Plant Virology

DR. L. O. KUNKEL—1884–1960

In Memoriam

PLANT VIROLOGY

edited by

M. K. CORBETT

and

H. D. SISLER

University of Florida Press ‡ Gainesville ‡ 1964

A University of Florida Press Book

Published with assistance from the National Science Foundation

Copyright © 1964 by the Board of Commissioners of State Institutions of Florida

Lithoprint edition, april, 1967

Library of Congress Catalog Card Number: 64–23327

Lithoprinted by Paramount Press, Inc., Jacksonville, Florida
Bound by Universal Dixie Bindery, Inc., Jacksonville, Florida

THIS BOOK has been compiled from a series of lectures and laboratory exercises presented during a Southern Regional Graduate Summer Session in Plant Virology, which was held at the University of Maryland, June 24 to August 2, 1963. The curriculum for the course was designed to provide students with the fundamentals and recent advances in the field of plant virology. The science of plant virology had its beginning near the end of the nineteenth century when Beijerinck described the filterable infectious extract from mosaic diseased tobacco plants as a virus or a *contagium vivum fluidum*. Today plant virology encompasses many disciplines as exemplified by the table of contents of this book. The subject matter ranges over a wide variety of topics including symptomatology, vector relationships, chemical nature, electron microscopy, and structure and substructure of viruses, which requires a student who wishes to master the science of virology to have a wide knowledge in the biological and physical sciences. It is difficult for one individual to accumulate sufficient knowledge to be an authority in all phases of virology. Thus, to cover each of these topics, specialists in the various areas were invited to participate in the course for periods of 1–2 weeks and present lectures and laboratory exercises in their field of specialization. Each lecturer prepared a review of his subject matter so that it would

be available to a much larger audience than the 32 students enrolled from the 15 participating southern institutions. These lectures have been published in anticipation that they will stimulate further research and development in the science of virology. The need for a textbook of plant virology has long been evident by the number of review articles that have appeared in the last few years in many scientific journals. It is recognized that this text will not make a virologist out of a student but it is hoped that it will suffice as an introduction to the subject of plant virology and provide a stimulus for students to continue in the search for knowledge rather than to accept dogma.

The success of this course depended greatly upon the cooperation of the following to whom special recognition and acknowledgment is hereby given: to the Regional Committee of the Southern Regional Education Board for its work in the initial planning stages; to Drs. S. J. P. Chilton and J. P. Fulton, members of the Executive Committee, for assistance in preparing the curriculum, selection of lecturers, and preparation of the grant proposal; to Dr. William L. Bowden, Associate Director for Regional Programs, Southern Regional Education Board, who worked with the Regional and Executive Committees throughout the course of the project; to Dr. Ronald Bamford, Dean of the Graduate School and former Head of the Department of Botany, University of Maryland, who served as representative of the Regional Advisory Council on Graduate Education in the Agricultural Sciences and made many valuable contributions at all stages of the program; to the University of Maryland, for so generously providing the necessary facilities for conducting the course; to the staff of the Botany Department, University of Maryland, for their assistance and cooperation; to the lecturers and students who made the course so suc-

cessful; and finally to the National Science Foundation for providing the grant which made the course possible.

Appreciation is expressed to President J. Wayne Reitz and Provost for Agriculture E. T. York, Jr., of the University of Florida for their cooperation in arranging for publication of this volume by the University of Florida Press.

Acknowledgment is made to Mrs. J. C. McCollum, Mrs. N. E. Link, and Mrs. A. A. Bell for typing manuscripts, and to Mr. R. K. Jones for assistance in proofreading.

M. K. CORBETT
Chairman Executive Committee and Program Coordinator

H. D. SISLER
Program Director

Contributors

ELLEN M. BALL
U.S.D.A. - A.R.S.
PLANT PATHOLOGY DEPARTMENT
UNIVERSITY OF NEBRASKA
LINCOLN, NEBRASKA

F. C. BAWDEN
ROTHAMSTED EXPERIMENTAL STATION
HARPENDEN, HERTFORDSHIRE, ENGLAND

R. H. E. BRADLEY
DIVISION OF PLANT PATHOLOGY
AGRICULTURAL RESEARCH STATION
FREDERICTON, NEW BRUNSWICK, CANADA

L. BROADBENT
DIVISION OF PLANT PATHOLOGY
GLASSHOUSE CORPS RESEARCH INSTITUTE
LITTLEHAMPTON, SUSSEX, ENGLAND

D. L. D. CASPAR
THE CHILDREN'S CANCER RESEARCH
    FOUNDATION, INC.
THE CHILDREN'S MEDICAL CENTER
THE HARVARD MEDICAL SCHOOL
BOSTON, MASSACHUSETTS

M. K. CORBETT
PLANT VIRUS LABORATORY
UNIVERSITY OF FLORIDA
GAINESVILLE, FLORIDA

ROBERT W. FULTON
DEPARTMENT OF PLANT PATHOLOGY
COLLEGE OF AGRICULTURE
UNIVERSITY OF WISCONSIN
MADISON, WISCONSIN

C. E. HALL
DEPARTMENT OF BIOLOGY
MASSACHUSETTS INSTITUTE OF TECHNOL-
    OGY
CAMBRIDGE, MASSACHUSETTS

B. D. HARRISON
ROTHAMSTED EXPERIMENTAL STATION
HARPENDEN, HERTFORDSHIRE, ENGLAND

F. O. HOLMES
THE ROCKEFELLER INSTITUTE
NEW YORK, NEW YORK

C. A. KNIGHT
VIRUS LABORATORY
UNIVERSITY OF CALIFORNIA
BERKELEY, CALIFORNIA

FRANK LANNI
DEPARTMENT OF MICROBIOLOGY
EMORY UNIVERSITY
ATLANTA, GEORGIA

MAX A. LAUFFER
DEPARTMENT OF BIOPHYSICS
UNIVERSITY OF PITTSBURGH
PITTSBURGH, PENNSYLVANIA

ROBERT A. MANAKER
LABORATORY OF VIRAL ONCOLOGY
NATIONAL CANCER INSTITUTE
BETHESDA, MARYLAND

KARL MARAMOROSCH
THE BOYCE THOMPSON INSTITUTE FOR
    PLANT RESEARCH, INC.
YONKERS, NEW YORK

W. C. PRICE
PLANT VIRUS LABORATORY
UNIVERSITY OF FLORIDA
GAINESVILLE, FLORIDA

D. A. ROBERTS
DEPARTMENT OF PLANT PATHOLOGY
UNIVERSITY OF FLORIDA
GAINESVILLE, FLORIDA

A. F. ROSS
DEPARTMENT OF PLANT PATHOLOGY
CORNELL UNIVERSITY
ITHACA, NEW YORK

H. D. SISLER
BOTANY DEPARTMENT
UNIVERSITY OF MARYLAND
COLLEGE PARK, MARYLAND

KENNETH M. SMITH
DEPARTMENT OF BIOPHYSICS
UNIVERSITY OF PITTSBURGH
PITTSBURGH, PENNSYLVANIA

R. L. STEERE
PLANT VIROLOGY LABORATORY
U.S.D.A. - A.R.S.
CROPS RESEARCH DIVISION
BELTSVILLE, MARYLAND

WILLIAM N. TAKAHASHI
DEPARTMENT OF PLANT PATHOLOGY
UNIVERSITY OF CALIFORNIA
BERKELEY, CALIFORNIA

K. M. Smith

C. E. Hall

K. Maramorosch

R. H. E. Bradley

H. D. Sisler

L. Broadbent

R. L. Steere

F. Lanni

Ellen M. Ball

D. L. D. Caspar

W. N. Takahashi

F. C. BAWDEN

A. F. ROSS

W. C. PRICE

F. O. HOLMES

M. K. CORBETT

B. D. HARRISON

R. W. FULTON

D. A. ROBERTS

M. A. LAUFFER

R. A. MANAKER

C. A. KNIGHT

Contents

Contents

3—R. W. FULTON

Transmission of plant viruses by grafting, dodder, seed, and mechanical inoculation—39

4—A. F. ROSS

Identification of plant viruses—68

5—W. C. PRICE

Strains, mutation, acquired immunity, and interference—93

Contents

6–B. D. HARRISON

The transmission of plant viruses in soil–118

7–R. H. E. BRADLEY

Aphid transmission of stylet-borne viruses–148

8–KARL MARAMOROSCH

Virus-vector relationships: Vectors of circulative and propagative viruses–175

9–D. A. ROBERTS

Local-lesion assay of plant viruses–194

Contents

Contents

Contents

Contents

A3—R. A. MANAKER

An introduction to the tumor viruses—457

M. K. CORBETT

Introduction

THE WORD *virus* was described in the Phillips dictionary of 1720 as "a poison, venom, also a rammish smell as of the armpits; also a kind of watery matter, whitish, yellowish, and greenish at the same time, which issues out of ulcers and stinks very much; being indued with eating and malignant qualities." The modern concept of a virus as a pathogenic agent did not develop immediately, but required years of painstaking observation and research. By 1950, a virus was described by Bawden (1950) as an "obligately parasitic pathogen with dimensions of less than 200 mμ." Holmes (1948) proposed that viruses are "etiological agents of disease, typically of small size and capable of passing filters that retain bacteria, increasing only in the presence of living cells, giving rise to new strains by mutation, not arising *de novo*." Luria (1959) defined viruses as "submicroscopic entities, capable of being introduced into specific living cells and reproducing inside such cells only." Various other definitions have been proposed from time to time, but these few will suffice to demonstrate how the connotation of the word *virus* has been altered as knowledge has accumulated. In the following pages, I wish to show, by presenting some of the important findings, how this knowledge developed and how these discoveries have contributed to the present meaning of the word *virus* and to the science of virology.

Undoubtedly, many of the plant diseases which we now know are caused by viruses were recognized many years ago, but few of them attracted attention before the turn of the nineteenth century. Perhaps one of the oldest such plant diseases is that of tulip mosaic, or "breaking" as it was commonly called. The condition has been termed beneficial by some investigators because it induced color changes in the tulip flowers that enhance their beauty. They were so sought after by tulip fanciers during the sixteenth and seventeenth centuries that speculators gambling on the tulip market created the craze "tulipomania." Although the cause of the breaking was unknown at that time, planters knew how to transmit the condition by bulb grafts, and Blagrave in 1675 gave exact procedures and details for grafting such bulbs (McKay and Warner, 1933). The actual association of "breaking" with a virus had to wait until 1926 when it was shown that the virus could be transmitted mechanically and by aphids (McKay and Warner, 1933). Another early recognized plant virus disease was that of Jessamine (Jasminum) mottle. In a letter published in the philosophical transactions in 1720 Mr. Henry Cane reported that in 1692 he had transmitted the mottle condition to a common white Jasminum by grafting to it a yellow-striped Jasminum. In the words of Mr. Cane: "I have tried several other sorts of variegated

1

plants but do not find any of them transmute as that Jessamine will do." A similar situation was noted by Vibert in 1863 to occur in trees. He reported that apple trees budded with buds from "aucuba" plants produced variegated leaves on the stock the following spring. In some cases the buds failed, but the tree still produced variegated leaves. He concluded that the scion and stock need only be together long enough to allow sap to pass from the scion to the stock. He also reported a similar condition to occur in grafts between plants of rose and dog-rose.

1–1. DEVELOPMENT OF THE SCIENCE OF VIROLOGY

Virus diseases undoubtedly damaged many crop plants and ornamentals at this early date, but little was done to find their cause until the middle of the nineteenth century. Mayer (1886), an agricultural chemist working at Wageningen, the Netherlands, investigated a mosaic disease of tobacco, which had been termed "bunt," "rust," or "smut" by growers. To prevent confusion, Mayer suggested the international name of "mosaic disease of tobacco." The causal agent of the disease was unknown, though many theories had been proposed. Mayer attempted many experiments on the etiology of the mosaic disease and found that the causal agent was transmissible to healthy plants in juice extracts. He postulated that the disease was caused by an unorganized or organized ferment and that an unorganized ferment like an enzyme, capable of self-reproduction was unheard of. He found that continual heating at 60°C did not alter the infectivity but that it became weaker at 65°–75°C and was lost after several hours heating at 80°C. He was unable to retain infectivity after clarification and precipitation with weak alcohol. Thus, he concluded that the infectious agent was subject to the living conditions of organized ferments such as bacteria and fungi. Fungi were ruled out as the causal agent because they were too large to go through the filter paper. He concluded that the causal agent of the mosaic disease of tobacco was a bacterium

about which little was known concerning its mode of life or infectious form. Peach yellows disease, according to Smith, may have been recognized as early as 1750, but nothing was known about the nature of the disease until 1891 when he showed that it was contagious, had a long incubation period, and was bud transmitted.

In 1890, Ivanowski (1892) noted two diseases of tobacco in the Crimea. One was a pox-disease, and the other a mosaic disease similar to that reported by Mayer. He believed that the two diseases were independent rather than different stages of one disease. He verified Mayer's results on transmission, thermostability, and the absence of fungi and other parasites. He did not agree with Mayer, however, with respect to his statement on filtration through double filter paper. Ivanowski's preparation was still infectious after filtering through double filter paper and he knew that such filtration would not retain bacteria. Furthermore, he found that his preparation was still infectious even after filtering through a Chamberland filter-candle that would retain bacteria. Ivanowski thought his results were due either to a toxin secreted by the bacteria or to the penetration of the bacteria through the pores of the filter. The cause of these unknown diseases was still thought to be corpuscular, but they were now known to be caused by agents transmissible mechanically and by grafting. The first departure from the corpuscular theory for the etiology of the tobacco mosaic disease came with the work of Beijerinck (1898), who concluded after experiments on agar diffusion that the disease was not caused by microbes but by a *contagium vivum fluidum*. He also concluded from serial inoculation that the contagium reproduced itself in the living plant. It is also in Beijerinck's work that the word *virus* is used to describe the contagium. He found that the virus would infect and invade young tissue more rapidly than mature tissue, moved in both the xylem and the phloem, was graft transmissible and able to infect plants by means of the roots. He also reported that the virus was still infectious after drying for two years in diseased leaves, would survive the winter in soil, and was inactivated after exposure to formalin or boiling.

According to Fukushi the importance of insects as vectors of viruses was first shown by Hashimoto, who proved the relationship of a leafhopper to the dwarf disease of rice in 1894–95. It was thought at that time that the disease was caused by a leafhopper, and it was not until 1900 that it was found that only one species of leafhopper, *Nephotettix apicalis* var. *cincticeps,* was capable of producing the disease. In 1906–8 it was recognized that leafhoppers from certain areas of Japan induced the disease whereas leafhoppers from other areas did not and that these noninfective leafhoppers became able to induce the disease if they fed for about five days on diseased plants. Thus it became evident that the leafhopper *N. apicalis* did not cause the disease but was only transmitting its causal agent (1934).

It was thought by some that cutting tobacco plants back caused the mosaic disease, and Woods (1902) proposed that the trouble could not be due to parasites but must be attributed to a disturbance of a normal physiological activity of the cells in question. These disturbances, he proposed, were due to the enzymes peroxidase and oxidase.

Baur (1904), working with the variegation of Abutilon that he termed infectious chlorosis (*chlorosis infectiosa*), stated that the infectious substance could not be a living organism because in Europe variegated and nonvariegated plants were growing side by side without any evidence of transmission. Such a limited capacity for movement, according to Baur, was inconsistent with parasitic organisms. He thought that it was important to recognize that there were infectious diseases for which living organisms could not be considered the cause. He stated: "For a further insight into the etiology of these diseases the old dogma of the unconditionally parasitic nature of all infectious diseases seems to me to be only an obstruction."

From 1904 to 1935 many discoveries were made concerning the nature of virus diseases and the nature of the disease-causing entity. The published contributions during this period were numerous. Some of the outstanding discoveries that have affected our interpretation of the word *virus* and contributed to the characterization of viruses will be discussed. Allard in 1914 showed that of the various plants tested only those from the family *Solanaceae* were susceptible to tobacco mosaic virus. He also reported that pokeweed mosaic and tobacco mosaic were distinct diseases. He confirmed much of the earlier work and showed that clear filtrates obtained by the passage of sap from diseased plants through Berkfeld filters were as infectious as the unfiltered sap. In 1915 Allard showed that the disease could be caused by very small amounts of the virus. He found that the virus could withstand dilutions of 1:10,000 and in some cases 1:1,000,000. He argued that this small amount of material needed to cause infection was inconsistent with the enzymatic theory of Woods. He proposed that there was something in the virus quite extraneous to the protoplasmic constitution of healthy plants and that once introduced into healthy plants it rapidly increased and was parasitic in nature. Working on the properties of tobacco mosaic virus, Allard (1916) partially purified the virus by precipitation with aluminum sulfate. The precipitate was still infectious whereas the clear supernatant was not, even though it had good peroxidase activity. He concluded that there was no correlation between peroxidase or catalase activity and the infectious agent. He believed that tobacco mosaic was caused by an ultramicroscopic parasite. Although the necessity of wounds for infection was recognized earlier, Allard (1917) showed that tobacco plants were readily infected through the trichomes by rubbing leaves or stem with juice from diseased plants. He also found that washing with soap and water was a practical and efficient means of removing the virus from the hands.

Mild and severe forms of the sugar-beet curly-top virus were recognized by Carsner (1925a). He passed a severe form of the virus through plants of *Chenopodium murale, Rumex crispus,* or *Suseda moquini* and found that it then caused a mild form of the curly-top disease in beets. Similar mild forms were found to occur in beet leafhoppers collected in their natural breeding areas. Carsner proposed that the virus was attenuated, but he was most likely sorting out strains of the virus. Strains of viruses were also noted by McKinney (1929) to occur in isolates of a virus from *Nicotiana glauca* collected in the Canary Islands. Most plants had a light green or mild dark green mosaic. One plant had a pure yellow mosaic that produced yellow spots on subsequent inoculation. Subinoculation from these yellow spots produced a pure yellow mosaic type. McKinney proposed that such plants may be infected by mixtures of viruses or that the virus may become altered in the plant, producing mutations.

After extensive study on the aster yellows virus, Kunkel (1926) showed that both nymphs and adult leafhoppers were able to transmit the disease only after a 10-day incubation period. He proposed that this period of time was necessary for the causative agent to develop or multiply in the tissues of the leafhopper. He found that the virus was not transmitted through the eggs of the insect carrier or through the seeds of the aster, nor was it mechanically transmitted.

Studies on the nature of tobacco mosaic virus (TMV) led Mulvania (1926) to propose that the virus behaves as a typical colloid with regards to isoelectric point and mobility. Vinson (1927) showed that the virus could be precipitated out of solution by means of acetone, absolute alcohol, or ammonium salts. The precipitate in all cases was infectious whereas the supernatant was not.

The antigenic nature of plant viruses was discovered when Dvorak (1927) produced antisera in rabbits to sap from healthy potatoes and to sap from potatoes infected with a mosaic inducing virus. She was able to show that both sera had antibodies in common but that they exhibited a higher titer for the homologous than the heterologous reaction. In the preceding year Mulvania (1926) had injected a TMV preparation into the marginal ear veins of rabbits and had attempted to reisolate the virus from blood of the opposite ear. He made no attempt to produce a specific antiserum. More extensive studies were conducted on the antigenic nature of viruses by Purdy (1928, 1929). She found that antiserum contained a highly specific antibody for virus sap and that the specific antiserum would neutralize infectivity.

One of the most significant discoveries in the field of plant virology was that local lesions could be used for quantitative studies with TMV (Holmes, 1929). Until then, very little attention had been given to the reaction of viruses at the site of inoculation. Holmes found that several species of *Nicotiana* reacted by producing necrotic lesions at the site of infection with TMV and that the numbers of such lesions correlated with virus concentration in the inoculum when an efficient method of inoculation, such as rubbing with a gauze pad, was used. The reaction to TMV of plants of *N. glutinosa* made this host-virus combination a very desirable one for quantitative work. Holmes pointed out that the method could be compared with the poured-plate method for counting bacteria.

Another interesting phenomenon noted to occur in virus-infected plants was that of recovery from severe necrotizing diseases. Wingard (1928) was apparently the first to notice that leaves in the final or recovery stage of tobacco ringspot disease, although containing active virus, would not show necrotic spots as the result of reinoculation. Wingard suggested that the plants were immune. A type of interference phenomena was also suggested from the work of Thung (1931), who found that tobacco plants inoculated with mixtures of yellow and common strains of TMV developed symptoms of both diseases and that the viruses could be recovered separately. Thus, Thung concluded that only one type of virus could occupy any given cell. He also found that a tobacco plant affected with the yellow mosaic did not develop additional symptoms when it was inoculated with the common TMV.

Little was known about the morphology of virus particles, except that they were very small in size, until Takahashi and Rawlins (1933) ingeniously utilized the technique of stream double refraction and showed that the virus of tobacco mosaic was composed of rod-shaped particles.

INTRODUCTION

During the 30-year period 1904–35, many virus diseases were described on the basis of symptomatology and methods of transmission. The virus as a disease-causing agent during this period was shown to differ from bacteria in more ways than size alone. It was shown to exist and to increase only in living cells, to have host specificity, in some cases to behave like a proteinaceous colloid of rod-shaped particles, to mutate to different strains, to be antigenic, to be transmitted by insects in which it may multiply, and, in some instances, to induce in some plants a type of acquired immunity. In the next period, from 1935 to date, many changes occurred in our thinking concerning the nature of viruses. The first major contribution came in 1935, when Stanley obtained crystals of TMV. He found that sap from infected tobacco plants could be fractionated with ammonium sulfate until a crystalline protein was obtained. He was able to associate infectivity with the crystalline protein and proposed that TMV could be regarded as an autocatalytic protein which required the presence of living cells for multiplication. The next year Bawden *et al.* (1936) showed that the liquid crystalline preparations of TMV consist of a protein and nucleic acid of the ribose type and that the virus particles were composed of subunits in a rod shape which exhibited the phenomenon of anisotropy of flow. Immediately following 1936 numerous papers characterizing this virus by physical and chemical methods were published. The early X-ray studies of Bernal and Fankuchen (1941) demonstrated that the virus particles are built up of subunits arranged in a regular way. The electron microscope, although developed earlier, was used in 1939 by Kausche *et al.* to demonstrate that virus particles associated with tobacco mosaic are slender rods. Although the quality of the electron micrographs was poor as judged by today's standards, the morphology of other viruses was studied by Stanley and Anderson (1941). Some were found to be rods whereas others were spherical. The use of the electron microscope to study virus particle morphology received a new stimulus in 1945 when Williams and Wyckoff demonstrated the use of shadow casting to improve contrast. The visualization of viruses within their host cells was soon accomplished when techniques of embedding and sectioning were improved (Porter *et al.*, 1945). Although multiplication of a plant virus in its insect vector was suggested by earlier workers, the first direct evidence was presented by Maramorosch (1952) for multiplication of aster-yellows virus in the leafhopper *Macrosteles divisus*. The chemical composition of tobacco mosaic virus has been studied in detail, and the importance of the nucleic acid portion of the virus particle to infectivity was pointed out by Epstein (1953), when he showed that the radiosensitive portion of the virus was the nucleic acid and not the protein. Treatment of the virus with phenol by Gierer and Schramm (1956) showed that the protein could be removed and that the ribonucleic acid portion of the virus particle was infectious. Other procedures (Fraenkel-Conrat, 1956) have been used for deproteinization studies of viruses, and some of the rod-shaped viruses have been reconstituted. Thus, most viruses are now considered to consist of an infectious nucleic acid surrounded by a large number of protein subunits all of which may be identical. The use of negative staining techniques for electron microscopy (Hall, 1955; Brenner and Horne, 1959) has greatly enhanced the use of the electron microscope for studies on the morphology and structure of viruses. These studies, coupled with modern X-ray crystallography and physiochemical data, have given us much information on the nature of viruses, the details of which will be discussed in later chapters. The fortuitous discovery of tobacco mosaic virus and its unique characteristics which permit it to be studied so easily by so many procedures immediately becomes apparent, and from this brief review of some of the outstanding contributions to our knowledge on the nature of viruses one realizes how much we know and how much there is left to know before the questions, what is a virus, is it animate or inanimate, and how did it arise, may be answered in full. The fallacy of attempting to describe all viruses under one definition when the information is not complete is readily recognized from the changes made by recent studies in virology. Today we may define a virus as an infectious nucleoprotein or an infectious nucleic acid only to have our definition drastically changed in the near future to a group of bases or a single base or to a single compound. Who knows what wonders await us?

1–2. NOMENCLATURE AND CLASSIFICATION

Nomenclature and classification of plant viruses have been in a state of chaos and confusion ever since the first virus was named. This confusion arose in part from research workers giving different names and descriptions to the same virus. Most of these investigators received their training in a biological discipline where the use of Latinized names, keys, and methods of classification were a very important part of their formal education. The carry over of this training to the field of plant virology becomes very evident to the reader who, after attempting to unscramble the proposed systems of nomenclature and classification of plant viruses, is left completely confused.

At first, plant virus diseases were named for the most conspicuous symptom in the host, and the cause of the disease received the same name with the word virus attached. That this system is merely based upon symptoms is immediately evident, and the pitfalls of such a system are recognized when consideration is given to the variability of symptoms. The investigators who describe new virus diseases and propose new systems of classification should be the first to recognize this variability, and should rely upon a more complete study of the disease and the causal agent before proposing new names and systems of classification. The point is well put by Bawden (1950): "Virus literature contains many detailed descriptions of symptoms, usually first accounts of 'new' viruses, in which differences from clinical pictures previously recorded are stressed as evidence of newness. How valueless such comparisons can be is evident from the number of times potato viruses X and Y, cucumber mosaic and tobacco mosaic viruses, have been identified as new viruses and given new names. Nevertheless, virus workers seem reluctant to appreciate the fact that variability is the normal, and they continue to describe with a wealth of picturesque detail symptoms that may never again be exactly reproduced."

Regardless of the confusion that has been created, work on the various systems of classification has contributed to our understanding of virology and has stimulated much research. It is easy for us today to look at the problem of classification and nomenclature and to think how worthless all the controversy over what you should call a particular virus and how you should classify it, when it is easy just to distinguish them by common names. This was not so true in 1927 when Johnson proposed a system for classifying viruses. In 1927, little information concerning the causal agent of mosaic was available, beyond the fact that it was filterable, invisible, and infectious. Investigators were just realizing that there is considerable variability in the number and type of hosts that are susceptible and that there is variability in the symptoms produced. When this was realized, the need for a system of classification seemed important so that research workers would have a means of identifying the virus with which they were working. Johnson (1927) found that the diagnostic features of some symptoms, when properly interpreted from comparative studies, had some value in classification of the viruses of tobacco, but that it was difficult to give a descriptive name to all the viruses that occur in one host. That he recognized the value of such symptom variability is noted from the following: "Nowhere in the realm of plant pathology are symptoms of less value in description than in plant virus diseases, because of the remarkable influence of environmental factors, and the possible coexistence of two or more viruses in a single plant." He proposed that a system be established of naming viruses based upon the host in which each virus was first discovered together with a number to indicate the specific virus. Under this system, TMV would become *tobacco virus 1* and the other viruses of tobacco would receive a number in their order of discovery. In 1927, this system had its merits for the number of known viruses affecting tobacco was small, and it was possible for a research worker to remember and associate certain important features of a virus with a number. Today, such a system would be impossibly abstruse, for there is nothing characteristic or meaningful about a number that will associate it with a particular virus or disease. It also classes together viruses that have nothing in common except that they infect the same host. The system also raises the difficulty of what becomes of the number if a specific virus is removed from the system after further research shows that it does not belong to the particular group in which it was classified. Johnson (1929) further attempted to classify the virus diseases of potatoes that had been reported from the United States and Europe. He used several diagnostic features, such as symptoms in the Bliss Triumph potato variety, physical properties (thermal-inactivation, longevity *in vitro*, and dilution end point), influence of chemicals, methods of transmission, incubation period, host range, variation in cytological and histological detail, and filterability. He concluded that such a study was more meaningful than symptomatology alone and that "rugose mosaic" was the same as "crinkle mosaic."

Smith (1931), working with a composite potato virus disease of the mosaic group, designated the letters X and Y for the two components. This use of letters and common names has persisted and is perpetuated even today for the naming of the virus diseases of potatoes.

Use of the relationship of viruses to their vectors as means of classification was first proposed by Elze (1931). He proposed three classes: (1) viruses not spread by insects; (2) viruses spread by different insects; and (3) viruses adapted to particular insects. The third class was subdivided into (a) those viruses which, in addition, are mechanically transmitted, and (b) those which are adapted for a short incubation period and those with a long incubation period. Storey (1931) proposed that the species of insect vector is usually characteristic of the virus and that the virus is better characterized by its insect vector than by the host or the symptoms induced in the host. He cautioned that the specificity of the virus to its vector may not be absolute and that strains of the virus and races of the insect vector may determine the possibility of transmission.

Another departure from classification of viruses by symptomatology was proposed by Chester (1935), who demonstrated the usefulness of specific serological reactions for determining relationships among viruses. He showed that the viruses could be divided into serological groups such as the TMV group including the virus of tomato aucuba mosaic, Johnson's yellow tobacco mosaic 1, Holmes' symptomless tobacco mosaic, and Jensen's brilliant yellow, white, and slow-moving types. Although very diverse in symptomatology, these viruses were serologically related. Similarly, latent-mosaic of potato virus, X virus, healthy-potato virus, potato ringspot virus, and British Queen streak virus all belonged to the same group. The system of serology, undoubtedly one of the most reliable means of grouping viruses, is however not infallible. Chester (1935) obtained reactions suggesting that the vein-banding virus of potato (potato virus Y) was serologically related to cucumber mosaic virus and that they might be strains of one virus. These two viruses have since been shown to be distinct entities (Ross, 1950), and Chester's results may be explained on the basis that the viruses he was working with were not separate isolates of Y or cucumber mosaic virus or that his virus isolates were contaminated.

Smith (1937) proposed a variation of Johnson's system of classification for about 144 viruses, excluding strains, in his book *A Textbook of Plant Virus Diseases*. He adopted Johnson's use of numbers but used the Latin generic name of the host instead of the common name. This has the same disadvantages as Johnson's system, but did make it possible to be consistent with the naming of the host, especially in those cases where no generally accepted popular name of the host is available. Ainsworth (1939) recognized the difficulty of obtaining international conformity to any detailed list that included all strains. He proposed that a convenient method of distinguishing strains would be to add a number (in roman type) to the italicized name of the virus with any particular designation given by the author who described the variant. Thus, TMV would be designated *Nicotiana tabacum virus 1* and strains would be distinguished as follows: *Nicotiana tabacum virus 1,* masked strain, Holmes 1934. Ainsworth's recommendation may have some merit with regard to distinguishing strains, but it has the same faults as the already proposed systems.

On behalf of the Committee for Virus Nomenclature appointed by the Council of the American Phytopathological Society, Bennett (1939) selected five characteristics of viruses that he believed were most important. These were (1) type of symptoms produced on different species and varieties of susceptible plants; (2) morphological and cytological disturbance produced; (3) relation of insect vector to virus transmission; (4) antigenic reactions in animals and plants; and (5) the chemical and physical properties of the viruses themselves. He thought, at the time, that the host plant in all probability was the most logical basis for generic distinction of viruses but that purification and crystallization of the virus protein may lead to a more logical and natural basis for grouping them. Of the various possibilities, three were suggested. (1) Viruses might be considered as organisms and given binomial designations following the practices already used for recognized organisms. (2) They might be considered chemical compounds. (3) Arbitrary systems having no reference to the nature of the entities might be used as a basis for names. He proposed that, due to the difficulties of the systems in use, names should replace numbers. Thus, tobacco virus 1 of Johnson might become *tobacco virus altathermus* or *Nicotiana virus altathermus*. If, on subsequent investigations, viruses were shown to be organisms, then they might be given proper generic binomial names such as *paracrystalis altathermus*. If, on the other hand, they proved to be

chemical compounds, the suffix "vir" might be used to signify virus in the same way as the termination "ase" designates enzymes. Thus, tobacco virus 1 would become *altathermovir*.

In the same volume, same number, of *Phytopathology*, Holmes (1939a) proposed an extension of the binomial system of nomenclature to include viruses. He pointed out that such a system had the advantages of grouping viruses on fundamental similarities such as serological and immunological tests, type of disease, and all other accumulated data. The system has the further advantage of allowing names to be removed or added without affecting the continuity of the system. He proposed a kingdom *Vira* with two divisions, *Phytophagi* for plant viruses and *Zoophagi* for animal viruses. Each division consisted of classes, families, and genera with Latinized binomials for the individual viruses. Holmes (1939b) later expanded the system in his *Handbook of Phytopathogenic Viruses* to include descriptions of 129 individual viruses. As with all new proposals, as soon as the binomial system of nomenclature was published it had its critics, its supporters, and those who wanted to modify it. Soon after Holmes proposed the Latinized binomial-trinomial system, Valleau (1940) classified the viruses causing diseases of tobacco. He was dissatisfied with Holmes' genus *Marmor* because it was too heterogeneous and ill-defined. Thus, he suggested that the genus be used as a catchall. In place of the *Marmor* genus, he substituted a new genus, *Musivum*, based on Holmes' *Marmor tabaci* var. *vulgare* as a type species. He set up several new genera and redefined some of Holmes' original genera. He did not consider any groupings above the genus level.

Fawcett (1940) proposed a system of nomenclature which, in his judgment, combined the best of the systems proposed by Johnson (1927), Smith (1937), and Holmes (1939a). He described it briefly as a simplification of Smith's system without the confusion of Johnson's numbers, and Holmes' generic difficulties. He proposed using the binomials as suggested by Bennett (1939), obtaining the genus from the host plant in the way proposed by Johnson (1927) and Smith (1937), and using specific names as does Holmes, instead of numbers. Fawcett's rule of obtaining generic names was simply to apply the stem "vir" to the Latin genitive of the name of the genus of the host in which the virus was first reported. Thus, the viruses of peach rosette, sugar-beet curly-top, and potato yellow-dwarf become *Prunivir rosettae*, *Betavir eutetticola* and *Solanivir vastans*, respectively. Fawcett also recognized that such a system would create names that would be difficult to pronounce, such as *Chrysanthemivir*. Using his system, Fawcett proposed names for citrus viruses. Here again is a system of nomenclature and classification based mainly on the host and symptoms. Thornberry (1941) proposed that all intracellular infectious agents that do not increase in a cell-free medium be assigned to one order, *Biovirales*, an adjunct to the bacteria (class *Schizomyceta* phylum *Thallophyta* of the Plant Kingdom). The plant viruses were to be assigned to the genus *Phytovirus* of the family *Phytoviraceae*, and the classification of the genus *Phytovirus* was to be based upon host range, methods of transmission, and symptoms in standard hosts. The species portion of the binomial was to be based upon the first or more syllables of the generic names of an important host prefixed to a Latin word implying one or more of the characteristic symptoms in a standard host. Thus tobacco mosaic virus would presumably become *Phytovirus nicomosaicum* variety *vulgare*. To master such a system, one would have to be a Latin scholar and etymologist in addition to being a plant pathologist.

Bawden (1941) opposed the binomial system and suggested that nomenclature of viruses should be based on a system of classification so that the virus names would indicate some characteristic property of the virus or their interrelationships and that any permanent virus classification should be on the virus and not on the host plant. He suggested that it might be possible to classify those viruses about which serological, morphological, and chemical information was known and that all others be put in a group with a name to indicate that they were

there because of ignorance and not because of our knowledge. He proposed that a list of approved common names would be useful for the virus worker or plant pathologist to distinguish or make reference to the virus in question. Similar to all other proposals, Bawden's suggestions precipitated three more papers on the subject in volume 7 of *Chronica Botanica* (Fawcett, 1942; Johnson, 1942; Valleau, 1942).

Ainsworth (1943) suggested that the work of a plant pathologist would be greatly facilitated by a list of standardized English names of virus diseases from which the common name of the virus could be derived, similar to that compiled for the fungi in 1939 (common names of British plant diseases) and that a distinction should be made between obligate synonyms (those based on the same type) and facultative synonyms (based on different types).

McKinney (1944) proposed a kingdom *Phyta* with a division *Viriphyta* for the plant viruses. He described type species for 12 genera, again based on a binomial system. Holmes (1948) expanded his earlier classification to include all viruses, and he grouped 67 species in the genus *Marmor*, which contain the viruses of the mosaic group. Some of these he admitted were not described in sufficient detail and needed additional investigation. But he argued that they could be reclassified, as relationships with other groups were determined. To date, this has been his most ambitious treatment of the subject, and recently he has stated that he would most likely not revise it (personal communication).

The whole subject of virus classification and nomenclature was discussed in a series of papers presented at a conference on "Virus and Rickettsial Classification and Nomenclature," held in New York City, January 1952, by the Section of Biology of the New York Academy of Science, and edited by R. W. Miner (Vol. 56, 381–622, 1953). The authors of the previously discussed papers again presented their views, objections, and opinions on the subject without reaching any conclusive accepted procedure for plant virus nomenclature and classification.

Another binomial, Latinized system of

virus nomenclature, in which the generic name is composed of symbols representing three independent characteristics of the virus, was proposed by Hansen (1960). The symbols refer to direct transmission, to vector transmission, and to particle type. He proposed that a combination of these three characteristics would define the virus in question; thus potato virus X would be *Minflexus solani* (*M* = mechanical transmission; *in* = virus without specific arthropod vector; *flexus* = flexible threadlike particle). In this case the specific epithet (*solani*) is derived from the main host.

Recently, work on classifying viruses in relation to their morphological and serological relationships is being attempted on the viruses with elongated particles (Brandes and Wetter, 1959). Thus far, they have classified 46 plant viruses on the basis of particle morphology, normal length of the particle, and serological reactions. This is really the first attempt to classify viruses on natural relationships rather than on host reactions, and it should meet with approval of the critics of earlier classification. Brandes and Wetter have continued to use common names derived from the host reactions for the viruses. This system allows for expansion to include new viruses as they are shown to have virus particles of similar morphology and serological reactions and to remove viruses if they should be more closely related to another group. It also allows for the use of common names (*Review of Applied Mycology*, 1957) by which viruses are so frequently named and called, especially by the plant pathologists.

An extension of this natural classification was proposed recently by Lwoff *et al.* in 1962. They suggested that the system include only those entities that exhibit in their life cycle an infectious particle containing only one type of nucleic acid. The system is based mainly on morphology, structure, and symmetry of the virus particle as determined by electron microscopy, negative staining, and X-ray diffraction. In their system the mature virus is the *virion*, which is composed of a *capsid* built of *structure units*. The structure units can associate into symmetric units termed the *capsomeres*, and the capsid (protein) plus

nucleic acid is the *nucleocapsid*. Thus, virions were divided into 2 groups on the basis of their nucleic acid: group D, deoxyribonucleic acid (DNA), and group R, ribonucleic acid (RNA). These groups were subdivided on the basis of symmetry, helical (H) and cubic (C). All virions belong to one of 2 categories: some having a *naked capsid* (N), some an *enveloped capsid* (E). The groups were further subdivided on the number of capsomeres for the cubic capsids and on the diameter of the helical capsids. Thus, TMV would be an RHN, 170–200Å virus, and turnip yellow mosaic virus would belong to the REO group designated RCN, 32c. Such a system, although based on natural characteristics of the virus, would require that every laboratory have X-ray equipment and a crystallographer to classify a virus. Eventually such a system may be useful, but at present I believe it is long before its time in the field of plant virology.

1–3. ECONOMIC IMPORTANCE

Since 1898, more than 400 plant viruses have been described and named. The total number of diseases caused by these viruses has not been calculated. Some viruses, like cucumber mosaic virus, affect many kinds of crop plants. Others, like southern bean mosaic virus, affect only a few kinds. Almost all known forms of plant life suffer from the effects of plant viruses. In the plant world only the Gymnosperms and Pteridophyta still appear to have escaped their effects, but until recently the fungi and algae were also included in this group, and now even the fungi and algae have been reported to have virus diseases (Gandy and Hollings, 1962; Safferman and Morris, 1963). Why virus diseases have not been discovered in gymnosperms and ferns is unknown. It is probable that these groups are affected by viruses which will be revealed as they become economically important and extensively studied.

Plants of economic importance all suffer from losses due to viruses. The extent of the losses will vary greatly, depending upon the value of the crop and the type of damage. Losses may be either quantitative or qualitative. Quantitative losses are those which are directly associated with yield reduction, such as fewer or smaller potato tubers per plant, or fruit per tree, whereas qualitative losses are usually involved in lower market values, which result when such symptoms as internal necrosis of potatoes, color breaks in ornamentals, or size reduction in flowers are present. The difficulty in obtaining a monetary evaluation of any crop loss due to virus diseases is immediately recognized when consideration is given to the complexity of the market situation. In some areas, a particular grower or group of growers may lose an entire crop to one virus disease, while at the same time another grower or group of growers in a different location will receive an increased evaluation on their harvest because of the law of supply and demand. Thus, all crop losses are only estimates on an individual basis, and extrapolation of such losses to a world market is meaningless.

Both annual and perennial plants are affected. Sometimes, the annual crops are more dramatically affected as judged from symptoms and immediate losses. Crops such as potatoes, citrus, bananas, strawberries, raspberries, fruit trees, and sugar cane which are vegetatively propagated, will collect various viruses and eventually suffer severe losses. Not only does the grower lose the immediate yield in the case of perennial crops but the cost of replacement is much greater than that of annual crops. Numerous reports of losses due to virus diseases are available in the literature, but few contain actual market values. Some specific examples will be given in both annual and perennial crops to illustrate the extent to which virus diseases may occur and their drastic effects upon yield. Roque and Adsuar (1941) reported that a mosaic disease of chili peppers (*Capsicum frutescens*) occurred in epiphytotic proportions at the Agricultural Experiment Station at Isabela and later spread to other parts of Puerto Rico. The estimated crop losses due to the disease was 50–80%. The "big-bud" virus of tomatoes has been reported to cause losses in all parts of Australia (Samuel *et al.*, 1933). Usually, only a small percentage of plants is affected, scattered at random over the field, but infections of

50–100% have been reported in New South Wales.

Virus diseases of crucifers such as swedes, rape, turnip, and cauliflower have been reported from various parts of the world. It was recognized in New Zealand in 1932 (Chamberlain, 1936) that losses in rape equivalent to 25% occurred during 1934–35. Ling and Yang (1940) reported that a mosaic of rape destroyed more than 30% of the crop in China and that the reduction in seed yields ranged from 37 to 86% of the samples examined. Commercial plantings of cauliflower in the coastal areas of central California are severely affected by a virus disease that causes 20–30% loss in some fields (Tompkins, 1934). A similar virus disease was reported to be widespread in Devon and Cornwall and to have affected as many as 75% of the plants in a field; entire crops were rendered unmarketable (Caldwell and Prentice, 1942). Strains of turnip mosaic virus have been reported to damage commercial plantings of horseradish in Wisconsin, Illinois, Missouri, and Washington. In some areas 100% of the crop was infected (Pound, 1948).

In certain areas of Western Australia, farmers were not aware of the insidious nature of bean mosaic virus, which caused widespread damage in bean crops ranging from 20 to 50% (Cass Smith, 1945). This yield reduction is seldom noticed and records are often not available. Van Hoof (1956) determined from small plots of rhubarb in the Heemstkerk and Zwolle district of the Netherlands that the diseased plants were not appreciably less productive than healthy plants in the first year but that they were 23.6% less productive in the second year.

A yellow mosaic virus has been reported to cause severe damage to grasses in the New Delhi area, where 50–80% of the plants were affected (Vasudeva *et al.*, 1948). In 1935 a survey of the spotted wilt disease of lettuce in the Salinas Valley of California indicated that the virus has become progressively more destructive. Fields which formerly were unaffected showed a slight loss in the early summer but, as the season advanced, the loss increased until at the beginning of autumn it amounted to more than ¾ of the crop in some plantings (Harris, 1939). In the lettuce-growing areas of southeastern North Carolina, the virus diseases big vein and mosaic contributed significantly to the low yields and poor quality of the spring crop of lettuce, and seed from mosaic-free lettuce yielded 14,448 lbs per acre as compared to 12,432 lbs from fields planted with regular seed (Aycock and Winstead, 1955). Chupp and Paddock (1949) reported an epidemic of lettuce big vein virus in Long Island, New York, in 1949. In some counties the losses ranged from 10 to nearly 100% of the crop. Big vein virus in 10 commercial lettuce fields in the Salinas Valley was found by Zink and Grogan in 1954 to affect the yield of marketable lettuce without necessarily causing any economic loss. Profits obtained from fields almost 100% infected occasionally surpassed those obtained from predominantly healthy fields. The profits were apparently directly related to the consumer demand at the time of harvest: if demand was great, poor quality lettuce was accepted. Cucumber mosaic virus has been shown to cause severe losses to cucumbers both in the field and in the greenhouse. Doolittle (1924) reported that losses from this virus had been on the increase for five years in the greenhouse industry and that losses in a single locality in 1922 were estimated at $75,000. Losses were so continuous that in some areas cucumbers were being replaced by other crops. Tobacco ringspot virus has been reported by Pound (1949) to cause losses of 10% to watermelons in Wisconsin. The same virus has been reported to have caused up to 50% losses to watermelons in Texas (Rosberg, 1953).

Cereal crops are affected by at least 20 viruses causing various estimated losses. Sill et al. (1955) estimated that the soil-borne wheat mosaic virus caused a loss of $3,000,000 to farmers in Kansas in 1953–54. Losses caused by wheat streak mosaic virus were estimated at $14,000,000. The disease was very widespread in most parts of the state. Barley false stripe virus present in most states of the upper Mississippi Valley has been reported by Timian and Sisler (1955) to occur in 93% of the 214 barley fields examined in North Dakota. Infection ranged from a trace to 15%. The yield reduction depended upon the variety but ranged from 17 to 24%. A mean loss in yield of 10.8% was recorded for winter wheat varieties grown in soil infested with soil-borne wheat mosaic virus (Bever and Pendleton, 1954).

Oswald and Houston (1951) reported a new outbreak of barley yellow dwarf virus in barley in California in 1951 and estimated that it caused a 10% loss in the barley crop (Oswald and Houston, 1953). The virus is widespread around the world and infects oats, barley, wheat, many forage grasses, and numerous wild grasses. Rochow (1961) concluded that the virus is as destructive as any cereal virus yet discovered. Mosaic of winter wheat has been reported by Zazhurilo and Sitnikova (1939) to occur each year in the Voronczh Province in Russia where, under favorable conditions, up to 15–20% of the plants are affected; infected plants yield less than healthy ones.

Lupines have been used in various parts of the world as a forage, cover, or green-manure crop, and during the past 15 years they have been rather extensively grown in southeastern United States. In 1950 Weimer reported that two virus diseases occurred in epiphytotic proportions in the state of Georgia. Corbett (1955) reported that the United States Department of Agriculture, Bureau of Agricultural Economics, showed that the acreage of lupines grown for seed production in Florida decreased between 1950 and 1954. In 1950, 130,000 acres were planted, of which 16,000 acres were harvested for seed with a production value of $510,000. In 1954, 120,000 acres were planted, of which only 7000 were harvested with a production value of $172,000. The reduction in crop value was attributed mainly to infection by bean yellow mosaic virus.

The motley virus disease of carrots has been reported by Stubbs (1948) to be widespread in Australia and to cause severe losses to all carrot varieties. He reported the same disease from California (Stubbs, 1956) but noted that losses were correlated with vector population. Aster yellows virus, in addition to causing losses in crops such as lettuce, onions, and spinach, has been reported by R. D. Watson (1945) to have affected 80–90% of the carrots in the Lower Rio Grande Valley in 1943–44.

Sugar beets are grown throughout the world. In the United States they are grown in 22 states and contribute approximately 20% of the national sugar production. The by-products of the sugar-beet industry, consisting of tops, molasses, and pulp, are used for feeding livestock. Unfortunately, sugar-beet production is seriously affected by virus diseases. Carsner (1925a) reported that only about 25% of the normal sugar-beet crop was harvested from large acreages in 1924 in the Yakima Valley of the state of Washington. The rapid expansion of the sugar-beet industry was abruptly checked in Idaho in 1919 after the first very severe outbreak of curly-top virus (Murphy, 1946). Bennett *et al.* (1954) inoculated sugar beet with yellows virus by aphids and found that the average reduction due to virus infection was 39.9% in root weight and 35.8% in sucrose content. The potential damage of the yellows disease to sugar production was pointed out by M. A. Watson (1942) as being underestimated in Great Britain. She reported that the yields of roots and sugar were considerably reduced. Early infection of late-sown beets caused a loss of 67% of the root and 71% of the sugar yield. Watson *et al.* (1946) reported that the average yield of sugar beets for Great Britain during the years of severe outbreaks of beet yellows virus was 1.6 tons per acre less than during the other years. It appeared that the yield reduction of sugar was proportional to the percentage of diseased plants, which was estimated to be 5%. In Great Britain, Hull (1954) calculated a loss of 0.39 tons per acre of sugar-beet roots due to infection by sugar-beet yellows. Total losses from sugar-beet yellows in Great Britain in 1957 (Hull, 1958) were about 1,000,000 tons. In Denmark, where the disease has been reported to occur sporadically, losses of up to 3% of the sugar content have occurred (Gram, 1942). In Western Germany (Heiling, 1953), where severe outbreaks of beet yellows virus occur, the root yield is approximately 50–60% of the normal, and sugar yield is 60–70% of normal. In addition, the leaves wilted and decayed more rapidly than healthy ones, and virus-infected plants contained 30–50% less protein. Losses of from 29 to 35% of the sugar were reported for late infection of sugar beets in Sweden (Bjorling, 1949). In addition, the quality of the root is poor and the weight of seed per plant, percentage germination, and number of seed balls per ounce are reduced (Brewbaker, 1942).

Losses are very great in crops such as sugar cane and potatoes that are planted from vegetative parts when healthy propagative material is not used. In addition to causing losses in the individual plant, the virus in the infected "seed" provides a source of inoculum for within-field spread. Sugar cane is affected by at least five major virus diseases; mosaic, streak, sereh, Fiji, and ratoon stunting. Field experiments in Puerto Rico (Landrau and Adsuar, 1953) showed that cane grown from noninfected seed pieces produced significantly higher yields (42 tons per acre) than infected stock (34 tons per acre). Ratoon stunting has been reported to cause losses of from 11 to 37% in the Q-28 variety in Queensland (Hughes, 1955). In India, Chona (1944) reported that losses due to the sugar-cane mosaic in the Co. 213 variety, even though 100% infected, was only 10–12% reduction in yield of sugar; there was no loss in extraction or quality of juice. He concluded that mosaic virus does little damage to the Co. canes in India, but that even losses of 10% would amount to 3,300,000 rupees per annum.

The effects of viruses upon the yields of potatoes were probably noted in the late eighteenth century in Europe. Since then, about 18 viruses have been reported as causing diseases of potatoes. Each has its various effects upon yield, and without certification it would most likely be impossible to grow potatoes profitably. Scott (1941) reported that the yield of potatoes may be reduced 14–25% by a mild mottle caused by mild strains of potato virus X or A. Mild mosaic caused by virus X reduced the yield by 30–40%, whereas borderline severe mosaic, generally due to a combination of viruses A and X, and severe strains of virus X reduced the yield by 50–60%. Various combinations of these viruses caused yield reductions of 65–85%, and the leaf-roll virus reduced the yield by 50–95%. He also found that, in addition to reducing the yield, virus infections tended to induce early ripening of the potatoes. Bonde *et al.* (1943) reported results similar to Scott for the rate of virus spread and effects upon the yield of potatoes in Maine and in Long Island, New York. They found that the spread of potato viruses in Maine during a 19-year period varied from season to season. Mild mosaic varied from 4 to 97%, leaf-roll from 2 to 100%, and spindle tuber from 1 to 61% of plants infected. The spread was most extensive in seasons most favorable for the aphid vectors common in Maine. They reported that two potato varieties, Green Mountain and Bliss Triumph, when completely infected with leaf-roll, spindle tuber, or different types of mosaic yielded significantly less than when disease free. The reduction ranged between 18 and 56% in Maine and between 26 and 64% in Long Island. Schultz and Bonde (1944) found that potato virus X was harbored by potatoes more generally than any other virus and that it was responsible for losses of 9–22% in yield, representing annual losses of millions of bushels. Bald and Norris (1941) assumed that more than 90% of potatoes grown in Australia were infected with potato virus X. They estimated that losses from this virus were as heavy as those from all other viruses combined and probably amounted to a loss of $1,750,000 a year.

Peach trees in the eastern temperate region of North America have been suffering from the effects of peach yellows virus for about 150 years. In 1891, Erwin F. Smith wrote, "In July, 1891, I saw hundreds of bushels of this worthless fruit in upper Maryland and Delaware, and the entire loss thereby in 1891 certainly exceeded half a million dollars." Peaches are susceptible also to phony peach, little peach, X or yellow-red disease, and peach mosaic, all of which cause losses. Stout (1939) reported that during 1938 approximately 18,000 new infections of peach mosaic were found in southern California, and this figure amounts to only one-half that of 1937. Approximately 81,000 diseased trees were found of which 63% were removed; 200,000 trees were abandoned.

Similarly, citrus is greatly affected by virus diseases, but actual losses to the citrus industry are difficult to determine. Psorosis has been reported in 8% (15,100) of the mature trees in 220 orange orchards in southern and central California (Moore *et al.*, 1955). The reduction in yield varied with the stage of the disease. The yield in stage one was not significantly different from that in the controls, whereas trees in stage three yielded 28% less than those in stage one. Tristeza was first observed in Argentina in 1930–31. It probably occurs in all the major citrus-producing areas of Brazil, Argentina, and Uruguay. Bennett and Costa (1949) reported that in about 12 years the virus spread to all citrus-producing areas of the state of São Paulo, infecting and destroying upwards of 6,000,000 trees, or about 75% of the orange trees in the state.

The Manila hemp plant, widely used for the production of rope fibers, was reported by Ocfemia (1949) to be infected by a mosaic virus that caused losses ranging from 90% in some plantings to almost 100% in others in the eastern part of Mindanao of the Philippine Islands. One of the most devastating viruses on record is that of cacao swollen shoot. Posnette (1945) reported that in the eastern province of the Gold Coast more and more cacao farms were being completely destroyed by the disease. On one farm over a five-year period, the virus killed 74% of the 30- to 40-year-old trees and 43% of the 20- to 30-year-old trees. The total production decreased from 30 tons per annum in 1926–29 to 20 tons in 1936–39, and to only 6 tons in 1943–44. In 1947, Posnette reported that over 1,000,000 cacao trees had been destroyed in the eastern province, and production was reduced from 116,000 tons in 1936 to 64,000 tons of cacao in 1945. One of the more dramatic diseases of recent times that is causing extensive losses is that of cadang-cadang (yellow mottle decline)

INTRODUCTION

of coconut palms in the Philippines. Although the disease is still of unknown etiology, it is thought to be caused by a virus. De Leon (1952) reported that over 1,500,000 trees were dying from the disease in the Bicol area, with yearly losses amounting to $1,800,000. Price (1958) reported that approximately 7,927,000 diseased trees, or about 47% of all trees, were destroyed or diseased in the Bicol region, representing a direct loss to the farmers of 33,293,000 pesos in 1956.

From these few cases it becomes evident that viruses extract an annual loss from most commercial crops. With an ever-increasing world population, this loss of food is very important to peace and the well-being of mankind. With increased knowledge of the nature of viruses, it is anticipated that these losses will be reduced if not eliminated.

* * *

This work was supported in part by Research Grant AI-03148 from the National Institute of Allergy and Infectious Diseases, National Institutes of Health, U.S. Public Health Service.

1–4. LITERATURE CITED

Ainsworth, G. C. (1939). Chronica Botan. **5**, 193.
Ainsworth, G. C. (1943). Ann. Appl. Biol. **30**, 187.
Allard, H. A. (1914) U.S. Dept. Agr. Bull. **40**.
Allard, H. A. (1915). J. Agr. Res. U.S. **3**, 295.
Allard, H. A. (1916). J. Agr. Res. U.S. **6**, 649.
Allard, H. A. (1917). J. Agr. Res. U.S. **10**, 615.
Aycock, R., and Winstead, N. N. (1955). Res. Farming N. Carolina **14**, 7.
Bald, J. G., and Norris, D. O. (1941). J. Council Sci. Ind. Research Aust. **14**, 187.
Baur, E. (1904). Ber. Deut. Botan. Ges. **22**, 453. (Phytopathological Classic **7**, 55. 1942).
Bawden, F. C. (1941). Chronica Botan. **6**, 385.
Bawden, F. C. (1950). Plant Viruses and Virus Diseases. Chronica Bot. Co., Waltham, Mass.
Bawden, F. C., Pirie, N. W., Bernal, J. D., and Fankuchen, I. (1936). Nature **138**, 1051.
Beijerinck, M. W. (1898). Verhandel. Koninkl. Ned. Akad. Wetenschap. (Amsterdam) **65**, 3. (Phytopathological Classic **7**, 33).
Bennett, C. W. (1939). Phytopathology **29**, 422.
Bennett, C. W., and Costa, A. S. (1949). J. Agr. Res. U.S. **78**, 207.
Bennett, C. W., Price, C., and Gillespie, G. E. (1954). Proc. Am. Soc. Sugar Beet Technologists **8**, 236.
Bernal, J. D., and Fankuchen, I. (1941). J. Gen. Physiol. **25**, 111.
Bever, W. M., and Pendleton, J. W. (1954). Plant Disease Reptr. **38**, 366.
Bjorling, K. (1949). Socker Handl. **5**, 119.
Bonde, R., Schultz, E. S., and Raleigh, W. P. (1943). Maine Agr. Exp. Sta. Bull. **421**, 128.
Brandes, J., and Wetter, C. (1959). Virology **8**, 99.
Brenner, S., and Horne, R. W. (1959). Biochim. et Biophys. Acta **34**, 103.
Brewbaker, H. E. (1942). Proc. Am. Soc. Sugar Beet Technologists **3**, 381.

Caldwell, J., and Prentice, I. W. (1942). Ann. Appl. Biol. **29**, 366.
Cane, Henry. (1720). Roy. Soc. [London] Phil. Trans. B. **31** (**366**), 102.
Carsner, E. (1925a). Phytopathology **15**, 745.
Carsner, E. (1925b). U.S. Dept. Agr. Official Rec. **4**, 3.
Cass Smith, W. P. (1945). J. Dep. Agr. W. Australia **22**, 20.
Chamberlain, E. E. (1936). New Zealand J. Agr. **53**, 321.
Chester, K. S. (1935). Phytopathology **25**, 686.
Chona, B. L. (1944). Indian Farming **5**, 178.
Chupp, C. H., and Paddock, W. C. (1949). Plant Disease Reptr. **33**, 280.
Corbett, M. K. (1955). Soil Sci. Soc. Florida Proc. **15**, 35.
De Leon, D. (1952). Foreign Agr. **16**, 103.
Doolittle, S. P. (1924). U.S. Dept. Agr. Circ. **321**.
Dvorak, M. (1927). J. Infectious Diseases **41**, 215.
Elze, D. L. (1931). Phytopathology **21**, 675.
Epstein, H. T. (1953). Nature **171**, 394.
Fawcett, H. S. (1940). Science **92**, 559.
Fawcett, H. S. (1942). Chronica Botan. **7**, 7.
Fraenkel-Conrat, H. (1956). J. Am. Chem. Soc. **78**, 882.
Fukushi, T. (1934). J. Fac. Agr. Hokkaido Imp. Univ. **37**, 41.
Gandy, D. G., and Hollings, M. (1962). Rep. Glasshouse Crops. Res. Inst. **1961**, 103.
Gierer, A., and Schramm, A. (1956). Nature **177**, 702.
Gram, E. (1942). Tidsskr. Planteavl. **47**, 338.
Hall, C. E. (1955). J. Biophys. Biochem. Cytol. **1**, 1.
Hansen, H. P. (1960). Am. Potato J. **37**, 187.
Harris, M. R. (1939). Calif. Dept. Agr. Bull. **28**, 201.
Heiling, A. (1953). Zucker. **6**, 27.
Holmes, F. O. (1929). Botan. Gaz. **87**, 39.

Holmes, F. O. (1939a). Phytopathology 29, 431.

Holmes, F. O. (1939b). Handbook of Phytopathogenic Viruses. Burgess, Minneapolis.

Holmes, F. O. (1948). The Filterable Viruses, in Bergey's Manual of Determinative Bacteriology. Suppl. 2, 1127. Williams and Wilkins, Baltimore.

Hughes, C. G. (1955). Cane Growers Quart. Bull. 18, 71.

Hull, R. (1954). Plant Pathol. 3, 130.

Hull, R. (1958). Agriculture (London) 65, 62.

Ivanowski, D. (1892). St. Petersb. Acad. Imp. Sci. Bull. 35, 67. (Phytopathological Classic 7, 27).

Johnson, J. (1927). Wisconsin Univ. Agr. Expt. Sta. Research Bull. 76.

Johnson, J. (1929). Wisconsin Univ. Agr. Expt. Sta. Research Bull. 87.

Johnson, J. (1942). Chronica Botan. 7, 65.

Kausche, G. A., Pfankuch, E., and Ruska, H. (1939). Naturwissenschaften 27, 292.

Kunkel, L. O. (1926). Am. J. Botany 13, 646.

Landrau, P., and Adsuar, J. (1953). J. Agr. Univ. Puerto Rico 37, 19.

Ling, L., and Yang, J. Y. (1940). Phytopathology 30, 338.

Luria, S. E. (1959). General Virology. John Wiley and Sons, Inc., N.Y.

Lwoff, A., Horne, R., and Tournier, P. (1962). Cold Spring Harbor Symp. Quant. Biol. 27, 51.

McKay, M. B., and Warner, M. F. (1933). Nat. Hort. Mag. 12, 179.

McKinney, H. H. (1929). J. Agr. Res. U.S. 39, 557.

McKinney, H. H. (1944). J. Wash. Acad. Sci. 34, 139.

Maramorosch, K. (1952). Phytopathology 42, 59.

Mayer, A. (1886). Landwirtsch. Vers. Sta. 32, 451. (Phytopathological Classic 7, 11).

Moore, P. W., Nauer, E., and Yendol, W. (1955). Calif. Citrograph 40, 82.

Mulvania, M. (1926). Phytopathology 16, 853.

Murphy, A. M. (1946). Proc. Am. Soc. Sugar Beet Technologists 4, 408.

Ocfemia, G. O. (1949). Philippine Agriculturist 33, 142.

Oswald, J. W., and Houston, B. R. (1951). Plant Disease Reptr. 35, 471.

Oswald, J. W., and Houston, B. R. (1953). Phytopathology 43, 128.

Phillips, Edward (1720). New World of Words or Universal English Dictionary. 7th ed. Kings Arm in St. Paul's Church Yard, London.

Porter, K. R., Claude, A., and Fullam, E. F. (1945). J. Exptl. Med. 81, 233.

Posnette, A. F. (1945). Cacao Res. Conf. 1945, 114.

Posnette, A. F. (1947). Ann. Appl. Biol. 34, 388.

Pound, G. S. (1948). J. Agr. Res. U.S. 77, 97.

Pound, G. S. (1949). J. Agr. Res. U.S. 78, 647.

Price, W. C. (1958). Food and Agr. Organization, U.N. Report 850.

Purdy, H. A. (1928). Proc. Soc. Expt. Biol. Med. 25, 702.

Purdy, H. A. (1929). J. Exp. Med. 49, 919.

Rochow, W. F. (1961). Advances in Agronomy 13, 217.

Roque, A., and Adsuar, J. (1941). J. Agr. Univ. Puerto Rico 25, 40.

Rosberg, D. W. (1953). Plant Disease Reptr. 37, 392.

Ross, A. F. (1950). Phytopathology 40, 445.

Safferman, R. S., and Morris, Mary-Ellen (1963). Science 140, 679.

Samuel, G., Bald, J. G., and Eardley, C. M. (1933). Phytopathology 23, 641.

Schultz, E. S., and Bonde, R. (1944). Am. Potato J. 21, 278.

Scott, R. J. (1941). Scot. J. Agr. 23, 258.

Sill, W. H., Fellows, H., and King, C. L. (1955). Plant Disease Reptr. 39, 29.

Smith, E. F. (1891). U.S. Dept. Agr. Div. Veg. Path. Bull. 1.

Smith, K. M. (1931). Nature 127, 852.

Smith, K. M. (1937). A Textbook of Plant Virus Diseases. P. Blakiston's Son and Co., Inc., Philadelphia.

Stanley, W. M. (1935). Science 81, 644.

Stanley, W. M., and Anderson, T. F. (1941). J. Biol. Chem. 139, 325.

Storey, H. H. (1931). 2nd Intern. Congr. Path. Paris II Compt. rend. Comm. 471.

Stout, G. L. (1939). Calif. Dept. Agr. Bull. 28, 117.

Stubbs, L. L. (1948). Australian J. Sci. 1, 303.

Stubbs, L. L. (1956). Plant Disease Reptr. 40, 763.

Takahashi, W. N., and Rawlins, T. E. (1933). Science 77, 26.

Thornberry, H. H. (1941). Phytopathology 31, 23.

Thung, T. H. (1931). Handel. Ned. Ind. Natuur. Cong. 6de, 450.

Timian, R. G., and Sisler, W. W. (1955). Plant Disease Reptr. 39, 550.

Tompkins, C. M. (1934). Phytopathology 24, 1136.

Valleau, W. D. (1940). Phytopathology 30, 820.

Valleau, W. D. (1942). Chronica Botan. 7, 152.

Van Hoof, H. A. (1956). Mededeel. Proefsta. Groenteteelt Ned. 3, 761.

Vasudeva, R. S., Raychaudhuri, S. P., and Pathanian, P. S. (1948). Current Sci. (India) 17, 244.

Vibert, M. (1863). J. Soc. Imp. Centrale. Hort. 9, 144.

Vinson, C. G. (1927). Science 66, 357.

Watson, M. A. (1942). Ann. Appl. Biol. 29, 358.

Watson, M. A., Watson, D. J., and Hull, R. (1946). J. Agr. Sci. 36, 151.

Watson, R. D. (1945). Plant Disease Reptr. 29, 317.

Weimer, J. L. (1950). Plant Disease Reptr. 34, 376.

Williams, R. C., and Wyckoff, R. W. G. (1945). Proc. Soc. Exp. Biol. Med. 58, 265.

Wingard, S. A. (1928). J. Agr. Res. U.S. 37, 127.

Woods, A. F. (1902). U.S. Dept. Agr. Bur. Plant Ind. Bull. 18.

Zazhurilo, V. K., and Sitnikova, G. M. (1939). C. R. Acad. Sci. U.S.S.R., N. S. 25, 798.

Zink, F. W. and Grogan, R. G. (1954). Plant Disease Reptr. 38, 844.

2

F. O. HOLMES

Symptomatology of viral diseases in plants

2–1. INTRODUCTION

AN IMPRESSIVE array of symptoms can be recognized today as expressions of viral diseases in plants. This is largely a result of the rapid growth of scientific literature on this subject in relatively recent years. New techniques have enriched observations. Our present data are far more varied in character than the initial findings of investigators three or four decades ago, when relatively few viral diseases of plants had been studied.

Pioneers in virology confined their attention almost entirely to foliage abnormalities, failing to note many of the changes that occurred in other parts of infected plants. Various modifications of chlorotic effects in leaves were the principal phenomena that led to recognition of the fact that viruses could cause diseases in plants just as fungi and bacteria had long been known to do.

An all-inclusive category, known under the name of "infectious chloroses," seemed adequate at first to contain all the viral diseases of plants. No sharp distinction was made between constituent types. Some variations were noted from the beginning, of course, but were not explicitly defined or differentiated until a considerable number of viral diseases had been studied with some care.

Gradually it came to be recognized that one large group of infectious chloroses, the

mosaic diseases, could be differentiated from another large group, the true yellows diseases. Both were found to be transmissible through graft unions, but the mosaic diseases were seen to be typically chlorotic-spotting maladies whereas the true yellows diseases were observed never to show any spotting patterns at all.

Further studies disclosed that the mosaic-type diseases could in many cases, although not invariably, be transmitted mechanically and that they usually had aphid vectors in nature. They proved generally resistant to brief heat treatments and characteristically did not terminate flowering or affect dormancy of buds. In these respects they differed sharply from the yellows-type diseases.

The true yellows diseases showed a tendency to produce virescent flowers and eventual cessation of blossoming, to break dormancy of all axillary buds, and to be leafhopper-transmitted. They seemed in general to be susceptible of cure by brief exposures at relatively high temperatures, such as 50°–55°C.

The ringspot diseases were recognized later as a third group. They resembled the mosaic diseases in having spotlike primary and secondary lesions, but had a strong tendency to disappearance of symptoms soon after onset and to development of what has been called "nonsterile" immunity to reinfection (that is, an immunity when

17

reinoculated, insofar as reinfection would be shown by recurrence of symptoms of onset after conditions of chronic disease were once established). They have proved not to be transmitted by aphids or by leafhoppers, but some of them are now known to be transmitted by nematodes (as summarized by Raski and Hewitt, 1963).

Additional major and minor groupings of viral diseases have been suggested in the recent literature, in some cases partly because of symptom resemblances (Bawden and Pirie, 1942; Hollings, 1957; Bos and van der Want, 1962); but in other cases largely on the basis of characteristics such as physical properties of the etiological agents (Broadbent and Heathcote, 1958; Cadman and Harrison, 1959; Harrison and Nixon, 1960), vector relationships (Freitag *et al.*, 1952; Harrison *et al.*, 1961; Brunt and Kenten, 1962), serological overlaps (Bagnall *et al.*, 1958; Bercks and Brandes, 1961), and tendencies to mutual suppression in plant hosts (Bawden and Kassanis, 1941, 1945; Valenta, 1959).

Symptomatology may be expected to extend far beyond our current conceptions eventually, for the presently known symptoms are largely such gross abnormalities as are discernible without recourse to careful laboratory-based studies. Virology has developed vigorously in recent years but obviously has not yet reached its culmination of growth.

Viruses and their innumerable strains appear able to upset in almost every conceivable way the processes by which plants grow and maintain themselves. Hence symptom expressions are of many kinds. Such discrete symptoms as have been reported in the virological literature form a discontinuous spectrum of abnormalities covering nearly the whole range of plant physiology.

It should not be concluded, however, that reported symptoms represent the only levels of abnormality that exist in nature. They seem to represent only a large number of deviations observed at random along a partially explored and fundamentally continuous spectrum, just as the inch markings and their subdivisions represent arbitrary points of reference along a foot rule.

Primary lesions illustrate this to advantage. They have been variously described in such terms as necrotic spot lesions, distinctly yellow primary lesions, chlorotic or faintly chlorotic spot lesions, ringlike lesions, chlorophyll-retaining lesions, and masked lesions that can be disclosed only by appropriate stains for starch content. Actually it is possible to produce lesions of intermediate character over this whole range of symptoms, by choosing sometimes more virulent and sometimes less virulent strains of each virus or by changing host plants to attain slightly higher or slightly lower levels of tolerance. Other variations in symptoms can be induced by utilizing the subtle effects of changes in light intensity and temperature that superpose on the virus-host system a great range of physiological modifications. Hence the specific symptoms that have been reported in the literature must be regarded as mere samples from a potentially unlimited range of symptoms of each type.

In the future we may expect to see additions to our present knowledge in the form of altogether unanticipated classes of symptoms. There will be, of course, a great number of intensity variants of these new kinds as well as new intensity variants of previously recognized types.

In reviewing the symptoms that have been reported thus far, it will not be feasible to refer to all of the viral diseases that can display each one. It seems important, however, to mention at least one or a few diseases in connection with each, because the cited diseases can then be looked up in textbooks or library records to locate the original literature dealing with the specific symptoms. It is not feasible to give specific literature citations for the very large number of symptoms specified here nor is it possible to guarantee that the diseases mentioned as examples are the first reported, the most conspicuous, or the most appropriate ones that might have been selected to exemplify each symptom. When a disease name includes the name of a host plant, the symptom under discussion will be understood to occur in the host thus implied unless some other host is explicitly named.

The following account represents as accurately as possible our present accumulation of factual data in respect to the symptomatology of viral diseases in plants. The symptoms are treated here by dealing first with the extensive list of those that are expressed in diseased foliage and then with the relatively few, although still numerous, symptoms that are concerned with other parts of the plant hosts, such as flowers, fruits, stems, buds, and roots, or that involve the plant as a whole. Masked symptoms are discussed in a final section.

2–2. FOLIAGE SYMPTOMS

Foliage symptoms include abnormalities in leaves with respect to color, number, shape, size, texture, luster, and position, as well as abnormalities of histology, cytology, and basic physiological processes; a variety of effects also involve premature death of whole leaves or of macroscopic parts of leaves.

A. ABNORMALITIES OF LEAF COLOR

Leaves affected by viral diseases show a great number of color abnormalities. These may be separated into the following categories: Abnormalities of over-all color, vein patterns, mottling patterns, spotting patterns, ring patterns, and line patterns.

1. *Abnormalities of over-all color in leaves.*—Foliage is usually less green than normal in plants affected by viral diseases, but a few diseases are characterized by darker than normal green foliage.

Foliage is reported to be abnormally green in peach phony disease, dark green in Fiji disease of sugar cane, potato spindle tuber, raspberry alpha leaf curl, and black-raspberry streak. It is described as dark bluish green in blue dwarf of oats. Leaves are normally green or abnormally dark green in potato green dwarf (potato curly top), and darkened at first in tobacco yellow dwarf.

On the other hand, chlorosis appears in all newly developing foliage in aster yellows and many other yellows-type diseases. Leaves are lighter green than normal in strawberry witches' broom, light in color in potato infected by potato virus S, and pale in sugar-cane dwarf.

A yellow cast of foliage appears in potato plants carrying the yellow mottle strain of potato X virus. Flavescence of leaflets is seen in potato witches' broom. Leaves are yellowed in later stages of potato yellow dwarf. Young leaves are yellowed in tomato bushy stunt. Extreme chlorosis of foliage, somewhat resembling the effect of magnesium deficiency, is shown by soybean after infection by the virus of alfalfa mosaic. Brightly yellowed foliage in the early season is characteristic of yellow mosaic in grapevines. Outer leaves are yellowed in sugar-beet yellows.

A diffuse bleaching of uninoculated trifoliate leaves has been reported in cowpea systemically affected by pea wilt. Leaves of sweet orange trees on sour orange roots acquire a dull ashen color in quick decline (tristeza) disease. Silvery upper leaf surfaces are said to be characteristic of cherry vein-clearing disease as seen by reflected light. Bronzed leaves that are slightly glistening are reported for raspberry alpha leaf curl. Leaves become uniformly golden bronze green to olive brown as early as June in cherry albino disease. Young leaves are usually purplish underneath in tomato big bud.

A diffused and blended yellow and red discoloration of foliage has been noted in peach yellow-red virosis. This same disease in another host plant produces even more striking color changes, a brilliant red to yellow coloration of foliage six to seven weeks after growth starts in spring, intensifying with the season, in chokecherry in its first year of manifesting yellow-red virosis; there is a dulling of reddened foliage in the second and third years of this disease in chokecherry.

Yellowing of tips of leaves in summer with later premature reddening of leaf margins occurs in blueberry stunt. Foliage is reddened or orange-yellow in carrot affected by motley dwarf disease. A bronzy red color is acquired early in ocean-spray witches' broom. Red to purple discoloration appears in leaves affected by the Mesa Central type of corn stunt disease, but only a tinge of red appears in leaves affected by the Rio Grande type of this disease. Leaves are at first dull green but later prematurely bright red in strawberry green petal disease. On the other hand, leaves may remain green after normal foliage takes on autumn coloration in Muir peach dwarf disease.

Old leaves become chlorotic near their tips in wheat streak mosaic. The margins of leaves are yellow in strawberry yellow edge. Areas of leaves appear rusty in cherry rusty mottle.

2. *Vein patterns.*—The movement of viruses along veins is more rapid than through tissues of the leaf lamina in general. This causes a variety of vein-oriented symptoms.

A transitory chlorotic vein-clearing is the first observable evidence of systemic disease in aster yellows and tobacco mosaic, as well as in many other yellows-type and mosaic-type diseases. It has been reported also in cacao swollen shoot disease. A pronounced yellow clearing of veins is characteristic of the onset of turnip yellow mosaic. Veins show clearing and thickening in peach rosette. Flecks of vein-clearing in lime foliage are hailed as the first evidences of the presence of tristeza virus after experimental transmission by grafting.

Veins appear greener and hence darker than normal in tobacco leaf curl. Dark green veins are reported also in Pierce's disease of grape, caused by the virus of alfalfa dwarf. Veins of young leaves are blackened in broad bean vascular wilt.

Veinbanding mosaic, in which green bands of tissue border the veins in otherwise mottled leaves, is characteristic of infections by potato Y virus in tobacco, as well as of mild mosaic in potato. Brown veinbanding is reported in some rose varieties affected by rose streak.

Persistent yellowing occurs along veins in Euonymus mosaic. Yellowing along veins has been reported in red clover vein mosaic; the causative virus of this disease induces the appearance of whitish bands along veins in infected plants of *Vicia faba* L. Yellowing of veins that tends to be masked in summer is said to be characteristic of alfalfa vein yellowing disease. Foliage is yellow veined in yellow vein disease of grapevines. Bright yellow chlorosis of veins and veinlets accounts for the name of sugar-beet yellow net disease. Yellow chlorosis of veins and veinlets is observed in yellow net disease of tomato. A network of yellow veins encloses islands of green tissue in yellow vein-mosaic of okra. Yellowing along the margins of veins is found in peach golden-net disease. Yellow spots and blotches on the larger veins, extending into the adjacent parenchyma a distance of one millimeter or more, characterize sugar-beet yellow vein disease.

Chlorotic starlike lesions occur along veins in peach asteroid spot disease. Starlike spots, consisting of coalescent pellucid veins, are found in asteroid mosaic of grape. Chlorotic flecking, mostly along veins of dwarfed and puckered leaves, occurs in apple leaf-pucker disease. Chlorotic spots appear on veins in strawberry veinbanding.

Interveinal reddish browning on both leaf surfaces, extending from margins inward, has been reported as a summer symptom in crimson clover infected by the virus of potato yellow dwarf. Interveinal areas become reddish in filaree red leaf disease. Interveinal chlorosis occurs in barley yellow dwarf and hop yellow net. Fine brown lines parallel to main veins, followed by death and dropping out of included areas, are recorded for tatter leaf disease in sweet cherry.

3. *Mottling in leaves.*—Chlorotic mottling, apparently caused by the nonuniform establishment of secondary lesions in developing leaves, is typical of mosaic diseases in general. If the degree of chlorosis is slight, the condition is sometimes described as green mottling; when extreme, it may be referred to as yellow mottling or even white mottling.

Green mottling is attributed to typical cucurbit mosaic and tobacco mosaic. Mild dark green mosaic mottling is caused by an isolate of so-called mild dark green mosaic virus from *Nicotiana glauca* L. when this is introduced into plants of cultivated tobacco. Yellow mottling is mentioned as occurring in Hyoscyamus (henbane) mosaic, turnip yellow mosaic, and lettuce yellow mosaic. Yellow mottle is seen in potato aucuba mosaic and dandelion yellow mosaic. White mottling has been reported in connection with a mosaic caused in tobacco by cucumber mosaic virus of Price's strains

2 and 4. Gray mottling is said to be found with yellow mottling in Ornithogalum mosaic.

Systemic chlorotic variegation occurs in Abutilon mosaic. The chlorotic spots in this disease have a tendency to be limited by veins more than is the case in such diseases as tobacco mosaic or cucumber mosaic.

Feathery chlorotic patterns, consisting of finely branched yellow mottle along small veins with or without many small diffusely margined spots, account for the name of sweetpotato feathery mottle disease. Feather-like mosaic mottling is said to occur also in cacao swollen shoot disease. Vein feathering is mentioned in connection with yellow bud mosaic in almond.

4. *Spotting patterns in leaves.*—Spotting of leaves sometimes represents the local damage at sites of infection in foliage (primary lesions) but often is caused in systemic disease by the formation of relatively few and hence widely separated and discrete secondary lesions.

Yellowish-green primary lesions are occasionally seen in tobacco mosaic, although they tend to be so faintly contrasted with the color of the healthy leaf surface as to be overlooked. Yellowish primary lesions in *Nicotiana rustica* L. infected by typical potato yellow dwarf virus are used for quantitative estimation of viral concentrations in inocula. Raised yellow primary lesions have been described in pineapple infected by tomato spotted wilt virus.

Primary lesions are disclosed by chlorophyll retention in older leaves of tomato affected by bushy stunt disease. Chlorophyll is retained in lesions as leaves turn yellow in peach asteroid spot disease.

Pale spotting of leaf bases is reported in maize streak. Leaves show a fine chlorotic stippling in *achaparramiento,* or corn stunt, disease. Small pale-yellow to paper-white spots aggregated near tips of leaves are reported in plum white spot disease. Pale spots between veins near tips of older leaves are found in maize leaf fleck. Pale spots appear in leaves in cotton leaf curl. Petioles are white-streaked or spotted in western celery mosaic. Yellow spotting occurs in interveinal areas of leaves in red clover vein mosaic. Small bright yellow dots appear on leaves in bean yellow dot disease. Small yellow spots in irregular patches on leaves are characteristic of bean yellow stipple. Small, circular, stellate, or dendritic yellowish spots occur in spring in Pelargonium leaf curl; the centers of these spots usually become necrotic and leaves become twisted by unequal growth of unaffected and affected tissues.

Orange to reddish blotches appear on leaves in red leaf of oats. Purple or purple-brown spotting on young leaves occurs in pea streak. A red pigmentation in spots that later become dry and drop out has been reported for vine mosaic. Chlorosis at leaf base extends upward in plum blotch; the chlorotic blotches in developing foliage become reddish brown and develop shot holes. A blotching type of chlorosis has been reported in sugar-beet mosaic. A reddish discoloration of pulvini of leaves and leaflets occurs in bean red node.

5. *Ring patterns in leaves.*—Whitish necrotic rings and concentric markings are typical of tobacco ringspot and allied diseases. Incomplete chlorotic rings develop interveinally on newly formed leaves in Bergerac ringspot of tobacco. Rings consisting of nonnecrotic areas alternating with necrotic patches are characteristic of tobacco broken ringspot. Bronze ringlike secondary lesions are characteristic features of tomato spotted wilt. Ringlike necrotic primary lesions are found in tomato bushy stunt. Small black necrotic rings or spots appear in cabbage black ringspot. Both local and systemic lesions appear as small, black, necrotic rings in tomato black-ring disease; if the rings coalesce, affected tissues often collapse and die.

6. *Line patterns in leaves.*—Line patterns are especially common in the viral diseases of grasses. In these they may represent distortions of spotting patterns or fused spotting patterns. In other plants, line patterns are doubtless related often to extensive ring patterns.

Chlorotic streaks near the bases of young leaves, later fusing to form continuous stripes, have been observed in maize stripe. Fine chlorotic striae followed by yellowing of leaves occur in wheat striate mosaic. Broken chlorotic streaks on tips of young leaves characterize wheat streak mosaic.

Yellow bands or irregular chlorotic rings on mature leaves have been noted in delphinium ringspot; yellow streaks at the bases of developing leaves, in onion yellow dwarf; and green and yellow zigzag bands, in celery calico.

Long, narrow, longitudinal streaks of creamy or white tissues have been reported in sugar-cane chlorotic streak disease; light colored line patterns, in Prunus line pattern disease; and pale stripes from midrib to margin of leaf, in marble disease of cardamom.

Necrotic or yellowish concentric lines on affected leaves have been seen in Odontoglossum orchid ringspot; reddish brown to blackish pitting and sunken streaks in leaves and pseudo-bulbs, in Cattleya orchid virosis; chlorotic elongate areas and later necrotic spots and streaks, in black-streak disease of Cymbidium orchids.

Oak-leaf patterns, extending farther along main veins than between these, are occasionally noted in many and perhaps all mosaic-type and ringspot-type diseases.

B. Abnormalities of Leaf Number

Tobacco plants infected by severe etch virus show an increased rate of leaf production as well as a delay of flowering; hence more leaves are produced by infected than by normal plants.

Fewer than normal leaves appear in sweet cherry necrotic rusty mottle because some buds and leaf spurs die in this disease. Leaves are few in pear stony pit.

In general, leaves are more numerous than is normal in viral diseases that break the dormancy of buds and less numerous than normal in those that induce premature defoliation.

C. Abnormalities of Leaf Shape

A well-nigh universal expression of viral diseases in plants is distortion of leaf contours. This distortion varies greatly in degree. There are almost imperceptible deviations from normal shape in leaves of so-called "recovered" (i.e., chronically diseased as opposed to acutely diseased) plants affected by ringspot diseases. Better recognized are the moderately pinched leaf tips and intermediate irregularities of leaf margins displayed in many mosaic diseases. Occasionally one may see extreme conditions of fern-leaf and shoe-string manifestations, in which the leaf lamina between veins is poorly developed or hardly developed at all, as is sometimes the case in tomato plants affected by cucumber mosaic, by special strains of tobacco mosaic, or by complexes including one or both of these as constituents. Leaves are distorted and sometimes filamentous in the eggplant mosaic of India. Filiform leaves characterize late stages of teasel mosaic.

Leaves are almost round and lack teeth in their margins in spoon leaf of red currant, caused by a strain of raspberry ringspot virus. In contrast to this, leaves become lobed because of varying degrees of imperfect growth of lamina in tobacco streak.

Definite enations, which are leafy outgrowths of variable size, appear conspicuously in sweet cherry rasp leaf and pea enation mosaic. In the latter disease, although the enations are usually blister-like or ridgelike pseudo-enations or true lamina-like enations on the undersides of pea leaflets and stipules, they have been observed also as imbricated, prominently veined, leaflike tissue with a short stalklike attachment to the main stem of the pea plant. Conspicuous enations occur in aspermy disease in *Nicotiana glutinosa* L., generally as leafy outgrowths from the lower surface of the leaf but occasionally as outgrowths from the upper surface of the midrib, producing a structure resembling a small new leaf.

Lamina-like enations seem to be the extreme members of a series of abnormalities that would include veins greened and thickened, as in tobacco leaf curl and cotton leaf curl (which sometimes also show fully developed enations), veins swollen in sugar-beet leaf curl, and unevenly thickened veins that are depressed below the upper surface of the leaf (also sometimes with full enations) in crimson clover big vein disease (caused by wound tumor virus). In Fiji disease of sugar cane, galls appear on the lower surfaces of leaves, formed on vascular bundles through proliferation of phloem and nearby cells. Sharp protuberances on lower surfaces of veins as well as knotlike swellings resembling galls on distorted veins occur in sugar-beet curly top. Enations develop on veins within 18 to 33 days after transmission to lime of citrus vein-enation virus by the aphid *Myzus persicae* (Sulz.).

Leaves are thickened in tomato big bud, sugar-beet curly top, potato yellow dwarf, potato leaf roll, and sugar-beet yellows. They are thinner than normal, in their yellow areas, in sugar-beet mosaic and mosaic diseases in general.

Leaves are described as shortened and crumpled in Fiji disease of sugar cane, short in sugar-beet yellows, dwarfed in peach rosette, and dwarfed and curled downward in beet savoy.

Leaves are blistered in cucurbit mosaic, cotton leaf curl, and citrus infectious mottling, sometimes savoyed in clover club leaf, and crinkled in tobacco leaf curl, raspberry leaf curl, and bean mosaic.

Leaves are said to be rolled in sugar-beet curly top and potato leaf roll, rolled upward in cherry leaf roll, rolled downward in grape leaf roll, rugose, rolling downward, thickened, and later savoyed in tobacco yellow dwarf. They are cupped at tips of terminal shoots in autumn in apple star-crack disease, cupped inward in grape fan leaf, and cupped outward in filaree red leaf. They are cupped upward in potato green dwarf, but are said to resemble inverted spoons, with their margins curled downward, in tobacco rattle disease.

Leaves are described as curled in black-raspberry streak, curled upward in hop nettlehead, curled lengthwise and upward in quick decline of citrus, and arched downward in flowering cherry rough bark disease.

Leaves are tattered in peach yellow-red virosis (X disease). They are perforated by the dropping out of spots in vine mosaic and tatter leaf of sweet cherry. Late in the season, usually after harvest, affected areas fall out of leaves, producing a conspicuous shot-hole effect, in sweet cherry necrotic rusty mottle.

Leaves are described as narrow and flat in black currant reversion disease; short, narrow, and stiff in abacá bunchy top; short

and rigid in blue dwarf of oats. They are simple rather than normally compound in shoots from potato tubers formed in potato witches' broom. Leaves become sickle-shaped as a result of unsymmetrical chlorosis in olive sickle-leaf disease. Leaf blades are often bilaterally unequal in cherry twisted leaf.

Leaves of onion, which are normally more or less circular in cross section, are described as flattened in onion yellow dwarf. Leaves of raspberry are fluted along veins in raspberry decline. Leaves are said to be folded in strawberry stunt. They have a ribbed appearance in tobacco yellow dwarf. They are folded along their midveins in cherry vein-clearing.

Leaves are warped in citrus psorosis and twisted in rape savoy. The leaf spindle is twisted in sugar-cane dwarf.

Leaflets are described as recurved in rose wilt; narrow, cupped, and twisted in western celery mosaic; and slightly cupped convexly in cowpea mosaic.

Midribs are said to be curved in cauliflower mosaic, tortuous in strawberry stunt, split and cracked underneath in flowering cherry rough bark disease, and bent downward in cherry twisted leaf. Midveins of leaflets arch downward in strawberry witches' broom.

Veins are reduced in number in black currant reversion disease. They are shortened in raspberry leaf curl. Veins are crooked in tobacco infected by tobacco vein-distorting virus.

Petioles are undulating in crimson clover affected by big vein (wound tumor) disease, thickened in anemone alloiophylly, spindly in strawberry witches' broom, and slender in potato spindle tuber. They curve outward in filaree red leaf disease. In carrot motley dwarf, petioles are twisted and sometimes S-shaped or bent backward so that undersurfaces of leaves are exposed to view. Stipules are enlarged in cherry Western X disease.

Leaf margins turn down in strawberry stunt. They are puckered in cotton leaf curl, rolled down in bean mosaic, curling down in raspberry leaf curl, curled downward in a spoonlike fashion in red currant spoon leaf (caused by a strain of raspberry ringspot virus), and curved downward in strawberry witches' broom. Fissures are formed at leaf edges in rape savoy.

D. Abnormalities of Leaf Size

In respect to leaf size, there seem to be almost no reports of gigantism in leaves, despite greatly increased size of calyx lobes in some yellows-type diseases. Leaves that have been reduced in width often seem longer than normal and may even be so without this having been specifically noted in published literature. Attention should be given in the future to clarification of this point. Already there have been some hints. Leaves on the Drake almond tree when affected by bud failure disease are reported to be possibly somewhat larger than those on nonaffected trees. Some leaves on tobacco plants, produced after infection by severe etch virus, have proved both longer and wider than comparable leaves on healthy control plants (their thicknesses and weights are not reported).

Reduction of leaf size, on the other hand, is exceedingly common and perhaps in one degree or another nearly universal. In some cases leaves become so small that a host species becomes almost unidentifiable. In potato witches' broom, black locust witches' broom, and eggplant little leaf, successively formed leaves are progressively smaller until even a trained botanist would find difficulty in recognizing the host plants as potato, black locust, and eggplant, respectively. Except among the yellows-type diseases, however, such uniform and extreme reduction of leaf size seems not to occur, yet there is very commonly an appreciable degree of reduction, as in alfalfa dwarf where leaves are small. Individual leaves are occasionally greatly reduced in size, as in tomato affected by cucumber mosaic, in which there may be formed no more than a miniature petiole and midvein to represent a particular leaf. Absence of the leaf lamina or narrowing of its apical portion greatly distorts tobacco leaves affected by the Brazilian disease, *necrose branca,* or white necrosis.

Shortened young petioles are described as occurring in western celery mosaic, and this is the more important because petioles are the commercially desirable parts of celery leaves. Petioles are short in strawberry stunt and potato yellow dwarf also.

E. Abnormalities of Leaf Texture

Leaves are described as less rigid than normal, when young, in corn infected by the mottle strain of maize streak virus. They may droop and appear somewhat wilted in cherry vein-clearing. Leaves appear wilted but are stiff in cherry leaf roll.

Leaves are described as stiff in sugarcane dwarf, stiff and small in potato yellow dwarf, brittle in rose wilt, rigid in Phenomenal berry after infection by the virus of loganberry dwarf, leathery in little peach disease, pea leaf roll, and potato leaf roll, but unusually tender in citrus psorosis.

An interesting feature of strawberry stunt is that leaves give a papery rattle when they are brushed by hand. In leaf roll of cherry, also, leaves rattle when shaken. In sugar-beet yellows, in which leaves are thickened and brittle, they are said to crackle or rustle when brushed. Tobacco leaves rattle when disturbed in tobacco rattle disease.

F. Abnormalities of Leaf Luster

Leaves are glazed in prune dwarf. They show a glazed-appearing upper surface in tobacco infected by tomato big bud virus.

Foliage appears dry in raspberry leaf curl. It is dull in strawberry stunt. It is sometimes less glossy than normal in peach line pattern disease.

G. Abnormalities of Leaf Position

Leaves are abnormally erect in most yellows-type diseases. They are rigidly upright in Drake almond bud failure disease instead of bending away from the twig as in normal trees. They are unusually close together, forming rosettes on terminals, in yellow-red virosis of chokecherry. Short stems bear leaves in rosettes in peach rosette disease. The leaves are bunched in tobacco yellow dwarf. Yellowed or reddened leaves curl downward close to the ground on dwarfed plants in lily rosette, or yellow flat, disease. Rosetting occurs in barley and other cereal plants affected by *enanismo,* or dwarf disease, in Colombia.

In black-raspberry streak, leaves are abnormally close together on canes and often are twisted so as to be upside down. Leaves are mostly restricted to the tips of branches, giving a "lion's tail effect," in citrus xyloporosis. Leaflets are crowded in rose wilt.

Leaves may be prostrate in onion yellow dwarf. They hang close to the stem in tobacco after infection by tomato big bud virus. They droop at the pulvini in southern bean mosaic. Petioles of older leaves become horizontal in western celery mosaic.

Small incurved new leaves form a compact head in sugar-beet leaf curl. Lettuce mosaic, on the other hand, is characterized by defective heading of plants.

H. Abnormalities of Leaf Histology

Vascular bundles in leaves are enlarged, irregular in shape, and fused in sugar-cane dwarf. They are said to be more numerous than usual in anemone alloiophylly. Vascular tissues are described as darkened in sugar-beet mosaic.

Phloem degeneration is followed by formation of supernumerary sieve tubes in sugar-beet curly top. Necroses occur in phloem and adjoining sheath tissues in lily rosette. Phloem necrosis has been noted in winter wheat mosaic.

Palisade cells are reported as abnormally short in anemone alloiophylly; chloroplasts are smaller and fewer in these cells. Winter wheat mosaic is also reported to show chloroplasts that are few and small in affected tissues, as do many other infectious chloroses, such as sugar-cane streak.

I. Abnormalities of Leaf Cytology

Intracellular inclusions of kinds not found in healthy plants characterize many viral diseases. Some of these inclusions are found only in the cytoplasm but others are intranuclear or intranucleolar.

Abnormal intracellular inclusions are spherical or oval in Fiji disease of sugar cane. Vacuolate intracellular bodies have been described in connection with sandal spike, rice dwarf, tobacco mosaic, Hippeastrum mosaic, and potato mottle.

Amoeboid intracytoplasmic bodies are abundant in subveinal epidermis in turnip mosaic.

Intracytoplasmic crystalline inclusions occur commonly in tobacco mosaic, but never in the closely mimicking mosaic induced by infection with cucumber mosaic virus. Intracytoplasmic amorphous inclusions that tend to crystallize, forming needle-shaped birefringent bodies, are reported in tobacco etch. Crystalline inclusions in red clover vein mosaic are said to contain ribonucleic acid but not deoxyribonucleic acid, starch, or fats; amorphous inclusions are reported in this disease also. Protein crystals are found in affected cells in oat pupation disease. Cigar-shaped inclusion bodies are found in cactus virosis.

Isometric crystals occur in host cell nuclei and cytoplasm of *Vicia faba* L. affected by pea mosaic. Intranuclear crystalline inclusions, in the form of thin rectangular plates, occur in tobacco etch. Spherical, sometimes multiple, inclusion bodies in hypertrophic nuclei of phloem parenchyma cells have been reported in cotton leaf crumple disease.

Nuclei are enlarged and contain extra nucleoli in winter wheat mosaic. Intranucleolar inclusions of proteinaceous type are recorded for bean yellow mosaic in broad bean.

J. Abnormalities of Miscellaneous Physiological Processes in Leaves

A wide variety of disturbances of physiological processes not obviously associated with abnormalities of structure have been noted as symptoms of viral diseases.

Early unfurling of new leaves is characteristic of abacá bunchy top. In contrast to this, young leaves are said to be slow to unfold in crimson clover affected by clover club leaf. Delay in foliage development has been reported for red raspberry mosaic, Pierce's disease of grape, star-crack disease of apple, and weak peach disease.

Leaf tissues are described as having excessive starch content, as well as an increased concentration of reducing sugars, in potato leaf roll; serine and aspartic acid are less, but γ-aminobutyric acid more, concentrated than normal in this disease. In sugar-beet yellows, old leaves contain an abnormally large content of carbohydrate, and the greater part of the additional carbohydrate consists of reducing sugars; also, two substances are formed that fluoresce and appear as white spots in chromatograms. Sugar-beet mild yellows is not characterized by these fluorescent substances but produces at least six yellow or orange pigments in addition to those in healthy leaves.

Starch is slow to accumulate in primary and secondary lesions of tobacco mosaic in young tobacco leaves; once accumulated, it is slow to disappear from these same lesions during subsequent periods of darkness; thus, at appropriate times it is possible to detect starch-deficient and starch-retaining lesions by the use of iodine stains. Starch is said to be removed abnormally slowly from darkened leaves in citrus tristeza disease.

Ribonuclease activity is said to increase twice as much in leaves of cowpea inoculated with cucumber mosaic virus as in leaves abraded without inoculum.

It has been noted that there is a slightly decreased respiration just before, and a strongly increased respiration immediately after, the appearance of primary necrotic lesions in leaves of *Nicotiana glutinosa* L. as a result of infection by tobacco mosaic virus (TMV). Infection of tobacco leaves by tobacco etch virus does not change respiration rates until leaves show external symptoms, but respiration then rises sharply and remains high throughout the life of the leaves.

An excess of proline in midsummer distinguishes peach Western-X-diseased leaves from normal; abnormal retention of pipecolic acid after springtime has also been noticed and introduction of D,L-pipecolic acid into leaves of healthy trees produces reddening of veins and other effects resembling the symptoms of the disease in nature.

The attraction of vascular bundles for dodder as a parasite is said to be lowered in sugar-beet curly top. The attractiveness of peach trees to Japanese beetles is increased by peach yellows.

Leaves absciss prematurely in sour cherry yellows, peach yellow-red virosis (X disease), cacao swollen shoot, and cherry rusty mottle. All infected leaves absciss

promptly after the appearance of necrotic primary lesions in Tabasco pepper plants inoculated with tobacco mosaic virus, thus saving the plants from systemic infection. Pea plants tend to be defoliated when infected by alsike clover mosaic virus 2.

Inoculated leaves wilt but remain attached in pea wilt. Leaves yellow and die but remain attached when dry in olive die-back. Leaves drop or dry on tree in quick decline of citrus (tristeza disease).

A clear viscid exudate, which may later turn black and sticky, appears on petioles, midribs, or veins on the lower surface of leaves affected by sugar-beet curly top.

K. Abnormalities Comprising Death of Whole Leaves or of Macroscopic Parts of Leaves

The usefulness of so-called local-lesion hosts for measuring relative concentrations of viruses in samples of inoculum has led to conscious search for plants capable of responding sharply to initial infections and specifically for plants in which tissues tend to die promptly in the immediate vicinity of the first infected cells, thus producing conspicuous necrotic primary lesions. Experience has shown that most mosaic-type and most ringspot-type diseases have such hosts among potentially susceptible but not usually infected herbaceous species, but that no such local-lesion hosts can be found for yellows-type diseases.

Necrotic primary lesions are described in the literature as brown in leaves of Tabasco pepper infected by tobacco mosaic virus, dull red in cowpea infected by cucumber mosaic virus, reddish in cowpea infected by tomato bushy stunt virus, white in tobacco infected by tobacco ringspot, and black in tomato infected by alfalfa mosaic virus. They may be simple dead spots as in cucumber infected by tomato bushy stunt virus or zonate lesions as in pea wilt and most ringspots. Leaves may show brown necrotic primary lesions with gray centers as in *Nicotiana rustica* L. infected by an especially severe strain of potato yellow dwarf virus. A light yellow nonnecrotic halo may surround a dark brown necrotic peripheral ring which in turn surrounds a light brown center, as in primary lesions in cucumber infected by the virus of pea streak. Sometimes indistinct yellowish primary lesions, resembling the haloes mentioned above, become slowly necrotic, as in tobacco broad ringspot. Necrotic primary lesions may be surrounded by chlorotic haloes in *Physalis peruviana* L. after inoculation with tobacco etch virus. Similar necrotic lesions usually lack conspicuous chlorotic haloes in *Nicotiana glutinosa* L. after inoculation with TMV. In hybrid derivatives of *Nicotiana rustica* L. inoculated with TMV, individual plants characteristically display such necrotic lesions surrounded by conspicuous chlorotic haloes if a recessive gene is present but the necrotic lesions lack haloes and appear more promptly after inoculation if a dominant allele replaces this.

Secondary necrotic lesions in young leaves may be isolated spots or rings, or may be large numbers of spots so close together as to cause collapse of whole leaves. Sometimes whitish secondary necrotic lesions may appear not as solid spots but as indistinct flecks or arcs and rings, as in tobacco infected by the virus of alfalfa mosaic. Necrotic flecking is reported in chlorotic areas of leaves affected by cauliflower mosaic. Necrotic etching along veins and peripherally around chlorotic primary and secondary lesions occurs in tobacco etch disease.

Necrotic lesions produced by tobacco necrosis virus as a result of inoculation of leaves of French bean are smaller, and sometimes more numerous, if the so-called satellite virus is also present; this satellite virus has been found to multiply detectably only in the presence of tobacco necrosis virus, from which, however, it is serologically distinct.

When necrosis occurs within the creamy or white streaks of sugar-cane chlorotic streak disease, it begins in mesophyll and involves vascular bundles late.

Necrotic spots of irregular shape and of blackish-brown color occur in foliage of doubly-infected tomato plants wherever tobacco mosaic virus and potato X virus invade the same individual cells. Necrotic flecks in leaves of Easter lily are distinctive features of the double-virus infection that involves lily-symptomless virus plus cucumber mosaic virus.

Outer leaves are reported to die from their tips back in spinach affected by sugarbeet mosaic. Leaf edges are scorched in some varieties of lettuce affected by lettuce mosaic. Foliage shows burning and scalding, with death of leaf margins, in Pierce's disease of grape. Inoculated leaves are killed in pea and bean plants infected by alsike clover mosaic virus. They are reported to collapse in *Nicotiana rustica* L. infected heavily by potato yellow dwarf.

Veinal necrosis of older leaves appears in tobacco that has been infected by tomato big bud virus. Young leaves show a bronze veinal necrosis in lettuce infected by dandelion yellow mosaic virus. Interveinal necrosis is described as a feature of sugarbeet yellows disease in spinach.

2–3. FLOWER SYMPTOMS

Flower symptoms include abnormalities of flower color, size, number, shape, position, pollen and egg viability, time of blossoming, and persistence.

A. Abnormalities of Flower Color

"Broken" or variegated flowers have long been recognized as features of some viral diseases. In the case of tulip mosaic the resulting patterns were once valued as ornamental and still are sometimes admired despite the relatively poor growth of affected plants. Streaks on petals may be a result of decreased pigmentation, as is usual in tulip mosaic, or a result of increased pigmentation, as in tulip color-adding disease. Streaks as a result of local intensification of flower pigments characterize cranberry false blossom.

Transparency of flowers has been noted in black currant reversion disease. Opaque frostlike streaks on perianth and cup of flower are reported for narcissus mosaic. White boat-shaped spots and streaks, sometimes with pink centers, are seen in pink-flowered peach affected by peach mosaic. Vinca flowers that normally are white with red centers show progressive suppression of red pigment after infection by the virus of corn stunt. Blotches of light and dark green on flower stalks occur in Ornithogalum mosaic.

One of the commonest abnormalities of flower color is virescence, or greening of petals, a nearly universal characteristic of the true yellows diseases, especially note-worthy in aster yellows, tomato big bud, and strawberry green petal.

B. Abnormalities of Flower Size

Flowers are dwarfed to a greater or less extent in many viral diseases, as for ex-ample in chrysanthemum flower distortion disease. Occasionally parts of flowers be-come abnormally large. A bladder-like structure may result from fusion of en-larged sepals, as in tomato big bud. Gigan-tic though often still discrete calyx lobes may be produced, as in tomato experimen-tally infected by cranberry false blossom virus. In strawberry green petal disease, also, sepals are enlarged. Enlarged sepals on male flowers but not on female flowers are reported in cucumber witches' broom.

C. Abnormalities of Flower Number

Abnormally profuse blooming has been noted as a feature of sandal spike and cherry vein-clearing diseases. Flower buds are more often geminate (with two com-plete flower buds on a common receptacle, enclosed by a single set of bud scales) in peach mosaic than in healthy peach trees.

Fewer than the normal number of flowers develop in each inflorescence in chirke disease of cardamom. Blossoming ceases in pigeon-pea sterility disease. Flo-rets are blasted in oat yellow leaf disease. First-formed floral heads sometimes are killed in lettuce mosaic, but side shoots later produce seeds.

Yellows-type diseases usually show an unfruitfulness of flowers that is often a prel-ude to complete suppression of flowering, as in alfalfa witches' broom. There is grad-ual suppression of flowering in Vinca in-fected by chrysanthemum flower distortion virus.

D. Abnormalities of Flower Shape

Petals are narrow and distorted in prune dwarf. The corolla tends to split and petals are curiously "apiculated," showing thread-like tips, in the Brazilian disease *necrose branca*, or white necrosis, which is probably the same as the North American tobacco streak. The calyx and corolla may be twisted and distorted in sour cherry ne-crotic ringspot.

Diseases that produce virescent flowers tend to produce a modified floral axis bear-ing small leaves (phyllody) or proliferating flower buds, as in aster yellows in some host species, sunn-hemp phyllody, and clo-ver phyllody.

E. Abnormalities of Flower Position

In yellows-type diseases flowers as well as branches are often abnormally erect. This is conspicuous in cranberry false blos-som disease, because cranberry flowers are pendant on healthy plants. Flower stalks are sometimes bent in onion yellow dwarf. Flower pedicels are short in cherry leaf roll.

F. Abnormalities of Pollen and Egg Viability in Flowers

In tomato aspermy disease, many pollen cells and egg cells fail to function. Abortive pollen grains are reported to be numerous in tobacco ringspot. Pollen from cherry trees affected by sour cherry yellows in-duces poorer sets of fruit than normal when applied to healthy or diseased cherry trees. Ovules are said to become leaflets in kok-saghyz yellows.

G. Abnormalities in Time of Blossoming

Blossoming may occur prematurely or, in contrast to this, it may be delayed as a result of viral infection.

Flowers are sometimes formed prema-turely, i.e., during the first year of growth, in normally biennial species, as in carrot bolting disease. Premature flowering in citrus is characteristic of quick decline (tristeza disease). New Zealand flax blos-soms prematurely when affected by Phor-mium yellow leaf. Flowers are reported to appear early in chrysanthemum stunt.

Flowering in spring may be slightly de-layed in Muir peach dwarf. Retarded blos-soming has been reported for sweet cherry necrotic rusty mottle. Affected trees blos-som late in spring in sour cherry pink fruit disease. Tobacco plants affected by severe etch disease are said to be delayed in flowering.

H. ABNORMALITIES OF FLOWER PERSISTENCE

Flowers may abort, as in cowpea mosaic. Pistils of flowers are described as aborted in prune dwarf. Flowers drop off from tomato plants after infection by sugar-beet curly-top virus.

2–4. FRUIT SYMPTOMS

Fruits express symptoms as abnormalities of number, size, shape, habit, color, texture, ripening, flavor, seed content, persistence, and total yield; some viral diseases also cause death of parts of fruits.

A. ABNORMALITIES OF FRUIT NUMBER

Fruit production is often seriously decreased in viral diseases but rarely if ever is increased.

Complete sterility occurs eventually in most yellows-type diseases, usually as a result of gross flower abnormalities or failure of plants to continue the production of blossoms. Complete unfruitfulness without damage to pollen has been reported in connection with female sterility disease of tobacco. Fruiting is slight in tomato aspermy disease because pollen cells and ovules are largely nonfunctional.

Mature fruits are few, although blossoms are numerous, in prune dwarf. The crop of fruits is reduced or wanting, despite abnormally abundant blossoms, in cherry vein-clearing disease. Fruits are fewer than normal in peach phony disease, Drake almond bud failure, and cucumber mosaic. Cone production is greatly reduced in hop nettlehead. Only occasional fruits are left on trees in peach X-disease, because of abnormal fruit drop. The crop is progressively reduced in successive years in Muir peach dwarf and in advanced cases there may be no more than a dozen fruits on each tree. Lambert cherry trees set only a light crop when affected by Lambert mottle. Fruit is lacking or scanty in grape yellow vein disease.

B. ABNORMALITIES OF FRUIT SIZE

Reduction of fruit size is a common but not invariable symptom of viral diseases.

Fruits are much reduced in size in little peach disease, which is caused by infection with a mild strain of peach yellows virus. Despite good foliage to support their growth, cherry fruits remain small because of deficient cell division in otherwise normal-appearing trees affected by little cherry disease. Kernels of maize are reduced in size by corn stunt but remain viable and edible. Fruits are small, pale, and conical in cherry buckskin disease. They are small and turn white in cherry albino disease. Infected seeds tend to be small in barley false stripe.

Cotton bolls are reduced in size by cotton leaf crumple disease. Cantaloupe fruits are small, poorly netted, and low in sugar on plants infected by sugar-beet curly-top virus.

Fruits are often larger than normal and of excellent quality, but few, in prune dwarf disease. Fruits are larger than normal and are said to be of good quality in sour cherry yellows, but the number of fruiting spurs is reduced.

C. ABNORMALITIES OF FRUIT SHAPE

Fruits, like leaves, are likely to be changed to some extent in shape, and sometimes are radically distorted, by viral diseases.

Cucumbers are conspicuously misshapen as well as small and mottled in cucumber mosaic. Navel orange fruits are misshapen, with rind abnormally thick near the stem end but thin near the stylar end, in stubborn disease of citrus. Fruits become spineless in Datura distortion mosaic.

Dwarfed, ribbed, or lobed fruits have been reported in apple decline. Flattened patches of green skin distort fruits in dapple apple disease. Irregular fruits are formed in cranberry false blossom. Fruits are deformed in apple false sting disease and lumpy in apple green crinkle. They are severely deformed and pitted in stony pit of pear. Symmetry of fruits is destroyed in side rot (spotted wilt disease) of pineapple, which causes fruits to bend toward the affected side. The suture sides of fruits often bulge in peach red suture disease. Fruits may be blistered, welted, or warty in peach wart disease. In ring pox of apricot, about two weeks before ripening, fruits develop protuberances that tend to disappear during the ripening process and to be supplanted by discolored blotches within which cracks may develop.

Fruits may show small depressions in which the skin is abnormally pigmented, sometimes with superficial russet ring patterns, in leaf-pucker disease of apple. Coarse depressed rings, sometimes concentric, have been noted on fruits in psorosis B, more rarely in psorosis A, of citrus (grapefruit). Depressed light-yellowish longitudinal streaks appear on green fruits of avocado affected by graft-transmissible sun blotch disease. Water-soaked blemishes, later appearing as scars on fruits, characterize apple scar-skin. Star cracks on fruits characterize star-crack disease of apple. Shallow skin depressions or furrows are underlaid by brown corky flesh in transmissible corky pit of the Flemish Beauty pear.

D. Abnormalities of Fruit Habit

Cranberry fruits are small and erect in cranberry false blossom disease. Fruit pedicels may be short and curved in Lambert mottle of sweet cherry.

E. Abnormalities of Fruit Color

Fruit color is often defective in viral diseases but occasionally is intensified or radically changed instead.

Fruits are usually more highly colored in peach trees affected by phony disease than in normal trees of the same varieties. In peach varieties that normally develop some red color in the skin and around the pit, the skin may become abnormally highly colored and spotted with red and purple in peach yellows disease; at the same time the flesh of the fruit may become streaked with crimson, with a pronounced red coloring around the pit.

On the other hand, fruits often fail to reach full color, as in tomato spotted wilt, which induces production of yellow mottling or concentric-ring patterns, sometimes involving subepidermal necrosis that appears externally as concentric brown bands. Light or rusty spots are reported on figs affected by fig mosaic. Circular patches of green skin fail to color properly at ripening time in dapple apple disease. Apple fruits affected by ringspot in New Zealand display patches of russeted tissue edged with smooth dark brown bands and occasional dark brown concentric rings. Cherry varieties that normally have red or pink fruits develop little or no red pigment in cherry albino disease.

Reddish concentric-ring patterns occur on pods in red node of bean. Pods may be blotched with dark green, shiny, short, malformed, and sometimes curled in southern bean mosaic. They are purple or marked with purple in pea streak. They are darker green than normal and severely mottled as well as short, curled, twisted, and warty in bean pod mottle.

Green or dark brown rings occur on yellowing fruits in Puerto Rican papaya mosaic. Chlorotic or yellow rings conspicuously distinguish ripening fruits affected by the Hawaiian papaya-"ringspot," which is in fact an aphid-transmitted mosaic-type malady.

F. Abnormalities of Fruit Texture

Fruits may be woody, as in tomato big bud. Woody fruits, with thickened pericarp and deficient pulp as well as deepened color, are reported for passionfruit woodiness disease.

Watermelon fruits are warty with necrotic spots that exude drops of a viscous liquid when infected by tobacco ringspot virus. Warty tissues in fruits may be hard and bony or just leathery and tougher than usual in peach wart disease; they are superficial, with underlying tissues coarse and containing gum pockets.

Fruits are described as dry in mild streak of black raspberry. Fruits show drying when foliage wilts in Pierce's disease of grape. Hard, seedy, small fruits may be produced in strawberry stunt.

Concentric hemispheres or spheres with corky or watersoaked boundaries have been reported in winter squash infected by tomato ringspot virus. Punky areas are reported to occur in fruits in virus gummosis of apricot. Fruits may show corky spots in citrus psorosis.

In red suture disease, peach fruits may show coarse and stringy flesh that is exceptionally watery. Crumbly fruits, which are also abnormally globose and irregular, have been noted in raspberry decline.

G. Abnormalities of Fruit Maturation

Fruits that do not shrivel and fall may ripen prematurely in peach yellow-red virosis (X disease). Uneven ripening is reported in loganberry dwarf and peach red suture disease. Fruits seldom ripen in strawberry green petal disease. Peaches ripen several days to three weeks later than usual in little peach disease.

H. Abnormalities of Fruit Flavor

Cherries are said to be insipid as a result of cherry rusty mottle disease. Peach fruits generally have an insipid flavor in little peach disease. Lack of flavor and of sweetness characterizes fruits in little cherry disease. Fruits are poor in flavor in mild streak of black raspberry. Tomato fruits affected by internal browning disease are unsatisfactory in flavor. Ripe berries have an unpleasant flavor in blueberry stunt disease. Cherries at picking time are somewhat bitter in small bitter cherry disease; they are delayed in ripening but eventually lose their bitterness and then taste somewhat fermented. Fruits are bitter and unpalatable, and seeds do not develop within the pits, in peach yellow-red virosis.

I. Abnormalities of Seed Content of Fruits

Seed number is reduced to some extent in virtually all viral diseases; it is rarely if ever increased, even temporarily. Set of seeds is almost completely suppressed in tomato aspermy disease, because pollen viability and egg cell viability are both greatly lowered. Grain is rarely formed in spring wheat, barley, and oats infected by the virus of winter wheat mosaic. Partial sterility of heads of infected plants is reported in wheat streak mosaic. Seed formation is inhibited in peanut rosette. Pods often contain aborted ovules in bean pod mottle. Fruits are often seedless in grape yellow vein disease.

J. Abnormalities of Persistence of Fruits

The number of mature fruits may be reduced by abscission of fruits when young, as in black currant reversion disease. Many fruits shrivel and fall soon after the appearance of foliage symptoms in peach yellow-red virosis. Fruits drop prematurely in fig mosaic. On the other hand, ripe berries stick abnormally tightly to the stem in blueberry stunt disease.

K. Abnormalities of Yield of Fruits

Reduction in yield of fruits is nearly universal in viral diseases, usually being slight when foliage symptoms are mild and progressively more serious when these are increasingly severe. It has been studied with care in tomato infected by a variety of strains of TMV introduced at various stages in the growth of the host plant. Reduction of crop is often due to a combination of reduced fruit size and reduced fruit number. Retardation of tree growth reduces the crop in cherry rasp leaf.

Reduction of yield in cowpea mosaic has been reported as greater in some varieties of cowpea than in others. Yield of seeds is said to be reduced in onion yellow dwarf.

No reduction in yield of fruits has been noted in almond calico, despite well-defined leaf symptoms (chlorotic blotches).

L. Death of Parts of Fruits

Fruits may contain dead embryos in chokecherry affected by yellow-red virosis. Necrotic lesions are found in seeds of pea plants that have been infected by tomato spotted wilt virus. In early browning disease of pea, pods show flecklike and ringlike purplish brown necrotic patterns, and seeds in affected pods become chlorotic and wrinkled. Necrotic spots, rings, or streaks appear on pods in bean stipple streak. Necrosis occurs in pineapple fruits affected by side rot. Spots and flecks of necrosis in internal tissues of tomato fruits characterize tomato internal browning disease. Necrosis of the fruit pedicel occurs in cherry twisted leaf disease.

2–5. STEM SYMPTOMS

Stem symptoms involve abnormalities in growth habit, internode length, number, shape, bark characteristics, color, rigidity, histology, physiology, chemical constitution, and gum production, as well as premature death of parts.

A. ABNORMALITIES OF GROWTH HABIT OF STEMS

Yellows-type diseases tend to change the angle of growth of branches, making new shoots abnormally erect. After cure by heat the normal angle of growth is resumed, only to be lost again if reinfection occurs, as has been demonstrated in peach yellows.

Aerial tubers are formed in potato witches' broom, and underground tubers are abnormally small in this disease. In purple top wilt, potato tubers sometimes are formed in leaf axils; underground tubers, which are often soft and spongy, may fail to germinate, form weak sprouts, or develop secondary tubers without formation of shoots and foliage.

B. ABNORMALITIES OF INTERNODE LENGTH OF STEMS

Internode length may be much modified. It is reduced moderately in many diseases, as in tobacco yellow dwarf and rice dwarf. Rosette diseases, such as peach rosette, show extreme reduction of internode length. Runners of strawberry are conspicuously short in strawberry witches' broom. Soon after infection newly developing internodes are abnormally short in tomato bunchy top, but subsequently formed internodes again lengthen to produce a spindly type of growth. Unusually long internodes and enlarged nodes are reported as occurring in potato witches' broom.

C. ABNORMALITIES OF NUMBER OF STEMS

All yellows-type diseases tend to break the dormancy of axillary buds and hence to increase the number of branches in their host plants. Abnormally numerous laterals with extra branches are shown in ocean-spray witches' broom. Canes are weak and more numerous than usual in Rubus stunt. Profuse branching is reported to occur in winter wheat mosaic, profuse shoot development in oat pupation disease.

Lateral branches are fewer than normal in flowering cherry rough bark disease.

D. ABNORMALITIES OF STEM SHAPE

Upward bending of runner tip is caused in cucurbitaceous plants by infection with sugar-beet curly-top virus; affected stems in this disease may be deep green. Lateral bending of the stem tip occurs in broad bean vascular wilt. A tendency of stems to zigzag at the nodes has been noted in grape fan leaf and tea phloem necrosis.

Spines are suppressed in Ceiba by infection with cacao swollen shoot virus. Thorns are attenuated or absent in thorny varieties of eggplant affected by little leaf disease.

Branchlets are thin and wiry in ocean-spray witches' broom. Axillary and basal branches are spindly in potato witches' broom. Twigs become slender and pendulous in peach willow twig disease. Tubers are cylindrical, tapered, long, smooth, soft, and have tender skins and conspicuous eyes in potato spindle tuber. Loganberry dwarf disease produces short and spindly new canes.

Stubby stems are recorded in connection with peach stubby twig disease. Twigs are short and thick in Muir peach dwarf; these twigs tend to be pale green instead of the normal reddish brown color, presumably because of heavy shade from abnormally compact foliage.

Stems are swollen or die back in areas of recent ligneous growth in cacao swollen shoot disease. Slightly swollen parts appear in twigs of Napoleon sweet cherry affected by black canker of cherry; later rough black cankers occur at the same sites. Apical swelling in flax occurs as a result of double infection by aster yellows virus and the virus of flax crinkle (oat blue dwarf virus), but not in singly-infected plants.

Woody galls develop near the infection site after grafting, or elsewhere later, in citrus vein-enation disease, especially appearing in wounded tissues. Galls develop on stems of sweetclover plants infected by wound-tumor virus (clover big vein virus), especially at the sites of natural or artificial wounds.

E. Abnormalities of Bark of Stems

Bark is rough and split in flowering cherry rough bark disease; it may also be unusually deep brown. Bark is cracked in pear stony pit. Bark splitting occurs in apple bark-splitting disease.

Bark may be increased in thickness in stubborn disease of citrus. It becomes thickened and roughened, often in a diamond-shaped area around a wound, in prune diamond canker disease. Blisters and bark splitting on the main stem characterize blister canker disease of the Williams pear; severe phloem necrosis in this disease may kill susceptible scions. Blisters and concentric ring cankers on bark surface produce extremely rough bark with marked ridges and flutes in pear bark-measles disease. Bark is roughened by blister-like lesions and cankers in sweet cherry necrotic rusty mottle.

Scaling of bark is characteristic of citrus exocortis. Outer bark scales away in citrus psorosis; gum may exude before the bark scales away, with necrosis after scaling, producing concavities on trunks and large limbs or troughlike pockets in bark or wood; the wood is sometimes gray to red in this disease.

The smooth interface between the bark and wood of trees is sometimes deformed by death of parts and compensatory growth of adjacent tissues. Minute holes on the inner surface of bark of sour orange occur just below the bud union in citrus tristeza, producing the macroscopic symptom called honeycombing; minute pegs from the woody cylinder fit into the holes. Pegs of wood fit into pits in thickened bark in stem-pitting of coffee. In contrast to this, pegs of bark fit into pits in wood in rootstocks of citrus affected by xyloporosis. Wood-pitting occurs in Virginia crabapple trees affected by stem-pitting disease. Mild stem-pitting has been noted sometimes in apple chlorotic leaf spot disease. Pitting in wood and cambial face of bark is reported for citrus cachexia.

F. Abnormalities of Stem Color

Bluish violet dots, spots, or stripes appear near the bases of new canes that are affected by black-raspberry streak. Brownish or greenish ring patterns, often appearing watersoaked, are found on canes in rose streak. Light yellowish sunken streaks occur on green stems in avocado sun blotch. Browning at nodes and brownish or purplish necrotic streaks in petioles and stem are characteristic of Wisconsin pea streak. A reddish discoloration of nodes accounts for the name of red node of bean.

G. Abnormalities of Stem Rigidity

Brittle stems characterize pea streak disease. Trunks and branches are especially subject to breakage in windstorms in sour cherry yellows.

Flexible stems occur in rubbery wood of apple as a result of inhibition of lignification in many xylem fibers and vessels. Stems are less woody than normal in black currant reversion disease. Affected branches are more flexible than normal branches of the same diameter in peach willow twig disease.

H. Abnormalities of Stem Histology

Vascular bundles are reddened by a colored gum in sugar-cane sereh disease and are darkened in sugar-beet mosaic. They are larger than usual and also abnormally numerous in anemone alloiophylly. They show a reddish-yellow discoloration near nodes in sugar-cane ratoon stunting disease; a feature of this disease is failure to show a blue-green color at the leaf scar level in parenchyma around fibrovascular bundles when longitudinal sections of basal nodes of stems are flooded with 3% hydrogen peroxide for 10–15 seconds, then blotted dry, and flooded with concentrated hydrochloric acid.

Inner phloem is hypertrophied in tomato big bud. Stems of tomato are hollow when affected by potato witches' broom disease. Phloem necrosis occurs in mahaleb rootstock carrying scions of sweet cherry affected by buckskin disease. Phloem necrosis is contained within circular hyperplastic areas in the primary phloem of stems in potato rosette of Tasmania.

I. Abnormalities of Stem Physiology

Raspberry canes are easily winterkilled when affected by raspberry leaf curl. Shoots are reddish and late to develop in spring as a result of raspberry-decline disease.

J. Abnormalities of Chemical Constitution of Stems

Ray cells stain red in phloroglucinol-HCl in exocortis disease of *Poncirus trifoliata* Raf. A fluorescent substance, characteristic of carnation mosaic, is found in extracts of infected terminal shoots; butanol is added to the extract, which is shaken, allowed to settle, and made slightly alkaline; on exposure to ultraviolet light fluorescence is pink. Glutamine and glutamic acid are reported to occur in abnormal amounts in eyes of spindle-tuber potatoes.

K. Abnormalities of Gum Production in Stems

Gum exudes profusely through fissures in bark in leaf roll of cherry. Gumming is profuse on branches and trunk in apricot gummosis. Gum is deposited in phloem and in rings of xylem in citrus cachexia. Gummosis of conductive elements is said to be common in sugar-cane chlorotic streak. Gummosis has been observed in the xylem, accompanied by excessive formation of tyloses, in Pierce's disease of grapevine.

L. Death of Stems or Parts of Stems

Progressive die-back of branches occurs in rose wilt. Terminal die-back is found in apple chlorotic leaf spot disease. Die-back of year-old shoots is reported for apple star-crack disease. New shoots die back in apricot gummosis. Branches die back in cherry leaf roll.

Death of growing points permits subsequent growth of axillary buds in tomato bushy stunt. Top necrosis in some field-resistant varieties of potato is caused by infection with potato mottle virus. Death of growing points induces new growth from stem buds of *Vicia faba* L. infected by red clover vein mosaic. Death of terminal shoots is caused by the tip-blight strain of tomato spotted-wilt virus. Stem tips grow unilaterally, curve toward the affected sides, and eventually die, become brittle, and break off in bud blight of soybean caused by infection with tobacco ringspot virus.

Stem streak occurs in southern bean mosaic. Streaking of blue lupine stems by pea mosaic causes bending of the growing point toward the injured side. Stem streaks and crookneck have been reported in tobacco affected by tomato spotted wilt. Dark brown or black necrotic streaks occur on stems, petioles, and leaf veins in bean stipple streak. Stem necrosis is seen in potato yellow dwarf. Corky, raised necrotic streaks are found in stems and petioles of geraniums affected by Pelargonium leaf curl.

Stem cankers occur occasionally in sugar-cane mosaic. Cankers are reported around buds in star-crack disease of apple.

Certain hybrid tea roses show necrotic primary lesions, sometimes girdling the canes, at the places where buds from plants affected by rose streak are inserted; necrotic secondary lesions may appear on young lateral branches below the inserted buds. Pea stems are sometimes girdled by necrotic lesions in Wisconsin pea streak. Phloem destruction below bud unions girdles trees in quick decline (tristeza) of citrus.

Necrosis of cortex and pith in potato tubers has been noted in potato aucuba mosaic. Phloem necrosis occurs in tubers of some potato varieties as a result of potato leaf roll; the tubers affected by leaf roll are inclined to be small, crisp, and few; sprouts from them are often spindly. Tuber necrosis is reported in the Red La Soda potato after infection by a strain of alfalfa mosaic.

In potato yellow dwarf, seed tubers that germinate may show dying shoots, but tubers often remain hard, glassy, and unrotted in the ground instead of germinating; newly formed tubers are close to the stem, few, small, and often cracked, with flesh discolored by scattered brown flecks.

2–6. BUD SYMPTOMS

Symptoms shown by buds include abnormalities of dormancy, of structure, and of viability.

SYMPTOMATOLOGY

A. Abnormalities of Dormancy of Buds

Yellows-type diseases stimulate axillary buds of stems to grow prematurely; this produces the witches'-broom type of growth of affected plants. Tuber buds share in this lack of dormancy in potato witches' broom disease.

In green dwarf of potato, the small tubers that are formed are slow to germinate. Lateral buds fail to grow in pear stony pit. Buds fail to grow in peach and almond after graft transmission of bud failure disease of Drake almond.

B. Abnormalities of Structure of Buds

Flower buds are enlarged in tomato big bud, and their sepals fail to separate as buds mature.

C. Abnormalities of Viability of Buds

Lateral leaf and fruit buds die and are shed in winter in peach willow twig disease. Buds grow to a length of a few millimeters and then appear yellow and remain at a standstill for several weeks in peach yellow bud mosaic; later some of the abnormal buds die and others produce rosettes of small distorted leaves, with or without mottling. Upper buds die in late spring in Lambert mottle of sweet cherry; the development of lower leaf buds and flower buds is late and irregular. In necrotic rusty mottle of sweet cherry, part of the buds are killed; this produces bare, rangy branches.

2–7. ROOT SYMPTOMS

Symptoms expressed by roots include abnormalities of number, size, shape, texture, color, and chemical composition; in some cases there may also be premature death of parts.

A. Abnormalities of Root Number

An increased number of rootlets has been noted in sugar-beet curly-top. Excessive numbers of adventitious roots are reported in connection with sugar-cane sereh disease. Root development in cuttings of alfalfa is reduced in alfalfa mosaic.

B. Abnormalities of Root Size

Fiji disease of sugar cane is described as characterized by small roots that appear bunchy. Carrot roots are reduced in growth in carrot motley dwarf disease. Roots are severely stunted in corn stunt disease.

C. Abnormalities of Root Shape

Numerous galls develop on roots of Rumex and sweetclover plants after infection by wound-tumor virus, especially at the sites of natural or artificial wounds. Roots are reported to be abnormally swollen in cacao swollen shoot disease. The tap root may be reduced to a shrivelled vascular cylinder in broad bean vascular wilt.

D. Abnormalities of Root Texture

Roots are said to be brittle in black locust witches' broom disease; in this disease, also, rootlets have been reported as branching excessively. Roots snap instead of bending in horseradish brittle root disease, caused by infection with sugar-beet curly-top virus; these brittle roots show brown to almost black streaks when sliced longitudinally. Dark, hard, corky spots in the flesh of sweet potatoes appear during storage, most conspicuously at 70°–85°F, in internal cork disease.

E. Abnormalities of Root Color

Discolored wood in roots is reported in alfalfa dwarf. Slight external browning and phloem browning have been recorded in abnormally small root systems that are characteristic of tobacco yellow dwarf.

F. Abnormalities of Chemical Composition of Roots

Roots of peach trees that are affected by phony disease show flecked wood, and root sections show red to purple spots after treatment with methyl alcohol and hydrochloric acid. Root sections stain yellow by the phloroglucinol-nitrophenolic acid technique in peach mosaic, but pink in normal trees.

A yellow to brown discoloration of phloem tissues, accompanied by a faint odor of wintergreen, occurs in roots of elm trees after infection by elm phloem necrosis; affected roots soon die, causing death of trees.

G. Death of Roots or Parts of Roots

Root decay occurs in tomato affected by sugar-beet curly-top. Roots die in citrus tristeza disease. Death of roots causing subsequent death of plants has been reported in Phormium yellow leaf disease. Phloem necrosis occurs spottily in roots as well as in stems and leaves in tea phloem necrosis. Phloem necrosis in roots is reported also for beet savoy.

Our knowledge of symptoms in roots is still scanty because of the relative paucity of root records. This is especially true for root systems under field conditions.

2–8. SYMPTOMS EXPRESSED BY THE PLANT AS A WHOLE

It is difficult to separate the discussion of symptoms that are expressed by the plant as a whole from the discussion of those that concern only parts of the plant. Yet there are some features of viral diseases that logically fall under the more inclusive category.

A. Abnormalities of Yield

Some degree of reduction in total yield has been found in nearly all viral diseases of plants. It may be slight in masked infections, such as paracrinkle in King Edward potato, or devastating, as in potato yellow dwarf, potato leaf roll, and cotton leaf curl. A reduced rate of increase has been noted for planting stock of bulbous iris affected by iris mosaic. Onion yellow dwarf is characterized by production of abnormally small bulbs. Dry matter yield is much reduced in alfalfa mosaic. A slight increase in tuber yield of potatoes claimed to occur after infection by mild strains of potato X virus requires confirmation, as does a claim of increased height and weight of *Cleome spinosa* L. after infection of roots by tobacco necrosis virus.

B. Abnormalities of Turgidity

Wilting is rather a rare symptom of viral diseases, but occasionally it is striking. When it occurs, it often is a forerunner of death of the entire plant.

Wilting of Tabasco pepper, but not of most varieties of the garden pepper, is characteristic of infection by tobacco-etch virus. Wilting at midday is recorded for sugar-cane chlorotic streak. Individual leaves or whole stems wilt in bean stipple streak.

Wilting followed by death in potato is said to be a result of infection by parastolbur virus. Elm phloem necrosis is characterized by wilting and sudden death in the summer of the second year of disease, or by gradual decline over a period of 12–18 months before death. Wilting and death occur in peach rosette and in sudden-death disease of the clove tree. Wilting is followed by death in blue lupine affected by pea mosaic. Wilting and death may occur in yellow wilt disease of sugar beet in Argentina. Loss of turgidity throughout the whole plant may be followed by death in broad bean vascular wilt.

C. Abnormalities of Length of Life

Death ensues within a few years after infection of cherry by leaf roll. Apricot trees affected by virus gummosis characteristically show gumming and necrosis in small branches during three or four successive years and then die. Fuller's teasel is soon killed by teasel mosaic.

Systemic necrosis may occur in, but be limited to, a few uninoculated parts of plants that tend to localize mosaic-type infections, and in this case length of life may not be appreciably affected; but if necrotic secondary lesions become very numerous, as in very young Black Beauty eggplants infected by TMV, the plants may collapse and die within a few days.

Peach trees affected by peach yellows do not stop growing as cold weather approaches but continue vegetative growth until the tender tips of branches are frozen and killed. Winter hardiness of Ladino clover is reduced by infection with alfalfa mosaic virus.

Premature death of oat plants is a feature of blue dwarf disease. On the other hand, prolongation of life has been reported in oats affected by red leaf disease.

China aster plants remain alive later than normal when affected by aster yellows, perhaps because this disease reduces and finally stops seed production. Potato plants grown in greenhouses ordinarily mature their foliage, produce tubers, and die; if infected by witches' broom disease, however, they produce tubers but continue vegetative growth throughout successive years.

D. Abnormalities of Growth Rate

Growth rate is markedly reduced in sugar-cane chlorotic streak; this disease was first discovered by observation of the comparative growth rates of heated and unheated cuttings, cure of the disease occurring regularly in cuttings immersed in a water bath for 20 minutes at 52°C. Many other viral diseases tend to share this characteristic of producing a more or less conspicuously reduced growth rate. Almost complete cessation of upward growth has been reported in tomato bushy stunt. On the other hand, diseased vines are said to be sometimes abnormally vigorous vegetatively in yellow vein of grape, perhaps because their fruits are few and often seedless.

E. Abnormalities of Size of Plant

Dwarfing of the whole plant is a very common attribute of viral diseases. It has been noted, for example, as a characteristic of tomato big bud, Pierce's disease of grape, blueberry stunt, potato yellow dwarf, barley yellow dwarf, cucurbit mosaic, and potato leaf roll. A slight dwarfing, associated with premature flowering, is sometimes the only obvious symptom of chrysanthemum stunt. Plants that grow all new parts above ground each year actually become smaller progressively, as has been noted for alfalfa dwarf and for black-raspberry streak. Dwarfing of trees occurs in flowering cherry rough bark disease. Severe dwarfing of the affected side of the plant, and later of the whole plant, is characteristic of sugar-beet yellow vein.

F. Abnormalities of Transpiration

Decreased transpiration probably occurs in viral diseases much more often than has been reported. It has been noted in alfalfa dwarf. Some lowering of transpiration has been found also in connection with the sudden-death disease of clove trees.

Increased transpiration seems to have been observed rarely. Tomato plants after infection by tobacco mosaic virus are reported to show a sharp drop in transpiration at the time of first appearance of symptoms; after this the transpiration rate increases gradually; in long-infected plants, mosaic leaves transpire at a substantially faster rate than the healthy leaves of uninfected control plants.

G. Abnormalities of Chemical Composition

Marked reduction of ribose nucleic acid content has been found in *Prunus mahaleb* L. seedlings doubly-infected with prune dwarf virus and Prunus recurrent-ringspot virus. Catalase activity is low but peroxidase activity is high in barley yellow dwarf.

H. Abnormalities of Histology

Degeneration of sieve tubes and hypertrophy of ray and cortical parenchymas have been noted in rapid decline of apple. Breakdown of tissue in and around vascular bundles of affected foliage is reported for artichoke curly dwarf; this structural change is associated with decline of vigor, sometimes followed by death of the plant. Phloem degeneration, involving death of phloem parenchyma and companion cells with resultant collapse of sieve elements, is recorded in connection with barley yellow dwarf. Phloem cells proliferate and the supernumerary cells assume the characteristics of sieve elements in sugar-beet curly-top and aster yellows.

I. Abnormalities of Latex Flow

Latex flow on wounding ceases in papaya bunchy top; removal of the affected tops of trees effects cure.

J. Abnormalities of Growth Habit

Growth is erect, stiff, and spindly in potato spindle tuber. Plants as a whole are abnormally erect in strawberry stunt. On the other hand, plants appear flat in strawberry yellow edge and western celery mosaic. The top of the plant has a flattened appearance in broad bean vascular wilt and in lily yellow flat disease. Sugar-cane stools are bushy in Fiji disease.

2–9. MASKING OF SYMPTOMS

All symptoms are masked at high environmental temperatures in red raspberry mosaic. Many viral diseases share this masking effect of high temperature to a greater or less degree at some stage of the disease or at some season of the year. A conspicuous example is pelargonium leaf curl, which shows no symptoms in leaves produced in summer and autumn, but reappears as a leaf spotting disease in late winter and spring each year unless cured by consistently maintained high temperatures.

Several so-called latent viruses appear to produce no obvious symptoms at any time in their natural hosts. Thus carnation latent virus is said to produce no symptoms in carnation and Sweet William plants, dodder latent virus is not known to produce definite symptoms in dodder, and strawberry latent virus is regarded as producing no reliable symptoms, but perhaps a slight reduction of vigor, in *Fragaria vesca* L., when no other viruses are present. King Edward potatoes were regarded as healthy in appearance when only stocks infected by paracrinkle virus were available for study, but after the variety had been freed from virus by meristem culture it became evident that virus-free plants produced slightly more leaves, larger leaves, and greater dry weight than the supposedly symptomless infected plants. Presumably nearly all, if not all, symptomless carriers are slightly less vigorous than their virus-free counterparts.

The symptoms of viral diseases are not limited to effects that can be seen at a hasty glance or detected by touch. If they were so, most of the symptoms that we now consider important would be of little value for an investigator with poor eyesight, yet all these symptoms and what we now regard as masked symptoms would be present and awaiting the coming of a more gifted or a more resourceful investigator.

The study of masked infection has shown that leaf tissues may be strikingly affected chemically even when leaf shape and color are not noticeably modified. In affected but outwardly symptomless leaves, patterns of starch distribution may be as revealing as our more frequently recognized patterns of chlorophyll damage. Such patterns have been sought principally when more obvious expressions of disease processes have not been present to appease the curiosity of the investigator.

In diseases in which symptoms are conspicuous, we may predict that unnoticed but important changes are about as frequently present as in masked infections. When these less obvious, but perhaps highly significant, symptoms come to be fully described in the scientific literature, we shall have a more complete picture on which to base our attempts to understand viral diseases and the ever changing relationships of invading viruses to their plant hosts.

2–10. LITERATURE CITED

Bagnall, R. H., Wetter, C., and Larson, R. H. (1958). Phytopathology **48**, 391. (Abstract.)

Bawden, F. C., and Kassanis, B. (1941). Ann. Appl. Biol. **28**, 107.

Bawden, F. C., and Kassanis, B. (1945). Ann. Appl. Biol. **32**, 52.

Bawden, F. C., and Pirie, N. W. (1942). Brit. J. Exptl. Pathol. **23**, 314.

Bercks, R., and Brandes, J. (1961). Phytopathol. Z. **42**, 45.

Bos, L., and van der Want, J. P. H. (1962). Tijdschr. Plantenziekten **68**, 368.

Broadbent, L., and Heathcote, G. D. (1958). Ann. Appl. Biol. **46**, 585.

Brunt, A. A., and Kenten, R. H. (1962). Virology **16**, 199.

Cadman, C. H., and Harrison, B. D. (1959). Ann. Appl. Biol. **47**, 542.

Freitag, J. H., Frazier, N. W., and Flock, R. A. (1952). Phytopathology **42**, 533.

Harrison, B. D., Mowat, W. P., and Taylor, C. E. (1961). Virology **14**, 480.

Harrison, B. D., and Nixon, H. L. (1960). Virology **12**, 104.

Hollings, M. (1957). Ann. Appl. Biol. **45**, 44.

Raski, D. J., and Hewitt, Wm. B. (1963). Phytopathology **53**, 39.

Valenta, V. (1959). Acta Virol. (Prague, English Edition) **3**, 145.

ROBERT W. FULTON

Transmission of plant viruses by grafting, dodder, seed, and mechanical inoculation

3–1. INTRODUCTION

THE PROPERTY of transmissibility is a fundamental characteristic of viruses as it is of other biological agents that cause disease. In the development of knowledge of plant viruses, however, transmission has played a more fundamental role than with microscopically visible pathogens. For years the transmission of a virus provided the only experimental evidence of its existence as an independent entity.

The pathologist is concerned with virus transmissibility both from the practical standpoint of trying to prevent or circumvent natural transmission and from an experimental standpoint in that most research depends on his ability to transmit virus at will under controlled conditions. This chapter is concerned mainly with experimental transmission.

3–2. GRAFT TRANSMISSION

Grafting is the most nearly universally applicable method of virus transmission, requiring only that the virus become systemic in plants that can be joined by grafting. Grafting is an ancient horticultural practice (Roberts, 1949), and it might be pertinent here to point out that the word "inoculate" originally referred to the insertion of an "eye" (i.e., bud) into another plant. Baur (1904), in one of the early classical papers on graft transmission, points out that horti-culturists had known for 200 years that certain types of leaf variegation could be transferred to healthy plants through a graft union. Dubos (1958), in describing "tulipomania," points out that grafting was employed in the early fifteenth century to induce the highly desirable "breaking" or white streaking of solid-colored petals of tulip. As Baur (1904) points out, the distinction of transmissibility (as opposed to mere perpetuation in the part grafted on) is a fundamental one, indicating an infectious disease. He goes further and points out that although his infectious variegation appears to have no other means of spread, it would not exist naturally unless it did have some other means of perpetuating itself.

One of the early and very extensive investigations of a virus disease transmitted by grafting was that of Smith (1888) on peach yellows. He pointed out that practical growers had known for years that yellows was transmitted by budding.

Numerous examples could be cited of the transmission a century and more ago of rather poorly defined conditions by grafting. The distinguishing feature of the work of Smith and of Baur, however, was their recognition that they were dealing with an unusual agent of some sort. Speculation about the nature of these agents, and tobacco mosaic virus, presented problems for which no solution was then apparent. The apparently anomalous differences between virus and living, microscopic pathogens have stimulated virology ever since.

Before inoculation by leaf rubbing with Carborundum was introduced, mechanical inoculations were often uncertain or impossible. Thus, much of the early work in virology involved grafting. This is particularly true with potato virus diseases. Quanjer *et al.* (1916) pointed out that leaf roll of potatoes could be transmitted by stem and tuber grafts. These were used very commonly in early work (Schultz and Folsom, 1920, 1921; Quanjer, 1920; Atanasoff, 1924). In 1926, Murphy and McKay (1926) and Goss (1926) described core grafting of potato tubers in which a plug of tuber tissue removed with a cork borer is inserted in a hole made with a slightly smaller cork borer in another tuber. This was more rapid and more efficient than binding the cut surfaces of two tubers together as had been done previously.

Other types and modifications of grafts are too numerous to describe here. Basically, a shoot (scion) is severed from its stem and the cut is closely matched by a reverse cut in a rooted plant (stock). The scion is then bound to the stock so that the cambium of the two is as closely matched as possible. As Muzik and LaRue (1954) point out, the presence of meristematic cells at the graft union is of importance, rather than cambium per se.

The scion will be subject to damaging dehydration unless it is dormant or without leaves. All but bud leaves are usually removed from actively growing scions to prevent water loss. Propagating chambers supplied with intermittent mist can be used for grafted plants until the graft union has healed. Enclosing individual scions in polyethylene bags is convenient and effective.

Slanting cuts of the same length in stock and scion are often used. Increasing the cut surface by an additional vertical cut, to form a tongue of exposed tissue, increases the surface for tissue union and helps prevent slippage when wrapping the graft. For virus transmission it is often convenient to trim a shoot tip, or the nodal portion of a young stem bearing a bud, to a wedge shape and insert this into a cut slanting inward in the stem of the stock plant.

Approach grafting or inarching is done by binding cut surfaces of two plant stems together without severing either from its own roots. Thus, both plants are supplied water through their own roots until the graft union heals.

To hold tissues together firmly until they unite and to prevent water loss, grafts must be wrapped. For this, strips of rubber are convenient because they disintegrate out-of-doors in a few weeks. Grafts wrapped with raffia, string, or cloth, and then covered with wax must be cut away to prevent girdling when the stem enlarges.

Budding is a specialized form of grafting in which the scion consists of a bud, usually dormant, and the underlying bark. This is inserted beneath the bark flaps resulting from a T-shaped cut in the bark of a young stem, and bound in place.

Finally, as these methods of mechanical inoculation became more widely used, it was found that although some diseases could be transmitted in this way, others could not, and viruses were grouped on the basis of how they could be transmitted. Eventually it became evident that this distinction reflected deficiencies in methods of mechanical transmission required to transmit less infectious viruses.

Grafting is successful in transmitting some viruses, where other methods fail, either because a sufficient concentration of infective virus cannot be obtained in extracts, or because mechanical inoculation methods do not introduce virus into tissue in which it can multiply. Leafhopper-transmitted viruses are apparently confined to vascular tissue, or are in higher concentration in this tissue than in parenchymatous tissue. The transmission of these viruses thus seems to require a period sufficiently long to allow some development of vascular tissue at the graft union. Kunkel (1938) pointed out that peach yellows and rosette viruses moved across a graft union only after 8–14 days, whereas peach mosaic virus passed the union in 2–3 days. None of these viruses has yet been transmitted mechanically; the 2–3-day period required for transmission of peach mosaic suggests that some tissue interaction was involved rather than simple mechanical transmission. Bennett (1943) found similar differences in comparing sugar-beet curly-top virus with tobacco ringspot and cucumber mosaic viruses. The curly-top virus passed a graft union in tobacco only after 6 days or more; the 2 mechanically transmissible viruses passed in 2 or 3 days.

In the experiments reported by Bennett (1943), strains of tobacco ringspot and cucumber mosaic viruses were used that were transmissible mechanically with some difficulty. These 2 viruses did not pass graft unions in contact for 24 hours. As with peach mosaic, certain tissue changes, perhaps the development of plasmodesmata between parenchymatous cells of the stock and scion, may have occurred after 48 hours that permitted virus transmission.

Evidence also indicates that with at least some viruses in certain hosts a response that might be described as an unsuccessful graft will still result in virus transmission. The insertion of pieces of infected leaves under flaps of bark of healthy trees has been a technique used successfully rather commonly (Sreenivasaya, 1930; Cochran and Rue, 1944; Wallace, 1947). Wallace demonstrated tissue union between the leaf tissue and the stock. Usually this occurred at the cut edges of veins; transmission was improved by increasing the amount of cut surface on the piece of leaf. J. D. Moore (personal communication) transmitted cherry necrotic ringspot virus by placing under bark flaps of healthy cherry, pieces of leaves, sepals, pistils, anthers, and filaments of diseased trees. Transmission was not obtained, however, from pollen or petals.

Virus may also be transmitted by inserting other types of tissue under bark flaps or into stem slits. Jorgensen (1957) described transmission of strawberry viruses by inserting pieces of petioles with the edges trimmed to expose vascular bundles into slits in the petioles of healthy strawberries. Such transmission is not unexpected when tissue of the same species is inserted; a degree of tissue fusion may occur even though no permanent union is evident and the inserted tissue lacks the capability of

continued growth. Transmission of virus by inserting in healthy plants tissue that would not appear to make a union in any accepted sense suggests that a continuous protoplasmic connection did not exist, and that a form of "mechanical" transmission of virus occurred. Blattný and Limberk (1956) have described transmission of stolbur virus (leafhopper-transmitted) by implanting Convolvulus tissue into stems of tomato and tobacco plants. Boyle et al. (1949) reported transmitting necrotic ringspot virus by implanting infected cucumber tissue beneath cherry bark. The author has confirmed this, but as Boyle et al. pointed out, the rate of transmission was so low that reliability of the results was uncertain. Kegler (1959) reported transmission of apple mosaic virus without the graft partners fusing.

Disadvantages of grafting in transmitting virus are numerous. It is time consuming, and is often limited by compatibilities of stock and scion. Unless woody plants are beginning a stage of active terminal growth, symptom expression may be delayed. Kunkel (1930) pointed out that peach yellows symptoms appear earlier if grafts are made near the tips of rapidly growing shoots than if made low. Also, many woody species that have stopped growing within the previous month or so may be stimulated to produce a new flush of leaves by defoliating. Hildebrand (1941, 1942) pointed out advantages of stimulating a flush of new growth by pruning graft-inoculated plants.

Quite commonly it is pointed out that graft transmission applies to viruses affecting dicotyledons, because monocotyledonous plants cannot be grafted. One can only wonder if this statement has not been repeated more often than graft transmission has been tried with monocotyledonous tissue. Muzik and LaRue (1954) have described grafts with grasses. While the lack of a ring of cambial tissue might prohibit permanent tissue union as it occurs in the dicotyledons, the fact that a structurally sound union is not always necessary for virus transmission in the dicotyledons should encourage trials with monocotyledons.

An idea seems more or less prevalent that graft transmissions are highly efficient in transmitting virus. Published data indicate that this is not the case. Reasons for failure to transmit are not always clear. Probably one of the commonest reasons is that the virus is not completely systemic in the plant supplying scions, and that scions are chosen that carry no virus. Rozendaal and van der Want (1948) point out that potato stem mottle virus, known not to invade potato completely, was not transmitted by tuber grafts, and not by all stem grafts. Davidson (1955) reported up to 48% transmission of potato leaf roll virus by tuber grafts. The highest percentage transmission occurred when the diseased core was within one-fourth inch of a healthy eye, suggesting that the virus did not move readily or rapidly from the diseased core, or that vascular tissue was necessary for virus movement, and that this did not always develop. Valenta (1962) has pointed out that the rate of graft transmission of stolbur and potato witches' broom viruses varied with the hosts grafted, and that failure to transmit did not necessarily indicate immunity of the stock plant. J. P. Fulton (1957) and Cropley (1958) have recorded erratic transmission of strawberry viruses with the leaf grafting technique of Bringhurst and Voth (1956). Even though tissue union occurred, some viruses were transmitted more often than others.

Natural transmission of viruses by grafting is apparently quite rare because of the relatively rare occurrence of natural grafts. Hunter *et al.* (1958) described the transmission of apple mosaic virus through naturally occurring root grafts. Thomas and Baker (1952) described transmission of carnation mosaic virus through root grafts when plants were growing in the same pot but otherwise prevented from touching. Sheffield (1952) described transmission of the sudden-death disease of cloves through natural root grafts.

3–3. DODDER TRANSMISSION OF PLANT VIRUSES

One of the drawbacks of virus transmission by grafting is the difficulty or impossibility of obtaining an organic union between unrelated plants sufficient to permit passage of virus. In part, this difficulty may be circumvented by dodder transmission. Kunkel (1943a) pointed out that it is seldom that one host is suitable for all types of experimental work with plant viruses. Dodder is one method of transferring "difficult" viruses to new hosts.

Dodder (*Cuscuta* spp.) is a parasitic vine, lacking chlorophyll and leaves, of the family Convolvulaceae. It parasitizes higher plants by twining around them and forming haustoria that ultimately connect with the vascular tissue of the host. Lackey (1953) has pointed out that both the beet leafhopper and dodder are apparently attracted to the vascular bundles of sugar beet. Dodder haustoria formed on beet petioles opposite vascular bundles, not between them. Phloem degeneration in curlytop-infected beet adversely affected the accuracy of the dodder in locating the vascular bundles.

The species of dodder commonly used in virus transmission work will parasitize a rather wide range of host plants. A given species of dodder may flourish on some hosts but be unable to maintain growth on another host (Lackey, 1949). Different species of dodder will parasitize each other; Lackey (1946) has described the parasitism of each other by *C. californica* and *C. subinclusa.*

A. THE MECHANISM OF DODDER TRANSMISSION

Bennett (1940a) and F. Johnson (1941a) described the transmission of a number of plant viruses by *C. subinclusa* and *C. campestris,* the two species subsequently used most widely. Many species of dodder will transmit one or more viruses, but there is some specificity (Table 3–1). Bennett was able to separate cucumber mosaic virus from tobacco mosaic virus (TMV) because it persisted in the dodder when the dodder was grown on hosts immune to both viruses. TMV did not persist in the dodder, and there was thus no evidence that it multiplied in the dodder. Its transmission is evidently a passive movement from the vascular system of one host plant to the other. Costa (1944a) found a few cases in which TMV was transmitted by dodder removed from infected plants, but usually this did not occur, and there was never transmission after one or two transfers on plants immune from TMV.

G. W. Cochran (1946) presented further evidence that TMV is carried passively in the food stream of dodder when he showed that pruning the dodder (to remove growing points) and shading the healthy "recipient" plant gave 75% transmission; unshaded plants did not become infected. Cochran (1947) also described a "dodder graft" by which a detached stem tip was attached to an intact plant by winding growing tips of dodder around each. The detached stem tips were kept moist and sprayed with indole butyric acid.

The evidence is good (Costa, 1944b; Bennett, 1944a; Kunkel, 1943b, 1944, 1945) that many viruses multiply in the dodder species that will transmit them; stems of such dodder growing on infected plants will transmit the virus when detached and transferred to another host plant. Bennett (1944b) pointed out that in addition to making direct tracheal connections with the xylem and phloem of the host, there were also indications of plasmodesmatal connections between parasite and host.

It seems probable that certain species of dodder do not transmit certain viruses because they do not infect and multiply in the dodder. The evidence seems clear that TMV is merely carried in the dodder food stream, and is transmitted without infecting the dodder. Its transmission may be aided by the high concentration reached in many hosts, a concentration not closely approached by many other viruses that are not transmitted by dodder.

There are peculiarities of dodder transmission that remain unexplained. Peach X-disease virus can be transmitted by *C. campestris* from peach to periwinkle, carrot, and other hosts. It has not, however, been transmitted from the herbaceous hosts back to peach. Possibly this is due to some interaction, or lack of it, between the peach and the dodder, since Kunkel (1945) transmitted cranberry false-blossom virus from tomato back to cranberry, a rather woody host. Hildebrand (1945) was unable to transmit cucumber mosaic virus to peach with dodder, although peach has been found infected by this virus. Canova (1955) reported that *Cuscuta epithymum* failed to transmit cucumber mosaic virus to beet but that aphids acquired the virus by feeding on dodder growing on diseased beets. This would indicate that the dodder had acquired the virus, but that it was unable to transmit it.

A number of insects feed readily on dodder, and Giddings (1947) pointed out that the beet leafhopper will feed more readily on dodder and will transmit curly-top virus more readily from the dodder than from the species on which the dodder is growing.

A number of mechanically transmitted viruses have been recovered from the pressed juice of dodder, indicating that the viruses occur in appreciable amounts in the dodder. A number of species of dodder, however, contain substances inhibiting virus infection when mixed with the virus *in vitro* (Miyakawa and Yoshii, 1951; Schmelzer, 1956a). There is no evidence that such inhibitors are involved in the specificity of virus transmission by dodder.

B. Practical Aspects of Dodder Transmission

Dodder is probably seldom, if ever, involved in virus transmission in nature to economically important plants. In annual crops its occurrence is usually rare, except when seed is grossly contaminated with dodder seed. The possibility of dodder seed carrying virus over from one annual crop to the next has not often been considered. Bennett (1944a) described dodder latent virus, which causes a severe disease on some hosts, and which is transmitted through the seed of *C. californica*. Cranberry false blossom was not transmitted through seed of *C. campestris* (Kunkel, 1945).

C. Methods of Using Dodder

For experimental work dodder can be started conveniently from seed. Sowing dodder seed with the seed of a congenial host will result in the parasitism of the young green seedlings after germination. A somewhat more rapid method of obtaining a quantity of vigorous dodder is to germinate the dodder seed on filter paper. When the dodder seedlings are an inch or two long the rootlike "peg" can be immersed in a very small tube of water and attached near the top of a stem of a host large enough and growing vigorously enough to support rapid and abundant growth of dodder. Growth movements of the dodder in making initial contacts with its host are facilitated if the "peg" is immobilized.

Dodder will flower rather abundantly when it has produced considerable vegetative growth. Once flowering starts, vegetative growth slows markedly. Transfers from the dodder plant after flowering starts are likely to continue flowering without making much vegetative growth, thus, fairly frequent transfers are needed to keep dodder vegetative. Removal of flowers as soon as they form also may help keep dodder vegetative.

3–4. SEED TRANSMISSION OF PLANT VIRUSES

The possibility that virus diseases might be transmitted through the seed of infected plants was not neglected in the earliest work. Mayer (1886) mentions that there was no more mosaic in plants grown from seed of diseased tobacco than in plants grown from seed of healthy plants. Later, when the highly infectious nature and systemic distribution of the virus were better understood, the puzzling question was, why are so few plant viruses transmitted through the seeds? Although 30 or more viruses are now known to be seed transmitted (Table 3–2), the problem of why there are not more is still not entirely solved.

McClintock (1916, 1917) presented some of the first evidence that plant viruses are transmitted through seed in the case of cucumber mosaic and lima bean mosaic viruses. The evidence, however, was more suggestive than conclusive. Reddick and Stewart (1919) and Doolittle and Gilbert (1919) presented uncontestable evidence of seed transmission of bean mosaic and cucumber mosaic in 1919. Seed transmission of a number of other viruses was demonstrated in the next few years.

A. THE RATE OF VIRUS TRANSMISSION IN SEED

The frequency with which a seed-transmitted virus appears in the seed from an infected plant varies greatly with the virus and with the species infected. Up to 100% transmission has been found in seed of individual soybean plants infected with tobacco ringspot virus (Athow and Bancroft, 1959); lettuce plants infected with lettuce mosaic may produce 3–10% of the seed carrying the virus (Newhall, 1923; Couch, 1955). Seed transmission of virus at very low rates might be overlooked or ignored as being due to contamination from some other source. There are, however, relatively few reports of very low rates, suggesting that when seed transmission does occur, the percentage of seed carrying virus is usually high enough to be detectable without extensive testing or elaborate precautions against contamination.

Where rates of seed transmission from individual plants have been compared, rather wide differences have been found. Differences in rates of transmission of barley stripe mosaic virus were associated with different varieties (McNeal and Afanasiev, 1955; Singh et al., 1960). Varietal resistance factors may be involved in this variation. Clinch and Loughnane (1948) found sugar-beet yellows seed transmitted in 47.5% of the seed of one breeding line of beets, but not in other lines. Nikolic (1956), however, reported a low incidence of seed transmission of this virus in sugar-beet varieties. Grogan and Bardin (1950) found that lettuce mosaic virus was consistently transmitted through the seed in higher percentages in some varieties than in others. This virus apparently is not seed transmitted in the variety Cheshunt Early Giant (Kassanis, 1947; Couch, 1955). Fajardo (1930) found the percentage of transmission of bean mosaic virus higher with late varieties than with early varieties. Couch (1955) found considerable variation between different flower heads in their rates of seed transmission of lettuce mosaic virus. Fajardo (1930) found that the location in the pod of bean seed carrying bean mosaic virus was random. Nelson (1932) found that plants infected during the growing season transmitted virus to fewer seeds than plants infected the entire season.

Variation in rate of seed transmission may also be due to the stage at which the plant became infected. A high percentage of transmission resulting from early infection has been reported for barley stripe mosaic virus (Singh *et al.,* 1960), tobacco ringspot virus in soybean (Athow and Bancroft, 1959), lettuce mosaic virus in lettuce (Couch, 1955), and with several viruses by Crowley (1959). On the other hand, Eslick and Afanasiev (1955) reported the highest percentage of infection with barley stripe mosaic in barley when plants were inoculated ten days before heading than from earlier or later infections. Harrison (1935a) reported that, with bean mosaic virus, pods set early contained more seeds with virus than pods set late. Some reports indicate that plants grown from infected seed produce a higher percentage of infected seeds than plants that contract infection during the growing season. Other reports indicate that this is not always the case; the difference may lie in differences in times of "current season infection." Crowley (1959) found that southern bean mosaic, tobacco ringspot, and barley stripe mosaic viruses infected the gametes of their hosts. Embryos were infected in early stages of their development, but in lower percentages, and were not infected in later stages.

B. POLLEN TRANSMISSION

Pollen transmission of bean mosaic virus was reported by Reddick (1931). Nelson and Down (1933) found that the virus was seed-transmitted in about the same percentage when flowers on infected plants were pollinated with pollen from healthy plants as when flowers on healthy plants were pollinated with pollen from infected plants. This was confirmed with bean mosaic virus by Medina and Grogan (1961) and with elm mosaic virus by Callahan (1957). As far as tested, most seed-transmitted viruses appear to be pollen-transmitted also (Way and Gilmer, 1958; Gold *et al.,* 1954). Thus, self-pollination will result in more infected seed than pollinations of infected plants by healthy, or vice versa.

The presence of virus in pollen immediately raises the question of virus transmission to healthy plants by pollination. Reddick (1931) suggested this might occur, and Das and Milbrath (1961) described the infection of healthy plants (squash) by pollination with pollen from infected squash. Crowley (1959) pointed out earlier, however, the notable lack of evidence of this type of virus transmission. Thus far, the evidence indicates that if it does occur with seed-transmitted viruses, it must be rare or occur with only a few of the viruses. Elm mosaic virus, for example, is transmitted by pollen to seed in fairly high percentages. Since elm is wind-pollinated and sets seed copiously even a low rate of transmission of virus from pollen to a mature tree would mean a high incidence of disease.

C. ELIMINATION OF VIRUS FROM SEED

With most seed-transmitted viruses there is good evidence that the virus is carried internally. Attempts to treat the seed in ways that should inactivate external virus have not reduced the percentage containing demonstrable virus (Harrison, 1935b; Athow and Bancroft, 1959). Heat treatment of infected seed has not eliminated the virus. Muskmelon mosaic (squash mosaic?) and bean mosaic viruses are not highly tolerant of heat *in vitro,* but temperatures far above their thermal inactivation points have failed to eliminate the virus from seed (Reddick and Stewart, 1919; Rader *et al.,* 1947; Harrison, 1935b). Well-dried seed is surprisingly resistant to high temperature; virus in such seed appears to tolerate as much heat as the seed tolerates, suggesting that it, too, is less hydrated than in sap and thus has acquired greater resistance to heat denaturation.

Most attempts to eliminate virus from seed by heat have been done with rather high temperatures for relatively short periods. The apparent disappearance of virus from seed stored for a number of years suggests that elimination of virus might be hastened by moderate heat for longer periods.

Valleau (1939) found a lower percentage of tobacco seed carrying tobacco ringspot virus after 5½-years storage. He pointed out, however, that a differential loss of viability might account for the results. R. W. Fulton (unpublished) found that the percentage of *Prunus pensylvanica* seed carrying cherry necrotic ringspot virus (60–70%) remained relatively constant the first 4 years of storage at 2°C, but by the 6th year less than 5% of the seed produced infected seedlings. Loss of viability was minor, indicating a true loss of virus from the seed. Similar marked decreases in percentage of seed carrying muskmelon mosaic virus after 3-years storage were reported by Rader *et al.* (1947). Presumably this virus is the same or closely related to squash mosaic virus, which Middleton (1944) found did not disappear from squash seed stored 3 years. Athow and Bancroft (1959) found no decrease in percentage of soybean seed infected with tobacco ringspot virus after 10-months' storage.

The chief exception to the statement that most virus is carried internally in seed is TMV on tomato seed. Early workers disagreed on whether the virus was seed-transmitted (Dickson, 1922; Gardner and Kendrick, 1922; Bewley and Corbett, 1930; Doolittle and Beecher, 1937). Differences in results may have been due to differences in methods of extracting and cleaning seed from infected fruit. Chamberlain and Fry (1950) and Taylor *et al.* (1961) found that most of the virus present with tomato seed is in and on the seed coat. This could be eliminated by acid extraction or trisodium phosphate treatment, but not by thorough washing in detergent solutions. A small number of seeds had virus in the endosperm; this was not affected by acid or phosphate treatment, but was inactivated slowly during storage. Howles (1961) reported that virus associated with tomato seed could be reduced by heat treatment.

The infection of tomato seedlings by TMV carried with the seed occurs during and after germination (Taylor *et al.*, 1961), and may occur, partly at least, because virus from the seed coat is transferred mechanically to the seedlings when they are handled. Taylor (1962) found that germinating seed remained healthy when accompanied by trash containing TMV.

Evidently the transmission depends on fairly intimate association of virus with parts of the seed other than the embryo. McKinney (1952) reported transmission of TMV in pepper seed, but it is not known whether the virus was carried internally or externally or whether the strain of virus or line of pepper were determining factors.

D. Latent Virus in Seed

Of considerable practical importance is the fact that a number of seed-transmitted viruses are of the ringspot-type; infected seedlings are in the "recovered phase" from the time the seed germinates, and may not be readily detected. Valleau (1939), however, noticed that tobacco seedlings carrying yellow tobacco ringspot are more chlorotic than normal seedlings. Seedlings of a number of species of *Prunus* carrying necrotic ringspot virus may show no detectable symptoms. Wallace and Drake (1962) reported that some avocado trees, symptomless themselves, produce seedlings that carry the sunblotch virus without symptoms. McKinney (1953) described a barley line with a high rate of seed transmission of barley stripe mosaic in nearly symptomless seedlings.

E. Correlation of Seed Transmission with Other Virus Characteristics

There has been some tendency to describe certain plant families, Leguminosae for example, as particularly prone to seed transmission of infecting viruses. As more examples of seed transmission have been investigated, however, it seems more likely that seed transmission is a characteristic of the virus rather than a plant family. Lister (1960) has pointed out the general tendency for soil-borne viruses also to be seed-transmitted. Nitzany and Gerechter (1962) found that seed transmission of barley stripe mosaic virus occurred rather generally in many grasses.

F. Mechanisms Restricting Seed Transmission

The problem of explaining the lack of seed infection by many plant viruses has stimulated investigations of mechanisms and tissues involved in seed transmission.

Duggar (1930) suggested that TMV might be inactivated in the seed. Kausche (1940) described virus inactivation by aqueous extracts of tobacco seed. As Crowley (1955) pointed out, however, virus inactivators occur commonly in many plant extracts, and there is no evidence that any of them affect virus *in vivo*. Crowley (1957a) could find no evidence of any diffusible substance associated with developing tomato embryos on White's medium that was capable of reducing the infectivity of TMV in the culture.

Cheo's (1955) results with southern bean mosaic virus, on the other hand, indicated that this virus was present in embryos of immature seeds, but disappeared very rapidly as maturing seed became dehydrated. This loss of virus did not occur when seed coats or leaves were dried. Crowley (1957b) found that bean yellow mosaic, tomato spotted wilt, and tobacco mosaic viruses (not seed-transmitted) did not occur in the embryos.

Thus, two mechanisms may operate to prevent seed transmission: (1) elimination of virus from embryos of maturing seed, and (2) exclusion of virus from developing seed. Too few viruses not seed-transmitted have been investigated to know whether they are consistently absent from embryos and pollen. It might be assumed that both exclusion and elimination must be operative to prevent seed transmission in plants infected before reproductive organs are formed. There is some doubt, however, that many viruses completely invade meristematic tissue (Valleau, 1935; Bennett, 1940b; Limasset and Cornuet, 1949; Crowley and Hanson, 1960). Thus, virus might not reach reproductive cells until they were sufficiently differentiated to be "insulated" from the rest of the infected plant. Sheffield (1941) found inclusion bodies of severe etch virus in the testa, but not in other parts of tobacco seeds. Bennett (1940b) pointed out that tobacco mosaic and beet mosaic viruses, not seed-transmitted, but easily transmitted mechanically could not be transmitted mechanically from pollen.

It is easy enough to see, as pointed out by Bennett and Esau (1936), how the absence of direct phloem connections between the developing seed and the maternal parent could prevent a phloem-limited virus from entering the seed. Bennett (1940b) suggested that the absence of plasmodesmatal connections between the seed and the maternal plant might prevent virus from entering the seed. The extent to which viruses depend on plasmodesmata to pass from cell to cell is uncertain. Kassanis *et al.* (1958) found no plasmodesmata in cultured tobacco tumor tissue, but TMV spread through such tissue at about the same rate as through leaf tissue, where cells were connected by plasmodesmata. There must be some barrier, however, usually preventing virus movement between developing seed and maternal plant. Not only do nonseed-transmitted viruses fail to enter developing seeds, but many viruses that are seed-transmitted fail to pass from seed to maternal plant when introduced into the seed by pollen.

Bennett (1940b) suggested that plant viruses that are not seed-transmitted are unable to maintain themselves in gametophytic tissue. Crowley (1957b) concluded that this explanation was the only one fitting all the data. The general failure of citrus viruses to enter nucellar seed (Weathers and Calavan, 1959) would seem to indicate that the meristematic condition might be the critical factor rather than the haploid nuclear condition. Caldwell (1962) has suggested that a smaller amount of high energy phosphate compounds in embryos than in leaves may be concerned with inability of virus to maintain itself in embryos.

3–5. MECHANICAL INOCULATION

Such a large part of our knowledge of plant viruses has depended on mechanical inoculation that its importance as an experimental technique cannot be overestimated. This was emphasized in a review by Yarwood (1957b).

Investigations of virus outside the host are all dependent, in the final analysis, on the ability to demonstrate and measure the infectiousness of the material. The methods of doing this have improved greatly in the past 50 years, and improvements in efficiency are still being made.

Mechanical inoculation techniques have been described as highly inefficient in terms of numbers of infections obtained with the numbers of virus particles applied (Steere, 1955). The nature of the plant cell, with its cellulose cell wall, and the necessity for introducing virus into such cells make it seem probable that inoculation efficiency of plant viruses will never approach the highly efficient bacteriophage, equipped with its own mechanisms for penetrating the bacterial cell. Improvements in efficiency of plant virus inoculation in recent years, however, have resulted in mechanical transmission of many viruses once designated "not mechanically transmissible." A more realistic goal may be the mechanical transmission of all plant viruses rather than the ability to cause infection with each virus particle.

A. HISTORICAL

The earliest investigators of TMV used a variety of inoculation methods. Mayer (1886) sucked juice of diseased plants into glass capillaries and inserted these into midribs of healthy plants. Beijerinck (1898) injected juice with a syringe and inserted pieces of dry leaf in wounds in the stem. Both Clinton (1915) and Allard (1917) mention that a high percentage of infection was obtained by lightly rubbing tobacco leaves with diseased plant extract on hands or a brush. Schultz and Folsom (1920) inoculated potatoes by bruising leaves with their fingers and then applying juice of virus diseased potato leaves. They later (1923) characterized the "pin-prick" method of inoculation as useless. Fromme *et al.* (1927) and McKinney (1928) pointed out the apparent efficiency of wiping or swabbing leaves with juice or extracts of diseased plants.

Despite this evidence of the efficiency of lightly rubbing leaves with juice of an infected plant, until about 1930 inoculations were commonly made by pricking through drops of juice into healthy leaves with fine pins. In 1929, Holmes (1929a) published results that greatly stimulated the study of viruses. He demonstrated that the numbers of necrotic lesions on certain *Nicotiana* species were proportional to the dilution of the inoculum. Such lesions had been observed previously, but their quantitative significance apparently had not been appreciated. This provided a method, long needed for quantitative measurement of virus. It also demonstrated unequivocally the superiority of wiping inoculum on the surface of leaves. The relative efficiency of various inoculation methods could be compared quickly and far more accurately than by the use of large numbers of plants reacting with systemic symptoms. Apparently the previous evidence of the efficiency of the leaf-wiping method had not been widely accepted because of skepticism of the data on its reliability. There also may have been some tendency to equate plant virus inoculation methods with the injection or scarification methods used in animal virology; it did not seem quite logical that much virus was going to be introduced into a plant by lightly rubbing the leaves.

B. METHODS OF APPLYING INOCULUM

There have been many refinements of the basic technique of applying inoculum to the surface of leaves gently enough to avoid lethal damage to the cells. Some of these have been introduced as matters of convenience, some have increased the efficiency or uniformity of application. Commonly, inoculum is applied with a pad of cheesecloth or gauze periodically dipped in the inoculum. This, and the necessity of supporting the leaf during inoculation, means that the operator's hands will be contaminated with virus. This can be avoided by using a fairly stiff brush as an applicator (Allard, 1917; McKinney, 1928; Takahashi, 1947; and Yarwood, 1952b) with the leaf supported with some impervious material such as waxed paper. Spatulas made by flattening one end of a glass rod and roughening the bearing surface with abrasive are often used (Samuel, 1931). These are convenient in conserving inoculum or when making inoculations with single lesions (McWhorter, 1951). Single lesions can be ground between two spatulas, which are then used to transfer inoculum to plants. MacClement (1937) described an apparatus involving a ground glass disc mechanically rotated against the leaf surface. This permitted application of a measured amount of inoculum with uniform pressure provided by a tension spring.

Many other types of applicators have been used. The operator's forefinger is quite convenient, but necessitates thorough decontamination. McKinney (1948) noted the relative ease with which grass leaves can be inoculated by drawing them between the thumb and forefinger, compared with rubbing with a cloth pad. The end of the pestle used for grinding inoculum can be used, mainly as a matter of convenience rather than efficiency. Bent and twisted pipe cleaners (Krietlow, 1961) make cheap disposable applicators, as do "Q-tips."

The optimum amount of rubbing and pressure to apply probably vary with the host being inoculated. Usually, more than one or two passes over a leaf area will result in successively fewer lesions, probably because of increasing injury to the cells. Ross (1953) found that continued use of a cloth pad without redipping in inoculum resulted in a rapid progressive reduction in lesion counts of potato virus Y on *Physalis floridana*.

The relative efficiency of rubbing methods of inoculating suggests at once that leaf hairs are involved in virus transmission. Boyle and McKinney (1937) found, however, that trichomes were not unusually susceptible. When only the trichomes of a leaf were damaged in the presence of virus, there was considerably less infection than when the whole leaf surface was rubbed. Benda (1956) also found that direct wounding of individual hair cells did not result in a high rate of infection. Boyle and McKinney (1937) and Yarwood (1962b) have pointed out that some plants with few or no trichomes are nevertheless quite susceptible to virus infection. Kontaxis and Schlegel (1962), using C^{14}-labeled TMV found that virus might be deposited in basal septa of broken trichomes and enter uninjured cells via plasmodesmata.

C. Spraying Methods of Applying Inoculum

One drawback to applying inoculum to leaves by wiping or rubbing is that it is somewhat laborious if large numbers of plants are involved. A technique that has been used with some success on large numbers of plants is pressure spraying of inoculum. Richards and Munger (1944) used this method for field inoculation of large numbers of plants with bean mosaic and cucumber mosaic viruses. Subsequently, McKinney and Fellows (1951), Timian *et al.* (1955), and Dean (1960) found the method useful in inoculating wheat streak-mosaic, potato virus X, and sugar-cane mosaic viruses to large populations of plants to detect resistance. With the type of agricultural spray apparatus used the method was not highly effective in terms of complete infection of every susceptible plant. It did, however, provide a quick method for eliminating a large part of the susceptible population.

Lindner and Kirkpatrick (1959) refined the spraying technique by using an artist's air brush, a tool conveniently handled for inoculating individual plants and one lending itself to close standardization of pressure, fineness of spray, and distance from leaf surface. They reported a 10–20-fold increase in efficiency over the conventional rubbing method of inoculation of tobacco mosaic virus on cucumber cotyledons.

Optimum conditions for infection of cucumber cotyledons by tobacco mosaic virus were: 60 psi spraying pressure, a distance of 1 cm from the spray nozzle to the cotyledon, an inoculum delivery rate of 10 ml/min, a spraying time of 4 sec to cover a cotyledon, and the presence of 1% (w/v) 600-mesh Carborundum in the inoculum. The spraying distance was closely regulated by fitting over the spray nozzle a cork with a funnel-shaped opening. During spraying the cork was kept from contacting the inoculated surface by a cushion of air from the nozzle. Toler (1962) has reported better infection with oat mosaic virus using an air brush than by rubbing.

D. Pricking and Injection Application of Inoculum

In spite of the general convenience and efficiency of applying inoculum by rubbing there are a few diseases for which pin pricking seems to be a better, or the only method, of mechanical transmission. There is much evidence that sugar-beet curly-top virus is closely associated with, or limited to, the phloem. Apparently, the virus is unable to multiply in epidermal tissues or is unable to move from the epidermis. Severin (1924) infected sugar beets with curly top by pricking through drops of juice into the crowns. Dana (1932) infected healthy plants by pricks through young infected leaves. Others have confirmed this (Bennett, 1934). Fulton (1955) infected tobacco with curly-top virus by pricking inoculum into axillary buds. Brakke *et al.* (1954) transmitted wound-tumor virus to a low percentage of *Trifolium incarnatum* plants by pricking drops of tumor extract into the crowns.

Sugar-cane mosaic virus has been transmitted with various degrees of success by hypodermic injection or by needle pricking through drops of extract into the base of young leaves (Brandes, 1920; Matz, 1933; Bain, 1944; Liu, 1949). Bruner (1922) transmitted the virus by pricking through young infected leaves into the bases of young healthy leaves. The virus can also be transmitted by leaf rubbing (Matz, 1933), but the percentage of infection is low. Bain (1944) and Costa *et al.* (1952) obtained better infection by leaf rubbing with Carborundum than by leaf pricking, but Bain infected only about half the plants inoculated. Liu (1949) reported 95% infection by pin pricking. Bird (1961) obtained higher infection with an air brush operated at 75 psi than by pin pricking.

Hypodermic injection of infectious extracts has been used sporadically with plant viruses, usually without marked success. Harpaz (1959), however, reported 25% transmission of a maize virus by hypodermic injection of stalks, where leaf rubbing with abrasives failed. Pfaeltzer (1960) infected a higher percentage of cherry seedlings with cherry Pfeffinger virus by injecting sap into stems than by rubbing leaves. Symptoms appeared in one month after leaf rubbing, however, compared with one year for injection.

E. HOST SUSCEPTIBILITY; THE USE OF ABRASIVES

The leaf-rubbing and local-lesion techniques immediately revealed differences in susceptibility among leaves on one plant, and among plants (Holmes, 1929a). It seems obvious that differences in the thickness or toughness of the cuticle and the external cell wall of the epidermis would affect the efficiency of the rubbing method of inoculation. Probably the most important improvement of the leaf-rubbing method was the introduction of Carborundum (silicon carbide) as an abrasive by Rawlins and Tompkins (1934, 1936). This apparently provided a means of making the small, nonlethal wounds needed for the introduction of virus. The numbers of primary lesions with a number of viruses are increased 10 to 100 times when virus is applied to leaves lightly dusted with Carborundum. Rawlins and Tompkins (1936) reported much higher percentages of infection by tomato spotted wilt, celery mosaic, broad bean mosaic, cauliflower mosaic, and sugar-beet mosaic viruses. These were all difficult to transmit without Carborundum.

The use of abrasives was not new; Harrison (1935b), Fajardo (1930), and Fajardo and Maranon (1932) had used fine sand in transmitting bean mosaic and sincamas mosaic viruses. Vinson and Petre (1931) had noted increased infection with tobacco mosaic in the presence of charcoal. These abrasives, however, had been used so as to produce visible injury to the epidermis, in an approximation of needle scratching or pricking, and quantitative methods for estimating increased infections were not available. A combination of Carborundum and gentle wiping of virus on a local-lesion host left no doubt of the efficiency of nonlethal wounds for inoculation.

There have been many modifications in the use of abrasives. Kalmus and Kassanis (1945) pointed out that Celite (diatomaceous earth), charcoal, aluminum oxide (corundum), and kaolin (aluminum silicate) were all effective. Celite has an advantage in that it is light and does not settle out as rapidly when mixed with inoculum as Carborundum. Different grades of charcoal had various effects, possibly due to varying adsorptive capacities.

The use of abrasives has become routine in mechanical inoculation. Thus, the number of viruses mechanically transmissible with abrasive, but not transmissible without abrasive is not known. Kassanis (1949) credits mechanical transmissibility of sugarbeet yellows to the use of Celite or Carborundum, and Bawden *et al.* (1950) were able to transmit mechanically potato paracrinkle virus (long an enigma) using abrasives. Probably many other viruses belong in this category.

It seems obvious that finely divided abrasive will wound or penetrate epidermal cells. That this is its main effect seems probable from the fact that different abrasives are all relatively effective (Costa, 1944b; Kalmus and Kassanis, 1945; Beraha and Thornberry, 1952). Particle fineness of various grades of abrasive is expressed as the spacing of screen mesh per inch that will permit passage. Various reports on the effect of abrasive particle size have indicated greater efficiency for one size or another in the 150–800 mesh range. As Lindner *et al.* (1959) pointed out, however, the size range of particles varies in different lots of the same grade. Beraha *et al.* (1955) presented evidence indicating that efficiency was related to the numbers of particles present rather than their size. Lindner *et al.* (1959) thought that infectivity was not directly proportional to the amount of Carborundum in the inoculum, but was proportional to the calculated number of particles/epidermal cell up to one particle/cell. The inference here is that one wound/cell is optimum for infection and that greater wounding may kill cells or damage them so greatly that they will not support virus multiplication.

The question of whether the effect of Carborundum was only in wounding or whether it carried adsorbed virus into the cell was considered by Costa (1944b) and Beraha *et al.* (1955), who found no evidence that virus was adsorbed to the Carborundum particles.

F. Physiological Factors of Host Susceptibility

Although by breaching physical barriers of epidermal cells to virus penetration abrasives decrease variations in susceptibility among leaves and plants, the remaining variation is still great. The basis of much of this variation is obscure; to say it is due to physiological factors covers much ignorance.

Certain species of plants seem to have an inherent susceptibility to many different viruses. *Phaseolus vulgaris, Nicotiana tabacum, Cucumis sativus, Chenopodium amaranticolor* are representative of plants used widely in virus research, partly because of their general susceptibility. Many plants are susceptible to fewer viruses or are more difficult to infect. Tomato, for example, is relatively difficult to infect mechanically with tobacco ringspot virus. Undoubtedly, many plants have an absolute immunity to many viruses. To what extent this category is determined by the efficiency of inoculation methods, however, is not clear. Most investigators refrain from reporting a species "immune"; "not infected" is a much safer category in view of the wider and wider host ranges found as improved methods of transmission are developed.

Inherent variation in susceptibility within species was described by Holmes (1939) in *Lycopersicon esculentum*. Certain lines tended to escape infection by TMV, and this tendency was inherited (Holmes, 1943, 1954). The same characteristic in tobacco was reported by Schwartz and Cuzin (1951). Troutman and Fulton (1958) showed that this characteristic in tobacco was relatively nonspecific against a number of different viruses.

G. Effect of Illumination

Bawden and Roberts (1947, 1948) reported that in summer reduced light intensity increased susceptibility of plants to virus. The virus content of plants was higher under reduced light intensity. This effect seemed not related to leaf morphology because it could be obtained by darkening the plants for 24 or 48 hours.

The effect of darkness on susceptibility indicates that there should be diurnal variations in susceptibility. These have been found frequently, but high susceptibility has not always been associated with a previous dark period. Matthews (1953a) reported maximum susceptibility of beans to TMV in the afternoon. This was between

March and May in New Zealand. In Madison, Wisconsin, during the short days of winter, tobacco is most susceptible to TMV late in the afternoon. Matthews (1953b) reported that the daily variation in susceptibility persisted even when plants were kept in a constant environment. Yarwood (1956a, 1962a) found beans were more susceptible to TMV in the early afternoon than in the early morning. He also reported that other factors interacted with light in altering susceptibility.

With viruses difficult to transmit, darkening plants before inoculation may permit transmission otherwise impossible. Costa and Bennett (1955) and Mundry and Rohmer (1958) have reported that preinoculation darkening increased susceptibility of sugar beets to beet yellows virus.

The basis of the dark-induced susceptibility is not known. The evidence indicates that certain amount of light or length of day is optimum for susceptibility. Darkening may counteract superoptimal light. Humphries and Kassanis (1955) attempted to correlate dark-induced susceptibility with changes in chemical composition of the leaves. An increase in nitrate nitrogen was correlated with increased susceptibility, but they concluded that the relationship was indirect. Troutman and Fulton (1958) found that the susceptibility of a variety somewhat difficult to infect was increased much more by darkening than the susceptibility of a rather susceptible variety, indicating inherent differences among plants in the response of susceptibility to changes in light.

H. Effect of Host Nutrition on Susceptibility

Because the multiplication of viruses is so dependent on the biochemical apparatus of the plant, it is not surprising that it is nearly an axiom that young, well-nourished, vigorous plants are most susceptible. Spencer (1935a) pointed out that the amount of nitrogen supplied to beans and tobacco affected susceptibility to TMV. Susceptibility was highest when growth was somewhat retarded by excess nitrogen, indicating that factors other than host growth were involved. Moderately high potassium decreased susceptibility without affecting plant growth (Spencer, 1935b). With variations in phosphorus supply, susceptibility was correlated directly with growth of the plants. Bawden and Kassanis (1950) found that susceptibility of N. glutinosa to TMV was decreased by a deficiency or an excess of either nitrogen or phosphorus. Chessin and Scott (1955) reported that calcium deficient N. glutinosa were less susceptible to TMV than normal plants.

I. Effect of Heat Treatments on Susceptibility

Kassanis (1952) found with a number of viruses that keeping plants at 36°C for some time before inoculation increased their susceptibility. This was not simply an effect of temperature stimulating virus reproduction, since with those viruses multiplying at 36°C, plants kept at 36°C after inoculation developed fewer lesions than those kept at lower temperatures. Tobacco necrosis, tomato bushy stunt, and cucumber mosaic viruses apparently did not multiply at 36°C, and keeping inoculated plants at this temperature a day or more after inoculation prevented lesion formation altogether.

Yarwood (1956b) has investigated heat-induced susceptibility with a number of viruses. Beans were treated by dipping them in water at various temperatures (40–55°C) for periods up to 30 sec. Greatest increases in susceptibility were obtained with leaves that had become somewhat resistant to infection due to age. The increased susceptibility of bean leaves was observed for up to 3 days after treatment. The effect of heat in increasing susceptibility was observed only with bean. Yarwood et al. (1962) later found that the effect of heat was not a local phenomenon. Heating one of a pair of primary bean leaves increased the susceptibility of the opposite leaf.

In some cases (Yarwood, 1958) the appearance of lesions was delayed by heating leaves 20 sec at 50°C between 6 hr and 3 days after inoculation. More and larger lesions developed, however, and lesions appeared on plants inoculated with peach yellow bud mosaic virus, which ordinarily did not induce lesions. The increase in lesion numbers by treatment after inoculation evidently resulted from the activation of virus latent under ordinary conditions. Increases in susceptibility may result from the destruction of some material, or the temporary inhibition of some normal process of the plant that tends to oppose infection.

J. Other Factors Affecting Susceptibility

There are a number of chemical and physical factors that affect the susceptibility of leaves to viruses. Kalmus and Kassanis (1944) found that exposing plants to 30–60% CO_2 reduced susceptibility. Yarwood (1954) found that immersion of bean leaves 10 min in low concentrations of zinc sulphate increased their susceptibility, as did soaking them in water (Yarwood, 1959). Rubbing the lower surface of bean leaves increased the susceptibility to virus applied on the upper surface (Yarwood et al., 1962).

Yarwood (1953b) found that application of pressure to bean leaves just before or after inoculation increased the number of lesions produced by TMV, tobacco ringspot virus, and tobacco necrosis virus. Panzer (1959), however, found no effect of atmospheric pressures as high as 20 psi after inoculation of N. glutinosa with TMV or bean with alfalfa mosaic virus.

Tinsley (1953) found that tobacco and N. glutinosa receiving unlimited water before inoculation were more susceptible to tomato bushy stunt virus and potato viruses X and Y than plants receiving only enough water to prevent wilting. The differences decreased when plants were grown under shade or inoculated with Celite in the inoculum and may have been due to structural differences associated with succulence. Panzer (1957) found that lowest lesion counts were obtained on leaf disks floated on relatively concentrated sucrose solutions or on plants with their stems immersed in these solutions. He suggested that variations in osmotic pressure of the tissues inoculated may be involved in variations in susceptibility.

K. Infectivity of Inoculum; the Phosphate Effect

In any inoculation, it is essential that inoculum be infective. There are many factors that may increase or decrease the infectivity of plant viruses. The evidence is good that many of these factors affect the susceptibility of the host rather than affecting the virus directly. They are treated here, however, as inhibitors of infectivity because their net effects are rather similar to materials directly affecting virus, and the methods of dealing with such inhibitors usually involve methods of handling inoculum.

Mechanical inoculation usually involves virus suspended in a liquid medium, and the nature of this medium may greatly affect the efficiency of inoculation. Thornberry (1935a) reported that dibasic phosphate salts in inoculum greatly increased infectivity of TMV. This has been repeatedly confirmed, although not for all viruses on all hosts (Yarwood, 1952c). The relative effect of phosphate may be greater on one host than another. Yarwood (1952c) has interpreted the effect of phosphate as being on the host. It seems more probable, however, that it affects some part of the initial process of the entry or attachment of virus to a susceptible site on a wounded cell. Kahn and Schachtner (1954a,b), analyzed the effect of phosphate by abrading leaves dry and then applying solutions, or inoculum in various sequences. Applying water after abrasion and before applying inoculum resulted in less infection than applying buffer or applying inoculum. The effect of phosphate in increasing infection was apparent at the time of inoculation or immediately after, but not when applied before inoculation. As Kahn and Libby (1958) point out, however, more lesions were produced if dry-abraded leaves did not receive either water or phosphate before inoculum was applied. Yarwood (1962a) also found that the maximum effect of phosphate is obtained when it is present at the time virus is applied and the cells are wounded. Application of phosphate before or after application of virus had less effect.

The hydrogen ion concentration of the suspending medium also may markedly affect the amount of infection obtained. Thornberry (1935a) reported that the optimum for infectivity of TMV was between pH 7 and 8.5. Yarwood (1952c) commonly uses a solution of K_2HPO_4; this, unadjusted would have a pH of about 8.5. In general, slightly alkaline inocula are more infectious than slightly acid inocula; infectivity decreases rapidly with additional increase in acidity.

The concentration of salts dissolved in inoculum also affects infectivity. Thornberry (1935a) found greatest infectivity with 0.1 M phosphate, and this concentration is commonly used. Certain viruses, however, are more infectious in 0.03 M or even lower concentrations of phosphate than in 0.1 M (R. W. Fulton, 1957). The leaves of some plants may be damaged by 0.1 M phosphate (or with any salt at this concentration) which may account for fewer lesions developing. The buffering capacity of 0.03 M phosphate is not great; there is no assurance that pH is maintained in inocula containing any quantity of extraneous material. Some other salts also seem to improve transmission to some extent; Yarwood (1956a) pointed out that sodium sulphite had a beneficial effect that could not be explained on the basis of its antioxidant properties. Ross (1953) found that 0.1 M borate buffer was superior to phosphate when inoculating *Physalis floridana* with potato virus Y. Inoculated leaves were severely injured, however, unless they were rinsed within one minute.

L. INHIBITORS IN PLANT EXTRACTS

The presence of inhibitors in plant extracts has been known since Duggar and Armstrong (1925) described the inhibition of TMV infectivity by extracts of *Phytolacca decandra*. These materials either have little or no effect on the virus *in vivo* or they are formed only after the tissue is ground (Bawden, 1954). The chemical nature of many of these inhibitors is unknown; undoubtedly they are a heterogeneous group. Kassanis and Kleczkowski (1948) found the inhibitor in *Phytolacca* was a mucoprotein; Kuntz and Walker

(1947) described two inhibitors in spinach juice, one which absorbed to charcoal, the other, removed by adding $CaCl_2$ and filtering, was probably an oxalate.

Part of the evidence that the action of one type of inhibitor is on the host rather than on the virus is that the full effect of a given amount of inhibitor is obtained immediately on mixing with viruses; incubating mixtures does not increase the amount of virus inactivated. Many inhibitors apparently do not permanently inactivate viruses. Dilution of inhibitor-virus mixtures usually results in an increase in infectivity (Stanley, 1934; Black, 1939; Ross, 1941; Kuntz and Walker, 1947; Bawden, 1954). The action of these inhibitors is conditioned by the host inoculated. Gendron and Kassanis (1954) found that several plant saps inhibited infection when inoculations were made to other species, but not when inoculated to the species supplying the sap.

Tannins are of particular interest and importance in the transmission of plant viruses because of their wide occurrence and virus-inhibiting properties. Allard (1918) and Stanley (1935) demonstrated inhibition of infectivity of TMV by tannic acid. Thornberry (1935b) found that the degree of inhibition depended on the concentration of tannic acid and on the time it was in contact with the virus. Bawden and Kleczkowski (1945) found that extracts of strawberry leaves contained material, presumably tannin, that precipitated proteins from the extracts.

Thornberry (1935b) and Hirth (1951) found evidence that tannin formed a loose complex with TMV, and that this complex dissociated at pH 8.2–8.5. TMV presumably is unusually resistant to denaturation by tannin. Other viruses may be denatured; in fact, the characterization of many viruses as "unstable" probably reflects their tendency to become rapidly and permanently destroyed by tannins or other substances in plant extracts.

Numerous methods have been devised to avoid the effects of tannins in transmitting virus. Tannins form insoluble precipitates with proteins; Thornberry (1935b) partially restored infectivity of tannic acid-TMV mixtures by adding gelatin. Alkaloids form insoluble complexes with tannin. Thung and van der Want (1951) used nicotine sulphate precipitation to remove tannins from extracts of raspberry leaves. Thresh (1956) pointed out that nicotine sulphate was only partially effective in preventing precipitation of TMV by tannin in raspberries and that by itself it reduced infectivity of the virus. Cadman (1956), however, has transmitted raspberry viruses by grinding leaves with 4 ml of 40% nicotine sulphate, centrifuging and then dialysing overnight to remove the nicotine sulphate.

Cadman (1959) later found nicotine base more effective than the sulphate. He pointed out that the degree to which infection was inhibited depended on the virus rather than the host. Inactivation could be reversed by dilution or raising the pH to 8 with some viruses but not with others. Lister (1958) used nicotine treatment in preparing antigen from infected strawberry.

Diener and Weaver (1959) have used a 0.5% solution of caffeine as an aid in improving transmissibility of cherry necrotic ringspot virus from cherry leaves to herbaceous hosts.

Cornuet (1952) reported transmission of a virus of strawberry using inoculum prepared by freeze-drying infected tissue, then extracting it with alcohol to remove tannins. Vaughan (1956a) described a modified Soxhlet apparatus for extracting frozen dried tissue with alcohol or chloroform so as to avoid hydration of the tissue or solvent during the process. The method was effective in removing tannins, but attempts to transmit raspberry and strawberry viruses using the method were unsuccessful (Vaughan, 1956b). It may be that not all viruses will withstand the freezing and extraction procedures.

Another promising method of removing tannins is by adsorption. Cadman (1959) found that alumina effectively removed inhibitors from raspberry and strawberry leaves. Lister (1959) used extracts containing alumina in mechanically transmitting cassava brown streak virus.

Other inhibitive substances in extracts also may be removed with resulting increase in infectivity. J. Johnson (1941) showed with a variety of materials that diffusing the inhibitor away from the virus resulted in an increase in infectivity.

The beneficial effect of charcoal on infectivity of TMV was noticed by Vinson and Petre (1931), Stanley (1935), and Bald (1937). This effect was also thought due to the abrasive action of charcoal, but Stanley found that filtrates after removal of charcoal were more infectious than untreated extracts. TMV was adsorbed by charcoal, particularly at pH 3–5, but adsorbed virus was still infective. Kalmus and Kassanis (1945) found that charcoal from various sources had widely different effects on TMV; some lots were inhibitory. Presumably inclusion of charcoal in extracts of citrus infectious variegation virus by Grant and Corbett (1960, 1961) is effective because it removes inhibitors. Thung and Dijkstra (1958) and Thung and Noordam (1959) removed virus-inhibiting material from carnation extract by adsorption to montmorillonite. They pointed out that this clay mineral removed some virus also.

Less clear is the nature of action of some other compounds reported to stabilize virus in extracts or to improve transmissibility. The nature and chemical characteristics of virus-stabilizing compounds, however, provide a key that eventually may be used in explaining unusual instability of some viruses. Englebrecht and Regenmortel (1960) reported that salicylic acid and "deinhibited rabbit serum" prolonged infectivity of a stone fruit ringspot virus. Kegler (1961) stabilized Stecklenburger and Pfeffinger viruses with hydroxylamine hydrochloride. He found increased infection when infected *Prunus* leaves were homogenized with sodium diethyldithiocarbamate (DIECA).

Grant and Corbett (1961) and Desjardins and Wallace (1962) used sucrose as well as charcoal in the inoculum of citrus psorosis virus. Sucrose increased infectivity and was thought to act by preventing rupture and release of enzymes from mitochondria.

M. POLYPHENOLS AND ANTIOXIDANTS

A class of compounds related to tannins and important in interfering with mechanical transmission of viruses are the oxidizable phenolic compounds. These apparently are relatively innocuous in the reduced state, but oxidize readily when tissue extracts are exposed to air, and become highly inhibitory. Perhaps most of the viruses characterized as highly unstable are sensitive to this type of inactivator. Bald and Samuel (1934) investigating tomato spotted wilt virus found that the rate of loss of infectivity was increased by aeration and retarded in an atmosphere of nitrogen. Chemical oxidizing agents increased inactivation; reducing agents (sodium sulphite) retarded inactivation. Best and Samuel (1936) concluded that the effects of oxidation were not primarily on the virus. Best (1939) found that sodium salts of glutathione, thioglycollic acid, ascorbic acid, and potassium cyanide all had preservative effects on the virus in extracts.

Numerous viruses have since been found that are stabilized in extracts by antioxidants (Ainsworth and Ogilvie, 1939; R. W. Fulton, 1949; Limasset, 1951; Hougas, 1951; Martin, 1952; Hildebrand, 1956b). Usually the transmission of these viruses is possible without antioxidants, but such materials increase efficiency. This is particularly true with concentrated extracts. Use of undiluted sap in an effort to inoculate with as high a concentration of virus as possible may be self-defeating. R. W. Fulton (1957) showed that undiluted extracts of cherry necrotic ringspot virus lost most of their infectivity 90 sec after grinding the tissue. More dilute extracts lost infectivity more slowly, and those containing antioxidants lost little or no infectivity for several hours. Since chemical reactions are involved it might be expected that the speed of the reaction would be greater with more concentrated reagents.

Sulphur-containing compounds have been used commonly as antioxidants. Other compounds that combine more readily with oxygen than do the phenols in the extract are effective if they do not adversely affect infectivity otherwise. Iron filings, for example, partially stabilize tobacco streak virus (R. W. Fulton, 1949).

Enzymes are involved in the oxidation of phenolic compounds in plant extracts. Hampton and Fulton (1961) found that

sodium diethyldithiocarbamate (DIECA) stabilized infectivity of extracts of cherry necrotic ringspot virus without the use of antioxidants. DIECA inhibits polyphenol oxidase activity by sequestering copper, necessary for enzymatic activity. Cyanide also forms complexes with copper ion, and it is also effective in stabilizing a number of viruses (Best, 1939; R. W. Fulton, 1949, 1957), although less so than DIECA. Azide and citrate helped stabilize tobacco necrosis virus (Bawden and Pirie, 1957). Other compounds inhibiting polyphenol oxidase by providing a competitive substrate (p-nitrophenol, benzaldehydeoxime) also stabilized infectivity of cherry necrotic ringspot virus (Hampton and Fulton, 1961).

The intensity of the phenol-polyphenol oxidase reaction varies with different tissues and at different seasons of the year. Hampton and Fulton (1961) found that prune dwarf virus retained infectivity in extracts of infected squash leaves longer in the late spring and early fall than during the winter. This was apparently due to less enzyme as well as less substrate because the addition of either to the extract hastened inactivation.

The polyphenol-polyphenol oxidase system is also of interest because it appears to be much more prominent in virus-infected than in healthy tissue. Best (1937) found that an enzyme catalyzing the oxidation of several phenols was present in tomatoes infected with tomato spotted wilt virus, but was not demonstrable in healthy tissue. It was present in infected tobacco, but not in *Tropaeolum majus*.

Martin (1954) found that tyrosinase activity was higher in mosaic-infected dahlias than in healthy plants. He later (1958) reported one maximum in the activity of this enzyme 24–72 hours after inoculating tobacco with several viruses, and another maximum after 10 days when symptoms developed. Martin and Morel (1958) found that chlorogenic acid and its derivatives—substrates of polyphenol oxidase—were present in greater amounts in infected tissue. Similar increase in this enzyme-substrate system was found by Hampton and Fulton (1961) in squash and cucumber infected with stone fruit viruses. Bawden and Pirie (1957) found stronger inactivation of tobacco necrosis virus by material sedimented from tobacco ringspot virus-infected plants than from healthy plants.

The virus-inactivating action of oxidized phenolic compounds apparently results in irreversible loss of infectivity with some viruses. Some oxidized phenolic compounds can be reduced by proper reducing agents. Once cherry necrotic ringspot virus had been in contact with o-quinone (oxidized) loss of infectivity was not reversed by reducing the o-quinone to catechol, the reduced form, which was innocuous to the virus (Hampton and Fulton, 1961). The "stable" viruses are evidently not sensitive to oxidized phenolic materials, or require much higher amounts for their inactivation. How many of the "unstable" viruses are permanently inactivated is not known. The mechanism of inactivation is rather subtle, since serological specificity is retained (Hampton and Fulton, 1961).

When a virus inactivator is formed after tissue is ground, and permanently inactivates virus, its formation must be prevented if inoculations are to be consistently successful. Antioxidants provide one means of doing this. Other attempts to avoid oxidative changes have involved making inoculations without grinding tissue and preparing extracts. Yarwood (1953a) described a technique involving rubbing the freshly cut edges of a stack of leaf disks over the surface of leaves previously dusted with Carborundum and sprayed with phosphate. Hildebrand (1956a) used the method to transmit sweet-potato internal cork virus. Berg (1962a, 1962b) has transmitted a virus disease of poplars using a modification of the method.

N. Sources of Inoculum

It should be obvious that tissue selected to provide inoculum should contain a high concentration of virus. Ordinarily this will be young tissue, in which the virus concentration is highest within a relatively few days after infection, whether by virus introduced directly, or virus entering systemically from another part of the plant. Tissue with the highest virus concentration, how-ever, may not always supply the most infectious inoculum. Results (unpublished) have indicated maximum infectivity of cherry necrotic ringspot virus in cucumber cotyledons 3–4 days after inoculation. After 7–10 days, virus concentration measured serologically was high, but infectivity of extracts of the leaves was quite low. Evidently in newly infected leaves virus increased more rapidly than inactivating substances accumulated, but after a few additional days the concentration of inactivating material was sufficiently high to depress infectivity to low levels.

Some methods for transmitting "difficult" viruses involve selection of tissue with a low inhibitor content for preparing inoculum. Sill and Walker (1952) found that cucumber corollas contained little or no inhibitor of cucumber mosaic virus, in contrast to the rest of the plant. Milbrath (1953), McWhorter (1953), and Willison et al. (1956) have used petals as a source of readily transmissible virus, or of virus free of undesirable material present in leaf extracts. Tomlinson (1955) reported that a latent virus of cherry was more infectious and more stable in extracts of cucumber roots than in extracts of leaves.

Yarwood (1957a) described an inoculation method based on the demonstrated high concentrations of some viruses in the epidermis. The surface of infected plants was stroked with a stiff poster brush, which was then immediately stroked on a healthy leaf dusted with Carborundum and sprayed with phosphate. Transmission from nonhairy leaves with this method was usually poor.

Schmelzer (1957a) avoided the effect of an inhibitor in carnation by first transmitting carnation virus to Stellaria media. Presumably this species, a member of the same family as carnation, was less affected by the inhibitor in carnation than other hosts. The virus then was readily transmissible from S. media to tobacco.

O. The Mechanism of Infection and Factors Affecting It

Infection of a susceptible cell by a virus particle is a process rather than a single event. A number of factors appear to affect this process, some of which will be considered here. Differentiation of these factors from those considered previously, however, is rather arbitrary. Many virus inhibitors, for example, are more or less effective if applied to inoculated leaves soon after inoculation (Bawden, 1954). Evidently the virus (or the host) remains sensitive to these effects until a certain stage is reached in the process of infection.

A factor in the amount of infection obtained by mechanical inoculation is the washing the leaves received after inoculation. Holmes (1929b), in determining whether the time of contact between virus and epidermal cells was important, found that washing leaves after inoculation increased the amount of infection. This practice has been widely followed, and it is easy to understand why it might be effective, since some plant extracts kill epidermal cells if allowed to dry on leaves. Yarwood (1952a) reported, however, that leaves to which dry virus was applied developed fewer lesions if they were washed after inoculation than when they were left unwashed. Leaves dried rapidly after inoculation developed more lesions than leaves dried slowly. When abrasion and application of inoculum were done as successive steps, abrading the leaves wet, then applying inoculum resulted in fewer lesions than dry abrasion before inoculation. In a later report Yarwood (1955a) found that washing was not detrimental if the period of washing was 10 sec or less. The deleterious effect of washing could be demonstrated up to 3 hours after inoculation at 31°C and 9 hours at 20°C. When inoculum contained phosphate, washing always decreased infection. When inoculum was prepared with water, a brief washing often increased infection, particularly when the wash water contained phosphate. Kahn and Schachtner (1954a) found that washing cowpea leaves after inoculation decreased infection regardless of the presence or absence of phosphate in the inoculum.

These results, in general, have been confirmed by other workers (Allington and Laird, 1954b; Dale, 1956). Some workers have reported negligible effects from washing (Crowley, 1954); others have found sharp reduction in infection after washing (R. W. Fulton, 1957). Yarwood (1955a) believed that the effect of water was to dilute or remove from the tissue certain ions that were necessary for infection.

Statistical evidence (Lauffer and Price, 1945) indicates that each infection by a virus results from the action of a single infectious particle. With a few viruses, however, there is evidence that two or more particles are required at an infection site for successful infection (R. W. Fulton, 1962). This characteristic makes the amount of virus of great importance in transmission if the concentration in infected tissue were lower than that necessary to provide the required number of particles at an infection site.

Hildebrand (1943) described the extrusion of a droplet of cytoplasm from a wounded cell and its rapid withdrawal back into the cell. Benda (1956) described this extrusion and retraction when a *Nicotiana* hair cell was punctured through a droplet of inoculum. D. J. Rossouw and the author (unpublished) readily observed the retraction of the protoplasmic droplet when a cell in air was punctured. When immersed in liquid, however, protoplasmic granules were extruded from the wound, but there was no evidence of a return of any material into the cell regardless of the composition or concentration of the surrounding liquid.

How a cell behaves when wounded by rubbing with an abrasive in the presence of liquid is not known. It may be significant, however, that application of dry inoculum is more effective than inoculum suspended in water or buffer (Yarwood, 1952a; Kalmus and Kassanis, 1945; Kahn and Libby, 1958). Sheffield (1936) found that it was not necessary (although it was more efficient) to wound a cell in the presence of virus to obtain infection. The loss of susceptibility, however, was rapid after wounding. Allington and Laird (1954b) found that after dry abrasion plants that had received a low potassium nutrient supply were more susceptible to TMV than those receiving normal potassium. In fact, the susceptibility of some potassium-deficient plants increased with time for 60 sec or more. Later Jedlinski (1956) found that a number of plants retained susceptibility after dry abrasions for periods up to 10 min after wounding. As the authors of both these papers point out, it is apparent that more is involved in infection than the mere introduction of virus into susceptible cells. There seem to be different degrees of probability of successful infection of a cell, conditioned by events preceding inoculations as well as after inoculation. While the rapid retraction of a droplet of cytoplasm into a wounded cell can be envisioned as carrying virus with it, it is difficult to reconcile this view with retention of high infectability of dry abraded cells for 5–10 min.

The effects of humidity are probably involved indirectly in transmission by determining the length of time a leaf remains wet after inoculation. Howles (1947), Yarwood (1952a), Panzer (1959), and Lindner *et al.* (1959) obtained more infection on plants placed at low humidity after inoculation than on plants at high humidities. Yarwood (1952a) found that somewhat wilted leaves were more susceptible than fully turgid ones.

P. RIBONUCLEASE AND VIRUS TRANSMISSION

After Schramm *et al.* (1955) demonstrated the infectivity of the nucleic acid portion of TMV there was some basis for supposing that some plant viruses might exist only as "naked" nucleic acid, and that mechanical transmission of these might be prevented by ribonuclease in leaf extracts. Babos and Kassanis (1962) described a variant of tobacco necrosis virus more readily transmissible in water-saturated phenol extracts of infected leaves or in 0.5 *M* borax, than in sap. They suggested that the variant usually existed largely as nucleic acid. Brandenburg (1962) reported mechanically transmitting potato leaf roll virus, using phenol extracts of diseased leaves (ribonuclease being removed by the phenol treatment). Govier (1963), however, was unable to repeat this.

Gordon and Smith (1960) reported infecting *Rhoeo discolor* by TMV nucleic acid, whereas the plant could not be infected by intact virus. It was soon found, however, that the plant was also susceptible to intact TMV, but that the virus increased only at high illumination (Gordon and Smith, 1961). Bawden (1961) pointed out that virus increase after inoculation with intact virus was less readily detected than with nucleic acid inoculation because of residual virus on the leaves.

There is little evidence in the literature that many attempts have been made to transmit "nonmechanically transmissible viruses" by phenol extracts or extracts prepared with bentonite to check inhibitive effects of ribonuclease in leaf extracts. While the hypothesis is attractive, there is very little evidence indicating that many plant viruses exist in the plant solely as "naked" nucleoprotein.

3–6. CONCLUSIONS

Increasing the efficiency of mechanical inoculation may be desirable to reduce variability in quantitative measurement of infectivity, and to permit transmission of viruses from hosts in which their study is difficult to hosts better adapted for experimental work. Viruses present problems in woody hosts, for example, that are avoided in herbaceous hosts. Woody plants are subject to periods of dormancy; cultivated woody plants are usually clones, which necessitates clonal propagation of experimental material; most woody plants are not only difficult to transmit virus from, they are also difficult to infect by mechanical inoculation. Annual plants have obvious advantages as experimental hosts, particularly if the seed is reasonably uniform genetically or can be made so by selfing.

There seems to be no method of predicting where susceptible plants may be found for unknown viruses. Certain families (Leguminosae, Cucurbitaceae, Solanaceae, Chenopodiaceae) contain species that are susceptible to a wide range of viruses. Possibly suitable hosts for an unknown virus are more common in these families than in others; or these families may only appear as susceptible to a wide range of viruses because they have been tested more often.

The author has gained the impression in

his own work as well as in reviewing the literature that no one factor in transmission techniques can be credited with permitting mechanically transmission of "difficult" viruses. Success may depend on many factors of technique, each relatively minor. It is to be hoped that what appear as relatively minor improvements in technique will be documented as far as possible with quantitative data.

3–7. TABLES

TABLE 3–1. VIRUSES REPORTED AS TRANSMITTED BY VARIOUS SPECIES OF *Cuscuta*

Species of *Cuscuta*	Diseases, the viruses of which have been transmitted	Diseases, the viruses of which have been reported as not transmitted
C. americana	Cucumber mosaic (Schmelzer, 1956b)	Tobacco etch, bean yellow mosaic, potato Y, and potato bouquet (Schmelzer, 1956b)
C. australis	Ageratum yellow veinbanding, crotalaria witches' broom (Thung and Hadiwidjaja, 1950)	
C. californica	Tobacco etch, sugar-beet curly-top, cucumber mosaic, tomato spotted wilt (Bennett, 1944b), dodder latent (Bennett, 1944a)	Bean yellow mosaic, potato Y, potato bouquet, alfalfa mosaic, tobacco etch (Schmelzer, 1956b), tobacco mosaic, sugar-beet mosaic, sugar-beet yellow vein, tomato ringspot, peach mosaic (Bennett, 1944b), sugar-beet rosette (Bennett and Duffus, 1957), tobacco rattle (Schmelzer, 1955), tomato aspermy (Schmelzer, 1957b)
C. campestris	Tobacco mosaic, aster yellows, tomato bushy stunt, cucurbit mosaic (Johnson, 1941a,b), sugar-beet rosette (Bennett and Duffus, 1957), lilac witches' broom (Brierly, 1955), chrysanthemum flower distortion (Brierly and Smith, 1957), white clover mosaic (Bos *et al.*, 1959), clover phyllody (Frazier and Posnette, 1957), potato stem mottle (tobacco rattle) (Schmelzer, 1955), tomato big bud (Hill and Mandryk, 1954), tomato spotted wilt (Bennett, 1944b), potato witches' broom (Kunkel, 1943b), peach X-disease (Kunkel, 1944), cranberry false blossom (Kunkel, 1945), Vinca yellows (Maramorosch, 1956), tomato stolbur (Misiga and Valenta, 1957), cucumber mosaic (Bennett, 1940b), alfalfa mosaic (Schmelzer, 1956b), Centrosema mosaic (Van Velsen and Crowley, 1961), Tulare apple mosaic (Yarwood, 1955b), dodder latent mosaic (Bennett, 1944a), sugar-beet yellow wilt (Bennett and Munck, 1946), Asclepias yellows (Kunkel, 1950)	Tobacco etch, sugar-beet mosaic, sugar-beet yellow vein, tomato ringspot, citrus psorosis, peach mosaic (Bennett, 1944b), lettuce bigvein (Campbell and Grogan, 1963), tobacco yellow dwarf (Hill and Mandryk, 1954), tobacco ringspot (Johnson, 1941a), pea wilt virus (Johnson, 1942), bean yellow mosaic, potato Y, potato bouquet (Schmelzer, 1956b), tomato aspermy (Schmelzer, 1957b), potato leaf roll (Williams, 1957)
C. chinensis	Potato witches' broom (Fukushi and Shikata, 1955)	
C. epilinum	Tomato stolbur (Misiga and Valenta, 1957), alfalfa mosaic (Schmelzer, 1956b)	Tobacco etch, bean yellow mosaic, potato Y, potato bouquet (Schmelzer, 1956b)

TABLE 3–1.—*Continued*

Species of *Cuscuta*	Diseases, the viruses of which have been transmitted	Diseases, the viruses of which have been reported as not transmitted
C. epithymum	Cucumber mosaic (Schmelzer, 1956b)	Beet yellows, beet yellow net (Bennett, 1944b), alfalfa mosaic, bean yellow mosaic, potato Y, potato bouquet, tobacco rattle, tobacco etch (Schmelzer, 1956b), tomato aspermy (Schmelzer, 1957b)
C. europaea	Cucumber mosaic, alfalfa mosaic, potato stem mottle (Schmelzer, 1956b), tomato aspermy (Schmelzer, 1957b)	Tobacco etch, bean yellow mosaic, potato Y, potato bouquet (Schmelzer, 1956b)
C. gronovii	Beet yellows (Beiss, 1956), clover phyllody (Chiykowski, 1962), cucumber mosaic, potato stem mottle (Schmelzer, 1956b)	Lettuce big-vein (Campbell and Grogan, 1963), tobacco etch, bean yellow mosaic, potato Y, potato bouquet (Schmelzer, 1956b)
C. japonica	Potato witches' broom (Fukushi and Shikata, 1955), tobacco mosaic (Miyakawa and Yoshii, 1951)	
C. lupuliformis	Cucumber mosaic (poorly), alfalfa mosaic, potato stem mottle, tobacco etch (Schmelzer, 1956b)	Bean yellow mosaic, potato Y, potato bouquet (Schmelzer, 1956b)
C. petagona	Tobacco mosaic (Gualaccini, 1955)	
C. reflexa	A mosaic of Rubus (Azad and Sehgal, 1958)	
C. repens	Cucumber mosaic (Hildebrand, 1945)	
C. sandwichiana	Cucumber mosaic (Sakimura, 1947)	Tomato spotted wilt (Sakimura, 1947)
C. subinclusa	Cucumber mosaic (Bennett, 1940b), tobacco mosaic (Bennett, 1940b), lilac witches' broom (Brierly, 1955), strawberry veinbanding (Frazier, 1955), strawberry green petal (Frazier and Posnette, 1956), blueberry stunt (Hutchinson et al., 1960), potato stem mottle (Schmelzer, 1955), alfalfa mosaic (Schmelzer, 1956b), tomato aspermy (Schmelzer, 1957b), potato leaf roll (Williams, 1957), Tulare apple mosaic (Yarwood, 1955b), dodder latent mosaic (Bennett, 1944a)	Tobacco etch, sugar-beet mosaic, citrus psorosis, tomato ringspot, sugar-beet yellow vein, peach mosaic (Bennett, 1944b), sugar-beet rosette (Bennett and Duffus, 1957), bean yellow mosaic, potato Y, potato bouquet (Schmelzer, 1956b), sugar-beet yellow wilt (Bennett and Munck, 1946)
C. trifolii	Tomato stolbur (Misiga and Valenta, 1957)	

TABLE 3–2. SEED TRANSMITTED VIRUSES

Virus of:	Host	Citation
Abutilon mosaic	*Abutilon thompsoni* × *A. mulleri*	Keur (1933)
Alfalfa mosaic	*Capsicum annuum*	Sutic (1959)
Arabis mosaic	*Glycine max* *Petunia hybrida*	Lister (1960)
Avocado sun-blotch	*Persea americana*	Wallace and Drake (1962)
Barley stripe mosaic	*Hordeum vulgare* *Triticum aestivum*	McKinney (1951) McNeal and Afanasiev (1955)
Bean mosaic	*Phaseolus vulgaris*	Reddick and Stewart (1919)
Bean red node	*Phaseolus vulgaris*	Thomas and Graham (1951)
Broadbean mosaic	*Vicia faba*	Quantz (1953)
Cineraria mosaic	*Senecio cruentus*	Jones (1944)
Coffee ringspot	*Coffea excelsa*	Reyes (1961)
Cowpea mosaic	*Vigna sinensis*	McLean (1941)
Cucumber mosaic	*Cucumis sativus* *Echinocystis lobata* *Lupinus luteus* *Vigna sesquipedalis* *V. sinensis*	Doolittle (1920) Doolittle and Gilbert (1919) Troll (1957) Anderson (1957) Anderson (1957)
Dandelion yellow mosaic	*Lactuca sativa*	Kassanis (1947)
Datura "Q" virus	*Datura stramonium*	Blakeslee (1921)
Dodder latent mosaic	*Cuscuta campestris*	Bennett (1944a)
Elm mosaic	*Ulmus americana*	Callahan (1957)
Hop chlorosis	*Humulus lupulus*	Salmon and Ware (1935)
Lettuce mosaic	*Lactuca sativa*	Newhall (1923)
Muskmelon mosaic	*Cucumis melo*	Rader *et al.* (1947)
Peach necrotic leafspot	*Prunus persicae*	Wagnon *et al.* (1960)
Peanut marginal chlorosis	*Arachis hypogaea*	Van Velsen (1961)
Prune dwarf virus	*Prunus cerasus*	Gilmer and Way (1960)
Raspberry ringspot	*Glycine max* *Petunia hybrida*	Lister (1960)
Sour cherry necrotic ringspot (peach ringspot)	*Prunus avium* *P. persicae* *P. mahaleb* *P. americana* *Cucurbita maxima*	Cochran, L. C. (1946) Cation (1949, 1952) Gilmer (1955) Hobart (1956) Das and Milbrath (1961)
Sour cherry yellows	*Prunus persicae*	Cation (1949, 1952)
Southern bean mosaic	*Vigna sinensis*	Shepherd and Fulton (1962)
Sowbane mosaic	*Chenopodium murale* *C. album* *Atriplex pacifica*	Bennett and Costa (1961)

TABLE 3–2.—*Continued*

Virus of:	Host	Citation
Squash mosaic	*Cucurbita maxima* *C. moschata* *C. pepo* *Cucumis melo*	Middleton (1944) Grogan *et al.* (1959)
Sugar-beet yellows	*Beta vulgaris*	Clinch and Loughnane (1948)
Tobacco mosaic virus	*Lycopersicon esculentum*	Bewley and Corbett (1930)
Tobacco ringspot	*Glycine max* *Petuna hybrida* *Nicotiana tabacum* *Cucumis melo*	Desjardins *et al.* (1954) Henderson (1931) Valleau (1932) McLean (1962)
Tomato black ring	*Glycine max* *Fragaria* *Capsella bursa-pastoris* *Fumaria* sp. *Senecio vulgaris* *Nicotiana rustica*	Lister (1960)
Tomato bunchy top	*Solanum incanum* *S. aculeatissimum* *S. diploservatum* *Physalis peruviana* *Lycopersicon esculentum*	McClean (1948)
Tomato ringspot	*Glycine max*	Kahn (1956)
Western bean mosaic	*Phaseolus vulgaris*	Skotland and Burke (1961)
Xyloporosis	*Citrus* spp.	Childs (1956)

3–8. LITERATURE CITED

Ainsworth, G. C., and Ogilvie, L. (1939). Ann. Appl. Biol. **26**, 279.

Allard, H. A. (1917). J. Agr. Res. **10**, 615.

Allard, H. A. (1918). J. Agr. Res. **13**, 619.

Allington, W. B., and Laird, E. F., Jr. (1954a). Phytopathology **44**, 297.

Allington, W. B., and Laird, E. F., Jr. (1954b). Phytopathology **44**, 546.

Anderson, C. W. (1957). (Abstr.) Phytopathology **47**, 515.

Atanasoff, D. (1924). Phytopathology **14**, 521.

Athow, K. L., and Bancroft, J. B. (1959). Phytopathology **49**, 697.

Azad, R. N., and Sehgal, O. P. (1958). Indian Phytopathology **11**, 159.

Babos, P., and Kassanis, B. (1962). Virology **18**, 206.

Bain, D. C. (1944). Phytopathology **34**, 844.

Bald, J. G. (1937). Ann. Appl. Biol. **24**, 77.

Bald, J. G., and Samuel, G. (1934). Ann. Appl. Biol. **21**, 179.

Baur, E. (1904). Ber. Deutschen Bot. Gesellschaft **22**, 453.

Bawden, F. C. (1954). Advan. Virus Res. **2**, 31.

Bawden, F. C. (1961). J. Biol. Chem. **236**, 2760.

Bawden, F. C., and Kassanis, B. (1950). Ann. Appl. Biol. **37**, 46.

Bawden, F. C., and Kleczkowski, A. (1945). J. Pomol. Hort. Sci. **21**, 2.

Bawden, F. C., and Pirie, N. W. (1957). J. Gen. Microbiol. **16**, 696.

Bawden, F. C., and Roberts, F. M. (1947). Ann. Appl. Biol. **34**, 286.

Bawden, F. C., and Roberts, F. M. (1948). Ann. Appl. Biol. **35**, 418.

Bawden, F. C., Kassanis, B., and Nixon, H. L. (1950). J. Gen. Microbiol. **4**, 210.

Beijerinck, M. W. (1898). Verhandel. Koninink. Ned. Akad. Wettensch. (Amsterdam) **65 (2)**, 3.

Beiss, U. (1956). Phytopathol. Z. **27**, 83.

Benda, G. T. A. (1956). Virology **2**, 820.

Bennett, C. W. (1934). J. Agr. Res. **48**, 665.

Bennett, C. W. (1940a). (Abstr.) Phytopathology **30**, 2.

Bennett, C. W. (1940b). Botan. Review **6**, 427.

Bennett, C. W. (1943). Phytopathology **33**, 818.

Bennett, C. W. (1944a). Phytopathology **34**, 77.

Bennett, C. W. (1944b). Phytopathology **34**, 905.

Bennett, C. W., and Costa, A. S. (1961). Phytopathology **51**, 546.

Bennett, C. W., and Duffus, J. E. (1957). Plant Disease Reptr. **41**, 1001.

Bennett, C. W., and Esau, K. (1936). J. Agr. Res. **53**, 595.

Bennett, C. W., and Munck, C. (1946). J. Agr. Res. **73**, 45.

Beraha, L., and Thornberry, H. H. (1952). (Abstr.) Phytopathology **42**, 2.

Beraha, L., Varzandeh, M., and Thornberry, H. H. (1955). Virology **1**, 141.

Berg, T. M. (1962a). Nature **194**, 1302.

Berg, T. M. (1962b). Tijdschr. Plantenziekten **68**, 231.

Best, R. J. (1937). Australian J. Exptl. Biol. Med. Sci. **15**, 191.

Best, R. J. (1939). Australian J. Exptl. Biol. Med. Sci. **17**, 1.

Best, R. J., and Samuel, G. (1936). Ann. Appl. Biol. **23**, 759.

Bewley, W. F., and Corbett, W. (1930). Ann. Appl. Biol. **17**, 260.

Bird, J. (1961). J. Agr. Univ. Puerto Rico **45**, 1.

Black, L. M. (1939). Phytopathology **29**, 321.

Blakeslee, A. F. (1921). J. Genetics **11**, 17.

Blattný, C., and Limberk, J. (1956). Preslia **28**, 413.

Bos, L., Delević, B., and van der Want, J. P. H. (1959). Tijdschr. Plantenziekten **65**, 89.

Boyle, J. S., Moore, J. D., and Keitt, G. W. (1949). (Abstr.) Phytopathology **39**, 3.

Boyle, L. W., and McKinney, H. H. (1937). Science **85**, 458.

Brakke, M. K., Vatter, A. E., and Black, L. M. (1954). Brookhaven Symp. Biol. **6**, 137.

Brandenburg, E. (1962). Phytopathol. Z. **43**, 420.

Brandes, E. W. (1920). J. Agr. Res. **19**, 131.

Brierley, P. (1955). Plant Disease Reptr. **39**, 719.

Brierley, P., and Smith, F. F. (1957). Phytopathology **47**, 448.

Bringhurst, R. S., and Voth, V. (1956). Plant Disease Reptr. **40**, 596.

Bruner, S. C. (1922). Rev. Agr. Com. y Trab. (Cuba) **5**, 11.

Cadman, C. H. (1956). J. Hort. Sci. **31**, 111.

Cadman, C. H. (1959). J. Gen. Microbiol. **20**, 113.

Caldwell, J. (1962). Nature **193**, 457.

Callahan, K. L. (1957). (Abstr.) Phytopathology **47**, 5.

Campbell, R. N., and Grogan, R. G. (1963). Phytopathology **53**, 252.

Canova, A. (1955). Ann. Sper. Agrar. (Rome) **9**, 549.

Cation, D. (1949). Phytopathology **39**, 37.

Cation, D. (1952). Phytopathology **42**, 4.

Chamberlain, E. E., and Fry, P. R. (1950). New Zealand J. Sci. Technol. (A) **32**, 19.

Cheo, P. C. (1955). Phytopathology **45**, 17.

Chessin, M., and Scott, H. A. (1955). Phytopathology **45**, 288.

Childs, J. F. L. (1956). Plant Disease Reptr. **40**, 143.

Chiykowski, L. N. (1962). Can. J. Botany **40**, 397.

Clinch, Phyllis E. M., and Loughnane, J. B. (1948). Sci. Proc. Roy. Dublin Soc. (N.S.) **24**, 307.

Clinton, G. P. (1915). Conn. Agr. Expt. Sta. Ann. Rept. 1914, 357.

Cochran, G. W. (1946). Phytopathology **36**, 396.

Cochran, G. W. (1947). Phytopathology **37**, 5.

Cochran, L. C. (1946). Science **104**, 269.

Cochran, L. C., and Rue, J. L. (1944). (Abstr.) Phytopathology **34**, 934.

Cornuet, M. (1952). Compt. Rend. Acad. Sci. (Paris) **235**, 171.

Costa, A. S. (1944a). Phytopathology **34**, 151.

Costa, A. S. (1944b). Phytopathology **34**, 288.

Costa, A. S., and Bennett, C. W. (1955). Phytopathology **45**, 233.

Costa, A. S., de Aguirre, J. M., Segalla, A. L., and Alvarez, R. (1952). Bragantia **12**, 7.

Couch, H. B. (1955). Phytopathology **45**, 63.

Cropley, R. (1958). Ann. Rept. East Malling Res. Sta. (Kent) 1957, 124.

Crowley, N. C. (1954). Australian J. Biol. Sci. **7**, 141.

Crowley, N. C. (1955). Australian J. Biol. Sci. **8**, 56.

Crowley, N. C. (1957a). Australian J. Biol. Sci. **10**, 443.

Crowley, N. C. (1957b). Australian J. Biol. Sci. **10**, 449.

Crowley, N. C. (1959). Virology **8**, 116.

Crowley, N. C., and Hanson, J. B. (1960). Virology **12**, 603.

Dale, J. L. (1956). Dissertation Abstr. **16**, 1566.

Dana, B. F. (1932). (Abstr.) Phytopathology **22**, 997.

Das, C. R., and Milbrath, J. A. (1961). Phytopathology **51**, 489.

Das, C. R., Milbrath, J. A., and Swenson, K. G. (1961). (Abstr.) Phytopathology **51**, 64.

Davidson, T. R. (1955). Can. J. Agr. Sci. **35**, 238.

Dean, J. L. (1960). Plant Disease Reptr. **44**, 874.

Desjardins, P. R., and Wallace, J. M. (1962). Plant Disease Reptr. **46**, 414.

Desjardins, P. R., Latterell, R. L., and Mitchell, J. E. (1954). Phytopathology **44**, 86.

Dickson, B. T. (1922). Macdonald College J. Ser. Tech. Bull. No. 2.

Diener, T. O., and Weaver, M. L. (1959). Phytopathology **49**, 321.

Doolittle, S. P. (1920). U. S. Dept. Agr. Bull. **879**.

Doolittle, S. P., and Beecher, F. S. (1937). Phytopathology **27**, 800.

Doolittle, S. P., and Gilbert, W. W. (1919). Phytopathology **9**, 326.

Dubos, R. J. (1958). In M. Pollard (ed.) Perspectives in Virology. 291–99. Wiley and Sons, Philadelphia.

Duggar, B. M. (1930). (Abstr.) Phytopathology **20**, 133.

Duggar, B. M., and Armstrong, J. K. (1925). Ann. Missouri Botan. Garden **12**, 359.

Engelbrecht, D. J., and Regenmortel, M. H. V. (1960). S. African J. Agr. Sci. **3**, 617.

Eslick, R. F., and Afanasiev, M. M. (1955). Plant Disease Reptr. **39**, 722.

Fajardo, T. G. (1930). Phytopathology **20**, 469.

Fajardo, T. G., and Marañon, J. (1932). Philippine J. Sci. **48**, 129.

Frazier, N. W. (1955). Phytopathology **45**, 307.

Frazier, N. W., and Posnette, A. F. (1956). Nature **177**, 1040.

Frazier, N. W., and Posnette, A. F. (1957). Ann. Appl. Biol. **45**, 580.

Fromme, F. D., Wingard, S. A., and Priode, C. N. (1927). Phytopathology **17**, 321.

Fukushi, T., and Shikata, E. (1955). Mem. Fac. Agr. Hokkaido Univ. **2**, 47.

Fulton, J. P. (1957). (Abstr.) Phytopathology **47**, 521.

Fulton, R. W. (1949). Phytopathology **39**, 231.

Fulton, R. W. (1955). Plant Disease Reptr. **39**, 799.

Fulton, R. W. (1957). Phytopathology **47**, 683.

Fulton, R. W. (1962). Virology **18**, 477.

Gardner, M. W., and Kendrick, J. B. (1921). J. Agr. Res. **22**, 111.

Gardner, M. W., and Kendrick, J. B. (1922). Botan. Gaz. **68**, 469.

Gehring, F. (1957). Nachrbl. Deut. Pflanzenschutzdienst (Braunschweig) Stuttgart **9**, 172.

Gendron, Y., and Kassanis, B. (1954). Ann. Appl. Biol. **41**, 183.

Giddings, N. J. (1947). Phytopathology **37**, 278.

Gilmer, R. M. (1955). Plant Disease Reptr. **39**, 727.

Gilmer, R. M., and Way, R. D. (1960). Phytopathology **50**, 624.

Gold, A. H., Suneson, C. A., Houston, B. R., and Oswald, J. W. (1954). Phytopathology **44**, 115.

Gordon, M. P., and Smith, C. (1960). J. Biol. Chem. **235**, PC28.

Gordon, M. P., and Smith, C. (1961). J. Biol. Chem. **236**, 2762.

Coss, R. W. (1926). Phytopathology **16**, 233.

Govier, D. A. (1963). Virology **19**, 561.

Grant, T. J., and Corbett, M. K. (1960). Nature **188**, 519.

Grant, T. J., and Corbett, M. K. (1961). In W. C. Price (ed.), Proc. Second Conf. Int. Org. Citrus Virologists. 197. Univ. of Florida Press.

Grogan, R. G., and Bardin, R. (1950). (Abstr.) Phytopathology **40**, 965.

Grogan, R. G., Hall, D. H., and Kimble, K. A. (1959). Phytopathology **49**, 366.

Gualaccini, F. (1955). Boll. Staz. Pat. Veg. (Rome) **12**, 137.

Hampton, R. E., and Fulton, R. W. (1961). Virology **13**, 44.

Harpaz, I. (1959). Nature **184**, B.A. 77-B.A. 78.

Harrison, A. L. (1935a). N.Y. State Agr. Expt. Sta. (Geneva) Tech. Bull. **235**, 48.

Harrison, A. L. (1935b). N.Y. State Agr. Expt. Sta. Bull. **236**.

Helms, Katie. (1962). Australian J. Biol. Sci. **15**, 278.

Henderson, R. G. (1931). Phytopathology **21**, 225.

Hildebrand, E. M. (1941). Contrib. Boyce Thompson Inst. **11**, 485.

Hildebrand, E. M. (1942). Science **95**, 52.

Hildebrand, E. M. (1943). In J. A. Reyniers (ed.), Micrurgical and Germ-free Techniques. 72–92. C. C. Thomas, Baltimore.

Hildebrand, E. M. (1945). Plant Disease Reptr. **29**, 196.

Hildebrand, E. M. (1956a). Science **123**, 506.

Hildebrand, E. M. (1956b). Phytopathology **46**, 233.

Hill, A. V., and Mandryk, M. (1954). Australian J. Agr. Res. **5**, 617.

Hirth, L. (1951). Ann. Inst. Pasteur **80**, 458.

Hobart, O. F. (1956). (Abstr.) Iowa State Coll. J. Sci. **30**, 381.

Holmes, F. O. (1929a). Botan. Gaz. **87**, 39.

Holmes, F. O. (1929b). Botan. Gaz. **87**, 56.

Holmes, F. O. (1939). Phytopathology **29**, 215.

Holmes, F. O. (1943). Phytopathology **33**, 691.

Holmes, F. O. (1954). Phytopathology **44**, 640.

Hougas, R. W. (1951). Phytopathology **41**, 483.

Howles, R. (1947). Exp. Research Sta. Turner's Hill, Cheshunt, Herts. Ann. Rept., **33d**, 22.

Howles, R. (1961). Plant Pathol. **10**, 160.

Humphries, E. C., and Kassanis, B. (1955). Ann. Appl. Biol. **43**, 686.

Hunter, J. A., Chamberlain, E. E., and Atkinson, J. D. (1958). New Zealand J. Agr. Res. **1**, 80.

Hutchinson, M. T., Goheen, A. C., and Varney, E. H. (1960). Phytopathology **50**, 308.

Jedlinski, H. (1956). Phytopathology **46**, 673.

Johnson, F. (1941a). (Abstr.) Phytopathology **31**, 13.

Johnson, F. (1941b). Phytopathology **31**, 649.

Johnson, F. (1942). Phytopathology **32**, 103.

Johnson, J. (1941). Phytopathology **31**, 679.

Jones, L. K. (1944). Phytopathology **34**, 941.

Jorgensen, P. S. (1957). Plant Disease Reptr. **41**, 1009.

Kahn, R. P. (1956). Phytopathology **46**, 295.

Kahn, R. P., and Libby, J. L. (1958). Phytopathology **48**, 57.

Kahn, R. P., and Schachtner, N. D. (1954a). (Abstr.) Phytopathology **44**, 389.

Kahn, R. P., and Schachtner, N. D. (1954b). (Abstr.) Phytopathology **44**, 494.

Kalmus, H., and Kassanis, B. (1944). Nature **154**, 641.

Kalmus, H., and Kassanis, B. (1945). Ann. Appl. Biol. **32**, 230.

Kassanis, B. (1947). Ann. Appl. Biol. **34**, 412.

Kassanis, B. (1949). Ann. Appl. Biol. **36**, 270.

Kassanis, B. (1952). Ann. Appl. Biol. **39**, 358.

Kassanis, B., and Kleczkowski, A. (1948). J. Gen. Microbiol. **2**, 143.

Kassanis, B., Tinsley, T. W., and Quak, F. (1958). Ann. Appl. Biol. **46**, 11.

Kausche, G. H. (1940). Biol. Zbl. **60**, 423.

Kegler, H. (1959). Phytopathol. Z. **37**, 170.

Kegler, H. (1961). Tidsskr. Planteavl. **65**, 163.

Keur, J. Y. (1933). (Abstr.) Phytopathology **23**, 20.

Kontaxis, D. G., and Schlegel, D. E. (1962). Virology **16**, 244.

Kreitlow, K. W. (1961). Phytopathology **51**, 808.

Kunkel, L. O. (1930). Science **71**, 516.

Kunkel, L. O. (1938). Phytopathology **28**, 491.

Kunkel, L. O. (1943a). In Rockefeller Institute for Medical Research, Virus Diseases. 63–82. Cornell Univ. Press.

Kunkel, L. O. (1943b). Proc. Am. Phil. Soc. **86**, 470.

Kunkel, L. O. (1944). (Abstr.) Phytopathology **34**, 1006.

Kunkel, L. O. (1945). Phytopathology **35**, 805.

Kunkel, L. O. (1950). (Abstr.) Phytopathology **40**, 16.

Kuntz, J. E., and Walker, J. C. (1947). Phytopathology **37**, 561.

Lackey, C. F. (1946). Phytopathology **36**, 386.

Lackey, C. F. (1949). Phytopathology **39**, 562.

Lackey, C. F. (1953). Am. J. Bot. **40**, 221.

Lauffer, M. A., and Price, W. C. (1945). Arch. Biochem. **8**, 449.

Limasset, P. (1951). Atti Soc. Ital. Patol. **2**, 911.

Limasset, P., and Cornuet, P. (1949). C. R. Acad. Sci. (Paris) **228**, 1971.

Lindner, R. C., and Kirkpatrick, H. C. (1959). Phytopathology **49**, 507.

Lindner, R. C., Kirkpatrick, H. C., and Weeks, T. E. (1959). Phytopathology **49**, 78.

Lister, R. M. (1958). Nature **182**, 1814.

Lister, R. M. (1959). Nature **183**, 1588.

Lister, R. M. (1960). Virology **10**, 547.

Liu, H. P. (1949). Rept. Taiwan Sugar Expt. Sta. **4**, 210.

MacClement, W. D. (1937). Parasitology **29**, 266.

Maramorosch, K. (1956). Plant Disease Reptr. **40**, 1109.

Martin, C. (1952). Ann. Inst. Nat. Rech. Agron. (C) **3**, 395.

Martin, C. (1954). Ann. Inst. Rech. Agron. (C) (Ann. Epiphyt.) **5**, 63.

Martin, C. (1958). Compt. Rend. Acad. Sci. (Paris) **246**, 2026.

Martin, C., and Morel, G. (1958). Compt. Rend. Acad. Sci. (Paris) **246**, 2283.

Matthews, R. E. F. (1953a). Ann. Appl. Biol. **40**, 377.

Matthews, R. E. F. (1953b). Ann. Appl. Biol. **40**, 556.

Matz, J. (1933). J. Agr. Res. **46**, 821.

Mayer, A. E. (1886). Die Landwirtschaftlichen Versuchstationen **32**, 451. (Phytopathological Classic No. 7.)

McClean, A. P. D. (1948). Union S. Africa Dept. Agr. Sci. Bull. **256**.

McClintock, J. A. (1916). Science **44**, 786.

McClintock, J. A. (1917). (Abstr.) Phytopathology **7**, 60.

McKinney, H. H. (1928). Science **68**, 380.

McKinney, H. H. (1948). Phytopathology **38**, 1003.

McKinney, H. H. (1951). (Abstr.) Phytopathology **41**, 563.

McKinney, H. H. (1952). Plant Disease Reptr. **36**, 184.

McKinney, H. H. (1953). Plant Disease Reptr. **37**, 292.

McKinney, H. H., and Fellows, H. (1951). Plant Disease Reptr. **35**, 264.

McLean, D. M. (1941). Phytopathology **31**, 420.

McLean, D. M. (1962). (Abstr.) Phytopathology **52**, 21.

McNeal, F. H., and Afanasiev, M. M. (1955). Plant Disease Reptr. **39**, 460.

McWhorter, F. P. (1951). Phytopathology **41**, 185.

McWhorter, F. P. (1953). (Abstr.) Phytopathology **43**, 479.

Medina, A. C., and Grogan, R. G. (1961). Phytopathology **51**, 452.

Middleton, J. T. (1944). Phytopathology **34**, 405.

Milbrath, J. A. (1953). (Abstr.) Phytopathology **43**, 479.

Misiga, S., and Valenta, V. (1957). Biologia, Bratislava **12**, 652.

Miyakawa, T., and Yoshii, H. (1951). Sci. Bull. Fac. Agr., Kyushu Univ. **12**(2), 143.

Mundry, K. W., and Rohmer, Irmgard (1958). Phytopathol. Z. **31**, 305.

Murphy, P. A., and McKay, R. (1926). Sci. Proc. Roy. Dublin Soc. **18**, 169.

Muzik, T. J., and LaRue, C. D. (1954). Am. J. Botany **41**, 448.

Nelson, R. (1932). Mich. State Univ. Agr. Expt. Sta. Tech. Bull. **118**.

Nelson, R., and Down, E. E. (1933). (Abstr.) Phytopathology **23**, 25.

Newhall, A. G. (1923). Phytopathology **13**, 104.

Nikolic, V. J. (1956). Zasht. Bilja (Plant Prot., Beograd) **35**, 79.

Nitzany, F. E., and Gerechter, E. K. (1962). Phytopathology Medit. **2**, 11.

Panzer, J. D. (1957). Phytopathology **47**, 337.

Panzer, J. D. (1959). Plant Disease Reptr. **43**, 845.

Pfaeltzer, Hillegonda J. (1960). Tijdschr. Plantenziekten **66**, 24.

Quanjer, H. M. (1920). Phytopathology **10**, 35.

Quanjer, H. M., van der Lek, H. A. A., and Botjes, J. O. (1916). Meded. Rijks Hoogere Land-, Tuinen Boschbouwschool **10**, 92.

Quantz, L. (1953). Phytopathol. Z. **20**, 421.

Rader, W. E., Fitzpatrick, H. F., and Hildebrand, E. M. (1947). Phytopathology **37**, 809.

Rawlins, T. E., and Tompkins, C. M. (1934). (Abstr.) Phytopathology **24**, 1147.

Rawlins, T. E., and Tompkins, C. M. (1936). Phytopathology **26**, 578.

Reddick, D. (1931). Deuxieme Congress Internat. de Path. Comp. **1**, 363.

Reddick, D., and Stewart, N. B. (1919). Phytopathology **9**, 445.

Reyes, T. T. (1961). Plant Disease Reptr. **45**, 185.

Richards, B. L., Jr., and Munger, H. M. (1944). (Abstr.) Phytopathology **34**, 1010.

Roberts, R. H. (1949). Botan. Rev. **15**, 423.

Ross, A. F. (1941). Phytopathology **31**, 410.

Ross, A. F. (1953). Phytopathology **43**, 1.

Rozendaal, A., and van der Want, J. P. H. (1948). Tijdschr. Plantenziekten **54**, 113.

Sakimura, K. (1947). Phytopathology **37**, 66.

Salmon, E. S., and Ware, W. M. (1935). Ann. Appl. Biol. **22**, 728.

Samuel, G. (1931). Ann. Appl. Biol. **18**, 494.

Schmelzer, K. (1955). Naturwissenschaften **42**, 19.
Schmelzer, K. (1956a). Zbl. Bakt. II. Abt. **109**, 382.
Schmelzer, K. (1956b). Phytopathol. Z. **28**, 1.
Schmelzer, K. (1957a). Phytopathol. Z. **28**, 457.
Schmelzer, K. (1957b). Phytopathol. Z. **30**, 449.
Schmelzer, K. (1960). Z. Pflanzen Krankheiten **67**, 193.
Schramm, G., Schumaker, G., and Zillig, W. (1955). Nature **175**, 549.
Schultz, E. S., and Folsom, D. (1920). J. Agr. Res. **19**, 315.
Schultz, E. S., and Folsom, D. (1921). J. Agr. Res. **21**, 47.
Schultz, E. S., and Folsom, D. (1923). J. Agr. Res. **25**, 43.
Schwartz, D., and Cuzin, J. (1951). Ann. Inst. Exptl. Tab. Bergerac **1**, 167.
Severin, H. H. P. (1924). Phytopathology **14**, 80.
Sheffield, F. M. L. (1936). Ann. Appl. Biol. **23**, 498.
Sheffield, F. M. L. (1941). J. Roy. Microscopical Soc. (III) **61**, 30.
Sheffield, F. M. L. (1952). Ann. Appl. Biol. **39**, 103.
Shepherd, R. J., and Fulton, R. W. (1962). Phytopathology **52**, 489.
Sill, W. H., Jr., and Walker, J. C. (1952). Phytopathology **42**, 349.
Singh, G. P., Arny, D. C., and Pound, G. S. (1960). Phytopathology **50**, 290.
Skotland, C. B., and Burke, D. W. (1961). Phytopathology **51**, 565.
Smith, E. F. (1888). U.S. Dept. Agr. Bot. Div. Bull. **9**.
Spencer, E. L. (1935a). Phytopathology **25**, 178.
Spencer, E. L. (1935b). Phytopathology **25**, 493.
Sreenivasaya, M. (1930). J. Indian Inst. Sci. **13a**, 113.
Stanley, W. M. (1934). Phytopathology **24**, 1055.
Stanley, W. M. (1935). Phytopathology **25**, 899.
Steere, R. L. (1955). Phytopathology **45**, 196.
Sutic, D. (1959). Phytopathol. Z. **36**, 84.
Takahashi, W. N. (1947). Am. J. Botany **34**, 496.
Taylor, R. H. (1962). Australian J. Expt. Agr. Animal Husbandry **2**, 86.
Taylor, R. H., Grogan, R. G., and Kimble, K. A. (1961). Phytopathology **51**, 837.
Thomas, W. D., Jr., and Baker, R. R. (1952). (Abstr.) Phytopathology **42**, 21.
Thomas, W. D., Jr., and Graham, R. W. (1951). Phytopathology **41**, 959.
Thornberry, H. H. (1935a). Phytopathology **25**, 618.
Thornberry, H. H. (1935b). Phytopathology **25**, 931.
Thresh, J. M. (1956). Ann. Appl. Biol. **44**, 608.
Thung, T. H., and Dijkstra, J. (1958). Tijdschr. Plantenziekten. **64**, 411.
Thung, T. H., and Hadiwidjaja, T. (1950). Tijdschr. Plantenziekten **56**, 349.
Thung, T. H., and Noordam, D. (1959). Mededel. Landbouwhogeschool Opzoekingssta, Staat Gent **24**, 775.

Thung, T. H., and van der Want, J. P. H. (1951). Tijdschr. Plantenziekten **57**, 173.
Timian, R. G., Peterson, C. E., and Hooker, W. J. (1955). Am. Potato J. **32**, 411.
Tinsley, T. W. (1953). Ann. Appl. Biol. **40**, 750.
Toler, R. W. (1962). Dissertation Abstr. **22**, 3804.
Tomlinson, N. (1955). Plant Disease Reptr. **39**, 148.
Troll, H. J. (1957). Nachrbl. Deut. Pflanzenschutzdienst (Berlin) **11**, 218.
Troutman, J. L., and Fulton, R. W. (1958). Virology **6**, 303.
Valenta, V. (1962). Biologia, Bratislava **17**, 415.
Valleau, W. D. (1932). Kentucky Agr. Expt. Sta. Bull. **327**, 43.
Valleau, W. D. (1935). Kentucky Agr. Expt. Sta. Bull. **360**, 202.
Valleau, W. D. (1939). Phytopathology **29**, 549.
Van Velsen, R. J. (1961). Papua New Guinea Agr. J. **14**, 38.
Van Velsen, R. J., and Crowley, N. C. (1961). Nature **189**, 858.
Vaughan, E. K. (1956a). Tijdschr. Plantenziekten **62**, 266.
Vaughan, E. K. (1956b). Tijdschr. Plantenziekten **62**, 271.
Vinson, C. G., and Petre, A. W. (1931). Contrib. Boyce Thompson Inst. **3**, 131.
Wagnon, H. K., Traylor, J. A., Williams, H. E., and Weinberger, J. H. (1960). Plant Disease Reptr. **44**, 117.
Wallace, J. M. (1947). Phytopathology **37**, 149.
Wallace, J. M., and Drake, R. J. (1962). Phytopathology **52**, 237.
Way, R. D., and Gilmer, R. M. (1958). Plant Disease Reptr. **42**, 1222.
Weathers, L. G., and Calavan, E. C. (1959). In J. M. Wallace (ed.), Citrus Virus Diseases. 197. Univ. of California Press.
Williams, W. L. (1957). Dissertation Abstr. **27**, 2784.
Willison, R. S., Weintraub, M., and Ferguson, J. D. (1956). Can. J. Botany **34**, 86.
Yarwood, C. E. (1952a). Nature **169**, 502.
Yarwood, C. E. (1952b). Am. J. Botany **39**, 119.
Yarwood, C. E. (1952c). Phytopathology **42**, 137.
Yarwood, C. E. (1953a). Plant Disease Reptr. **37**, 501.
Yarwood, C. E. (1953b). Phytopathology **43**, 70.
Yarwood, C. E. (1954). Phytopathology **44**, 230.
Yarwood, C. E. (1955a). Virology **1**, 268.
Yarwood, C. E. (1955b). Hilgardia **23**, 613.
Yarwood, C. E. (1956a). (Abstr.) Phytopathology **46**, 32.
Yarwood, C. E. (1956b). Phytopathology **46**, 523.
Yarwood, C. E. (1957a). Phytopathology **47**, 613.
Yarwood, C. E. (1957b). Advan. Virus Res. **4**, **243**.
Yarwood, C. E. (1958). Phytopathology **48**, 39.
Yarwood, C. E. (1959). Plant Disease Reptr. **43**, 841.
Yarwood, C. E. (1962a). Phytopathology **52**, 206.
Yarwood, C. E. (1962b). Plant Disease Reptr. **46**, 317.
Yarwood, C. E., Resconich, E. C., and Kado, C. I. (1962). Virology **16**, 414.

4

A. F. ROSS

Identification of plant viruses

4–1. INTRODUCTION

PLANT VIROLOGISTS, who as a group show a degree of heterogeneity comparable to that shown by the viruses with which they work, have not yet agreed upon a well-defined species concept. Thus, there is not yet a clear-cut unified system of classification for the plant viruses; this absence of a firm basis for identification means that a systematic straightforward scheme for identification has not yet been formulated. The situation is likely to improve as more and more viruses are characterized in detail, as natural groupings become more evident, and as new bases for classification and identification are developed. The constantly changing criteria for classification and identification and the constantly changing relations and values of the criteria used are simply reflections of the fact that viruses resemble living things in many ways.

In general, the plant virologist has based his identifications on all information he could obtain; thus the reliability of identifications has paralleled the growth of knowledge in all phases of plant virology. The present-day virologist has the choice of many approaches to identification, and the approaches used will depend largely upon the virus or viruses concerned and the available facilities. Some viruses can be identified with a high degree of certainty on the basis of precise information concerning only a few properties; with others, a judgment can be made only after the acquisition of information on all of the properties that can be studied. Identification of any plant virus on the basis of a single criterion or property is rarely without its dangers.

Keys for the identification of plant viruses have been difficult to devise, and no one has been successful in devising a workable key embracing all known plant viruses. Two of the most important reasons for this are the facts that many viruses have been incompletely characterized and that almost all plant viruses exist as a large family of strains or variants. These variants may differ greatly in some traits while sharing others. Unfortunately, much of the missing information concerns the shared characteristics.

Historically, symptomatology has been the most widely used criterion for the identification of plant viruses. This is the natural consequence of the fact that the known plant viruses, with a few recent exceptions, have been discovered and recognized on the basis of the diseases they cause. The inadequacy of symptomatology as a basis for identification has long been recognized, and many of the early diagnoses based solely on symptomatology are questionable today. As information on the viruses accumulated, it became apparent that a given virus can cause widely different symptoms in different host species, that different viruses can cause similar symptoms in the same species, that different strains or isolates of the same virus can cause entirely different diseases, and that symptoms induced by a given strain in a given host species can vary greatly under different environmental conditions. Some of these things were recognized many years ago, and plant virologists began to look for other diagnostic characters.

Cross inoculations, first made in 1886 (Mayer, 1886), demonstrated that different viruses have different host ranges, and virus workers began to base identification in part on host-range studies. These were conveniently combined with studies on symptomatology, for symptoms induced in a number of species quite logically proved better for diagnosis than did just those symptoms in the original host species. As further knowledge accumulated, plant pathologists were able to characterize certain viruses still further on the basis of methods of transmission (mechanical, specific vectors, grafting only) and physical properties in crude juice (dilution end point, longevity *in vitro,* thermal inactivation point). Prior to about 1930, these were almost the only characters available for use in identification.

The demonstration of acquired immunity (McKinney, 1929; Thung, 1931; Wingard, 1928) and of the antigenic nature of some plant viruses (Purdy, 1929) provided two of the most useful diagnostic tools, i.e., cross-protection and serological tests, respectively. The development of these tools contributed greatly to the accuracy of identification; satisfactory cross-protection tests cannot be made with some viruses, however; and many viruses have not yet been shown to be antigenic. More recent *in vivo* reactions shown to be of diagnostic value are the interaction of viruses in mixed infections (Holmes, 1956) and the response to infection of plant varieties containing specific genes (Holmes, 1958).

Following the crystallization of tobacco mosaic virus (TMV) (Stanley, 1935) and proof that it is a nucleoprotein (Bawden *et al.,* 1936), a vast amount of information has accumulated on the chemical and physical properties of several plant viruses. This wealth of precise information, by which some viruses can be accurately characterized in terms of morphology and chemical structure, provides still further criteria for use in identification. Unfortunately, such biochemical and biophysical studies can be made only with some viruses and only in laboratories with the required specialized equipment.

Actually, almost any fact known about a virus may be of value in identification, for the more information used for an identification, the more certain is the identification. Practically, identification of an "unknown" consists of the demonstration of a sufficient number of similarities between it and a described virus to establish its identity beyond reasonable doubt. Even today, plant virus identification is not an exact science, and cases do occur in which identification is no more than a judgment. Authorities differ on the relative weight to give different criteria, so any identification should be supported by statements on the bases used for identification.

The basic information on which identifications are made, and most of the methods used, will be found in other chapters in this book. This chapter will deal largely with some practical aspects of identification, the application of various facts and concepts to the problem, and an evaluation of various tests and techniques in terms of applicability and limitations. Methods and special procedures will be given only in those areas not dealt with elsewhere or where the choice of a particular method may be of importance.

4–2. ESTABLISHING THAT THE "UNKNOWN" IS A VIRUS

All too often a pathogenic agent is assumed to be a virus if it is shown to induce "virus-like symptoms" following transmission by graft or by other methods commonly used for viruses. Such assumptions have been proved true in many cases by subsequent work, but they have been in error in others. For instance, "beet latent virus" was described several years ago (Smith, 1950, 1951a), and this virus name has appeared many times in the literature. The agent was considered to be a virus largely on the basis of the occurrence of the pathogen in symptomless beets and mangolds, the production of "virus-like" lesions in cowpea and other plants rubbed with nonfiltered juice, the ease of transmission by methods used routinely for viruses, and the production of systemic infection of cowpea (Smith, 1951a). In 1961, Yarwood *et al.* (1961) showed that "beet latent virus" is actually not a virus but a bacterium, *Pseudomonas aptata.*

Viruses can be differentiated from toxins and other nonliving agents capable of causing physiological disturbances (by their presence or absence) on the basis of transmissibility in series. Viruses are usually distinguished from other pathogens on the basis of size, for a pathogenic agent with one dimension less than 200 mμ is generally considered to be a virus (Bawden, 1950). The cause of a disease, therefore, can be identified reliably as a virus on the basis of transmissibility in the absence of pathogens visible in the light microscope. The classical method for testing an agent by these two criteria is to attempt transmission with juice passed through a filter that retains bacteria. If juice passed through such a filter is infectious, the presence of a virus is generally considered to have been established. Filterable forms of other agents do exist; hence such evidence may not constitute rigorous proof. Another historical approach to the problem of size is the application of ordinary microscopic and cultural methods in attempts to detect presence of bacteria, fungi, or other microscopic organisms. If careful examination of infected tissue does not reveal the presence of organisms, and if no organisms can be cultured from such tissue, the size criterion is generally considered to have been met. Modern methods of purification and electron microscopy have provided still another approach to this question, for they make possible the determination of the size and shape of some viruses. Virus particles are not always easy to find, and showing that a virus-like particle is indeed the causal virus is a still more difficult problem; therefore these methods are not universally applicable.

4–3. ESTABLISHING THAT ONLY ONE VIRUS IS PRESENT

Many diseases are the result of infection by two viruses, and indeed infection by more than two viruses is not at all unusual. One should always keep in mind, therefore, that an "unknown" may actually be a mixture of viruses. One of the first problems to consider is whether one or more viruses are present, and steps should be taken to separate the viruses if more than one are found.

Sometimes careful examination of the original infected plants will provide evidence of a mixture. Presence of more than one virus may be indicated by the presence of two or more distinct types of symptoms or by the presence of two or more types of crystalline inclusion bodies. If the "unknown" is collected from a field or greenhouse where likely contaminants are few in number, then specific tests can be made for those contaminants by serological tests or by attempted transmissions to so-called indicator plants. Preliminary tests for contamination should be made by inoculations to several different species, and these should be followed in two to three weeks by return inoculations to the original plant species from both the inoculated leaves and noninoculated ones. If the return inoculations do not reproduce the original disease, then a mixture is indicated. The original inoculations to the test species should be made with different dilutions of juice where possible and by different inoculation methods.

If a mixture is detected, separation may be accomplished by any of several methods or a combination of methods. A single method is generally effective only for the separation or elimination of one virus from a mixture; thus, several different methods must be used to separate each component from the others.

Separation may possibly be effected simply by inoculations to a number of different test species and thence back to the original species. One test species may be susceptible to one component and immune from the others, or one component may be able to cause systemic infection in a particular host whereas other components may be localized in the inoculated leaves. A host that is systemically invaded by all components may be useful in separation if the viruses move at different rates; attempts to recover virus from the tip or other remote portions at different times after inoculation may result in recovery of one virus free from the others. If local-lesion hosts are inoculated with dilute inocula, recovery from single lesions may result in recovery of one or more of the viruses free from the others.

Separation also may be accomplished by use of different methods of transmission; one component of the complex may be transmitted—and others not—by mechanical methods, by dodder, or by specific vectors. With insect-transmitted viruses, advantage may be taken of differences in virus-vector relationships and of the fact that a single vector carrying more than one virus and given a series of test feedings on healthy plants may transmit one virus to some plants in the series and another to other plants. Mechanical inoculations with highly diluted juice may free one virus from others of the mixture. This procedure is particularly useful when one of the component viruses has a much higher dilution end point than the others, but separation may be effected even where the component viruses have about the same dilution end point: if many plants are inoculated with dilutions such that transmission is somewhat less than 100%, some plants may become infected by chance with one virus and some with another. The viruses in a mixture also may differ in stability; thus, heating juice at various temperatures or allowing juice to age at room temperature for different periods may eliminate one or more viruses from a mixture.

Specific antisera can be used for removal of known viruses from a mixture. Separation also may be effected by such techniques as filtration through membranes differing in size of pores (Smith, 1951b), sedimentation in density-gradient columns (Brakke, 1953), or electrophoresis (Brakke, 1955).

All attempts at separation should be followed by return inoculations to the original host species. If symptoms induced by a return inoculation differ from the original ones, loss of one or more viruses from a mixture is to be expected. Should return inoculations following other procedures result in still different symptoms, further separation of the component viruses may have been successful. All viruses thus separated should be recombined and the mixture used for inoculation of the original host species. Reproduction of the original symptoms would show that all components have been accounted for. One should keep in mind, however, that some of the procedures used may merely have separated out one or more minor strains from the original inoculum, which almost certainly consisted of a mixture of predominant and minor strains (Bawden, 1950). Remixing such strains would very likely be in a proportion different from that in the original inoculum, in which case the original symptoms might not be reproduced. Whether or not this happened will become apparent upon final identification of the separated components.

There is no guarantee that any method or combination of methods will result in separation of a mixture of unidentified viruses. Some virus pairs are extremely difficult to separate; hence failure to effect a separation is not proof of biological purity. Furthermore, isolation of two or more types of virus entities from an inoculum is no guarantee that each separated component is itself a single virus. During subsequent attempts at identification, therefore, one should always be alert for evidence indicating that a mixture is still being dealt with.

4–4. GENERAL APPROACH TO IDENTIFICATION

Identification is perhaps best accomplished by a step-wise series of characterizations at progressively higher levels of specificity. Thus, studies on symptomatology in a number of host species may be sufficient to place a virus in one of several large groups, e.g., mosaic, yellows, ringspot, witches' broom, etc. Further tests on host range, on transmission, and on properties in crude juice should narrow the possibilities to just a few viruses. At this stage, tests for specific viruses can be applied, e.g., serological or cross-protection tests. If these result in a tentative identification, they should be followed by further confirming tests such as examination in the electron microscope, interaction with other viruses, and inoculation of additional plant species. Still further characterization may be necessary if identification is not certain at this stage or if it is desirable to carry identification through to the strain level. The specific tests to be used at this stage can be determined only by a careful search of the original literature.

The approach suggested above is most generally applicable to viruses that are mechanically transmissible. Identification of a virus that is not mechanically transmissible must of necessity be based largely on symptomatology, host range, and (if the vector is known) the identity of the vector and the virus-vector relations. Fairly satisfactory cross-protection tests can sometimes be made where the only known method of transmission is by grafting. If transmission by the insect vector is dependent upon multiplication within the insect, tests for cross protection within the insect may provide useful information. Modern techniques have made possible the use of other methods with some of the persistent viruses transmitted by leafhoppers or aphids. Some of these in plant or insect extracts can now be transmitted by mechanical methods to insects, which then transmit them to plants, making it possible to measure virus stability, to purify the viruses in some cases, and perhaps to characterize them by means of electron microscopy. Also, some of the leafhopper-transmitted viruses have proved to be antigenic, making it possible to use serology in their identification.

Prior knowledge about the "unknown," or of the conditions under which it was found, may make it feasible to by-pass some of the steps in the suggested approach. Thus if an "unknown" were suspected to be TMV, its reaction with TMV-antiserum might be the most logical first step. If a strong reaction is obtained, then a dependable identification might be made on the basis of this fact and a few additional confirming tests, such as the diseases induced in a few selected plant species, comparative effects in to-

bacco varieties with and without the *N* gene from *Nicotiana glutinosa* L. (Holmes, 1958), thermal inactivation point, and examination in the electron microscope.

Present methods for the identification of plant viruses have been developed for use with viruses as they generally exist in natural infections—as intact nucleoproteins. Recently, naturally occurring unstable variants of some viruses have been found to exist free of the usual specific protein coat (Sänger and Brandenburg, 1961; Cadman 1962; Babos and Kassanis, 1962). These variants differ from the parent virus in stability, in ease of transmission by conventional methods (although vector relations may be the same), in host reactions, and in particle morphology. Being free of the specific viral protein, they are not antigenic. Quite obviously, application of the usual identification methods to one of these unstable variants would very likely fail to connect it with the parent virus. This type of virus is indicated if the "unknown" is very difficult to transmit by ordinary mechanical means but easily transmitted following phenol extraction (Schlegel, 1960). Host-range studies, cross-protection tests, and vector relations might be used as aids in identifying such viruses, but it is apparent that new methods are needed.

4-5. TECHNIQUES AND TESTS USED IN IDENTIFICATION

Usually, the objective in work with a new virus or virus "unknown" is not simply to establish its identity. Since the identity is not known in advance, and since soundness of an identification increases progressively with the amount of information obtained, the identification procedure normally should be designed to provide a full characterization of the virus. Usually, further work on the virus after it is identified is to be anticipated, which means that one will need precise information on such things as transmissibility, host range, symptomatology, stability, possible local-lesion hosts, and host species suitable for virus maintenance and increase. Choice of procedures to use, therefore, should not be limited to the minimum needed to establish a reasonable identification but instead should include all those that are applicable to the virus at hand and that are possible with the available facilities.

A. SYMPTOMATOLOGY AND HOST RANGE

One objective of studies on host range and symptomatology is, of course, to characterize the "unknown" in terms of the reactions or lack of reactions it induces in host plants selected on the basis of their reactions to known viruses. Such information serves at least two purposes. First, it may point directly to the identity of the virus or at least narrow the investigation to a workable number of "possibilities" and thus make possible the application of more specific tests. Second, information on symptomatology and host range will almost always be needed, after other tests have identified the virus of which the "unknown" is a strain, for the final determination to the strain level.

A second important objective is the discovery of a suitable test or "indicator" plant. A good test plant is needed in identification studies for testing for possible virus increase in inoculated plants that failed to develop symptoms, for determining the so-called physical properties of the virus in crude juice, and for checking on the potency of the inocula used in various kinds of tests. This test plant should be one that develops distinct symptoms soon after inoculation and preferably one that is self-pollinated, homozygous, and rapidly grown from seed; for mechanical inoculations, a plant that reacts to inoculation by the formation of local lesions is much to be preferred.

Many times, the plant species in which the "unknown" is discovered may be unsatisfactory for maintenance of the culture or as a source for high-potency inocula. Consequently, a frequent third objective is the discovery of a suitable species for use as a source plant.

1. *Selection of test species.*—Approximately one-third of the known plant viruses have extremely wide host ranges, including species from widely related families; the host ranges of some viruses include both monocots and dicots and both herbaceous and nonherbaceous species. Another third, more or less, have host ranges embracing several species in a number of genera and perhaps a few families, whereas the remaining ones appear to have very restricted host ranges, usually including only a few closely related species in no more than a few genera. A newly discovered virus in one species may be a well-known virus commonly associated with an entirely different type of plant species or group of species. The list of test plants used in studies on host range and symptomatology should include, therefore, not only other varieties of the source species (the species in which the "unknown" was found) and other closely related species but also species known to be susceptible to a large number of viruses. The last-named group should include species from several genera and families. If the source species is nonherbaceous, for example, the test species used may logically include some herbaceous species, for many viruses found in woody plants also have herbaceous hosts.

Some herbaceous species have been found to be susceptible to a large number of viruses (Table 4–1). Another species in the same category is *Nicotiana clevelandii* Gray (Hollings, 1959). Some of these are susceptible to a broad spectrum of viruses, including ones normally found in woody plants. There may be other species that show the same range of susceptibility as those listed, for this list may be in part a reflection of the frequency with which certain species are used in host-range studies. Whatever the reason for the apparent unusual susceptibility of the listed species, it would seem advisable to follow the suggestion of Thornberry (1961) that the species listed in Table 4–1 be used in host-range investigations. They would perhaps be most useful where mechanical transmission is attempted, but many of them should be included also when other transmission methods are used.

Several varieties of most of the species listed in Table 4–1 are available, and sometimes the choice of varieties is highly important. Virus workers have not been particularly in agreement concerning the best varieties to use, and choice has probably

TABLE 4–1. NUMBER OF VIRUSES KNOWN TO INFECT OR NOT INFECT SOME SPECIES OF PLANTS (*Information from Coded-Card File of Susceptible and Insusceptible Plant Species*)[*]

Species of Plants	Number of Viruses	
	Infecting species	Not infecting species
Beta vulgaris L.	33	62
Brassica oleracea L.	23	46
Chenopodium amaranticolor Coste & Reyn.	47	6
Cucumis sativus L.	67	77
Datura stramonium L.	70	67
Gomphrena globosa L.	26	16
Lycopersicum esculentum Mill.	60	76
Nicotiana glutinosa L.	78	67
Nicotiana tabacum L.	115	95
Phaseolus vulgaris L.	60	71
Pisum sativum L.	42	39
Solanum melongena L.	31	32
Solanum tuberosum L.	60	45
Vicia faba L.	35	40
Vigna sinensis Endl.	48	34
Zinnia elegans Jacq.	45	39

[*] Reproduced from Thornberry (1961) by permission.

Sometimes the method of inoculation, e.g., grafting, will dictate the age of test plant to use. In general, it is best to use young, rapidly growing plants at about the time two or three leaves become fully expanded or nearly so. Some species seem to give the best results when inoculated within a fairly narrow age range. For example, cucumbers are usually used before the first true leaf has expanded appreciably, and only the cotyledons (and perhaps one true leaf) are usually inoculated. The primary leaves of beans and cowpeas are generally the only leaves inoculated mechanically, and this is usually done just before the trifoliolate leaves begin to expand.

The number of test plants to use is largely determined by the availability of plants, of greenhouse space, and of time. At least three plants of each species or variety should be used, and it would be preferable to use six or more. Tests with any species giving questionable or variable results should be repeated, with an increase in the number of test plants.

Ideally, all tests should be made at normal greenhouse temperatures (20°–22°C), with other conditions (light, nutrition, etc.) near those optimal for growth of the species depended as much on easy availability as on any other single thing. Table 4–2 lists the varieties of some of these species that appear to have been used most frequently in the past or are known to offer some particular advantage. Workers with a particular type of virus may find it desirable to substitute others or to use additional ones.

Those who work with viruses attacking a particular kind of plant generally use more or less the same test species, and a few attempts have been made to establish standard lists. Thus, Bos *et al.* (1960), as a part of a suggested procedure for the international identification of legume viruses, listed 30 species and recommended that these species be used by all workers with legume viruses throughout the world.

2. *Procedure.*—Systemic symptoms usually develop best in plant parts that are growing rapidly, but local lesions sometimes develop best in expanded mature leaves.

TABLE 4–2. SUGGESTED LIST OF VARIETIES OR SELECTIONS FOR USE IN STUDIES ON HOST RANGE AND SYMPTOMATOLOGY

Species	Variety
Cucumus sativus	A & C, National Pickling
Gomphrena globosa	Cornell selection[*]
Lycopersicum esculentum	Bonny Best
Nicotiana tabacum	Turkish, Samsun, White Burley, Samsun NN[†]
Phaseolus vulgaris	Pinto, Bountiful
Solanum tuberosum	USDA seedling 41956[‡] Saco[§]
Vigna sinensis	Black

[*] Wilkinson and Blodgett (1948).

[†] Or other variety containing the *N* gene from *N. glutinosa*.

[‡] Immune from, or resistant to, potato virus X but likely to be infected by potato virus S.

[§] Immune from, or resistant to, potato viruses X and S.

being used. Often this is not possible, because of the difficulty of doing large-scale experiments under standardized conditions and because the plant species themselves may vary greatly in their requirements for optimal growth. As temperature is perhaps the most important single environmental factor affecting symptoms, the practical solution to the problem is to do the tests when near-normal temperatures can be maintained and when other conditions are not particularly limiting for plant growth. In any case, the conditions used should be reported and the results interpreted accordingly.

The method of inoculation used will depend upon the virus. Mechanical inoculations should be attempted and used where possible, but inoculations may be by any feasible method (mechanical, grafting, dodder, tissue insertion, insects, etc.). Presumably, the investigator will have to determine something about the transmissibility of the "unknown" before he undertakes a host-range study. It should be kept in mind, however, that the reported host range of a virus may depend upon the method of inoculation used, e.g., some species may be found susceptible when inoculated by grafting but not when inoculated mechanically or by means of insects. It is not particularly uncommon for one to encounter difficulty in mechanical transmission of a virus from plant to plant within the species in which the virus is commonly found in nature and yet encounter little difficulty in transmitting it by mechanical means to other species. For example, necrotic ringspot virus of Prunus is virtually nontransmissible by mechanical means from cherry to cherry, but it is rather easily so transmitted to cucumber. If transmission of the "unknown" is seemingly restricted to graft inoculations, it may be possible to increase the number of usable test species by use of dodder or by tissue implantations.

Results of mechanical inoculations are likely to be inconclusive unless highly infectious inocula are used. With herbaceous species, the first systemically infected leaves to show well-developed symptoms are generally satisfactory as source of inocula. These should be used within a few days after symptom development—usually 10–14 days after inoculation. Leaves inoculated directly with highly infectious juice are generally satisfactory virus sources about a week after the inoculation. In most of the inoculated test species, positive reactions should occur in either 100% or 0% of the plants. Unless this occurs or unless tests on local-lesion hosts indicate a satisfactory inoculum, steps should be taken to find a better virus source or to improve the inoculation technique.

Inoculated plants must be examined at daily intervals following inoculation, so that the sequence of symptoms may be recorded. Some symptoms, such as vein-clearing, are transient and thus may be missed unless frequent observations are made. Incubation periods, i.e., the time required after inoculation for symptoms to develop, may be an aid in identification. Also, some viruses induce a characteristic sequence of disease symptoms. Many of the ringspot diseases, for example, are characterized by a local phase (in inoculated leaves), a subsequent acute stage (in first leaves invaded systemically) where symptoms may be quite severe, and eventually a chronic phase (in leaves developing after the infection is systemic) in which symptoms may be mild or absent.

Absence of symptoms must never be taken as evidence of lack of infection. In other words, a symptomless plant should not be judged insusceptible unless attempts to recover virus from it are consistently unsuccessful. Similarly, species developing symptoms only in inoculated leaves must not be judged insusceptible to systemic invasion unless recovery tests from noninoculated leaves are negative. Recovery tests should be made first (about a week after inoculation) from the inoculated leaves. With a stable virus, sufficient inoculum may remain on the surface of the rubbed leaf to give a "positive" recovery test. The amount of such virus recovered will generally be small and thus indicated by only a few lesions in a local-lesion test plant or by a low percentage of "takes" in systemic hosts. When there is any question concerning possible virus increase in the inoculated leaves, the test should be repeated and attempts made to detect an actual increase in virus by making quantitative tests immediately and at various intervals following the original inoculation. Viruses vary considerably in the rate at which they move systemically, hence recovery from noninoculated leaves should be made two or more weeks following inoculation.

Even though distinct symptoms develop in all inoculated plants of a given species, return inoculations should still be made to healthy plants of the source species. This practice not only will confirm the susceptibility of the test species concerned, but it also will serve as a check on possible separation of components of a mixture or the possible filtering out of a particular strain from the original inoculum. Either of these things would be indicated by failure of the return inoculation to induce typical symptoms in the source species.

Because of the importance of the recovery tests in host-range studies, one should be on the alert for a good test or indicator plant, i.e., one that develops easily recognized symptoms soon after inoculation. Species or varieties that develop local lesions following inoculation are best to use for mechanically transmissible viruses. Hopefully, the investigator will find a suitable indicator plant among those being used in a host-range study, or perhaps the original source species will be suitable. If neither is the case, it normally would be good practice to screen still other species or varieties for possible use as indicator plants.

The observations or records made should be of three types; from the standpoint of their usefulness in identification, the order of importance of the three types is generally in the same order in which they will be mentioned. First, each species or variety should be recorded as infected or not infected. Development of reproducible symptoms may be taken as evidence of virus increase, but recovery tests should be made in any case where there is any doubt. Second, each infection should be classed as local or systemic. Again, this may be on the basis of symptoms supplemented where necessary by recovery tests. Third, the specific symptoms should be recorded in the sequence in which they appear and according to whether they occur in inoculated or systemically invaded leaves.

The failure of a virus to infect a particular plant species may be as important to its eventual identification as infection of another species. Consequently, reports on host-range studies should list the species not infected.

Plants should be examined for other than external symptoms. Many viruses induce characteristic inclusion bodies in certain hosts. The identity of the "unknown" may be suggested by the types of inclusion bodies induced, by the tissues or the parts of the cell in which the inclusion bodies are found, and sometimes by the staining reactions of the inclusion bodies (McWhorter, 1941). Also, information on the type and distribution of inclusion bodies can be used to differentiate between some pairs of viruses (McWhorter, 1960). Certain viruses also induce characteristic changes in specific tissues, such as phloem or xylem. The staining characteristics of affected tissues, or the reactions with certain chemicals, will occasionally be indicative of the causal virus (Lindner, 1961).

Selected plant species often can be used to differentiate between a particular virus and another. After an identification has been narrowed to just a few "possibilities," therefore, the literature should be consulted for information on plant species that react differently to the viruses still on the list. The differentiation may be on the basis of susceptibility, symptoms, or systemic vs. local infection.

3. *Interpretation.*—Data obtained in studies on host ranges and symptomatology seldom should be considered sufficient for a positive identification. Variability is the basic reason for this. Variability due to environmental conditions is of considerable importance from a practical standpoint, but the difficulty could be largely overcome by use of modern facilities for growing and testing of plants under controlled conditions. The most important source of variation, therefore, is the viruses themselves. The multiplicity of existing strains, plus the fact that new strains may arise at any time, should always be kept in mind by the virologist attempting an identification. The

fact that most new strains or mutants are at first recognized either on the basis of symptomatology or host range is ample evidence that the ability of a virus to induce certain symptoms or to infect certain species is not a particularly stable characteristic.

Despite the general inability of studies on host range or symptomatology to provide reliable identifications, they do provide the best criteria for identification of a few viruses. Potato spindle tuber virus, for instance, is best identified on the basis of the characteristic shape of infected potato tubers. Also the ability of experienced plant pathologists to make accurate diagnoses solely on the basis of symptomatology should not be discounted. This ability results from long experience with particular viruses in specific crop plants grown under a fairly narrow range of environmental conditions. That such diagnoses can be sufficiently accurate for all practical purposes is attested to by the fact that a great many productive field experiments and successful control measures are based on this type of diagnosis.

Symptomatology and host-range studies are of major importance in the identification of specific strains of a virus. Differentiation among virus strains has been largely on the basis of symptoms induced or on ability or inability to infect certain plant species. For many strains, there are no other methods for differentiating among them.

B. Properties in Crude Juice

Years ago, Johnson (1927) pointed out the difficulties of identifying viruses on the basis of symptomatology and suggested the use of other characters such as thermal inactivation point, resistance to aging *in vitro*, and dilution end point. Since then, most first accounts of mechanically transmitted viruses have included data on these properties. The original recommendations were concerned with properties in juice from infected plants (Johnson and Grant, 1932), and most of the subsequent determinations also have been made on this basis. Until recently (Bos *et al.*, 1960), no attempt has been made toward a widespread use of a standard source plant; workers have generally used as source the species in which the virus was first found or the species commonly used for maintenance and increase of the virus. Similarly, there has been no standardization of the species used for detecting virus activity, although local-lesion hosts have generally been used when available. Obviously, this lack of standardization has resulted in much variation in results, for the crude juice of infected plants of different source species is almost certain to differ in virus concentration, in content of other constituents that may be either protective or deleterious to the virus, and in pH. Results of such tests also will depend in part upon the sensitivity of the test plant. As a result of these and other sources of variation, published data on these properties actually do vary to a great extent. With cucumber mosaic virus, for example, different workers have reported thermal inactivation between 55° and 70° and dilution end points varying from 1/1000 to 1/100,000. This may be an extreme case; actually, there is fair agreement among most workers on the *in vitro* properties of many of the juice-transmitted viruses, and such properties have proved of considerable diagnostic value. This should continue to be the case provided there is general agreement that such data are not precise, that some variation in results is to be expected, that the data obtained do not necessarily reflect exactly the intrinsic properties of the viruses themselves, and that such tests are no more than aids in the characterization of viruses. The chief value of these *in vitro* properties lies in the fact that, in general, strains (except those variants lacking the specific protein) of a given virus are similar with respect to stability and to the extent to which they are able to multiply or accumulate in a given host species. It is true that many viruses have similar thermal inactivation points and dilution end points, yet there is a sufficient range in these properties to make them quite useful in identification. Furthermore, information obtained from such tests is of considerable value for other reasons; all *in vitro* work with a virus begins with crude juice, hence the virus worker should have some prior information on virus stability and concentration in such materials.

Some care in selection of source material is advisable. In general, source material should consist of leaves from relatively young plants showing typical symptoms. Usually, those systemically infected leaves showing the most distinct symptoms about 10–14 days following inoculation are used; where necessary, inoculated leaves can be used 7–10 days after inoculation. The leaves are ground by mortar and pestle or food chopper; the juice is separated from the pulp by passage through cheesecloth and used as soon as possible.

Since most of the published data have been obtained in tests with untreated crude juice, it seems desirable to continue on the same basis. Bos *et al.* (1960) recently recommended that the tests be based on juice diluted 1/10 with 0.01 M phosphate buffer at pH 7. The advisability of this change in procedure is doubtful. First, the data obtained would not be comparable with the bulk of the published data. Second, phosphate is deleterious to some viruses. Third, there is little evidence that the addition of this amount of phosphate to crude juice would necessarily "stabilize pH and ionic activity" in the crude juices from different species of plants. Precise characterization of the virus should be made with purified viruses under known ionic conditions; there seems little reason for attempting further rigorous standardization of these rather crude tests that have in general served the purpose for which they were intended. It is important, however, that reports of such tests carry full information on the source and test species used and on whether or not the crude juice was treated in any way prior to the tests.

Slight modification may provide useful information in special cases. Exposure of the crude juice to oxidation will result in the rapid inactivation of some viruses. Addition of reducing agents or of inhibitors of oxidizing enzymes may prolong longevity, raise the thermal inactivation point, and increase the dilution end point of such viruses. Thus, addition of such agents in tests with a particularly unstable virus may materially aid in its characterization.

Until recently, the tests discussed here have been applied for the most part to vi-ruses that can be transmitted mechanically from plant to plant. It is now possible to apply these or similar tests to viruses that can be mechanically transmitted from plant to insect vector or from insect to insect.

Since treatments involving heating, aging, or diluting of infectious juice are often used to separate viruses, it would be advisable to make return inoculations from plants inoculated with treated juice (but still infectious) to the source species as a check on the ability of the treated inoculum to induce the original disease.

1. *Thermal inactivation point.*—When infectious crude juice is heated, the rate of virus inactivation is dependent not only upon temperature but also upon virus concentration, pH, other materials present, etc. The time required for complete inactivation, or inactivation to a certain point, is affected by the same variables. Hence, some variation due to the source species can be expected, and dilution with water or buffers would also introduce variations. Consequently, it has been necessary to choose an arbitrary time and to effect some standardization of the type of extract used. The most commonly accepted definition of the thermal inactivation point of a virus (in crude juice) is the temperature required for the complete inactivation of the virus in untreated crude juice during a 10-minute exposure.

In a typical test, the crude juice is pipetted in narrow thin-walled test tubes previously warmed to the desired temperature; the tubes are placed in a constant-temperature water bath for exactly 10 minutes and then removed and immediately cooled in running water. The treated juice, and also unheated juice, is then rubbed on the leaves of suitable test plants, preferably local-lesion hosts. If nothing is known about the virus, a series of temperatures ranging from 45° to 95° at 5° intervals is commonly used; if something is known about the identity of the virus, then it may be possible to use a narrower range of temperatures. The test should be repeated, but the second test can be over a narrower temperature range and possibly at 2° intervals. Five-ml serological tubes, with walls about 0.7 mm thick, are suitable. The juice (2 ml) should be pipetted into the tubes in such a manner that no juice is left on the inner wall of the upper part of the tube. The level of the water in the bath should be at least 3 cm above the level of the juice.

In respect to their general behavior at elevated temperatures, viruses may be divided roughly into two groups. With those that have a high temperature coefficient ($Q_{10°}$), such as TMV and potato virus X, loss of infectivity is closely correlated with denaturation (coagulation) and precedes it by a very narrow margin. Others, such as tobacco necrosis virus and tomato bushy stunt virus, are characterized by a relatively low $Q_{10°}$, and virus inactivation proceeds well in advance of denaturation and more or less independently of it. With these viruses with a high $Q_{10°}$, temperature is the most important single factor affecting the amount of inactivation occurring in 10 minutes. Hence, most workers agree reasonably well on the thermal inactivation point of such viruses in crude juice. On the other hand, temperature is of less relative importance in determining the amount of inactivation of the other group of viruses; hence other factors become progressively more important. As a result, the reported thermal inactivation points of such viruses vary considerably. If an "unknown" is tentatively identified as a particular virus, its thermal inactivation point should be in reasonable agreement with the values reported in the literature. If it is a virus like tobacco mosaic virus or potato virus X, agreement should usually be within 5°. With others, perhaps agreement within 10° should be expected. Large discrepancies should be considered as good evidence but not proof of the nonidentity of one virus with another.

2. *Other measures of heat stability.*—The stability of a virus at elevated temperatures also can be characterized rather easily in other ways, particularly if local-lesion assays are possible. From an equivalent amount of data, for example, the velocity constant of inactivation at a specified temperature can be determined with greater accuracy than can the thermal inactivation point (Price, 1940). If velocity constants at different temperatures are determined, the temperature coefficient of inactivation, i.e., the ratio between velocity constants at two different temperatures, can be calculated (Price, 1940). The temperature coefficient customarily determined is $Q_{10°}$, the ratio of velocity constants at temperatures differing by 10°C. Values for $Q_{10°}$ are not constant over any appreciable temperature range, for they tend to increase as the temperature is increased. Another value, the energy of activation, is more nearly constant over different temperature ranges than is $Q_{10°}$ and can be calculated from the same data (Price, 1940).

Velocity constants, temperature coefficients, and the energy of activation have been determined for only a few viruses (tabulated by Pollard, 1953; and Bawden, 1950) and thus at present are of limited value in identification. These measures of heat stability would appear to be more accurate and more informative than thermal inactivation points and hence are of potential use in identification. For the present, parallel studies with an "unknown" and known viruses, either unpurified or purified, could be very useful in identification.

3. *Longevity in vitro.*—Different viruses behave differently when allowed to age *in vitro* at room temperature. The thermal inactivation point is not an index of ability to retain infectivity at room temperature; thus resistance to aging is yet another way to characterize a virus. Loss of activity during aging at room temperature may result from thermal inactivation, i.e., the same series of reactions that lead to rapid loss of infectivity at or near the thermal inactivation point, or it may result from action by microorganisms or from oxidative reactions. Thus TMV is remarkably stable at room temperature, even in crude juice, because it is not particularly subject to any of the three types of reactions. Tobacco necrosis virus, which has the same thermal inactivation point as TMV, is much less stable than is TMV at room temperature because thermal inactivation proceeds at an appreciable rate at room temperature. Potato virus X, which is similar to TMV in that inactivation and denaturation proceed at about the same rate, is rather unstable at room tem-

perature because it is subject to microbial action.

Tests on longevity *in vitro* are usually made with untreated crude juice stored in stoppered containers at room temperature (20°–22°C). Samples are removed at intervals and tested for infectivity on suitable test plants. Unless something is known about the general stability of the virus, the first series of intervals should be at a geometric progression (e.g., 1,2,4,8,16,32 . . . days) until infectivity is lost; shorter intervals over a narrower range should then be used in a confirmatory run.

As with thermal inactivation tests, results may vary with a number of factors, such as the exact temperature used, the source species, the sensitivity of the assay, and the microbial population of the juice. Reports should always specify the source plant, test plant, and temperature. Useful information may be gained by varying the technique, such as by adding reducing agents, by filtration to sterilize the juice, or by adding chemicals that inhibit bacteria and fungi; if such things are done, they should be described in detail in the report.

Small differences in longevity should not be considered to be significant. In general, longevity tests should be considered as doing no more than characterizing a virus in terms of whether its longevity *in vitro* can be measured in minutes, hours, days, weeks, months, or years.

Yarwood and Sylvester (1959) have suggested that the relative stability of viruses *in vitro* be measured and expressed in terms of "half-life," i.e., the time required for loss of one-half of the original activity. Nitzany and Friedman (1963) investigated the applicability of the half-life concept to the aging *in vitro* of several unpurified viruses and concluded that half-life is the more accurate expression of virus inactivation. Whether or not this concept will prove useful in identification work depends upon how widely it is accepted and applied. It is likely to be of limited use until the half-life of the known viruses is reported, until fiducial limits of the test are determined, until reproducibility of results by different investigators working with the same viruses has been determined, and until a standardized procedure is adopted. One should keep in mind the fact that the accuracy of a half-life test will be no greater than the accuracy of the assay. Also, tests on crude juice are still replete with uncertainties and probably will remain of limited diagnostic value.

4. *Dilution end point.*—The extent to which a virus multiplies and/or accumulates in a given host species is somewhat characteristic of the virus and most of its strains. Hence, a simple dilution test may serve as yet another pointer in attempts to identify a virus.

Dilution is usually on a logarithmic scale (i.e., 1/1, 1/10, 1/100, 1/1000, . . . 1/10,000,000), and each dilution should be rubbed on an equal number of uniform test plants. Water is the recommended diluent. The dilution end point is generally reported as being between two dilutions, i.e., between the highest dilution that was still infectious and the next highest one.

Like the other two tests on properties of viruses in crude juice, this test also is rather crude and is subject to several sources of variation. In addition to the identity of host and test species, the environmental conditions under which each is grown will influence the results. The temperature at which the source plant is maintained is of particular importance, for temperature can have a very marked effect on virus titer. Hence, the experimental conditions should always be reported. Since considerable variation is to be expected, dilutions at less than 10-fold steps are not necessary. In interpreting results, one should recognize that the test is designed to differentiate among viruses that differ greatly in dilution end point. The dilution end point, as determined by the prescribed method, should fall within the range reported in the literature, and 10- or 100-fold differences should be given no particular significance.

C. Transmission Characteristics

The extent to which facts about the transmission of a virus are used in identification depends largely upon the nature of the virus. Transmission characteristics may play a very minor role in the identification of a mechanically transmissible virus, for many other tools are available. On the other hand, transmission characteristics are of major importance in the identification of many viruses that are transmitted by specific vectors, that cannot be transmitted by mechanical means, and that cannot as yet be worked with serologically. Barley yellow dwarf virus, for instance, can be identified only on the basis of symptomatology, host range, the aphid species capable of transmitting it, and the virus-vector relationship.

Even with mechanically transmitted viruses, most of which are transmitted by living vectors, data on transmissibility may be of material aid in identification. On the one hand, these viruses can be grouped according to the relative ease of transmission by the usual mechanical methods and also according to whether or not transmission is facilitated by the addition of reducing agents or by phenol extraction. On the other hand, identification of one or more vectors of a virus would identify the virus as belonging to a certain group and thus greatly narrow the possible identities that might be considered. A tentative identification could be strengthened significantly by the discovery of one or more vectors, or it could be invalidated by this.

Identification of a vector is almost an essential step in the identification of many vector-borne viruses, i.e., those that are not antigenic and are difficult to characterize *in vitro*. An identification of an "unknown," as barley yellow dwarf virus for example, would be incomplete unless it is shown to be transmitted by one of the known aphid vectors of this virus.

Discovery of the vector of a virus is usually followed by studies on virus-vector relations; such studies are likely to aid in the identification of the virus. Of particular value would be information on whether the virus is persistent or nonpersistent in the vector, on the duration of the latent period (if such exists), on how long after acquisition the vector retains the ability to transmit, and on whether or not the virus multiplies within the vector.

The extent to which discovery of the vector of an unknown virus will contribute to its identification is related to the number of viruses transmitted by that vector. The green peach aphid, *Myzus persicae* Sulzer,

transmits 30 or more plant viruses, thus demonstration that an "unknown" is transmitted by this vector would be a relatively small step toward its identification. In contrast, tomato spotted wilt virus is the only one known to be transmitted by thrips; thus only a minimum amount of further characterization would be needed to establish the identity of a thrips-borne "unknown" as tomato spotted wilt virus.

Transmission characteristics are sometimes of value in differentiation among strains of the same virus. Mutants devoid of the specific protein coat may be difficult to transmit mechanically even though the parent virus is easily transmitted in this manner (Sänger and Brandenburg, 1961; Cadman, 1962; Babos and Kassanis, 1962). Potato virus C, a strain of potato virus Y, is not transmitted by the green peach aphid, the usual vector of potato virus Y (Bawden and Kassanis, 1947). One strain of potato yellow dwarf virus is transmitted specifically by one leafhopper species, and yet another strain is transmitted specifically by another species (Black, 1941). Similarly, there are several vector-specific strains of barley yellow dwarf virus, and these strains can be differentiated only on the basis of their specific aphid vectors (Rochow, 1961).

D. Interaction with Other Viruses

Various aspects of virus interaction following simultaneous or sequential inoculation with virus pairs may be utilized to obtain information on the identity of one member of the pair. For the most part, tests of this nature are designed to detect either relatedness or unrelatedness of the "unknown" and a "known" virus. Sometimes, however, the way in which the "unknown" interacts with a specific virus may help to establish the identity of the "unknown."

1. *Cross protection.*—The phenomenon of cross protection is discussed fully by W. C. Price, and his chapter should be consulted for additional information. The subject will be dealt with here in bare outline only, with emphasis on the role of cross protection in identification, on its limitations, and on some aspects of interpretation.

As might be expected, a plant completely infected by a virus suffers no further damage if reinoculated with the same virus. It is not surprising, then, that prior infection with one virus affords protection against closely related ones. This principle is the basis for the so-called cross-protection test, which is one of the more important and widely used tools for determining the identity of a virus. Basically, the cross-protection test is a test for the relatedness of two viruses. The test consists essentially of challenge inoculation with one virus of tissue previously infected by another. Thus, it can be used most effectively only after the identity of an "unknown" has been fairly well established by other methods and the investigator is ready to test the hypothesis that it is a particular virus. The success of such tests depends upon several things, the most basic of which is that the second or challenge virus be one whose multiplication or effects can be recognized in the presence of the first virus.

The test would be of little value if it were not for the additional fact that protection does not ordinarily occur between unrelated viruses. A plant infected by one virus is almost always susceptible to an unrelated virus, i.e., the second virus is almost always able to become established and multiply despite the presence of the first. There is much variation in the extent to which the first interferes with the multiplication of the second and with its ability to induce characteristic symptoms. Depending upon the virus used, the first may have very little or no effect on the behavior of the second, it may be appreciably inhibitory (Thomson, 1958), or it may have a stimulatory effect (Thomson, 1961). In the planning and interpretation of cross-protection tests, one should always bear in mind the fact that the control (healthy) and the test plant (infected by the first virus) are entirely different test materials and that they will not necessarily provide environments equally suitable for the establishment and propagation of the second virus.

Prior infection by one virus rarely results in total exclusion of an unrelated virus, hence some interference between unrelated viruses would be of little consequence if complete protection were always afforded against a related virus. Unfortunately, this is not always so. The degree of protection infection by one strain confers against the effects of another strain depends upon the closeness of the relationship of the two viruses (Matthews, 1949, 1957) and on the completeness of infection of the test tissue by the first virus. In addition, it sometimes depends on the host species used, the method by which the second virus is introduced, and the order in which the two viruses are used. Thus, results with some unrelated pairs used under certain conditions may be indistinguishable from those with some pairs of related viruses.

Anyone attempting cross-protection tests should keep in mind the fact that cross protection is relative. The fact that results are not always clear-cut does not mean that cross-protection tests are useless. It does mean, however, that failure to demonstrate cross protection does not necessarily indicate unrelatedness and that such "negative results," as well as partial or incomplete protection, should be interpreted with caution. On the other hand, positive results, i.e., complete protection, can usually be depended upon as indicating relatedness. Results of reciprocal or "mirror" tests in particular are highly dependable. If A protects completely against B, and B gives similar protection against A, the only valid conclusion is that A and B are identical or closely related. Relatedness would be strongly indicated where protection is complete in one direction but absent or incomplete in the other. One should remember, however, that unilateral protection involving three unrelated viruses has been reported from one laboratory (Bawden and Kassanis, 1941, 1945), although the results could not be confirmed in another (Schmelzer et al., 1960). The safest procedure, of course, is to consider results of cross-protection tests as evidence, not absolute proof, and to base final conclusions on several different criteria.

Since positive results are so much more dependable than negative ones, the investigator should choose the best available method for his test. Cross protection is relative, hence it is highly desirable to use a method in which a local-lesion-inducing virus can be used for the challenge inoculation. This makes it possible to obtain a quantitative estimate of the level of protection.

One of the best types of test is that involving chronic-stage or "recovered" leaves (Price, 1936). This test requires that both viruses be capable of inducing lesions in the inoculated leaf and also that at least one of the viruses be capable of inducing a disease characterized by "recovery." The "recovered" leaves, being infected but symptomless or nearly so, are challenge inoculated with a second virus. This test offers the advantage that tests for completeness of infection by the first virus can be made by challenge inoculation of some half-leaves with the first virus. Other half-leaves are challenge inoculated with the second virus, and still others can be inoculated with known strains of the first virus or with unrelated viruses. Another advantage is that reciprocal tests usually can be made, i.e., leaves on plants "recovered" from each virus can be challenged with the other virus.

The half-leaf test described by Kunkel (1934) is another excellent test. This test can be made when one of the viruses to be used induces local lesions in a host susceptible to both whereas the other does not. Half of each leaf is used as a control; these are rubbed with water or with juice from a healthy plant. The opposite halves are inoculated with the nonlesion-inducing virus. Later, after local multiplication has occurred, the entire leaf is challenge inoculated with the lesion-inducing virus. Preferably, different lots of plants should be challenge inoculated on different days, e.g., at 1- or 2-day intervals. This not only points to the best interval to use, but it also provides data showing the progressive development of protection in the inoculated halves (if the viruses are related).

Other methods, those involving an "all-or-none" reaction, are useful if interpreted with caution. In particular, introduction of the second virus by graft or by insects should be resorted to only when no other method is available. If the first tests made give only negative or inconclusive results, the possibility of obtaining good protection under different conditions or by means of other procedures should be explored. It sometimes is profitable to try other hosts, different strains of the "known" virus, or different environmental conditions. Even when protection is good in one direction, these and other things should be utilized in attempts to devise methods for conducting the reciprocal test. Regardless of the method used, cross-protection tests should not be used blindly. Before testing the "unknown" against a known, one should show that the known virus will protect against one or more of its known strains.

That cross protection may occur between two plant virus strains within their insect vector has been demonstrated (Kunkel, 1955; Maramorosch, 1958). Thus cross protection in an insect vector can sometimes be used in identification work, but so far it has been detected only in leafhoppers. Presumably, cross protection can occur in a vector only if both viruses are capable of infecting the vector and then only if transmission of the second virus is dependent upon multiplication within the vector. Cross protection of the second virus is dependent upon multiplication within the vector. Cross protection is considered to be involved when an insect allowed to acquire one virus some time before being given access to a second is unable to transmit the second even though it normally does so. In other words, ability of the vector to transmit the second virus is the sole criterion for determining whether the vector has become infected by the second virus. Thus, results will be meaningful only with an "unknown" with a "known" vector in which the virus must multiply before it can be transmitted by the vector. Such "unknowns" are likely to be rare. On the other hand, only a few methods are available for the identification of this type of "unknown," hence this technique should be extremely useful where it is applicable.

2. *Simultaneous-infection test for unrelatedness.*—Holmes (1956) pointed out that in mixed infections "closely related strains do not produce effects that transgress the limits set by the strains separately but . . . unrelated viruses often, although not always, do so. . . ." This general expe-

rience was proposed as a basis for demonstrating unrelatedness among virus isolates. The proposal appears sound, for the basic premise is in accord with the general experience of not only virologists but also investigators in all parts of the field of parasitology. The premise could be stated in another way: strains of the same virus have similar requirements and are thus competitive in mixed infections whereas unrelated viruses have different requirements and tend toward complete independence of each other.

The procedure for making such a test is very simple. A given pair of viruses, the "unknown" and a "known," are tested separately and together in a number of host species. The two viruses would be judged unrelated if the mixture induces a more severe disease than does either virus alone. The data recorded could concern any effect that can be measured more or less quantitatively. Holmes (1956) used plant stunting or plant height as an index of virus effects. He found, for example, that the average heights of tobacco plants (3 weeks after inoculation) were as follows: healthy controls—11.5 cm; inoculated with tomato aspermy virus—4.3 cm; inoculated with potato virus X—7.5 cm; and inoculated with both viruses—2.8 cm. Had the two viruses been strains of the same virus, the basic premise would have predicted that the height of the doubly infected plants would have been intermediate, i.e., between 4.3 and 7.5 cm.

Quantitative data are too meager to warrant a decision as to whether the reverse line of reasoning is valid, i.e., whether intermediate effects can be considered as good evidence of relatedness. It is true that the combined effects of unrelated mixtures are usually either additive or synergistic, but it is not known whether the exceptions to this are rare or numerous.

The test for unrelatedness should be applied only to systemic infections. If infections are local and independent, i.e., local lesions, the effects would presumably be approximately additive when two strains are mixed. Caution should perhaps be used in the application of this test even to systemic infections, for at least one apparent

exception to Holmes' general thesis has been reported (Hollings, 1957).

3. *Specific effects in mixed infections.*— Some pairs of viruses are known to interact in a characteristic manner (Bennett, 1953; Ross, 1959). Thus the ability or lack of ability of an "unknown" to interact with certain viruses may contribute to its characterization. This would be especially true with virus pairs that react synergistically. Potato virus X (Rochow, 1954) and dodder latent virus (Bennett, 1949), for example, interact synergistically with any of several viruses. Testing of an "unknown" in mixed infections with each of these viruses during the early stages of identification might very easily provide an early clue to the probable identity of a virus; also, such tests could be used to test the validity of a tentative identification.

E. RESPONSE TO PRESENCE OF SPECIFIC GENES IN THE HOST

A very specific test can be based on the use of plants containing a specific single gene that conditions the response of that plant to infection by a particular virus. Application of such a test was very nicely demonstrated by Holmes (1941) in identifying a *Plantago* virus as a strain of TMV. He used a segregating progeny of tobacco plants, some of which were bearing the dominant N gene from *Nicotiana glutinosa* and others the recessive allele n. Plants with the dominant gene N respond to infection with known strains of TMV by the production of necrotic local lesions like those developed in *N. glutinosa* (Holmes, 1938) whereas plants lacking it respond by forming very faint chlorotic lesions in the inoculated leaves and a subsequent chlorotic mottling or mosaic in noninoculated ones. The *Plantago* virus induced two types of disease in the segregating progeny, a result that would not be expected had the virus been other than a strain of TMV.

Inbred tobacco lines containing the N gene also can be used for similar tests. Samsun NN tobacco (Holmes, 1938), for example, responds to inoculation with all known strains of TMV (to which it is susceptible) by the formation of local lesions, whereas the otherwise similar nn varieties, Samsun and Turkish, are systemically infected by all but a few experimentally derived strains (Holmes, 1953). No other virus is known to induce the one distinct type of disease in NN plants and the other in nn plants. Thus, if an "unknown" induces local lesions in Samsun NN tobacco but systemic disease in Samsun or Turkish tobacco, it almost certainly is a strain of TMV.

This test has not been widely applied because suitable test plants are available for only a few viruses. This is perhaps the most specific test of all those based on a biological response and doubtlessly will be used more widely in the future.

F. Serological Tests

Many plant virologists have concluded that serology provides the most reliable evidence concerning the identity of a virus. This conclusion appears valid provided too much emphasis is not placed on weak cross reactions, particularly those obtained with antisera of very high titer. This section will deal primarily with some of the general aspects of serology as used in identification work, with some of its limitations, and with a few miscellaneous points that cannot be overemphasized. (See Chapter 11 by Ellen Ball for further information.)

Antisera have been prepared for more than 30 plant viruses, and antisera for many others will doubtlessly be obtained in the future. It is far from certain that serological procedures will eventually be applicable to all plant viruses, for many serious attempts to apply serological techniques to several plant viruses have consistently resulted in failure. Despite the lack of general applicability, serology is one of the most useful tools for the identification of plant viruses.

Serological tests are of special value in identification work because of the rapidity with which a meaningful test can be made. In a laboratory with a stock of antisera for several viruses, the testing of an "unknown" against each of the available antisera could very easily lead to a rapid identification of the virus. A positive reaction with a particular antiserum should, of course, be followed by more thorough characterization, but much preliminary work would have been by-passed.

Another advantage is that serological tests, like cross-protection tests, are group specific, not strain specific. In other words, an antiserum prepared by injection of a "type" virus will react with all strains of that virus, except proteinless ones, but not ordinarily with other viruses. An "unknown" may be readily identified by serology as a strain of a particular virus even though the "unknown" and the "type" virus induce entirely different diseases or have no hosts in common. Some strains of some viruses can be differentiated by means of cross-absorption tests, and the degree of relatedness of two or more strains can be determined in this way. Nevertheless, serological techniques are seldom useful in the identification of a particular strain other than to place it in a certain group.

Tests with a single antiserum can only indicate the presence or probable absence of a particular virus or one of its strains. The word "probable" is used because the failure of an infectious preparation to react with a specific antiserum does not necessarily mean that the virus being tested for is not present—it may be present but at a concentration too low to give a visible reaction. Thus, proof that an "unknown" is not a strain of the particular virus would require that a good antiserum of each virus be prepared and that it be demonstrated that each virus will react with its homologous antiserum but not with the heterologous antiserum. Actually, a rigorous identification should involve such reciprocal testing. The investigator should not be satisfied by finding that the "unknown" reacts with a particular antiserum, for the identification would be on a much firmer basis if an antiserum specific for the "unknown" were prepared and shown to react not only with the "unknown" but also with the "type" virus. The possibility of a mixed infection also should be kept in mind. A second virus would not be detected unless, by chance or by shrewd guess, the "unknown" also is tested against an antiserum specific for the second virus.

An identification based on serology will be no better than the antisera and methods used. One should make certain that each antiserum used is free from antibodies specific for normal plant constituents and also that it is free of antibodies that will react with other viruses. Any of several methods may be used for detecting the antigen-antibody reaction (Ball, 1961; Matthews, 1957), and it may be advantageous to use different methods for different antigen-antibody systems. The gel-diffusion method, for example, offers many advantages in tests for many viruses, but it is not suitable for testing for viruses with elongated particles. Adequate controls should be used to guard against conclusions based on false reactions.

The validity of serology as a basis for virus identification is based largely on the premise that all strains of a given virus are serologically related and will react with antiserum prepared against the "type" virus. The converse of this, i.e., that all serologically related viruses are strains, has been challenged (Bagnall *et al.*, 1959; Bercks, 1960; Brandes and Wetter, 1959; Wetter *et al.*, 1959) on the basis that a high-titer antiserum may cross react with viruses considered to be unrelated to the virus used for preparing the antiserum. Thus Bercks (1960) prepared antisera against bean yellow mosaic virus that had a titer of 1:256,000 and found that it reacted with potato virus Y and beet mosaic virus. Similarly, high-titer antisera against potato virus Y cross reacted with bean yellow mosaic virus and beet mosaic virus. Macleod and Markham (1963), who also used methods that result in high-titer antisera, reported cross reactions between turnip yellow mosaic virus and wild cucumber mosaic virus, two viruses that have no host in common. These weak cross reactions have been reported only between viruses that are very similar with respect to particle morphology and/or chemical composition. It may very well be that further work with high-titer antisera will reveal the existence of virus groups characterized by a few antigenic groupings, by similar morphology, and by nucleic acids with similar base ratios (Macleod and Markham, 1963). These findings of a possible serological relationship between viruses that are now considered as distinct viruses encourage the hope that groups of related viral species may be identified but emphasize the inadvisability of using serology as the sole basis for species identification. Until virologists agree upon the significance of these new findings, it would appear advisable to avoid the use of high-titer antisera in routine identification work and to interpret weak cross reactions with caution.

G. VIRUS PARTICLE CHARACTERISTICS

Little or nothing is known concerning the morphology and chemical composition of the infectious particles of many plant viruses; nevertheless, the number of viruses that have been well characterized is sufficiently large to provide an indication of the characteristics of greatest value in identification work. Any characteristic may be of use in identification, but some appear more useful than others. The most useful characteristics are those that differ little or none from strain to strain but that differ appreciably among distinct viruses. For example, strains of the same virus vary little in size and shape whereas different viruses possess a variety of sizes and shapes. Of course it is possible for two or more viruses to have particles of the same size and shape, but only a few such exceptions are known. Consequently, the coincidence of two viruses having particles of the same size and shape is good evidence that they are the same or related strains, whereas a marked difference in size or shape would be strongly indicative, if not proof, that they are two distinct viruses.

Other characters, besides size and shape, that appear most promising for pointing to or establishing the identity of a virus are composition (base ratios) of the nucleic acid (Macleod and Markham, 1963), the absolute weight of the virus particle (Macleod and Markham, 1963), the number of protein subunits (Knight, 1959), and the identity of the amino acid residue terminating the peptide chains (Knight, 1959). Unfortunately, most of these characters cannot be determined unless the virus can be obtained in a highly purified state, and they all require specialized equipment. Because of these facts, and also because this approach is not yet applicable to all plant viruses, most identifications will likely continue for some time to be based on other properties. Many virologists believe, however, that these intrinsic properties of the viruses, plus perhaps serological relationships and transmission characteristics, will eventually be the most generally acceptable bases for virus classification, nomenclature, and identification. Since a trend to place increasing weight on the physicochemical properties of viruses is discernible, any description of a newly described virus should report data on these properties, if possible, and an identification based in part on such properties will be more likely to be accepted in the future than will ones based mostly on host reactions.

Only those characters of greatest use at the present will be further discussed, and these will not be discussed in detail because of the more complete presentation in other papers in this series.

1. *Physical properties.*—Many different plant viruses have been visualized in the electron microscope, and precise information on the exact size and shape of several viruses is available. Particle morphology appears to be quite a constant characteristic feature of a given virus and its strains; thus the electron microscope is an important aid to identification.

Electron microscopy can sometimes be used at an early stage of an identification attempt, for viruses with elongated particles can often be detected and characterized without a preliminary purification or concentration. Examination of crude extracts may reveal the presence of rod-shaped or threadlike particles in crude extracts of infected plants and their absence in similar extracts in healthy plants. A determination of the particle width and the distribution of particle lengths could very well point to the probable identity of the virus or at least predict the group of viruses to which it probably belongs. On the other hand, such observation may lead one in the wrong direction, for the mere finding of virus-like particles in juices from a plant infected by the "unknown" is far from proof that the particles are actually those of the "unknown." Claims that particles of a specific size and shape are actually those of the "unknown" should eventually be supported by data correlating such particles with in-

fectivity (Lauffer, 1952; Lauffer, Appendix 1), but such data can be obtained after the assumed identity has been more nearly established.

Crude extracts may be prepared in a number of ways for examination with the electron microscope. Extracts may be obtained as a forced exudate (Johnson, 1948) or by the usual methods of obtaining clarified expressed juice. The latter can be diluted and applied directly to the grids or by means of an atomizer (Gold *et al.*, 1957). Perhaps the simplest method and the one least likely to fragment the particle is the "dip" method of Brandes (1957). A freshly cut edge of a leaf is dipped for 1–2 seconds in a small drop of distilled water placed directly on the grid. The drop is dried and shadow-cast by the usual methods. Polystyrene particles or a known virus (e.g., TMV) can be added as an internal standard.

The crude extract methods are applicable only to viruses with elongated particles, for plant juices contain normal constituents that are essentially spherical in shape and within the size range of viruses. A spheroid virus usually cannot be detected with certainty in such material, hence such viruses must be highly purified before they can be characterized in the electron microscope. Failure to find elongated virus-like particles in an extract does not necessarily mean that the virus particles are not elongated rods or threads. The virus simply may not be present in sufficient quantities in the extracts as prepared to make possible their detection. This is true even though the extracts are found to be infectious, for virus preparations too dilute for use in electron microscopy may still have sufficient particles present to be infectious.

Where it is feasible, the "unknown" should be purified and characterized by means of the electron microscope. The shadow-casting technique may be used for obtaining precise information on particle shape (Williams, 1954) and particle dimensions (Brandes and Paul, 1957). The so-called negative staining technique (Brenner and Horne, 1959) may provide additional information on structure, including data on number and arrangement of protein subunits. Precise data on these features would strengthen a correct tentative identification and likely detect an erroneous one.

A virus also may be characterized by its sedimentation constant, which is a function of size, shape, and density of the particles. Since these properties vary from virus to virus yet are usually constant for a given virus and its strains, the sedimentation constant of a virus is a fair index of its identity. Sedimentation constants are usually determined by means of the analytical ultracentrifuge; this is best done with purified preparations, although crude juice is usable in some instances (Markham, 1962). Brakke (1958) has developed a method for estimating sedimentation rates by density-gradient centrifugation in a Spinco Model L centrifuge. A comparison is made of the sedimentation rate of the unknown virus with that of a known virus (TMV) centrifuged through a density-gradient column at the same time under the same conditions. This method appears to be of potential use in identification work because it requires only equipment that is available in many laboratories, impure virus preparations can be used, low concentrations of virus can be used, and identification of the visible virus zone can be confirmed by infectivity assays.

Any virus that can be obtained in a reasonably pure state can be characterized in several other ways. Methods are available (Pollard, 1953; Schachman and Williams, 1959) for determining isoelectric point, "molecular weight" or absolute particle weight, electrophoretic mobility, diffusion coefficient, and X-ray diffraction; these properties are probably fairly constant for a given virus and its strains, although appropriate data are available for only a small proportion of the plant viruses.

2. *Chemical composition and structure.—* The nucleic acid content of viruses varies from about 5% to 35%. Most of those with elongated particles contain about the same amount (5–6%), but others vary considerably in the amount they contain. A significant point is that the nucleic acid content is constant for a given virus and all of its strains (Knight, 1959), hence analyses for these constituents may help in the characterization of a virus.

Of much greater significance may be the kind of nucleic acid in the virus, as indicated by the relative proportions of the four nitrogen bases (Macleod and Markham, 1963). Related viruses have similar base ratios (Markham and Smith, 1950) whereas unrelated viruses may differ appreciably in this respect. For example, wild cucumber mosaic virus and turnip yellow mosaic virus appear to be unique in that about 40% of their nucleotides are cytidylic acid (Yamazaki and Kaesberg, 1961a,b; Macleod and Markham, 1963) whereas the nucleic acid of several other viruses contains less than 25% (tabulated by Knight, 1959). This unusual composition of the nucleic acid of wild cucumber mosaic and turnip yellow mosaic viruses is one of the reasons that lead Macleod and Markham to consider these two viruses to be related.

Knight (1959) considers the amino acid residue terminating the polypetide chain (C-terminal amino acid) as a constant feature of a given virus and its strains. The C-terminal amino acid of 13 strains of tobacco mosaic virus was found to be threonine (Knight, 1955) whereas a different C-terminal amino acid was found in tomato bushy stunt virus and potato virus X (Niu *et al.*, 1958). The C-terminal amino acid is known for only a few viruses, hence the general applicability of this criterion has not yet been tested adequately.

The assumption that the protein moieties of all plant viruses are made up of subunits (Crick and Watson, 1957) is supported by every case so far examined. The number of subunits, as indicated by the number of terminal amino acid residues or possibly by electron microscopy involving the negative-staining technique, appears to be constant for a given virus and its strains (Knight, 1955), but it may be different for different viruses (Niu *et al.*, 1958).

4–6. CHOICE OF CRITERIA TO USE IN ESTABLISHING THE IDENTITY OF AN "UNKNOWN"

Since the various criteria differ greatly in applicability and since the viruses themselves vary greatly in the ease in which they can be identified, the number and nature of the criteria needed for a correct identification depend largely upon the virus. Any identification should be based on several criteria; the greater the number of criteria used, the more reliable is the identification. Choice also is governed to a considerable extent by the level of identification desired, i.e., whether the "unknown" is identified simply as a strain of a particular virus or as a specific strain.

The level of identification desired not only influences the number of criteria to use but also the relative weight that should be given to each criterion. In establishing that the "unknown" is a strain of a particular virus, one should place greatest weight on those criteria that are most specific, i.e., those properties that are changed least by mutation. Although not all virologists agree on the relative weight to give different criteria, no more than minor disagreements should result from the following grouping:

Group I: Chemical and physical properties of the virus particles, serological properties, and response to genetic change in the host.

Group II: Ability to cross protect, stability *in vitro*, general transmission characteristics, and interaction in simultaneous infections.

Group III: Symptomatology and host range.

Strains should be identical or nearly so with respect to the properties in Group I, except for serological properties; strains possess some common antigenic groupings, but they are not necessarily serologically identical. Strains are usually quite similar with respect to the Group II properties, but there is some variability and exceptions may occur. Strains usually, but certainly not always, show some resemblance with respect to Group III properties. Specific strains usually are identified on the basis of properties listed in Group III, although some strains are identified on the basis of transmission characteristics. Judgments based on any one of the more reliable criteria are generally in agreement with those based on any other, but exceptions may be encountered. When this happens, about the only recourse is to apply still other criteria and base the identification on the whole picture.

4–7. VIRUS DESCRIPTIONS AND NAMES

Perhaps the most extensive list of virus names and synonyms is that published by the *Review of Applied Mycology* (Hopkins, 1957). This is a good starting point for tracing descriptions published prior to about 1956. Other starting points are the summarized virus descriptions in the books by Holmes (1939, 1948), Smith (undated, 1957), and Klinkowski (1958). Of value also are publications on viruses (or the diseases they cause) attacking specific crops such as tobacco (Valleau *et al.*, 1954; Wolf, 1957), legumes (Hagedorn and Walker, 1954; Kreitlow *et al.*, 1957; Weiss, 1945a; Zaumeyer and Thomas, 1957), potatoes (Weiss, 1945b), ornamentals (Brierley, 1944, 1945), citrus (Knorr *et al.*, 1957), and stone fruits (U.S. Dept. Agr., 1951).

The relatively few keys that have been published may be of some help in tracing down an identity. Examples are those of Valleau (1940) for tobacco viruses and Weiss (1939) for legume viruses. Tables of chemical and physicochemical properties have been published by Bawden and Pirie (1938), of transmission characteristics and symptoms in differential hosts by Smith (1939), of insect vectors and virus-vector relations by Carter (1962), of serological grouping by Matthews (1957), and of the properties and morphology of viruses with elongated particles by Brandes and Wetter (1959).

The several compilations cited above are useful during all stages of an identification attempt, but the original literature must be consulted before the final decision is made. A compilation may be out of date or otherwise incomplete, and the descriptions given may be too short to permit a precise comparison. More importantly, the original literature must be referred to for information on the exact experimental conditions used by others or for other details that must of necessity be omitted from summarized descriptions.

If an "unknown" is reported as a previously undescribed virus, a full and very detailed description should be given, i.e., all of the properties that can be studied should be reported upon and precise information should be given on the procedures used and the environmental conditions under which the tests were made. It also is important to give the virus a distinctive common name. Reference to a virus simply as "a new virus of beans" or a "new bean mosaic virus" is highly unsatisfactory, for this leaves a virus without a differentiating name under which it can be discussed. Similarly, naming a virus by letter or number is to be avoided; such names tell nothing about the virus and thus provide no point of reference. The most common practice is to combine a host name with one or two words indicating some distinct feature of the virus or of the disease it causes; this practice is probably the best one to follow until a systematic system of nomenclature is accepted. Assignment of a Latin binomial is optional.

4–8. ROUTINE DIAGNOSES

Many plant virologists and plant pathologists are confronted with the task of making occasional or numerous diagnoses of virus-infected plants in the field or greenhouse or of submitted specimens. Obviously it is impossible, or at least impractical, to attempt rigorous identification of all such samples. Fortunately, most of these will be well-known viruses, and an experienced person can usually make reasonably accurate diagnoses without extensive testing. Only the occasional oddity or unusual isolate will require a more elaborate investigation into its identity.

Satisfactory routine diagnosis can sometimes be made on the basis of symptoms in the specimen plant, the identity of the infected plant, where and when it was found, and the experience of the investigator. Where possible, it is highly desirable (and often essential) to obtain confirmatory data by one or more additional methods.

Serological tests are of particular value for routine diagnoses because of their specificity and the speed with which results can be obtained. A strong reaction with a particular antiserum should be all the additional evidence needed to establish a reasonably reliable identification. If the observed symptoms do not agree with the serological diagnosis, then perhaps additional procedures will be needed to determine whether the "unknown" is a mixture of two or more viruses or simply an unusual strain of the virus indicated by the serological test.

Another method of obtaining confirmatory information is the inoculation of a few appropriate indicator plants. The plant species or varieties to use will depend upon the species in which the "unknown" was found, the suspected identity of the "unknown," and other possible identities that must be considered. Most laboratories have a favorite set of test plants or procedures for use in such routine identifications. These are usually chosen on the basis of the viruses likely to be encountered, the reliability of the plant species or procedures under the prevailing conditions, and the extent of the experience of the investigator with the specific plants and procedures. Only a few examples can be given here.

The reaction of a single indicator species is sometimes sufficient for a practical diagnosis. For example, tobacco etch virus appears to be the only one that induces a rapid wilt in Tabasco pepper. Of course, this single test might not detect the presence of a second virus, if present; hence it is best to use several indicator species. As mentioned previously, TMV can be identified by the comparative response of tobacco varieties with and without the N gene from *Nicotiana glutinosa*. Potato virus X can usually be identified on the basis of the strictly local reaction of *Gomphrena globosa* plus the ability of this virus to interact synergistically with potato virus Y in tobacco. Identification of potato virus Y can be based on the local-lesion reaction of USDA seedling 41956, the immunity of *Datura stramonium*, and the synergistic interaction with potato virus X. Tobacco necrosis virus is strongly indicated if a local-lesion response but no systemic infection is induced in a wide range of species. The examples cited are some of the easy ones.

Frequently, identification must be based on the susceptibility or insusceptibility of a number of species as well as the specific symptoms in the susceptible species.

The supplementary information needed for a routine identification also may be provided by a variety of other methods. Identification of the specific vector may provide the needed confirmatory information. If the "unknown" happens to have elongated particles, the needed information may be provided by dipping the cut edge of an infected leaf into a small droplet and examing the droplet by means of an electron microscope. This method has been used for such viruses as tobacco mosaic virus and wheat mosaic virus. The kind of inclusion bodies found in infected cells, or the staining reactions of such bodies, may point to the identity of the virus. Similarly, identification may be confirmed by certain chemical or histochemical tests.

In work with a relatively small group of viruses, as in a survey of the viruses found in a particular crop in a specified area, it often is possible to devise a key that will differentiate among the viruses likely to be encountered. Such a key may be based in part on specific symptoms but also on such things as the susceptibility or insusceptibility of selected species, systemic *vs.* local infection, virus stability, interaction with other viruses, and transmissibility by specified vectors.

A high percentage of routine identifications based on well-chosen testing are likely to be correct. A few erroneous diagnoses are to be expected, particularly with some of the less common viruses. Some of the "errors" may result from failure to detect a mixture; one component may be identified correctly but one or more others may be missed. Aberrant strains of some viruses may also give trouble as may also rare occurrences of viruses in species in which they seldom are found.

4–9. LITERATURE CITED

Babos, P., and Kassanis, B. (1962). Virology **18**, 206.

Bagnall, R. H., Wetter, C., and Larson, R. H. (1959). Phytopathology **49**, 435.

Ball, Ellen Moorhead (1961). Serological Tests for the Identification of Plant Viruses. Amer. Phytopathol. Soc., Ithaca, N. Y. 16 pp.

Bawden, F. C. (1950). Plant Viruses and Virus Diseases. Chronica Botanica Co., Waltham, Mass. 335 pp.

Bawden, F. C., and Kassanis, B. (1941). Ann. Appl. Biol. **28**, 107.

Bawden, F. C., and Kassanis, B. (1945). Ann. Appl. Biol. **32**, 52.

Bawden, F. C., and Kassanis, B. (1947). Ann. Appl. Biol. **34**, 127.

Bawden, F. C., and Pirie, N. W. (1938). Tabulae Biol. **16**, 355.

Bawden, F. C., Pirie, N. W., Bernal, J. D., and Fankuchen, I. (1936). Nature **138**, 1051.

Bennett, C. W. (1949). Phytopathology **39**, 637.

Bennett, C. W. (1953). Advances in Virus Research **1**, 39.

Bercks, R. (1960). Virology **12**, 311.

Black, L. M. (1941). Am. Potato J. **18**, 231.

Bos, L., Hagedorn, D. J., and Quantz, L. (1960). Tijdschr. Plantenziekten **66**, 328.

Brakke, M. K. (1953). Arch. Biochem. Biophys. **45**, 275.

Brakke, M. K. (1955). Arch. Biochem. Biophys. **55**, 175.

Brakke, M. K. (1958). Virology **6**, 96.

Brandes, J. (1957). Nachrbl. Deut. Pflanzenschutzdienst (Braunschweig) **9**, 151.

Brandes, J., and Paul, H. L. (1957). Arch. Mikrobiol. **26**, 358.

Brandes, J., and Wetter, C. (1959). Virology **8**, 99.

Brenner, S., and Horne, R. W. (1959). Biochim. et Biophys. Acta **34**, 103.

Brierley, P. (1944). Plant Disease Reptr. Suppl. **150**, 410.

Brierley, P. (1945). Plant Disease Reptr. Suppl. **158**, 168.

Cadman, C. H. (1962). Nature **193**, 49.

Carter, W. (1962). Insects in Relation to Plant Disease. Interscience, New York and London. 705 pp.

Crick, F. H. C., and Watson, J. D. (1957). In G. E. W. Wolstenholme and Elaine C. P. Millar (eds.), The Nature of Viruses. 5. Churchill, London.

Gold, A. H., Scott, H. A., and McKinney, H. H. (1957). Plant Disease Reptr. **41**, 250.

Hagedorn, D. J., and Walker, J. C. (1954). Wisc. Univ. Research Bull. **185**, 32 pp.

Hollings, M. (1957). Ann. Appl. Biol. **45**, 44.

Hollings, M. (1959). Plant Pathol. **8**, 133.

Holmes, F. O. (1938). Phytopathology **28**, 553.

Holmes, F. O. (1939). Handbook of Phytopathogenic Viruses. Burgess, Minneapolis. 221 pp.

Holmes, F. O. (1941). Phytopathology **31**, 1089.

Holmes, F. O. (1948). "The Filterable Viruses," in Bergey's Manual of Determinative Bacteriology. 6th ed., Suppl. No. 2, Williams and Wilkins, Baltimore.

Holmes, F. O. (1953). Indian Phytopathol. 5 (1952), 8.

Holmes, F. O. (1956). Virology 2, 611.

Holmes, F. O. (1958). Virology 5, 382.

Hopkins, J. C. F. (ed.). (1957). "Common Names of Virus Diseases Used in the Review of Applied Mycology." Review Appl. Mycology 35 (Suppl.), 78 pp.

Johnson, J. (1927). Wisconsin Univ. Agr. Expt. Sta. Res. Bull. 76, 16 pp.

Johnson, J. (1948). Science 108, 122.

Johnson, J., and Grant, T. J. (1932). Phytopathology 22, 741.

Klinkowski, M. (1958). Pflanzliche Virologie Vol. 2, Akademie-Verlag, Berlin.

Knight, C. A. (1955). J. Biol. Chem. 214, 231.

Knight, C. A. (1959). In F. M. Burnet and W. M. Stanley (eds.), The Viruses. 2, 127. Academic Press, New York.

Knorr, L. C., Suit, R. F., and DuCharme, E. P. (1957). Florida Univ. Agr. Expt. Sta. Bull. 587, 157 pp.

Kreitlow, K. W., Boyd, Helen C., Chamberlain, D. W., and Dunleavy, J. M. (1957). Plant Disease Reptr. 41, 579.

Kunkel, L. O. (1934). Phytopathology 24, 437.

Kunkel, L. O. (1955). Advances in Virus Research 3, 251.

Lauffer, M. A. (1952). Sci. Monthly 75, 79.

Lindner, R. C. (1961). Botan. Review 27, 501.

McKinney, H. H. (1929). J. Agr. Research 39, 557.

Macleod, R., and Markham, R. (1963). Virology 19, 190.

McWhorter, F. P. (1941). Stain Technol. 16, 143.

McWhorter, F. P. (1960). In Rept. 4th Annual Dry Bean Research Conf.

Maramorosch, K. (1958). Virology 6, 448.

Markham, R. (1962). Advances in Virus Research 9, 241.

Markham, R., and Smith, J. D. (1950). Biochem. J. 46, 513.

Matthews, R. E. F. (1949). Ann. Appl. Biol. 36, 460.

Matthews, R. E. F. (1957). Plant Virus Serology. Cambridge Univ. Press, Cambridge. 128 pp.

Mayer, A. (1886). Landw. Versuchs-Stat. 32, 451.

Nitzany, F. E., and Friedman, S. (1963). Phytopathology 53, 548.

Niu, C., Shore, V., and Knight, C. A. (1958). Virology 6, 226.

Pollard, E. C. (1953). The Physics of Viruses. Academic Press, New York. 230 pp.

Price, W. C. (1936). Phytopathology 26, 665.

Price, W. C. (1940). Arch. Ges. Virusforsch. 1, 373.

Purdy, Helen A. (1929). J. Expr. Med. 49, 919.

Rochow, W. F. (1954). Ph.D. Thesis, Cornell Univ., Ithaca, N. Y. 81 pp. (Abstr. in Dissertation Abstr. 14, 1890).

Rochow, W. F. (1961). Phytopathology 51, 809.

Ross, A. F. (1959). In Plant Pathology—Problems and Progress, 1908–1958. 511. Univ. Wisconsin Press.

Sänger, H. L., and Brandenburg, E. (1961). Naturwissenschaften 48, 391.

Schachman, H. K., and Williams, R. C. (1959). In F. M. Burnet and W. M. Stanley (eds.), The Viruses. 1, 223. Academic Press, New York.

Schlegel, D. E. (1960). Phytopathology 50, 156.

Schmelzer, K., Bartels, R., and Klinkowski, M. (1960). Phytopathol. Z. 40, 52.

Smith, K. M. (1939). Tabulae Biol. 17, 24.

Smith, K. M. (1950). Research 3, 434.

Smith, K. M. (1951a). Nature 167, 1061.

Smith, K. M. (1951b). Recent Advances in the Study of Plant Viruses. 2d ed. Blakiston, Philadelphia. 300 pp.

Smith, K. M. (1957). A Textbook of Plant Virus Diseases. 2d ed. Little, Brown and Co., Boston. 652 pp.

Smith, K. M. (Undated). Virus Diseases of Farm and Garden Crops. Littlebury, Worcester, England. 111 pp.

Stanley, W. M. (1935). Science 81, 644.

Thomson, A. D. (1958). Nature 181, 1547.

Thomson, A. D. (1961). Virology 13, 262.

Thornberry, H. H. (1961). Proc. 2nd Conf. Intern. Organization Citrus Virol. p. 256. Univ. Florida Press, Gainesville.

Thung, T. H. (1931). Handel. Ned.-Indish Natuurwetensch. Congr. Bandoeng, Java, 450.

United States Department of Agriculture (1951). "Virus Diseases and Other Disorders with Viruslike Symptoms of Stone Fruits in North America." U.S. Dept. Agr. Handb. 10, 276 pp.

Valleau, W. D. (1940). Phytopathology 30, 820.

Valleau, W. D., Johnson, E. M., and Diachun, S. (1954). Ky. Agr. Expt. Sta. Bull. 522, 65 pp.

Weiss, F. (1939). Plant Disease Reptr. 23, 352.

Weiss, F. (1945a). Plant Disease Reptr. Suppl. 154, 32.

Weiss, F. (1945b). Plant Disease Reptr. Suppl. 155, 82.

Wetter, C., Quantz, L., and Brandes, J. (1959). Phytopathol. Z. 35, 201.

Wilkinson, R. E., and Blodgett, F. M. (1948). Phytopathology 38, 28.

Williams, R. C. (1954). Advances in Virus Research 2, 183.

Wingard, S. A. (1928). J. Agr. Research 37, 127.

Wolf, F. A. (1957). Tobacco Diseases and Decays. 2d ed. Duke Univ. Press, Durham, North Carolina. 396 pp.

Yamazaki, H., and Kaesberg, P. (1961a). Nature 191, 96.

Yamazaki, H., and Kaesberg, P. (1961b). Biochim. et Biophys. Acta 51, 9.

Yarwood, C. E., and Sylvester, E. S. (1959). Plant Disease Reptr. 43, 125.

Yarwood, C. E., Resconich, E. C., Ark, P. A., Schlegel, D. E., and Smith, K. M. (1961). Plant Disease Reptr. 45, 85.

Zaumeyer, W. J., and Thomas, H. R. (1957). U.S. Dept. Agr. Techn. Bull. 868, 255 pp.

W. C. PRICE

Strains, mutation, acquired immunity, and interference

5–1. INTRODUCTION

THE SUBJECT matter of this chapter had its beginning in 1926 when McKinney reported the isolation of yellow mosaic viruses from tobacco plants infected with what was presumed to be a pure line of ordinary tobacco mosaic virus (TMV). Years passed, however, before the significance of this observation became fully apparent.

Several reviews have appeared from time to time (Price, 1940a, 1940b; Kunkel, 1947; Bennett, 1951, 1953; Köhler, 1954; Knight, 1959; Ross, 1959; Hitchborn and Thomson, 1960). The student is referred to these reviews for additional details.

5–2. MUTATION

The first law of nature is that "like begets like"; the second law is that "like begets unlike." Viruses obey these two laws with conspicuous regularity. If a virus such as that which causes ordinary tobacco mosaic (now commonly referred to as TMV) is passed by mass transfer from one host plant to another, as usually happens when the virus spreads in nature, the symptoms produced are remarkably constant from one generation of host plants to another. As the virus reproduces in a cell, the bulk of the virus particles produced are exactly "like" their progenitors, in properties as well as

morphology. Once in a while, however, a particle unlike its progenitors appears; the frequency of occurrence of these unlike particles is about 0.5–2% (Kunkel, 1940). These particles remain hidden by the other 98–99.5% of the particles unless an unusual event occurs; they must be separated from the other particles so that they can multiply independently in a separate plant or part of a plant. When this happens, a disease so unlike tobacco mosaic that the average person would not recognize it may be produced; a new strain of TMV has been segregated from the type.

The concept of virus strains is not very old. Between 1924 and 1932, plant viruses were "attenuated" by passing them through resistant host plants (Carsner and Stahl, 1924; Carsner, 1925; Lackey, 1929; Carsner and Lackey, 1928) or by growing them at a high temperature (Johnson, 1926) and were restored to virulence by passing them through susceptible plants (Lackey, 1931, 1932, 1937). The attenuated virus was thought to be qualitatively different. The modern explanation for such attenuation is that the procedures employed to "attenuate" were "unlikely events" that permitted an "unlike" progeny, or strain, to multiply by itself. In terms of classical genetics, it is simply selection of a mutation by the environment.

A. Evidence for Mutation

A mutation, in the sense in which it was used by de Vries (1909) in developing his "Mutation Theory," is a sudden change in a characteristic that breeds true. Modern geneticists recognize a mutation as a specific alteration of a single gene. Modern virologists recognize mutation in a virus particle as a specific alteration in its ribonucleic acid (RNA).

What is the evidence that viruses mutate? This question can best be answered by reviewing some research done with plant viruses during the late 1920's and early 1930's. The evidence consists in showing that a single strain of virus during the course of its reproduction in a susceptible host will give rise to new and different strains of the same virus. To obtain such evidence, it is necessary (a) to show that the virus strain used as starting material is free from all other viruses, and (b) to isolate new strains that can be shown to resemble the original strain in some respects and to differ from it in others. The plant virus literature provides ample evidence of this kind.

McKinney (1926) noted the occurrence of bright yellow spots, 1–5 mm in diameter, in leaves of tobacco plants that had been inoculated 3–6 weeks earlier with an isolate of TMV that appeared to be free of other viruses. He showed that such yellow spots contained a virus that would induce a bright yellow mosaic, strikingly different from ordinary mosaic, in tobacco plants to which it was transmitted. In a subsequent paper, McKinney (1931) reported that yellow spots developed in tobacco plants infected with any of many collections of TMV from various geographical locations and, secondly, that TMV transmitted from 120 single lesions in *Nicotiana rustica* and *N. glutinosa* produced yellow spots, in addition to ordinary green mottling. McKinney (1929) suggested the possibility that viruses may mutate.

Proof for mutation of TMV was supplied by Jensen (1933), who used the local-lesion method of Holmes (1929) to obtain pure strains of the virus (Kunkel, 1934a). It was reasoned that each local lesion was initiated by one virus particle, or at most only a few particles, and that subinoculating from local lesions through 10 successive passages would make it highly probable that virus present in the lesion on the 10th passage would have been derived from a single particle. When such pure strains were transmitted to tobacco, the infected plants produced yellow spots in addition to the ordinary mottling. Jensen concluded that the yellow mosaic viruses present in the yellow spots must have arisen during multiplication of the common strain. Jensen obtained 26 isolates from yellow spots and showed that many of them differed from one another in symptoms they produced; they all resembled TMV in having the same host range and in producing necrotic local lesions in *N. glutinosa*.

The evidence for mutation in TMV has been amplified and extended in further work. Among the techniques used to obtain pure strains of TMV, which could then be tested for ability to mutate, are high dilution (McKinney, 1935; Jensen, 1936), single pin-puncture inoculations, ultrafiltration, partial inactivation with various chemicals (Jensen, 1936), and partial inactivation by high temperature, subfreezing, and exposure to ultraviolet light (McKinney, 1935).

Evidence for mutation of cucumber mosaic virus (CMV) was developed by Price (1934), who showed that CMV transferred through 10 serial passages from necrotic local lesions in cowpea was capable of producing yellow spots in tobacco from which variant strains were isolated. During multiplication of CMV in necrotic local lesions in cowpea, a variant strain that caused a mottling disease in cowpea was obtained. It was concluded that strains of CMV arise by mutation.

B. Permanence of Mutants

Establishment of the fact that viruses mutate led immediately to the fact that variant strains also mutate, giving rise to submutants (Jensen, 1936; McKinney, 1937). How permanent, then, are these mutants and submutants? One attempt to evaluate the differences in mutation rate of four strains of TMV yielded evidence that the rate for some strains may be four times that for others (Kunkel, 1940). In this attempt, however, the only kind of mutant tested for was one capable of producing yellow spots in tobacco plants. Nevertheless, there is presently no reason for believing that some strains mutate with high frequency whereas others mutate with low frequency.

If there is no great difference in rate of mutation among strains, there are, on the other hand, very great differences among strains in ability to survive in more or less pure form. Some of the mutants isolated by Jensen (1936, 1937) were of the localizing type that tended to move with difficulty, or not at all, in tobacco and were difficult to transmit. Obviously, such virus strains have little chance of surviving in nature; as soon as a mutant that moves readily arises, it tends to move to the top of the plant and replace its progenitor. It was Jensen's experience and that of subsequent investigators that some virus strains were impermanent for this very reason.

The ordinary strain of TMV has been found to have greater invasive power in tobacco plants than does any of its mutants (McKinney, 1943). The ordinary strain could therefore be expected to occur in tobacco fields much more frequently than any other strain, since invasiveness of a virus provides high survival value for it. What is often referred to as the ordinary strain is actually a group of strains. Johnson and Valleau (1946) collected 54 isolates of TMV from naturally infected plants in tobacco fields during a 15-year period and compared their symptomatology in 4 tobacco varieties in the field and in the greenhouse. No two of the isolates produced identical symptoms. These workers believe that the number of TMV strains of natural occurrence is practically unlimited.

A virus strain that is more invasive than others for one kind of plant may not be more invasive for another kind. When Johnson (1947) inoculated sea-holly with a field strain of TMV, he invariably was able to recover only an attenuated, or mild, strain from the top of the plant. When inoculations were made with single-lesion pure-line strains that, for all practical purposes, arose from single particles, the severe strain remained localized whereas the mild strain became systemic. Tomato plants, on the contrary, tended to separate a severe strain from a mild strain present in mixtures with which they were inoculated. These observations present a plausible explanation for attenuation of viruses by passage through resistant hosts and restoration of virulence by passage through susceptible hosts (Giddings, 1950).

The many strains of potato virus Y (PVY) collected from field crops of potatoes by Bawden and Kassanis (1947) differed from one another in virulence but remained remarkably permanent with respect to behavior during a 3-year period when they were transmitted to many different plants. Potato virus C, previously shown by Bald and Norris (1945) to be a strain of PVY rarely transmitted by *Myzus persicae,* the most efficient vector of other strains of PVY, was one of the collection. According to Bawden and Kassanis, the most prevalent strains of a virus will be those most easily transmitted.

C. Rate of Mutation

Although the frequency with which virus strains arise has been mentioned in numerous papers and although reports of increased mutation rates occurring at high temperatures have been given (McKinney, 1937; Johnson, 1947), very few studies have been undertaken to determine specific mutation rates. Probably the best method of doing this is to "plate out" virus samples on a local-lesion host and then transfer the virus from a local lesion to another host in which symptomatological differences can be detected. Kunkel (1940) has plated out the sap from a tobacco plant diseased with TMV onto leaves of *Nicotiana glutinosa* and then subinoculated from individual lesions. He reported that about 1 lesion in 200 contained a variant strain if the tobacco plant had been diseased for a short time but that the rate was 1 in 100 or 1 in 50 if the tobacco plant had been diseased for several months. What Kunkel was doing, of course, was measuring the rate at which mutants had accumulated in the total population; only those mutants that could be differentiated by symptomatology on to-bacco were detected. A mutation rate of 1 in 200 might seem very large at first glance though it is not unreasonable when com-pared with mutation rates for Drosophila. On the basis of 5000–10,000 genes present in Drosophila, Muller (1950) calculated that 1 gamete in 20 has a new mutation, the rate being about 1 new mutation in 100,000 genes.

If one accepts Kunkel's estimate of 1 in 200 as the mutation rate for TMV particles and the rate in Drosophila of 1 mutant in 100,000 genes as an estimate of the rate of change of individual loci within the TMV particle, there will be $100,000/200 = 500$ loci within a particle capable of changing in such manner as to result in a new mutant form. If, as has been suggested (Fraenkel-Conrat, 1962), alteration in any one of the 6500 nucleotide units in the TMV-RNA chain, thereby altering the nucleotide se-quence, is sufficient to cause a mutation, many more than 500 mutants of TMV would be possible, since alteration in a single nucleotide unit does not preclude alteration in another unit.

The mutation rate determined by Gowen (1941) for a particular type of change in TMV—from localization in *N. sylvestris* to systemic mottling in *N. sylvestris* and the reverse change from systemic mottling to necrotic local lesions—was about 15×10^{-4}. Actually, this rate seems somewhat high when compared with Kunkel's rate of 50×10^{-4} for any kind of change that could be detected by symptomatology in tobacco; it would allow for only 3 or 4 kinds of mutants in Kunkel's isolations.

D. Characteristics Altered by Mutation

It was suggested by Holmes (1936) that there may be unit differences in a virus particle comparable to genic differences be-tween parts of chromosomes within plants and animals or to differences between sin-gle allelomorphic genes. In comparing de-rivatives from a masked strain of TMV with those from a distorting strain from which the masked strain itself had been derived, he found that ability of a strain to cause yellowing in tobacco plants was in-dependent of its ability to invade the plant.

Yellowing and invasiveness thus may be thought of as independent heritable units. The characteristic of invasiveness, once lost in the mutation from the distorting strain to the masked strain, did not reap-pear in yellow-mosaic type derivatives from the masked strain. Starting with a noninva-sive strain, Jensen's 14, which remains localized in necrotic lesions in tobacco, Norval (1938) obtained 62 derivatives of which 5 were of the distorting green-mosaic type. The factor for noninvasiveness is not identical with the factor for localization. Norval also observed that the ability of a strain to cause tissue destruction in tobacco and tomato plants was not necessarily con-nected with low infectivity and inability to become systemic.

Factors in TMV mutants that vary in-dependently have been listed by Kunkel (1947) as follows: (1) green mottling in tobacco and localizing in *Nicotiana sylves-tris,* (2) yellowing in tobacco and invasive-ness in tobacco, (3) necrosis, localizing, yellowing, and distorting, and (4) green mottling and rate of production of bright yellow spots. On the contrary, the following pairs of characteristics appear to be linked: (1) rate of movement in plants and rate of multiplication, and (2) infectivity and ability to move out of inoculated leaves. Holmes (1952) also found a linkage be-tween infectivity and ability to spread systemically.

In studying about 35 laboratory strains of TMV in comparison with the type, green aucuba, ribgrass, and rosette strains, Price (1954) found evidence for 6 heritable char-acteristics, or factors, that varied indepen-dently; these are (1) ability to cause yel-lowing in Turkish tobacco, (2) localization in *N. sylvestris,* (3) production of ringspots in Turkish tobacco, (4) ability to infect *Phaseolus vulgaris* L., (5) production of large lesions in *N. glutinosa,* and (6) pro-duction of strap leaf in Turkish tobacco. Holmes' factor for invasiveness should prob-ably be added to this list but was not studied in comparison with all 6 of the other factors listed.

Mutation in TMV affects other charac-teristics of the virus besides its ability to induce certain types of symptoms. So far as has been determined, the morphology of the virus is altered little, if at all, even by a series of mutations. One characteristic that has been studied in much detail is amino acid composition. Major differences in amino acid content were found among the 8 strains studied by Knight (1943, 1947); Holmes' ribgrass strain, for example, was found to contain histidine and methionine, which are not present in the other 7 strains. These differences in amino acid content are undoubtedly reflected in the observed differences in isoelectric point (Oster, 1951; Gordon and Price, 1953) and may be responsible, at least in part, for differences among strains in serological reactions (Chester, 1935, 1936; Weaver and Price, 1952). Knight (1947) suggested that, in some cases at least, mutation in TMV involves stepwise changes in amino acid content and that each mutation involves a change in amino acid composition. It has been observed, however, that mutations effecting no appreciable change in amino acid composition nevertheless effect profound changes in symptomatology, and it was pointed out that it is more likely that a mutation in TMV is accompanied by a corresponding alteration in the nucleic acid fraction of the virus and that any changes that occur in amino acid composition are incidental (Price, 1954). It was subsequently shown that there were greater amounts of cytidylic and uridylic acids in digests of the nucleic acid of Holmes' masked strain of TMV than in digests of the nucleic acids of the type strain, Holmes' ribgrass strain, or the yellow aucuba strain (Reddi, 1957, 1959; Knight, 1959). Additional evidence for differences among strains in structure of their nucleic acids will no doubt be obtained when new and better techniques are used to investigate the problem.

E. ARTIFICIAL INDUCTION OF MUTATION

Generally speaking, treatments that are known to induce mutation—treatments such as radiation—are those that also inactivate or kill. If it were possible to start with a virus preparation consisting of essentially one strain, to treat the preparation with a mutagenic agent, and then to show that a large proportion of the virus particles represented mutant forms, proof for the mutagenic action would be available. This is not likely to happen, with our present state of knowledge. It is necessary to start with a preparation that already contains mutant strains, perhaps 1 or 2%, because of the natural mutations that occur during multiplication of the virus. To prove, therefore, that a particular chemical or physical treatment can induce mutation in a plant virus is to prove that the treatment increases the *rate* of mutation. The most convincing way of doing this is to start with two preparations, one treated and one untreated, to plate these preparations out on a host plant in which a large number of strains of the virus are known to produce local lesions, and then to subinoculate from these local lesions to another kind of host plant in which mutant strains can be recognized by the symptoms they produce. The number of such isolations required to be statistically significant will depend upon how much the treatment increases the mutation rate. This procedure was used by Kausche and Stubbe (1939), who reported that 1–2% of the single lesions yielded virus with completely aberrant features, distinct from the type, aucuba mosaic, or yellow mosaic, and that the aberrant types remained constant in serial passage. They concluded that some virus particles are modified by the X-rays. The method was also used by Siegel (1960).

A second method of obtaining evidence for induced mutations in plant viruses is to use a strain that shows no apparent spontaneous mutation during successive local lesion transfers, to treat a leaf shortly after inoculation with this strain, and then to subinoculate from isolated lesions produced subsequently on that leaf. This technique was used by Larson *et al.* (1952) in studies on mutagenic effects of nitrogen mustard on potato virus X.

A third method involves the use of two strains of virus, one of which is localized in a specific host plant and the other of which is systemic. The effect of a specific treatment on the rate of change from localized infection to systemic, and vice versa, can then be compared with the natural rate.

This method was used by Gowen (1941) and by Gierer and Mundry (1958) in studies with X-rays and nitrous acid, respectively.

The most striking effect of exposing TMV to X-rays or to HNO_2 is inactivation, which proceeds exponentially with time. The ratio of the number of local lesions produced by a treated sample of virus in a host (such as bean, N. glutinosa, or Xanthi tobacco) to the number produced by an untreated sample is a measure of the inactivation induced by the treatment. If a part of the treated sample is simultaneously inoculated onto a host plant such as N. sylvestris or Java tobacco, the number of necrotic local lesions on the plant is a measure of the number of a particular type of mutant in the sample. The proportion of mutants in the sample is then the ratio of the number of necrotic lesions in N. sylvestris to the number in bean. Gowen (1941) found that the proportion of local-lesion type mutants increased from 7.9×10^{-4} in the untreated sample to 69.1×10^{-4} in a sample exposed to 490,000 roentgens; for the reverse change, from a local-lesion type to a systemic type, the proportion increased from 14.8×10^{-4} to 88.7×10^{-4} after 1,355,000 roentgens exposure. On the basis of the number of mutations per roentgen per virus particle, the ratios were 1.2×10^{-8} and 5.1×10^{-9}, respectively. These rates may be compared with 3.7×10^{-8} for mutations in Phytomonas stewartii, 1.0×10^{-7} for mutations from wild type genes in Drosophila melanogaster, and 1.2×10^{-8} for mutations from mutant genes in Drosophila.

Gierer and Mundry (1958) treated 1 volume of 0.19% TMV-RNA with 1 volume of 4 M sodium nitrate and 1 volume of 1 M acetate and found the percentage of mutants of the local-lesion type to increase from 0.8 after 1 min of treatment to 15.5 after 96 min. They concluded that the alteration of individual bases of the ribonucleic acid molecule in vitro is mutagenic.

Bawden (1959) very properly raised the question whether results of Gierer and Mundry might not equally well be interpreted on the basis of selection of mutants from a mixture; his comments apply also to the results of Gowen. When a mixture containing TMV and a small quantity of aucuba mosaic virus is rubbed over leaves of N. glutinosa and N. sylvestris, the ratio of the number of necrotic lesions produced in N. sylvestris to the total number produced in N. glutinosa will increase with increasing dilutions of the mixture used for inoculation. This is so because the TMV, being more invasive in N. sylvestris, interferes with the production of necrotic lesions by the aucuba mosaic virus that happens to be present. Therefore, the apparent rate of mutation from a systemic type virus strain to a local-lesion type is increased as the dilution factor is increased.

There are other sources of error in interpreting results such as those presented by Gowen and by Gierer and Mundry. One of these resides in the fact that the assay of the total virus remaining active after a specific treatment is made on one kind of host plant whereas assay of mutants remaining active is made on another kind. Any inaccuracies in assay on either host plant is compounded with those on the other. Moreover, it has been shown (Miller and Stanley, 1942) that certain treatments may reduce the infectivity for one kind of host plant much more drastically than it does for another. Another possible source of error may lie in assumptions regarding the nature of infection. If infection can be induced by single virus particles then calculating ratios of numbers of infections by mutant particles to numbers of infections by all particles may be an accurate means of calculating mutation rates. But Kleczkowski (1950) insists that individual areas of a leaf may vary in susceptibility to infection in such manner that different doses of virus are required to infect them. If this be so, presence of small numbers of mutant particles in a mixture could be obscured because, although present in the infection site, they would have little chance of being expressed. Finally, the possibility that inactive virus present in a treated preparation can interfere differentially with infection by active particles remaining in the preparation cannot be completely ruled out.

Despite the valid objections mentioned above, the weight of available evidence favors the conclusion that mutation in TMV can be induced by treatment with nitrous acid. For one thing, the increase in apparent mutation rate is much too large to be accounted for on the basis of interference (Mundry, 1959). For another, Siegel (1960) treated a TMV preparation with nitrous acid, plated it out by inoculating leaves of *N. glutinosa,* and then subinoculated from individual lesions to small tobacco plants to detect presence of mutants. From 154 such individual lesions, 42 mutants were obtained. Conversely, from 105 individual lesions produced on *N. glutinosa* by the control preparation of TMV, only 2 mutants were obtained. Treatment with nitrous acid increased the apparent mutation rate more than 14-fold on the average.

There is evidence also that nitrogen mustard induces mutations in potato virus X when infected leaves are exposed to its vapors, though not when the virus is exposed *in vitro* (Larson *et al.,* 1952). On the other hand, as many as 70% of the amino groups of TMV can be covered with either acetyl, phenylureido, carbobenzoxy, *p*-chlorobenzoyl, or benzenesulfonyl groups without apparent change in infectivity or genetic characteristics of the virus particle; also, 20–40% of the phenol plus indole groups can be similarly covered with similar results (Miller and Stanley, 1941a,b, 1942).

5–3. HYBRIDIZATION

If it could be shown that 2 strains of a plant virus undergo hybridization while multiplying in the same host cell, additional information about the method of reproduction of plant viruses would be provided. Evidence for hybridization presented in the literature is not convincing.

Evidence for hybridization of strains of tomato spotted wilt virus has been published by Best (1954, 1962) and by Best and Gallus (1955), for hybridization of potato virus Y by Watson (1960) and by Thomson (1961), and for hybridization of TMV by Sukhov (1956). In all these cases, the evidence consisted in introducing 2 different strains into a host plant simultaneously, allowing sufficient time for muliplication to occur, and then isolating from the infected plant new strains that have some of the characteristics of each of the 2 strains

with which the experiment was started. Best postulated that there is a transfer of "character determinants" from each of the parents to the progeny during multiplication. Thomson concluded that whereas hybridization—a transfer of character determinants—is a possibility, the evidence is inadequate to prove that genetic recombination actually does take place.

Actually, it is not difficult to duplicate the kind of results mentioned above with 2 strains of TMV reproducing separately in different plants. The aucuba mosaic strain differs from the ordinary strain in at least two respects, or characters; it produces local lesions in *N. sylvestris* in contrast to systemic mottling and it produces yellow mottling in Turkish tobacco in contrast to green mottling. One can inoculate tobacco plants with a single-lesion isolate of the ordinary strain and subsequently look for bright yellow spots on systemically affected leaves. From some of these yellow spots, one can isolate a strain that will produce bright yellow mosaic in Turkish tobacco, like the mosaic produced by the aucuba mosaic strain, but that will become systemic in *N. sylvestris,* as does the ordinary strain. Of the two characters, invasiveness in *N. sylvestris* and yellowing in tobacco, one is possessed by ordinary TMV and the other by aucuba mosaic virus. Essentially the same strain can be derived if one starts with a single-lesion isolate of aucuba mosaic virus and looks for a mutant that becomes systemic in *N. sylvestris.* Other pairs of strains of TMV with other pairs of characters could be selected for the demonstration. The simple explanation for the new strain is mutation, not hybridization. Consequently, an essential part of the evidence for the theory proposed by Best is that strains possessing the particular characters under investigation cannot be isolated from a single-lesion strain of PVX or spotted wilt virus during its multiplication in an infected plant. This has not been demonstrated despite the fact that such strains were not found.

It has been reported (Sukhov, 1958) that a new strain of PVX, more virulent than the ordinary strain, was obtained by inoculating tobacco leaves simultaneously with PVX and TMV and that the phenomenon occurs only when there is simultaneous infection with two viruses that are not closely related.

5–4. STRAINS

The strains of plant viruses found in nature can be divided into groups according to their serological, immunological, and physical properties. Generally speaking, the differences among strains within groups are minor compared with the differences among groups. In the next few pages, I shall show how strains resemble one another, how they differ, and how they may be identified as belonging to one or another group; I shall list some naturally occurring strains and some experimentally isolated ones, and, finally, I shall show how strains can be useful.

A. SIMILARITIES AND DIFFERENCES AMONG STRAINS

Strains of a virus resemble one another in host range, symptomatology, physical properties, chemical composition, serological reactions, and particle morphology. They also differ from one another in these various ways. The differences among strains are, however, generally smaller than the differences among different viruses. Apparent differences in physical properties may not be real, because such properties as thermostability are influenced by virus concentration, by pH of the solution, and by presence of normal constituents of sap. Moreover, evidence has recently been obtained that some strains exist in an unstable form (Köhler, 1956; Cadman and Harrison, 1959; Babos and Kassanis, 1962). Babos and Kassanis suggested that the instability may be due to lack of a full complement of protective protein, or to its absence, so that the strain may be present in sap in the form of nucleic acid.

Differences in virulence, or severity of symptoms produced, have been found among strains of sugar-beet curly-top virus (Carsner and Stahl, 1924; Carsner, 1925; Carsner and Lackey, 1928; Lackey, 1929, 1931; Giddings, 1938, 1944), TMV (McKinney, 1926, 1929; Jensen, 1933), potato virus X (Smith, 1929; Salaman, 1933;

Böhme, 1933), potato virus Y (Böhme, 1933), potato yellow dwarf virus (Black, 1940), sugar-cane mosaic virus (Summers, 1936, 1939), tomato spotted wilt virus (Norris, 1943, 1946), apple mosaic virus (Posnette and Cropley, 1952, 1956), tristeza virus of citrus (Grant and Costa, 1951), and many other viruses.

Generally speaking, mutation of a virus does not involve an apparent change in particle morphology (Knight, 1942; Takahashi and Rawlins, 1946, 1947) despite profound changes in chemical composition (Knight, 1947, 1959). Plant viruses differ in their serological affinities (Beale, 1934; Birkeland, 1934; Chester, 1935, 1936) thus making serology a useful tool for identification and classification of viruses. The cross-absorption technique was used by Chester (1936) to demonstrate serological differences among strains of the same virus. Strains also differ in the amount of virus required to reach equivalence with antiserum in precipitin tests (Kleczkowski, 1941) and in antiserum dilution end points and in the weight of virus required to react optimally with specific immune serum (Weaver and Price, 1952). In a series of sequential mutations from TMV, it was found that each mutation involved a small change in antigenic properties, a change that was retained in subsequent mutants in the series (Aach, 1957). These changes in antigenic properties were not correlated with changes in tyrosine and tryptophane content (Aach, 1958).

Strains of plant viruses have been found to differ in insect vector relationships, some being transmitted by a different species of insect and others being vectorless (Black, 1941, 1958; Bruehl, 1958; Rochow, 1958; Watson and Mulligan, 1960).

The amino acid composition of 8 strains of TMV was investigated by Knight (1947), who found substantial differences among them; the rib-grass strain, for example, contains histidine and methionine, which are absent from the other 7 strains. Preliminary work by Reddi (1957, 1959), Knight (1959), and Knight *et al.* (1962) indicates that strains of virus differ slightly in structure of their nucleic acids.

Since strains of a plant virus may differ

in their amino acid composition, it is to be expected that they differ in the charge carried on the surface of their particles and, therefore, in their isoelectric points. Such differences in isoelectric points have been found (Friedrich-Freksa *et al.*, 1946; Kahler and Woods, 1949; Singer *et al.*, 1951; Miller *et al.*, 1951; Gordon and Price, 1953). Ginosa and Atkinson (1955) have reported differences in ultraviolet absorption spectra of strains of TMV, reflecting in some cases differences in tyrosine, tryptophane, and histidine contents.

Strains differ in ability to multiply in host tissue at high temperature (Holmes, 1934). Finally, strains differ in their productivity —in the apparent concentration of virus they produce while multiplying in a local-lesion host (Veldee and Fraenkel-Conrat, 1962).

B. Identification of Strains

When one virus is known to have been derived from another, there is no question that the two are closely related strains. When, however, the origin of neither one of the two is known—when they are found occurring naturally—the question of what criteria should be used to establish their relationship may well be asked. This question will be answered by considering two papers that deal with the relationship between TMV and cucumber viruses 3 and 4. The latter two viruses were first described by Ainsworth (1935) and the similarities of their chemical and physical properties to those of TMV were pointed out by Bawden and Pirie (1937).

In discussing the question of relationship, Knight (1955) summarized seven commonly accepted criteria for establishing the relationship among strains and proposed three new criteria. In recapitulating these criteria here, I will also indicate how they can be applied to the question of relationship between TMV and CV 3–4.

1. *Similarity in host range.*—TMV has a wide host range, including some cucurbits in which it gives localized infection only, whereas CV 3–4 seems ordinarily to be restricted to the Cucurbitaceae.

2. *Similarity in chemical and physical properties.*—Both TMV and CV 3–4 are highly resistant to heat, aging, and certain chemicals. Both consist of 94% protein and 6% nucleic acid. Some other viruses, such as tobacco necrosis virus, have equally high thermal inactivation points but no other plant virus is known to denature with such high energies of activation, of the order of 150,000 cal/mole (Price, 1940; Lauffer and Price, 1940).

3. *Identical particle morphology.*—According to Knight, both viruses are rigid rods 15×300 mμ, though X-ray data suggest that CV 3–4 has a slightly smaller diameter, about 14.6 mμ. More recent work (Franklin *et al.*, 1959) reveals, however, that the maximum diameter is the same (18 mμ) but that the weight of the protein in the outer part of the CV 4 rod is considerably less than in the TMV rod and that the structure of CV 4 is as similar to that of TMV as to that of any of the other strains of TMV investigated.

4. *Cross protection.*—R. W. Fulton (1950) failed to demonstrate cross protection between CV 3–4 and TMV in cotyledons of cucumber, but Rochow (1956) subsequently showed that such cotyledons when heavily inoculated with CV 3–4 were almost completely refractory to infection by TMV after 11 days.

5. *Cross serological reactions.*—A cross serological reaction between CV 3–4 and TMV has been demonstrated (Bawden and Pirie, 1937; Knight and Stanley, 1941), but the reaction is considerably weaker than that between certain closely related strains of TMV.

6. *Response to a genetic change in a host.* —This criterion has not been applied to CV 3–4 and TMV.

7. *Method of transmission.*—Both viruses are transmitted by mechanical means; no true insect vectors are known for either. TMV is reported to be transmitted by a grasshopper in a mechanical manner (Walters, 1952).

8. *Nucleic acid composition.*—The nucleic acid composition of CV 3–4 is distinctly different from that of 16 tested strains of TMV.

9. *Number and termination of peptide chains.*—CV 3–4 have alanine (or serine) at the terminal ends of their peptide chains

whereas TMV has threonine. The number of peptide chains in the two viruses is also quite different.

10. *Any outstanding feature of chemical composition common to many strains.*—CV 3–4 contain no cysteine, no sulfur-containing amino acids, in contrast to TMV.

Despite the similarities between CV 3–4 and TMV, Knight considers the differences to be sufficient to conclude that neither CV 3 nor CV 4 is a strain of TMV. Rochow (1956) and Markham (1959), in contrast, consider the cross-protection reaction, combined with other similarities, sufficiently important to identify CV 3 and CV 4 as strains of TMV. There is no doubt that the relationship, if it exists, is not so close as that for other strains of TMV.

There is no single criterion that will enable an investigator to decide whether one virus is a strain of another. Several lines of evidence must be brought to bear on the question, and even then the decision may depend upon whether the investigator is a "lumper" or a "splitter."

C. Naturally Occurring Strains

The number of strains found in nature is extremely large and increases almost daily. Only a few need be mentioned to give some idea of the range of their occurrence.

Cucumber mosaic virus. Some naturally occurring diseases that have been identified as being caused, wholly or in part, by strains of CMV are southern celery mosaic (Wellman, 1934; Price, 1935b), lily mosaic (Ogilvie, 1928; Price, 1937; Ainsworth, 1938; Brierley, 1939), lima bean mosaic (Holmes, 1939), tulip mosaic (Ainsworth, 1938; McWhorter, 1938), a mosaic of hyacinth (Ainsworth, 1938), and a mosaic of pea and a mosaic of pea and bean (Whipple and Walker, 1941).

Tobacco mosaic virus. Strains of TMV have been found causing economically important, or otherwise interesting, diseases of various plants. Some diseases involving strains of TMV are aucuba mosaic of tomato (J. H. Smith, 1928; Kunkel, 1934a), enation mosaic of tomato (Ainsworth, 1937); mosaic of rib-grass (Holmes, 1941); tomato single-virus streak (Jarrett, 1930); cucurbit mosaic caused by CV 3 and CV 4

(Ainsworth, 1935; Bawden and Pirie, 1937; see also the discussion in section 5–4-B); a mosaic of cowpea and bean in Nigeria (Lister and Thresh, 1955), and a mosaic of sann hemp in India (Capoor, 1950) caused by strains of TMV (Bawden, 1956).

Tomato spotted wilt virus. The tipblight disease of tomato, which occurs in the Pacific Northwest, has been identified as due to a strain of tomato spotted wilt virus (McWhorter and Milbrath, 1938; Milbrath, 1939; Norris, 1943). Peach yellow bud mosaic has been shown to be caused by a strain of tomato ringspot virus (Thomas and Rawlins, 1951; Yarwood, 1956; Cadman and Lister, 1961).

Aster yellows virus. A strain of aster yellows virus has been shown to cause western celery yellows (Severin, 1929; Kunkel, 1932).

Peach yellows virus. Little peach disease is caused by a strain of the virus that causes peach yellows (Kunkel, 1936).

Alfalfa mosaic virus. Potato calico was demonstrated to be caused by a strain of alfalfa mosaic virus (Black and Price, 1940).

In addition to the strains enumerated above, numerous other strains differing from the type in symptoms they produce in a common host, in host range, or in other ways have been reported to occur naturally. As an example, natural occurrence of strains of PVX has been reported by Bawden and Sheffield (1944), Clinch (1944), Cockerham (1954), Ross and Köhler (1953), Salaman (1938), Johnson (1925), and Köhler (1937). To list all these strains, or a substantial number of them, would serve no useful purpose in this paper.

D. Useful Strains

Generally, strains of virus have not been useful to the growers of agricultural crops. On the other hand, some strains have been very useful to the experimentalist whose business it is to explore the nature of viruses and the diseases they cause. For this purpose, one of the most useful types of strains is one that can be used in cross-protection tests to ascertain relationships.

The indicator strain of CMV was isolated from a bright yellow spot on a tobacco plant infected with ordinary CMV (Price, 1934). Its most useful property is that it produces necrotic local lesions in zinnia whereas most strains of the virus produce mottling symptoms. When inoculated with the indicator strain, zinnia leaves mottled as a result of previous infection by CMV do not develop lesions but those mottled as a result of previous infection by other viruses, such as TMV, do develop lesions (Price 1935a). The indicator strain, consequently, has been used by many investigators to identify viruses suspected of being strains of CMV (Price, 1935a, 1937, 1941; Whipple and Walker, 1941; Faan and Johnson, 1951).

The aucuba mosaic strain of TMV was found occurring in nature (Bewley, 1934). Kunkel (1934b) showed that leaves of *N. sylvestris* mottled by ordinary strains of TMV did not produce necrotic local lesions when inoculated with the aucuba mosaic strain whereas previously noninfected leaves did. The aucuba strain has subsequently been used in many laboratories as an aid in identifying strains of TMV.

In a similar way, a necrotic local-lesion producing strain of bean yellow mosaic virus, isolated from pea by Hagedorn and Walker (1950), was shown by Corbett (1957) to produce necrotic local lesions in *Crotalaria spectabilis* and was used by him in cross-protection tests to identify other strains of the virus.

Strains are useful in another, quite different, way. By studying the similarities and differences among strains, we have learned much about the relationships between the chemical make-up of viruses and their biological activities. A large amount of research on the chemistry of TMV has been summarized by Knight (1959) and need not be repeated here. The excellent early research on the protein part of the particle failed to give much insight into the genetics and method of reproduction of TMV because, as has only recently been learned, it is not the protein but the nucleic acid part of the particle that controls these functions. Only a beginning has been made in research on the nucleic acid fraction, but already there is reason to believe that such research will be very illuminating.

5–5. ACQUIRED IMMUNITY

Acquired immunity is defined here as increased resistance to a disease resulting from previous infection by the pathogenic agent, or one of its strains. This definition is in conformity with general concepts of acquired immunity during the preceding half-century or more (Jordan, 1908; Buchanan and Murray, 1916; Conn and Conn, 1926; Taliaferro, 1929; Topley, 1933; Zinnser *et al.*, 1939; Rivers, (1948). It should be noted that the definition does not specify any particular mechanism for the increased resistance and that it does not require the individual to be immune from infection by the pathogenic agent.

Much of the controversy during the past 30 years about acquired immunity from plant virus diseases is due not to controversy about the facts that have been reported but rather to disagreement about terminology. What is more important is that this controversy contributes in no small way to misunderstanding about the significance of cross-protection tests as aids in identifying and classifying viruses.

Of recent years, there has been a tendency to distinguish between acquired immunity associated with humoral antibodies and a phenomenon known as interference. A very good review of interference among animal viruses has been given by Schlesinger (1959). According to Schlesinger, interference is involved when one virus so modifies cells of a host that a second virus, or even a closely related strain of the first virus, cannot multiply normally or cannot produce characteristic injury. Henle (1950) restricted the term interference to the inhibitory effect of one virus, or a component of it, upon propagation of another. In reviewing the literature, Bennett (1951) used the term interference in the sense of Schlesinger but also recognized that there might be a basic difference between the interference between two closely related strains of a plant virus and that between unrelated viruses.

In this paper, the term interference will have a more restricted meaning than given to it by either Schlesinger, Henle, or Bennett. It will be used in those instances in which one virus interferes either with the multiplication of a second unrelated virus or with its disease-producing capabilities. The basic difference between cross protection and interference lies in the fact that the former is specific and the latter nonspecific, and in the fact that either of 2 closely related viruses will protect against the other, provided a suitable host system can be found to demonstrate the protection, whereas interference between two unrelated viruses is in one direction only.

In a review paper (Price, 1940b), I classified acquired immunity into three types: the chronic-disease type, the carrier type, and the sterile type. In the chronic-disease type, the individual becomes immune from a severe type of disease but suffers from a chronic mild one. In the carrier type, the pathogenic agent is retained but obvious manifestations of disease disappear, or never appear. In the sterile type, the agent, as well as the disease, disappears. It was pointed out that the three types are not demarcated sharply but intergrade.

Acquired immunity from plant virus diseases can also be classified in another way, into the immunity following recovery from disease and cross immunity, or cross protection, in which infection with one strain of a virus confers protection against another strain. It will be convenient to use this classification in the discussion that follows.

A. Acquired Immunity Following Recovery from Disease

It is difficult to compare, or to contrast, virus infections in higher plants with those in vertebrate animals because of the vast differences in the structural organization of these divergent groups of organisms. Differentiation of cells and tissues is much more complicated in the animal than in the plant. Moreover, there is no circulatory system in plants comparable to that in animals. The plant's defense mechanisms against infection are less complex and less extensive than those of the animal; plants have no humoral antibodies nor do they possess specialized cells that can move through the vascular system to defend against an infection. Recovery from a disease takes a different form in plants from that in animals. A plant continues to grow from meristematic tissues, expanding in girth but producing new shoots from terminal or axillary buds.

Poliomyelitis is commonly a mild upper respiratory or gastro-intestinal disease, but in a small proportion of infections it is a paralytic disease involving neurons in the central nervous system (Howe, 1948). The patient may recover from poliomyelitis but be left with flaccid paralysis of skeletal muscles; the damaged neurons are not regenerated. Paralytic poliomyelitis is perhaps an extreme example, but many other virus infections of man leave their marks upon him and he seldom escapes a severe disease completely unscathed.

The cells of a leaf that are killed by a virus infection are not regenerated either. The leaf may fall off while new leaves are being produced from one or more growing points. It is true that the mottling produced by a virus in a leaf may fade but this is more of an aging phenomenon than a recovery; the distortion resulting from unequal growth and maturation of leaf cells usually remains. Recovery of a plant from a virus disease is brought about by production of new shoots with milder symptoms. In some cases, these shoots may have outgrown the virus and are essentially healthy; in other cases, they retain the virus. It is the latter cases that constitute the subject matter of this section.

Virus diseases from which plants recover and acquire immunity are tobacco ringspot (Wingard, 1928), tomato ringspot (Price, 1936b), Bergerac ringspot of tobacco (Smith, 1937), sugar-beet curly-top in tobacco and tomato (Lesley and Wallace, 1938) and in water pimpernel (Bennett, 1955), potato yellow dwarf (Black, 1937), and dodder latent mosaic (Bennett, 1949). Since the phenomenon of acquired immunity has been studied more extensively in tobacco ringspot than in the other diseases mentioned, this disease will be considered as a type and the others will be described only briefly.

Tobacco ringspot. Tobacco ringspot virus has a wide natural host range and has been transmitted experimentally to many species in a large number of families of flowering plants. Not all these species show the recovery phenomenon but many of them do. In tobacco, a ringspot type of local lesion develops on inoculated leaves in about 3 days and a similar type of systemic lesion appears on young leaves at the tip of the plants in 6 or 7 days. The systemic lesions cover the entire leaf, but in 12–35 or more days the new leaves that appear develop lesions in their apical portions, leaving the basal portions symptomless or nearly so. A wavy necrotic line resembling the outline of an oak leaf separates the two portions. Finally, leaves appear that are completely free of necrotic lesions, and all subsequently developed leaves are of this type. The plants have now recovered from the ringspot disease (Wingard, 1928; Henderson and Wingard, 1931; Price, 1932), though some plant virologists prefer to say that the disease has passed from the acute phase to the chronic phase (Valleau, 1935, 1941; McKinney, 1941a; McKinney and

nomenon, Wingard (1928) pointed out that leaves that had recovered were not always entirely free from symptoms; they were thicker, had a more leathery texture, and sometimes developed chlorosis or necrosis along their edges. Valleau (1941) found that this sort of chlorosis and necrosis was the rule for 5 strains of tobacco ringspot virus when recovered plants were grown at a temperature of 20°C, but that nearly normal growth occurred at 26°C. Henderson (1934) found that necrotic lesions did not develop on inoculated leaves when plants were held at temperatures above 34°C but did develop when the plants were returned to more normal temperature; this was confirmed by Benda and Naylor (1957).

Leaves from plants that have recovered from the ringspot disease contain active virus (Wingard, 1928) but in amounts only 10–20% of that in leaves having acute symptoms (Price, 1936; Stanley, 1939).

Fig. 5–1. Plants of *Nicotiana sylvestris* grown from cuttings. Left, from a plant that had recovered from tobacco ringspot. Center and right, from healthy plants. The plant on the left and the one in the center were inoculated with yellow ringspot virus one month before the photograph was taken; the plant on the right was not inoculated. Photograph by J. A. Carlile. (After Price, 1936b.)

Clayton, 1944). The duration of the acute stage depends upon the age of the plant at the time of infection, growth rate of the plant, and environmental conditions; some plants may flower and die before recovering (McKinney and Clayton, 1944). In his original description of the recovery phe-

This limitation on the concentration of virus in recovered leaves is very sharp; the basal, lesion-free, half of leaves with oak-leaf patterns also have only 10–20% of the virus content of the apical, lesion-bearing half, but there is no difference in virus content between apical and basal halves of either leaves with lesions or recovered leaves (Price, 1936a). Fulton (1949) found this virus concentration differential to hold, however, only for Xanthia tobacco; in Havana 38 about the same amount of virus was present in recovered leaves as in acutely diseased leaves. He reported also that the virus content of leaves of both Havana 38 and Xanthia tobacco recovered from tobacco streak disease was as high as, or even higher than, that in acutely diseased leaves.

Recovered leaves do not develop lesions when inoculated with one or another strain of the ringspot virus (Wingard, 1928; Price, 1932, 1936b) but do develop symptoms when inoculated with unrelated viruses (Price, 1936b). There are exceptions to the statement made above; when plants recovered from the disease produced by the Wingard strain of ringspot were inoculated with Valleau's yellow ringspot virus, they developed yellow lesions, sometimes with necrotic edges, 10 days after inoculation and systemic yellow lesions 40 days after, both types of symptoms being much delayed (Fig. 5–1).

The strain of tobacco ringspot virus used by Wingard and subsequently by Price is apparently not seed transmitted (Priode, 1928; Henderson and Wingard, 1931), but the strains studied by Valleau are seed transmitted to the extent of about 17% (Valleau, 1932). Valleau (1932, 1941) points out that various strains of the virus cause a large amount of pollen sterility in tobacco plants that recover before flowering. When the virus is transmitted through seed, the seedlings show symptoms characteristic of the chronic stage rather than the acute stage (Valleau, 1932, 1941).

Plants that have recovered from ringspot may be kept small and in an active state by growing them from cuttings; it is difficult to distinguish them from plants grown from cuttings of healthy plants. When grown from cuttings for more than a year, such plants retain the virus and do not develop acute symptoms (Henderson and Wingard, 1931; Price, 1932).

Wingard (1928) observed that shoots produced from axillary buds of recovered plants developed typical ringspot symptoms in a few instances, and this has been confirmed by Valleau (1941). Hitchborn (1957) found that the Wingard strain of tobacco ringspot virus would not multiply in tobacco plants kept at 36°C. Another strain, obtained from G. S. Pound, multiplied at this temperature without producing typical symptoms; when returned to a greenhouse, the plants developed both local and systemic symptoms within 4 days. Benda and Naylor (1958) were able to free recovered tissue from ringspot virus by keeping plants at a minimum temperature of 35°C for 10 days. When returned to lower temperatures, the new shoots developed typical symptoms from which they subsequently recovered; one plant went through a cycle of symptoms and recovery three times as a result of alternating temperatures. Leaves that were without symptoms when placed at the high temperature developed necrotic ring and line patterns when returned to the greenhouse 10 days later; freeing them from the virus rendered them susceptible to attack by the disease.

Tomato ringspot, Bergerac ringspot of tobacco, and tobacco streak. None of these diseases has been studied so extensively as has tobacco ringspot. Tomato ringspot virus has been differentiated from tobacco ringspot virus not only by cross-protection tests (Price, 1936b) but also by serological tests (Tall *et al.*, 1949). Bergerac ringspot virus has been differentiated from the other two on the basis of symptomatology, properties, and cross protection (Smith, 1937, p. 285–89). Tobacco streak virus has been differentiated from all 3 of the others by symptomatology, properties, and cross protection (Johnson, 1936, 1937). Recovery from tomato ringspot, Bergerac ringspot, and tobacco streak is similar to that from tobacco ringspot. The immunity that follows is specific; symptoms can be produced in recovered leaves by inoculating them with any one of a number of viruses not related to that from which the plant has recovered.

Potato yellow dwarf. The recovery of potato plants from yellow dwarf takes place by growth from axillary buds; the new shoots bear chronic symptoms of the disease. Plants may be grown from cuttings of such shoots through at least 5 vegetative generations without again developing acute symptoms (Black, 1937).

Dodder latent mosaic. Recovery of plants from dodder latent mosaic was studied by Bennett (1949) in sugar beet, pokeweed, cantaloupe, celery, tomato, and potato. The virus content of recovered plants was found to be extremely low—of the order of 5% or less—in recovered plants as compared with recently infected plants. A similar reduction in virus content was found in symptomless carriers, such as Turkish tobacco. When tomato plants that had recovered from dodder latent mosaic were inoculated with either tobacco mosaic or tobacco etch viruses, the dodder latent mosaic virus concentration increased in them to levels approximating those in recently infected plants and symptoms of dodder latent mosaic reappeared on them. Bennett suggested that the critical factor in recovery is control of virus multiplication and that this control was broken by infecting the plants with a second virus.

Sugar-beet curly-top in tomato, tobacco, and water pimpernel. About 10–20% of plants of certain races of tomato infected with sugar-beet curly-top virus recover from the disease by production of shoots from axillary buds (Leslie and Wallace, 1938). Tobacco plants infected with curly-top virus also recover from the disease; the new growth appears healthy or develops only mild symptoms (Bennett and Esau, 1936; Wallace, 1939). Water pimpernel infected with any one of several strains of curly-top virus of different degrees of virulence recover from the induced disease (Bennett, 1955). Recovery of these plants from curly top is accompanied by retention of virus but it is not known whether or not the virus is present in reduced concentration. When recovered plants of water pimpernel were inoculated with a more severe strain of the virus they developed symptoms of the severe strains, indicating either a low degree of protection or no protection at all (Bennett, 1955).

Mechanism of immunity following recovery. Attempts to elucidate the mechanism of recovery and subsequent immunity have not been very successful. There are good reasons for believing that the recovery phase is initiated when the virus parasitizes embryonic tissues of the host (Price, 1940a). Benda and Naylor (1954) conclude that the mechanism of recovery of a leaf from tobacco ringspot is within the leaf itself; in other words, recovery does not depend upon development of symptoms in roots, stems, or other leaves. This is in conformity with the observation that inoculated plants may pass into the recovered stage without developing necrotic symptoms if the leaves that would be expected to develop such symptoms are removed when small (Price, 1932). The type of local and systemic lesions is modified by the environment (Price, 1932; Benda and Naylor, 1957). It has been suggested (Valleau, 1941) that embryonic cells do not develop virus-precursor materials in the quantity that cells of mature leaves do and that this accounts for the lower virus content of recovered leaves. Even though there were evidence for specific virus precursors in cells, one would still have to ask why infected cells do not continue to produce such materials as they mature and thereby provide a substrate for virus multiplication. Now that the ribonucleic acid portion of the virus is known to be the essential part for reproduction (Gierer and Schramm, 1956; Fraenkel-Conrat, 1956; Fraenkel-Conrat *et al.*, 1957), one might speculate that about 80% of the tobacco ringspot RNA formed during multiplication in embryonic cells is of an aberrant type that leads neither to infectiousness nor to fully developed virus particles.

There is no reason for believing that immunity following recovery from plant virus diseases is due to antibody formation. Protective substances are not transported across a graft union in sufficient concentration to modify the course of the disease (Price, 1932) nor are they transmitted by means of dodder (Bennett, 1955). When curly top was transmitted by means of grafts from recovered plants, a mild disease usually resulted whereas the insect vector transmitted a severe disease from similar recovered plants. This led Wallace (1940) to suggest that antibodies were also transmitted by grafting whereas the insect vector transmitted only the virus. It was subsequently shown, however, that the severity of the disease resulting from insect transmission depended upon whether the insect fed upon tissues near the growing point of the healthy plant or upon tissues farther down the stem (Price, 1943). Attempts to demonstrate specific neutralizing antibodies by fractionating the sap from recovered plants and reacting it with sap from diseased plants have been unsuccessful (Price, 1940c).

B. Cross Protection

It was reported by McKinney (1929), by Thung (1931), and by Caldwell (1935) that tobacco plants infected with a green mosaic virus developed no further symptoms when inoculated with a yellow mosaic virus. Thung and Caldwell were unable to isolate the second virus from doubly inoculated plants, suggesting that little or no multiplication had occurred. Salaman (1933) found that tobacco plants that had been infected with a mild strain of PVX for as little as 5 days were solidly immune from a more virulent strain of X virus but not from PVY or TMV. He reported later (1936) that the immunity was not complete, the more virulent virus having infected the plant and produced an occasional systemic yellow spot; he recognized that the induced immunity is cellular rather than humoral.

The phenomenon referred to here as cross protection has been given various names: premunity (Quanjer, 1942), antagonism (McKinney, 1941a), and interference (Bennett, 1951).

The system set up by Kunkel (1934b) to demonstrate cross protection is classic and became the basis for many successful applications of cross-protection tests in identifying strains of virus. Recognizing that cross immunity is relative, he used as the challenge virus one that would produce local lesions and thereby give a quantitative measure of the extent of infection; this was the aucuba mosaic strain of TMV, which produces local lesions on *Nicotiana sylvestris*. Mature leaves mottled by TMV were refractory to infection by aucuba mosaic virus but not to viruses unrelated to TMV.

Fig. 5–2. Leaf of *Nicotiana sylvestris*. The left half was rubbed with the type strain of tobacco mosaic virus; 4 days later the entire leaf was rubbed with the rosette strain of tobacco mosaic virus. The type strain protected the left half from infection by the rosette strain.

Portions of leaves heavily inoculated with TMV at least a full day before being inoculated with aucuba mosaic virus developed few or no lesions whereas the remaining portions developed many lesions (**Fig. 5–2**); the protection was confined to those cells actually invaded by the first virus. It is the general consensus that in order to be immune a cell must be completely occupied by the protective virus. Recently, Benda (1956) has obtained evidence, but not proof, that two different strains of TMV can multiply simultaneously in the same cell. The presence of one particle of virus in a cell does not, therefore, prevent the cell from becoming infected by a related strain though it might or might not prevent multiplication of the second virus. Sadasivan (1940) concluded that acquired immunity depends upon the presence of fully active virus in cell tissues and that the degree of protection is directly proportional to the number of active particles of the protecting virus present in the cell. Fulton (1951a,b) found also that necrotic type strains of TMV are able to enter and multiply in cells containing a low concentration of another strain. On the other hand, Köhler (1955) concluded that the distribution of virus in host tissues is more important in providing protection from another strain of virus than is the total concentration of the first virus. Oortwijn Botjes (1933) reported that plants of certain potato varieties infected with mild strains of PVX are protected from infection by a severe strain. Ross (1948) reported that infection of *Physalis floridana* plants with mild strains of PVX protected them from severe strains of the virus. Siegel (1959) postulated an exclusion mechanism by which a single particle of one strain of a virus prevents a particle of another strain from infecting, but Benda (1959) interpreted Siegel's data to represent an altered response of infected tissue rather than exclusion. Evidence in favor of Siegel's hypothesis has been presented by Wu and Rappaport (1961) and by Wu and Wildman (1962).

A type of immunity extending beyond tissues actually invaded by virus has been reported by Yarwood (1953, 1960). The local lesions produced by TMV on leaves of bean stop enlarging about 2 days after inoculation, and no virus can be detected in tissues immediately adjacent to the lesion. Yet a second inoculation with TMV failed to induce lesions within a 2-mm zone adjacent to the lesion though numerous lesions developed in more distant areas. Lesions were produced in these zones by alfalfa mosaic virus and tobacco necrosis virus, indicating that the resistance is specific.

If the immunity to a virus afforded by previous infection with another strain of the virus is thought of as relative, cross-protection tests can be very useful in determining relationships but, if it is regarded as absolute, such tests can be misleading. Thus, R. W. Fulton's (1950) failure to protect cucumber cotyledons from infection by TMV by inoculating them with CV 3 or CV 4 was cited by Knight (1955) as evidence against a close relationship, but Rochow (1956) showed that protection was afforded when the concentration of CV 3 or CV 4 in the cotyledons was sufficiently high.

The indicator strain of CMV (Holmes, 1939) induces necrotic local lesions on zinnia (Price, 1935a) whereas many other strains produce mottling symptoms; the latter protect zinnia leaves from infection by the former. The indicator strain has been used by many investigators as an aid in identifying strains of CMV. Strains of the virus from spinach gave more or less complete protection in zinnia or cowpea against local-lesion-producing strains (J. P. Fulton, 1950).

A strain of bean yellow mosaic virus was found to induce necrotic local lesions in leaves of *Crotalaria spectabilis*. Corbett (1957) used it in identifying other strains.

Ringspot type strains of PVX cause local lesions in tobacco leaves. This localized reaction and the systemic reaction as well have been used to identify strains of PVX (Salaman, 1933; Ainsworth, 1934; Bawden, 1934; Clinch, 1942; Matthews, 1949a; Ladeburg *et al.*, 1950). Plants infected with mild strains of PVX are not always protected against severe strains, especially when development of systemic symptoms is used as a measure of protection. Bald (1948) was able to infect potato plants having a mild strain with a more severe one either by grafting or inoculating young leaves. Matthews (1949a,b) found a correlation between the degree of cross protection among strains and the closeness of relationship judged by serological reactions.

A number of studies have shown that plants infected with strains of PVY acquire immunity from other strains of the virus

(Salaman, 1937; Darby *et al.*, 1951; Silberschmidt, 1957). Ross (1950b) differentiated between CMV and PVY on the basis of cross-protection tests in *Physalis floridana,* these viruses previously having been classed together on the basis of serological tests (Chester, 1935). On the other hand, tobacco veinal necrosis virus, isolated by Nobrega and Silberschmidt (1944) and considered by them to be a special strain of PVY despite inconclusive results from cross-protection tests, was classed by Bawden and Kassanis (1951) as a strain of PVY on the basis of serology despite the failure of the virus to protect tobacco, *N. glutinosa,* or potato from infection by known strains of PVY.

Peach yellows and little peach viruses were considered by Kunkel (1936) to be closely related on the basis of cross-protection tests but to be unrelated to peach rosette virus.

The virus of curly top of sugar beet seems to be unusual in that none of its strains protect against one another either in sugar beet or in water pimpernel (Giddings, 1940, 1941, 1950; Bennett, 1955). There may, however, be other plant viruses that behave similarly. Bennett (1957) recently reported on yellow-vein virus, which apparently arose as a mutant from curly-top virus. Tobacco plants recovered from curly top seem to be immune from yellow vein when transmission is by the beet leafhopper but only resistant when transmission is by grafting. Yellow-vein virus also protects tomato plants from the severe disease caused by curly-top virus.

Tobacco and *N. glutinosa* plants invaded by potato calico virus were refractory to infection by alfalfa mosaic virus, suggesting a close relationship between them (Black and Price, 1940). Other strains of alfalfa mosaic virus have been identified by cross-protection tests in tobacco (Berkeley, 1947) and in potato (Oswald, 1950). Cross-protection tests have been used to confirm the presence of tobacco etch virus in Puerto Rico (Adsuar and Perez, 1956). On the basis of cross-protection tests, host range, and properties, Grogan and Walker (1948) concluded that common bean mosaic and bean yellow mosaic viruses are closely related, a

relationship suggested also by serological reactions (Beemster and van der Want, 1951). Two strains of pea mosaic virus were demonstrated to have a close relationship to bean yellow mosaic virus by cross-protection tests and serological reactions (Goodchild, 1956). Cross-immunity tests have been applied to viruses that cause disease in cacao, with results suggesting that more than two groups of virus strains are involved (Crowdy and Posnette, 1947; Brunt and Kentin, 1962). Wallace (1957) reported that sweet orange seedlings infected either with concave gum, blind pocket, crinky leaf, or infectious variegation viruses were protected from the severe effects induced by grafting with a severe form of psorosis A virus, thus bringing evidence for close relationships among these viruses.

5–6. INTERFERENCE

In this chapter, the term interference is used in reference to instances in which a virus or viral component interferes with the multiplication of an unrelated virus or its disease-producing capacities. When tobacco plants are inoculated separately or concurrently with tobacco mosaic and tobacco etch viruses (TEV), both viruses infect and multiply simultaneously in the same cells of the plant (McWhorter and Price, 1949), the plants are stunted more than when infected by either virus alone, but the characteristic morphological symptoms are those of etch alone; the mottling characteristic of tobacco mosaic is masked. This is not interference!

In contrast, when PVY and severe etch virus are introduced separately or concurrently into potato or tobacco plants, multiplication of PVY is prevented and PVY may even be replaced by TEV (Bawden and Kassanis, 1945). This is interference! The mild strain of TEV reduces the concentration of PVY but does not prevent its multiplication completely. CMV multiplies normally in plants infected either with TEV or PVY. Bawden and Kassanis reasoned that the interference between TEV and PVY is not due to blocking of multiplication sites but to interference at some later stage of the infection.

TEV and PVY are not closely related, on the basis of properties and serological reactions. Were they closely related, it would be expected that PVY would protect potato or tobacco plants from infection by severe TEV. But this was not the case; interference took place in only one direction. Interference by TEV differs from cross protection in which either strain of a virus will protect against the other. It should be mentioned at this point that Schmelzer *et al.* (1960) did not confirm the results of Bawden and Kassanis on interference between TEV and PVY; Schmelzer *et al.* found that inoculation of Samsun tobacco plants with severe TEV did not protect them from infection by various strains of PVY for, although no additional symptoms were observed, presence of PVY in doubly inoculated plants was easily detected by differential hosts and by serological tests.

So far as I am aware, the interference between TEV and PVY is unique, though there may be other pairs of plant viruses that behave similarly. On the other hand, there are other types of interference to which reference should be made.

Recent literature on interference among plant viruses suggests that several different phenomena, with different mechanisms, are involved. Full justice to this literature cannot be given in a short discussion. Moreover, it is probably too early to generalize about the various results that have been reported.

A. INTERFERENCE RESULTING FROM USE OF MIXED INOCULA

One type of interference is that involving a reduction in infectivity of a virus by virtue of the presence in the inoculum of another virus or virus-related substance. This type can be illustrated with PVY and PVX. Although USDA potato seedling 41956 is considered to be immune from PVX, infection of it by PVY is inhibited if the inoculum also contains PVX; the inhibition increases as the amount of PVX in the inoculum increases (Ross, 1950a).

When the rib-grass strain of TMV, which produces neither local lesions nor systemic infections in bean leaves, was mixed in increasing concentration with a relatively low concentration of ordinary TMV and the mixture was rubbed over bean leaves, successively smaller numbers of local lesions were produced (Beale, 1947).

B. INTERFERENCE WITHIN AN INOCULATED LEAF

Another type of interference is that in which inoculation of a leaf with one virus reduces its susceptibility for another, unrelated, virus. *Physalis floridana* plants inoculated simultaneously with PVY and a non-lesion-forming strain of PVX develop lesions at a slower rate than when PVX is not present. That this sort of interference may be caused by an inhibitory substance was suggested by the work of Sela and Applebaum (1962). Sap of leaves of *Nicotiana repanda, N. glutinosa,* or *Physalis floridana* infected with either TMV, PVY, or a local-lesion strain of PVY was adsorbed with hydrated calcium phosphate to remove the virus. When the adsorbed sap was mixed with a virus solution it reduced the infectivity by 39–94%. A similar, or identical, inhibitor was found in the upper leaves of *N. glutinosa* 5 days after inoculation of the lower leaves with TMV. The inhibitory substance was nonspecific for the host-virus combinations tested. Inoculation of half-leaves of *Chenopodium amaranticolor* with alfalfa mosaic virus (AMV) reduced the number of lesions produced by inoculating them 3, 6, and 9 days later with CMV by 60–80% but did not interfere with production of lesions by TMV or a cucurbit mosaic virus in the same host (Nitzany and Cohen, 1960). On the other hand, *N. glutinosa* plants systemically infected with CMV were fully susceptible to a strain of AMV that causes local lesions in this host. Furthermore, zinnia plants systemically infected with CMV were susceptible to strains of AMV that induce necrosis in zinnia.

Interference between CMV and TMV in zinnia, *Nicotiana repanda* Wild, and *N. glutinosa* was studied by Nitzany and Sela (1962). A strain of CMV (CMV-LL) that produces local lesions in zinnia was used as the challenge virus in zinnia and as the protecting virus in *N. repanda* and *N. glutinosa.* Half-leaves of *N. repanda* that were inoculated with CMV-LL developed significantly fewer lesions when inoculated subsequently with TMV than did the opposite half-leaves, which had been rubbed previously with sap of healthy plants. The reduction increased from 0% on the third day after the first inoculation to a maximum of 60% on the fifth day and then declined to 0% on the tenth day. Results with *N. glutinosa* as the test plant were similar. There was no reduction in numbers of lesions produced by TMV, however, when the ordinary strain of CMV was used as the protecting virus. The two youngest pairs of leaves of zinnia plants systemically infected with TMV developed 49–57% fewer lesions when inoculated with CMV-LL than did the controls. The authors suggested, in agreement with Siegel (1959), that there is competition among viruses for infection sites or loci within cells.

On first thought, it might seem that results such as those of Nitzany and Cohen are comparable to cross protection. There are, however, significant differences. The interference reported by these authors was only about 50% complete, was restricted to certain pairs of viruses, and lasted for only a short period. In cross protection, on the other hand, the protection is more nearly complete, persists for a longer period, and is, generally, not restricted to special strains. For example, zinnia plants that had been infected with any one of several strains of CMV long enough for their leaves to have become mottled (18 days) were completely refractory to the indicator strain of CMV, the protection being restricted, of course, to tissues actually invaded by the "protecting" virus (Price, 1935a). In the same test, significantly fewer lesions were produced by the indicator strain in zinnia leaves previously infected with TMV or with tobacco ringspot virus (TRSV), than in the controls. In the reciprocal tests, using a strain of TMV (302A) that induced necrotic local lesions in zinnia, leaves infected with ordinary TMV or with the aucuba strain of TMV were completely refractory to TMV-302A. Again, there were fewer lesions produced by the challenge virus (TMV-302A) in leaves previously infected with some strains of CMV, with TRSV, or with tobacco severe etch virus, the difference

being statistically significant only for strain 9 of CMV.

The degree of protection against the challenge virus by viruses not closely related to it is of a different order of magnitude from that afforded by viruses that are closely related to it.

According to Zachos (1957), the multiplication of TMV was partially suppressed when TMV and PVX were inoculated simultaneously into tomato plants, or when PVX was inoculated first, but not when TMV was inoculated first. Simultaneous infection of tobacco plants with PVY and Datura necrosis virus leads to decrease in concentration of PVY as compared with controls, but the decrease was not observed when *N. glutinosa* was the host plant (Badami and Kassanis, 1959).

C. Localized Interference in Hypersensitive Hosts

Another type of interference was reported by Ross (1961a). A 1–2-mm zone around each local lesion produced by TMV in Samsun *NN* tobacco was resistant to subsequent infection by TMV, tobacco necrosis virus, tobacco ringspot virus, and tomato ringspot virus. The resistant zone increased in size and in degree of protection during 6 days after the first inoculation while the lesion was enlarging. This type of resistance is similar to that reported by Yarwood (1953) for TMV in bean plants except that the latter was specific.

D. Systemic Interference in Hypersensitive Hosts

In 1952, Gilpatrick and Weintraub reported an unusual type of protection against carnation mosaic virus in *Dianthus barbatus*. In 1961, Weintraub and Kemp reported that the protection apparently ceased to operate about $2\frac{1}{2}$ years after originally being observed, but they gave additional details. Three clones of carnation were involved; clones 20 and 26 developed only necrotic local lesions after inoculation whereas clone 21 developed a systemic mosaic disease. The upper leaves of clones 20 and 26 developed only about 25% as many lesions after inoculation with carnation mosaic virus when lower leaves had been previously

Fig. 5–3. Systemic interference in Samsum *NN* tobacco leaves (Ross, 1961b). A. Test leaf, inoculated first on left half with tobacco ringspot virus and 7 days later on right half with tobacco mosaic virus. B. Control leaf, rubbed on left half with water and 7 days later with tobacco mosaic virus. Photograph by H. H. Lyon.

infected than when the lower leaves had not been infected. The protection was not due to presence of a masked form of the virus in upper leaves at the time of the challenge inoculation. The agent responsible for protection passed across a graft union between protected and healthy clones; it did not protect clone 21 against systemic infection when this clone was grafted to protected clones 20 and 26.

This type of interference was studied in detail by Ross and Bozarth (1960) and by Ross (1961b). Inoculation of half-leaves of *NN* tobacco with TMV, followed 3 days later with a challenge inoculation of the other halves, led to fewer and smaller lesions than in the control halves. Local infections in lower leaves of decapitated plants induced resistance in upper leaves. Resistance was detected 3 days after the first inoculation, reached a maximum in 7 days, and persisted at least 20 days; it varied with the ratio of the area first inoculated to the area challenged. It could be detected in detached leaves, in darkened plants, and in plants of various degrees of vigor. But it was not specific; the resistant

leaves were almost as resistant to tobacco necrosis, tobacco ringspot, tomato ringspot, and turnip mosaic viruses as they were to TMV. Fig. 5–3 illustrates the resistance induced by TRSV. Ross pointed out that the resistance is not the direct result of virus multiplication per se; it is caused only by those viruses that induce necrosis during their reproduction. On the other hand, necrosis caused by agents other than viruses does not induce systemic resistance. Basically, the resistance seems to be of the kind that reduces the size of lesions induced by the challenge inoculation; under ultraviolet light, a leaf challenged by inoculation had a number of small fluorescing spots, the number corresponding to the number of lesions on the control leaves. This would seem to indicate that resistance did not consist in blocking infection sites but rather to restricting multiplication of virus after infection had taken place. Ross suggested two possible mechanisms for the resistance: (a) a diffusable by-product of virus-induced necrosis, and (b) preferential movement of metabolites essential for virus reproduction from normal areas of the plant to the necrotic areas produced by the first inoculation. The resistance resembles interferon-induced resistance in animal tissues described by Isaacs and Lindenmann (1957) but differs from it because interferon is stimulated by inactive virus whereas the resistance in plants is not.

Systemic interference in hypersensitive host plants was observed by Loebenstein (1963) in other host-virus combinations— TMV in *Datura stramonium* L. and PVX in *Gomphrena globosa* L. In both combinations, the reduction in numbers of lesions in noninoculated halves of leaves was not significant when the challenge inoculation was made 4 days after the first inoculation but was significant when it was made 6 or 8 days after. Sap taken from apical halves of Datura leaves inoculated on their basal halves 10 days previously with TMV was found to contain an inhibitory material. When the sap was extracted, centrifuged at 5000 rpm for 10 min, and mixed 1 : 1 with a 70 μg/ml TMV solution, it reduced the numbers of lesions produced by this solution on *N. glutinosa* L. by about 50% in some instances. This reduction suggests either the development of an inhibitory substance in Datura leaves infected with TMV or an increase in concentration of the inhibitory substance normally present in Datura leaves.

E. INTERFERENCE BY INACTIVE VIRUS

A final type of interference in plant virus infections, which does resemble the interferon phenomenon, needs to be mentioned. Both local and systemic resistance to TMV was induced in plants of *N. glutinosa* and *Datura stramonium* by rubbing their leaves with native protein prepared by degrading purified TMV (Loebenstein, 1960, 1962). The resistance was present 4 days after the rubbing but not 1 day after. Two rubbings, a day apart, with protein were more effective than one rubbing. The resistance was not entirely specific; TMV protein protected plants of *Gomphrena globosa* and *D. stramonium* from infection with PVX but not from infection with CMV. Loebenstein concludes that his results suggest the formation of protective substances in plants and their translocation and are thus analagous to the interferon phenomenon.

* * *

This work was supported in part by Research Grant AI 03148 from the National Institute of Allergy and Infectious Diseases, National Institutes of Health, United States Public Health Service.

5-7. LITERATURE CITED

Aach, H. G. (1957). Z. Naturforsch. **12**, 614.

Aach, H. G. (1958). Z. Naturforsch. **13**, 165.

Adsuar, J., and Perez, J. E. (1956), J. Agr., Univ. Puerto Rico **40**, 83.

Ainsworth, G. C. (1934). Ann. Appl. Biol. **21**, 581.

Ainsworth, G. C. (1935). Ann. Appl. Biol. **22**, 55.

Ainsworth, G. C. (1937). Ann. Appl. Biol. **24**, 545.

Ainsworth, G. C. (1938). Ann. Appl. Biol. **25**, 867.

Babos, P., and Kassanis, B. (1962). Virology 18, 206.

Badami, R. S., and Kassanis, B. (1959). Ann. Appl. Biol. **47**, 90.

Bald, J. G. (1948). J. Council Sci. Ind. Res. **21**, 247.

Bald, J. G., and Norris, D. O. (1945). Phytopathology **35**, 591.

Bawden, F. C. (1934). Proc. Roy. Soc. (London), Ser. B. **116**, 375.

Bawden, F. C. (1956). Nature **177**, 302.

Bawden, F. C. (1959). Nature **184**, B. A. 27–B. A. 29.

Bawden, F. C., and Kassanis, B. (1945). Ann. Appl. Biol. **32**, 52.

Bawden, F. C., and Kassanis, B. (1947). Ann. Appl. Biol. **34**, 503.

Bawden, F. C., and Kassanis, B. (1951). Ann. Appl. Biol. **38**, 402.

Bawden, F. C., and Pirie, N. W. (1937). Brit. J. Exptl. Pathol. **28**, 275.

Bawden, F. C., and Sheffield, F. M. L. (1944). Ann. Appl. Biol. **31**, 33.

Beale, H. P. (1934). Contrib. Boyce Thompson Inst. **6**, 407.

Beale, H. P. (1947). Phytopathology **37**, 847.

Beemster, A. B. R., and van der Want, J. P. H. (1951). Antonie van Leeuwenhoek **17**, 285.

Benda, G. T. A. (1956). Virology **2**, 820.

Benda, G. T. A. (1959). Virology **9**, 712.

Benda, G. T. A., and Naylor, A. W. (1954). Am. J. Botany **41**, 799.

Benda, G. T. A., and Naylor, A. W. (1957). Am. J. Botany **44**, 443.

Benda, G. T. A., and Naylor, A. W. (1958). Am. J. Botany **45**, 33.

Bennett, C. W. (1949). Phytopathology **39**, 637.

Bennett, C. W. (1951). Ann. Rev. Microbiol. **5**, 295.

Bennett, C. W. (1953). Advan. Virus Res. **1**, 39.

Bennett, C. W. (1955). Phytopathology **45**, 531.

Bennett, C. W. (1957). Virology **3**, 322.

Bennett, C. W., and Esau, K. (1936). J. Agr. Res. **53**, 595.

Berkeley, G. H. (1947). Phytopathology **37**, 781.

Best, R. J. (1954). Australian J. Biol. Sci. **7**, 415.

Best, R. J. (1962). Virology **15**, 327.

Best, R. J., and Gallus, H. P. C. (1955). Enzymologia **17**, 207.

Bewley, W. F. (1934). Cheshunt Expt. Res. Sta. Ann. Rept. **9** (1933), 66.

Birkeland, J. M. (1934). Botan. Gaz. **95**, 419.

Black, L. M. (1937). Cornell Univ. Agr. Expt. Sta. Mem. **209**, 23 pp.

Black, L. M. (1940). Am. J. Botany **27**, 386.

Black, L. M. (1941). Am. Potato J. **18**, 231.

Black, L. M. (1958). Proc. 10th Intern. Congr. Entomol. **3**, 201.

Black, L. M., and Price, W. C. (1940). Phytopathology **30**, 444.

Böhme, R. W. (1933). Phytopathol. Z. **6**, 517.

Brierley, P. (1939). Phytopathology **29**, 3.

Bruehl, G. W. (1958). Plant Disease Rep. **42**, 909.

Brunt, A. A., and Kentin, R. H. (1962). Virology **16**, 199.

Buchanan, R. E., and Murray, C. (1916). Veterinary Bacteriology. Ed. 2. W. B. Saunders Co., Philadelphia.

Cadman, C. H., and Harrison, B. D. (1959). Ann. Appl. Biol. **47**, 542.

Cadman, C. H., and Lister, R. M. (1961). Phytopathology **51**, 29.

Caldwell, J. (1935). Proc. Roy. Soc. (London), Ser. B. **117**, 120.

Capoor, S. P. (1950). Current Sci. (India) **19**, 22.

Carsner, E. (1925). Phytopathology **15**, 745.

Carsner, E., and Lackey, C. F. (1928). Phytopathology **18**, 951.

Carsner, E., and Stahl, C. F. (1924). J. Agr. Res. **28**, 297.

Chester, K. S. (1935). Phytopathology **25**, 686.

Chester, K. S. (1936). Phytopathology **26**, 778.

Clinch, P. E. M. (1942). Sci. Proc. Roy. Dublin Soc. **23**, 18.

Clinch, P. E. M. (1944). Sci. Proc. Roy. Dublin Soc. **23**, 273.

Cockerham, G. (1954). Proc. 2nd Conf. Potato Virus Diseases. 89.

Conn, H. W., and Conn, H. J. (1926). A Study of Microorganisms and Their Relation to Human Welfare. 3d ed. Williams and Wilkins Co., Baltimore.

Corbett, M. K. (1957). Phytopathology **47**, 573.

Crowdy, S. H., and Posnette, A. F. (1947). Ann. Appl. Biol. **34**, 403.

Darby, J. F., Larson, R. H., and Walker, J. C. (1951). Univ. Wisconsin Res. Bull. **177**, 32 p.

de Vries, H. (1909). The Mutation Theory. Vol. 1. The Origin of Species by Mutation. (Translated by J. B. Farmer and A. D. Darbishire.) The Open Court Publishing Company, Chicago.

Faan, H. C., and Johnson, J. (1951). Phytopathology **41**, 11.

Fraenkel-Conrat, H. (1956). J. Am. Chem. Soc. **78**, 882.

Fraenkel-Conrat, H. (1962). Design and Function at the Threshold of Life: The Viruses. Academic Press, New York. 117 pp.

Fraenkel-Conrat, H., Singer, B., and Williams, R. C. (1957). Biochim. Biophys. Acta **25**, 87.

Franklin, R. E., Caspar, D. L. D., and Klug, A. (1959). In C. S. Holton, G. W. Fischer, R. W. Fulton, H. Hart, and S. E. A. McCallan (eds.), Plant Pathology—Problems and Progress, 1908–1958. 447–61. Univ. Wisconsin Press.

Friedrich-Freksa, H. Melchers, G., and Schramm, G. (1946). Biol. Zentr. **65**, 187.

Fulton, J. P. (1950). Phytopathology **40**, 729.

Fulton, R. W. (1949). Phytopathology **39**, 231.

Fulton, R. W. (1950). Phytopathology **40**, 219.

Fulton, R. W. (1951a). Phytopathology **41**, 13.

Fulton, R. W. (1951b). Phytopathology **41**, 579.

Giddings, N. J. (1938). J. Agr. Res. **56**, 883.

Giddings, N. J. (1940). Phytopathology **30**, 786.

Giddings, N. J. (1941). Phytopathology **31**, 8.

Giddings, N. J. (1944.) J. Agr. Res. **69**, 149.

Giddings, N. J. (1950). Phytopathology **40**, 377.

Gierer, A., and Mundry, K. W. (1958). Nature **182**, 1457.

Gierer, A., and Schramm, G. (1956). Nature **177**, 702.

Gilpatrick, J. D., and Weintraub, M. (1952). Science **115**, 701.

Ginosa, W., and Atkinson, D. E. (1955). Virology **1**, 253.

Goodchild, D. J. (1956). Australian J. Biol. Sci. **9**, 231.

Gordon, R. B., and Price, W. C. (1953). Arch. Biochem. Biophys. **45**, 117.

Gowen, J. W. (1941). Cold Spring Harbor Symp. Quant. Biol. **9**, 187.

Grant, T. J., and Costa, A. S. (1951). Phytopathology **49**, 114.

Grogan, R. G., and Walker, J. C. (1948). Phytopathology **38**, 489.

Hagedorn, D. J., and Walker, J. C. (1950). Phytopathology **40**, 684.

Henderson, R. G. (1934). Phytopathology **24**, 10.

Henderson, R. G., and Wingard, S. A. (1931). J. Agr. Res. **43**, 191.

Henle, W. (1950). J. Immunol. **64**, 203.

Hitchborn, J. H. (1957). Virology **3**, 243.

Hitchborn, J. H., and Thomson, A. D. (1960). Advan. Virus Res. **7**, 163.

Holmes, F. O. (1929). Botan. Gaz. **87**, 39.

Holmes, F. O. (1934). Phytopathology **24**, 845.

Holmes, F. O. (1936). Phytopathology **26**, 896.

Holmes, F. O. (1939). Handbook of Phytopathogenic Viruses. Burgess Publ. Co., Minneapolis. 221 pp.

Holmes, F. O. (1941). Phytopathology **31**, 1089.

Holmes, F. O. (1952). Indian Phytopathology **5**, 8.

Howe, H. A. (1948). In T. M. Rivers (ed.), Viral and Rickettsial Infections of Man. 245–68. J. B. Lippincott Co., Philadelphia.

Isaacs, A., and Lindenmann, J. (1957). Proc. Roy. Soc. (London), Ser. B. 147, 258.

Jarrett, P. H. (1930). Ann. Appl. Biol. 17, 248.

Jensen, J. H. (1933). Phytopathology 23, 964.

Jensen, J. H. (1936). Phytopathology 26, 266.

Jensen, J. H. (1937). Phytopathology 27, 69.

Johnson, E. M., and Valleau, W. D. (1946). Phytopathology 36, 112.

Johnson, J. (1925). Wisconsin Univ. Agr. Expt. Sta. Res. Bull. 63, 12 p.

Johnson, J. (1926). Science 64, 210.

Johnson, J. (1936). Phytopathology 26, 285.

Johnson, J. (1937). Trans. Wisconsin Acad. Sci. Arts Letters 30, 27.

Johnson, J. (1947). Phytopathology 37, 822.

Jordan, E. O. (1908). A Textbook of General Bacteriology. W. B. Saunders Company, Philadelphia.

Kahler, H., and Woods, M. W. (1949). Arch. Biochem. 22, 393.

Kausche, G. A., and Stubbe, H. (1939). Naturwissenschaften 27, 501.

Kleczkowski, A. (1941). Brit. J. Exptl. Pathol. 22, 41.

Kleczkowski, A. (1950). J. Gen. Microbiol. 4, 53.

Knight, C. A. (1942). J. Biol. Chem. 145, 11.

Knight, C. A. (1943). J. Biol. Chem. 147, 663.

Knight, C. A. (1947). J. Biol. Chem. 171, 297.

Knight, C. A. (1955). Virology 1, 261.

Knight, C. A. (1959). In F. M. Burnett and W. M. Stanley (eds.), The Viruses. 2, 127. Academic Press, New York.

Knight, C. A., and Stanley, W. M. (1941.) J. Biol. Chem. 141, 29.

Knight, C. A., Silva, D. M., Dahl, D., and Tsugita, A. (1962). Virology 16, 236.

Köhler, E. (1937). Phytopathol. Z. 10, 467.

Köhler, E. (1954). In E. Köhler and M. Klinkowski (eds.), Handbuch der Pflanzenkrankheiten. 98. Paul Parey, Berlin and Hamburg.

Köhler, E. (1955). Phytopathol. Z. 23, 323.

Köhler, E. (1956). Nachrbl. Deut. Pflanzenschutzdienst (Stuttgart) 8, 93.

Kunkel, L. O. (1932). Contrib. Boyce Thompson Inst. 4, 405.

Kunkel, L. O. (1934a). Phytopathology 24, 13.

Kunkel, L. O. (1934b). Phytopathology 24, 437.

Kunkel, L. O. (1936). Phytopathology 26, 201.

Kunkel, L. O. (1940). In F. R. Moulton (ed.), The Genetics of Pathogenic Organisms. AAAS Publ. No. 12, 22.

Kunkel, L. O. (1947). Ann. Rev. Microbiol. 1, 85.

Lackey, C. F. (1929). Phytopathology 19, 975.

Lackey, C. F. (1931). Phytopathology 21, 123.

Lackey, C. F. (1932). J. Agr. Res. 44, 755.

Lackey, C. F. (1937). J. Agr. Res. 55, 453.

Ladeburg, R. C., Larson, R. H., and Walker, J. C. (1950). Wisconsin Agr. Expt. Sta. Res. Bull. 165, 47 pp.

Larson, R. H., Stahmann, M. A., Walker, J. C., and Colburn, R. W. (1952). Phytopathology 42, 25.

Lauffer, M. A., and Price, W. C. (1940). J. Biol. Chem. 133, 1.

Lesley, J. W., and Wallace, J. M. (1938). Phytopathology 28, 548.

Lister, R. M., and Thresh, J. M. (1955). Nature 175, 1047.

Loebenstein, G. (1960). Nature 185, 122.

Loebenstein, G. (1962). Virology 17, 574.

Loebenstein, G. (1963). Phytopathology 53, 306.

Markham, R. (1959). In F. M. Burnett and W. M. Stanley (eds.), The Viruses, 2, 33. Academic Press, New York.

Matthews, R. E. F. (1949a). Nature 163, 175.

Matthews, R. E. F. (1949b). Ann. Appl. Biol. 36, 460.

McKinney, H. H. (1926). Phytopathology 16, 893.

McKinney, H. H. (1929). J. Agr. Res. 39, 557.

McKinney, H. H. (1931). 2nd Congr. Intern. Path. Comp. v. 2. Compt. Rend. et Commun. 449.

McKinney, H. H. (1935). J. Agr. Res. 51, 951.

McKinney, H. H. (1937). J. Heredity 28, 51.

McKinney, H. H. (1941a). Phytopathology 31, 1059.

McKinney, H. H. (1941b). Am. J. Botany 28, 770.

McKinney, H. H. (1943). Phytopathology 33, 551.

McKinney, H. H., and Clayton, E. E. (1944). Phytopathology 34, 60.

McWhorter, F. P. (1938). Ann. Appl. Biol. 25, 254.

McWhorter, F. P., and Milbrath, J. A. (1938). Oregon Agr. Expt. Sta. Circular 128, 14 p.

McWhorter, F. P., and Price, W. C. (1949). Science 109, 116.

Milbrath, J. A. (1939). Phytopathology 29, 156.

Miller, G. L., and Stanley, W. M. (1941a). Science 93, 428.

Miller, G. L., and Stanley, W. M. (1941b). J. Biol. Chem. 141, 905.

Miller, G. L., and Stanley, W. M. (1942). J. Biol. Chem. 146, 331.

Miller, G. L., Eitelman, E. S., and Golder, R. H. (1951). Arch. Biochem. Biophys. 34, 162.

Muller, H. J. (1950). Am. Scientist 38, 33–59, 126, 399.

Mundry, K. W. (1959). Virology 9, 722.

Nitzany, F. E., and Cohen, S. (1960). Virology 11, 771.

Nitzany, F. E., and Sela, I. (1962). Virology 17, 549.

Nobrega, N. R., and Silberschmidt, K. (1944). Arquiv. Inst. Biol. (São Paulo) 15, 307.

Norris, D. O. (1943). J. Council Sci. Indust. Res. 16, 91.

Norris, D. O. (1946). Council Sci. Ind. Res. Bull. 202, 51 pp.

Norval, I. P. (1938). Phytopathology 28, 675.

Ogilvie, L. (1928). Ann. Appl. Biol. 15, 540.

Oortwijn Botjes, J. G. (1933). Tijdschr. Plantenziekten 39, 249.

Oster, G. (1951). J. Biol. Chem. 190, 55.

Oswald, J. W. (1950). Phytopathology 40, 973.

Posnette, A. F., and Cropley, R. (1952). Report E. Malling Res. Sta. 1951, pp. 128, 130.

Posnette, A. F., and Cropley, R. (1956). J. Hort. Sci. 31, 119.

STRAINS

Price, W. C. (1932). Contrib. Boyce Thompson Inst. 4, 359.

Price, W. C. (1934). Phytopathology 24, 743.

Price, W. C. (1935a). Phytopathology 25, 776.

Price, W. C. (1935b). Phytopathology 25, 947.

Price, W. C. (1936a). Phytopathology 26, 503.

Price, W. C. (1936b). Phytopathology 26, 665.

Price, W. C. (1937). Phytopathology 27, 561.

Price, W. C. (1940a). Arch. Ges. Virusforsch. 1, 373.

Price, W. C. (1940b). Quart. Rev. Biol. 15, 338.

Price, W. C. (1940c). Am. Naturalist 74, 117.

Price, W. C. (1941). Phytopathology 31, 756.

Price, W. C. (1943). Phytopathology 33, 586.

Price, W. C. (1954). Trans. N. Y. Acad. Sci. Ser. 2, 16, 196.

Priode, C. N. (1928). Am. J. Botany 15, 88.

Quanjer, H. M. (1942). Tijdschr. Plantenziekten 48, 1.

Reddi, K. K. (1957). Biochim. Biophys. Acta 25, 528.

Reddi, K. K. (1959). Biochim. Biophys. Acta 32, 386.

Rivers, T. M. (1948). In T. M. Rivers (ed.), Viral and Rickettsial Infections of Man. 1–17. J. B. Lippincott Co., Philadelphia.

Rochow, W. F. (1956). Phytopathology 46, 133.

Rochow, W. F. (1958). Plant Disease Rep. 42, 905.

Ross, A. F. (1948). Phytopathology 38, 930.

Ross, A. F. (1950a). Phytopathology 40, 24.

Ross, A. F. (1950b). Phytopathology 40, 445.

Ross, A. F. (1959). In C. S. Holton, G. W. Fischer, R. W. Fulton, H. Hart, and S. E. A. McCallan (eds.), Plant Pathology—Problems and Progress, 1908–1958. 511–20. Univ. Wisconsin Press, Madison.

Ross, A. F. (1961a). Virology 14, 329.

Ross, A. F. (1961b). Virology 14, 340.

Ross, A. F., and Bozarth, R. F. (1960). Phytopathology 50, 652.

Ross, H., and Köhler, E. (1953). Züchter 23, 179.

Sadasivan, T. S. (1940). Ann. Appl. Biol. 27, 359.

Salaman, R. N. (1933). Nature 131, 468.

Salaman, R. N. (1936). Rep. Intern. Congr. Comp. Pathol. 1, 167.

Salaman, R. N. (1937). Nature 139, 924.

Salaman, R. N. (1938). Phil. Trans. Roy. Soc. (London), Ser. B. 229, 137.

Schlesinger, R. W. (1959). In T. M. Rivers and F. L. Horsfall (eds.), Viral and Rickettsial Infections of Man. 3d ed. 145–55. J. B. Lippincott Co., Philadelphia.

Schmelzer, K., Bartels, R., and Klinkowski, M. (1960). Phytopathol. Z. 40, 52.

Sela, I., and Applebaum, S. W. (1962). Virology 17, 543.

Severin, H. H. P. (1929). Hilgardia 3, 543.

Siegel, A. (1959). Virology 8, 470.

Siegel, A. (1960). Virology 11, 156.

Silberschmidt, K. M. (1957). Turrialba 7, 34.

Singer, S. J., Bald, J. G., Wildman, S. G., and Owen, R. D. (1951). Science 114, 463.

Smith, J. H. (1928). Ann. Appl. Biol. 15, 155.

Smith, K. M. (1929). Ann. Appl. Biol. 16, 382.

Smith, K. M. (1937). A Textbook of Plant Virus Diseases. P. Blakiston's Son and Co., Inc., Philadelphia. 615 pp.

Stanley, W. M. (1939). J. Biol. Chem. 129, 429.

Sukhov, K. S. (1956). The Problem of Hereditary Variation of Phytopathogenic Viruses. Publication Akad. Nauk. S.S.S.R., Moscow.

Sukhov, K. S. (1958). Tr. Inst. Genet., Moscow, 24, 117.

Summers, E. M. (1936). Iowa State Coll. J. Sci. 11, 118.

Summers, E. M. (1939). Proc. 6th Congr. Intern. Soc. Sugar-Cane Technologists 1938, 564.

Takahashi, W. N., and Rawlins, T. E. (1946). Am. J. Botany 33, 740.

Takahashi, W. N., and Rawlins, T. E. (1947). Phytopathology 37, 73.

Taliaferro, W. H. (1929). The Immunology of Parasitic Infections. The Century Co., New York.

Tall, M. G., Price, W. C., and Wertman, K. (1949). Phytopathology 39, 288.

Thomas, H. E., and Rawlins, T. E. (1951). In Virus Diseases and Other Disorders with Viruslike Symptoms of Stone Fruits in North America. U.S.D.A. Handbook No. 10, 276 pp.

Thomson, A. D. (1961). Virology 13, 507.

Thung, T. H. (1931). Handel. Nederl. Ind. Natuurwetenshap. Congr. 6de, 1931, 450.

Topley, W. W. C. (1933). An Outline of Immunity. William Wood and Co., Baltimore.

Valleau, W. D. (1932). Kentucky Agr. Expt. Sta. Bull. 327, 43.

Valleau, W. D. (1935). Kentucky Agr. Expt. Sta. Bull. 360, 181.

Valleau, W. D. (1941). Phytopathology 31, 522.

Veldee, S., and Fraenkel-Conrat, H. (1962). Virology 18, 56.

Wallace, J. M. (1939). Phytopathology 29, 743.

Wallace, J. M. (1940). Phytopathology 30, 673.

Wallace, J. M. (1957). Hilgardia 27, 223.

Walters, H. J. (1952). Phytopathology 42, 355.

Watson, M. A. (1960). Virology 10, 211.

Watson, M. A., and Mulligan, T. (1960). Ann. Appl. Biol. 48, 711.

Weaver, E. P., and Price, W. C. (1952). Proc. Soc. Exp. Biol. Med. 79, 125.

Weintraub, M., and Kemp, W. G. (1961). Virology 13, 256.

Wellman, F. L. (1934). Phytopathology 24, 695.

Whipple, O. C., and Walker, J. C. (1941). J. Agr. Res. 62, 27.

Wingard, S. A. (1928). J. Agr. Res. 37, 127.

Wu, J., and Rappaport, I. (1961). Virology 14, 259.

Wu, J., and Wildman, S. G. (1962). Phytopathology 52, 758.

Yarwood, C. E. (1953). Phytopathology 43, 490.

Yarwood, C. E. (1956). Plant Disease Rep. 40, 299.

Yarwood, C. E. (1960). Phytopathology 50, 741.

Zachos, D. G. (1957). Ann. Inst. Phytopathol. Benaki, N. S. 1, 1.

Zinnser, H., Enders, J. F., and Fothergill, L. D. (1939). Immunity. Principles and Application in Medicine and Public Health. 5th ed. of Resistance to Infectious Diseases. The Macmillan Co., New York.

B. D. HARRISON

The transmission of plant viruses in soil

6–1. INTRODUCTION

SOME VIRUSES spread below ground and have no known vectors among organisms that infest the aerial parts of their host plants. These are the soil-borne plant viruses, which are defined as viruses "with an underground natural method of spread which does not depend simply on contact between tissues of infected and healthy plants" (Harrison, 1960). As early as 1898, Beijerinck showed that tobacco seedlings became infected with tobacco mosaic virus (TMV) when grown in soil taken from around the roots of a diseased tobacco plant, but the transmission of plant viruses in soil was for long neglected, and much that is now known has been discovered only during the last five years. Before then, the possibility that soil-inhabiting organisms might be concerned in the spread of soil-borne viruses was very rarely mentioned, whereas today we are in danger of assuming that organisms invariably are involved.

TMV is most commonly spread among tobacco plants when their tops are handled, and the credit for establishing that some plant viruses normally infect plants through their roots must go to McKinney and Webb (McKinney, 1923, 1925; McKinney et al., 1925; Webb, 1927, 1928) for their work on wheat mosaic, a disease generally accepted as being caused by a virus although the published critical evidence is still slight. Other diseases found by early workers to result from growing plants in infested soil, and which were shown at the time or later to be caused by viruses, include tobacco rattle (Behrens, 1899; Böning, 1931), grapevine arriciamento (probably the same as grapevine fanleaf; Petri, 1929), lettuce big-vein (Jagger and Chandler, 1934) and tobacco necrosis (Smith, 1937a). These viruses belong to several different groups, of which some are spread by nematodes and others by fungi. That plant-parasitic nematodes can transmit plant viruses was first shown by Hewitt et al. (1958) with grapevine fanleaf virus and Xiphinema index, and several other viruses are now known to have other species of nematodes as vectors. Recently, fungi of the genus Olpidium were implicated in the transmission of tobacco stunt (Hidaka, 1960), tobacco necrosis (Teakle, 1960), and lettuce big-vein (Campbell et al., 1961) viruses. Indeed, the ways in which plant viruses spread in soil are probably as varied as the methods of transmission of viruses that spread above ground.

For other recent reviews dealing specifically with soil-borne or nematode-transmitted plant viruses, the reader is referred to articles by Harrison (1960), Hewitt and Raski (1962), Raski and Hewitt (1963), and Cadman (1963).

6–2. ECONOMIC IMPORTANCE OF SOIL-BORNE VIRUSES

A few soil-borne viruses cause great losses of crop over wide areas and most cause diseases that are important at least locally, but a few are only of academic interest. A very rough estimate of the importance of soil-borne viruses in general is obtained by comparing their number with the number of viruses known to have aerial vectors. Smith (1957) lists about 150 viruses with aerial vectors, and about 20 are known to be soil-borne; but these relative numbers probably underestimate the losses caused by soil-borne viruses, because there are also many viruses with unknown means of spread, and fewer of these will have been tested for transmission in soil than for spread by aerial vectors. Also, many soil-borne viruses have extremely wide host ranges among crop plants.

Crops as diverse as cereals, cherries, soy beans, and spearmint are affected by soil-borne viruses, but only a few examples can be mentioned here. The grapevine is one of the crops most seriously affected, particularly in Europe where there are thousands of acres of diseased vines, but also in most other countries where the crop is grown. The commonest diseases are caused by strains of grapevine fanleaf virus, and can be grouped into two main types, each of which has different names in different countries, and some intermediate forms. The two main types are known as fanleaf (= *court-noué, Reisigkrankheit, urticado*) and yellow mosaic (= *panachure, clorose infecciosa*). Fanleaf causes greater losses of crop than yellow mosaic and is also more prevalent; some varieties are 100% infected with viruses that cause diseases of the fanleaf type. The proportion of yield lost through infection depends on the scion variety and on the rootstock; for instance, on one rootstock, the variety Chasselas lost 18% of its yield and on another 43% (Gallay *et al.*, 1955). Quality is probably also affected.

Soil-borne viruses seriously affect the yields of cereals in the United States. For instance, wheat mosaic virus, which occurs over large areas in several states, was esti-mated to have decreased the value of the 1957 wheat crop in Kansas State by $4 million (Sill and King, 1958). Disease-escaping varieties, however, are now grown in many places. In winter oats, Coffman *et al.* (1963) concluded that oat mosaic virus, which occurs in the southeastern states and in the state of Washington (McKinney, 1946; Bruehl and Damsteegt, 1961), is now a serious threat to the crop.

Lastly, among soft fruit crops, the diseases affecting raspberry and strawberry in Britain have probably received most attention. Arabis mosaic virus is common in strawberry in some parts of England (Lister, 1960a) and raspberry ringspot virus is prevalent in raspberry in eastern Scotland (Cadman, 1956), where the success of any new raspberry variety depends on its reaction to the virus.

6–3. GENERAL PROPERTIES OF THE VIRUSES

Table 6–1 groups soil-borne viruses according to their method of spread and some of their general properties. This list does not include viruses that seem to spread occasionally by root grafting (Hutchins, 1933) or root contact (Roberts, 1948). Aphid-transmitted viruses are also omitted, because although some of the species that spend part of their lives below ground feeding on roots are vectors (e.g., *Anuraphis subterranea* transmits cucumber mosaic virus; Heinze, 1950), tests seem only to have been made when they were feeding on shoots.

Harrison (1960) called the viruses in Group 1 the "soil-borne ringspot viruses," but Cadman (1963) suggests that "NEPO-viruses," i.e., NEmatode-transmitted viruses with POlyhedral particles, is a better name; it avoids the ambiguities that arise because the viruses do not cause ringspot symptoms in all their hosts, and because ringspot lesions can be caused by viruses outside the group. Similarly, the viruses in Group 2 can be called "NETU-viruses," i.e., NEmatode-transmitted viruses with TUbular particles. The other groupings given in Table 6–1 are more tentative than these two, and further names would be premature.

TABLE 6-1. SOME GENERAL PROPERTIES OF SOIL-BORNE VIRUSES

Virus	Particle Shape and Size	Thermal Inactivation Point (°C)	First Species Infected From Soil	Reference
Group 1. (NEPO-viruses)				
A. With nematode vectors				
Arabis mosaic				
Arabis mosaic form	polyhedral, c. 30 mμ diameter	60	Raspberry, sugar beet	(Harrison, 1958c)
Grapevine fanleaf form	"	65	Grapevine	(Petri, 1929) (Cadman, 1956; Harrison, 1956)
Raspberry ringspot	"	70	Raspberry	(Lister, 1963)
Strawberry latent ringspot	"	56	Cucumber	(Hendrix, 1961)
Tobacco ringspot	"	60	Tobacco	
Tomato black ring				
Beet ringspot form	"	65	Sugar beet, etc.	(Harrison, 1957)
Lettuce ringspot form	"	65	Lettuce	(Smith & Short, 1959)
Tomato ringspot				
Peach yellow bud mosaic strain	"	60	Peach	(Wagnon & Breece, 1955)
Group 2. (NETU-viruses)				
Pea early browning	tubular, 210 mμ and 105 mμ long	70–78	Pea, etc.	(Bos & van der Want, 1962)
Tobacco rattle	tubular, 185 × 25 mμ and 75 × 25 mμ	80	Tobacco	(Böning, 1931)
B. With fungus-assisted spread				
Group 3.				
Tobacco necrosis	spherical, c. 30 mμ diameter	85–95	Tobacco	(Smith, 1937a)
Cucumber necrosis	–	80	Cucumber	(McKeen, 1959)
Unnamed *Chrysanthemum* virus	–	92	Tobacco	(Brierley & Travis, 1958)
C. Method of spread unknown				
Group 4.				
Lettuce big-vein	–	–	Lettuce	(Jagger & Chandler, 1934)
Tobacco stunt	–	–	Tobacco	(Uozumi, 1954)
Group 5.				
U.S.A. wheat mosaic & wheat yellow mosaic	rod, 130 × 25 mμ	65	Wheat	(McKinney, 1923)
Japanese wheat mosaic & wheat yellow mosaic	rod, 120–180 × 25 mμ	–	Wheat	(Wada & Fukano, 1937)
Barley yellow mosaic	–	–	Barley	(Miyamoto, 1958a)
Oat mosaic	–	46	Oat	(McKinney, 1946)
Sugar-cane chlorotic streak	–	–	Sugar cane	(Antoine, 1957)
Group 6.				
Tobacco mosaic	tubular, 300 × 16 mμ	93	Tobacco	(Beijerinck, 1898)

TABLE 6–2. SYNONYMS OF NEPO-VIRUSES

Virus	Synonym	Evidence for synonymy
Arabis mosaic	Cherry rasp-leaf (in part)	Cadman, 1960
	Raspberry yellow dwarf	Cadman, 1960
	Rhubarb mosaic	Cadman, 1960; Schade, 1960
	Strawberry mosaic	Jha, 1961
	Strawberry yellow crinkle	Jha, 1961
Grapevine fan-leaf	Grapevine yellow mosaic*	Dias and Harrison, 1963
Tomato black ring	Beet ringspot†	Harrison, 1958a
	Celery yellow vein	Hollings and Stone, 1962
	Lettuce ringspot	Harrison, 1958a
	Potato bouquet	Harrison, 1958a
	Potato pseudo-aucuba†	Bercks and Gehring, 1956; Bercks, 1962
Raspberry ring-spot	Cherry Pfeffingerkrankheit†	Cadman, 1960
	Cherry rasp-leaf (in part)†	Cadman, 1960
	Raspberry (Scottish) leaf curl	Cadman, 1956
	Red currant spoon leaf*	Harrison, 1961a
Tomato ringspot	Cherry (Eola) rasp-leaf	Milbrath and Reynolds, 1961
	Grapevine yellow vein	Gooding, 1963
	Peach yellow bud mosaic	Cadman and Lister, 1961
Tobacco ringspot	Lettuce calico	Grogan and Schnathorst, 1955

* Produces distinctive symptoms but shares many antigenic groups with the type strain.

† Shares only a few antigenic groups with the type strain.

A. NEMATODE-TRANSMITTED VIRUSES WITH POLYHEDRAL PARTICLES (NEPO-VIRUSES)

Four of the viruses in Group 1 (arabis mosaic, raspberry ringspot, strawberry latent ringspot, and tomato black ring) have been found only in Europe, some in several different countries; two (tobacco ringspot and tomato ringspot) are found in America, and one (grapevine fanleaf) occurs in many countries on several continents. Reports of tobacco ringspot virus in Europe seem of doubtful validity or to refer to virus imported in vegetatively propagated plants. Except for arabis mosaic and grapevine fanleaf viruses, which share a few antigenic groups (Cadman et al., 1960), these viruses seem not to react with antisera to other members of Group 1, although distant relationships cannot be excluded. NEPO-viruses, however, have several properties in common in addition to those implicit in this name; they all have particles about 30 mµ in diameter (Steere, 1956; Cadman et al., 1960; Harrison and Nixon, 1960; Cadman and Lister, 1962), wide host ranges, and thermal inactivation points in the range 55°–70°C. Tomato black ring (Harrison, 1958a; Bercks, 1962), raspberry ringspot (Harrison, 1958b; Cadman, 1960), and tobacco ringspot (Kahn et al., 1962) viruses each occur in forms which differ greatly from one another in antigenic constitution. The different forms of raspberry ringspot and tomato black ring viruses, respectively, seem to have different specific vectors.

Because they mostly have a wide natural host range, NEPO-viruses cause crop diseases too numerous to mention individually, and several of the viruses have received different names when found by different workers in different plants (Table 6–2). A factor that has helped to establish the synonymy of different names is the introduction of improved methods for transmitting viruses to herbaceous species by manual inoculation from plants containing tannins (Cadman, 1959a; Diener and Weaver, 1959) or with acid sap (Cadman et al., 1960). However, symptoms alone often do not greatly help in establishing the relationship of two viruses. One virus may cause different diseases in the same crop plant. For instance, grapevine fanleaf and grapevine yellow mosaic diseases, which both result from growing plants in infested soil (Hewitt and Delp, 1953; Hewitt, 1956), look very different although caused by closely related strains of the same virus (Dias and Harrison, 1963). Another example is raspberry ringspot virus, which causes different diseases in different raspberry varieties, e.g., leaf curl in Norfolk Giant and ringspot in Malling Jewel (Cadman, 1956). Or, similar diseases in a crop may be caused by different viruses; in different localities cherry diseases of the rasp-leaf type are associated with either raspberry ringspot, arabis mosaic, or tomato ringspot viruses (Cadman, 1960; Cropley, 1961; Milbrath and Reynolds, 1961). Indeed, symptoms caused by NEPO-viruses do no more than permit an intelligent guess at the identity of the virus involved, and critical identifications are best done by serological tests. Strawberry latent ringspot virus, which causes symptoms in herbaceous plants like those caused by arabis mosaic virus, was discovered only because it did not react with antiserum to arabis mosaic virus (Lister, 1963).

NEPO-viruses are transmitted through a large proportion of the seeds of several of their hosts (Henderson, 1931; Kahn, 1956; Lister, 1960b; Brückbauer and Rüdel, 1961), including weed as well as crop species. The virus may come from either ovule or pollen, and infected progeny seedlings often show slight or no symptoms (Lister and Murant, 1962). Typically, NEPO-viruses cause severe symptoms in the first parts of a plant to be invaded systemically, whereas leaves formed later contain the virus but look almost normal. Seedlings infected with seed-borne virus often behave like experimentally infected plants already recovered from the phase of showing severe symptoms, which is consistent with the idea

that severe symptoms develop in tissues invaded after they have started to differentiate from the meristem but not in those invaded when meristematic.

B. Nematode-transmitted Viruses with Tubular Particles (NETU-viruses)

Tobacco rattle and pea early browning viruses both have wide host ranges (Schmelzer, 1957; Bos and van der Want, 1962). Tobacco rattle virus occurs naturally in Europe and North America in over 100 plant species, which include bulbous (van Slogteren, 1958) and nonbulbous (Uschdraweit and Valentin, 1956) ornamental plants, crop plants such as tobacco and potato, and weed species (Noordam, 1956; Cadman and Harrison, 1959). In tobacco, the diseases called Mauche (Behrens, 1899) and Steifen und Kräuselkrankheit (Böning, 1931) in early German papers are probably the same as that known in the Netherlands as ratel (rattle) or partridge (Quanjer, 1943).

An interesting feature of tobacco rattle virus is that it often fails to become systemic or becomes only partially systemic; in many species it is restricted to the roots of naturally infected plants. Only one or a few of the shoots produced by an infected potato plant may show symptoms of stem-mottle and some of the tubers set by a plant with stem-mottle may give rise to healthy progeny plants. The infected tubers are often misshapen and may contain small brown internal spots (Rozendaal, 1947). These tuber symptoms differ from the corky arcs (Fig. 6–1), known in different countries as spraing, corky ringspot, kringerigheid, and Pfropfenbildung, which occur in tubers of normal shape. Spraing lesions probably result from infections of tobacco rattle virus that occur when vector nematodes feed on the superficial tissue of the developing tuber. Spraing is essentially a symptom of primary infection and, in Britain, rarely recurs in tubers produced by plants grown from tubers with spraing; such progeny seem free of virus. Whether this is because the virus strains that cause spraing have even less ability to invade plants systemically than those that cause stem-mottle,

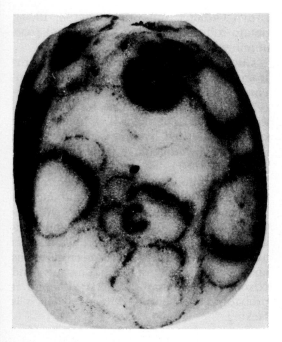

Fig. 6–1. Tuber of potato (*Solanum tuberosum* var. Olympic) with skin removed to show the lesions of spraing disease.

none; isolates of the first type give rise to those of the second but not vice versa (Cadman and Harrison, 1959). Plants infected with isolates that are difficult to transmit contain considerable amounts of infective virus nucleic acid, but little or none of this gets incorporated into the stable rod-shaped particles characteristic of tobacco rattle virus (Sänger and Brandenburg, 1961; Cadman, 1962). Infectivity of the unstable particles can be preserved by extracting leaves in water-saturated phenol or other media that remove or inhibit enzyme systems that inactivate free virus nucleic acid in leaf sap. Isolates that have unstable particles have also been found with tobacco necrosis (Babos and Kassanis, 1962), tobacco mosaic (Siegel *et al.*, 1962), and pea early browning (Gibbs and Harrison, 1964) viruses. Isolates of tobacco rattle virus having unstable particles are common in naturally infected plants, but whether they arise as variants in plants initially inoculated with stable particles (Cadman and Harrison, 1959), or whether vector nematodes can infect plants directly with unstable particles is not known.

The stable rod-shaped particles of tobacco rattle virus are of two main lengths, about 75 mμ and 185 mμ respectively, only the longer of which is infective (Harrison and Nixon, 1959); the short particles, which predominate in some preparations, are not known to play any role in infection.

Pea early browning virus occurs naturally in pea and lucerne crops in the Netherlands and in Britain (Bos and van der Want, 1962; Gibbs and Harrison, 1963). Like tobacco rattle virus it does not readily invade plants systemically. In pea, for instance, the symptoms may be limited to part of the stem or to one of the leaflets. The particles of pea early browning virus also are of two main lengths, but unlike those of tobacco rattle virus the shorter (105 mμ) is about half as long as the longer (210 mμ).

C. TOBACCO NECROSIS AND ALLIED VIRUSES

Those of the viruses in Group 3 that have been examined in the electron microscope have particles similar in size and gross

whether the varieties that develop spraing are those that do not become infected systemically, or whether the small brown spots associated with stem-mottle are a consequence of virus entering the tuber through the stolon is uncertain. There is, however, good evidence that spraing and stem-mottle are caused by strains of the same virus (Lihnell, 1958; Walkinshaw and Larson, 1958; Cadman, 1959b), for tobacco rattle virus can be obtained from infected but not from normal tubers, though often only with difficulty from those with spraing. Eibner (1959) obtained further evidence from a survey, which showed that spraing developed only on soils that were infested with tobacco rattle virus, and concluded that this was its cause.

Another interesting feature of tobacco rattle virus is that isolates differ greatly in the ease with which they can be transmitted by manual inoculation of sap. Single lesions of some isolates may give rise to hundreds of lesions when juice from them is inoculated to other plants, whereas single lesions of other isolates may give few or

morphology to those in Group 1, but higher thermal inactivation points. The best known are the tobacco necrosis viruses, which are particularly common in glasshouse soils and take their name from their effects on young tobacco seedlings (Smith and Bald, 1935). Recent work on several of these viruses isolated in Britain and the Netherlands shows that among them there are two serologically distinguishable forms which share only few antigenic groups, whereas many are shared by isolates belonging to any one form (Babos and Kassanis, 1963a). It had long been known that different tobacco necrosis viruses could be distinguished serologically (Bawden, 1941; Bawden and Pirie, 1942), but Babos and Kassanis (1963a) now propose to use serological tests to define the group as well as to differentiate its members. They suggest that the name tobacco necrosis virus should be reserved for viruses with some antigenic groups in common with their strain A. Thus Canadian cucumber necrosis virus, which did not react with antiserum to either of the forms, is considered a separate entity, whereas a necrosis virus from cucumber in the Netherlands (van Koot and van Dorst, 1955) is considered a tobacco necrosis virus because it is antigenically related.

Tobacco necrosis viruses are common in the roots of many species grown in unsterilized soil at Rothamsted. In winter they often invade the shoots of young tobacco seedlings, producing necrotic lesions on the petioles and basal parts of the older leaves. At other seasons, small amounts of virus occasionally occur in symptomless tobacco shoots. In bean (*Phaseolus vulgaris*), most strains rarely move out of the inoculated leaves, but one, stipple streak, first found in the Netherlands, causes systemic necrosis (Bawden and van der Want, 1949). Tobacco necrosis viruses also cause the necrotic disease of tulips known as *Augusta-ziek*, a name taken from a variety of tulip in which outbreaks were prevalent in earlier years (de Bruyn Ouboter and van Slogteren, 1949; Kassanis, 1949). The viruses are usually restricted to the underground parts of plants, and they rarely seem to produce obvious symptoms, but lesions have been reported on tulip bulbs (de

Bruyn Ouboter and van Slogteren, 1949), potato tubers (Noordam, 1957), and roots of mung bean (Teakle, 1962a).

Cucumber necrosis virus and the virus from *Chrysanthemum* are tentatively included in Group 3 because they have properties similar to tobacco necrosis virus, although it is not known whether their spread is assisted by fungi. The two seem not to have antigenic groups in common (McKeen, 1959).

The satellite virus of tobacco necrosis virus must also be mentioned, although it does not share antigenic groups with tobacco necrosis virus and is only 17 mμ in diameter. It seems to multiply only in cells also infected with tobacco necrosis virus and is extremely stable (Kassanis and Nixon, 1961; Kassanis, 1962); although it probably is soil-borne, critical evidence is lacking.

D. LETTUCE BIG-VEIN AND ALLIED VIRUSES

The study of lettuce big-vein disease has an interesting history. Jagger and Chandler (1934) noted that the symptoms resembled those of a virus disease, and when Doolittle and Thompson (1945) showed that big-vein developed when leaves of healthy lettuce were inoculated with sap from the roots of diseased lettuce, this was taken as evidence that a virus was involved. However, Allen (1948) found that the disease did not develop when precautions were taken to prevent the inoculum from reaching the soil, and in 1958 Grogan *et al.* concluded that no previous workers had proved virus etiology. Big-vein disease was shown to be closely associated with the fungus *Olpidium brassicae* (Grogan *et al.*, 1958; Fry, 1958). Although careful not to dismiss the idea that a virus was involved, Grogan *et al.* then favoured the hypothesis "that the symptoms of big-vein disease are caused by some substance produced by *Olpidium* that induces symptoms after being translocated to the leaves." Later work, however, shows that the causal agent of the disease is transmitted by grafting diseased scions onto healthy stocks, again suggesting that big-vein is a virus disease (Campbell *et al.*, 1961; Tomlinson *et al.*, 1962). The disease has been maintained for six successive transfers to healthy plants by grafting (Campbell and Grogan, 1963).

There is little information on the properties of the presumed virus. No symptoms developed in lettuce or other species inoculated with leaf sap from diseased lettuce, whether or not the inocula were made with the aid of diethyldithiocarbamate, nicotine, alumina or phenol, plus bentonite clay (Campbell and Grogan, 1963). Although a culture of *Olpidium* sp. from a plant with big-vein disease had a fairly wide host range (Sahtiyanci, 1962), it is not clear whether the virus infects plants outside the genera *Lactuca* and *Sonchus* (Tomlinson and Smith, 1959). Grogan *et al.* (1958) found that lettuce seedlings developed big-vein when washed roots of celery, radish, onion, or broccoli plants that were naturally infected with *Olpidium* were added to pots containing steam-sterilized soil, but not when *Olpidium*-infected roots of several other species were added. This, however, does not prove that these plants are hosts for the virus, which possibly persisted in the fungus through its life cycle without being replenished from plants, or may have persisted in adhering resting sporangia (Campbell, 1962).

Tobacco necrosis virus often occurs in the roots of field-infected plants with big-vein (Fry, 1952; Yarwood, 1954), but isolates obtained from lettuce do not produce big-vein symptoms when inoculated to lettuce, and only exceptionally is tobacco necrosis virus found in the roots of plants infected experimentally with big-vein virus (Fry, 1952; Tomlinson and Smith, 1958; Tomlinson and Garrett, 1962; Campbell *et al.*, 1961; Campbell and Grogan, 1963). The most plausible explanation of the inconsistent association between tobacco necrosis virus and lettuce big-vein disease is that conditions favouring the spread of one virus by *Olpidium* will probably also favour the spread of the other.

In many ways tobacco stunt, a disease reported from Japan, behaves like lettuce big-vein. The pathogen is transmitted by grafting infected scions to healthy stocks but not by manual inoculation (Hidaka, 1956), it seems to have a limited host range

(i.e., the genus *Nicotiana;* Hidaka, Uozumi, and Hiruki, 1956), and the disease is associated with a species of *Olpidium* (Hidaka, 1960). Tobacco stunt and lettuce big-vein both develop best at about 15°C. Symptoms of tobacco stunt developed in plants kept at 17°C but not at 25°C, although there was evidence of some infection at the higher temperature (Hidaka and Hiruki, 1956a). By comparison, symptoms of lettuce big-vein developed at 10°–15°C (7°–10°C at night) but not at 18°–24°C (10°–15°C at night) (Thompson and Doolittle, 1942). Also, both diseases occur in plants grown in infested soil which has been air-dried (Hidaka, Uozumi, and Shimizu, 1956; Pryor, 1946). However, the grouping of tobacco stunt virus with lettuce big-vein virus must be considered provisional.

E. WHEAT MOSAIC AND ALLIED VIRUSES

The viruses listed in Group 5 behave very like those in Group 4. Each affects only one or a few genera of plants, and symptoms often develop best at 15°–18°C; but whereas some of the cereal mosaic viruses can be transmitted with difficulty by manual inoculation of sap, the viruses in Group 4 have not been transmitted in this way. The viruses causing wheat mosaic and wheat yellow mosaic are reported from various parts of North America and from Japan; an apparently similar virus is described from Italy (Dijkstra and Grancini, 1960). However, although many of these viruses seem to behave similarly (Sill, 1958), there is no critical evidence that isolates from different countries or localities are related. Barley yellow mosaic virus, found in Japan, does not infect wheat, and oat mosaic virus, found in the United States, infects only *Avena* spp. Sugar-cane chlorotic streak virus, which has a wide distribution, is the most tentative member of Group 5; sugar cane and species of *Pennisetum* (Bird, 1961; Sturgess, 1961) are almost its only recorded hosts and nothing is known about its properties *in vitro*. None of these pathogens is easy to study, and the best evidence that they are viruses is that plants infected with some of them have yielded characteristic rod-shaped virus-like particles (Gold *et al.*, 1957; Saito *et al.*, 1961). Also, in the United States and Japan, leaves of wheat plants with mosaic sometimes contain characteristic inclusion bodies (McKinney *et al.*, 1923; Wada and Fukano, 1934), suggesting that plants may contain considerable amounts of virus, and that difficulty in infecting plants by manual inoculation may be, at least in part, caused by difficulty in extracting the viruses from source plants or in making suitable entry points in inoculated leaves.

F. Tobacco Mosaic Virus

TMV is considered on its own because although a great deal is known about the virus itself, little is known about the way it infects plants from soil and there is no evidence that it should be included in any other group. Soil-borne TMV often appears to play a part in starting outbreaks of mosaic in tomato and tobacco crops (Doolittle, 1928; Johnson and Ogden, 1929). Although some infections presumably occur through the roots, Fulton (1941) found that the virus did not spread readily from root to shoot in experimentally inoculated tobacco plants and Johnson (1937) suggested that most primary infections of tobacco shoots are caused by contact of stems and leaves with contaminated soil. Once the virus reaches the shoots of a few primarily infected plants, spread to other plants by direct contact or during cultural operations is rapid. It would be interesting to know whether wild strains of the virus, such as the ribgrass strain (Holmes, 1941) often spread through the soil.

The other viruses listed in Table 6-1 are included only for completeness, for nothing is known about their properties or how they are transmitted in the soil.

6-4. METHODS OF TRANSMISSION

A. Transmission by Nematodes

1. *Evidence that nematodes are vectors.* —There are several types of evidence that nematodes transmit plant viruses. One comes from correlating the occurrence of a specific nematode with that of diseased plants in fields where the diseased plants are in patches. Thus, the distribution of arabis mosaic virus in raspberry and strawberry crops was closely correlated with that of *Xiphinema diversicaudatum*, and the distribution of tomato black ring virus (beet ringspot form) with that of *Longidorus elongatus*, whereas neither virus could be related to the occurrence of other plant-parasitic nematodes (Harrison and Cadman, 1959; Harrison *et al.*, 1961). Similarly, patches of plants infected with tobacco ringspot virus in a spearmint crop coincided with infestations of *X. americanum* (Stone *et al.*, 1962). Where diseased plants are not patchily distributed, a correlation can sometimes be obtained by comparing the nematode population in soils where the virus spreads with that where it does not spread. Thus, *X. index* was found in most of the vineyards where grapevine fanleaf virus was spreading and not in those where the virus occurred but was not spreading (Hewitt *et al.*, 1958; Raski and Hewitt, 1963).

It is, however, highly desirable that handpicked nematodes should be used in any attempt to establish the identity of a nematode vector. One such experiment, which is particularly suitable for perennial plants, was first made by Hewitt *et al.* (1958), who showed that when diseased and healthy grapevines were grown in the same container, fanleaf virus spread from one to the other only when *X. index* was added to the containers. No spread took place in containers with healthy plants and *X. index*.

In another type of experiment, bait plants are exposed to hand-picked nematodes. Bait plants may be any species susceptible to the virus in question and which, after a suitable length of exposure to the nematodes, are inspected for symptoms or, preferably, tested for virus by inoculating sap from their roots and shoots to indicator species, of which *Chenopodium amaranticolor* is one of the most useful. Shoot symptoms may take many months to appear with some combinations of virus and species of bait plant, and with others the virus rarely or never spreads systemically. Hence more complete results are obtained sooner by inoculating sap from the roots of bait plants to indicator plants, usually after exposing the bait plants to the nematodes for 4–6 weeks.

Infective nematodes are obtained either by sampling virus-carrying populations in field soil or by allowing virus-free populations to feed on infected plants. Large nematodes, such as *Xiphinema* spp. and *Longidorus* spp., are usually extracted from the soil by sieving; but *Trichodorus* spp., smaller nematodes, are often extracted by other methods, such as that using a Seinhorst elutriator (Sol and Seinhorst, 1961). The method of extraction is important, because *L. elongatus* extracted in Baermann funnels did not transmit tomato black ring virus, whereas those extracted by sieving did (Harrison *et al.*, 1961). The nematodes to be tested are picked out of a suspension, which also contains other species and varying amounts of debris, transferred to distilled water one or more times, and added in water to peat, sand, or sterilized soil in which suitable plants are grown. In their early work, Hewitt *et al.* (1958) showed that batches of *X. index* obtained in this way transmitted grapevine fanleaf virus, and in later work the virus was transmitted by single nematodes (Raski and Hewitt, 1960). The nematode species listed in Table 6–3 have transmitted other viruses in similar tests, usually using 1–50 nematodes per pot. In tests of this type, it is important to add to other pots the mixture of nematodes and debris that remains after all individuals of the chosen nematode species are removed. Only when these residues give no transmissions can it be argued that the soil contained only one vector species (Harrison and Cadman, 1959; Harrison *et al.*, 1961).

Nematodes from infective populations sometimes transmit more readily when allowed to feed on healthy plants, which are hosts of the virus, before bait plants are grown, than when bait plants are grown in freshly collected field soil. Thus Walkinshaw *et al.* (1961) found tobacco rattle virus was transmitted to tobacco more often when soil infested with *Trichodorus christiei* was first cropped with initially healthy maize, than when tobacco was planted directly in field soil. Maize was a good host for both nematode and virus, whereas to-bacco was a poor host of the nematode. Feeding the vectors on favourable preliminary hosts may be an important aid in obtaining nematodes that feed readily on bait plants.

Experiments in which bait plants are grown in soil that is contaminated with virus, but which does not contain nematodes, also show that a vector is necessary for transmission. For example, when large amounts of sap containing tomato black ring or raspberry ringspot viruses were added to sterilized soil in which bait plants were growing, or when sterilized soil was used to grow artificially infected crops and their roots left in the soil when the bait seedlings were planted, the viruses did not spread (Harrison, 1958b). There was also no spread of virus when washed roots of plants naturally infected with tomato black ring virus were added to pots containing bait plants (Cadman and Harrison, 1960), showing that any vector present was not closely associated with plant roots; indeed, vector nematodes are rarely found adhering to roots.

Valuable circumstantial evidence of the role of nematodes is given by tests made to see whether subjecting infested soil to a variety of treatments has parallel effects on the nematodes and on the virus-transmitting system in soil. Neither survived air-drying for a week in soil infested with tomato black ring or arabis mosaic viruses (Cadman and Harrison, 1960), and in soil infested with tobacco rattle virus neither survived rubbing between a block of wood and a tile (Sol *et al.*, 1960). Also, treating soil with chemicals that have no effect on the infectivity of sap containing tomato black ring or arabis mosaic viruses killed the vector nematodes and prevented bait plants becoming infected (Harrison and Cadman, 1959; Cadman and Harrison, 1960). At the doses used some of these chemicals, e.g., pentachloronitrobenzene, did not kill nonvector plant-parasitic nematodes belonging to the Tylenchida. Finally, when suspensions of soil infested with arabis mosaic virus were passed through a series of sieves of decreasing pore size, and bait seedlings grown in the material retained by each sieve, the seed-

TABLE 6–3. NEMATODE VECTORS OF PLANT VIRUSES

Virus		Vector (Reference)
A. NEPO-viruses		
Arabis mosaic	Type form	*Xiphinema diversicaudatum* (Jha & Posnette, 1959; Harrison & Cadman, 1959)
	"	*X. paraelongatum* (Fritzsche & Schmidt, 1963)
	"	*X.* sp. (Fritzsche & Schmidt, 1963)
	Grapevine fanleaf form	*X. index* (Hewitt *et al.*, 1958)
	Grapevine yellow mosaic strain	*X. index* (Hewitt *et al.*, 1962)
Strawberry latent ringspot		*X. diversicaudatum* (Lister, 1963)
Tobacco ringspot		*X. americanum* (Fulton, 1962)
Tomato ringspot	Peach yellow bud mosaic strain	*X. americanum* (Breece & Hart, 1959)
Raspberry ringspot	Scottish form	*Longidorus elongatus* (Taylor, 1962)
	English form	*L. macrosoma* (Harrison, 1962)
Tomato black ring	Beet ringspot form	*L. elongatus* (Harrison *et al.*, 1961)
	Lettuce ringspot form	*L. attenuatus* (Harrison *et al.*, 1961)
B. NETU-viruses		
Tobacco rattle	Dutch culture	*Trichodorus pachydermus* (Sol & Seinhorst, 1961)
	U.S.A. culture	*T. christiei* (Walkinshaw *et al.*, 1961)
	British culture	*T. primitivus* (Harrison, 1961b)
Pea early browning	Dutch culture	*T. teres, T. pachydermus* (van Hoof, 1962)
	British culture	*T. viruliferus* (Gibbs & Harrison, 1963)

lings became infected only in the fractions containing *X. diversicaudatum* (Harrison and Cadman, 1959).

These different kinds of evidence all lead directly or indirectly to the conclusion that the viruses listed in Table 6–3 are transmitted by nematodes, and apparently only by nematodes, in ways directly comparable to those in which viruses are transmitted by arthropods.

2. *Relation between virus and vector.—a. Range of vector species and mode of feeding.* The vector nematodes fall into two groups, which correspond to the two groups of viruses. NEPO-viruses are transmitted by *Xiphinema* and *Longidorus* spp. and NETU-viruses by *Trichodorus* spp. (Harrison *et al.*, 1961). *Xiphinema* and *Longidorus* are closely allied genera in the subfamily Tylencholaiminae of the family Dorylaimidae, and are large nematodes, adults of most species measuring at least 3 mm long. *Trichodorus* is classified in the family Trichodoridae and has adults about 1 mm long. All three genera belong to the Order Dorylaimida, in which they are the only well-known plant parasites, whereas the great majority of plant-parasitic species

belong to the Order Tylenchida (Goodey, 1963). Several members of the Tylenchida have been tested specifically (Sol *et al.*, 1960) or incidentally in work with several of the nematode-transmitted viruses, but have not transmitted them.

Within the vector genera, species are separated on minor anatomical differences, which may be difficult or impossible to observe without killing the specimen. Identification to species is, however, important and the reader is referred to the following papers for help: for *Xiphinema index* to Thorne and Allen (1950); for *X. diversicaudatum* to Goodey *et al.* (1960); for *Longidorus* spp. to Hooper (1961); for *Trichodorus* spp. to Allen (1957) and Hooper (1962, 1963).

The three vector genera all have fairly long stylets, but tylenchid nematodes with long stylets, such as species of *Hemicycliophora,* seem unable to transmit (Sol *et al.,* 1960). Whether the apparent restriction of vectors to the Dorylaimida depends on differences from the Tylenchida in anatomy or in physiology is not clear although, as Raski and Hewitt (1963) have pointed out, the dorsal salivary gland discharges into the anterior part of the oesophagus in most Tylenchida but much nearer the junction of oesophagus and intestine in the vectors. How such a difference might affect ability to transmit is speculative.

The stylet is tubular in *Xiphinema* (Fig. 6–2) and *Longidorus;* in *Trichodorus* it is a slightly curved tooth. Many of the feeding punctures seem to occur near root tips, where gall formation may be induced by *X. diversicaudatum* and *X. index* (Schindler, 1957; Raski and Radewald, 1958; Fig. 6–3); root-tip feeding by *Trichodorus* may arrest growth (Rhode and Jenkins, 1957; Zuckerman, 1961). These effects are produced in varieties of plants that seem immune to virus infection (Harrison and Winslow, 1961). However, some instances of poor crop growth that are attributed to damage caused by nematodes in vector genera may well be caused by viruses transmitted by the nematodes. Little is known about the details of the feeding process in *Xiphinema* or *Longidorus,* but Zuckerman (1961) found that *T. christiei* fed only on epidermal root cells, usually near the root cap (Fig. 6–4). The cells were punctured by a rapid probing motion of the stylet and their contents then withdrawn. After 1–4.5 min the nematodes moved to another cell, which sometimes was punctured only 10 sec after leaving the first. One nematode was observed feeding in this manner for 8 hours. Most vectors apparently have a wide host range.

b. *Acquisition and transmission of virus.* The minimum reported periods for nematodes to acquire viruses from plants and, having acquired them to transmit them to other plants, are access periods, not feeding periods. Thus, using batches of 5–10 nematodes, Jha and Posnette (1961) showed that *X. diversicaudatum* could acquire arabis mosaic virus in 1 day and that nematodes which had already acquired the virus

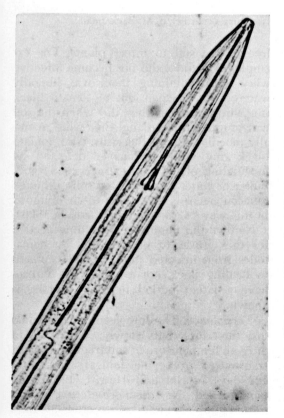

Fig. 6–2. Anterior end of larval *Xiphinema diversicaudatum.* Note the functional spear and the tripartite expanded basal flanges on the spear extension; also the developing spear posterior to the functional one.

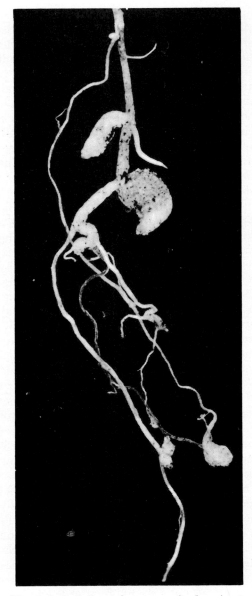

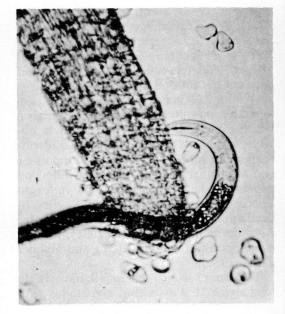

Fig. 6–4. *Trichodorus christiei* feeding on root of cranberry (courtesy B. M. Zuckerman).

Fig. 6–3. Galls formed on roots of celery (*Apium dulce*) exposed to *X. diversicaudatum* (Harrison and Winslow, 1961).

in the field could transmit it to bait plants in 3 days. Raski and Hewitt (1960) found that a few grapevine cuttings became infected with grapevine fanleaf virus when each was infested for 1 day with 600 *X. index* from an infective population. Feeding on infected plants is the only known way nematodes can acquire virus; nematodes do not seem to enable virus that is free in the soil to infect plants. For example, nematodes did not become infective when soil containing them was liberally watered with suspensions of tomato black ring virus, whereas they did when the soil was cropped with plants that were manually inoculated with the virus. Also, tomato black ring virus was never detected by inoculating plants with extracts made with buffer or water from infested soils although tobacco necrosis virus was often obtained in this way (Cadman and Harrison, 1960).

Neither the minimum total time needed for the viruses to be acquired by nematodes from infected plants and inoculated to healthy ones, nor whether the viruses have a latent period in their vectors, is known.

c. *Persistence.* The few vectors yet studied lose their infectivity slowly. *X. index* kept at room temperature in soil free from plants transmitted grapevine fanleaf virus after 122 days (Raski and Hewitt, 1963) and hand-picked *X. diversicaudatum* transmitted arabis mosaic virus after 31 days (Jha and Posnette, 1961). When infective populations of *X. diversicaudatum* were placed on a variety of raspberry that does not become infected with arabis mosaic virus when grafted with infected scions (Cadman, 1961), the populations were still infective after 8 months on raspberry but not after 11 months (Harrison and Winslow, 1961). Thus adult nematodes can probably retain and transmit these two viruses for much of their lives. The vectors remain infective for longer than does sap from infected plants, which loses infectivity within a few weeks at 18°C (Harrison, 1958c; Cadman *et al.*, 1960), but there is no critical evidence either for or against the idea that the viruses multiply in the nematodes. Sol (1963) finds that tobacco rattle virus, which is stable for long periods *in vitro*, persists in fasting *T. pachydermus* for at least 36 days.

d. *Retention of virus through the moult.* The ability of *Xiphinema* spp. to retain and transmit viruses for long periods suggests an analogy with the "persistent" viruses transmitted by aphids. It is therefore of interest to know whether the nematode-transmitted viruses are, like aphid-transmitted persistent viruses, retained through the moult; retention would show that the virus is not held solely on the anterior part of the stylet of the nematodes, because this is cast at moulting. A final conclusion is not yet possible because there have only been a few tests; *X. diversicaudatum* did not transmit arabis mosaic virus after moulting but too few nematodes were tested to exclude the possibility that infectivity is occasionally retained (Harrison and Winslow, 1961).

e. *Efficiency of transmission by larvae and adults.* Grapevine fanleaf virus is transmitted by both larval and adult *X. index* (Raski and Hewitt, 1960), and arabis mosaic virus by both larval and adult *X. diversicaudatum*, although somewhat more readily by adults of either sex (Harrison and Winslow, 1961). Larvae, adult females, and adult males of *T. pachydermus* each transmitted tobacco rattle virus (Sol, 1963). By contrast, larvae of *L. elongatus* transmitted tomato black ring virus but adults did not (Harrison *et al.*, 1961), although both adults and larvae can transmit raspberry ringspot virus (Taylor, 1962).

f. *Transmission to progeny through the egg.* Raski and Hewitt (1960) got no evidence that grapevine fanleaf virus is trans-

mitted through the eggs of *X. index*. Direct evidence on this has not been sought with other viruses but the behaviour of arabis mosaic virus in *X. diversicaudatum* shows that it is seldom if ever carried through the egg. Thus the infectivity of a population disappeared after 11 months on a variety of raspberry that is not susceptible to arabis mosaic virus, although the population was increasing in numbers; individuals can be expected to survive up to this time (Harrison and Winslow, 1961).

g. *Detection of virus in nematodes.* Tobacco rattle virus was detected in *Trichodorus* spp. by cutting infective nematodes in a drop of liquid, which was then inoculated to assay plants (Sänger *et al.*, 1962; Sol, quoted by Raski and Hewitt, 1963). Raski and Hewitt (1963) claim that grapevine fanleaf virus can be detected in *X. index* by similar methods. This technique may prove useful for studying the mechanism of virus transmission but, equally, it may only be detecting virus in the intestine that is playing no part in transmission. No effect of plant viruses on their nematode vectors has been reported, but Loewenberg *et al.*, (1959) described effects on *Meloidogyne incognita* which they attributed to a virus-like agent.

h. *Vector specificity.* The association of specific nematodes with natural infections of specific viruses suggests that within vector genera only one or a few species transmit any one virus. Thus, infections with tomato black ring and raspberry ringspot viruses are always associated with *Longidorus* spp., whereas those with tobacco ringspot and arabis mosaic viruses are associated with *Xiphinema* spp.

A still greater specificity exists among antigenically related viruses, for natural infestations of arabis mosaic and grapevine fanleaf viruses, which share a few antigenic groups, are associated with different species of *Xiphinema* and, in experiments, *X. diversicaudatum* transmitted the first but not the second (Dias and Harrison, 1963). Vector specificity also seems linked to antigenic form in tomato black ring and raspberry ringspot viruses. The beet ringspot form of tomato black ring virus, found in Scotland, is transmitted by *L. elongatus*, and the lettuce ringspot form, found in England, is transmitted by *L. attenuatus* (Harrison *et al.*, 1961). Harrison's (1958a) suggestion that the difference between these forms in antigenic constitution could be accounted for by geographical variation now seems wrong, because viruses indistinguishable from beet ringspot occur in Northern Ireland, where they also are associated with *L. elongatus* (Calvert and Harrison, 1963) and viruses resembling each form occur in Germany (Harrison, 1958a; Bercks, 1962). The Scottish and English forms of raspberry ringspot virus also have different vectors, namely, *L. elongatus* and *L. macrosoma*. Preliminary work suggests that *L. macrosoma* and *L. attenuatus* rarely or never transmit the forms of the two viruses that are associated in the field with *L. elongatus* (Harrison, 1964).

Whether this type of vector specificity also occurs among the NETU-viruses is not established. Three different species of *Trichodorus* have been implicated as vectors of tobacco rattle virus in three different countries, but there is no evidence of whether or not one species will transmit all three isolates, and little on the degree of relationship between the viruses studied in the different countries. Again, different species of *Trichodorus* are also implicated in the spread of pea early browning virus in the Netherlands and in Britain and, as with the NEPO-viruses, the viruses associated with the different species share only a few antigenic groups (Gibbs and Harrison, 1964).

In general there is much less information about the details of transmission of the NETU-viruses than of the NEPO-viruses, and no reason to assume that the virus-vector relations of the one group are the same as those of the other, but there are as yet few indications of differences.

B. Fungus-Assisted Transmission

Olpidium, a chytrid, is the only fungal genus known to be involved in the transmission of viruses to plants; the zoospores are the active stage. Although *Olpidium* spp. have not been proved to assist virus spread in aseptic conditions, there is,

equally, no good evidence that other organisms are involved in the spread of tobacco necrosis and lettuce big-vein viruses, and much to implicate species of *Olpidium.* The fungi involved in transmission would, until recently, have been included in the species *O. brassicae,* but it is now clear that several different forms, possibly different species, have been grouped under this name, and as their taxonomy requires further study they will be referred to below by the unqualified name *Olpidium.* The fact that tobacco necrosis virus is sap-transmissible and lettuce big-vein virus is not has influenced the type of experiment made with the two viruses. Results of experiments with lettuce big-vein virus are assessed by inspecting plants for systemic symptoms over a period of several weeks, whereas tobacco necrosis virus, or the lesions it causes, are readily detected in roots only a few days after exposure to infection. Experiments with tobacco necrosis virus have dealt mainly with the early stages of infection by virus added to zoospore suspensions, and those with lettuce big-vein virus have mainly concerned zoospores obtained from virus-infected roots.

1. *Life history of* Olpidium.—*Olpidium* has a simple life history (Sampson, 1939; Sahtiyanci, 1962). Zoosporangia, usually in cells close to the root surface, liberate uniciliate zoospores (Fig. 6–5) through exit

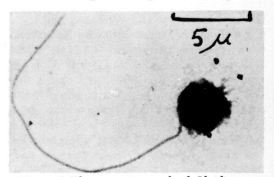

Fig. 6–5. Electron micrograph of *Olpidium* zoospore: not shadowed (courtesy I. Macfarlane and H. L. Nixon).

tubes into the surrounding medium. The zoospores, which swim with the cilium behind, infect other root cells and give rise to new zoosporangia. Occasionally, zoospores are thought to fuse in pairs before infecting and giving rise to thick-walled resting sporangia. In due course the resting sporangia, which readily resist drying, germinate to give zoosporangia, which liberate zoospores as before.

Sahtiyanci (1962) has distinguished three forms of *Olpidium* which previously would have been included in the species *O. brassicae*, one heterothallic and two homothallic, given all three specific rank, and referred them to the genus *Pleotrachelus*. Each form parasitized several different plant species; a culture obtained from lettuce with big-vein, for example, infected eggplant, sugar beet, spinach, tobacco, tomato, and grasses. It is not known how many of the forms can aid the transmission of either of the viruses, although Teakle (1962b) obtained spread of tobacco necrosis virus when using cultures of *Olpidium* from lettuce but not with those from crucifers.

Zoospores, of the culture of *Olpidium* from lettuce with big-vein, infected roots in the following way (Sahtiyanci, 1962). The zoospore settled on the surface of the root, withdrew its cilium, and in a few minutes produced a thin superficial membrane. No further change was seen for two hours. An infection canal then formed, and after another hour the zoospore contents had moved into the cell, leaving the membrane outside. The thallus grew and developed within the cell until, after 2–3 days, a new ripe zoosporangium with exit tube had formed and zoospores were liberated when the root was placed in water. Some resting sporangia were formed about 6 days after infection and some germinated 2–3 weeks later.

2. *Transmission of tobacco necrosis virus.*—Smith (1937a,b) found that roots of many normal-looking plants growing in the glasshouse were infected with tobacco necrosis virus, whether or not the soil in which they were planted was previously sterilized. Plants grown on sterile media and protected from dust and water-splash did not become infected. He found small amounts of virus in dust trapped by drawing glasshouse air through a moist pad of cotton wool (Smith, 1937c), and also in soil water, and he showed that tobacco necrosis

virus infected plants dosed with virus-contaminated water (Smith, 1937a). The importance of water was also implied by Frazier (1955), who found that *Fragaria vesca* roots became infected when they grew in contact with the moist surface of the glasshouse bench.

Bawden and Kassanis (1947) attempted to transmit tobacco necrosis virus with the soil-inhabiting fungi *Rhizoctonia solani* and *Thielaviopsis basicola*, but without success, and its transmission remained unexplained until Teakle (1960) associated *Olpidium* with spread of the virus. He found that few lettuce seedlings became infected when watered with suspensions of virus alone, or *Olpidium* zoospores alone, but many when they were watered with mixed suspensions of virus and zoospores. Later, he showed that some roots became infected when exposed for only a minute to virus plus zoospores before they were washed in running tap water (Teakle, 1962b); presumably the zoospores attached themselves to the roots within this time. He suggested that the virus entered the root cells at the same time as *Olpidium*, about 3 hr after the zoospores adhere to the roots. Thus, virus infections did not develop when roots were dipped for 10 sec in water at 50°C at times up to 2 hr after exposure to virus plus zoospores, whereas the virus did multiply in roots dipped in hot water 3 or more hr after the exposure. *Olpidium* seems to do more than make entry points for the virus, because when roots were heated 1, 2, 3, or 4 hr after exposure to *Olpidium* alone, virus added after the heating did not infect.

Teakle (1962b) also found that the number of virus infections seemed related to the activity and number of the zoospores. Various treatments, such as adding dilute copper sulphate to suspensions of virus plus *Olpidium*, inactivated the zoospores and prevented the virus from infecting roots although they did not inactivate the virus in the inoculum. The effect of number of zoospores was shown by tests in which *Olpidium*-infected, virus-free roots were transferred to fresh lots of water every 2 min; no zoospores were released in the first 2 min, several in the second, and many in the third. Virus was then added to the three suspensions, and susceptible roots were put in each; the numbers of lesions that later developed were related to the zoospore concentration of the suspensions.

That virus and zoospores are closely associated in mixed suspensions is suggested by the claim that adding virus antiserum to virus 5 min before mixing with zoospores prevented the virus infecting roots later exposed to the mixture, whereas adding antiserum 5 min after mixing virus and zoospores did not (Teakle and Gold, 1963). Also, the fact that the zoospore wall, which forms when the zoospore settles on a root, is left outside when the zoospore contents enter the cell suggests that the virus may be carried internally. It is uncertain whether tobacco necrosis virus is carried by zoospores produced in virus-infected cells or from virus-containing zoosporangia, as well as by zoospores that acquire it from suspensions. Teakle and Gold (1963) state that zoospores released from virus-infected roots into 1% antiserum gave several, but somewhat fewer, infections than zoospores released into normal serum; but it is not clear whether this concentration of antiserum would completely have prevented *Olpidium* acquiring virus released into the medium independently of the zoospores.

Taken together, this evidence leaves little doubt that *Olpidium* behaves like a vector in the transmission of tobacco necrosis virus, but some infection occurs without the fungus and possibly without organisms of any kind. Experiments of Babos and Kassanis (1963b) suggest two kinds of transmission, one fungus-dependent and the other not; the fungicide captan prevented bait plants grown in naturally infested soil from becoming infected with tobacco necrosis virus but it did not prevent infection by virus suspensions watered onto sterilized soil. It seems probable that soil water is important for the dissemination of tobacco necrosis virus, which was found by Smith (1937a) in soil extracts, and that the virus is efficiently acquired and carried into root cells by *Olpidium* zoospores, but occasionally gets in by other methods.

Teakle and Gold (1963) found *Olpidium* did not promote the infection of roots by six other sap-transmissible viruses, three of which have nematode vectors. The satellite virus of tobacco necrosis virus, however, seems more likely to be transmitted in a similar way to tobacco necrosis virus, for concomitant spread would provide a ready explanation for the common association of the two viruses in naturally infected plants in glasshouses.

3. *Transmission of lettuce big-vein virus.* —The cause of lettuce big-vein will be referred to as a virus because it is graft-transmitted and there is no evidence that infected lettuce leaves contain any visible pathogen, but that it is a virus is still not established.

The spread of big-vein virus differs in two ways from that of nematode-transmitted viruses. Seedlings will contract big-vein when grown in infested soil previously kept air-dry for several years (Pryor, 1946) and in sterilized soil contaminated either with the washed roots of naturally infected plants or with their superficial scrapings but not with their deeper tissues. Both these differences reflect the behaviour of *Olpidium*, which is consistently associated with lettuce big-vein in the field (Fry, 1958; Grogan et al., 1958). Spread depends on the presence of viable *Olpidium*. Thus big-vein infects plants treated with root sap from infected plants but not those treated with leaf sap (Doolittle and Thompson, 1945), and some fungicides prevent virus spread from naturally infected roots to healthy plants (Grogan et al., 1958).

More direct evidence of the role of *Olpidium* was given by experiments with zoospores, suspensions of which readily transmit big-vein virus from infected to healthy plants. The zoospores are killed and transmission is prevented by heating the suspensions to 60°C for 10 min but after heating to 55°C some survive and the virus occasionally is transmitted. Similarly, when zoospore suspensions were passed through a series of filters, the filtrates from filters with nominal pore sizes of 40–60 μ and 10–15 μ contained many zoospores and readily transmitted big-vein virus, and a filtrate that passed through pores of 4–5.5 μ contained few zoospores and caused few infections (Campbell and Grogan, 1963). Tomlinson and Garrett (1962) showed that when a virus-free culture of the fungus was cultured for three weeks on *Lactuca* plants previously infected with virus by grafting, zoospore suspensions then obtained from the roots transmitted the virus, whereas root washings from *Olpidium*-free, virus-infected *Lactuca* did not.

In contrast to experiments with tobacco necrosis virus, those with lettuce big-vein virus mainly concern virus carried by *Olpidium* from host tissues in which virus and fungus probably multiply together, and the virus has not been acquired by zoospores in suspensions. This is despite the apparently more sensitive techniques of handling *Olpidium* used in work with lettuce big-vein virus. Thus although big-vein symptoms did not develop in all the plants exposed to a few virus-bearing zoospores, the virus could in some instances be detected later by transferring zoospore suspensions from these symptomless plants to other plants, in which symptoms developed (Campbell and Grogan, 1963).

Campbell (1962) found that plants became infected with big-vein virus when they were infested with resting sporangia obtained from plants with big-vein symptoms and stored dry for 2–5 months. Treating the resting sporangia for 2 hr at pH 0.5 with hydrochloric acid or for 30 min at pH 12 with 10% trisodium phosphate did not free all of them from the virus, suggesting that it is carried internally. Also, when the fungus was actively multiplying, he obtained indications that the virus may persist for some weeks. Thus, when a virus-transmitting culture of *Olpidium* from lettuce was transferred serially from sugar beet to sugar beet and then back to lettuce, the lettuce became infected with big-vein virus after 4 transfers lasting 12 weeks on sugar beet but not after 5 transfers lasting 14 weeks. However, Tomlinson and Garrett (1963) found that when big-vein carrying zoospores were added to *Plantago major* or *Veronica persica,* some cultures recovered from these plants 3 weeks later did not carry the virus. Campbell (1962) suggests that the virus does not multiply either in sugar beet or in *Olpidium;* hence the virus would persist in *Olpidium* but not multiply. However, several other interpretations also seem possible.

Hidaka (1960) stated that the occurrence of tobacco stunt is correlated with that of *Olpidium,* although experimental evidence is lacking; but the behaviour of this virus-transmitting system in soil is compatible with the idea that *Olpidium* has a role similar to that played in the transmission of lettuce big-vein virus. The presumed virus-transmitting agent of tobacco stunt survived and transmitted the virus after 4 years in air-dry soil and it passed through a 300-mesh sieve (Hidaka, Uozumi, and Shimizu, 1956; Hidaka and Hiruki, 1956b).

With the increasing evidence that plant-parasitic fungi act as vectors of some viruses, viruses that cause diseases of fungi are of special interest. Hollings (1962) has obtained one or more viruses, with particles resembling in the electron microscope those of some plant viruses, from the sporophores of mushrooms with die-back disease. One of these viruses, which seems to spread by hyphal anastomosis, distorts and depresses the growth of the hyphae, as in the contagious disease previously observed by Lindberg (1959) in *Helminthosporium victoriae.* Whether any of these agents causes diseases in higher plants as well as in fungi is not known.

C. Method of Transmission Unknown

1. *Transmission with evidence that agents in soil are needed.*—In general, the behaviour in soil of the cereal mosaic viruses and sugar-cane chlorotic streak virus, which are included in this section, resembles that of lettuce big-vein virus. For instance, American wheat mosaic virus infects plants grown either in infested soil kept air-dry for several years (McKinney, 1923) or in the fraction of infested soil that passes through a 250-mesh sieve (McKinney, 1953). Spread of wheat mosaic and oat mosaic viruses seems associated with agents which, like *Olpidium* but unlike vector nematodes, are closely associated with roots. Thus, healthy plants became infected when grown in soil contaminated with the roots of naturally infected plants

but not in soil contaminated with virus-containing roots from plants infected by manual inoculation (McKinney *et al.*, 1957). Although some quite different mechanism of virus spread may be involved, experiments with the cereal mosaic viruses and root-inhabiting parasites seem indicated; three kinds of organisms that appear to have the properties required of the agents that aid virus spread are the myxomycete *Polymyxa graminis*, reported from the roots of plants with wheat mosaic (Linford and McKinney, 1954) and with oat mosaic (Bruehl and Damsteegt, 1961), *Helminthosporium* spp., which McKinney (1923) once suggested were associated with wheat mosaic, and *Olpidium* spp., which occur in the roots of plants with oat mosaic (Bruehl and Damsteegt, 1961).

Bird *et al.* (1958) showed that sugar-cane chlorotic streak virus spreads readily from plant to plant when diseased and healthy plants are grown in water culture in separate containers and culture solution is circulated between the containers. This, when considered together with the observation that the virus infects plants when their roots are immersed for 7 days in sap from roots of infected plants but does not infect plants immersed in leaf or stalk sap (Sturgess, 1961), suggests that virus spread may depend on an agent closely associated with roots and able to be carried in water. Indeed, a chytrid-like organism was reported from sugar cane with chlorotic streak by Carpenter (1940), although Abbott and Sass (1945) concluded that bodies of the type observed by Carpenter were an effect of virus infection on the host.

In the soil, barley yellow mosaic virus seems to behave very like wheat mosaic virus (Miyamoto, 1958a,b; 1959a,b) and is therefore considered in this section. An important difference, however, is that a few barley plants were infected by inoculating their leaves with a slowly sedimenting fraction of soil from infested fields. Another difference is that a few seedlings became infected when grown in clay preparations to which sap from infected plants was added several months previously. Thus the virus was detectable in soil fractions, it infected plants when added to the potting medium, and there was no evidence that soil-inhabiting organisms were involved in transmission. These results, however, do not exclude the possibility that spread may be assisted by an agent similar to that involved in the spread of wheat mosaic virus. The infective soil fraction may have contained this agent, some of which, when inoculated to the leaves, was perhaps borne by liquid running off the leaves into the soil, where it then carried the virus into root cells. This is the type of infection that occurs when lettuce leaves are inoculated with sap from the roots of plants with big-vein disease (Allen, 1948). Similarly, a small amount of barley root included in the material used to prepare the inoculum added to the clay may have contained the agent which spread the virus.

2. *Transmission without evidence that agents in soil are needed.*—Tobacco mosaic is now the only virus included in this section, and its spread in soil has not been studied in the light of recent findings about organisms that assist viruses to infect. But if viruses do exist that spread in soil by means of some process resembling mechanical inoculation, TMV is an obvious candidate. It overwinters in infected plant debris (Johnson and Ogden, 1929) and as virus leached from infected debris into the soil (Hoggan and Johnson, 1936), where it can be adsorbed by clays (van der Want, 1952). Infectivity appears to be maintained best in conditions that least favour the activity of aerobic micro-organisms. Thus, virus in dried plant debris lost infectivity more rapidly in moist than in dry aerobic soil, and in moist aerobic than in moist anaerobic sand. Also, when the virus was added as a suspension, infectivity was lost more rapidly in moist soil than in dry or waterlogged soil; but when virus and moist soil were kept together in aseptic conditions, little infectivity was lost in 6 months (Johnson and Ogden, 1929). Although plants become infected when grown in soil contaminated with the sap or roots of plants infected with TMV by manual inoculation (McKinney, 1927), the possibility that soil-inhabiting organisms are sometimes or often concerned in the field spread of the virus is not excluded.

6–5. VIRUS ECOLOGY

A. METHODS OF SURVIVAL

Virus ecology depends on the behaviour of the virus and of its vector, if any, in relation to the plant hosts of each; it also depends on the relation between virus and vector. Hence, in considering the survival of a vector-transmitted virus, the ecology of the vector is as important as the behaviour of the virus in the vector and host plant.

Nearly all nematode-transmitted viruses and also their vector nematodes have extensive host ranges, which ensure survival on weed hosts when immune crops are grown. Among wild species, woody plants seem particularly important as hosts of arabis mosaic virus and its vector *X. diversicaudatum;* in some parts of Britain both virus and vector are restricted to woods and to hedgerows containing woody plants (Harrison and Winslow, 1961; Pitcher and Jha, 1961). Both virus and vector are probably much less widely distributed now than before the advent of agriculture, when much land was forested, their distribution decreasing as increasing areas of land were taken for farming.

Most nematode-transmitted viruses seem best considered as pathogens of wild plants which become important in crops when infested land is taken into cultivation. Grapevine fanleaf virus, however, is an exception to this rule; in the field it is rarely found infecting anything other than grapevine although it is transmissible experimentally to many herbaceous (Dias, 1963) and woody (Ciferri *et al.,* 1959) species. The reason for this restriction in the field is probably that *X. index* feeds readily on only a few species (Radewald and Raski, 1962), and that both virus and vector owe their present distribution largely to man (Raski and Hewitt, 1963), who has carried them to many parts of the world with the grapevines, which live for many years; changes of host species are frequently not necessary for survival.

A second factor aiding virus survival is the longevity of the vector nematodes. *Xiphinema* and *Longidorus* spp. survive in fallow soil for long periods; for instance,

L. elongatus survived in moist soil kept at room temperature in polythene bags without plants for well over 2 years, the longest period tested (Harrison and Hooper, 1963). The viruses can persist for weeks or months in nematodes kept without plants, although the longest recorded persistence, 4 months for grapevine fanleaf virus in *X. index* (Raski and Hewitt, 1963), is a good deal less than the maximum reported longevity of the nematode. That the viruses persist in their vectors is not surprising, because the nematodes probably feed infrequently and any virus held in a transmissible form for only a short time would be unlikely to survive and spread.

The viruses may persist on infested land in two other ways. The first is in dormant seeds, through which several viruses are transmitted to a sizeable proportion of the progeny seedlings of many species, including weeds (Lister, 1960b). Surviving roots of perennial plants provide another virus reservoir; grapevine roots, for example, may survive in soil for 2 years or more after the vines are dug up (Hewitt *et al.,* 1962).

Both the viruses and their vector nematodes thus have effective ways of persisting through a sequence of crops and through periods of fallow. The vectors can survive some adverse soil conditions although they have no resistant resting stage. When the top-soil becomes dry, many probably move into the sub-soil and migrate back when the top-soil again becomes moist. The nematodes also survive long periods of freezing; some individuals and eggs of *X. americanum* survived soil temperatures at or below $0°C$ for 116 days and gave rise to large populations in the following spring and summer (Norton, 1963). Migration up from unfrozen sub-soil may, however, have played a part in this increase.

By contrast to the nematode-transmitted viruses, lettuce big-vein, tobacco stunt, and wheat mosaic viruses apparently have narrow host ranges, but their vectors more readily survive adverse soil conditions. These viruses will persist for many years in dry soil without plants, presumably because the resting stages of *Olpidium* and other agents involved in virus spread are resist-

Fig. 6–6. Outbreak of raspberry ringspot virus in strawberry var. Talisman. Infected plants are severely stunted (courtesy Scottish Horticultural Research Institute).

ant and long-lived. Hence susceptible plants are infected when they occur and these viruses can survive long periods without them. Tobacco necrosis virus probably behaves differently from these three viruses; it has a wide host range, as have *Olpidium* spp. (Sahtiyanci, 1962), but it usually infects roots only locally and may need a succession of hosts to survive. There is no evidence of whether or not it is carried through the resting sporangia of *Olpidium*. The satellite virus that often accompanies it is extremely stable (Kassanis, 1962) and conceivably might survive free in the soil, like TMV.

B. DISTRIBUTION AND SPREAD

The distribution of nematode-transmitted viruses within a crop can often be correlated with that of their vectors. Both virus and vector may be patchily distributed (Fig. 6–6; Harrison and Cadman, 1959; Harrison *et al.*, 1961), both may differ in incidence from one part of a field to another (Calvert and Harrison, 1963), or both may occur throughout (Raski and Hewitt, 1963). Viruses newly brought in with crop plants or seed are usually sporadically distributed in the crop and not correlated with any specific nematode. Wheat mosaic and lettuce big-vein viruses too may be either patchily or more generally distributed through a crop, but correlations have not been described between the patches and any soil-inhabiting organisms.

Disease outbreaks are often related to soil type. Wheat mosaic (McKinney, 1925), sugar-cane chlorotic streak (Antoine, 1959), and lettuce big-vein (Jagger and Chandler, 1934) diseases occur predominantly on heavy soils, or where drainage is poor or the rainfall heavy, presumably because water is important for the active stage of the agents that assist virus spread. Among the nematode-transmitted viruses, tobacco rattle and tomato black ring viruses occur on light soils (Rozendaal, 1947; Harrison, 1957), and arabis mosaic virus is found on several types of soil that resist drying out but not on nearby light soils (Harrison and Winslow, 1961); these distributions each reflect the soil preferences of the vector nematodes (Sol and Seinhorst, 1961; Harrison and Winslow, 1961).

The vertical distribution of vectors in soil is particularly important in relation to controlling them by chemical treatments. It differs with different vectors. Wheat mosaic virus was transmitted in soil collected at depths down to 60 cm in one field but only down to 45 cm in another (Koehler *et al.*, 1952; Sill, 1958). Most tobacco rattle virus was carried in the top 10 cm of a podzolic soil that had been cultivated, and none below 40 cm (Eibner, 1959). However, although their vertical distribution is probably greatly dependent on soil type and weather, the peak population of vector nematodes is usually not in the top 10 cm of soil. Peak populations of *X. diversicaudatum* were usually about 15–20 cm deep, with few nematodes below 100 cm (Harrison and Winslow, 1961), and most *X. index* occur where grapevine roots are most abundant, sometimes 200 cm deep, with some individuals down to 300 cm (Hewitt *et al.*, 1962; Raski and Hewitt, 1963).

Several patterns of virus spread in the field can be distinguished. In the first, the spread is only apparent. It occurs in perennial crops, such as raspberry, in which plants exposed to populations of infective nematodes may not show shoot symptoms for a year or more after their roots are infected; thus the initial distribution of infective nematodes is gradually revealed. True spread is usually slow. Typically, it is a gradual increase in size of an affected area in a crop and can be related to the spread of vectors in the soil. For example, Harrison and Winslow (1961) estimated that a population of *X. diversicaudatum* invaded uncultivated woodland at a rate of about a foot a year. Movement of soil containing vectors during cultivations and with drainage water will often supplement the movement of the vectors themselves and may be particularly important for organisms which, like *Olpidium* spp., will not move far on their own.

Bringing viruses into fields already infested with potential vectors is another type of spread. Tomato black ring virus becomes established when land infested with *L. elongatus* is planted with virus-infected potato tubers (Cadman and Harrison, 1960) or is contaminated by virus-containing weed seeds dispersed from other fields (Lister and Murant, 1962). Carriage of virus in weed seeds during dispersal may account for the high proportion of populations of *L. elongatus* in eastern Scotland that harbour tomato black ring virus. Indeed, virus-free populations of some vector nematodes, for example, *X. diversicauda-*

tum, are difficult to find for experimental work. Viruses can be expected to spread more rapidly where their vectors are already established than where spread depends on the movement of vectors. Infection of a root of a plant with an extensive root system, e.g., a tree, might be followed within a year or two by systemic invasion of the root system by the virus, which could then be obtained by vectors feeding many yards away from the original infection.

A fourth type of spread is seen when the viruses and their vectors are brought into a field together, as for instance in soil carried on plant roots, boots, or farm implements. Wheat mosaic virus survives drying in soil and is carried by fine particles, which presumably may be carried by wind to adjacent land (McKinney *et al.*, 1925). However, only small numbers of a vector are introduced in any of these ways and their subsequent multiplication is important. *Olpidium* spp. have a life cycle of only a few days and probably multiply rapidly in suitable conditions. Infestations of wheat mosaic virus may also build up relatively rapidly; attacks became severe within four years of adding 1 part of infested soil to 10,000 parts of virus-free soil (Koehler *et al.*, 1952). Some vector nematodes, by contrast, increase slowly; *X. diversicaudatum* only quadrupled in numbers during two years of cropping with strawberry, a good host, most of the increase coming in the second year (Harrison *et al.*, 1963). Populations of *X. index*, however, increased up to sixty-fold during three and a half months in pot cultures (Hewitt *et al.*, 1958), and *Trichodorus teres* reached populations of over 3,400 nematodes per litre of soil in a part of the Netherlands reclaimed from the sea only three years previously (Kuiper and Loof, 1962). *T. christiei* is another vector species which multiplies rapidly in culture (Rohde and Jenkins, 1957). It may be significant that these three rapidly multiplying species reproduce parthenogenetically and rarely produce males, whereas males of *X. diversicaudatum* are common and apparently functional. Also, one individual of a parthenogenetic species can establish an infestation, but a mating colony of at least two individuals of opposite sex will be needed to start an infestation of other species.

C. Incidence of Infection

Many factors affect the proportion of infected plants in a crop. Both the number and feeding activity of vector nematodes are important. Thus in a series of plots in which the numbers of *X. diversicaudatum* were altered by chemical treatments, the incidence of arabis mosaic virus in strawberry plants was directly related to the number of nematodes in the soil (Fig. 6–7; Harrison *et al.*, 1963). Little is known about feeding activity in different conditions, but the proportion of virus-carrying nematodes in infective populations differs

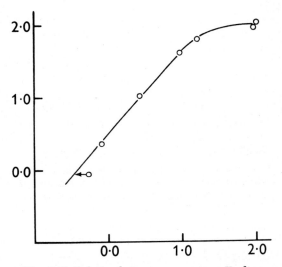

Fig. 6–7. Relation between percentage *X. diversicaudatum* surviving various chemical treatments of soil and incidence of arabis mosaic virus in a subsequent strawberry crop. Ordinate, log. percentage surviving nematodes: abscissa, log. virus incidence in treated plots as a percentage of that in control plots (Harrison *et al.*, 1963).

greatly, probably mainly because sources of virus are commoner in some places than in others. In one population of *X. diversicaudatum*, about one in six of the nematodes was estimated to be carrying arabis mosaic virus, and in another only about one in 1,800; the different proportions were not related to any innate difference between the populations in ability to transmit (Harrison and Winslow, 1961).

Viruses that invade many of their hosts systemically will be more readily available to vectors than those which cause local infections in roots. Perhaps nematodes are more attracted to infected roots than to healthy ones, or plants systemically infected with some viruses are commoner than supposed; *Trichodorus* spp., for instance, seem unlikely often to acquire tobacco rattle virus by feeding at random on locally infected roots.

Factors affecting the susceptibility of plants to infection by soil-borne viruses have been little studied. Hosts of two viruses with the same vector may be more susceptible to one virus than the other. For example, in Scotland, raspberry ringspot virus is commoner in perennial than in annual plants, but tomato black ring virus is commoner in annuals than in perennials although the two viruses often occur in the same fields (Harrison, 1958b) and are both transmitted by *L. elongatus*. When a range of strawberry varieties was planted on land infested with both viruses, most infected plants contained raspberry ringspot virus alone and a few contained both viruses; the variety Redgauntlet, however, differed from the others in being more readily infected by tomato black ring virus. Neither these differences nor differences between varieties in incidence of infection seemed related to differences in ability to support the vector *L. elongatus* (Lister, 1962). Similarly, although both tobacco ringspot and tomato ringspot viruses are transmitted by *X. americanum*, tobacco ringspot virus causes more diseases of economic importance in herbaceous annuals and tomato ringspot virus more in woody perennials. Susceptibility to infection also differs with age of plant; wheat seedlings were most susceptible to infection with wheat mosaic virus when 1–4 weeks old (Webb, 1927) and turnip seedlings were most susceptible to infection with tomato black ring virus during the first week after germination (Cadman and Harrison, 1960). Hence, if conditions are unfavourable for infection when the crop is most susceptible, virus incidence may remain small; early-sown winter wheat is more severely affected by mosaic than late-sown (McKinney, 1923), presumably because the late-sown crops avoid the conditions that are most suitable for infection.

Moisture and temperature are the two soil factors that most influence virus spread. Wheat mosaic (Webb, 1927), tobacco stunt (Hidaka and Hiruki, 1956a), and lettuce big-vein (Thompson and Doolittle, 1942) become more prevalent at 15°–18°C than at higher soil temperatures. Wheat mosaic (Webb, 1927), sugar-cane chlorotic streak (Abbott, 1947), and lettuce big-vein (Pryor, 1944) viruses also spread most when the soil contains most moisture, lettuce big-vein virus presumably because *Olpidium* zoospores are then most active. Indeed, in Germany, Haeske (1958) was able to relate the incidence of big-vein disease in lettuce crops planted on different dates to the monthly rainfall. Information on the effect of soil temperature and moisture on the numbers and activity of vector nematodes is badly needed. However, freezing pots of soil containing infective *L. elongatus* decreased the incidence of tomato black ring virus in sugar-beet seedlings grown subsequently; and long periods of cold weather seemed related to decreases in the frequency with which plants grown in soil, collected subsequently from the field, became infected (Cadman and Harrison, 1960).

Agricultural practices greatly affect virus incidence. For instance, those kinds of cultivation that made residues of a tobacco crop decay soonest were also those that most decreased the incidence of mosaic in a subsequent tobacco crop (Lehman, 1934). Cultivations also probably affect vector nematodes adversely, if only because they decrease the amount and distribution of live roots in the soil. Different crop sequences may have large effects. Thus, outbreaks of wheat mosaic virus became increasingly severe when four successive wheat crops were taken, but decreased greatly in severity when four successive maize, soybean, or oat crops were grown on infested land between wheat crops (Koehler *et al.*, 1952). Similarly, when a strawberry crop was grown for two years on land uniformly infested with *X. diversicaudatum*, half having previously carried strawberry infected with arabis mosaic virus and half a variety of raspberry that seems immune to infection, 69% of the plants on the strawberry ground were infected and only 8% of those on the raspberry ground (Harrison *et al.*, 1963). Also, tulips seem to suffer most severely from tobacco necrosis virus on land previously cropped with potato or tobacco (de Bruyn Ouboter and van Slogteren, 1949).

6–6. METHODS OF CONTROL

Although much more is now known about the soil-inhabiting organisms involved in virus transmission than when methods of control were reviewed previously (Harrison, 1960), no new principles of control have been evolved and the same headings will be used again. The relative value of different methods of control differs with the virus and vector, and from annual to perennial crops. Methods that are successful and economic with an annual crop may not prevent infection of perennial crops. Conversely, measures which are too expensive to be justified by the increase in crop obtained in a single season may pay well with plantation crops over a period of several years. In general, soil-borne viruses spread more slowly than viruses with aerial vectors, but they are difficult to eradicate.

A. Prevention of Spread to New Sites

To prevent vectors reaching new sites, as little soil as possible should be carried from one field to another on farm machinery or by other means, because although the soil may not come from a virus-infested field, it may contain potential vectors. Soil should be removed from plant roots at transplanting; some strawberry growers in Britain transplant strawberry runners with a ball of soil adhering to their roots, a practice that might have been designed to start new infestations of *X. diversicaudatum* and arabis mosaic virus (Harrison and Winslow, 1961). Also, the fact that *X. index* carrying grapevine fanleaf virus is found in California only in areas where *Vitis rupestris* var. St. George rootstocks were used in earlier years suggests that the nematode was carried onto the land with the rootstocks (Raski and Hewitt, 1963). *Olpidium* spp. presumably are disseminated on plant roots, and a general fungicidal and nematicidal dip at transplanting would probably be worth while: Staniland (1963) suggests that iodine solution would be suitable for killing *Xiphinema* spp. Another approach is to treat land to be used for propagation beds with steam or suitable chemicals.

Such treatments would also greatly decrease the chance that plants may become infected with soil-borne viruses in propagation beds. Graft-indexing, and inoculating sap manually to indicator plants, are two ways of revealing symptomless infections of vegetatively propagated planting material; with a few viruses serological tests are useful. Some viruses can be eliminated from planting material by heat treatment; for example, sugar-cane setts are freed from chlorotic streak virus by immersion in water at 52°C for 20 min (Martin and Conant, 1939). A few viruses, however, seem to be self-eliminating; in Britain potato tubers with spraing disease give rise to healthy progeny and there is no evidence that they establish tobacco rattle virus in previously virus-free land.

Soil-borne viruses can also be imported with true seed. Thus, Bos and van der Want (1962) showed that pea early browning virus sometimes was seed-borne in pea and recommended that seed should not be taken from infected pea crops. Good control of weeds will decrease the chance that infected weed seeds will be distributed from virus-infested fields to fields infested with virus-free vectors.

B. CONTROL MEASURES ON INFESTED LAND

1. *Crop hygiene.*—The amount of TMV reaching the soil can be decreased by removing and burning root and shoot debris from infected tobacco crops. Removing debris containing tobacco necrosis virus is also desirable but, with this and other viruses with a wide host range, good weed control may more effectively decrease the level of infestation and, particularly with the nematode-transmitted viruses, would decrease the importance of dormant weed seed as a virus reservoir.

2. *Rotation of crops.*—Johnson and Ogden (1929) found that alternating tobacco and maize crops prevented the tobacco from becoming infected by soil-borne TMV; but other soil-borne viruses are less readily eliminated, although their incidence can be decreased by growing crops in suitable sequences. This applies both to viruses with a wide host range among weeds and crops and to viruses with a narrow host range that survive in the resistant dormant stage of some soil-inhabiting organism. The effects of growing a nonsusceptible variety of raspberry on the incidence of arabis mosaic virus and of growing oats, soybeans, or maize on the incidence of wheat mosaic virus, have already been mentioned and illustrate the behaviour of viruses with different methods of survival. In rotations, crops which are not hosts of either virus or vector are preferable to those which maintain the vector but are not infected by the virus.

Fallowing land for short periods seems to have little effect on virus incidence. Summer fallowing did not affect the incidence of wheat mosaic virus (McKinney, 1923), and grapevine fanleaf virus infected grapevines planted after 3–4 years of fallow; after 2 years of fallow, there were as many *X. index* in the soil as initially (Raski and Hewitt, 1963).

3. *Disease-escaping varieties.*—Disease-escaping varieties are used with wheat and wheat mosaic virus (McKinney, 1923); oat and oat mosaic virus (McKinney *et al.*, 1949); barley and barley yellow mosaic virus (Miyamoto, 1958b); tobacco and tobacco stunt (Hidaka, Uozumi, and Hiruki, 1956) and tobacco mosaic (Holmes, 1954) viruses; raspberry and raspberry ringspot, tomato black ring and arabis mosaic viruses (Cadman, 1961); grapevine and grapevine fanleaf virus (Petri, 1937); and potato and tobacco rattle virus, the cause of both spraing and stem-mottle diseases (Noordam, 1956). Varieties that escape wheat mosaic (Fig. 6–8), raspberry ringspot, and potato spraing, respectively, give excellent crops on infested land. Many of the disease-escaping wheat varieties seem to become infected but tolerate infection. Others do not become diseased in the field although they develop obvious symptoms when inoc-

Fig. 6–8. Two selections of wheat var. Harvest Queen sown in soil infested with wheat mosaic virus. Left, selected for tolerance of infection; right, selected for sensitivity (courtesy H. H. McKinney).

ulated with infective sap (McKinney, 1948); Toler and Hebert (1963) suggest that this type of behaviour, which also occurs with oats and oat mosaic virus, may indicate that the plants are not good hosts of the vector although susceptible to the virus. By contrast, the Malling Jewel variety of raspberry does not become infected with arabis mosaic virus even when grafted with infected scions (Cadman, 1961), but is a good host of the vector *X. diversicaudatum* (Harrison and Winslow, 1961). This type of immunity to raspberry ringspot, tomato black ring, and arabis mosaic viruses occurs independently in different raspberry varieties (Table 6–4); in genetical tests immunity to each virus was dominant to susceptibility (Jennings, 1960).

4. *Soil treatments.*—Steam sterilization is particularly applicable to glasshouses and seedbeds, and should prevent the spread of any of the viruses, but is unlikely to be economic for field crops. Harrison (1960) listed many chemicals, some of which are general poisons and some virus inactivators, that will prevent virus infection when applied to soil in experimental conditions, but few had then been tested in field conditions, and of those now tested few are effective. However, Vuittenez (1957, 1958,

TABLE 6–4. REACTION OF RASPBERRY TO
INFECTION BY ARABIS MOSAIC, RASPBERRY
RINGSPOT, AND TOMATO BLACK RING VIRUSES
(from Cadman, 1961)[*]

Variety	Arabis mosaic virus	Raspberry ringspot virus	Tomato black ring virus
Malling Exploit	+	+	+
Norfolk Giant	−	+	+
Malling Seedling K	−	+	+
Malling Jewel	−	+	−
Malling Promise	−	+	−
Burnetholm Seedling	−	−	+
Malling Seedling V	−	−	+
Lloyd George	−	−	−

[*] + = susceptible to infection by grafting.
− = immune to infection by grafting.

1960, 1961), working in France, claimed that infection of young grapevines with grapevine fanleaf virus was greatly decreased by treating the soil of old diseased vineyards with chemicals before replanting with young grapevines. For example, in one experiment the incidence of fanleaf seven years after planting was 1% in plots treated with methyl bromide, 3% after dichloropropane-dichloropropene (D-D), 18% after carbon disulphide, and 93% in plots not treated with chemicals. The results of such treatments seem to depend greatly on local conditions, because in California these same three chemicals, although the most effective of those tested, did not give worthwhile results (Hewitt *et al.*, 1962). However, grapevine fanleaf virus is probably one of the most difficult of the nematode-transmitted viruses to control by chemical treatment of the soil, and the reasons for this are worth noting. Roots of the previous grapevine crop go deep and may survive for several years after the tops are removed, providing a possible source of virus (Raski and Hewitt, 1963); *X. index* occurs at least three metres deep in the soil (Hewitt *et al.*, 1962), where it is difficult to kill; *X. index* is parthenogenetic, and isolated survivors may multiply quite rapidly to form new colonies (Raski, 1962); finally, the grapevine is more exposed to infection than many crop species because it has a large root system and an intended cropping life of 40–60 years.

The control of arabis mosaic virus in strawberry crops presents less serious difficulties. *X. diversicaudatum* often infests only the top metre of soil, it does not multiply rapidly, and the crop is in the ground for only 1–4 years. Of several chemicals tested, applications (800 lb/acre) of either methyl bromide or D-D gave excellent results. On land where almost 80% of the plants in control plots became infected within one year after planting, fewer than 1% became infected in plots treated with D-D. The effects of the chemicals on virus incidence were directly related to their effects on nematode numbers (Fig. 6-7); hence to check virus spread usefully at such

sites it is necessary to kill *X. diversicaudatum* at all depths and to kill more than 99% of the initial population (Harrison *et al.*, 1963).

There seem to be no claims for successful control by chemical treatments in the field of the spread of *Olpidium*-transmitted viruses. However, Miyamoto (1961) claimed that treating land with pyroligneous acid before planting wheat or barley prevented the spread of wheat yellow mosaic and barley yellow mosaic viruses, and suggested that formaldehyde in this material might be responsible for the effect.

6-7. CONCLUDING REMARKS

Although emphasis has shifted in recent years from the hypothesis that soil-borne viruses spread and infect plants by some sort of mechanical process to the idea that transmission involves soil-inhabiting organisms, it would be premature to assume that organisms always are needed. The organisms that appear to assist the spread of some viruses have not been identified; with some viruses there is evidence of transmission without the vector usually concerned, and with other viruses there is no reason to suppose that organisms are ever needed; but there is also no adequately documented record of transmission in soil in aseptic conditions. Nor is there any critical evidence that more than one class of organism is concerned in the spread of any one soil-borne virus. Where vectors of soil-borne viruses are known, studies of how they transmit, of their ecology, and of their activity in the field in relation to virus spread are developing along similar lines to those in comparable work with arthropod vectors.

6-8. LITERATURE CITED

Abbott, E. V. (1947). Phytopathology **37**, 162.

Abbott, E. V., and Sass, J. E. (1945). J. Agr. Research **70**, 201.

Allen, M. W. (1948). Phytopathology **38**, 612.

Allen, M. W. (1957). Nematologica **2**, 32.

Antoine, R. (1957). Rept. Mauritius Sugar Ind. Research Inst., p. 53.

Antoine, R. (1959). Proc. 10th Cong. Intern. Soc. Sugar-Cane Technologists, p. 1091.

Babos, P., and Kassanis, B. (1962). Virology **18**, 206.

Babos, P., and Kassanis, B. (1963a). J. Gen. Microbiol. **32**, 135.

Babos, P., and Kassanis, B. (1963b). Virology **20**, 498.

Bawden, F. C. (1941). Brit. J. Exptl. Pathol. 22, 59.

Bawden, F. C., and Kassanis, B. (1947). Ann. Appl. Biol. 34, 127.

Bawden, F. C., and Pirie, N. W. (1942). Brit. J. Exptl. Pathol. 23, 314.

Bawden, F. C. and van der Want, J. P. H. (1949). Tijdschr. Plantenziekten 55, 142.

Behrens, J. (1899). Landwirtsch. Vers.-Sta. 52, 442.

Beijerinck, M. W. (1898). Verhandel. Akad. Wetenschap. (Amsterdam) 6, 3.

Bercks, R. (1962). Phytopathol. Z. 46, 97.

Bercks, R., and Gehring, F. (1956). Phytopathol. Z. 28, 57.

Bird, J. (1961). J. Agr. Univ. Puerto Rico 45, 8.

Bird, J., Cibes, H., and Tio, M. A. (1958). Univ. Puerto Rico Agr. Exptl. Sta. Tech. Paper 27.

Böning, K. (1931). Z. Parasitenk. 3, 103.

Bos, L., and van der Want, J. P. H. (1962). Tijdschr. Plantenziekten 68, 368.

Breece, J. R., and Hart, W. H. (1959). Plant Disease Reptr. 43, 989.

Brierley, P., and Travis, R. V. (1958). Plant Disease Reptr. 42, 1030.

Brückbauer, H., and Rüdel, M. (1961). Wein-Wissenschaft 16, 177.

Bruehl, G. W., and Damsteegt, V. D. (1961). Plant Disease Reptr. 45, 884.

Cadman, C. H. (1956). J. Hort. Sci. 31, 111.

Cadman, C. H. (1959a). J. Gen. Microbiol. 20, 113.

Cadman, C. H. (1959b). European Potato J. 2, 165.

Cadman, C. H. (1960). Virology 11, 653.

Cadman, C. H. (1961). Horticultural Research 1, 47.

Cadman, C. H. (1962). Nature 193, 49.

Cadman, C. H. (1963). Ann. Rev. Phytopathology 1, 143.

Cadman, C. H., and Harrison, B. D. (1959). Ann. Appl. Biol. 47, 542.

Cadman, C. H., and Harrison, B. D. (1960). Virology 10, 1.

Cadman, C. H., and Lister, R. M. (1961). Phytopathology 51, 29.

Cadman, C. H., and Lister, R. M. (1962). Plant Disease Reptr. 46, 770.

Cadman, C. H., Dias, H. F., and Harrison, B. D. (1960). Nature 187, 577.

Calvert, E. L., and Harrison, B. D. (1963). Horticultural Research 2, 115.

Campbell, R. N. (1962). Nature 195, 675.

Campbell, R. N., and Grogan, R. G. (1963). Phytopathology 53, 252.

Campbell, R. N., Grogan, R. G., and Purcifull, D. E. (1961). Virology 15, 82.

Carpenter, C. W. (1940). Hawaiian Planters' Record 44, 19.

Cation, D. (1951). U.S. Dept. Agr. Handbook 10, 14.

Ciferri, R., Corte, A., and Scaramuzzi, G. (1959). Atti. Ist. Bot. Univ. Pavia Ser. 5, 16, 335.

Coffman, F. A., Hebert, T. T., Gore, U. R., and Byrd, W. P. (1963). Plant Disease Reptr. 47, 54.

Cropley, R. (1961). Ann. Appl. Biol. 49, 530.

de Bruyn Ouboter, M. P., and van Slogteren, E. (1949). Tijdschr. Plantenziekten 55, 262.

Dias, H. F. (1963). Ann. Appl. Biol. 51, 85.

Dias, H. F., and Harrison, B. D. (1963). Ann. Appl. Biol. 51, 97.

Diener, T. O., and Weaver, M. L. (1959). Phytopathology 49, 321.

Dijkstra, J., and Grancini, P. (1960). Tijdschr. Plantenziekten 66, 301.

Doolittle, S. P. (1928). Phytopathology 18, 155.

Doolittle, S. P., and Thompson, R. C. (1945). Phytopathology 35, 484.

Eibner, R. (1959). Doctoral Dissertation, Justus-Liebig-Universität, Giessen, Germany.

Frazier, N. W. (1955). Plant Disease Reptr. 39, 143.

Fritzsche, R., and Schmidt, H. B. (1963). Naturwissenschaften 50, 163.

Fry, P. R. (1952). New Zealand J. Sci. Technol. A. 34, 224.

Fry, P. R. (1958). New Zealand J. Agr. Research 1, 301.

Fujikawa, T. (1955). Agr. and Hort. (Tokyo) 30, 721.

Fulton, J. P. (1962). Phytopathology 52, 375.

Fulton, R. W. (1941). Phytopathology 31, 575.

Gallay, R., Wurgler, W., Bovey, R., Staehelin, M., and Leyvraz, H. (1955). Rev. Romande Agric. Vitic. Arboric. 11, 17.

Gibbs, A. J., and Harrison, B. D. (1963). Rept. Rothamsted Expt. Sta. for 1962, p. 113.

Gibbs, A. J., and Harrison, B. D. (1964). Ann. Appl. Biol. (in press).

Gold, A. H., Scott, H. A., and McKinney, H. H. (1957). Plant Disease Reptr. 41, 250.

Goodey, J. B., Peacock, F. C., and Pitcher, R. S. (1960). Nematologica 5, 127.

Goodey, T. (1963). Soil and Freshwater Nematodes, 2d ed. revised by J. B. Goodey. Methuen, London.

Gooding, G. V. (1963). Phytopathology 53, 475.

Grogan, R. G., and Schnathorst, W. C. (1955). Plant Disease Reptr. 39, 803.

Grogan, R. G., Zink, F. W., Hewitt, W. B., and Kimble, K. A. (1958). Phytopathology 48, 292.

Haeske, E. (1958). Doctoral Dissertation, Justus-Liebig-Universität, Giessen, Germany.

Harrison, B. D. (1956). Nature 178, 553.

Harrison, B. D. (1957). Ann. Appl. Biol. 45, 462.

Harrison, B. D. (1958a). J. Gen. Microbiol. 18, 450.

Harrison, B. D. (1958b). Ann. Appl. Biol. 46, 571.

Harrison, B. D. (1958c). Ann. Appl. Biol. 46, 221.

Harrison, B. D. (1960). Advances in Virus Research 7, 131.

Harrison, B. D. (1961a). Tijdschr. Plantenziekten 67, 562.

Harrison, B. D. (1961b). Rept. Rothamsted Expt. Sta. for 1960, p. 118.

Harrison, B. D. (1962). Rept. Rothamsted Expt. Sta. for 1961, p. 105.

Harrison, B. D. (1964). Virology 22, 544.

Harrison, B. D., and Cadman, C. H. (1959). Nature 184, 1624.

Harrison, B. D., and Hooper, D. J. (1963). Nematologica **9**, 159.

Harrison, B. D., and Nixon, H. L. (1959). J. Gen. Microbiol. **21**, 569.

Harrison, B. D., and Nixon, H. L. (1960). Virology **12**, 104.

Harrison, B. D., and Winslow, R. D. (1961). Ann. Appl. Biol. **49**, 621.

Harrison, B. D., Mowat, W. P., and Taylor, C. E. (1961). Virology **14**, 480.

Harrison, B. D., Peachey, J. E., and Winslow, R. D. (1963). Ann. Appl. Biol. **52**, 243.

Heinze, K. (1950). Nachrbl. Deut. Pflanzenschutzdienst (Braunschweig) **2**, 49.

Henderson, R. G. (1931). Phytopathology **21**, 225.

Hendrix, J. W. (1961). Phytopathology **51**, 194.

Hewitt, W. B. (1956). Phytopathology **46**, 15.

Hewitt, W. B., and Delp, C. J. (1953). Phytopathology **43**, 475.

Hewitt, W. B., and Raski, D. J. (1962). Biological Transmission of Disease Agents. Ed. K. Maramorosch. 63. Academic Press, New York.

Hewitt, W. B., Raski, D. J., and Goheen, A. C. (1958). Phytopathology **48**, 586.

Hewitt, W. B., Goheen, A. C., Raski, D. J., and Gooding, G. V. (1962). Vitis **3**, 57.

Hidaka, Z. (1956). Bull. Hatano Tobacco Exptl. Sta. **40**, 19.

Hidaka, Z. (1960). Quoted by C. H. Cadman, Rept. Scottish Horticultural Research Inst. for 1960–61 (1961), p. 76.

Hidaka, Z., and Hiruki, C. (1956a). Bull. Hatano Tobacco Exptl. Sta. **40**, 67.

Hidaka, Z., and Hiruki, C. (1956b). Bull. Hatano Tobacco Exptl. Sta. **40**, 53.

Hidaka, Z., Uozumi, T., and Hiruki, C. (1956). Bull. Hatano Tobacco Exptl. Sta. **40**, 47.

Hidaka, Z., Uozumi, T., and Shimizu, T. (1956). Bull. Hatano Tobacco Exptl. Sta. **40**, 31.

Hoggan, I. A., and Johnson, J. (1936). J. Agr. Research **52**, 271.

Hollings, M. (1962). Nature **196**, 962.

Hollings, M., and Stone, O. M. (1962). Nature **194**, 607.

Holmes, F. O. (1941). Phytopathology **31**, 1089.

Holmes, F. O. (1954). Advances in Virus Research **2**, 1.

Hooper, D. J. (1961). Nematologica **6**, 237.

Hooper, D. J. (1962). Nematologica **7**, 273.

Hooper, D. J. (1963). Nematologica **9**, 200.

Hutchins, L. M. (1933). Georgia Offic. State Entomol. Bull. **78**.

Jagger, I. C., and Chandler, N. (1934). Phytopathology **24**, 1253.

Jennings, D. L. (1960). Rept. Scottish Hort. Res. Inst. for 1959–60, p. 14.

Jha, A. (1961). J. Hort. Sci. **36**, 219.

Jha, A., and Posnette, A. F. (1959). Nature **184**, 962.

Jha, A., and Posnette, A. F. (1961). Virology **13**, 119.

Johnson, J. (1937). J. Agr. Research **54**, 239.

Johnson, J., and Ogden, W. B. (1929). Wisc. Univ. Agr. Expt. Sta. Res. Bull. **95**.

Kahn, R. P. (1956). Phytopathology **46**, 295.

Kahn, R. P., Scott, H. A., and Monroe, R. L. (1962). Phytopathology **52**, 1211.

Kassanis, B. (1949). Ann. Appl. Biol. **36**, 14.

Kassanis, B. (1962). J. Gen. Microbiol. **27**, 477.

Kassanis, B., and Nixon, H. L. (1961). J. Gen. Microbiol. **25**, 459.

Koehler, B., Bever, W. M., and Bonnett, O. T. (1952). Illinois Univ. Agr. Expt. Sta. Bull. **556**, 567.

Kuiper, K., and Loof, P. A. A. (1962). Versl. Meded. Plantenz. k. Dienst. **136**, 193.

Lehman, S. G. (1934). N. Carolina State Coll. Agr. Expt. Sta. Tech. Bull. **46**.

Lihnell, D. (1958). Proc. 3rd Conf. Potato Virus Diseases, Lisse-Wageningen, 1957, p. 184.

Lindberg, G. D. (1959). Phytopathology **49**, 29.

Linford, M. B., and McKinney, H. H. (1954). Plant Disease Reptr. **38**, 711.

Lister, R. M. (1960a). Plant Pathology **9**, 102.

Lister, R. M. (1960b). Virology **10**, 547.

Lister, R. M. (1962). Rept. Scottish Hort. Res. Inst. for 1961–62, p. 66.

Lister, R. M. (1963). Rept. Scottish Hort. Res. Inst. for 1962–63, p. 69.

Lister, R. M., and Murant, A. F. (1962). Rept. Scottish Hort. Res. Inst. for 1961–62, p. 68.

Loewenberg, J. R., Sullivan, T., and Schuster, M. L. (1959). Nature **184**, 1896.

Martin, J. P., and Conant, R. K. (1939). Hawaiian Planters' Record **43**, 277.

McKeen, C. D. (1959). Can. J. Botany **37**, 913.

McKinney, H. H. (1923). J. Agr. Research **23**, 771.

McKinney, H. H. (1925). U.S. Dept. Agr. Bull. **1361**.

McKinney, H. H. (1927). J. Agr. Research **35**, 13.

McKinney, H. H. (1946). Phytopathology **36**, 359.

McKinney, H. H. (1948). Phytopathology **38**, 1003.

McKinney, H. H. (1953). Yearbook Agr. U.S. Dept. Agr. for 1953, p. 350.

McKinney, H. H., Eckerson, S. H., and Webb, R. W. (1923). J. Agr. Research **26**, 605.

McKinney, H. H., Paden, W. R., and Koehler, B. (1957). Plant Disease Reptr. **41**, 256.

McKinney, H. H., Webb, R. W., and Dungan, G. H. (1925). Illinois Univ. Agr. Expt. Sta. Bull. **264**.

McKinney, H. H., Stanton, T. R., Seal, J. L., Rogers, T. H., Paden, W. R., Middleton, G. K., and Gore, U. R. (1949). U.S. Dept. Agr. Circ. **809**.

Milbrath, J. A., and Reynolds, J. E. (1961). Plant Disease Reptr. **45**, 520.

Miyamoto, Y. (1958a). Ann. Phytopathol. Soc. Japan **23**, 69.

Miyamoto, Y. (1958b). Ann. Phytopathol. Soc. Japan **23**, 199.

Miyamoto, Y. (1959a). Virology **7**, 250.

Miyamoto, Y. (1959b). Virology **9**, 290.

Miyamoto, Y. (1961). Ann. Phytopathol. Soc. Japan **26**, 90.

Noordam, D. (1956). Tijdschr. Plantenziekten **62**, 219.

Noordam, D. (1957). Tijdschr. Plantenziekten **63**, 237.

Norton, D. C. (1963). Phytopathology **53**, 66.

Petri, L. (1929). Boll. Regia Staz. Patol. Vegetale (N.S.) **9**, 101.

Petri, L. (1937). Boll. Staz. Patol. Vegetale (N.S.) **17**, 1.

Pitcher, R. S., and Jha, A. (1961). Plant Pathology **10**, 67.

Pryor, D. E. (1944). J. Agr. Research **68**, 1.

Pryor, D. E. (1946). Phytopathology **36**, 264.

Quanjer, H. M. (1943). Tijdschr. Plantenziekten **49**, 37.

Radewald, J. D., and Raski, D. J. (1962). Phytopathology **52**, 748.

Raski, D. J. (1962). Plant Disease Reptr. **46**, 516.

Raski, D. J., and Hewitt, W. B. (1960). Nematologica **5**, 166.

Raski, D. J., and Hewitt, W. B. (1963). Phytopathology **53**, 39.

Raski, D. J., and Radewald, J. D. (1958). Plant Disease Reptr. **42**, 941.

Roberts, F. M. (1948). Ann. Appl. Biol. **35**, 266.

Rohde, R. A., and Jenkins, W. R. (1957). Phytopathology **47**, 295.

Rozendaal, A. (1947). Tijdschr. Plantenziekten **53**, 93.

Sahtiyanci, S. (1962). Arch. Mikrobiol. **41**, 187.

Saito, Y., Takanashi, K., and Iwata, Y. (1961). Ann. Phytopathol. Soc. Japan **26**, 16.

Sampson, K. (1939). Trans. Brit. Mycol. Soc. **23**, 199.

Sänger, H. L., and Brandenburg, E. (1961). Naturwissenschaften **48**, 391.

Sänger, H. L., Allen, M. W., and Gold, A. H. (1962). Phytopathology **52**, 750.

Schade, C. (1960). Phytopathol. Z. **37**, 422.

Schindler, A. F. (1957). Nematologica **2**, 25.

Schmelzer, K. (1957). Phytopathol. Z. **30**, 281.

Siegel, A., Zaitlin, M., and Sehgal, O. P. (1962). Proc. Nat. Acad. Sci. Wash. **48**, 1845.

Sill, W. H. (1958). Plant Disease Reptr. **42**, 912.

Sill, W. H., and King, C. L. (1958). Plant Disease Reptr. **42**, 513.

Smith, K. M. (1937a). Parasitology **29**, 86.

Smith, K. M. (1937b). Parasitology **29**, 70.

Smith, K. M. (1937c). Nature **139**, 370.

Smith, K. M. (1957). A Textbook of Plant Virus Diseases. 2d ed. Churchill, London.

Smith, K. M., and Bald, J. G. (1935). Parasitology **27**, 231.

Smith, K. M., and Short, M. E. (1959). Plant Pathology **8**, 54.

Sol, H. H. (1963). Tijdschr. Plantenziekten **69**, 208.

Sol, H. H., and Seinhorst, J. W. (1961). Tijdschr. Plantenziekten **67**, 307.

Sol, H. H., van Heuven, J. C., and Seinhorst, J. W. (1960). Tijdschr. Plantenziekten **66**, 228.

Staniland, L. N. (1963). Plant Pathology **12**, 91.

Steere, R. L. (1956). Phytopathology **46**, 60.

Stone, W. J., Mink, G. I., and Bergeson, G. B. (1962). Plant Disease Reptr. **46**, 623.

Sturgess, O. W. (1961). Sugar y Azúcar **56**, 29.

Taylor, C. E. (1962). Virology **17**, 493.

Teakle, D. S. (1960). Nature **188**, 431.

Teakle, D. S. (1962a). Phytopathology **52**, 1037.

Teakle, D. S. (1962b). Virology **18**, 224.

Teakle, D. S., and Gold, A. H. (1963). Virology **19**, 310.

Thompson, R. C., and Doolittle, S. P. (1942). Phytopathology **32**, 542.

Thorne, G., and Allen, M. W. (1950). Proc. Helm. Soc. Wash. **17**, 27.

Toler, R. W., and Hebert, T. T. (1963). Plant Disease Reptr. **47**, 58.

Tomlinson, J. A., and Garrett, R. G. (1962). Nature **194**, 249.

Tomlinson, J. A., and Garrett, R. G. (1963). Rept. Nat. Veg. Res. Sta. Wellesbourne for 1962, p. 57.

Tomlinson, J. A., and Smith, B. R. (1958). Plant Pathology **7**, 19.

Tomlinson, J. A., and Smith, B. R. (1959). Rept. Nat. Veg. Res. Sta. Wellesbourne for 1958, p. 38.

Tomlinson, J. A., Smith, B. R., and Garrett, R. G. (1962). Nature **193**, 599.

Uozumi, T. (1954). Virus (Osaka) **4**, 359.

Uschdraweit, H. A., and Valentin, H. (1956). Nachrbl. Deut. Pflanzenschutzdienst (Braunschweig) **8**, 132.

van der Want, J. P. H. (1952). Proc. Conf. Potato Virus Diseases, Wageningen-Lisse, 1951, p. 71.

van Hoof, H. A. (1962). Tijdschr. Plantenziekten **68**, 391.

van Koot, Y., and van Dorst, H. J. M. (1955). Tijdschr. Plantenziekten **61**, 163.

van Slogteren, D. H. M. (1958). Tijdschr. Plantenziekten **64**, 452.

Vuittenez, A. (1957). Compt. Rend. Acad. Agr. France **43**, 185.

Vuittenez, A. (1958). Compt. Rend. Acad. Agr. France **44**, 901.

Vuittenez, A. (1960). Compt. Rend. Acad. Agr. France **46**, 89.

Vuittenez, A. (1961). In Les Nématodes. Fédération Nationale des Groupements de Protection des Cultures. Versailles.

Wada, E., and Fukano, H. (1934). Agr. and Hort. (Tokyo) **9**, 1778.

Wada, E., and Fukano, H. (1937). J. Imp. Agr. Expt. Sta. Japan **3**, 93.

Wagnon, H. K., and Breece, J. R. (1955). Phytopathology **45**, 696.

Walkinshaw, C. H., and Larson, R. H. (1958). Nature **181**, 1146.

Walkinshaw, C. H., Griffin, G. D., and Larson, R. H. (1961). Phytopathology **51**, 806.

Webb, R. W. (1927). J. Agr. Research **35**, 587.

Webb, R. W. (1928). J. Agr. Research **36**, 53.

Yarwood, C. E. (1954). Plant Disease Reptr. **38**, 263.

Zuckerman, B. M. (1961). Nematologica **6**, 135.

7

R. H. E. BRADLEY

Aphid transmission of stylet-borne viruses

WHY FOCUS on this *one* type of transmission by *one* group of insects? Because it is important just now—not only to a few specialists but also to many who deal in plants and their products. In their *Conspectus of Aphids as Vectors of Plant Viruses*, Kennedy *et al.* (1962) list 84 viruses as being stylet-borne and another 18 that probably are. No other group of viruses looms so large; none other affects more crops or causes greater losses; and none other is proving more difficult to control. Surely these are reasons enough for stalking this giant so closely.

7-1. INTRODUCTION

The obvious way to prevent aphids from spreading virus—that is, by killing them—has been tried repeatedly. Yet in spite of the high kills possible with modern insecticides, seldom has the spread of stylet-borne viruses been reduced enough to give practical control (Broadbent, 1957). As the reasons for this emerge it looks more and more as though it may not be feasible to kill migrant aphids before they can alight and probe the few seconds required to transmit stylet-borne virus. Since migrant aphids are often the main vectors in nature, spread by them may have to be checked some way that does not depend on killing them before they probe. So there is a need to find other ways to block this transmission. This departure from the traditional approach to control will require among other things a launching pad built of firm ideas about how aphids transmit stylet-borne virus. Such a pad could also be put to good use in other research on aphid vectors, so it is important enough to be our focus point here.

Fortunately the launching site was cleared some time ago and construction is well under way. Several bird's-eye views of it have been made from various vantage points (Bawden, 1950; Day and Irzykiéwicz, 1954; Sylvester, 1954, 1962; Heinze, 1957; van Hoof, 1958; Schmidt, 1959; Carter, 1962). With these available, the time is ripe for a tour down into the site and a closer look at what is being done.

Beware of your first impression of how aphids transmit stylet-borne virus. It looks deceivingly simple. An aphid takes up virus during a brief probe into an infected plant, can then transmit it at once during the next probe or so, but usually does not remain viruliferous for long after leaving the source of virus. Even without direct evidence that such virus is stylet-borne, it is little wonder that pioneers in the field decided that the mouthparts must get contaminated with virus and then act like an inoculating needle (Doolittle and Walker, 1928; Hoggan, 1933; Osborn, 1937). They did not know and many still do not realize that, unlike TMV, stylet-borne viruses are not easily transmitted by pricking with a needle.

Anyway, before long, Watson (1938) persisted until she showed that there is far more to this type of transmission than meets the eye. After this the contaminated mouthparts idea appeared to have gaping holes in it (Watson and Roberts, 1940). Now some 20 years later we are still undecided whether to patch up the idea or replace it altogether with an up-to-date model. One thing has become clear: this transmission may still turn out to be a rather simple process in the final analysis, but the final analysis is by no means simple. Let me tell you about it.

7–2. FRAMEWORK

Many of us in the stylet-borne corps can be justly proud of one thing; that is, we stick close to the problem. So close in fact that seldom do we investigate anything outside of the transmission process itself. This has the drawback that for the most part our experimenting has to be done with aphids, viruses, and plants all being used together. And as if this is not enough, the experimenter can unknowingly have a marked effect on the transmission results. Each of these things can vary from within and be varied from without. Few other problems carry such a load of potential variability.

Nor is that all. The amount of virus carried by an aphid's stylets is so small that as yet it cannot be measured quantitatively or otherwise studied directly. At best it can only be detected and even this has to be done in a roundabout way. Each aphid has to be given an opportunity to transmit virus to one or more suitable test plants, and then these have to be observed after a time to learn if they develop symptoms characteristic of the virus.

Aphid transmission of stylet-borne virus is not as it may sound one single event. Rather it is a chain of events, only some of which can ever be fathomed from the results of plant to plant transmission trials. Yet such results have always been the main raw materials for our ideas about how this transmission takes place. The chain of events involved in this transmission can be divided into the following three steps: (a) first the aphid takes up virus from an infected plant; (b) then for a time, usually not long, the virus is carried by the aphid; and (c) finally the aphid must inoculate the virus to a plant in such a way that infection occurs. Let these steps be called *uptake, carry over,* and *inoculation,* respectively.

In any given test the probability of an aphid transmitting virus (P_t) will depend on the probabilities of uptake, carry over, and inoculation successfully taking place. If the probabilities for these steps be represented by P_u, P_c, and P_i, respectively, then:

$$P_t = P_u P_c P_i$$

An estimate of P_t can be obtained experimentally by carrying out repeated tests under the same conditions. This is normally done by using similar aphids from the same colony, but it could also be done by using the same aphid over and over. If each aphid is tested on a separate plant as is commonly done, P_t is simply the number of test plants infected divided by the number used. For example, if after a probe on the source plant 50 aphids are tested on as many plants and later 30 of these prove to be infected, then: $P_t = 30/50$, or 0.6; and substituting in the above formula we get: $0.6 = P_u P_c P_i$. Obviously the individual values of the three unknowns cannot be determined without more data; and ordinary transmission tests do not give nearly enough data to do this. So what is done in practice is that certain deductions are made about the values of P_u, P_c, and P_i and conclusions made accordingly. If, for example, $P_t = 0.6$ as above, then it follows that P_u, P_c, and P_i cannot have values less than 0.6; and if one of them should have this minimum value the other two would have to equal one.

A single break in the chain of events necessary for transmission and the result will be an uninfected test plant. But such a plant does not mean, as is sometimes assumed, that none of the events took place. A break can occur during any of the three steps; for each involves a series of lesser events, some of which are known to fail to occur at times. For example, aphids do not

TABLE 7–1. PROBABILITY OF TRANSMISSION OVER 0.5 WITH SINGLE APHIDS

Vector and Virus	Source and Test Plants*	Reference
M. persicae		
Henbane mosaic	Tobacco	Watson (1938)
Potato Y	Tobacco	Watson and Roberts (1939)
Tobacco etch	Tobacco	Kassanis (1941)
Beet mosaic	Sugar beet	Watson (1946)
Squash mosaic	Cantaloupe	Dickson *et al.* (1949)
Turnip mosaic	*Brassica juncea* Coss.	Sylvester (1954)
Bean common mosaic	Bean	van der Want (1954)
Sweet-potato feathery mottle	*Ipomoea setosa* Ker.	McLean (1959)
Bean yellow mosaic	Broad bean to pea	Swenson (1962)
Pea mosaic	Broad bean	Cockbain *et al.* (1963)
M. certus		
Potato Y	Tobacco	MacGillivray and Bradley (1960)
M. circumflexus		
Celery mosaic	Celery	Simons and Sylvester (1953)
A. gossypii		
Cucumber mosaic	Pepper	Simons (1959)
Potato Y	Pepper	Simons (1959)
Sweet-potato feathery mottle	*Ipomoea setosa* Ker.	McLean (1959)

* When only one species of plant is given it was used both as a source of virus and as test plants.

always insert their stylets when they appear to probe as viewed with a hand lens (Bradley, 1961; Papasolomontos, 1961), so at such times uptake or inoculation would not occur. Also a delay of as little as two minutes between uptake and inoculation will cause some aphids to cease to be viruliferous (Sylvester, 1949); yet even if aphids are transferred to test plants immediately after uptake, some will usually wander about for a while without attempting to probe—you can lead an aphid to a plant but you cannot make it probe. Or consider inoculation. The virus has to be introduced into the plant tissues in such a way that it survives until it becomes established, after which it must multiply by utilizing the plant's resources. Surely plants have some defences against viruses inoculated to them by probing aphids; and if so, these defences must sometimes overcome the virus and thereby prevent infection from occurring.

The highest values of P_t thus far reported have been around 0.8 (Watson, 1938; Sylvester, 1949; Simons, 1958). Using methods essentially the same as those discovered by Watson (1938), various workers have shown that P_t can be maintained above 0.5 in repeated trials with any of the viruses and vectors listed in Table 7–1. Undoubtedly the same can be done with many other viruses and vectors. Nearly all work on the transmission process has been done under conditions where P_t is high, and then a treatment applied during one of the three steps to learn what effect it has on transmission. Knowing what the effect of the treatment is likely to be, one can usually tell whether it affected uptake, carry over, or inoculation. But there is always the possibility that a treatment applied during uptake may affect P_c, or P_i; and one applied during carry over may affect P_i. Under conditions where P_t is low for no apparent reason, the first problem is usually to find whether it is because of a low probability of uptake, carry over, or inoculation. If it is uptake, probably a richer source of virus is needed; if it is inoculation, perhaps a more susceptible test plant can be found.

In experiments that involve aphids, viruses, plants, and even the experimenter, not only must many variables be contended with but many interactions are also possible. Aphids can affect both plants and viruses; plants can affect both aphids and viruses; and viruses can affect plants, perhaps aphids too, though as yet there is no evidence of this for a stylet-borne virus. How experimenters unconsciously affect results is still not known, but there are plenty of possibilities. Let us briefly look at some of the ways that aphids, viruses, and plants have already been shown to affect transmission of stylet-borne virus. This will clear the way for a discussion of uptake, carry over, and inoculation.

A. APHIDS

Kennedy *et al.* (1962) found reports of only 242 species of aphids having been tested as vectors. Since this is less than 10% of the known species, these authors wisely caution that much of the canvas has yet to be filled in. This can also be said about our understanding of how aphids transmit stylet-borne virus; for most work on this has been done with a mere handful of species. One of these, *Myzus persicae* (Sulz.), has been used more than all others together—the workhorse of the trade. Of necessity, therefore, much of what follows will be based on results with *M. persicae*, which may be taken as the species intended hereafter if none other is named. How far our understanding applies generally remains to be seen; but so far there is every reason to be optimistic that a close look at a few of the trees will reveal what the rest of the forest will be like.

Fortunately not all species of aphid vectors transmit all of the known stylet-borne viruses. Nor does any one species. As a rule several species have been shown to transmit each virus but some appear unable to do so, experimentally at least (Kennedy *et al.*, 1962). The most interesting cases of this specificity are when one species fails to transmit a virus under conditions where another species of the very same genus is an efficient vector (Kvíčala, 1945; Doncaster and Kassanis, 1946; Kassanis, 1947). If a species does not transmit a given virus there is no way of knowing whether it is because uptake does not occur, or the virus does not survive carry over, or inoculation is unsuccessful. Although it is easy to check whether a nonvector species does in fact probe into both the source and test plants, often this is not even done. But there is more to this specificity than failure to probe; for example, from cruciferous plants simultaneously infected with cabbage black ring spot and cauliflower mosaic viruses,[*] *Myzus ornatus* Laing will transmit only the latter virus whereas *M. persicae* will transmit both (Kvíčala, 1945). Also, *Myzus ascolonicus* Donc. will transmit either cucumber mosaic or henbane mosaic viruses from tobacco to tobacco, but not potato Y or tobacco etch viruses (Doncaster and Kassanis, 1946). These early reports of extreme cases of specificity merit further study with the more detailed methods of today; at least someone should take the trouble to confirm such interesting reports.

When those species that transmit a given virus are compared as vectors of it, usually each one causes a different level of transmission. A species that transmits one virus efficiently will often do so with others, but there are notable exceptions to this. For example, Sylvester (1952) found that *M. persicae* was a more efficient vector of beet mosaic virus than *Myzus circumflexus* (Buckt.), but it was quite the reverse when these species were compared as vectors of celery mosaic virus (Simons and Sylvester, 1953). It is difficult to say how much importance should be attached to such differences when the comparisons are made at different times; for many variables are now known to affect the level of transmission obtained. There is always the possibility that at one time the aphids are collected from a vigorous colony but from a depleted one another time, which Swenson (1962) has reported can affect the level of transmission. It can also be affected by rearing

[*] The names of viruses used throughout this chapter are those suggested as the preferred name in the Supplement to Vol. 35 of the *Review of Applied Mycology* (1957).

aphids on different hosts (Simons, 1955). Also, what may appear as an unimportant change can increase the level of transmission with one species and decrease it with another. Sylvester and Simons (1951) drove this point home with an experiment in which *M. persicae* and *Rhopalosiphum pseudobrassicae* (Davis) were compared as vectors of a turnip mosaic virus. When mustard seedlings were used as test plants, *M. persicae* was the more efficient vector; but it was just the reverse when Chinese cabbage was used.

Species of aphids often differ from one another in their probing behaviour and this would be expected to affect their transmission of stylet-borne virus. But there is no reason to believe that this is by any means the main factor that determines the efficiency of a species (Watson and Roberts, 1939). Even when each aphid is only allowed what appears to be a single probe on the source plant followed by one probe on a test plant, there are still marked differences in the level of transmission by different species (Sylvester, 1952; Bradley and Rideout, 1953). But such care as this cannot be relied upon to make the probing of different species comparable. For one thing aphids do not always insert their stylets when they appear to probe (Bradley, 1961), so the experiments referred to above would be improved by studying at the same time how often the aphids of each species insert their stylets. Also there may be subtle differences in the ways that aphids insert their stylets during the brief probes when transmission of stylet-borne virus so characteristically occurs. This is not to imply that species differ in their efficiencies primarily because of differences in probing behaviour. Rather it is to stress that probing is so important to this transmission that much more needs to be learned about it.

Why species differ in their efficiency as vectors of stylet-borne virus is the one question that nearly every worker in the field has attempted to answer at one time or another. Yet after all that has been said and done it is difficult to go beyond what Watson and Roberts (1939) concluded some years ago after what was perhaps the most extensive study of the problem ever made.

They summed up their ideas by saying that the different levels of transmission obtained with different vector species and viruses depends on "several interacting factors." Nor is anyone apt to disagree. Still most of the discussion about vector efficiency seems determined to attribute it to one over-all important factor.

Experimenting with a single species is no assurance that the aphids will behave more or less the same as vectors. Most species occur in various seasonal forms, which often differ morphologically and live on quite different host plants. The differences between these seasonal forms as vectors may be as great as those between species (Orlob, 1962). Most laboratory work has been done with the summer forms, which appear to be the main vectors in nature, though there is at least one report of the spring form being so (Paine and Legg, 1953). Although winged aphids are believed to be the most important vectors in nature, wingless adults or large nymphs are generally used in the laboratory because they are easier to rear and handle. Comparisons between winged and wingless aphids as vectors of stylet-borne viruses have sometimes shown that the wingless ones are the better (Sylvester, 1955; Broadbent, 1960), or the reverse (Cockbain *et al.*, 1963), or no differences between them (Hamlyn, 1953). But in all such comparisons made thus far there was a possibility that any differences in transmission were caused by differences in probing behaviour, though Cockbain and associates went a long way towards eliminating these.

Simons (1959) has reported that clones of a species can differ in their efficiency as vectors of two stylet-borne viruses. In view of the evidence of this for certain of the circulative-borne viruses (Stubbs, 1955; Björling and Ossiannilsson, 1958; Rochow, 1960), there is no reason why the same would not apply to stylet-borne viruses; for clones are often distinguished because of differences in host preferences or feeding behaviour. But this is no reason to accept the first claim of this for stylet-borne virus without questioning it. Besides, Simons used the term *clone* for two different things about aphids. The separate field collections that he identified as *Aphis gossypii* Glover, one from pepper and the other from kenaf, may well have been clones of the one species. Those from pepper were certainly more efficient at transmitting both cucumber mosaic and potato Y viruses than were those from kenaf. Indeed the differences were so striking that it would seem worth while to study these two collections further to see if they deserve the status of separate species rather than clones. Presumably Simons had his identifications of these two collections confirmed by an outside authority, but he did not mention it in his report of the work. The second way that he used *clone* was to denote aphids of the same line reared on different species of plants. The differences in transmission that he obtained with aphids from such colonies were surely a reflection of an effect of the rearing plant as Simons (1955) himself reported earlier.

Of the various other ways that aphids can affect the transmission of stylet-borne virus, there is one that might easily be overlooked but can hardly be overstressed. It has only recently been pointed out, and then somewhat indirectly (Swenson, 1962). Disturbed by the variability of his transmission results with bean yellow mosaic virus, Swenson made a determined effort to find the reasons for this; and after various lines of work he found that the condition of the colony from which aphids were collected had an effect on both the level of transmission and its variability from test to test. With aphids from vigorous uniform colonies Swenson obtained a probability of transmission of 0.7 compared with one of 0.5 with aphids from variable colonies. Although he reared the two types of colonies under different environments, I have no doubt whatever that similar results can be obtained by comparing the transmission by aphids from young vigorous colonies with that by aphids from old depleted colonies reared under the same conditions. For aphids to transmit stylet-borne virus efficiently it is imperative that they make definite probes on both the source and test plants, preferably without hesitating. Vigorous aphids do this and withstand being handled far better than puny ones. Because

aphids reproduce so readily on a plant, there is probably a tendency to go on collecting them from the same plant as long as the required numbers can be found. But don't do it. Instead, infest two or three medium-aged host plants every week with vigorous handpicked adults and distribute them well over the plants. About two weeks later when the first generation of young has matured into large vigorous adults, collect the best of these for your transmission experiments over the next few days, and then discard the plants before they become overcrowded with aphids. This extra care will be well repaid in higher and less variable transmission results.

B. VIRUSES

Why aphids transmit many viruses via their stylets yet not certain ones such as potato X and tobacco mosaic viruses has long been a puzzling question. Recently it has become even more so with reports that aphids not only ingest both of these viruses (Ossiannilsson, 1958; Kikumoto and Matsui, 1962), but after aphids feed on plants infected with tobacco mosaic virus (TMV) they can transmit virus-like particles when they probe through a membrane into water (Matsui *et al.*, 1963). It remains to be shown whether these particles are infective or not.

Certain properties of a virus must determine whether it is transmitted via the stylets of aphids. A few of the stylet-borne viruses have had some of their properties studied *in vitro*, mostly in sap extracts. For a time it looked as though the stylet-borne viruses might form a group with similar properties such as: (a) thermal inactivation points around 60°C; (b) inactivated within a few days at ordinary room temperatures; (c) readily inactivated by acid and alcohol; and (d) filamentous particles. But at least two of these viruses are now believed to be isometric particles, namely, cucumber mosaic (Sill *et al.*, 1952) and cauliflower mosaic (Pirone *et al.*, 1960). Also the latter virus has a thermal inactivation point around 80°C (Tompkins *et al.*, 1938), which is considerably higher than that of other stylet-borne viruses.

Not only do stylet-borne viruses differ

from one another in the degree that they are transmitted by aphids, but so do strains of a single virus (Watson and Roberts, 1939; Bhargava, 1951). Furthermore some strains appear not to be transmitted at all by aphids (Bawden and Kassanis, 1947; Swenson, 1957). Badami (1958) has even reported that a strain once transmitted by aphids later lost the property to be transmitted by two species of aphids while remaining transmissible by two other species.

For years potato virus C, which is serologically and immunologically related to potato virus Y, could not be transmitted by aphids (Bawden and Kassanis, 1947) or was so very rarely (Bald and Norris, 1945). Then an isolate of virus C that had been maintained for years in *N. glutinosa* was unexpectedly found to have become transmissible by aphids, though less readily so than ordinary strains of virus Y (Watson, 1956). Watson also showed that this aphid-transmissible strain of virus C usually ceased to be so if it was passed through potato and then returned to tobacco. More intriguing still, Watson (1960) later reported that when a strain of virus C not transmitted by aphids was inoculated to *N. glutinosa* simultaneously with virus Y, from the resulting infection aphids sometimes transmitted virus that had some of the properties of both virus C and virus Y. Of the various possible explanations of this considered by Watson, she concluded that some sort of interaction or genetic recombination must have occurred between the two viruses as they multiplied in the same plant.

Simultaneous infection of a plant with two stylet-borne viruses can affect the concentration of one or both within the plant and thereby affect the level of transmission obtained by aphids (Bawden and Kassanis, 1941; Simons, 1958). Bawden and Kassanis also found that sometimes one stylet-borne virus can supplant another already established within a plant; for example, tobacco etch virus can supplant potato Y virus in tobacco.

A virus may not be transmitted by aphids unless it infects a plant simultaneously with another stylet-borne virus. An example of this is potato acuba mosaic virus, which is not transmitted from plants that it alone infects, but is from plants also infected with either potato A or Y viruses (Kassanis, 1961). Although viruses A and Y both increased the concentration of acuba mosaic virus in plants, its transmission by aphids was not in general correlated with its concentration as measured by serological tests. So to explain the results on the basis of an increase in concentration it would be necessary to postulate increased concentration in a specific tissue such as the epidermis, which might not be reflected in sap extracts of whole leaves. Among other possible explanations of his results, Kassanis suggested that phenotypic mixing may have occurred between the unrelated viruses in such a way that acuba mosaic virus obtained properties that made it transmissible by aphids.

C. PLANTS

Aphid transmission of stylet-borne virus normally cannot occur without plants being involved in at least the following ways: (a) the aphids are reared on one of their host plants; (b) the source of virus is an infected plant; and (c) the aphids have to be given an opportunity to transmit the virus to healthy test plants. Transmission can be affected by plants affecting the aphids during any of these stages, or by plants affecting the virus during either of the latter two stages. With so many possibilities here it is surprising that more has not been done on the effects of plants on this transmission.

As a rule aphids are reared on a host that is immune to the virus being used, for this is the easiest way to assure that aphids are not carrying the virus at the start of an experiment. By contrast, the source and test plants are often the same species (Table 7–1), probably as a matter of convenience. Transferring aphids from one plant species to another as is usually done from the rearing plant to the source, probably would affect their probing behaviour and thereby affect transmission as Bawden *et al.* (1954) and others have suggested. Simons (1955, 1957) has demonstrated that the species of rearing plant can affect the level of transmission. Presumably they may do so in various ways. Besides the one already mentioned another that seems likely is the species of rearing plant may affect the vigour of the aphids and thereby affect transmission (Swenson, 1962).

The species of plant used either as a source of virus or as a test plant can affect the level of transmission (Watson, 1936; Simons, 1955, 1957), as can also different varieties of the one species (Bawden and Kassanis, 1946; Sylvester, 1953b; Simons, 1960). When a certain species or variety is used as a source of virus and is found to be the cause of a low level of transmission, it is apt to be the result of a low concentration of virus in such plants. Not only do species and varieties differ in their susceptibility to aphid inoculation with stylet-borne virus, but they may do so to a greater extent with one vector species than with another (Sylvester and Simons, 1951).

Although various treatments to plants are known to increase their susceptibility to mechanically inoculated virus, as a rule the same treatments appear to have little or no effect on susceptibility to aphid inoculation. For example, unlike with mechanical inoculation, keeping plants in the dark some hours before aphid inoculation has not increased their susceptibility to at least three stylet-borne viruses (Bradley, 1952; Sylvester, 1953a; van Hoof, 1958), but appeared to do so with lettuce mosaic virus (Sylvester, 1955). Also, Bawden and Kassanis (1950) found that fertilizer treatments that increased the susceptibility of plants to mechanical inoculation did not increase the susceptibility of tobacco or potato to aphid inoculation with potato virus Y. Recently, Swenson and Sohi (1961) reported that changes in the nutrition of beans affected their susceptibility to aphid inoculation with bean yellow mosaic virus; but the experimental results have yet to be published.

7–3. UPTAKE

Let us start with a simple case and keep clear of the underbrush as long as possible. It so happens that the simplest case of uptake known also appears to be the usual one —that is, when it occurs within seconds after an aphid alights or is placed on an infected plant. What takes place then is still mainly presumed from what can be seen outwardly. Briefly the aphid stops,

protracts its labium until the distal end is in contact with the plant, remains this way for a while as if inserting its stylets, then lifts its labium free with an upward jerk of its forebody. To depict these actions the term *probe* has come to be generally used. It will be used here too, but with reservations; for it implies that the stylets penetrate into the plant, yet at times they do not (Bradley, 1961).

A. During Superficial Probes

Uptake of stylet-borne virus often occurs during the first probe on a source plant. Were it not so, much of the work in this field during the past decade could not have been done. Sylvester (1949) pioneered the use of single probes; he and others have since shown that under favourable conditions the probability of uptake during one probe can be maintained above 0.5 with any of the viruses and vectors listed in Table 7–1.

Besides a good source of virus, the most important requirement for efficient uptake appears to be for the aphids to make a brief probe or so before they settle down to feed. A simple way to condition aphids to behave this way is to keep them off plants for an hour or so before placing them on the source, an important practice introduced by Watson (1938). This is so widely done that it will apply to all work referred to hereafter unless otherwise stated. The transmission increases will be discussed later.

The effect of the duration of the source probe on uptake has been studied a great deal. In general, two approaches have been used: (a) to allow each aphid to complete its source probe; (b) to interrupt the probe at a predetermined time by dislodging the aphid. Strictly speaking, the duration of a probe should be the actual time the stylets are inserted into a plant. But since there is no easy way of determining this, the duration is simply taken as the time in seconds that the labium remains in contact with the plant.

After aphids have been kept off plants for a while, usually well over half of them probe initially for less than 30 sec and hardly 1 in 10 does so for more than a min (Bradley, 1952). This applies not only to

M. persicae but also to other species such as *Macrosiphum euphorbiae* (Thos.) and *Aphis nasturtii* Kltb. (Bradley and Rideout, 1953) and *Aphis fabae* Scop. (van der Want, 1954); but not to *Brevicoryne brassicae* (L.) (Chalfant, 1959). Uptake of stylet-borne virus has been reported to occur in as little as 5 sec (Jensen, 1950; Simons, 1956; McLean, 1959). But with uninterrupted probes it is after those lasting anywhere from about 10 sec to a min or so that aphids are most apt to be viruliferous (Bradley and Rideout, 1953; van der Want, 1954; Simons, 1956; Swenson, 1960; Zettler, 1963). Within this time range uptake occurs as readily during the shorter probes as during the longer ones, sometimes even more so. If the source probe lasts over 5 min the aphid is less apt to be viruliferous than after a shorter probe (Bradley, 1954).

Grouping aphids according to the durations of their first probe on the source involves the risk that it may select some behavioural trait that is favourable or unfavourable to transmission. One way to avoid this is to interrupt each aphid at some predetermined time during the source probe as Sylvester and his associates at California have usually done. But when this is done the time range that can be tested is only from 0 to about 20 sec, for most aphids do not probe initially for longer than this. Interrupting the source probe at 15 sec or so has been reported twice to decrease the level of transmission to about half that obtained with uninterrupted probes (Bradley, 1952; Sylvester, 1954); but at other times it has had little or no effect (Sylvester, 1949; 1952; Simons and Sylvester, 1953; McLean, 1959). There is no reason to believe that dislodging aphids from the source in itself affects transmission (McLean, 1959), so the effect of interrupting the source probe at 15 sec or earlier must simply be to pull out the stylets before uptake occurs. Simons (1956) found that for interruption to affect the level of transmission it had to be done during the first 15 sec of the source probe, and the earlier it was done the greater the effect.

Whether the source probe is interrupted or not, clearly uptake often occurs within the first 15 sec or so. Whether it occurs after this time is less easily decided as will be discussed later. Besides there is so much evidence that uptake usually occurs during the first 15 sec of a probe that this is obviously the period that merits the greatest attention in any discussion of uptake.

How far does an aphid insert its stylets within 15 sec? Not far, probably just beneath the cuticle during the first brief probes when uptake so characteristically occurs. It usually takes a minute or more for an aphid to penetrate through stripped epidermis (Bradley, 1952; van Hoof, 1958). Van Hoof obtained a few penetrations through epidermis in less than a minute and Pollard (1958) reported that *A. gossypii* does so in 42 sec, but these may have been unusually rapid cases. If aphids are anaesthetized *in situ* with carbon dioxide at any time during their first 15 sec or so of probing, the stylets usually do not extend even 5 μ beyond the end of the labium, which is one measure of the depth they have penetrated (Papasolomontos, 1961; Bradley, 1964). So uptake not only occurs from the epidermis of the source plant, but probably does so soon after the stylets penetrate through the cuticle, which presumably is devoid of virus.

Let us now consider what takes place when uptake occurs during superficial probes into the epidermis of a source plant. And let us do so by considering the answers to the following questions. Where does uptake usually occur on the source plant? How is the labium affixed to the epidermis in relation to the cells? Does uptake occur from within or between epidermal cells? And finally, is there saliva around the stylets when uptake occurs?

B. WHERE ON THE SOURCE?

Usually aphids probe the source initially within a few steps of where they are placed on it. This in turn will depend on where the experimenter believes they should go. Since the various leaves of an infected plant will differ in the virus that is available to aphids (Broadbent, 1954; Bagnall and Bradley, 1958; Bradley, 1962a), it is necessary to make tests or learn by experience which type of leaf is the best source for aphids. Once this has been done, my experience is that aphids are usually placed on the upper surface to one side of the midvein. When this is done most aphids probe initially on the upper surface, whereas the others usually do so soon after they move to the underside, which is where aphids prefer to feed. In either case the first probe or so is nearly always made interveinally, though the veins are the preferred feeding sites. It is generally accepted that the availability of virus to aphids is similar for both surfaces of a leaf, but surprisingly few tests of this appear to have been made (Stevenson, 1959; Bradley, 1962a). It also appears to be tacitly assumed that the availability of virus is similar for the different areas of a leaf, but this is unlikely to be so. For example, with a mature tobacco leaf showing well-developed symptoms of infection with potato virus Y, the tip third is a better source than the middle or base, and interveinal areas are better than veins (Bradley, 1962a). Other viruses probably are distributed differently in leaves. With a little care in placing aphids they can be made to probe on any part of a leaf, so it is a straightforward matter to determine the availability of virus for different leaf areas. Since aphids first probe interveinally and later settle on veins, the distribution of virus in a leaf could affect transmission results, especially when aphids are tested after various times on the source (Bradley, 1962a).

C. How Is the Labium Placed in Relation to the Epidermal Cells?

Recently Swenson (1962) stressed that after aphids have been kept off plants for a while their first probes are usually made abruptly without the aphid tapping the leaf surface with its labium as it often does later. He suggested that it is by this labial tapping that aphids locate the intercellular probing sites for their later probes (van Hoof, 1958), so he proposed that the first brief probes are made by the labium being placed more or less at random on the epidermis. If this is so, the labium would be placed on the surface of a cell far more often than on the transverse walls of adjoining cells. This led Swenson to postulate that uptake occurs more readily when stylets penetrate into rather than between the cells of the epidermis. Earlier, van der Want (1954) made a similar proposal.

As already mentioned, at first aphids usually probe the source interveinally. At such times it is not possible to observe how the labium is placed, because pigments in the underlying tissues obscure the irregular outlines of the transverse walls of the epidermal cells. But if aphids are placed astride a vein they will usually probe into it and then one can easily see how the labium is placed; for there are so few pigments in the underlying tissues that the epidermal cells stand out like tightly packed cylinders lying side by side. I have observed some 300 aphids as they probed initially on a tobacco vein (Bradley, 1964). Not one aphid did so without placing the tip of its labium in a surface depression between adjoining cells. These depressions seemed to be the natural place for the labium to go as this helped to hold it firm for the start of probing. When the tip of the labium contacted the epidermis on the crest of a cell, the labium invariably slid into an adjacent depression as the aphid pushed downwards to probe. These probes into veins were initiated abruptly without any tapping of the labium, and they usually terminated in less than 30 sec. Also, by using veins from senescent leaves of plants infected about two months with potato virus Y, I found that the probability of uptake occurring during the first probe was above 0.5, which was comparable to that obtained with aphids allowed to probe interveinally on such leaves. So the probes observed on veins were characteristic of those when uptake occurs. And since interveinal epidermis of tobacco also has surface depressions between adjoining cells, I expect that the first brief probes on it are also made with the labium in one of these depressions. On tobacco, therefore, the initial probes are not made by the labium being placed at random as proposed by Swenson (1962). Presumably this applies to other plants too.

D. Is Uptake from Within or Between Epidermal Cells?

With the labium being placed in a surface depression between cells and with van

Hoof's (1958) evidence that aphids usually penetrate between the transverse walls of the epidermis, it would seem like an open and shut case for intercellular uptake as proposed by van Hoof. But it could still be argued that during the initial brief probes when uptake occurs, the stylets penetrate at an angle and thereby enter one of the adjoining cells instead of passing between them. And it could be pointed out that no one has claimed to have directly observed stylets during initial brief probes. The nearest to this that has been done is to observe the stylets as they penetrate *through* stripped epidermis. Of those who have done this, van Hoof (1958) has given by far the best account of what takes place. He was the first to use the shape of the salivary sheath formed around the stylets as a guide to whether penetration was through or between the cells of the epidermis. Sheaths formed within a cell are beaded and thicker than the smooth cylindrical ones formed between transverse walls of the epidermis. Using this as a guide and by observing the stylets under high magnification, van Hoof found that both *M. persicae* and *A. fabae* usually penetrate between the transverse walls of the epidermis, i.e., intercellularly.

When observations of aphids probing through stripped epidermis are related to the uptake of stylet-borne virus, there are at least two reasons for caution. First, stripped epidermis is a poor source of virus (Bradley, 1952; van Hoof, 1958). Secondly and more important, the probes observed passing through stripped epidermis are not the brief initial ones when uptake so characteristically occurs. Rather they are probes made by aphids that have first probed briefly and then settled down long enough to penetrate through the epidermis, which takes about a minute or so. To observe stylets penetrating through stripped epidermis, the aphid first has to be followed under low magnification until it stops walking and begins to probe. Then one must change to a much higher magnification, which takes about 15 sec; and even after this my experience is that another 15 sec or so passes before the stylets can be seen emerging from the shadow cast by the end of the labium, and still more time passes

before enough of the salivary sheath can be seen to decide whether it is beaded or not. So probes observed in stripped epidermis have to last upwards of a minute and preferably longer. Such probes may not be typical of those when uptake occurs as will be discussed later. Anyway by the time the stylets can be seen uptake will already have occurred. Presumably it is because of this technical difficulty of observing stylets at the start of probing that led Swenson (1962) to question van Hoof's evidence that uptake occurs intercellularly.

But van Hoof also obtained other evidence for intercellular uptake. He plasmolyzed source leaves until the cytoplasm of the epidermal cells shrunk away from the cell walls, and then he found that uptake still occurred during 15-sec probes, which were not long enough for the stylets to penetrate into the shrunken cytoplasm. This evidence and that already discussed makes almost inescapable the conclusion that uptake occurs intercellularly as claimed by van Hoof. Whether it can also occur during probes into epidermal cells has yet to be shown.

E. SALIVA?

Bradley (1952) and van der Want (1954) suggested that uptake occurs during the first brief probes on the source because little or no saliva surrounds the stylets at such times. The only bit of evidence offered in support of this was Bradley's claim that he did not see saliva being ejected during the first brief probes into stripped epidermis. But as explained earlier, the stylets cannot be seen during the first 15 sec or so of probing, so it would be necessary to note the exact position of the labium on the epidermis and then look there for saliva after the aphid moved away. Since these observations would have to be made through the epidermis and since the probes would usually be intercellular, the small amount of saliva that would be ejected during a superficial probe might well pass undetected. So Bradley's claim in this respect need not be taken seriously. More detailed observations will be needed to settle whether or not aphids eject saliva around the stylets during their first brief probes.

Van Hoof (1957) reasoned that since aphids eject saliva on the leaf surface even before penetration, it is unlikely they would stop ejecting it as the stylets entered the leaf. Is it so unlikely? If the first brief probes are made to test the suitability of the plant (Wensler, 1962), the stylets may penetrate beyond the saliva as they apparently do in sieve tubes when feeding is in progress (Zimmermann, 1961). Nor is there convincing evidence that aphids do eject saliva on the leaf surface during their initial brief probes when uptake occurs. And if they do, is it the gelling type that forms the surface flange and later the sheath around the stylets, or is it the nongelling watery type recently reported by Miles (1959)? As yet there is too little evidence to say whether or not stylets are surrounded by saliva when uptake occurs. If not, it offers a ready explanation of some of the characteristics of this transmission discussed later.

F. Uptake Other Than During Superficial Probing?

This question cannot be answered straightforwardly because all sorts of complicating factors become involved. But as a rule aphids are as apt to be viruliferous after one brief source probe as after additional ones (Sylvester, 1950a; Bradley, 1954), and since allowing aphids to remain on the source for more than a few minutes decreases the level of transmission obtained (Watson, 1938), it is certainly not necessary to postulate that uptake occurs other than during the first 15 sec or so of a probe.

One thing that should be understood from the outset is that probing for 15 sec, or even much longer, *does not* greatly decrease the probability that uptake will occur at the *start* of the very next probe. For example, if aphids probe first on a healthy plant and then on the source, uptake occurs as readily as when they probe the source immediately (Sylvester, 1950a). Also, if aphids probe continuously on the source for 20 min or more and then withdraw their stylets themselves, they are rarely viruliferous; but often become so at the start of their next probe on the source plant (Bradley, 1954; Cockbain *et al.,* 1963).

At times the probability of uptake during the first 15 sec of probing may be so high that further uptake after this time might not be detected if it did occur. For example, it is not unusual for the probability of transmission to be as high as 0.7 after a 15-sec probe, which means that during this time the probability of uptake would be between 0.7 and 1. If it should be near the upper limit, further uptake probably would not increase the level of transmission in ordinary trials. Even working with a level of transmission around 0.5, Sylvester (1950a, 1954) found that additional brief source probes *did not* increase the numbers of infections that aphids would cause during a series of brief test probes. Presumably aphids differ in the relative amounts of virus they carry, but as yet there is no way of proving this. So if a viruliferous aphid takes up additional virus after the first 15 sec or so of a probe, there is still no way of detecting it.

This question of uptake of transmissible virus after the first 15 sec or so of a probe can be approached another way. It takes about a minute for stylets to penetrate through the epidermis of a source plant (van Hoof, 1958); so if after doing this an aphid acquires transmissible virus from subepidermal tissues it would prove that uptake occurred after the first 15 sec of the probe. Subepidermal tissues contain transmissible virus, for aphids sometimes become viruliferous when they probe directly into such tissues after the epidermis has been removed (Bradley, 1956; van Hoof, 1958; Namba, 1962).

Many workers in this field may believe that under normal conditions subepidermal uptake occurs at times, but Bawden *et al.* (1954) appear to be the only ones who have argued in support of it. They did so on the basis of the transmissions they obtained from leaves that had been exposed to ultraviolet irradiation that would inactivate virus. Irradiation of both leaf surfaces greatly reduced the numbers of aphids that became viruliferous within 2 min but had little or no effect on the numbers that were so after 1 or 24 hr on such leaves. Since more aphids were always viruliferous after the longer periods on irradiated leaves,

159

Bawden and associates reasoned that at least the additional aphids must have transmitted virus they acquired from subepidermal tissues where it was believed the irradiation did not inactivate much of the virus. Yet to explain certain other aspects of their results, these workers postulated that in parts of the epidermis the virus was not inactivated, because the uneven leaf surfaces were not uniformly irradiated. Presumably the sides of veins and perhaps nearby areas partly shielded by the protruding veins of the lower surface would receive less irradiation than other areas. During the first few minutes on the leaves most aphids would probe interveinally, but in time more and more of them would move to the underside and find their way to the veins where they prefer to feed. This movement to the veins could have taken them to the very parts of the epidermis that were not fully irradiated, which could explain the increased numbers of viruliferous aphids after 1 or 24 hr without postulating subepidermal uptake.

Working with potato virus Y in tobacco, Bradley (1956) also irradiated infected leaves and tested whether aphids were viruliferous after various periods on them. Since no aphids proved to be so after short or long periods on such leaves and since sap extracts of the leaves contained mechanically transmissible virus, Bradley interpreted this as evidence that subepidermal uptake rarely occurs. He too believed that irradiation would not inactivate much of the virus in subepidermal tissues. That this is not so has since been shown by Hitchborn (1958), who found that irradiation greatly reduced the infectivity of sap extracts of subepidermal as well as epidermal tissues. Hitchborn did not test whether irradiation produced inhibitors in leaves, presumably because Bawden et al. (1954) had done so and found no evidence of them. But van Hoof (1958) reported that sap extracts of irradiated leaves inhibited both tobacco mosaic and turnip mosaic viruses when inoculated to plants by rubbing; the inhibition only reduced the numbers of lesions formed by about half, whereas it had a much greater effect on reducing the availability of virus to aphids. Until the effects of irradiation on both leaves and viruses are better understood (Kleczkowski, 1960), results with this method cannot settle whether aphids normally acquire transmissible virus from subepidermal tissues.

Bradley (1963b) approached the problem another way. He tested whether aphids become viruliferous when they probe through a membrane into an infected leaf disc. Since aphids that did this seldom proved to be viruliferous, this was interpreted as evidence that uptake rarely occurs other than at the start of a probe. Bradley also pointed out that his membrane results can be interpreted another way. A membrane between the aphid and the source of virus would probably prevent the stylets from entering the source intercellularly as they usually do, and uptake may not occur during intracellular probing.

Though all of the evidence for or against uptake of stylet-borne virus after the first 15 sec or so of a probe is equivocal, at least this conclusion seems justified. If uptake normally occurs after this time it does so much less readily than before.

G. Why Does Uptake Mainly Occur During Superficial Probing?

In one sense this question is simply another way of looking at an earlier problem. That is, why are aphids usually more apt to be viruliferous after a minute or so on the source than after some time on it? Most attempts to explain this have also tried at the same time to explain why keeping aphids off plants before uptake increases the transmission of stylet-borne virus. Watson (1938) not only discovered both of these phenomena, but her explanation of them has received more support than any other. Briefly her hypothesis was as follows: (a) while feeding, aphids produce a substance that renders the virus noninfective; (b) keeping aphids off plants arrests the production of this substance; and (c) for a while after aphids are returned to plants they can take up and transmit the virus until feeding again stimulates the production of the substance. When it is considered that this hypothesis was advanced some 20 years ago and that it has influenced work in this field more than any other single idea, Watson's foresight deserves the respect that it still commands.

The core of Watson's hypothesis was that soon after aphids are returned to plants something begins to impede transmission. Whatever it is must act by interfering with the uptake of transmissible virus, for keeping aphids off plants *after* uptake does not increase transmission (Watson, 1938). Watson and most others who have since discussed this problem have incriminated the aphid's saliva as the most probable thing that would interfere with transmission. And opinion continues to be in favour of the saliva containing substances that render the virus noninfective. For further discussion of the various ideas about this consult Watson and Roberts (1939), Day and Irzykiewicz (1954), Sylvester (1954), and Schmidt (1959). I have always been wary of this idea. Admittedly such substances may well occur in the saliva. But my experience is that after accepting the idea one inevitably extends it to explain more and more of the characteristics of this transmission; and the more necessary the idea appears to become, the greater the danger that it will go on being accepted without being questioned or tested experimentally.

Some workers have tried to explain uptake during superficial probing without postulating inactivators or inhibitors in the saliva. For example, Bradley (1952) and van der Want (1954) proposed that uptake occurs mainly at the start of a probe because little or no saliva surrounds the stylets at such times. Bradley postulated that in the absence of saliva the food or salivary duct becomes clogged by the unfiltered plant sap, causing the aphid to withdraw. Then at the start of the next probe or so the aphid might have to clear the clogged duct by forcing liquid outwards at which time virus could pass from the stylets into a healthy plant. For this hypothesis to be true it would mean that transmissible virus would probably be carried a considerable distance up the food or salivary duct; and this now seems unlikely in view of the evidence that the virus is carried at the stylet tips (Bradley and Ganong, 1955a). Van der Want's hypothesis is much simpler and therefore

to be preferred. He pointed out that in the absence of saliva the stylets would be in direct contact with the plant tissues and therefore more apt to acquire virus than later when saliva is being ejected ahead of the advancing stylets and molded into the salivary sheath. Certainly the salivary sheath separates the stylets from the plant tissues. Whether plant sap passes through the sheath and surrounds the length of the stylets within the sheath is not known.

Some workers have postulated hypotheses without incriminating the saliva as interfering with transmission. For example, Bawden *et al.* (1954) postulated that stylet-borne viruses are much more concentrated in the epidermis of infected plants than in subepidermal tissues. This would explain why aphids are more apt to be viruliferous after superficial probing than after they settle and insert their stylets deeply. But it fails to explain why aphids do not become viruliferous when they probe through a membrane into infected leaves (Bradley, 1963b). Bawden and associates supported their hypothesis with results obtained by exposing infected leaves to ultraviolet irradiation and then testing them as sources of virus for aphids and comparing the infectivity of sap extracts of such leaves with unirradiated controls. Although later evidence does not support the claim that stylet-borne viruses are more concentrated in the epidermis than in subepidermal tissues (Hitchborn, 1958; van Hoof, 1958; Namba, 1962), the hypothesis served a useful purpose in that it stimulated considerable work.

Van Hoof (1958) observed that once stylets penetrate through the epidermis of a leaf they often pass through the intercellular spaces of the spongy parenchyma. So he pointed out that uptake would be less apt to occur from subepidermal tissues; for there the stylets are in less close contact with cells than as they penetrate through the epidermis. This too would explain why uptake mainly occurs during superficial probing, and the simplicity of this hypothesis has much to recommend it. But it also fails to explain why uptake seldom occurs when aphids probe through a membrane into an infected leaf.

Although it has long been accepted that as a rule aphids are far more apt to be viruliferous after a brief time on the source than after an hour or more on it, Papasolomontos (1961) has recently questioned this in an interesting and original way. He suggests that an experimental artifact is mainly responsible for this belief. He points out that the longer aphids remain on the source the more they settle down and insert their stylets deeply. When an aphid that has done this is removed from the source for testing, the stylets are pulled from the plant before the labium can extend over them. This exposes the stylets to air, a treatment that Papasolomontos suggests would quickly inactivate stylet-borne virus. And he presents convincing evidence that exposing stylets to air for about 2 or 3 min causes most aphids to become nonviruliferous with cucumber mosaic virus. It is also possible that this is the reason that Sylvester and Richardson (1963) obtained a marked drop in transmission when they exposed the stylets of aphids carrying a virus that they referred to as cabbage mosaic. But other results appear not to support this hypothesis. For example, with aphids carrying potato virus Y, exposing the stylets to air for upwards of 10 min often does not render the aphids nonviruliferous (Bradley, 1959). Also when an aphid with its stylets inserted deeply withdraws itself, it does so slowly and extends the labium over the stylets while doing so. This would prevent the stylets from being exposed to air, and yet aphids are seldom viruliferous when they withdraw their stylets from the source after some time on it (Bradley, 1954; Cockbain *et al.*, 1963). Furthermore, if aphids are in fact viruliferous after they penetrate deeply into the source as postulated by Papasolomontos, it would mean that transmissible virus would have to be acquired from the deeper tissues to replace that scoured from the stylets by the action of probing (Bradley, 1959). Yet as discussed earlier there are various reasons for believing that uptake rarely occurs from subepidermal tissues. Though exposure of stylets to air will in time cause aphids to become nonviruliferous and apparently does so sooner with some viruses than with others, it is unlikely that this is the main reason for the reduced transmission obtained when aphids remain on the source for some time.

H. Effect of Keeping Aphids Off Plants Prior to Uptake

As mentioned earlier, aphids are usually kept off plants an hour or so before being placed on the source of virus, an important practice introduced by Watson (1938). This usually increases the level of transmission several times over that obtained when aphids are interrupted from feeding and placed immediately on the source. It now seems that with careful handling aphids will transmit virus as readily after about 5 min off plants as after longer periods (Sylvester, 1949; McLean, 1959; Bradley, 1961). All that appears to be required is for each aphid to make a definite brief probe on the source and then probe the test plant without undue delay.

When aphids are interrupted from feeding and immediately placed on the source plant, various things about their behaviour obviously reduce the chances of uptake of stylet-borne virus (Bradley, 1961; Papasolomontos, 1961). Such aphids are sluggish and reluctant to probe. As a rule their stylets have been pulled out of the previous plant before the labium could be extended over them; and as the aphid ensheathes its stylets it often appears to be probing but is not. Even after the stylets are ensheathed and the aphid begins to probe within a minute or so, it usually remains probing some time and inserts its stylets more than superficially into the source. And when recently collected aphids make long initial probes on the source, they rarely become viruliferous even if they are interrupted and tested after probing for only 20 sec or so (Bradley, 1964). Thus uptake seems not to occur at the start of probes that characteristically last long enough for the stylets to be inserted some way into the source.

Aphids probe into plants for at least two reasons and probably more. One reason is to test the suitability of the plant as a host; another is to ingest food. Apparently aphids test the suitability of a plant during their first brief probes (Wensler, 1962), which is also when uptake of stylet-borne virus normally occurs. After aphids accept a plant they probe deeper, for as a rule ingestion takes place mainly from vascular tissues (Auclair, 1963). Since these two types of probes are made for different reasons, they may also be made in different ways. I am thinking along these lines for my own future work and am speculating as follows. For its *test* probes on a plant an aphid may insert its stylets without saliva around the tips and thereby receive the stimuli that enable it to accept or reject the plant. At such times saliva may or may not be ejected on the leaf surface and into the plant; and if it is it may be the watery type rather than the gelling type (Miles, 1959). After the aphid accepts the plant and makes a probe that goes deeper in search of food, presumably it ejects gelling saliva on the leaf surface and ahead of the stylets so as to form the salivary sheath with its surface flange (van Hoof, 1958). To account for uptake of stylet-borne virus during the superficial test probes and yet not at the start of deeper probes, it seems necessary to incriminate the saliva as impeding uptake. Whether it does so simply by forming a barrier between the stylets and plant (van der Want, 1954), or by containing substances that make the virus noninfectious, or by some other way, remains to be shown. I favour van der Want's hypothesis, simply because it is the least complex yet advanced and therefore less apt to be accepted without being tested. By thinking along these lines I see various studies that can be made with existing methods.

Keeping aphids in a container without food is one way that conditions certain species at least to make test probes, which appear to be best for uptake of stylet-borne virus. Some species may not respond to this treatment; for example, *B. brassicae* (Hamlyn, 1955; Chalfant, 1959). Perhaps the transmission obtained with species that do not probe readily after being kept in a container without food would be increased by using winged aphids and flying them for a time before the source probe; for Cockbain *et al.* (1963) found that this was more effective with *A. fabae* than keeping them in a container without food. The brief probing that results in the highest level of trans-

mission in the laboratory is also characteristic of the behaviour of winged aphids that have flown for a time in the field (Kennedy, 1960). And such aphids are believed to be the main vectors of stylet-borne viruses in nature.

I. Sundries

Thus far only uptake of stylet-borne virus from living plants has been considered. Schmidt (1959) found that aphids transmitted beet mosaic virus from infected leaves that had been frozen. But van Hoof (1958) obtained no transmissions of lupin mosaic virus from infected broadbean leaves that had been killed by freezing, by heating, or by dipping into various chemicals. Since extracts of frozen leaves contain mechanically transmissible virus, van Hoof postulated that the failure of aphids to transmit virus from killed leaves may be because aphids transmit virus nucleic acid, which would be inactivated by enzymes released when the cells were killed. If this hypothesis is correct, it should be possible to render aphids nonviruliferous by treating their stylets with ribonuclease; but Simons and Moss (1963) found that this did not affect subsequent transmission by aphids carrying potato virus Y.

Various workers have reported that aphids do not become viruliferous when they probe through a membrane into a solution of a stylet-borne virus or into concentrated TMV, nor when the stylets are inserted directly into such a solution (Hamilton, 1935; Bradley, 1952; Day and Irzykiewicz, 1954; Heinze, 1959; Schmidt, 1959; Orlob, 1963). Heinze (1959) appears to be the only one who has obtained uptake of transmissible stylet-borne virus other than from infected plants; he reported that aphids occasionally were viruliferous after probing into paper that had been infiltrated with a solution of beet mosaic virus.

Throughout this discussion I have intentionally avoided any mention of aphids *feeding* during the brief probes when uptake of stylet-borne virus characteristically occurs. There is no evidence that feeding in the sense of ingestion has anything to do with this transmission; for no appreciable amount of it seems to occur until after aphids remain on plants for some minutes (Day and Irzykiewicz, 1953; Watson and Nixon, 1953). Indeed, were it not for the uptake and subsequent transmission of stylet-borne virus there would still be no way of telling that aphids take up material from plants during their first 15 sec of probing. Using autoradiographic tests, Nishizawa et al. (1959) have shown that when aphids probe for as little as 30 sec on radish plants infected with radish mosaic virus and also containing P^{32}, they subsequently transmit both the virus and P^{32} during their next two or three probes. With a test as sensitive as this it should be possible to determine whether during brief probes aphids acquire material other than at the tips of their stylets, which is where transmissible stylet-borne virus appears to be carried.

7–4. CARRY OVER

With stylet-borne viruses, aphids are most apt to be viruliferous immediately after uptake and they do not remain so for long after leaving the source. So there is no need to consider that such viruses multiply during carry over as do certain others carried internally (Maramorosch, 1963).

Most studies concerned with the carry over period of stylet-borne viruses have dealt with the factors that cause aphids to cease to be viruliferous. Since this transmission always involves a certain minimum carry over period, it is against this that the effects of any factor have to be judged. The minimum carry over period that can be obtained in practice involves at least the following. The aphid either has to withdraw its stylets from the source or they can be pulled out by dislodging the aphid. It seems not to matter which way it is done (McLean, 1959). At least 15 sec and usually longer elapse between uptake and the start of the first probe on a test plant (Sylvester, 1949). After the labium is affixed to the test plant, the stylets have to be pushed out of the labial groove and presumably must penetrate at least through the cuticle before inoculation can occur. Nor does an aphid always cause infection during its first probe; it may not do so until after two, three, or even more probes (Sylvester,

1950a). So even the minimum carry over period takes some time and involves probing with all of its ramifications. And since both time and probing are factors that cause aphids to cease to be viruliferous, some probably do so before they successfully inoculate their virus.

Until recently most work on the carry over period has been concerned with how long aphids remain viruliferous under different conditions. The conditions that have been studied can be broadly divided into (a) when aphids are on plants, and (b) when they are not.

A. On Plants

The length of time that aphids remain viruliferous on plants depends in part on the virus being used. Those that appear to be more or less typical of the group are bean mosaic, henbane mosaic, potato Y, and tobacco etch viruses. When aphids carrying one of these are placed on a host plant, they often cease to be viruliferous within minutes and nearly always within half an hour if they are left undisturbed. Two viruses that appear to be atypical are those that cause cucumber mosaic and cauliflower mosaic. With the first, aphids usually cease to be viruliferous within a few minutes (Bhargava, 1951); whereas with the second, aphids often remain viruliferous for some hours on plants (Hamlyn, 1955), and B. brassicae has been reported to do so for more than two days on turnip seedlings (Day and Venables, 1961). Why viruses differ this way is not known. Day and Venables suggested that aphids remain viruliferous with cauliflower mosaic virus for a relatively long time because it is more stable than other viruses of the group. Their main reason for claiming that this is a comparatively stable virus appears to be its relatively high thermal inactivation point, which is around 80°C (Kvíčala, 1948). By the same reasoning, the spinach strain of cucumber mosaic virus is also relatively stable; for its thermal inactivation point is around 70°C, which is higher than for most other stylet-borne viruses; yet aphids carrying this virus usually cease to be viruliferous within minutes of being placed on tobacco plants (Bhargava, 1951).

When aphids are placed on healthy plants for various periods after uptake of stylet-borne virus and then tested, the object is to learn how long they remain viruliferous while "feeding." The plants are therefore ones that the aphid will feed upon. But they may or may not be susceptible to the virus being used. Whether they are or not seems not to affect the time that aphids remain viruliferous (Bradley, 1959), so there is no need to consider that susceptible plant tissues attract virus from the stylets.

Watson and Roberts (1940) were the first to report that transferring aphids to a series of healthy plants at brief intervals causes them to remain viruliferous longer than if they are left on a plant without being interrupted. They interpreted this as evidence that cleansing of virus from the stylets as a result of probing is *not* the main thing that causes aphids to cease to be viruliferous while on plants. Transferring aphids to a series of plants at 2-min intervals would increase the number of times they probed as Watson and Roberts claimed; but it would not necessarily increase the over-all amount of probing. Indeed it would probably decrease it, because some probing time would be lost with each transfer. Also, the aphids being transferred would probe mainly in the epidermis where the stylets advance slower, move less vigorously, and less saliva is ejected than during probing in the intercellular spaces of the spongy parenchyma (van Hoof, 1958). Thus the deeper probes of interrupted aphids may well be more effective in removing virus from the stylets than the superficial probes of aphids transferred at 2-min intervals.

Bradley (1959) attempted to determine more precisely what it is about probing that causes aphids to cease to be viruliferous. Working with potato virus Y, he found that during comparable amounts of probing aphids ceased to be viruliferous at the same rate while probing into tobacco, potato, *Datura stramonium* L., or through a Parafilm membrane. Nor did it seem to matter whether the probes through the membrane were into water or air. He therefore concluded that normally the following things

are not important in causing aphids to cease to be viruliferous: (a) the species of plant or material probed; (b) the presence of liquids other than saliva around the stylets; and (c) ingestion, which could not occur during probing through a membrane into air. He also claimed that in the absence of probing the ejection of saliva or movements of the stylets were not in themselves important factors in rendering aphids nonviruliferous. The test for the effect of these two things by themselves was to tether aphids by the back with their feet in the air and their stylets exposed from the labium. Within 5–10 min such aphids would eject considerable saliva and move their stylets as if probing; yet they were as apt to be viruliferous after doing these things as were controls treated the same way, but not tethered and allowed to recover on glass where it was claimed they did not eject saliva. There are at least two possible loopholes in this experiment. First, it is quite possible that aphids moved their stylets *within* the labial groove, where any movements could easily have passed undetected. Secondly, it is even possible that the control aphids also ejected saliva; they were checked for this as they recovered from being anaesthetized and extended the labium over their stylets, but not during the few minutes that they walked about on the glass before they were transferred to test plants. Aphids sometimes try to probe on glass, and in so doing they not only eject saliva but presumably insert their stylets in and out of it as they try to probe. With both the tethered aphids and the controls the probability of transmission was 0.3, which is roughly half that for aphids tested immediately after uptake. It is not surprising that half the aphids ceased to be viruliferous when it is considered that they were anaesthetized for about 2 min, had their stylets bared, and were not placed on test plants for about 10 min after uptake. But it could be argued that half the aphids in both groups ceased to be viruliferous mainly as a result of salivating or moving their stylets or both. The point of questioning this experiment here is not that I doubt my earlier conclusion, but to stress that claims such as these should not be accepted without question as so often happens in this field.

Bradley (1959) concluded that on host plants aphids cease to be viruliferous mainly because their probing scours virus from the stylets. Other factors may also be involved, but it would be hazardous to incriminate any on the evidence available. The idea that keeps getting verbal support is that the saliva contains substances that inactivate or inhibit such viruses. For further discussion of the reasoning behind this idea consult Watson and Roberts (1939), Day and Irzykiewicz (1954), Sylvester (1954), Heinze (1957), and Schmidt (1959). As yet the idea can be supported only by circumstantial evidence, all of which can be interpreted otherwise as readily as not. Saliva certainly has every opportunity to come in contact with stylet-borne virus during probing. So much so that if saliva contains virus inactivators I fail to see how aphids can remain viruliferous after building a salivary sheath 70 μ or more in length (Bradley, 1956). If aphids could be made to probe that same amount into water without a salivary sheath around the stylets, it would surely wash all virus from the stylets (Bradley, 1959). So it is possible that saliva helps prolong the time that aphids remain viruliferous.

What the idea of virus inactivators or inhibitors in the saliva needs is direct evidence to substantiate it. Nishi (1959) may have taken a step in this direction with his evidence that plants infested by aphids contain inhibitors of TMV inoculated to plants by rubbing.

B. OFF PLANTS

Aphids carrying stylet-borne virus remain viruliferous somewhat longer off plants than on them. The increase can be up to several hours at room temperature. The main point of testing how long aphids can remain viruliferous off plants is usually to gain some idea how long migrant aphids may remain so in the field, a point of obvious practical importance. What is most stressed about such experiments is that the aphids are kept from "feeding," the term being used in a broad sense to include all that aphids do on plants. Whether feeding in the sense of ingestion causes aphids to cease to be viruliferous is questionable (Bradley, 1959), but there can be no doubt that probing does. So in testing how long aphids remain viruliferous off plants, the important thing is probably to keep the aphids from probing in so far as is possible. It is not easy to do, for at ordinary temperatures aphids will repeatedly try to probe even on an impenetrable surface such as glass, and in so doing they eject saliva on the surface and presumably insert their stylets in and out of it in their attempts to probe. Aphids can insert their stylets and probe when confined in such containers as cellophane-covered dishes (Watson, 1936), gelatin capsules (Sylvester, 1952), or containers lined with filter paper (Severin and Tompkins, 1948). Yet even in such containers aphids remain viruliferous longer than on plants, so they obviously do not probe nearly as much as on a food plant. The time that aphids remain viruliferous in a container without food is generally accepted as what would occur with migrant aphids in the field, other factors being the same. That this is probably so has recently been further substantiated by comparisons between aphids kept in a container without food and with others flying tethered (McLean, 1961) or better still while flying free (Cockbain et al., 1963).

The lower the temperature the longer aphids remain viruliferous with stylet-borne viruses (Kassanis, 1941; Heinze, 1959; Cockbain et al., 1963). Heinze has reported that at temperatures just under 0°C, aphids often remained viruliferous for 6 days with turnip mosaic virus, and occasionally did so up to 40 hr with cucumber mosaic virus. Temperatures near 0°C would not only slow inactivation of stylet-borne virus by ageing, but would also immobilize aphids so that they would not so much as attempt to probe and probably not even move their stylets within the labium. Under these conditions it would seem that aphids cease to be viruliferous mainly because their virus is inactivated by ageing.

If aphids probe under certain artificial conditions they cease to be viruliferous much sooner than would normally occur. The first instance of this was found accidentally in certain trials where aphids carrying potato virus Y were allowed to probe through a membrane made of a low melting paraffin (Bradley, 1956). One brief probe into this paraffin and nearly every aphid ceased to be viruliferous. Later Bradley *et al.* (1962) showed that this effect was caused by a trace of oil in the paraffin; and simply coating any of various oils on a leaf gave similar results. Subsequent work (Bradley, 1963a) has revealed that oil also impedes aphid transmission when it is coated on the source plant or when aphids probe through a membrane into oil. The effect even occurs if a viruliferous aphid merely taps its labium to an oil-coated leaf. Probing on an oil-coated leaf also reduces for a few minutes the ability of an aphid to take up and transmit new virus. How oil impedes transmission is not yet understood. The data can be explained most simply by postulating that oil removes virus from the stylets. But much more important than how the effect occurs is the possibility that oils and perhaps other materials may be a means of preventing field spread of stylet-borne viruses without having to kill the vectors before they probe.

Chalfant and Chapman (1962) have reported another way that quickly renders probing aphids nonviruliferous. Working with *B. brassicae* and cauliflower mosaic virus, they found that aphids usually ceased to be viruliferous when they probed through a membrane into 1.25% formalin and 10% sucrose. The sucrose alone not only did not cause the effect, but for some unexplainable reason it seemed to increase the chances of transmission occurring thereafter. Chalfant and Chapman claimed that probing into formalin rendered *B. brassicae* nonviruliferous if they had spent 2 min on the source plant but not if they had remained on it for one or two days. This is part of their evidence that *B. brassicae* not only carries transmissible cauliflower mosaic virus via its stylets but also carries it some other way, presumably internally. Some of their evidence for this could not be confirmed by Orlob and Bradley (1961). Nor is the evidence from aphids probing into formalin strong enough to substantiate the claim that *B. brassicae* transmits this

virus two ways. In these experiments the aphids were placed individually on a Baudruche membrane, which was then inverted, and it was assumed that the aphid probed through the membrane into the formalin if it remained in the feeding position 1–3 min. It would probably take at least a minute for the stylets to penetrate through the membrane. After a day or two on the source plant, presumably the aphids would be well fed and therefore would not probe through a membrane nearly as readily as those that had been kept off plants several hours and then were placed on the source for only 2 min. This latter treatment might even stimulate aphids to probe subsequently. The experiment could be strengthened by observing the stylets of each aphid to be sure that they entered the formalin and remained there about the same time for all treatments. Also tests should be made to learn whether probing into formalin affects the ability of aphids to take up and transmit new virus; if so, possibly the treatment affects the chance of inoculation occurring.

C. Stylet Treatments

Within the past decade it has been found that aphids can be rendered nonviruliferous by certain treatments applied directly to their stylets. Since aphids soon cease to be viruliferous with stylet-borne virus, stylet treatments must of necessity be brief; all those used thus far have been for 30 sec or less. Treatments that have been reported to render all but occasional aphids nonviruliferous are: (a) insertion into certain liquids such as 0.03% or stronger formalin (Bradley and Ganong, 1955b), oil (Bradley, 1963a), or 4 M urea (Simons and Moss, 1963); (b) exposure of the stylet tips to ultraviolet irradiation (Bradley and Ganong, 1955a; Wade, 1962); (c) an electrostatic discharge to the stylet tips (Bradley, 1962b). By contrast, the following treatments are not effective: (a) insertion into water (Bradley and Ganong, 1955b); (b) exposure of much of the stylets except the tips to ultraviolet irradiation (Bradley and Ganong, 1955a); (c) insertion into various virus inhibitors such as 8-azaguanine, ribonuclease, and milk (Simons and Moss, 1963).

When a stylet treatment renders aphids nonviruliferous, one thing that has to be considered is whether it does so by affecting the virus or by affecting the aphid and thereby reducing the probability of inoculation occurring. If, for example, aphids do not probe after being treated, as happens after an electrostatic discharge to the stylet tips (Bradley, 1962b), inoculation cannot possibly occur. Since the early work on stylet treatments it has been found that stylets are much more sensitive than was believed earlier when it was assumed they are only tactile structures. Various treatments are now known to completely inhibit probing for some hours or even permanently. Examples are: (a) removal of the tip of a single stylet (Bradley, 1960); (b) treatment for 30 sec with 1 M nitric acid or 10% formalin; (c) separation of the two mandibular stylets from the interlocked maxillae, allowing the parted stylets to dry briefly, and then treating the tips of the two mandibles with water (Bradley, 1962d). All of these treatments also stimulate aphids to larviposit. Such results and the finding that the mandibular duct contains liquid led Bradley to postulate that the mandibles have nerves running to their tips.

Even if a stylet treatment has no obvious effect on the probing behaviour of aphids, it cannot be assumed that the treatment does not affect the probability of inoculation. One way of testing for this is to determine if the treatment affects an aphid's ability to take up and transmit virus within minutes after the aphid recovers from being anaesthetized. If a treatment does not affect uptake and transmission of virus, it is unequivocal evidence that the probability of inoculation was not affected. But if a treatment greatly reduces the uptake and transmission of virus, there is as yet no way of determining whether its effect is on the probability of uptake, carry over, or inoculation.

Of the stylet treatments that have been reported to render aphids nonviruliferous without inhibiting probing by the aphid soon after it recovers from being anaesthetized, only two have been tested for their effect on uptake and transmission of virus.

They are treatment of the stylets with dilute formalin, and exposure of the stylet tips to ultraviolet irradiation. Bradley and Ganong (1955b) reported that treating stylets for 30 sec with 0.25% formalin did not affect uptake and transmission of potato virus Y any more so than did treatment with water. Recently Simons and Moss (1963) reported that treating stylets for 20 sec with 1.0% formalin somewhat reduced the ability of aphids to take up and transmit virus about an hour after treatment. But this was not nearly as marked as the effect that the same treatment had on viruliferous aphids, which always failed to transmit virus Y when tested immediately after treatment. Sylvester and Bradley (1962) found that treating stylets for 30 sec with 0.25% or 1.0% formalin somewhat reduced the numbers of aphids that appeared to be probing after one or four hours on Swiss chard seedlings, and there was also a reduction in the depth that aphids inserted their stylets. But they observed no such effects after treating stylets for 30 sec with 0.05% formalin, which also renders aphids carrying virus Y nonviruliferous (Bradley and Ganong, 1955b). Even with this recent evidence that treating stylets with 1.0% or 0.25% formalin affects both probing and the uptake and transmission of virus an hour after treatment, it still seems that such treatments render aphids nonviruliferous mainly because they inactivate the transmissible virus carried by the aphid. But this conclusion needs the support of the unconfirmed report that a 30-sec treatment with 0.25% formalin does not affect the uptake and transmission of virus any more so than water (Bradley and Ganong, 1955b). And as a precaution against affecting the probing of aphids in future, it would be wise to treat their stylets with the weakest formalin that will render them nonviruliferous.

Even if it is accepted that treating stylets with dilute formalin renders aphids nonviruliferous by inactivating the transmissible virus, at best it is only circumstantial evidence that the virus is stylet-borne. Whenever stylets are inserted into a liquid there is always the possibility that it passes up the food or salivary ducts by capillarity, or it may pass up the outside or between the stylets and thence into the labial groove. A treatment that does not have these drawbacks is exposing the stylet tips to ultraviolet irradiation, especially since irradiating much of the stylets except the tips does not render aphids nonviruliferous (Bradley and Ganong, 1955a). Irradiating aphids with the tips of their stylets exposed to the irradiation has been reported to render all but occasional aphids nonviruliferous with cauliflower mosaic, cucumber mosaic, henbane mosaic, potato Y, and tobacco etch viruses; but not with the circulative-borne virus that causes barley yellow dwarf (Bradley and Ganong, 1955a, 1957b; Orlob and Bradley, 1961). Unfortunately, irradiating aphids also greatly reduces the uptake and transmission of virus during the early minutes after they recover from being anaesthetized, though within an hour such aphids acquire and transmit virus as readily as unirradiated controls (Bradley and Ganong, 1955a). But unlike aphids being rendered nonviruliferous by irradiation, the effect on uptake and transmission of virus seemed not to depend on the stylet tips being exposed to the irradiation. The evidence that Bradley and Ganong gave in support of this point was not extensive, nor has it been confirmed. Also, Sylvester (1963) has informed me that the irradiation technique does not produce the expected results.

In view of the growing evidence that stylets are far more sensitive than was believed earlier, I have made further experiments on irradiating stylets (Bradley, 1964); and have used an improved method that permits irradiating only the stylets and not the rest of the aphid (Wade, 1962). I have confirmed that irradiating only the stylet tips of aphids carrying potato virus Y renders all but an occasional one nonviruliferous. But I have also found that irradiating only the stylet tips also reduces the ability of aphids to take up and transmit virus Y for at least 15 min after they recover from being anaesthetized; but within 30 min such aphids take up and transmit virus Y as readily as controls that have not been treated in any way except being kept off plants an hour or so before they probed the source. Irradiation of the stylet tips

makes aphids somewhat restless and reluctant to probe; but with careful handling they will probe, especially if placed on the underside of the source leaf. The effect of irradiating stylet tips on the uptake and transmission of virus is not as marked as that on viruliferous aphids, which rarely transmit virus Y after irradiation of their stylet tips. I suspect that the effect on uptake and transmission of virus is mainly that irradiation of stylet tips somehow affects aphids so that they often fail to take up virus when they probe the source; for their behaviour for some minutes after recovery is similar to that of aphids that have just been disturbed from feeding. Other recent experiments with ultraviolet irradiation of the stylets have failed to give any concrete evidence against the hypothesis that transmissible virus is mainly carried at the stylet tips. Admittedly the argument is not nearly as straightforward as it first appeared to be. So there is still a need for further work, especially by those who can approach the problem with a fresh outlook.

Certain stylet-borne viruses may not be suitable for experiments in which treatments are applied to the stylets of viruliferous aphids. Sylvester and Richardson (1963) reported that merely exposing the stylets from the labium for 2 or 3 min caused over 70% of the aphids to cease to be viruliferous with a virus they referred to as a strain of cabbage mosaic virus. The difficulty may have been that the virus became inactivated when the stylets were exposed to air, as Papasolomontos (1961) showed happened with cucumber mosaic virus. If exposure to the air inactivates certain viruses carried by the stylets, it may still be possible to carry out stylet treatments with such viruses by reducing the time that the stylets are exposed. One way the exposure time could be reduced considerably is by pulling the labium out over the stylets immediately after treatment rather than leaving them exposed until the aphid recovers from being anaesthetized and extends its labium.

It is still not known just where virus is carried at the tips of the stylets. Some workers have supposed that it is carried within the food duct (Bawden et al., 1954;

Sylvester, 1954; Carter, 1962), others that it is probably carried externally (Day and Irzykiewicz, 1954; van der Want, 1954; Sylvester, 1962). Van Hoof's (1958) excellent electron micrographs of individual stylets clearly show numerous chitinous barbs on the distal part of the maxillae and the outer side of the two mandibles. He suggested that plant material containing virus gets caught behind these barbs as the stylets withdraw from the source plant.

For nearly a decade I have tried repeatedly to determine whether transmissible virus is carried by the pair of interlocked maxillary stylets or by the two mandibles that flank them. The answer continues to elude me, though at times it seemed within reach. My main approach has been to part the mandibles from the maxillae and then treat one pair of stylets or the other with either formalin or ultraviolet irradiation. The difficulty has been that merely parting the stylets for the 2 or 3 min needed to carry out the treatment causes all but occasional aphids to cease to be viruliferous with potato virus Y or cauliflower mosaic virus. But parting the stylets for this time does not greatly reduce the uptake and transmission of virus within minutes after an aphid recovers from being anaesthetized. So it seems that parting the stylets exposes the virus more directly to the air and thereby causes it to be rapidly inactivated. On the basis of this admittedly weak evidence, I suspect but have not been able to prove that at least some of the transmissible virus is carried between the stylets. It may be simply trapped there or it may adhere to either the outside of the maxillae or the inner side of each mandible. Of these possibilities, I favour the last; for there is circumstantial evidence that the proposed mandibular nerve terminates on the inner side of the mandible near the tip (Bradley, 1962d). And this would provide a living surface where stylet-borne virus might be carried for reasons briefly discussed by Watson (1958).

7–5. INOCULATION

This third and final step in the transmission of stylet-borne virus has much in common with the first. Like uptake, inoculation has been reported to occur within as little as 5 sec after an aphid affixes its labium to a plant (Sylvester, 1950b; Bradley, 1952; van der Want, 1954; Simons, 1956). The effect of the duration of a probe on inoculation has been studied both by allowing the probe to be completed and by interrupting it at a predetermined time by dislodging the aphid. When viruliferous aphids are allowed to complete their probes on the test plants, the probability of infection resulting is as high for probes that last from 15 to 30 sec as for those that last longer (Bradley, 1952; Bradley and Rideout, 1953; van der Want, 1954). And when aphids are interrupted at various intervals during their first probe on a test plant, the probability of infection resulting reaches its maximum by about 15 sec and sometimes earlier (Sylvester, 1949, 1950b; McLean, 1959). So inoculation, like uptake, readily occurs during the first 15 sec of a probe. From what is known about probing during this time as was discussed earlier under *Uptake* (Section 7–3), it follows that inoculation often occurs soon after the stylets penetrate through the cuticle of a plant; and at such times usually the virus would be introduced between the transverse walls of the epidermal cells (van Hoof, 1958).

The mechanics of inoculation appear so similar to those of uptake that as yet only three possible differences between them can be pointed out. First is the obvious difference in the direction that the virus moves—towards the stylets for uptake and away from them for inoculation. Secondly, when comparisons have been made of the minimum time required for uptake or inoculation of each virus, usually it has been found that inoculation occurs slightly sooner than uptake (McLean, 1959; Toba, 1963). This may be a real difference between the two processes, or it may be no more than a reflection of the speed at which penetration occurs. Having probed into the source plant, an aphid may then probe faster during its first probe on the test plant. The third possible difference between uptake and inoculation has been reported by Bradley (1963b), but it has not been confirmed. It is that uptake of potato virus Y rarely occurs when aphids probe through a membrane into tobacco, but inoculation occurs as readily as could be expected when allowance is made for the virus lost from the stylets as they penetrate through the membrane. Thus inoculation seems more apt to occur after the first 15 sec or so of a probe than does uptake. The reason for this may be that the ejection of saliva would cause movement away from the stylet tips and this could carry virus to the plant tissues, but it would hinder the passage of virus from the plant to the stylets.

Since virus Y can be inoculated to plants by aphids probing through a membrane, possibly under normal conditions infection sometimes results from virus inoculated to subepidermal tissues. It remains to be shown that this does occur; and if so, how readily compared with infection from virus inoculated to the epidermis. Cunningham and Schultz (1963) claimed that potatoes sometimes become infected with potato virus Y that passes from the stylets into the mesophyll tissues. Their evidence for this is that when aphids probed on healthy plants for 56 to 75 sec the level of infection was higher than for those that probed 15 to 55 sec. The account of this work does not make clear whether the longest probing periods tested were single probes or not; and if they were it is difficult to understand how the aphids were made to co-operate to the extent that those that made long probes on the source also made long ones on the test plants. Besides, the selection of aphids according to the durations of their probes may also have selected some behavioural trait favourable or unfavourable to transmission. More direct evidence will be needed to prove that infection sometimes results from virus inoculated to subepidermal tissues of a plant.

The probability of infection resulting from probes by viruliferous aphids is always highest immediately after uptake. The first probes on test plants, like those on the source, are usually brief and are made for the most part interveinally. So infection can result from virus inoculated to interveinal epidermis. It can also occur from virus inoculated to epidermis of petioles or stems (Sylvester, 1953a), or that of leaf veins

(Bradley, 1962c). Sylvester compared the susceptibility of various areas of the aboveground parts of mustard seedlings to aphid inoculation with turnip mosaic virus, and found they were much the same except that petioles may have been more susceptible than other areas. Bradley found no differences in the susceptibilities of the midveins, secondary veins, and interveinal areas of tobacco leaves to aphid inoculation with potato virus Y. It will be surprising if some areas of a plant cannot be shown to differ in susceptibility to aphid inoculation with stylet-borne virus. Perhaps this can be shown by using much older plants than have been tested heretofore.

Infection does not always occur each time that a viruliferous aphid appears to probe a susceptible plant. The infections that occur during each of a series of probes have been determined by a few workers; some have done so by allowing the probes to terminate naturally (Bradley, 1952; van der Want, 1954), while others have kept the duration of each probe constant by interrupting the aphid each time at a predetermined period such as 10, 15, or 20 sec (Sylvester, 1950a, 1954; McLean, 1959). During a series of probes the probability of obtaining infection decreases successively. Partly this is because some aphids cease to be viruliferous after their first probe, some after their second, and so on. Also it appears that the probability of inoculation occurring decreases as the virus carried by an aphid becomes depleted. Evidence of this can be found in the results of serial transmission tests. For example, when McLean (1959) determined the infections caused by aphids during a series of 10 brief probes, 20 of 38 viruliferous aphids caused infections on or after the seventh probe; of these, the probability of infection during any of the first 3 probes was about 0.6, but it was only 0.3 during the fifth, sixth, and seventh probes.

Why does infection not occur each time that a viruliferous aphid appears to probe a susceptible plant? Presumably failures occur for various reasons such as: (a) the aphid may appear to probe but does not insert its stylets; (b) the stylets penetrate into the plant but no virus passes from them; or (c) virus enters the plant tissues but becomes inactivated before it gets established and multiplies.

That infection can be inhibited *after* virus is inoculated into a plant is not a new idea. Many substances are known to inhibit viruses inoculated to plants by rubbing, and apparently they often do so by altering the metabolism of cells so that virus does not become established (Bawden, 1954). When such inhibitors have been applied to plants that are subsequently inoculated by aphids carrying stylet-borne virus, usually they have not inhibited infections (Bradley and Ganong, 1957a; Simons and Moss, 1963). Yet Bradley and Ganong did find that spraying plants with the inhibitor trichothecin either before or after aphid inoculation with potato virus Y greatly reduced the numbers of infections. Thiouracil applied both before and after inoculation also inhibited infections; but unlike trichothecin it did so only at concentrations that visibly damaged plants. The reason why trichothecin and thiouracil inhibit infections of stylet-borne virus inoculated to plants by aphids is probably that these substances diffuse into the plants (Bawden and Freeman, 1952), whereas most other inhibitors are not diffusible and therefore depend for their entry on the wounds made by rubbing inoculation. A diffusible inhibitor such as trichothecin is another possible way of preventing the spread of stylet-borne viruses and one that does not depend on killing the vectors before they probe.

From time to time it has been suggested that certain species or varieties of plants are resistant to virus infection because of naturally occurring inhibitors of infection. The idea is plausible, but how can it be proven? Recently Simons and Moss (1963) claimed that the resistance of the pepper variety Italian El to potato virus Y is caused by such an inhibitor. Their main evidence for this is an experiment in which pepper seedlings of a susceptible variety, California wonder, were vacuum infiltrated with a freeze-dried concentrate of Italian El plants. After this the probability of seedlings being infected by single aphids was 0.4 compared with 0.7 for untreated controls or seedlings infiltrated with water. Infiltrating seedlings with an extract of another variety surely would cause foreign substances to enter the plant cells, and this in turn could affect cell metabolism so that virus inoculated to the cells by aphids or by rubbing sometimes would not become established and cause infection. But this does not prove that these same inhibitors are responsible for the natural resistance of Italian El to potato virus Y. Nor does the experiment prove that Italian El contains inhibitors that are not also present in other varieties of pepper; for even sap from susceptible varieties contains inhibitors of virus inoculated to plants by rubbing (Simons *et al.*, 1963). To prove that Italian El pepper contains inhibitors not present in susceptible varieties, Simons and Moss should have infiltrated the control seedlings not with water but with a similar concentrate from a susceptible variety of pepper such as Red Cayenne (Simons, 1960). Also, two other experiments did not give any evidence in support of the hypothesis that the natural resistance of Italian El is caused by an inhibitor; the susceptibility of California Wonder plants to aphid inoculation was not affected by spraying Italian El sap on the plants, nor by grafting them to Italian El roots. Another point that fits poorly with the hypothesis is that with rubbing inoculation, inhibitors from plants are usually not effective inhibitors of infection in the same species from which they are derived (Gendron and Kassanis, 1954).

Finally, there is yet another way that infection may be inhibited in plants inoculated by aphids carrying stylet-borne virus. Sylvester (1954) postulated that the saliva of aphids may contain substances that alter the metabolism of cells and thereby make them resistant to infection. If, as many workers believe, the saliva of aphids contains inhibitors of stylet-borne viruses, Sylvester's hypothesis is the most plausible explanation of how they would affect transmission; for it is similar to the presently accepted hypothesis of how inhibitors of virus inoculated to plants by rubbing cause their effects (Bawden, 1954). It is well known that the saliva of aphids affects plants in various ways ranging from local reactions at the feeding site to systemic toxemias. The problem that remains is how to test

Sylvester's hypothesis. Nishi (1959) has made a start by showing that sap from plants fed upon by aphids contains an inhibitor of tobacco mosaic virus inoculated to plants by rubbing. It would be strong circumstantial evidence in support of the hypothesis if it could be shown that aphids probing into plants made them resistant to virus inoculated to them by aphids. Sylvester (1955) attempted this with lettuce mosaic virus and found no evidence that aphids feeding on lettuce seedlings reduced their susceptibility to infection. For these tests Sylvester used the aphid *M. persicae*, which is one of the most efficient vectors of stylet-borne virus, so possibly its saliva is less apt to contain inhibitors than that of other species. It would seem worth while to make similar experiments with a species that is an inefficient vector of stylet-borne virus and is also known to eject saliva that is toxic to plants.

7–6. LITERATURE CITED

Auclair, J. L. (1963). Ann. Rev. Entomol. **8**, 439.

Badami, R. S. (1958). Ann. Appl. Biol. **46**, 554.

Bagnall, R. H., and Bradley, R. H. E. (1958). Phytopathology **48**, 121.

Bald, J. G., and Norris, D. O. (1945). Phytopathology **35**, 591.

Bawden, F. C. (1950). Plant Viruses and Virus Diseases. 3d ed. Chronica Botanica, Waltham, Mass.

Bawden, F. C. (1954). Advan. Virus Res. **2**, 31.

Bawden, F. C., and Freeman, G. G. (1952). J. Gen. Microbiol. **7**, 154.

Bawden, F. C., and Kassanis, B. (1941). Ann. Appl. Biol. **28**, 107.

Bawden, F. C., and Kassanis, B. (1946). Ann. Appl. Biol. **33**, 46.

Bawden, F. C., and Kassanis, B. (1947). Ann. Appl. Biol. **34**, 503.

Bawden, F. C., and Kassanis, B. (1950). Ann. Appl. Biol. **37**, 46.

Bawden, F. C., Hamlyn, B. M. G., and Watson, M. A. (1954). Ann. Appl. Biol. **41**, 229.

Bhargava, K. S. (1951). Ann. Appl. Biol. **38**, 377.

Björling, K., and Ossiannilsson, F. (1958). Socker Handl. II, **14**, 1.

Bradley, R. H. E. (1952). Ann. Appl. Biol. **39**, 78.

Bradley, R. H. E. (1954). Can. J. Zool. **32**, 64.

Bradley, R. H. E. (1956). Can. J. Microbiol. **2**, 539.

Bradley, R. H. E. (1959). Virology **8**, 308.

Bradley, R. H. E. (1960). Nature **188**, 337.

Bradley, R. H. E. (1961). Recent Advances in Botany. 1, Sec. 5, 528. Univ. of Toronto Press, Toronto, Canada.

Bradley, R. H. E. (1962a). Virology **16**, 366.

Bradley, R. H. E. (1962b). Virology **17**, 95.

Bradley, R. H. E. (1962c). Virology **17**, 357.

Bradley, R. H. E. (1962d). Can. Entomol. **94**, 707.

Bradley, R. H. E. (1963a). Can. J. Microbiol. **9**, 369.

Bradley, R. H. E. (1963b). Virology **21**, 152.

Bradley, R. H. E. (1964). Unpublished data.

Bradley, R. H. E., and Ganong, R. Y. (1955a). Can. J. Microbiol. **1**, 775.

Bradley, R. H. E., and Ganong, R. Y. (1955b). Can. J. Microbiol. **1**, 783.

Bradley, R. H. E., and Ganong, R. Y. (1957a). Virology **4**, 172.

Bradley, R. H. E., and Ganong, R. Y. (1957b). Can. J. Microbiol. **3**, 669.

Bradley, R. H. E., and Rideout, D. W. (1953). Can. J. Zool. **31**, 333.

Bradley, R. H. E., Wade, C. V., and Wood, F. A. (1962). Virology **18**, 327.

Broadbent, L. (1954). Ann. Appl. Biol. **41**, 174.

Broadbent, L. (1957). Ann. Rev. Entomol. **2**, 339.

Broadbent, L. (1960). Ann. Appl. Biol. **48**, 377.

Carter, W. (1962). Insects in Relation to Plant Diseases. Interscience Publishers, New York and London.

Chalfant, R. B. (1959). Ph.D. Thesis, Univ. Wisconsin.

Chalfant, R. B., and Chapman, R. K. (1962). J. Econ. Entomol. **55**, 584.

Cockbain, A. J., Gibbs, A. J., and Heathcote, G. D. (1963). Ann. Appl. Biol. **52**, 133.

Cunningham, V. D., and Schultz, J. T. (1963). Ann. Entomol. Soc. Am. **56**, 334.

Day, M. F., and Irzykiewicz, H. (1953). Australian J. Biol. Sci. **6**, 98.

Day, M. F., and Irzykiewicz, H. (1954). Australian J. Biol. Sci. **7**, 251.

Day, M. F., and Venables, D. G. (1961). Australian J. Biol. Sci. **14**, 187.

Dickson, R. C., Swift, J. E., Anderson, L. D., and Middleton, J. T. (1949). J. Econ. Entomol. **42**, 770.

Doncaster, J. P., and Kassanis, B. (1946). Ann. Appl. Biol. **33**, 66.

Doolittle, S. P., and Walker, M. N. (1928). Phytopathology **18**, 143.

Gendron, Y., and Kassanis, B. (1954). Ann. Appl. Biol. **41**, 188.

Hamilton, M. A. (1935). Ann. Appl. Biol. **22**, 243.

Hamlyn, B. M. G. (1953). Ann. Appl. Biol. **40**, 393.

Hamlyn, B. M. G. (1955). Plant. Pathol. **4**, 13.

Heinze, K. (1957). Z. Angew. Zool. **44**, 187.

Heinze, K. (1959). Phytopathol. Z. **36**, 131.

Hitchborn, J. H. (1958). Ann. Appl. Biol. **46**, 563.

Hoggan, I. A. (1933). J. Agr. Res. **47**, 689.

Jensen, D. D. (1950). Phytopathology **40**, 976.

Kassanis, B. (1941). Ann. Appl. Biol. **27**, 238.

Kassanis, B. (1947). Ann. Appl. Biol. **34**, 412.

Kassanis, B. (1961). Virology **13**, 93.

Kennedy, J. S. (1960). Rept. 7th Commonwealth Entomol. Conf. 1960, 165.

Kennedy, J. S., Day, M. F., and Eastop, V. F. (1962). A Conspectus of Aphids as Vectors of Plant Viruses. Commonwealth Inst. Entomol. 114 pp.

Kikumoto, T., and Matsui, C. (1962). Virology **16**, 509.

Kleczkowski, A. (1960). Rept. Rothamsted Exptl. Sta. 1960, 234.

Kvíčala, B. A. (1945). Nature **155**, 174.

Kvíčala, B. A. (1948). Acta Univ. Agric. Silv., Brunn. **40**, 1.

MacGillivray, M. E., and Bradley, R. H. E. (1960). Can. Entomol. **92**, 367.

McLean, D. L. (1959). J. Econ. Entomol. **52**, 1057.

McLean, D. L. (1961). J. Econ. Entomol. **54**, 1135.

Maramorosch, K. (1963). Ann. Rev. Entomol. **8**, 369.

Matsui, C., Sasaki, T., and Kikumoto, T. (1963). Virology **19**, 411.

Miles, P. W. (1959). Nature **183**, 756.

Namba, R. (1962). Virology **16**, 267.

Nishi, Y. (1959). Ann. Phytopath. Soc. (Japan) **23**, 185.

Nishizawa, T., Nishi, Y., and Kimura, T. (1959). Virus **9**, 130.

Orlob, G. B. (1962). Virology **16**, 301.

Orlob, G. B. (1963). Phytopathology **53**, 822.

Orlob, G. B., and Bradley, R. H. E. (1961). Phytopathology **51**, 397.

Osborn, H. T. (1937). Phytopathology **27**, 589.

Ossiannilsson, F. (1958). Kungl. Lantbruks-Hogskol. Ann. **24**, 369.

Paine, J., and Legg, J. T. (1953). Nature **171**, 263.

Papasolomontos, A. (1961). Ph.D. Thesis, Cornell Univ.

Pirone, T. P., Pound, G. S., and Shepherd, R. J. (1960). Nature **186**, 656.

Pollard, D. G. (1958). Empire Cotton Growing Rev. **35**, 244.

Rochow, W. F. (1960). Phytopathology **50**, 881.

Schmidt, H. B. (1959). Biol. Zentr. **78**, 889.

Severin, H. H. P., and Tompkins, C. M. (1948). Hilgardia **18**, 389.

Sill, W. H., Burger, W. C., and Stahmann, M. A. (1952). Phytopathology **42**, 420.

Simons, J. N. (1955). Phytopathology **45**, 217.

Simons, J. N. (1956). Phytopathology **46**, 53.

Simons, J. N. (1957). Phytopathology **47**, 145.

Simons, J. N. (1958). Phytopathology **48**, 265.

Simons, J. N. (1959). Virology **9**, 612.

Simons, J. N. (1960). Phytopathology **50**, 424.

Simons, J. N., and Moss, L. M. (1963). Phytopathology **53**, 684.

Simons, J. N., and Sylvester, E. S. (1953). Phytopathology **43**, 29.

Simons, J. N., Swidler, R., and Moss, L. M. (1963). Phytopathology **53**, 677.

Stevenson, A. B. (1959). Ph.D. Thesis, Univ. Wisconsin.

Stubbs, L. L. (1955). Australian J. Biol. Sci. **8**, 68.

Swenson, K. G. (1957). J. Econ. Entomol. **50**, 727.

Swenson, K. G. (1960). Ann. Entomol. Soc. Am. **53**, 521.

Swenson, K. G. (1962). Australian J. Biol. Sci. **15**, 468.

Swenson, K. G., and Sohi, S. S. (1961). Phytopathology **51**, 67.

Sylvester, E. S. (1949). Phytopathology **39**, 417.

Sylvester, E. S. (1950a). Phytopathology **40**, 737.

Sylvester, E. S. (1950b). Phytopathology **40**, 743.

Sylvester, E. S. (1952). Phytopathology **42**, 252.

Sylvester, E. S. (1953a). Phytopathology **43**, 209.

Sylvester, E. S. (1953b). Phytopathology **43**, 541.

Sylvester, E. S. (1954). Hilgardia **23**, 53.

Sylvester, E. S. (1955). Phytopathology **45**, 357.

Sylvester, E. S. (1962). Biological Transmission of Disease Agents. Ed. Karl Maramorosch. 11–31. Academic Press, New York and London.

Sylvester, E. S. (1963). Personal communication.

Sylvester, E. S., and Bradley, R. H. E. (1962). Virology **17**, 381.

Sylvester, E. S., and Richardson, J. (1963). Virology **20**, 302.

Sylvester, E. S., and Simons, J. N. (1951). Phytopathology **41**, 908.

Toba, H. H. (1963). J. Econ. Entomol. **56**, 200.

Tompkins, C. M., Gardner, M. W., and Thomas, H. R. (1938). J. Agr. Res. **57**, 929.

van der Want, J. P. H. (1954). Doctoral Thesis, Wageningen Agr. Univ., H. Veenman & Zonen, Wageningen, The Netherlands.

van Hoof, H. A. (1957). Koninkl. Ned. Akad. Wetenschap. Proc. (Amsterdam) **60(c)**, 314.

van Hoof, H. A. (1958). Doctoral Thesis, Wageningen Agr. Univ., Van Putten & Oortmeijer, Aklmaar, The Netherlands.

Wade, C. V. (1962). Can. J. Zool. **40**, 673.

Watson, M. A. (1936). Roy. Soc. London Phil. Trans. **B226**, 457.

Watson, M. A. (1938). Proc. Roy. Soc. London **B125**, 144.

Watson, M. A. (1946). Proc. Roy. Soc. London **B133**, 200.

Watson, M. A. (1956). Ann. Appl. Biol. **44**, 599.

Watson, M. A. (1958). Proc. 10th Intern. Congr. Entomol. **3**, 215.

Watson, M. A. (1960). Virology **10**, 211.

Watson, M. A., and Nixon, H. L. (1953). Ann. Appl. Biol. **40**, 537.

Watson, M. A., and Roberts, F. M. (1939). Proc. Roy. Soc. London **B127**, 543.

Watson, M. A., and Roberts, F. M. (1940). Ann. Appl. Biol. **27**, 227.

Wensler, R. J. D. (1962). Nature **195**, 830.

Zettler, F. W. (1963). Phytopathology **53**, 894.

Zimmermann, M. H. (1961). Science **133**, 73.

8

KARL MARAMOROSCH

Virus-vector relationships: Vectors of circulative and propagative viruses

8–1. APHIDS

APHID TRANSMISSION of plant viruses at one extreme is characterized by the type in which the insect vectors can acquire and transmit virus within a matter of seconds or minutes, but soon lose the ability to transmit, unless they have renewed access to a fresh virus source. This relationship, earlier termed nonpersistent or mechanical, is the most common type of aphid–plant virus relationship. The other extreme, earlier called persistent or nonmechanical, is characterized by a lapse of several hours between acquisition and first transmission, and by a continuation of virus transmission for many days following the removal of the insects from the virus source.

Kennedy *et al.* (1962) suggested that with the increasing number of intermediates between the two extremes, that is, with the growing number of viruses found to be neither persistent nor nonpersistent, actual routes of virus transport in the vector should be used as criteria for classifying viruses. Only two such routes of virus transport have been recognized so far. Watson (1960) designated them as external and internal, but these terms have been changed by Kennedy *et al.* (1962) to "stylet-borne" and "circulative." The latter has been adopted from Black's (1959) definition of certain leafhopper-borne viruses.

Circulative viruses are acquired by aphid vectors through their mouthparts, accumulated internally, then passed through the insect tissues and introduced into plants again via the mouthparts of the aphid. The viruses may multiply in their respective vectors and are then termed propagative, or they may be transmitted without undergoing intrinsic multiplication in the insect vector. The terms "propagative" and "circulative" are thus not mutually exclusive.

Circulative viruses include the aphid-borne viruses described in the earlier literature under the term "persistent." The new system of classification and the terms "stylet-borne" and "circulative" have so many advantages over those used earlier that they will most likely become widely accepted.

Circulative aphid-borne viruses are much less common than stylet-borne viruses. Until now, less than a dozen have been described and only a few have been studied carefully. The best-known relationship in this group is that between potato leafroll virus and its vector *Myzus persicae*.

The retention of potato leafroll virus in *M. persicae* has focused the attention of many workers on the possibility that this virus might be of the propagative type, that is, multiply within the body of the aphid that carries it from plant to plant. Until recently the only plant viruses shown to multiply intrinsically were several leafhopper-borne viruses (Maramorosch, 1963a). In 1955 Heinze showed that aphids can withstand severe wounding inflicted by steel or glass needles; attempts to transmit potato leafroll virus and pea enation mosaic virus by needle inoculation were made by Heinze (1955) while he worked at the laboratories of the Rockefeller Institute in association with the present writer. In the same year, Day (1955) published results of experiments with potato leafroll virus that were interpreted as indirect evidence that this circulative virus may perhaps multiply in *M. persicae*.

The major difficulty encountered in attempts to transmit potato leafroll virus from infective to noninfective aphids by needle inoculation was not the mechanical process of injection, but the inactivation of the virus. No bioassay of this virus was available until 1958. In that year, Stegwee and Ponsen (1958) presented the results of ingenious experiments from which they concluded that the virus was of the propagative type. Instead of using extracts of whole aphids, as is usually done in experiments on the mechanical transmission of propagative leafhopper-borne viruses, the authors used aphid hemolymph. This method was prompted by the finding that crushed whole aphids were unsuitable and that such preparations inactivated the virus. When virus-free *M. persicae* were injected with hemolymph obtained from virus-carrying aphids, nearly 50% of the injected insects became infective and transmitted the virus to susceptible plants after an incubation period of 20 or more hours. When, instead of undiluted hemolymph, saline dilutions were used as inoculum, the intrinsic incubation could be prolonged to as much as 7–10 days. Aphids rendered infective by mechanical inoculation did not lose their ability to transmit when transferred to a succession of fresh test plants.

The preliminary results were soon followed by an attempt to carry potato leafroll virus serially from insect to insect, to find whether it can propagate in injected aphids. Virus-free aphids, maintained on Chinese cabbage immune to leafroll, were injected with hemolymph of viruliferous aphids and kept for the following 7 days on immune plants. Afterwards small amounts of hemolymph were drawn into glass micropipettes and in turn injected into another group of virus-free aphids. This procedure was repeated 15 times at weekly intervals. In every passage the presence of virus could be demonstrated by removing a few injected aphids at random from Chinese cabbage, and testing them on plants susceptible to leafroll. The calculated dilution of the original virus inoculum, if no multiplication had occurred, would have reached 10^{-21}, but the authors found that hemolymph of viruliferous *M. persicae* diluted beyond 10^{-4} no longer rendered virus-free aphids infective. Stegwee and Ponsen (1958) concluded therefore that potato leafroll virus had multiplied in the injected aphids during the 15 serial passages.

It seems that the success of Stegwee and Ponsen in carrying out their serial passage experiment has been the result of using insect hemolymph rather than extracts of whole insects. Harrison (1958) reported that extracts from crushed *M. persicae* carrying potato leafroll virus rendered virus-free aphids infective, but that the ability to transmit the virus was gradually lost by injected vectors because of the exhaustion of the virus. During the initial 48 hr following virus acquisition by feeding, and preceding virus transmission, virus could be recovered from crushed insect bodies. When the insects once became infective, and later were crushed and used as virus inoculum, no recovery of virus could be obtained. This finding was considered by Harrison as evidence against virus multiplication in the vector. The rapid decrease in the ability of injected insects to transmit potato leafroll virus was at variance with the findings of Stegwee (1961) and also with the earlier findings of MacCarthy (1954). Whether this discrepancy could be explained solely on the basis of the different method of preparing the virus inoculum, in one case from whole insects and in the other from hemolymph only, is difficult to determine. It is hoped that the experiments with potato leafroll virus will be continued and that, with the recently introduced improvements in the injection technique described by Rochow (1963), accurate titrations and serial passages will be carried out soon. This would permit a clarification of the controversial findings. The method of transferring blood from one aphid to another is likely to circumvent the hazard of inactivation and thus permit the demonstration of leafroll virus in the blood long after the acquisition feeding.

The presence or absence of an incubation period in *M. persicae* in the transmission of potato leafroll virus presents another seemingly controversial issue. Kirkpatrick and Ross (1952), Klostermeyer (1953), and de Meester-Manger Cats (1956) reported that transmission may occur within minutes after aphids acquired the virus from diseased plants. Results obtained by MacCarthy (1954), Day (1955), and Heinze (1959) indicate, on the other hand, that a fairly long incubation period always must precede the transmission of this virus. Although several explanations for the discrepancy in results have been offered by various workers who reviewed these findings, no critical experiments have been carried out to explain the controversial issue. Day suggested that the strains of aphids used by the different workers might have resulted in the presence or absence of an incubation period, but Heinze (personal communication), using both European and American aphids of the same species, could find no difference in the transmission pattern and was unable to obtain transmission without previous incubation. MacCarthy pointed out that there appears to be no reason why the interval between acquisition and transmission of potato leafroll virus could not have been eliminated in a few cases through the acquisition of a very large amount of virus from a good source of inoculum, for instance from *Physalis floridana*, so that the circulative virus under optimal conditions could be transmitted in a stylet-borne manner. After brief transmission periods an incubation would follow, and the virus would be transmitted in the propagative manner afterwards. This possibility has not been checked experimentally so far as could be ascertained by this writer.

In addition to the insect injection technique, another ingenious technique has been used in recent years for the study of certain circulative viruses transmitted by aphids. Rochow (1960) transmitted barley yellow dwarf to aphids through semipermeable membranes in the same manner in which several leafhopper-borne viruses had been transmitted (Bennett and Wallace, 1938; Storey, 1933). The technique made possible many kinds of experiments and it provided a simple qualitative test for an aphid-borne virus in liquid preparations. In addition, Mueller and Rochow (1961) perfected the aphid injection technique and used it for the inoculation of barley yellow dwarf from plant and from insect extracts into aphid vectors. The injected insects often transmitted virus within one day but an inoculation test feeding period of five days was found most suitable for experimental purposes.

8–2. TREEHOPPERS

Treehoppers (Membracidae) were first shown to transmit a plant virus in 1958, when Simons and Coe in Florida established the pseudo-curly-top virus transmission by a species of *Micrutalis*. Simons (1962) studied the relationship between the virus and the treehopper vector and found that virus retention was correlated with length of acquisition feeding. There seemed to be no evidence of virus multiplication in the vector and transmissions were obtained after a 24- to 48-hr latent period. The circulative pseudo-curly-top virus showed a striking similarity in this respect to the curly-top virus of sugar beets. However, this similarity in nonpropagative aspects and in symptoms produced in a few hosts, while leading to the naming of the virus, has no bearing on any real relationship between the membracid-borne and the leafhopper-borne virus. Until serological tests are developed for these two viruses, it is safe to assume that they are unrelated. The finding, that plant virus vectors occur among groups or families that until recently have not been known to comprise vectors, should be kept in mind by those who search for transmitters of disease agents. It is apparent that such virus carriers are not limited to the already established groups but may occur as well among unsuspected taxa.

8–3. MITES

Eriophyid mites are now known to transmit at least six different plant viruses (Slykhuis, 1960; 1962). This group of mites (*Eriophyidae*) constitutes a distinct unit with no close relation to other mite groups. These arthropods feed by sucking plant juices, puncturing the plant cells with stylets that are inside a groove of the rostrum. The rostrum has two pads at its apex, serving as ducts for the saliva. The mites can only move to a very limited extent independently because of their small size. Desiccation easily kills them, nevertheless their main means of dispersion is wind (Slykhuis, 1955). More than once have mite injuries to plants been ascribed to air-borne viruses, because the injury simulates virus symptoms.

The small size of mite vectors creates a difficult problem in the study of virus-vector interrelationships in this group. With improved techniques and mounting interest in mite-borne viruses it can be expected that the number of known viruses and vectors will soon increase. Currant reversion in England was the first plant disease suspected to be caused by a mite-borne virus (Amos *et al.*, 1927; Massee, 1952). It has not yet been determined clearly whether currant reversion is or is not caused by a virus. It is not yet known whether disease symptoms would persist in currant after the plants are freed from mites through chemical treatment and no experiments have been reported on the possible effect of virus-free mites obtained from eggs hatched on healthy plants, nor on the acquisition of virus by such mites. Graft experiments should be carried out to test the viral nature of the disease.

Slykhuis (1962) found that the mite *Aceria tulipae* can transmit two viruses simultaneously—wheat streak mosaic virus and wheat spot mosaic virus. In 1955, Flock and Wallace (1955) discovered that the mite *A. ficus* transmits fig mosaic virus. In the same year Wilson *et al.* (1955) reported the transmission of peach mosaic virus by *Eriophyes insidiosus*. There are several other viruses suspected of being mite-borne, among them California's cherry mottle leaf virus.

As far as is known, none of the mite-borne viruses passes transovarially to the progeny of infective mites, but all seem to persist in the mites through the molts. Slykhuis (1962) noticed that nymphs acquire wheat streak mosaic virus, while adults do not. This is reminiscent of the thrips acquisition of tomato spotted wilt virus and suggests a biological relationship.

8–4. WHITEFLIES

Relationships between tropical viruses and whitefly vectors have been studied in only a few instances. The literature has been reviewed by Orlando and Silberschmidt (1946). The vector, *Bemisia tabaci*, which was proven by Orlando and Silberschmidt in 1946 to transmit the virus of infectious chlorosis of malvaceous plants in Brazil, has since been found to transmit a number of other tropical plant viruses in various parts of the world. In India, where whiteflies are probably the most important vectors of plant viruses, *B. tabaci* transmits tobacco leaf curl, tobacco yellow-net virus, and several viruses affecting other cultivated plants. According to Varma (1955), an individual whitefly vector may carry three different viruses simultaneously.

One of the best studies on virus retention in whiteflies was made by Costa and Bennett (1950) who found that *Euphorbia* mosaic virus was retained by whiteflies for prolonged periods, often for life. An incubation period of from 4 to 48 hr in *B. tabaci* preceded transmission of the virus. Therefore, this virus can be classified as circulatory. The transmitting ability of females was twice that of males. In infectious chlorosis in Brazil, the same finding was made (Orlando and Silberschmidt, 1946) and a feeding period of 30 min was adequate for virus acquisition. In addition, the ability to produce infection reportedly increased with prolonged acquisition feeding time. In Puerto Rico, Bird (1958) found that whiteflies acquired a *Sida* chlorosis virus in a 15-min acquisition feeding and that the virus also was retained by the vectors for long periods.

In the absence of serological tests, cross-protection tests have been used in addition to symptomatology to distinguish whitefly-borne viruses. Flores and Silberschmidt (1962) pointed out that whitefly-borne viruses frequently induce diseases with strikingly similar symptoms in host plants, although the viruses may not be closely related. The authors concluded from their results that cross-protection tests alone did not provide adequate criteria for the determination of whitefly-borne virus strains. It is hoped that serological tests will soon be developed for this important group. In recent years there were indications that the leaf curl disease of tobacco, described from South America and transmitted by *B. tabaci*, might also occur in several of the southern states, including Georgia. Serological tests would be of great value in determining the identity of the virus or viruses involved.

8–5. MEALYBUGS

Mealybugs are known as vectors of several tropical viruses. In West Africa the swollen shoot virus is spread from indigenous jungle trees to cacao and many virus strains have been isolated by Posnette (1953). A few species of mealybugs have been recognized as vectors in Ghana and Nigeria where the cacao trees are of great economic importance. The mealybugs are tended and dispersed by ants. Several hours of feeding are required before the vectors become infective, but they can infect a plant in less than one hour. According to Posnette and co-workers (Posnette and Robertson, 1950; Posnette and Strickland, 1948), the transmitting efficiency of the vector *Pseudococcus njalensis* increased with prolonged feeding on diseased plants. Maximum efficiency was reached after 10 hr of feeding, and longer acquisition feeding resulted in a decrease of efficiency. Infectivity was usually lost soon after removal from the virus source and not more than two plants could be inoculated. However, the virus was retained up to 36 hr when the acquisition feeding was preceded by fasting. The virus seems nevertheless to belong to the stylet-borne viruses.

While the cacao swollen shoot virus probably is the most destructive of all plant viruses economically because of the high price of the affected crop, another mealybug-borne virus, that of pineapple wilt, is of much lesser economic importance today through the development of preventive and control methods. In Hawaii, in spite of the fact that the same species of mealybugs existed in many locations where pineapples were grown, the wilt appeared only in some locations (Carter, 1963). The disease was not recognized as viral in nature and an insect toxin was suspected as the etiologic cause. Recently Carter (1951, 1952) found that unless mealybugs feed on diseased plants, they are unable to infect healthy seedlings. Also, mealybugs acquire virus by feeding on diseased plants, but soon lose infectivity, which is similar to the relationship between cacao swollen shoot virus and its mealy-bug vectors (Posnette, 1953). In Puerto Rico, Bird (1954) found that a single specimen of *Dysmicoccus brevipes* could transmit wilt virus to healthy susceptible pineapple seedlings when the mealybug was confined to test plants for 24 hr. The virus could also be recovered from plants that appeared to have recovered from the infection and no longer showed wilt symptoms (Carter, 1963; Maramorosch, 1963b).

8–6. THRIPS

Only one virus is known to be thrips-borne: tomato spotted wilt virus. This virus is world-wide in its distribution. The main vector, *Thrips tabaci* Lindeman, has been studied since Pittman in 1927 first described its role in the transmission of spotted wilt. It is now well established that adult thrips are unable to acquire the virus, and acquisition occurs solely during the larval stage. The reader is referred to critical reviews of this subject by Sakimura (1947, 1962). A definite latent period occurs in the vector, as has been established by Bald and Samuel (1931) and as was later confirmed by others. The shortest incubation period ranges from 3 days

(Razvyazkina, 1953) in the vector *T. tabaci* to as much as 12 days in *Frankliniella fusca* (Sakimura, 1962). The longest periods were found for larvae that changed into adults. When the virus completes its latent period before pupation, larvae may become infective, and the incubation period is comparatively shorter. Sakimura (1962) found an increase in percentage of infection when the feeding period increased. According to Razvyazkina (1953) the inoculation threshold was only 5 min after an acquisition feeding of 30 min. The virus is often retained throughout the life of the vector, but some individuals are poor transmitters so that erratic transmission patterns are commonly encountered, with sporadic transmission on certain days, and long periods of no transmission in between. So far no conclusive data exist to support or reject the possibility that the spotted wilt virus passes transovarially to the offspring of infective vectors. Sakimura (1962) pointed out that no experimental data have been obtained so far on the possible multiplication of the spotted wilt virus in thrips vectors, and that the virus-vector relationships in this group have been investigated less vigorously than those in the aphid- or leafhopper-borne viruses. The small size of the vectors is undoubtedly responsible for the lack of experimental studies of the type described for aphid- and leafhopper-borne viruses.

It might be proper to mention here that recombination of strains of spotted wilt virus has been reported by Best (1954) and Best and Gallus (1955). These recombinations were reportedly obtained in plants infected simultaneously with different strains of the virus, but the markers used by Best do not permit a definite conclusion as to the production of hybrid strains. As far as this writer is aware, no attempts have been made to confirm Best's findings in vectors inoculated simultaneously with different strains of the virus.

8–7. LEAFHOPPERS

Most leafhopper-borne viruses are either circulative or propagative. The terms are not mutually exclusive, as has been stated.

A. CIRCULATIVE TRANSMISSION

There is a good deal of evidence indicating that the sugar-beet curly-top virus is circulative in *Circulifer tenellus* Baker, and that it does not undergo multiplication in its vector (Bennett and Wallace, 1938). However, one ought to bear in mind the difficulties inherent in any attempts to prove lack of multiplication. A progressive decrease of the virus content, following a short acquisition feeding, has been considered one of the most significant findings in support of lack of multiplication (Bennett and Wallace, 1938). A similar decrease, as will be recalled, has been reported by Harrison (1958) for potato leafroll virus in *M. persicae*, and yet, in the latter case, strong evidence was provided by Stegwee and Ponsen (1958) for propagative transmission of that virus. However, old and poorly transmitting leafhoppers can regain sugar-beet curly-top virus by renewed feeding on a diseased plant, and a proportional relationship exists between the length of acquisition feeding and the transmitting ability of individual leafhoppers, which is in striking contrast to results obtained with leafhopper-borne propagative viruses such as aster yellows (Kunkel, 1954).

B. PROPAGATIVE TRANSMISSION

There are many propagative leafhopper-borne viruses which infect their leafhopper vectors and multiply in them just as they infect plants and multiply in their respective plant hosts. In most cases the infection of the leafhopper is not apparent. There are two techniques which provide unquestionable evidence for multiplication of viruses in vectors. The first is the serial passage technique in which the virus is carried from insect to insect by injection until the dilution attained exceeds with certainty the maximum dilution of the starting material that can be successfully inoculated. This technique was used successfully by Maramorosch (1952) with aster yellows virus and its vector, *M. fascifrons,* and by Black and Brakke (1952) with wound-tumor virus in *Agallia constricta* Van Duzee.

The second technique to prove multiplication is by transovarial passage of virus from generation to generation of vectors until the dilution attained exceeds with certainty the maximum possible without multiplication in the insect. Black (1950) estimated that a dilution of 10^{-12} should be exceeded in such a passage to provide evidence for virus multiplication. This technique was first used by Fukushi (1935, 1940) in his classical experiments on multiplication of rice stunt virus in *Nephotettix apicalis* var. *cincticeps*.

Rice stunt was the first plant virus shown to be transmitted by an insect. Onuku and Murata, according to Fukushi, discovered, about 1902, that leafhoppers, *N. apicalis* Motschulsky var. *cincticeps*, which hatched from eggs collected in the Shiga Prefecture, produced the dwarf disease in rice plants, whereas leafhoppers of the same species from the vicinity of Tokyo did not. They found later that noninfective leafhoppers from Tokyo became infective after feeding upon diseased plants. Murata noticed also, around 1914, that infectivity was transmitted from parents to progeny for 3 or 4 generations.

The vector, originally used by Fukushi, is known under the common name "green rice leafhopper." Earlier literature listed the species as *N. apicalis* Motschulsky var. *cincticeps*. Recent publications by Shinkai (1962), Nasu (1963), and Satomi *et al.* (personal communication) list the species as *N. cincticeps* Uhler. Yoshii (1959) and his co-workers, on the other hand, use the name *N. bipunctatus cincticeps* Uhler. *N. apicalis* is today considered to be a separate species.

Fukushi (1933, 1935, 1940) found that infective progeny hatched from eggs laid by viruliferous females. The virus was passed from insect to insect through the egg for 7 generations with only the original females in the experiment having had access to virus-infected plants. The virus appears able to perpetuate itself in leafhoppers in the absence of plants. This experiment also provided strong evidence that the virus multiplied in the leafhopper vector.

The clover club leaf virus, discovered by Black (1944) in *Agalliopsis novella* Say, was carried transovarially for more than 5 years through 21 generations, providing proof that this virus also multiplied in its insect vector (Black, 1950). Clover club leaf virus (Maramorosch, 1955) and rice dwarf virus (Fukushi and Kimura, 1958; Kimura and Fukushi, 1960) can also be transmitted to their respective vectors by injections, but the injection technique has not been used for serial passages. The injection method is essentially the same as for wound-tumor virus (Maramorosch *et al.*, 1949). Shinkai (1955) transmitted rice stripe virus transovarially to 40 generations of *Delphacodes striatella* (Fallen), a plant hopper belonging to the Delphacidae. Yamada and Yamamoto (1955, 1956) transferred this virus through 24 passages in the same vector. Shinkai (1960b) recently carried out transovarial passages of rice dwarf virus through *Inazuma* (*Deltocephalus*) *dorsalis* Motschulsky as well as through *Nephotettix cincticeps*.

Almost every year in the last decade new reports appeared of transovarially transmitted viruses in leafhoppers, which make it probable that this phenomenon is quite common. In the case of wound-tumor virus and potato yellow dwarf virus, transovarial passage is limited to less than 5% of the offspring (Black, 1953b, 1963) unless special selection and breeding for transovarial transmission is carried out (Nagaraj and Black, 1962). Grylls (1954) found that rugose leaf curl virus passes to a high percentage of the progeny of infective *Austroagallia torrida* (Evans). Průša *et al.* (1959) in Czechoslovakia found that oat sterile-dwarf virus does not pass through the egg of *Delphacodes pellucida* (Fab.), whereas the wheat striate virus carried by the same vector was shown to pass transovarially. Shinkai (1962) in Japan demonstrated recently that the virus causing stripe disease of rice passed to a high percentage of the progeny of infected *Delphacodes striatella* (Fallen) females, while the black-streaked dwarf virus, transmitted by the same plant hopper, does not pass to the progeny.

Thus far none of the viruses transmitted transovarially to the progeny of infective females have been transmitted through the sperm of infective males. This suggests that these viruses are primarily concentrated in the cytoplasm and not in the nucleus. Direct evidence for the presence of rice stunt virus in the cytoplasm of insect cells was recently obtained by Fukushi et al. (1960), who for the first time were able to photograph virus particles in ultrathin sections of an insect vector. The visualization of a plant virus within cells of its vector is one of the most outstanding contributions of recent years.

During 1962, Black and Markham (1963) found that wound-tumor virus contains double-stranded ribonucleic acid. No deoxyribonucleic acid was detected. This finding is of great importance, because heretofore it was not known what kind of nucleic acid any of the dual-host—"plant-insect"—viruses contained. The sedimentation coefficient of the virus was found to be 510 Svedberg units.

Recently, further studies were carried out on the morphology of the wound-tumor virus. Bils and Hall (1962) reported that the virus is about 600 Å in diameter and has the shape of an icosahedron. The surface of the virus consists of 92 subunits about 75 Å in diameter. The virus core stained heavily with uranyl acetate, confirming Black's finding that it consists of RNA. The core comprises about 20% of the volume of the virus particle.

The wound-tumor virus shows a striking similarity in its fine structure to the human-pathogenic reoviruses, formerly known under the name of ECHO type 10. These viruses are widely distributed throughout the world. Reoviruses were shown to contain double-stranded RNA, but no DNA (Gomatos and Tamm, 1963). In view of the morphologic and chemical similarity of the plant-pathogenic and the animal-pathogenic viruses, it was of interest to study the possible serological relationship between reoviruses and wound-tumor virus. This study was first suggested by Lwoff et al. (1962) during a symposium on animal virus classification, held during the summer of 1962 in Cold Spring Harbor. Serological tests were carried out by Streissle and Maramorosch (1963a). Serological cross reactivity was first found by comple-

ment fixation tests. Later neutralization tests confirmed these findings (1963b).

The positive results of preliminary tests were followed by a quantitative assay with the technique described for wound-tumor complement fixation by Windsor (1956) and by Ellen M. Ball (personal communication). Twofold serial dilutions of antigen and antiserum were made up to a dilution of 1 : 128 and tested against each other in a grid titration. Complement fixation took place up to and including a dilution of wound-tumor antiserum of 1 : 128, and of reovirus antigen dilution of 1 : 64, while the controls remained negative at 1 : 64 and 1 : 128. The finding that reoviruses and wound-tumor virus share a common antigen suggests a relationship between these animal-pathogenic and plant-pathogenic viruses. The possible implications and significance of such findings have been discussed by Macleod and Markham (1963) and by Streissle and Maramorosch (1963a). Certainly, similarities in host range can hardly continue to be considered as criteria for relationships among viruses (Lwoff et al., 1962).

This serological relationship between reoviruses and wound-tumor virus suggests the first known instance of common neutralizing and complement-fixing antigens between a human pathogenic and a plant pathogenic virus. The similarity in morphological structure and serological relationship indicates that wound-tumor and reoviruses should be classified as belonging to the same group (Lwoff et al., 1962; Streissle and Maramorosch, 1963a).

Work in Japan by Yoshii and Kiso (1959) indicated that rice stunt virus was also a RNA virus, because RNA isolated from stunt diseased rice plants was infectious when injected into the abdomen of leafhoppers. The authors reported that even ingested RNA rendered leafhoppers infective. The RNA preparation was inactivated by RNase. The authors did not test the RNA content of purified preparations, nor did they study RNA from insect vectors.

C. Virus Interrelationships and Virus Strains

Thirty years ago only two strains of aster

yellows virus were recognized in the United States, and the existence of the virus and its vectors in other parts of the world was not known. Today at least 5 strains of aster yellows virus have been isolated and studied in California (Freitag, personal communication), and 2 distinct strains are known to occur in the eastern United States. Aster yellows virus is known to be transmitted most efficiently by *Macrosteles fascifrons* throughout North America. A number of other, often less efficient, vectors have been reported from other areas. In recent years additional vectors have also been reported in the eastern parts of the United States and Canada.

Chiykowski (1963) found that a celery-infecting strain of aster yellows virus was transmitted by *Endria inimica* (Say) to barley and wheat. A very long latent period of the virus ranging from a minimum of 18–25 days to a maximum period of 73–81 days was reported for the virus-vector interrelationship. Differences in incubation of strains in the same vector have been reported earlier (Maramorosch, 1962b) and such differences were in the order of hours only. While Chiykowski (1963) considers that the virus that infected barley was a strain of aster yellows virus, this assumption is based solely on the symptoms caused in celery and on the ability of *M. fascifrons,* in addition to *E. inimica,* to transmit the infective agent. No tests were reported on the length of incubation of the barley infecting virus in *M. fascifrons,* and no cross-protection experiments were made in plants or in insects. Without such cross-protection tests, one is left in doubt as to whether the barley infecting virus merely resembles aster yellows virus in symptom induction, or whether it actually constitutes a strain of this virus.

Unfortunately no serological test is available to determine the identity and relationships of strains of aster yellows virus. It was assumed for many years that transmission by *M. fascifrons* is limited to aster yellows virus, and that positive transmission by this leafhopper identifies the causative agent of a yellows infection as aster yellows virus. Recent investigations showed that *M. fascifrons* acts as a vector of at least one virus, if

not several different viruses, in addition to transmitting strains of aster yellows virus. The symptoms of disease and the host range of different strains, as well as of other yellows-type and big-bud type viruses are not adequate as distinguishing criteria. Until a serological test becomes available, the identification of strains must depend on cross-immunity tests in plants and in *M. fascifrons.*

In Japan, Fukushi reported the presence of aster yellows in 1930 and more recently he and Nemoto demonstrated that the leafhopper *Ophiola flavopicta* (Ishihara) serves as its vector (Fukushi and Nemoto, 1953; 1954). Japanese aster yellows virus was transmitted by this leafhopper from tomato to *Nicotiana rustica* and other plants (Oshima and Goto, 1956), and from carrot to potato, petunia, and China aster (Fukushi and Shikata, 1959).

The aster yellows disease was first detected in Germany by Richter in 1936 and *Macrosteles laevis* Ribaut was found to be a vector by Heinze and Kunze (1955). *Aphrodes bicinctus* (Schrank) was also suspected as an additional vector. In Poland, in 1958, Kochmann and Książek (personal communication) transmitted aster yellows virus from onions by means of *M. laevis.* It has also been reported in onions from Czechoslovakia (Blattný, 1960). In Russia, aster yellows virus has been known for many years as the cause of Kok-sagyz yellows, and its transmission by a *Macrosteles* sp. has been studied (Ryshkow, 1940; 1943; Sukhov and Vovk, 1945).

In 1955 Kunkel found that the eastern and a western strain of aster yellows could be distinguished by symptom expression in *N. rustica* plants. Infected plants differed from normal ones by their striking development of secondary shoots. Similar differences were found in *Zinnia* plants. The distinguishing of the aster yellows strains by their symptoms in *N. rustica* enabled Kunkel to demonstrate for the first time that the presence of one virus in a leafhopper may interfere with the transmission of another. When one virus strain became well established in individual insects, which usually took place 14 days after virus acquisition, the insects were unable to acquire and transmit the second strain (Kunkel, 1957). This cross protection by virus strains provides an additional method for testing relationships between yellows viruses. In cases where the same insect vector transmits the viruses to different plants and the cross immunity cannot be tested in plant hosts, Kunkel's discovery may provide a means of testing for cross protection. Such a possibility was suggested by Black (1959) for testing the possible relationship between California aster yellows and cherry buckskin virus strains, transmitted by *Colladonus geminatus* (Van Duzee) (Jensen, 1956). While in aster yellows tests with two virus strains Kunkel found complete cross protection, Freitag (personal communication), working with 5 different strains, all of the western type, found a complicated relationship which could not be explained easily. Whereas some strains seemed to protect against transmission, others did not. These results are not surprising in view of the findings of Maramorosch (1958a) with 2 strains of corn stunt virus acquired consecutively by *D. maidis*. When the Rio Grande strain was acquired first, it prevented the transmission of the Mesa Central strain. However, in *D. maidis* protection in the reverse direction is incomplete. It was concluded that the Rio Grande strain was either more virulent or multiplied faster and thus protected the insects from acquiring and transmitting the second strain.

The rapid spread and increased occurrence of celery yellows in the eastern part of the United States might be explained on the basis of recent findings by Maramorosch (1962b). Contrary to preliminary findings (Maramorosch, 1960b), a shorter incubation period in plants and in insect vectors was found for the celery-infecting strain than for the ordinary eastern strain of aster yellows virus. The difference was not great, with a minimum incubation period in insects at 25°C for 8 days compared to 9 days for the eastern strain. However, the span between the first and the last plant infected with the celery strain in controlled conditions was only 2 days, compared to 8 days for the eastern strain. This shorter span between the first and last day

of the disease onset may play an important role in the spread of celery yellows, as cross immunity prevents reinfection with the slower-multiplying strain.

D. Loss of Transmissibility

A few years ago Black (1953c) discovered that certain leafhopper-borne viruses, maintained for many years in plants through grafting, had lost their affinity for the arthropod vectors, and no longer could be transmitted by their original insect carriers. It seems likely that vectorless strains of viruses have evolved artificially in the laboratory through a process of mutation or gradual selection. However, the possibility of the loss of a stage in the development of the virus cannot be excluded entirely, although at present there is no evidence supporting the existence of such virus forms or of different developmental stages in the life cycle of viruses multiplying in insects and plants.

E. Virus Acquisition and Transmission

In a study of virus acquisition and transmission, Maramorosch (1962a) found that *M. fascifrons* seldom acquires virus from older, symptomless leaves of diseased plants. Only 3% of insects became viruliferous in a single day of acquisition feeding on older leaves, while 80% acquired virus from the diseased inflorescence, and 90% from the leafless stem.

Virus transmission was not evenly distributed throughout the day, but occurred in distinct peaks, at 8:00 a.m., 11:00 a.m., 3:00 p.m., 5:00 p.m., and 8:00 p.m. Almost twice as many plants became infected during the afternoon hours, as during the morning hours. The increased transmission coincided with increased uptake of food, as measured by the uptake of C^{14}-labeled glucose from aster leaves, but no definite peaks were found in food uptake. The observed transmission peaks may indicate the existence of an independent mechanism governing virus transmission.

Nagaraj and Black (1962) have found that the abilities of *A. constricta* to transmit wound-tumor virus were unrelated to the abilities to transmit potato yellow dwarf virus. Their experiments indicated that the hereditary mechanisms which determine the abilities of a single leafhopper species to transmit two unrelated plant viruses were inherited independently. Actually the authors found that the ability to transfer wound-tumor virus from insect to insect transovarially, and that of transferring potato yellow dwarf by insects to plants, depended on either two alleles or two or more genes. It seems that individuals within a vector species, in much the same way as plants, have different specific genetic susceptibilities to virus infection. This conclusion is in accord with findings made by Storey (1932).

F. VIRUS INTERRELATIONSHIPS

Attempts to define the relationships of yellows type viruses are severely hampered not only by the lack of serological tests but also by the lack of a world-wide virus collection. A comparison between some of the European and Canadian viruses was made by Valenta (1958, 1959, 1961) and Valenta et al. (1961). Ryshkow (1961) pointed out that the stolbur group of viruses, transmitted primarily by *Hyalestes obsoletus* Sign., and in addition by at least 4 other leafhoppers, should be separated from the group to which the typical aster yellows virus belongs. The same view was often expressed by the late L. O. Kunkel (personal communication), who pointed out that big-bud symptoms were caused in tomato plants by stolbur virus and the Australian big-bud virus, but not by strains of aster yellows. The finding that several *Macrosteles* species, including *M. fascifrons*, can act as vectors of both types of viruses necessitates a revision of earlier conclusions concerning the identification of aster yellows virus and of its reported vectors in various regions.

G. SEROLOGY

The pioneering work of Black (1955) and of Brakke et al. (1951, 1954) on the purification and serology of leafhopper-borne viruses permitted the characterization of several viruses by electron microscopy, while the use of viral antigens made their accurate detection possible. Whitcomb and Black (1961) have measured the wound-tumor soluble antigen in the vector

Agallia constricta Van Duzee, and found that its titer increased rapidly between the fourth day when it could be first detected, and the tenth day, when it reached a plateau at which it remained for many weeks. This increase was caused by the rapid multiplication of the virus in the insect. On the other hand, the infectivity and efficiency of transmission seem to increase gradually, reaching their maximum at about 5 weeks after the injection of the virus into the vector. Although the level of soluble antigen remains high, the infectivity of the insects decreases in later weeks. Using the precipitin ring test, a method was developed to detect the presence or absence of wound-tumor virus in a single leafhopper. Although all insects injected with large doses of wound-tumor virus showed an increase of soluble antigen, some failed to transmit the virus. Thus, the serological method proved much more sensitive in detecting viruliferous insects than the testing of leafhoppers on susceptible plants.

It is not known in which tissues or organs of the vector the virus multiplies. Fluorescent antibody studies by Nagaraj et al. (1961) were perfected so that now a method exists by which the wound-tumor virus can be detected in cross sections of vectors. However, this technique has not yet revealed the site of viral multiplication. It has been speculated that the fat body, which in the case of some virus infections of vectors may show cytopathogenic changes, is the place where propagative viruses multiply, but this could not be proved. The mycetome has also been suspected because of the possible symbionts in which the multiplication of viruses could theoretically take place. This possibility was discussed by Black (1953a), but no indications of changes in the mycetome have been reported until very recently, when Nasu (1963) observed changes in the mycetome of viruliferous males of the black-streaked green rice leafhopper, *Nephotettix* sp. These and other virus-induced changes will be discussed in detail in the following pages.

Recently a new approach became possible for the determination of the site of plant virus multiplication in insect vectors.

Hirumi and Maramorosch (1963) used excised organs of inoculated aster leafhoppers as source of virus inoculum to determine the movement and location of aster yellows virus. After 5 days, small amounts of virus were detected in the gut, while 19 days later no virus was found there. However, by that time a high concentration of virus was demonstrable in the salivary glands. The possible multiplication of virus in salivary glands, mycetome, hemocytes, and fat body tissues is being tested further, using excised organs of vectors *in vitro*.

8–8. EFFECTS OF PLANT VIRUSES ON VECTORS AND NONVECTORS

Various deleterious and beneficial effects of plant viruses on insects have been reported in recent years. This subject has been reviewed by Maramorosch and Jensen (1963) and the reader is referred to their article for illustrations and details of this subject. The main aspects of this subject will be described below.

A. Aster Yellows Virus

Several years ago, Bawden (1950) pointed out that the insect pests that act as vectors constitute a possible source for the origin of plant viruses, for the vectors seem to be completely tolerant. However, this origin was not considered plausible until evidence became available that insect vectors can support multiplication of viruses they transmit. The demonstration of virus multiplication in both plants and insect vectors seemed to suggest that the presumably symptomless insect hosts may have been the original evolutionary source of these viruses. The multiplication cycles of viruses such as aster yellows virus, that can alternate between a plant and an arthropod, could have arisen either by very simple nutritive requirements or by a well-organized adaptation of all metabolic activities (Maramorosch, 1954). Biologically-transmitted plant viruses usually have a fairly large host range among plant species but a narrow one among the arthropod vectors. The harmful effects to plants are pronounced, but vectors are rarely affected. This seems to indicate that these viruses are well adapted to the animal host and that this adaptation, from an evolutionary point of view, is probably also of much longer existence. Until 1956 it was generally thought that insect vectors are completely tolerant of the otherwise highly virulent plant viruses, and that the long association between the insect host and virus parasite resulted in an ideally balanced, almost symbiotic relationship.

Littau and Maramorosch (1956, 1960) provided the first evidence against this hypothesis by finding a pathogenic action of the virus on the arthropod, an action that is quite drastic in some affected cells.

Cytological effects in the females appeared to be similar to those in the males, but the changes did not progress as far (Littau, 1960). Nuclei of fat body cells became stellate (star-shaped), but there was less tendency for spaces to appear in the tissue. That these processes were less marked in the females may have been a reflection of fat body activity related to egg production. No tests were made with virgin females to prove or disprove this assumption.

Viruliferous insects which remained the entire time on diseased plants showed more pronounced cytological changes than those which were allowed to acquire virus but were subsequently maintained on virus-free plants. If a constant supply of virus or virus by-products in the food is necessary for the full expression of the cytological effects, this could explain why changes failed to develop in many viruliferous insects that were maintained on healthy plants.

To exclude the possible effect of such changes, acquired through feeding on diseased plants, insects were mechanically infected by needle inoculation. Virus-free insects were injected with the juice of viruliferous ones and, after a suitable period of time on immune rye plants and healthy aster plants, the insects were examined cytologically. One-third of the injected viruliferous males were close to the extreme viruliferous condition, while the rest were intermediate, which demonstrated that feeding on the diseased plant was not the sole cause of the changes, but it suggested that such feeding might augment the effect of the virus.

The possible toxic effect of infected plants cannot be ruled out completely, although no evidence for toxicity has been found. On the contrary, aster leafhoppers were reported to breed more prolifically on diseased plants (Severin, 1946), which seems to deny the possibility of a toxic substance that might be acquired from diseased asters.

There has been a traditional assumption that if vectors are affected in any way at all by the virus they carry, it must be pathologically, because viruses are pathological by their very nature. Although there is no doubt that in diseased plants aster yellows virus is a pathogenic parasite, in the insect host it may be more like a commensal or even a symbiont and changes caused by it are not necessarily pathological. In this connection the work of Severin (1946) might again be recalled. Severin's experiments indicated that vectorship is a function of special biological significance in that it indirectly aids the insect's multiplication. The contrary is true for the infected plant, which becomes sterile in the course of the disease.

B. RICE VIRUSES

Fukushi (1931, 1934) reported the presence of several virus inclusion bodies in the tissues of rice and other grasses infected with rice dwarf virus. Subsequently, he (1940) examined viruliferous vectors and prepared numerous transverse and longitudinal sections but found no inclusion bodies or other evidence of virus in the salivary glands, the alimentary canal, the ovarian tubules, the mycetome, or other organs.

While neither virus particles nor histopathological changes due to virus were found with the help of the light microscope, recent electron micrographs (Fukushi et al., 1960, 1962; Shikata, 1962) have revealed the form of the virus, not only in partially purified preparations but also in ultrathin sections of insect vector tissue and infected rice leaves. The virus particles are spherical or hexagonal in shape with a darker central area surrounded by a relatively transparent zone.

In 1962 Fukushi et al. found virus particles in sections of the salivary glands of infected leafhoppers, as well as large clusters of virus particles in crystalline array in sections of the abdomen and sections of the malpighian tubules. Aggregates of virus particles were also encountered in sections through fat body cells, where they were arranged approximately in a hexagonal pattern. The property of forming crystallizing aggregates not only enables the identification of the virus in different organs but it will also facilitate, in the future, the study of the site and mode of virus multiplication within the vector.

Such conspicuous aggregations of virus in the vector might logically be expected to cause cytological changes and to alter the physiology of the infected leafhoppers. Recent publications and unpublished data received from Japan indicate that such is the case. Nasu (1963) reported cytological abnormalities in leafhopper vectors of rice viruses. The fat body was found to assume different forms depending upon the life stage of the leafhopper. Many vacuoles and granules were seen in fat body cells of young nymphs, but the granules disappeared at the end of the fifth instar. In adults the appearance of the fat body varied with the physiological condition of the insect, and pronounced changes were observed in the nuclei. Infected adults had larger numbers of vacuoles in their fat body cells, and the nuclei were stellate. The mycetome of vectors was also affected by two rice viruses—rice dwarf virus and rice stripe virus.

8–9. PLANT VIRUSES PATHOGENIC TO THEIR VECTORS

Although some of the work discussed previously indicated that certain viruses may affect the metabolism of insects or cause histopathologic changes in certain tissues, no drastic deleterious effects have been connected with the observed changes. The first finding of a direct injurious effect of a plant or animal virus on an insect vector was made by Jensen (1958), who demonstrated that the plant pathogenic virus, causing Western X-disease of stone fruits and a yellows disease in celery, significantly reduced the life span of one of its vectors, *Colladonus montanus* (Van Duzee). Jensen's subsequent papers (1959a, 1959b, 1962, 1963) present the most extensive study thus far made of deleterious effects of a virus on its arthropod vector. Western X-disease virus impairs the fecundity of *C. montanus.* Premature death of the viruliferous individuals appears to be due to the virus as such. An alternative explanation cannot be found in the possibility that there are genetic differences among the leafhoppers involving correlation between greater longevity and failure to acquire virus. All individuals appear to be potential vectors if given sufficient time on the inoculum plant.

Twenty years ago Sukhov (1943) reported that winter wheat mosaic virus induced the formation of numerous needle-shaped crystals in the intestine of the insect vector *Deltocephalus* (*Psammotettix*) *striatus* L. and also in the cells of infected wheat leaves. The crystals could be seen only after the plant cells and insect tissues were placed in an acid solution at pH 4.

In a recent article Lomakina *et al.* (1963) reported that considerable changes occur in the structure of fat body cells of the viruliferous vector of wheat mosaic virus, similar to the changes reported by Littau and Maramorosch (1960) for aster yellows virus vectors. In addition, a significant reduction was found in the amount of RNA in the cytoplasm and nucleoli, an alteration in the distribution of DNA in the nuclei, and a depletion of polysaccharides in the cytoplasm. These histochemical changes were considered to have been directly responsible for the impaired development and structure of transovarially infected nymphs. Peculiar inclusions were found in the cytoplasm of fat body cells of infected insects. No nucleic acids were detected in the inclusions, but they were found to contain histidine.

The report by Sukhov (1940) of needle-like crystals in the intestinal tract of *Delphacodes striatella,* carrying "zakuklivanie" or pseudo-rosette virus of oats, prompted a search for similar inclusions in *Colladonus montanus* carrying Western X-virus. Crystals were found in the enlarged portion of the midgut or stomach or first ventriculus and in the second ventriculus or narrowed portion of the midgut (Lee and Jensen, 1963). When part of an infective colony, having crystals in a high percentage of the individuals, was placed on healthy celery, the crystals gradually disappeared from an increasing number of leafhoppers.

A. EUROPEAN WHEAT STRIATE MOSAIC VIRUS

Another virus possibly pathogenic to its vector is that of European wheat striate mosaic. Watson and Sinha (1959) reported that virus infection caused a reduction in the number of progeny of the vector *Calligypona* (*Delphacodes*) *pellucida* (Fabricius). In several experiments, infective mothers produced fewer nymphs than non-infective mothers. This was further investigated and it was found that female nymphs that became infective as a result of feeding on infected plants produced fewer offspring than their sisters that were fed on healthy plants. Eggs deposited by viruliferous females often developed to a certain stage only and then shriveled and did not hatch. These authors suggested that the virus was pathogenic to the vector and that the poor reproductive ability of infective females tended to eliminate the virus from colonies that were unable to renew their infectivity by feeding on infected plants.

Kisimoto (personal communication) of the Shikoku Agricultural Experiment Station worked for one year at the Rothamsted Experiment Station with wheat striate mosaic virus. Although the reduction in offspring of viruliferous colonies of *C. pellucida* was consistently observed, he concluded that this reduction was the result of inbreeding and not of virus infection.

B. RICE DWARF VIRUS

The possible pathologic effect of rice dwarf virus on its leafhopper vectors has been under study recently. Shinkai (1958) reported that the premature death of *Inazuma dorsalis* leafhopper inheriting rice dwarf virus through the egg is a cause for the disappearance of the virus from insect colonies relying on transovarial passage.

Nephotettix cincticeps, the best-known vector of rice dwarf virus, is also a very favorable host of the virus. In fact, virus is passed transovarially to such a high percentage of the progeny that it apparently could survive long periods of time, if not indefinitely, in the absence of its host plant. This would suggest that the virus is noninjurious. However, deleterious effects of the virus in *N. cincticeps* are being found, although the virus appears to be much less lethal to the nymphs of this species than to those of *Inazuma dorsalis* (Shinkai, 1960a).

8–10. BENEFICIAL VIRUS EFFECTS

It may be that viruses serve constructive functions in nature as varied and universal as those played by bacteria, but difficult to detect because of their lack of obvious manifestations (Maramorosch, 1960a).

Several years ago, Severin (1946) found that 9 species of leafhoppers were able to complete their nymphal stages on celery or aster plants infected with California aster yellows virus, while the adults died within a few days after they were transferred to healthy celery or aster. Severin interpreted his findings as a demonstration that aster yellows virus in some way altered celery and aster plants so as to make them more suitable as source of food for the different species of leafhoppers.

Kennedy (1951) found that sugar-beet mosaic virus altered the physiology of the beet plant in such a manner that *Aphis fabae* produced more young aphids per mother on virus-infected leaves of all ages than on healthy leaves of comparable age.

A surprising effect of a virus upon a non-vector insect was found by Maramorosch (1958a, 1958b). At first, the finding and its interpretation seemed similar to the one made by Kennedy (1951). The leafhopper *Dalbulus maidis* (DeLong and Wolcott) can acquire and retain aster yellows virus in its haemolymph, but it cannot transmit the virus. The insect is highly host-specific and usually survives and breeds well only on maize (*Zea mays*) and on the related wild grass teosinte (*Euchlaena mexicana*). It dies within 4 days on most other plants, including healthy China asters (*Calliste-*

phus chinensis). However, if the asters are infected with aster yellows, the insects may survive for long periods, either as nymphs or as adults (Maramorosch, 1958c). More remarkable, however, is the fact that after the insects have survived for 7 days or longer on diseased aster plants, they are then able to survive on healthy asters and on other plants such as carrots and rye (Maramorosch, 1960a). The explanation of this intriguing phenomenon is still being studied. Suggested possibilities included alteration of aster by the virus to make this plant more palatable to the leafhopper. It was thought that such a "conditioned" leafhopper might then be more willing to feed on healthy asters. Orenski and Maramorosch (1962) found that it was not food acceptability but rather food digestion that had been altered in corn leafhoppers, following their access to diseased aster plants. The mechanism responsible for the increased survival of viruliferous *D. maidis* cannot yet be fully explained.

An interesting and somewhat unexpected finding was the difference between two aster yellows virus strains in influencing the ability of corn leafhoppers to feed on healthy asters. A celery-infecting strain that caused a more severe stunting of aster plants but failed to produce cytological changes in infected aster leafhoppers also failed to change the feeding ability of *D. maidis* (Maramorosch, 1960a).

The factors involved in the often observed sudden spread of certain virus vectors are not clearly understood. Could the acquisition of certain plant viruses by insects be responsible for such drastic expansions? Such an assumption is highly speculative, but it is mentioned here in view of the discussed metabolic changes induced in corn leafhoppers by aster yellows virus, and also in connection with an alarming series of outbreaks of corn stunt virus in various parts of the United States, and presumably transmitted by the corn leafhopper (Maramorosch, 1963c). The survival and overwintering of *D. maidis* has been limited in the past to the southernmost parts of the United States, and until 1962 no serious losses were attributed to corn stunt virus. In 1962 outbreaks

189

occurred in Mississippi and Louisiana, and in 1963, in addition to more severe outbreaks in those two states, a very serious outbreak was reported from Ohio (W. N. Stoner, personal communication).

Approximately 10,000 acres were involved, showing from a trace up to 70% of the plants affected. Estimates of losses averaged 15% in that area. It remains to be seen whether the disease is caused by the corn stunt virus and whether the vector is *D. maidis*. If this should be the case, it would be of great importance to establish the factors involved in the ability of this semitropical insect to spread into new territory. The possibility that such a change could have been induced by acquisition of a strange virus should not be overlooked. Cytological abnormalities found in a few instances in vectors of plant viruses, although not shown to be deleterious, may have altered the physiology of the respective vectors. Altered metabolism is not necessarily synonymous with deleterious effects, however.

8–11. CONCLUSIONS

After the evidence for multiplication of certain plant viruses in their respective vectors became overwhelming, there was a tendency to infer that all viruses that persisted in their vectors also multiplied in these vectors. While it is probable that a large number of viruses that require long incubation periods in their arthropod vectors also multiply in the respective vectors, one cannot safely accept this as a general, unqualified assumption. Curly-top virus of sugar beets, which has an incubation period in its vector somewhat shorter than most other leafhopper-transmitted viruses, apparently does not multiply in *Circulifer tenellus* (Baker) (Bennett and Wallace, 1938; Freitag, 1936). It is unlikely that this is the only case of a circulative virus that does not multiply in its vector, and probably a number of other circulative viruses will be found that have a similar relationship to their vectors.

Another widely held generalization has been that viruses in general, and plant viruses in particular, are not pathogenic to their insect vectors. This followed logically from the belief that most, if not all, vectors were carriers of virus but were supposedly not involved as true hosts. This viewpoint was bolstered further by early failures to find cytological changes or evidence of injury in leafhopper vectors of aster yellows and rice dwarf viruses.

The search for abnormalities in vectors of viruses was stimulated by the finding of changes in the fat body of leafhopper vectors of aster yellows virus (Littau and Maramorosch, 1956, 1960). A number of unrelated viruses were found in recent years to cause cytological changes in the fat body tissue of vector leafhoppers as well as vector aphids, and also other cytological changes.

It is to be expected that the intensive efforts in many laboratories, devoted to the study of effects of plant viruses on insects, will clarify whether unrelated viruses do cause similar effects in their vectors, or whether some of these effects are due to nonviral causes.

In spite of the meager knowledge of the effects exerted by plant viruses on insects, the accumulating evidence suggests that these relationships form a symbiotic spectrum showing mutual benefit at one end and lethal parasitism at the other. Examples of pathogenicity of plant viruses to insect vectors, reported from many laboratories, together with the well-established findings of transovarial infections and virus multiplication in insect vectors, indicate that certain leafhopper and aphid vectors are not mere fortuitous carriers of viruses, but hosts and reservoirs that have played a primary role in plant and animal virus evolution.

The transmission of viruses is a complex process, even in the simple stylet-borne viruses, and more so in the circulatory and propagative ones. New techniques are needed to study and understand the basic mechanisms involved. A very promising approach is offered through the recent development of insect tissue culture (Maramorosch, 1962c). The eventual goal of this approach is to provide accurate quantitative measurement of virus concentration by a plaque technique. It seems feasible to attempt an adaptation of propagative viruses to cells of insects, and even of higher cold- and warm-blooded animals grown *in vitro*. Another promising approach is the study of the histology and fine structure of organs and cells of vectors of circulatory and propagative viruses with the aid of the electron microscope. These studies may reveal changes caused by viruses and may help in the better understanding of virus-host inter-relationships.

* * *

This work was supported in part by grants from the U.S. Public Health Service, Nos. E-1537 and AI-04290, and from the National Science Foundation, Nos. G-17663 and GB-1199.

8–12. LITERATURE CITED

Amos, J., Haton, R. G., Knight, R. C., and Massee, A. M. (1927). Ann. Rept. East Malling Res. Sta., Kent 1925. II. Suppl. 13, 126.

Bald, J. G., and Samuel, G. (1931). Australia, Council Sci. Ind. Research Bull. No. 54.

Bawden, F. C. (1950). Plant Viruses and Virus Diseases, 3d ed. Chronica Botanica Co., Waltham, Mass.

Bennett, C. W., and Wallace, H. E. (1938). J. Agr. Res. U.S. 56, 31.

Best, R. J. (1954). Australian J. Biol. Sci. 7, 415.

Best, R. J., and Gallus, H. P. C. (1955). Enzymologia 17, 207.

Bils, R. F., and Hall, C. E. (1962). Virology 17, 123.

Bird, J. (1954). Ann. Rept. Dept. Plant Pathol., Agr. Expt. Sta., Univ. Puerto Rico. 1953–1954.

Bird, J. (1958). Puerto Rico Univ. Agr. Expt. Sta. Tech. Paper No. 26.

Black, L. M. (1944). Proc. Am. Phil. Soc. 88, 132.

Black, L. M. (1950). Nature 166, 852.

Black, L. M. (1953a). Ann. N.Y. Acad. Sci. 56, 398.

Black, L. M. (1953b). Phytopathology 43, 9.

Black, L. M. (1953c). Phytopathology 43, 466.

Black, L. M. (1955). Phytopathology 45, 208.

Black, L. M. (1959). In The Viruses. 2, 157. Academic Press, New York.

Black, L. M. (1963). Handbuch der Pflanzenphysiologie 15 (in press). Springer, Berlin.

Black, L. M., and Brakke, M. K. (1952). Phytopathology 42, 269.

Black, L. M. and Markham, R. (1963). Neth. J. Plant Pathol. 69, 215.

Blattny, C. S. (1960). Preslia 32, 406.

Brakke, M. K., Black, L. M., and Wyckoff, R. W. G. (1951). Am. J. Botany 38, 332.

Brakke, M. K., Vatter, A. E., and Black, L. M. (1954). Brookhaven Symp. Biol. 6, 137.

Carter, W. (1951). Phytopathology 41, 769.

Carter, W. (1952). Botan. Rev. 18, 680.

Carter, W. (1963). Mealybug Wilt of Pineapple: A Reappraisal. Ann. N.Y. Acad. Sci. 105, 741.

Chiykowski, L. N. (1963). Can. J. Botany 41, 669.

Costa, A. S., and Bennett, C. W. (1950). Phytopathology 40, 266.

Day, M. F. (1955). Australian J. Biol. Sci. 8, 498.

Flock, R. A., and Wallace, J. M. (1955). Phytopathology 45, 52.

Flores, E., and Silberschmidt, K. (1962). Phytopathol. Z. 43, 221.

Freitag, J. H. (1936). Hilgardia 10, 305.

Fukushi, T. (1931). Trans. Sapporo Nat. Hist. Soc. 12, 35.

Fukushi, T. (1933). Proc. Imp. Acad. (Tokyo) 9, 457.

Fukushi, T. (1934). J. Fac. Agr. Hokkaido Imp. Univ. 37(2), 41.

Fukushi, T. (1935). Proc. Imp. Acad. (Tokyo) 11, 301.

Fukushi, T. (1940). J. Fac. Agr. Hokkaido Imp. Univ. 45, 83.

Fukushi, T., and Kimura, I. (1958). Ann. Phytopathol. Soc. Japan 23, 54.

Fukushi, T., and Nemoto, M. (1953). Virus (Osaka) 3, 208.

Fukushi, T., and Nemoto, M. (1954). Ann. Phytopathol. Soc. Japan 18, 146.

Fukushi, T., and Shikata, E. (1959). Ann. Phytopathol. Soc. Japan 24, 62.

Fukushi, T., Shikata, E., and Kimura, I. (1962). Virology 18, 192.

Fukushi, T., Shikata, E., Kimura, I., and Nemoto, M. (1960). Proc. Japan Acad. 36, 352.

Gomatos, P. J., and Tamm, I. (1963). Proc. Natl. Acad. Sci. U.S. 49, 707.

Grylls, N. E. (1954). Australian J. Biol. Sci. 7, 47.

Harrison, B. D. (1958). Virology 6, 265.

Heinze, K. (1955). J. Econ. Entomol. 48, 751.

Heinze, K. (1959). Arch. ges. Virusforsch. 9, 396.

Heinze, K., and Kunze, L. (1955). Nachrbl. Deut. Pflanzenschutzdienst (Stuttgart) 7, 161.

Hirumi, H., and Maramorosch, K. (1963). Contrib. Boyce Thompson Inst. 22, 141.

Jensen, D. D. (1956). Virology 2, 249.

Jensen, D. D. (1958). Phytopathology 48, 394.

Jensen, D. D. (1959a). Virology 8, 164.

Jensen, D. D. (1959b). Pan-Pacific Entomologist 35, 65.

Jensen, D. D. (1962). Proc. Intern. Congr. Entomol., 11th, Vienna, 1960, 2, 789.

Jensen, D. D. (1963). Ann. N.Y. Acad. Sci. 105, 685.

Kennedy, J. S. (1951). Nature 168, 825.

Kennedy, J. S., Day, M. F., and Eastop, V. F. (1962). A Conspectus of Aphids as Vectors of Plant Viruses. Commonwealth Inst. Entomol., London, England.

Kimura, I., and Fukushi, T. (1960). Ann. Phytopathol. Soc. Japan 25, 131.

Kirkpatrick, H. C., and Ross, A. F. (1952). Phytopathology 42, 540.

Klostermeyer, E. C. (1953). Washington State Coll. Agr. Expt. Sta. Tech. Bull. 9.

Kunkel, L. O. (1954). In The Dynamics of Virus and Rickettsial Infections. 150–63. Blakiston Company, New York.

Kunkel, L. O. (1955). Advan. Virus Res. 3, 251.

Kunkel, L. O. (1957). Science 126, 1233.

Lee, P. E., and Jensen, D. D. (1963). Virology 20, 328.

Littau, V. C. (1960). J. Morphol. 106, 187.

Littau, V. C., and Maramorosch, K. (1956). Virology 2, 128.

Littau, V. C., and Maramorosch, K. (1960). Virology 10, 483.

Lomakina, L. Ya., Razvyazkina, G. M., and Shubnikova, E. A. (1963). Vopr. Virusol. 1963(2), 168.

Lwoff, A., Horne, R., and Tournier, P. (1962). Cold Spring Harbor Symp. Quant. Biol. 27, 51.

MacCarthy, H. R. (1954). Phytopathology 44, 167.

Macleod, R., and Markham, R. (1963). Virology 19, 190.

Maramorosch, K. (1952). Phytopathology 42, 59.

Maramorosch, K. (1954). Trans. N.Y. Acad. Sci. Ser. 2. 16, 189.

Maramorosch, K. (1955). Bull. Torrey Botan. Club 82, 339.

Maramorosch, K. (1958a). Virology 6, 448.

Maramorosch, K. (1958b). Proc. Intern. Congr. Microbiol., 8th, Stockholm, 260.

Maramorosch, K. (1958c). Tijdschr. Plantenziekten 64, 383.

Maramorosch, K. (1960a). Sci. Am. 203(2), 138.

Maramorosch, K. (1960b). Protoplasma 52, 457.

Maramorosch, K. (1962a). Phytopathology 52, 1219.

Maramorosch, K. (1962b). Phytopathology 52, 925.

Maramorosch, K. (1962c). Proc. Intern. Congr. Entomol., 11th, Vienna, 1960, 2, 801.

Maramorosch, K. (1963a). Ann. Rev. Entomol. 8, 369.

Maramorosch, K. (1963b). Ann. N.Y. Acad. Sci. 105, 683.

Maramorosch, K. (1963c). Plant Disease Reptr. 47, 858.

Maramorosch, K., and Jensen, D. D. (1963). Ann. Rev. Microbiol. 17, 495.

Maramorosch, K., Brakke, M. K., and Black, L. M. (1949). Science 110, 162.

Massee, A. M. (1952). Ann. Rept. East Malling Res. Sta., Kent 1951, 162.

Meester-Manger Cats, V. de. (1956). Tijdschr. Plantenziekten 62, 174.

Mueller, W. C., and Rochow, W. F. (1961). Virology 14, 253.

Nagaraj, A. N., and Black, L. M. (1962). Virology 16, 152.

Nagaraj, A. N., Sinha, R. C., and Black, L. M. (1961). Virology 15, 205.

Nasu, S. (1963). Bull. Kyushu Agr. Expt. Sta. 8, 153

Orenski, S. W., and Maramorosch, K. (1962). Phytopathology 52, 1219.

Orlando, A., and Silberschmidt, K. (1946). Arquiv. Instituto Biol. (São Paulo) 17, 1.

Oshima, N., and Goto, T. (1956). Res. Bull. Hokkaido Natl. Agr. Expt. Sta. 71, 56.

Pittman, H. A. (1927). J. Council Sci. Ind. Res. (Australia) 1, 74.

Posnette, A. F. (1953). Rept. Intern. Hort. Congr., 13th, 1952, 2, 1224.

Posnette, A. F., and Robertson, N. F. (1950). Ann. Appl. Biol. 37, 363.

Posnette, A. F., and Strickland, A. H. (1948). Ann. Appl. Biol. 35, 53.

Průša, V. Jermoljev, E., and Vacke, J. (1959). Biol. Plant. Acad. Sci. Bohemoslov. 1, 223.

Razvyazkina, G. M. (1953). Dokl. Vses. Akad. Sel'skokhoz. Nauk 18, 27.

Richter, H. (1936). Nachrbl. Deut. Pflanzenschutzdienst (Berlin) 16, 66.

Rochow, W. F. (1960). Virology 12, 223.

Rochow, W. F. (1963). Ann. N.Y. Acad. Sci. 105, 713.

Ryshkow, V. (1940). Sb. Akad. V. L. Kotarov. 696.

Ryshkow, V. (1943). Compt. Rend. Acad. Sci. URSS, N.S. 41, 90.

Ryshkow, V. (1961). Tagungsber. Deut. Akad. Landwirtsch. Berlin 33, 17.

Sakimura, K. (1947). Proc. Hawaiian Entomol. Soc. 13, 59.

Sakimura, K. (1962). In Biological Transmission of Disease Agents. 33. Academic Press, New York.

Severin, H. H. P. (1946). Hilgardia 17, 121.

Shikata, E. (1962). Program and Abstr. Symp. Plant Viruses, Tokyo, Jan. 18, 1962, 12.

Shinkai, A. (1955). Ann. Rept. Kanto and Tosan Phytopathol. Entomol. Soc. 1955, 5.

Shinkai, A. (1958). Ann. Phytopathol. Soc. Japan 23, 26.

Shinkai, A. (1960a). Ann. Phytopathol. Soc. Japan 25, 42.

Shinkai, A. (1960b). Plant Protect. 14, 146.

Shinkai, A. (1962). Bull. Natl. Inst. Agr. Sci. Ser. C. 14, 1.

Simons, J. N. (1962). J. Econ. Entomol. 55, 358.

Simons, J. N., and Coe, D. M. (1958). Virology 6, 43.

Slykhuis, J. T. (1955). Phytopathology 45, 116.

Slykhuis, J. T. (1960). Proc. Entomol. Soc. Ontario (1959) 90, 22.

Slykhuis, J. T. (1962). In Biological Transmission of Disease Agents. 41. Academic Press, New York.

Stegwee, D. (1961). In Recent Advances in Botany 2, 533. Univ. of Toronto Press, Toronto.

Stegwee, D., and Ponsen, M. B. (1958). Entomol. Exptl. Appl. 1, 291.

Storey, H. H. (1932). Proc. Roy. Soc. (London) 112B, 46.

Storey, H. H. (1933). Proc. Roy. Soc. (London) 113B, 463.

Streissle, G., and Maramorosch, K. (1963a). Science 140, 996.

Streissle, G., and Maramorosch, K. (1963b). Phytopathology 53, 891.

Sukhov, K. S. (1940). Mikrobiologia 9, 188.

Sukhov, K. S. (1943). Compt. Rend. Acad. Sci. URSS, N. S. 39, 73.

Sukhov, K. S., and Vovk, A. M. (1945). Compt. Rend. Acad. Sci. URSS, N. S. 48, 365.

Valenta, V. (1958). Proc. Conf. Potato Virus Diseases, 3rd, Lisse, Wageningen 1957, 246.

Valenta, V. (1959). Acta Virol. (Prague) 3, 65.

Valenta, V. (1961). Sb. Česk. Akad. Zéměděl. Věd, Rostlinná Výroba 7, 967.

Valenta, V., Musil, M., and Mišiga, S. (1961). Phytopathol. Z. 42, 1.

Varma, P. (1955). Current Sci. (India) 24, 317.

Watson, M. A. (1960). Rept. Commonwealth Entomol. Conf., 7th, London, 1960, 157.

Watson, M. A., and Sinha, R. C. (1959). Virology 8, 139.

Whitcomb, R. F., and Black, L. M. (1961). Virology 15, 136.

Wilson, N. S., Jones, L. S., and Cochran, L. C. (1955). Plant Disease Reptr. 39, 889.

Windsor, I. G. (1956). Serological Studies on Wound-tumor Virus. M.S. Thesis, Univ. of Illinois, Urbana. 44 pp.

Yamada, W., and Yamamoto, Y. (1955). Okayama Pref. Agr. Expt. Sta. Special Bull. 52, 93.

Yamada, W., and Yamamoto, Y. (1956). Okayama Pref. Agr. Expt. Sta. Special Bull. 55, 35.

Yoshii, H. (1959). Virus (Osaka) 9, 415.

Yoshii, H., and Kiso, A. (1959). Virus (Osaka) 9, 582.

D. A. ROBERTS

Local-lesion assay of plant viruses

9–1. INTRODUCTION

. . . when you can measure what you are speaking about, and express it in numbers, you know something about it; but when you cannot measure it, when you cannot express it in numbers, your knowledge is of a meager and unsatisfactory kind; it may be the beginning of knowledge, but you have scarcely, in your thoughts, advanced to the stage of science, whatever the matter may be.

—Lord Kelvin

ABILITY to assess viruses in number and in kind is the foundation stone upon which the body of knowledge of plant viruses has been built. Characteristic symptoms expressed in certain plants infected by virus are useful in identification of viruses and their strains. But symptoms are often unreliable criteria for identification, because different viruses may induce very similar symptoms in the same plant or the same virus may cause very different symptoms in different plants. Nevertheless, symptomatology in various test plants remains the only method for the qualitative assay of many plant viruses.

Quantitative assays of active virus make it possible to determine infectivity of one viral suspension relative to that of another, and results of properly conducted assays have made possible the correlation of infectivity with particles that are predominant in purified preparations of viruses. Indeed, purification procedures themselves would be unsound if infectivity of various fractions could not be determined by suitable assay methods. Quantitative assays also permit studies of physical and chemical properties of viruses, e.g., thermal stability, sedimentation constants, isoelectric points, longevity *in vitro*, resistance to certain enzymes and other chemicals. Moreover, the effects of factors that influence establishment of virus in the host and its subsequent replication can be assessed by quantitative assays. Without adequate assay techniques, little information could be obtained on the nature of plant viruses, their replication, and pathological effects upon host plants.

9–2. METHODS FOR ASSAYING PLANT VIRUSES

Infectiousness is an intrinsic property of viruses and can be determined only in biological systems. Once infectivity has been associated with a specific physical entity, however, viral preparations can be assayed by nonbiological methods, the most useful of which involve physical, chemical, and serological techniques. Weaknesses are inherent in both kinds of assay procedures. Biological assays are incapable of detecting total viral nucleoprotein, and nonbiological assays do not differentiate infectious from noninfectious material.

A. Physical

1. *Dry weight of virus in purified preparations.*—Perhaps the most obvious nonbiological assay procedure is the determination of the dry weight of material in a known volume of purified virus prepared from a measured amount of diseased plant material. With analytical balances that can weigh accurately to 5×10^{-6} mg, it would seem that the dry-weight determination might well be the most sensitive and reliable method of assaying plant viruses. The procedure has serious drawbacks, however. Its use is restricted to those viruses that can be prepared in purified form; moreover, it measures all solid material in the preparation and is incapable, therefore, of detecting impurities. Before the dry-weight method is used, the preparation should be subjected to all known tests for homogeneity and purity (Steere, 1955). Such tests include analysis by ultracentrifugation, electrophoresis, density-gradient centrifugation, chromatography, ultraviolet-absorption spectrometry, and electron microscopy. Although these tests have certain disadvantages, determination of homogeneity by 2 or more procedures is generally reliable.

2. *Optical density and ultraviolet-absorption spectra.*—Lavin and Stanley (1937) determined the ultraviolet absorption of crystalline tobacco mosaic virus (TMV) and reported that maximum absorption occurred at 265 mμ. This characteristic was the basis for an assay of total viral nucleoprotein (Takahashi, 1951). The concentration of nucleoprotein in a purified preparation was calculated from Kjeldahl nitrogen determinations of 3 aliquots. Known dilutions of the purified preparation were made and their optical densities at 265 mμ were determined. Optical density values plotted against concentration of virus yielded a straight line, and from this calibration curve it was possible to convert optical density of a purified preparation of unknown viral concentration at 265 mμ to mg of viral

nucleoprotein. This rapid and simple method gives reproducible results, and not only accounts for active virus units but for noninfective and aggregated units as well (Takahashi, 1951).

3. *The particle-count method.*—When examined with the electron microscope, highly infectious purified preparations have been found to consist of a suspension of particles of definite morphology. These particles (rigid or flexuous rods with high length/width ratios, short rods, spheres, or polyhedrons) are characteristic for a given virus, and probably are the infectious units. Numbers of such particles can be determined by a method developed by Backus and Williams (1950). A suspension of Dow polystyrene latex particles of uniform size and of known concentration is mixed in known proportions with a suspension of the virus to be assayed. The mixture is then applied by means of a spray gun to collodion-coated grids to be shadow cast and then viewed with the electron microscope. The droplets must be sufficiently small to permit photographing the residue of an entire droplet. A number of these residues are photographed, and the numbers of polystyrene latex particles and virus particles are counted. The volume of each droplet can be determined from the numbers of latex particles, and virus concentration, in terms of particles/ml, can be easily calculated.

The particle-count method is reliable and is one of the most sensitive assays of plant viruses (Steere, 1955). It can be used with dry-weight values to determine molecular weights. Rochow *et al.* (1955) used the particle-count method in conjunction with the local-lesion method and found the two methods in agreement with respect to determining the amount of potato virus X in doubly infected plants (potato viruses X and Y) relative to that in singly infected ones.

4. *Dilution end-point of stream double refraction.*—Stream double refraction (flow birefringence or anisotropy of flow) is exhibited by TMV in purified preparations because the characteristic particles are rod-shaped. The critical dilution of stream double refraction was used by Takahashi and Rawlins (1933, 1935) to demonstrate

differences in virus concentration in different preparations of virus. Lauffer and Stanley (1938) measured the intensity of stream double refraction with a photoelectric cell and attempted to relate intensity of the phenomenon with concentration of virus in different preparations. Unfortunately, values varied among preparations, not so much on the basis of varying concentrations of virus, but because of variations in techniques used in preparing the viral suspensions. Intensity of stream double refraction was significantly influenced by pH, there being an increased intensity as pH was changed from 7.0 to 5.0. Takahashi (1951) suggested that, under these conditions, stream double refraction was a function of particle length, because end-to-end aggregation of viral particles is favored at the lower pH (Takahashi, 1949). Thus, critical dilution of stream double refraction has but limited use as a quantitative assay procedure (Steere, 1955). It can be used as a rapid test for comparing concentration of rod-shaped particles in 2 suspensions, which may even be somewhat impure, provided the same procedure is used for preparing both suspensions and provided the pH is the same in both.

B. CHEMICAL

If a sufficient quantity of starting material is available, highly purified preparations of some viruses can be weighed and the percentage of some chemical constituent can be accurately determined. Then the quantity of 1 or more of these constituents in small samples can be determined and related to total viral protein. For example, the Kjeldahl nitrogen content of a small sample of purified TMV can be determined by microtechniques; since the virus contains 16.6% nitrogen, the Kjeldahl value is multiplied by the factor 6.06 to obtain a quantitative estimate of virus in the preparation.

Lojkin and Beale (1944) used a colorimetric procedure to assay TMV; microquantities of virus were determined on the basis of intensity of the blue color characteristic of the reaction between the Folin phenol reagent and 3 amino acids (tyrosine, tryptophane, and cysteine) present in the virus. Other constituents of viruses that may be used in assay techniques are phosphorus, ribose, arginine, and the purine and pyrimidine bases. Analyses for these components, as well as for those mentioned earlier, are laborious and time-consuming, and accuracy is dependent upon purity of the preparation being assayed. Also, it is necessary to have analytical data from a standard preparation of highly purified virus for comparative purposes.

C. SEROLOGICAL

Studies of antigenic properties of TMV by Purdy (1928) paved the way for extensive research on serological reactions between viral preparations and their immune sera. Serological activity of viral preparations can be demonstrated by 3 basic reactions: (1) precipitin and agglutination reactions, (2) neutralization of the infectivity of the antigen, and (3) complement fixation. All reactions have been used in qualitative assays, and some have proved to be particularly useful in determining taxonomic relationships among viruses and their strains. Most quantitative assays have been made by modified precipitin tests, but complement fixation reactions have also been used.

Six modifications of the precipitin test have been recently described in detail (Ball, 1961). These include the chloroplast agglutination, microprecipitin, ring interface precipitation, and 3 agar diffusion tests. Since the desired reaction occurs only when antigen and antibody are in proper proportions, concentrations of each should be made on the basis of results from a preliminary experiment involving grid titrations of dilutions of both reactants. Results of serological assays are usually expressed in terms of the dilution end-point of the reaction rather than upon weight of the precipitate.

Moorhead and Price (1953) described a serological test for TMV that was based on agglutination of sheep red blood cells in the presence of TMV antigen reacting with its antibodies. The erythrocytes apparently become entangled in the antigen-antibody network and fail to settle in the usual way. Although the method was used primarily to differentiate strains of TMV, a procedure for its use in quantitative assay was suggested. The test is as sensitive as the quantitative precipitin test, and requires but ⅕ as much virus. Although as satisfactory as the more laborious complement fixation test for differentiating strains of TMV, the sheep red cell test was much less sensitive to concentration of virus (Moorhead and Price, 1953).

D. BIOLOGICAL

1. *Qualitative assays using transmission by grafts, dodder, and insects.*—Ability to test for the presence of virus by graft-transmission is the basis for certification of propagative material, e.g., nursery stock and budwood for citrus and other fruit crops. Dodder has proved useful in transmitting certain plant viruses between hosts that may be graft-incompatible. Neither of these methods has been used in quantitative work, and it seems unlikely that they ever will be.

The fact that most plant viruses are insect-transmitted has permitted the development of several assay methods in which insects are used as the agents of inoculation. Some of these methods are qualitative and can be used only in detection and identification of viruses. Other methods, however, are quantitative.

2. *Quantitative biological assays.*—Although the quantitative assay methods thus far discussed have involved measurement of physical, chemical, or serological properties of viruses, quantitative procedures used in biological assay measure infectivity, the property that, by definition, is the true diagnostic of virus. Methods that have been used successfully in quantitative biological assays involve transmission of virus by insects or by mechanical means.

a. *Transmission by insects.* Three procedures have been followed in assays by insect transmission: (1) insects are permitted to become viruliferous by feeding upon diseased plants, (2) insects are allowed to feed through membranes upon virus-containing extracts, and (3) suspensions of virus are injected directly into the insects.

The first procedure has been used by Sylvester (1953) to study, among other subjects, the relative concentration of the *Brassica nigra* virus in mustard plants at intervals after inoculation. Aphids were fasted for 60–155 min, transferred singly to diseased plants for acquisition feeding (10–19 sec), and then moved to test plants for test feeding of 59–133 min. Plants that had been infected 15–20 days contained sufficient virus to permit 46–58% of the aphids to become viruliferous. Only 18–36% of the aphids fed upon plants diseased for 8–14 days became transmitters. There appeared to be a fall in concentration of active virus also at 21 and 22 days after inoculation. Despite a low number of samples within each treatment, reasonably consistent results were obtained when one aphid colony was used to acquire virus from a single source and to inoculate one group of uniform test plants within a 2-hr period (Sylvester, 1953). It is not certain, however, that this method measures relative concentration of active virus. Actually, it provides a qualitative estimate of the availability of virus to the insect; availability may or may not be determined by concentration of active virus in host cells.

Development of the membrane-feeding technique after an early report by Carter (1927) made it possible to assay such viruses as sugar-beet curly-top virus by determining the percentage of viruliferous insects in groups fed on food suspensions containing different dilutions of virus. Similar techniques are available for the study of the aphid-borne barley yellow dwarf virus (Rochow, 1960).

The third method of insect transmission permits determination of the number of infective insects and length of the incubation period in infective insects after their injection with preparations that differ with respect to concentration of virus. This method can be used with leafhoppers (Black, 1940; Maramorosch, 1952) and with aphids that transmit potato leafroll virus (Day, 1955; Heinze, 1955; Mueller and Ross, 1961) and those that transmit barley yellow dwarf virus (Mueller and Rochow, 1961). Perhaps the most extensive assay work by the insect-injection method was that of Brakke *et al.* (1954) with clover wound-tumor virus. Relative concentrations of virus in tumor and stem tissues and in the insects were determined and infectivity was correlated with characteristic particles observed in electron micrographs of the visible-zone fraction obtained by density-gradient centrifugation.

Few quantitative assays have been made by insect-transmission procedures because the methods are laborious and are subject to variables associated with the insect vector as well as to those contributed by the test plant, the virus itself, and the environment. Procedures involving insects, however, are the only ones available for assaying many of the most important plant viruses.

b. *Transmission by mechanical inoculation.* Of the biological assay methods, those involving mechanical transmission of infectious units have been the most useful. In one of these methods, dependent upon systemic infection, many test plants are inoculated with dilutions of a test preparation and others are inoculated with dilutions of a standard preparation. From the numbers of plants that become infected after inoculation with dilutions of each preparation, it is possible to estimate the concentration of active virus in one relative to that in the other. Holmes (1928), using the pin-prick method of inoculation, found that 1350 Turkish tobacco plants were required to differentiate between a ¼ and a ½ dilution of TMV. Differentiation between a ¼ dilution and dilutions of ¼, ⅛, ¹⁄₁₆, and ¹⁄₆₄, respectively, was possible in 240, 120, 60, and 30 plants. Despite the obvious disadvantage of requiring excessive numbers of test plants, the systemic-infection method is the best one available for the assay of certain viruses.

The second assay procedure based on infections following inoculation by mechanical means was made possible by Holmes' (1929) discovery that TMV induces localized necrotic lesions at sites of inoculation in leaves of certain hosts, notably *Nicotiana glutinosa* L. Holmes noted that the numbers of lesions in inoculated leaves of *N. glutinosa* were inversely correlated with dilution of the inoculum, and he recommended a method for quantitative bioassay of active TMV. This is the basis for the local-lesion assay of plant viruses.

9–3. THE LOCAL-LESION ASSAY

It should be emphasized that numbers of detectable infections at inoculation sites are correlated with infectivity of the inoculum; there may or may not be a concomitant correlation with concentration of total viral nucleoprotein (Bawden, 1950). Success of the local-lesion method depends upon concentration of active virus in the inocula, the kinds of tests used to detect active virus, and the interactions among the several factors that influence the production of lesions in inoculated leaves. Of fundamental importance is the fact that direct proportionality between numbers of lesions and concentration of active virus obtains only within specified limits of viral concentration. This point is amply illustrated by results of experiments on dilution series.

A. THE DILUTION CURVE

The nature of the relationship between numbers of lesions produced by a given inoculum and the concentration of active virus in that inoculum has been a subject for speculation ever since Holmes' (1929) original work on the local-lesion assay. Two major hypotheses have been proposed to explain this relationship.

The first hypothesis is based on the assumption that a single viral particle is capable of initiating an infection in a susceptible part of the host. The probability of obtaining an infection, therefore, would be simply the probability that a particle of active virus enters a susceptible host cell. If an inoculum consisting of a solution that contains n particles of active virus is diluted to a relative concentration x, the probability that an elemental volume, v, of the inoculum contains at least one particle of active virus can be expressed by the term $1 - e^{-vnx}$. If the volume v comes into contact with a susceptible region of the host, then $1 - e^{-vnx}$ is also the theoretical probability of obtaining an infection, or a lesion. The experimentally determined probability of obtaining a lesion can be expressed y/N, where y is the number of local lesions produced and N is the maximum number that could occur in the inoculated leaf or half-leaf. Thus, N represents the total number of susceptible regions in the inoculated leaf. Equating the experimentally determined probability and the theoretical probability gives

$$y/N = 1 - e^{-vnx}. \qquad (9\text{-}1)$$

A log-log plot of Eq. (9-1) is represented by the solid line in Fig. 9-1 (Price, 1945).

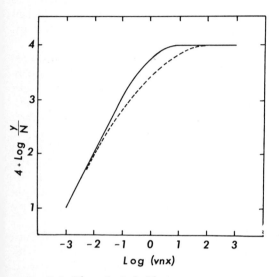

Fig. 9-1. Plot of viral dilution-curve equations based on the hypothesis that a single viral particle is capable of producing an infection in a susceptible portion of the host (Price, 1945). The solid line represents a plot of the basic equation; the broken line represents a plot of the equation as modified by the constant K, which is a measure of departure of data from the basic equation.

The principal characteristics of the curve are the flat portion at high concentrations of active virus, where log (vnx) is greater than zero, and the almost linear portion with unit slope at low concentrations, where log (vnx) is less than approximately −0.5. Data from dilution curves for plant viruses have been fitted to Eq. (9-1) by Youden *et al.* (1935), Bald (1937a,b,c), and others. The applicability of the equation has been discussed in some detail by Lauffer and Price (1945) and by Kleczkowski (1950).

It would be relatively easy to assay viral preparations if all dilution-curve data could be fitted to Eq. (9-1) with reasonable fidelity, since, for moderately dilute inocula,

concentration of active virus would be directly proportional to numbers of lesions. Bald (1937c) soon recognized, however, that many sets of data for plant viruses failed to fit Eq. (9-1) precisely; he suggested a modification of the basic equation to account for these failures. The modified equation may be written

$$y/N = 1 - e^{-(\sqrt{1+4Kvnx}-1)/2K}, \qquad (9\text{-}2)$$

where K is a constant. In this equation, the straight-line portion of the log-log plot is flattened; the broken line in Fig. 9-1 represents a plot in which K has a value of 10 (Price, 1945). The constant K, values for which vary between experiments, should be regarded merely as a measure of the departure of the data from Eq. (9-1). Bald (1937c) pointed out that the constant may correct for aggregation of viral particles in concentrated solutions and for dispersal of aggregates upon dilution. When aggregation occurs, the number of infections is determined by the number of aggregates rather than by the number of particles in the inoculum.

The second hypothesis that has been advanced to account for the slope of the viral dilution curve is based on the assumption that different regions of the host vary in susceptibility in such a way that different minimal amounts of virus are necessary to infect them. Thus, response of a host to inoculation with virus is comparable to response of living cells to various doses of drugs or poisons. This hypothesis was the basis for studies of animal viruses by Bryan and Beard (1940) and of plant viruses by Kleczkowski (1950). It can be expressed in terms of an equation

$$(9\text{-}3)$$

$$y/N = \frac{1}{\lambda\sqrt{2\pi}} \int_{-\infty}^{t} \exp\left\{-\tfrac{1}{2}\left(\frac{t-\xi}{\lambda}\right)^{2}\right\} dt$$

where y is the expected number of infections, N is the mean number of susceptible regions, t is the log of x, x being the actual concentration of virus, ξ is the log of x°, x° being that concentration which causes 50% of the susceptible regions to become infected and λ is the standard deviation

(Kleczkowski, 1950). If log y/N is plotted as a function of $\log\left(\dfrac{(x-\xi)}{\lambda}\right)$, a curve such as the one in Fig. 9–2 will be obtained.

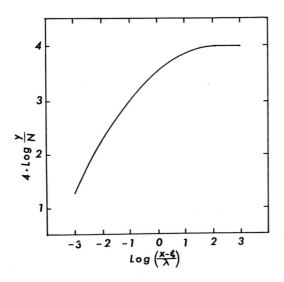

Fig. 9–2. Plot of a viral dilution-curve equation based on the hypothesis that different portions of the host vary in susceptibility such that the minimal amounts of virus required to infect them are normally distributed.

It is unlikely that the shape of the dilution curve will be explained by statistical analyses of existing data or of additional data obtained by present methods of making biological assays. Until techniques have been devised to increase the efficiency of transmission of plant viruses, the problem of the number of viral particles necessary for one infection must also remain unsolved.

B. Assessing Relative Infectivity

Dilutions of each of several inocula to be compared by the local-lesion assay should be such that their lesion counts fall within the straight-line portion of their respective dilution curves. As Best (1937) stated, ". . . that portion of the curves over which direct proportionality between lesion number and virus concentration holds, provides a useful working range in which to estimate relative concentrations with a reasonable degree of accuracy." Every well-conceived local-lesion assay, then, begins with preliminary experiments in which the dilution curve of each inoculum is determined in the test plant or plants. Whatever the explanation for the shape of the dilution curve and regardless of the number of viral particles required to induce an infection, the fact remains that accurate comparisons can be made between 2 properly diluted inocula.

1. *Schemes of inoculation.*—Because results of local-lesion assays may be seriously affected by a variety of factors other than concentration of active virus in the inoculum, experiments must be designed so they test what is meant to be tested, relative infectivity of inocula. The principle on which all bioassays should be based is that the experimental design permits identical treatment of all inocula, except for a single treatment whose effects are expressed by concentration of active virus.

In the first local-lesion assays, Holmes (1929) observed that the numbers of lesions produced by a given inoculum varied among plants and among leaves of the same plant. These variations, repeatedly confirmed, led to inoculation schemes in which each inoculum was rubbed an equal number of times on leaves at each position. Youden and Beale (1934) used a Latin square (Table 9–1), and were able to eliminate errors due to the effect of leaf position. This method, or the randomized complete block design, is satisfactory only when the

TABLE 9–1. A Latin-Square Design for Assaying Relative Infectivities of 6 Inocula[*] in 6 Plants, Each Having 6 Leaves

Leaf Position Number	Plant Number					
	1	2	3	4	5	6
1	A	D	B	E	C	F
2	E	B	D	A	F	C
3	D	A	F	C	E	B
4	C	E	A	F	B	D
5	B	F	C	D	A	E
6	F	C	E	B	D	A

[*] Each letter represents 1 inoculum.

number of inoculable leaves/test plant is as great as the number of inocula. When there are more inocula than leaves, the different inocula can be distributed evenly over the test plants when an incomplete-block design is used (Youden, 1937a,b). Treatments are distributed over the test plants in the form of a rectangle, with complete-block replications arranged along the rows or long axis (leaf positions), and with incomplete blocks running along the columns or short axis (plants). Youden (1937a) points out that the design is restricted for use with only certain combinations of block size and number of treatments. Three such combinations are presented in Tables 9–2

TABLE 9–2. MODIFIED INCOMPLETE BLOCK DESIGNS* FOR TESTING 13 ITEMS† IN BLOCKS OF 4 TREATMENTS

A	B	C	D	E	F	G	H	I	J	K	L	M
C	D	E	F	G	H	I	J	K	L	M	A	B
D	E	F	G	H	I	J	K	L	M	A	B	C
H	I	J	K	L	M	A	B	C	D	E	F	G
A	B	C	D	E	F	G	H	I	J	K	L	M
B	E	J	M	F	K	C	I	L	G	A	D	H
C	H	E	I	A	D	K	J	B	M	L	G	F
D	K	L	E	G	J	I	A	F	B	M	H	C

* Presented by Youden (1937a).

† If the number of items is just short of the requisite number, certain ones may be repeated. The blocks are so arranged that the treatments appear in the form of 4 replications in the horizontal rows.

and 9–3. Local-lesion assay data obtained from experiments in which randomized complete- or incomplete-block designs are used can be subjected to the analysis of variance to determine significance of differences among lesion numbers produced by different inocula. This analysis, with its 1 experimental error term, is unjust when several test inocula differ greatly from the

others. Youden and Beale (1934) recommended that the data obtained from the greatly different samples be segregated and analyzed separately. A better statistical practice would be to make the variance for low numbers of lesions the same as that for high numbers by transforming lesion numbers to log $(x + c)$, where x is the number of lesions and c is a constant (Kleczkowski, 1949). This transformation is discussed in the section on accuracy of the local-lesion method.

Although leaf position greatly influences numbers of lesions produced by a particular preparation, Samuel and Bald (1933) noted that practically the same number of lesions occurred in opposite halves of the same leaf inoculated with the same preparation. This led to development of the half-leaf method of assay. One procedure for using this method involves inoculation of half of each leaf with a standard; the other half of each leaf is then inoculated with a test inoculum. Youden and Beale (1934) pointed out that needless repetition of the standard reference treatment could be avoided by using an experimental design in which each inoculum appears an equal number of times at each half-leaf position.

The half-leaf method is probably the best one for use in local-lesion assays. Its reliability depends upon a design in which the experiment is balanced with respect to leaf position, half-leaf position, order of applying inocula to the different test plants, time of rinsing after inoculation, etc. Useful schemes have been devised for assays by the half-leaf method when test plants have 2 paired leaves (Spencer and Price, 1943), when they have several alternate leaves on 1 stem (Rochow, 1959), and when they have alternate leaves on several branches of each plant (Ross, 1953). Tables 9–4,

TABLE 9–3. MODIFIED INCOMPLETE BLOCK DESIGN FOR TESTING 21 ITEMS IN BLOCKS OF 5 TREATMENTS*

A	B	C	D	E	F	G	H	I	J	K	L	M	N	O	P	Q	R	S	T	U
D	E	F	G	H	I	J	K	L	M	N	O	P	Q	R	S	T	U	A	B	C
E	F	G	H	I	J	K	L	M	N	O	P	Q	R	S	T	U	A	B	C	D
J	K	L	M	N	O	P	Q	R	S	T	U	A	B	C	D	E	F	G	H	I
L	M	N	O	P	Q	R	S	T	U	A	B	C	D	E	F	G	H	I	J	K

* In one experiment, the 21 items were made up of 7 concentrations of TMV; each was prepared in 3 diluents (Youden, 1937a).

9–5, and 9–6 illustrate ways in which variations in lesion counts can be minimized.

TABLE 9–4. A BALANCED SCHEME OF INOCULATION FOR USE BY THE HALF-LEAF METHOD OF LOCAL-LESION ASSAY IN TEST PLANTS THAT HAVE OPPOSITE PRIMARY LEAVES[*]

Half-Leaf Position	Plant 1		Plant 2		Plant 3	
	L	R	L	R	L	R
Pots 1–3						
Leaf position 1	A	B	A	C	A	D
Leaf position 2	C	D	B	D	B	C
Pots 4–6						
Leaf position 1	B	A	C	A	D	A
Leaf position 2	D	C	D	B	C	B

[*] Each inoculum, represented by a capital letter, appears in each half-leaf position an equal number of times and is paired with every other inoculum an equal number of times. The scheme used to inoculate plants in pots 1–3 and 4–6 is repeated in plants in 2 additional 3-pot batches. The orders of inoculation recommended for plants in batches 1, 2, 3, and 4, respectively, are ABCD, BDAC, CADB, and DCBA.

TABLE 9–5. A BALANCED SCHEME OF INOCULATION FOR USE BY THE HALF-LEAF METHOD OF LOCAL-LESION ASSAY IN PLANTS HAVING SEVERAL ALTERNATE LEAVES SUITABLE FOR INOCULATION[*]

Leaf Position	Plant Number[†]											
	1		2		3		4		5		6	
	L	R	L	R	L	R	L	R	L	R	L	R
6	A	B	C	B	B	C	A	D	C	A	D	B
5	C	D	A	B	D	A	C	B	D	B	C	A
4	B	C	D	A	A	C	D	B	B	A	D	C
3	D	A	B	C	B	D	C	A	D	C	B	A
2	A	C	B	D	A	D	D	C	C	B	A	D
1	B	D	A	C	C	B	B	A	A	D	C	B

[*] A scheme used by Rochow (1959) to assay brome mosaic virus in *Chenopodium hybridum.* Capital letters represent the 4 inocula that were applied equally to left (L) and right (R) half-leaf positions.

[†] The design shown was reversed for plants 7–12. Plants were divided into 4 batches of 3 plants. Orders of inoculation for plants in the respective groups were: ABCD, DCBA, CADB, and BDAC. Plants in each group were rinsed immediately after their inoculation.

TABLE 9–6. A BALANCED SCHEME OF INOCULATION FOR USE BY THE HALF-LEAF METHOD OF LOCAL-LESION ASSAY IN PLANTS HAVING SUITABLE LEAVES ON DIFFERENT BRANCHES[*]

Leaf Position	Plant Number		1		2		3	
	Branch Number		1	2	1	2	1	2
6			A B	C D	C A	D B	B G	A D
			3	3	1	1	2	2
5			D C	B A	B D	A C	D A	C B
			3	3	1	1	2	2
4			B D	A C	D A	C B	A B	C D
			2	2	3	3	1	1
3			B C	A D	A B	C D	C A	D B
			1	1	2	2	3	3
2			C A	D B	B C	A D	D C	B A
			2	2	3	3	1	1
1			D A	C B	D C	B A	A B	D A
			1	1	2	2	3	3

Plant Number	Scheme	Order of Inoculation
1–3	as shown	ABCD
4–6	leaf-halves reversed	DCBA
7–9	as shown	CADB
10–12	as for plants 4–6	BDAC

[*] Used by Ross (1953) to assay potato virus Y in *Physalis floridana.* Capital letters representing different inocula are presented as they appear on left and right leaf-half positions. Numbers below the letters indicate the sequence of inoculation after renewal of inoculum on the pad. Each batch of 3 plants should be rinsed immediately after inoculation.

Several useful test plants have opposite leaves, and the experience has been that a given inoculum produces about as many lesions in one leaf of a pair as in the leaf opposite it. Rochow *et al.* (1955) used an opposite-leaf scheme (Table 9–7) to assay

TABLE 9–7. A BALANCED SCHEME OF INOCULATION FOR LOCAL-LESION ASSAYS BY THE OPPOSITE-LEAF METHOD[*]

Leaf Position	Plant Number					
	1	2	3	4	5	6
4	B A	B C	A C	D C	A D	D B
3	C D	D A	B D	A B	C B	C A
2	A C	A B	C B	B D	D C	A D
1	D B	C D	D A	C A	B A	B C

Scheme for plants 7–12 was the reverse of that shown.

[*] Used by Rochow *et al.* (1955) to assay potato virus X in *Gomphrena globosa*. Letters represent the 4 inocula, each of which was applied to 1 opposite-leaf position as shown. Plants were inoculated in groups of 6 and rinsed; order of inoculation was reversed in the second group of plants. Each leaf was rubbed 6 times, and inoculum was renewed on the pad after 2 leaves had been inoculated.

potato virus X in *Gomphrena globosa* L. In test plants with compound leaves that bear opposite leaflets, inoculation schemes have been used in which different inocula were compared in opposite leaflets (Corbett, 1961; Roberts and Corbett, 1961).

2. *Test plants for local-lesion assays.*— From the preceding discussions of the dilution curve and of schemes of inoculation, the false impression might have been gained that local-lesion assay procedures are applicable to all mechanically transmissible plant viruses.

a. *Local-lesion hosts.* Although theoretically possible, the fact is that only a few such viruses have been studied quantitatively by the local-lesion method. The explanation is simple: satisfactory local-lesion hosts have not been found for many plant viruses. The search should continue, and, however important "basic" studies may be, they should never be allowed to eclipse the less spectacular studies of local-lesion host range, tedious and dull as these searches may seem at times. Actually, less than a dozen

species of test plants have been used to any extent, and only 15–20 of the 400-odd plant viruses have been subjected to quantitative assay. As new local-lesion hosts are discovered, their usefulness in quantitative work should be determined experimentally.

b. *Starch-iodine lesions.* Failure to find a hypersensitive host need not preclude the possibility of making biological assays on the basis of numbers of infections at the points of inoculation. Holmes (1931) observed that indistinct yellowish spots sometimes developed in TMV-inoculated leaves of *Nicotiana tabacum* L. These spots were unreliable indicators of infection points, because they were not detectable under all conditions. When inoculated leaves were cleared in 95% ethanol and subsequently stained in a solution of I_2 and KI (10g I_2, 30g KI, 1500 ml H_2O), however, the infection points were made conspicuous as a result of the starch-iodine blue color reaction. When leaves were taken from plants in the afternoon, decolorized overnight, and then treated with iodine, infection points stained less deeply than the surrounding tissue. When plants were kept in the dark for several hr before leaves were harvested and then treated as described above, infection points stained darker than surrounding tissue (Holmes, 1931). These reactions are based on the fact that virus decreases the rate of carbohydrate synthesis in photosynthesizing tissues and also decreases the rate at which carbohydrate moves out of tissues kept in the dark (Bawden, 1950). Intensity of the starch-iodine color reaction varies widely, depending upon environmental conditions, and the method is usually less dependable than the local-lesion method. Under standardized conditions, however, the starch-iodine lesion method can be used with considerable accuracy. It was used by Rochow (1956) to demonstrate interference between TMV and cucumber viruses 3 and 4 in cucumber cotyledons. The starch lesion assay of TMV in cucumber cotyledons was refined by Lindner *et al.* (1959), who found it to be a sensitive method under standardized conditions.

3. *Accuracy of the local-lesion method.*— Knowledge of the dilution curve and use of appropriate schemes of inoculation make

203

possible reasonably accurate determination of relative active virus concentrations in 2 or more preparations. As Bawden (1950) has pointed out, however, no great emphasis should be placed on differences in lesion numbers until standard errors have been determined. Regrettably, too few experiments have been conducted to determine the accuracy of the local-lesion method as it applies to a given virus-host interaction tested by a particular inoculation scheme under certain environmental conditions.

When the half-leaf method was used in 40–50 leaves of bean, *Phaseolus vulgaris* L., var. Early Golden Cluster, a 10% difference was detected between 2 preparations of crystalline TMV at concentrations near 10^{-6} g/ml; when *N. glutinosa* was used as the test plant, however, or when different concentrations of virus were tested, differences in viral concentration of 20% were detected consistently (Loring, 1937). Only one dilution of each of 2 preparations was tested in each of these experiments; thus, only a single point on the dilution curve was used. In practice, many workers have determined accuracy to within 20% using only one dilution of the test inoculum. Because the slope of the dilution curve varies, however, reliability of experiments to determine accuracy of the local-lesion method is enhanced when 2 dilutions of each of 2 inocula are assayed (Spencer and Price, 1943; Price and Spencer, 1943a). This permits consideration of slope of the dilution curves in the analyses. The procedure recommended by Spencer and Price (1943) calls for application of both dilutions of each of the 2 preparations (differing in concentration by a known amount) to the 4 half-leaves of a single bean plant. Usually, 3 plants were grown in a 4-in pot, and 12–24 pots of plants were required for each assay. Best results were obtained when inocula were diluted so that 15–35 lesions were formed in each leaf. Log ratios of potencies (infectivities) were calculated from the formula below (Bliss and Marks, 1939a,b):

$$\log M = \frac{dI\Sigma x^2}{bN}. \quad (9\text{-}4)$$

In this equation, recommended for use with an even number of dilutions, log M is the log ratio of the potencies, d is a factor for difference in concentration between the 2 test inocula, I is the log interval between the dilutions, N is the number of dilutions, x is the factorial coefficient for slope, and b is the slope of the dilution curve. Spencer and Price (1943), using the 2-dilution procedure, consistently detected differences of only 10% between TMV preparations. Errors of only 11, 14, and 18% were obtained in similar experiments with, respectively, tobacco necrosis, tobacco ringspot, and alfalfa mosaic viruses (Price and Spencer, 1943a). With southern bean mosaic virus, Price (1945) found 10–15% errors in the method.

Later, Price and Spencer (1943b) found that the standard deviation of the log ratio of potencies is a reliable measure of experimental error. The standard deviation was in good agreement with true errors of estimate for tobacco mosaic, tobacco necrosis, and tobacco ringspot viruses, but not for alfalfa mosaic virus. The equation that was used can be expressed

$$S_{\log M} = \frac{KI}{B^2}\sqrt{B^2 V_D + D^2 V_B}, \quad (9\text{-}5)$$

in which $S_{\log M}$ is the standard deviation, K is a constant determined from the number of dilutions, I is the log interval between dilutions, B is the factor for slope, D is a factor for difference in concentration between the 2 inocula, V_D is the variance for difference, and V_B is the variance for slope.

Another formula used in calculating relative infectivities of 2 inocula is one proposed for calculating percentage potencies in assays of drugs (Sherwood, 1947). Two dilutions of a "standard" (S) and 2 of an "unknown" (U) preparation are used to inoculate plants in a scheme similar to one of those described above. Data are substituted in the formula

$$(9\text{-}6)$$

Percentage potency $=$ Antilog

$$\left[(2 \pm c) + \left(d \frac{(U_2 + U_1) - (S_2 + S_1)}{(U_2 + S_2) - (U_1 + S_1)} \right) \right]$$

where 2, the logarithm of 100, is the factor

for converting the ratio to percentage, c is the logarithm of the dilution interval between U and S, d is the logarithm of the dilution interval between S_1 and S_2 or between U_1 and U_2, and S_1, S_2, U_1, and U_2, respectively, are logarithms of lesion totals for S_1, S_2, U_1, and U_2. In this formula, as well as in the one suggested by Bliss and Marks and used by Spencer and Price, lesion numbers are converted to logarithms and consideration is given to factors for difference and for slope.

In analyses of local-lesion data by Eqs. (9–4), (9–5), or (9–6), lesion numbers were transformed to their logarithms before calculations were made. Although concentration of active virus is more closely related to logarithms of lesion numbers than to the numbers themselves, distribution around the means is skew, whichever statistic is used. Bawden (1950) points out that statistical analyses are based on the assumption that the variant is normally distributed around its mean; consequently, neither lesion numbers nor their logarithms are entirely satisfactory for statistical analyses. Kleczkowski (1949, 1955) suggested transformations that render standard deviations independent of means. One, for use when 10 or more lesions are produced in the inoculated unit (Kleczkowski, 1949), was expressed by the formula

$$z = \log\ (x + c), \qquad (9\text{–}7)$$

where x is lesion numbers and c is a constant. The value for c is determined by plotting standard deviations against means and extrapolating the regression line to the abscissa; c is read at the point of intersection. When fewer than 10 lesions/inoculated unit are produced, the formula

$$z = \log\ \tfrac{1}{2}\ (x + c + \sqrt{x^2 + 2\,cx}) \qquad (9\text{–}8)$$

has been suggested (Kleczkowski, 1955). Although Eq. (9–8) is satisfactory from the mathematical viewpoint, average lesion counts lower than 10 indicate that one might not be working within the straight-line portion of the dilution curve. When this occurs, no statistical transformation can properly relate lesion numbers to concentration of active virus in the inoculum. Equation (9–7), however, has been used

successfully (Kleczkowski, 1949; Fry and Taylor, 1954) in experiments where lesions/inoculated unit were greater than 10. The value for c was 12 when the half-leaf method was used to assay TMV in bean, tobacco, and *N. glutinosa;* its value was 21 in assays by the whole-leaf method in bean (Fry and Taylor, 1954).

Irrespective of the method of analysis, local-lesion assays usually do not differentiate between preparations unless their concentrations vary by 10–20%; no greater accuracy is required, however, in most experiments. Significant improvement in accuracy is not anticipated until it is possible to control biological, environmental, and technical factors that so greatly influence the numbers of lesions produced in a given test plant species by a single inoculum.

C. Factors Influencing the Local-lesion Assay

Accuracy of the local-lesion method can be improved through the application of statistical procedures, but gains are limited by ability to control the several factors, other than concentration of infective virus, that influence the number of lesions produced by a preparation. Some of these factors have already been mentioned; those relating to test plants, test inocula, environment, and experimental procedures will be discussed briefly in this section.

1. *The test plant.*—Choice of a local-lesion assay plant may affect results of basic studies of plant viruses. For example, Chessin (1951) assayed TMV purified from normal and from nitrogen-deficient plants, and used both bean and *N. glutinosa* as assay hosts. In 3 tests, activity of virus from nitrogen-deficient plants, as assayed in bean, was 32.5, 24.0, and 42.5% of that of virus from normal plants. When 4 assays were made in *N. glutinosa*, however, corresponding figures were 84.8, 47.2, 78.0, and 100.0%. Thus, conflicting results were obtained when different test plants were used in the assay of identical preparations.

Balanced inoculation schemes and the half-leaf method have already been recommended to compensate for the fact that different numbers of lesions are produced by a single preparation in different leaves of the same plant. The inherent variability among leaves may also be reduced by pre-inoculation removal of the growing tip and all leaves except those to be inoculated (Youden and Beale, 1934). When tobacco etch virus was assayed in *Physalis peruviana*, however, decapitation of test plants had no effect on production of local lesions; it hastened the development of systemic necroses, and, for that reason, the procedure was discontinued (Holmes, 1942). It is not known whether decapitation would be undesirable in other test plants in which virus moves systemically, nor is decapitation known to be of benefit in all test plants in which virus does not move systemically.

Genetic variations among individual test plants can be overcome by the use of pure lines, but variations among leaves may contribute to serious inaccuracies even when the half-leaf or the opposite-leaf method is used in a balanced design in uniform test plants. Since consistent results are expected only in leaves of the same age, it may be well to use only 3 or 4 leaves of a test plant that bears as many as 6–8 leaves apparently suitable for inoculation. Paul (1954) reported that leaves at the 3d and 4th nodes of *Gomphrena globosa* were more suitable for quantitative work with potato virus X than were leaves at nodes 1 and 2 or 5 and 6. Using selected lines of plants, however, Rochow *et al.* (1955) obtained highly satisfactory results in leaves at 4 nodes. Undoubtedly, the test plants were grown under different environmental conditions, making different the physiological state of the leaves used in the 2 experiments.

2. *Environment.*—Because environment strikingly influences the establishment and development of virus in test plants, it is of considerable importance in the local-lesion method of assay. What is pertinent to this subject, however, is the standardization of environmental influences and not so much the intrinsic effects of environment upon infection. Accurate assays are possible when the investigator is congnizant of environmental effects and when he performs assays under controlled conditions. Adequate reviews of environmental influences on infection by viruses have been published by Bawden and Pirie (1952), Kassanis (1957),

Yarwood (1957), and Harrison (1959); only a few facets of the subject will be considered here.

a. *Light.* Samuel *et al.* (1935) observed that the apparent susceptibility of test plants increased after several days of cloudy weather; also, more local lesions were produced in plants kept indoors at low light intensity for 24 hr before inoculation than in plants kept in the greenhouse. Bawden and Roberts (1947, 1948) found that preinoculation shading of test-plant leaves resulted in formation of 5–10 times as many lesions as in leaves that had not been shaded. Shading apparently did not increase the fragility of leaves to the extent that their susceptibility was increased. Other workers have reported that preinoculation darkening increased the numbers of lesions, but this effect has not always been obtained. Matthews (1953a) reported that tobacco necrosis virus produced the most lesions in bean plants that were inoculated in the afternoon, after they had been exposed all day to light in the greenhouse; the fewest lesions were produced in plants inoculated at the end of the night. Matthews' comment was: "The time of inoculation at which most local lesions were produced corresponded approximately to the maximum accumulation of sugars produced by photosynthesis; this renders unlikely a suggestion made by Bawden and Roberts (1948) that, during photosynthesis, products accumulate which tend to inhibit local lesion production." In later experiments, Matthews (1953b) found that lesion numbers were doubled in previously darkened (18–19 hr) plants that were exposed to light with intensity of 800 ft-c for 1 min immediately before inoculation. He suggested that susceptibility might be increased by some early product of photosynthesis.

This interpretation is not in disagreement with the suggestion made by Bawden and Roberts (1948), since it is possible that products formed early in photosynthesis and those produced after continued photosynthesis would affect viral replication differently. Matthews (1953b) kept bean plants at $69 \pm 0.5°F$ and $70 \pm 5\%$ relative humidity and exposed them to the following 4 treatments before and after inoculation with tobacco necrosis virus: (1) continuous light (13–25 ft-c) before and after inoculation, (2) darkness before and after inoculation, (3) light before, dark after inoculation, and (4) dark before, light after inoculation. In general, most lesions formed when plants were inoculated 6 hr after the start of the experiment. After that time, lesion numbers decreased until in plants inoculated 21 hr after the experiment had begun, lesion numbers again increased some. The influence of treatments varied widely with time. For example, plants illuminated before and after inoculation had significantly more lesions than those kept in the dark when inoculation occurred 6 hr after the start of the experiment. When test plants were inoculated 21 hr after treatment, however, the opposite relation obtained. In most instances, lesion numbers were not significantly influenced by the 4 treatments. This might be expected, because the light intensity used to illuminate treated plants was only 13–25 ft-c. The experiment compared darkened plants with plants that were, in effect, shaded. It would be of interest to know the influence of light at 500–1000 ft-c in a similar experiment.

Experience indicates that attempts to increase lesion numbers by light and dark treatments may meet with success or failure, depending upon the virus-host combination and upon environmental factors other than light. Of these factors, temperature is of prime importance.

b. *Temperature.* Kassanis (1957) considers temperature more important than light or nutrition as a factor influencing the number of lesions produced in test plants. In the development of a local-lesion assay procedure, the essential point is that, depending upon the virus and host, there may be more local lesions formed as temperature increases or there may be more infections as temperature decreases (Harrison, 1956). Within reasonable limits, it matters little at what temperature plants are kept during local-lesion assays, as long as all plants in the experiment are kept at the same temperature.

There are a number of reports that increased numbers of lesions formed in leaves that were heated before or after inocula-

tion. When *N. glutinosa* and bean plants were kept at 35°C for a day or so, their susceptibility to tobacco mosaic, tobacco necrosis, and tomato bushy stunt viruses was increased, as judged by numbers of local lesions (Kassanis, 1952). Yarwood (1958) found that lesion counts were doubled or trebled in Pinto bean leaves heated for 30–45 sec at 50°C 5–10 hr after inoculation. He suggested that activation of latent infections by heat might account for the appearance of more lesions in heated leaves than in nonheated controls.

Heat treatments of certain test plants might make otherwise latent infection points visible, and could be of value in local-lesion assays of some viruses. As with light and other environmental factors, though, the first consideration in a local-lesion assay is to maintain all test plants under uniform environmental conditions before and after inoculation.

3. *Inhibitors in the inoculum.*—The presence of unsuspected inhibitors in the inoculum has contributed to erroneous conclusions drawn from results of local-lesion assays. As Bawden (1954) states, "Failure to appreciate that it is usual rather than exceptional for the infectivity of an inoculum to depend as much on the nature of its other components as on the concentration of virus particles, has led to many mistaken interpretations of transmission experiments with plant viruses." Most local-lesion assays are made with dilutions of crude or clarified juice, and not with purified preparations of virus; results of many assays, then, are suspect until the possibility that inhibitors occurred in the inoculum has been ruled out. The literature on inhibition of infection by plant viruses has been reviewed by Bawden (1954). It suffices here to say that, in assays of nonpurified preparations, the interference by inhibitors can usually be escaped by dilution of the crude inoculum. When much dilution is required, one or more special treatments to increase lesion numbers may prove useful.

4. *Methods of inoculation.*—Thornberry (1935) observed that nonpurified preparations of TMV produced more local lesions when diluted in phosphate buffers than when diluted in water. Since that time,

other buffers and miscellaneous chemicals (Yarwood, 1957) have been found to increase numbers of local lesions. Samuel *et al.* (1935) showed that optimum concentration of neutral phosphate buffer was 0.05–0.2 M for use with TMV. They also discovered that tomato bushy stunt virus was inactivated by dilution in oxidizing agents but was preserved by certain reducing agents. In preparing inocula for assay, crude or clarified juice is usually diluted in buffer or another diluent, but with some viruses, considerable infectivity is lost before buffer can be added. Fezer and Ross (1959), for example, recommend that source plant tissue containing alfalfa mosaic virus should be bathed in 0.01 M neutral phosphate buffer while being ground in a mortar and pestle. A given buffer or other diluent may be beneficial to the assay of some viruses but deleterious in other instances. The effects of diluents, therefore, should always be determined during development of an assay procedure. Whatever the method of extracting and diluting preparations to be assayed for virus, the inoculum should be applied as soon as possible to test plants that have been selected for uniformity as to age, size, and physiological condition. Plants probably should be trimmed so that the only leaves remaining are those to be inoculated according to an appropriate experimental design.

Most workers dust leaves to be inoculated lightly and evenly with an abrasive, Carborundum (Rawlins and Tompkins, 1936) perhaps being the most popular. Using Celite as the abrasive, Kalmus and Kassanis (1945) found that leaves regained resistance to virus within 3 hr after rubbing, but breaks in the cuticle were not repaired for days. This indicates that the abrasive increased the number of infections only when virus was applied before wounds in epidermal cells could heal.

Costa (1944) found 500-mesh Carborundum superior to other grades, but Behara *et al.* (1956) obtained evidence that the number of particles and not the size of particles (240- to 800-mesh) was important. The abrasive may be applied to the leaves or mixed with the inoculum (Costa, 1944). Use of abrasives increases numbers of infec-

tions but does not insure accurate assays. Some workers routinely conduct assays without them, wounding as a result of rubbing the leaf surface being sufficient for introduction of virus into susceptible cells.

Inoculum should be applied evenly to leaves of test plants. Holmes (1929) used cloth pads saturated with inoculum to rub leaves of *N. glutinosa,* whereas Samuel (1931) used the thumb or finger or a glass spatula to apply the inoculum. Takahashi (1956) used stiff-bristled artist's brushes. The essential point is that the inoculum should be applied to each leaf in exactly the same manner. For example, when cloth pads are used, the inoculum should be renewed on the pad regularly, and each leaf or half-leaf should be rubbed with the same number of strokes and with the same pressure. During inoculation, most workers support the leaf with the palm of one hand, but others use a stiff card.

Rinsing inoculated leaves may increase local-lesion numbers (Holmes, 1929), may have no effect, or may even decrease the numbers of lesions, as when phosphate buffer is used as the diluent (Yarwood, 1952). Certainly no benefit would be expected from postinoculation rinsing when purified preparations are used as inocula; when nonpurified preparations are used, or when water is the diluent (Yarwood, 1952), rinsing may result in an increase in lesion numbers.

In local-lesion assays, each method must be used in such a way that its effect will be uniform throughout. Since uniformity is difficult to achieve, no unnecessary procedure should be adopted. Thus, if rinsing after inoculation and use of an abrasive do not increase accuracy of the method, they should not be used.

9–4. DISCUSSION

Because viruses are infective entities, the only direct methods for their assay are those that measure detectable infections. Of these biological methods, the local-lesion assay is by far the most useful. Properly designed assay experiments permit detection of differences of approximately 10% in concentration of active virus in 2 inocula.

LOCAL-LESION ASSAY

Results of local-lesion assays must be cautiously interpreted, since the number of infections obtained with a given preparation may depend as much on other components of the preparation as on the amount of virus that is present. Numbers of infections are also influenced by environmental factors and by the methods used to inoculate test plants. In practice, however, it is possible to minimize experimental errors by preliminary testing of carefully selected test plants and through the use of completely balanced experimental designs and standardized methods of inoculation.

The test plant selected for local-lesion assay work should provide lesions in numbers sufficient to give reproducible results (Hollings, 1956). The sensitivity of a potential assay host in which few lesions form can often be increased to a level satisfactory for local-lesion assay. Experience has indicated that treatments most likely to increase lesion numbers are the use of phosphate or other buffers as diluents, use of Carborundum or Celite evenly applied to leaves to be inoculated, and manipulation of environment, particularly with respect to light and temperature, before and after inoculation. Every local-lesion assay method should be based on preliminary experiments in which the dilution curve (Best, 1937; Youden, 1937b) is determined and accuracy of a recommended experimental design (Samuel and Bald, 1933; Youden and Beale, 1934) is assessed (Spencer and Price, 1943). The work of Ross (1953) on the use of *Physalis floridana* as an assay host for potato virus Y illustrates the kind of experimentation that is fundamental to reliable local-lesion assays. Takahashi (1956) increased the sensitivity of TMV assays in *N. glutinosa* 1200–1400 times through the combined use of Carborundum and 0.05 M neutral phosphate buffer, but whether increased sensitivity was accompanied by increased accuracy was not determined.

Innate sensitivity of the test plant is not nearly so important as reproducibility of results in local-lesion assays designed to determine concentration of active virus in a preparation relative to that in another. Sensitivity is of prime importance, however, in assays for absolute amounts of infective virus. According to Steere (1955), the major problem in the assay of plant viruses is that no positive evidence has been obtained to indicate whether or not a single characteristic particle is also an infectious unit. Statistical analyses of existing data from local-lesion assays neither prove nor disprove the 1 particle-1 infection hypothesis (Lauffer and Price, 1945; Price, 1946; Kleczkowski, 1950). It is unlikely that evidence adequate to test the hypothesis will be obtained until more sensitive hosts have been found, until more skill has been developed in making inoculations, and until environmental factors that increase susceptibility can be determined and controlled (Steere, 1955).

The local-lesion method of assaying plant viruses is insensitive relative to methods used for the assay of bacterial and some animal viruses (Harrison, 1959). In standardized tests by means of the local-lesion assay, however, accurate determinations of the relative infectivities of inocula can be made. Despite its relative insensitivity, the local-lesion assay remains one of the most useful experimental procedures for the study of the nature and properties of plant viruses.

* * *

This work was supported in part by Research Grant AI-03148 from the National Institute of Allergy and Infectious Diseases, National Institutes of Health, U.S. Public Health Service.

9–5. LITERATURE CITED

Backus, R. C., and Williams, R. C. (1950). J. Appl. Physics 21, 11.
Bald, J. G. (1937a). Ann. Appl. Biol. 24, 33.
Bald, J. G. (1937b). Ann. Appl. Biol. 24, 56.
Bald, J. G. (1937c). Australian J. Exp. Biol. Med. Sci. 15, 211.

Ball, Ellen Moorhead. (1961). Serological Tests for the Identification of Plant Viruses. Am. Phytopathol. Soc., Committee on Plant Virology, Plant Pathology Dept., Cornell Univ., Ithaca, N.Y. 16 pp.

Bawden, F. C. (1950). Plant Viruses and Virus Diseases. 3d ed. Chronica Botanica, Waltham, Mass. 335 pp.

Bawden, F. C. (1954). Advan. Virus Res. 2, 31.

Bawden, F. C., and Pirie, N. W. (1952). Ann. Rev. Plant Physiol. 3, 171.

Bawden, F. C., and Roberts, F. M. (1947). Ann. Appl. Biol. 34, 286.

Bawden, F. C., and Roberts, F. M. (1948). Ann. Appl. Biol. 35, 418.

Behara, L., Varzandeh, M., and Thornberry, H. H. (1956). Virology 1, 141.

Best, R. J. (1937). Australian J. Exp. Biol. Med. Sci. 15, 65.

Black, L. M. (1940). Phytopathology 30, 2.

Bliss, C. I., and Marks, H. P. (1939a). Quart. J. Pharm. Pharmacol. 12, 82.

Bliss, C. I., and Marks, H. P. (1939b). Quart. J. Pharm. Pharmacol. 12, 182.

Brakke, M. K., Vatter, A. E., and Black, L. M. (1954). Brookhaven Symp. Biol. 6, 137.

Bryan, W. R., and Beard, J. W. (1940). J. Infect. Diseases 67, 5.

Carter, W. (1927). J. Agr. Res. 34, 449.

Chessin, M. (1951). Phytopathology 41, 235.

Corbett, M. K. (1961). Virology 15, 8.

Costa, A. S. (1944). Phytopathology 34, 288.

Day, M. F. (1955). Australian J. Biol. Sci. 8, 498.

Fezer, K. D., and Ross, A. F. (1959). Phytopathology 49, 529.

Fry, P. R., and Taylor, W. B. (1954). Ann. Appl. Biol. 41, 664.

Harrison, B. D. (1956). Ann. Appl. Biol. 44, 215.

Harrison, B. D. (1959). In Isaacs, A., and Lacey, B. W. (eds.), Virus Growth and Variation. 34. Ninth Symposium Soc. Genl. Microbiol., Cambridge Univ. Press, Cambridge, England.

Heinze, K. (1955). Phytopathol. Z. 25, 103.

Hollings, M. (1956). Plant Pathol. 5, 57.

Holmes, F. O. (1928). Botan. Gaz. 86, 66.

Holmes, F. O. (1929). Botan. Gaz. 87, 39.

Holmes, F. O. (1931). Contrib. Boyce Thompson Inst. 3, 163.

Holmes, F. O. (1942). Phytopathology 32, 1058.

Kalmus, H., and Kassanis, B. (1945). Ann. Appl. Biol. 32, 230.

Kassanis, B. (1952). Ann. Appl. Biol. 39, 358.

Kassanis, B. (1957). Advan. Virus Res. 4, 222.

Kleczkowski, A. (1949). Ann. Appl. Biol. 36, 139.

Kleczkowski, A. (1950). J. Gen. Microbiol. 4, 53.

Kleczkowski, A. (1955). J. Gen. Microbiol. 13, 91.

Lauffer, M. A., and Price, W. C. (1945). Arch. Biochem. 8, 449.

Lauffer, M. A., and Stanley, W. M. (1938). J. Biol. Chem. 123, 507.

Lavin, G. I., and Stanley, W. M. (1937). J. Biol. Chem. 118, 269.

Lindner, R. C., Kirkpatrick, H. C., and Weeks, T. E. (1959). Phytopathology 49, 78.

Lojkin, Mary E., and Beale, Helen Purdy. (1944). Contrib. Boyce Thompson Inst. 13, 337.

Loring, H. S. (1937). J. Biol. Chem. 121, 637.

Maramorosch, K. (1952). Phytopathology 42, 59.

Matthews, R. E. F. (1953a). Ann. Appl. Biol. 40, 377.

Matthews, R. E. F. (1953b). Ann. Appl. Biol. 40, 556.

Moorhead, Ellen L., and Price, W. C. (1953). Phytopathology 43, 73.

Mueller, W. C., and Rochow, W. F. (1961). Virlogy 14, 253.

Mueller, W. C., and Ross, A. F. (1961). Am. Potato J. 38, 249.

Paul, H. L. (1954). Zentr. Bakteriol. Parasitenk., Abt. 2, 108, 7.

Price, W. C. (1945). Am. J. Botany 32, 613.

Price, W. C. (1946). Biometrics Bull. 2, 81.

Price, W. C., and Spencer, E. L. (1943a). Am. J. Botany 30, 340.

Price, W. C., and Spencer, E. L. (1943b). Am. J. Botany 30, 720.

Purdy, Helen A. (1928). J. Exp. Med. 49, 919.

Rawlins, T. E., and Tompkins, C. E. (1936). Phytopathology 26, 578.

Roberts, D. A., and Corbett, M. K. (1961). Phytopathology 51, 831.

Rochow, W. F. (1956). Phytopathology 46, 133.

Rochow, W. F. (1959). Phytopathology 49, 126.

Rochow, W. F. (1960). Virology 12, 223.

Rochow, W. F., Ross, A. F., and Siegel, B. M. (1955). Virology 1, 28.

Ross, A. F. (1953). Phytopathology 43, 1.

Samuel, G. (1931). Ann. Appl. Biol. 18, 494.

Samuel, G., and Bald, J. G. (1933). Ann. Appl. Biol. 20, 70.

Samuel, G., Best, R. J., and Bald, J. G. (1935). Ann. Appl. Biol. 22, 508.

Sherwood, Marion B. (1947). Science 106, 152.

Spencer, E. L., and Price, W. C. (1943). Am. J. Botany 30, 280.

Steere, R. L. (1955). Phytopathology 45, 196.

Sylvester, E. S. (1953). Phytopathology 43, 209.

Takahashi, W. N. (1949). Am. J. Botany 36, 642.

Takahaski, W. N. (1951). Phytopathology 41, 142.

Takahashi, W. N. (1956). Phytopathology 46, 654.

Takahashi, W. N., and Rawlins, T. E. (1933). Science 77, 26.

Takahashi, W. N., and Rawlins, T. E. (1935). Science 81, 299.

Thornberry, H. H. (1935). Phytopathology 25, 618.

Yarwood, C. E. (1952). Phytopathology 42, 137.

Yarwood, C. E. (1957). Advan. Virus Res. 4, 243.

Yarwood, C. E. (1958). Phytopathology 48, 39.

Youden, W. J. (1937a). Contrib. Boyce Thompson Inst. 9, 41.

Youden, W. J. (1937b). Contrib. Boyce Thompson Inst. 9, 49.

Youden, W. J., and Beale, Helen Purdy. (1934). Contrib. Boyce Thompson Inst. 6, 437.

Youden, W. J., Beale, Helen Purdy, and Guthrie, J. D. (1935). Contrib. Boyce Thompson Inst. 7, 37.

R. L. STEERE

Purification

10–1. INTRODUCTION

IT IS ASSUMED that the student or reader is about to attempt the purification of a virus never purified before and that no information whatsoever is available regarding shape or size of the virus or its relationship to any other virus. I will present here, in sequence, the various steps one might use in developing a satisfactory purification procedure. A spectrum of techniques which might be useful at each step will be described.

For additional ideas which may be useful in virus purification, the reader is referred to an earlier review on this same topic (Steere, 1959); to several books on virology (Bawden, 1950; Smith, 1957; Burnett and Stanley, 1959; Lauffer and Smith, 1953 through 1962); and to a large number of books and reports too numerous to list which describe purification procedures for and properties of viruses, proteins, nucleic acids, nucleoproteins, enzymes, and cell particulates.

10–2. HOST SELECTION

As in any experimental work involving host-pathogen interrelationships, it is well for the virologist who intends to obtain a purified virus suspension to examine various hosts or possible hosts with the aim of selecting the best ones for virus production and for the required assays. Virus purifica-

tion has little significance unless infectivity can be specifically associated with the characteristic purified particles.

A. ASSAY HOST

Whenever available, a local-lesion host is desired for assays of the infectiousness of a virus suspension. Sometimes two or more local-lesion hosts can be employed. If so, it behooves the researcher to conduct a sufficient test series to ascertain the relative sensitivities of the different local-lesion hosts under different growing conditions. Adjustment of nutrients, length of day, temperature, or light conditions and method of inoculation can be important in the number and visibility of local lesions produced. Sometimes no local-lesion host is available so a systemic host must be selected for assay work. One must make a choice of the assay host to be used and establish standard conditions to provide the greatest reliability within and between experiments. For a particular project, one may decide not to use the best assay host. Sometimes a slightly less satisfactory host may prove to be more easily grown or possess some other feature which dictates that it be used under the existing conditions.

B. PRODUCTION HOST

In the selection of a production host for a particular virus, one must keep in mind a number of important features. Other things being equal, one wants to use the host which produces the highest concentration of virus per gram of tissue. Some of the other things which might not be equal are: (a) various host components which interfere with the extraction of virus, inactivate or irreversibly precipitate the virus, adsorb to the surface of the virus, have size or physical properties too close to those of the virus to permit good separation; (b) rate of growth; (c) sensitivity to smog or fumigation; (d) susceptibility to other pathogens; and (e) ease of culture.

Another important point to keep in mind is that some viruses reach a peak of concentration (based on infectivity tests) at a certain time after inoculation, then drop to a low level (Black, 1955; Ross, 1941a, 1941b). For maximum recovery of infectious virus, one must harvest at the optimum time. Also, virus content of different tissues may vary considerably (Black, 1955; Stanley, 1939a, 1939b), making it sensible to dissect the plant and use only parts with the highest content of infective virus. Standardization of growing conditions for maximum yield from the production host may prove very worthwhile.

10–3. DETERMINATION OF INITIAL BUFFER

Once a satisfactory production host, a suitable test host, and the proper tissue for maximum virus content have been determined, some decision must be reached as to the appropriate buffer to be used during the maceration of tissues and purification of the virus. It is well to know how stable the virus is to storage in crude juice and in juice diluted with various buffers so that a buffer may be selected which will be most useful for the retention of activity and to prevent aggregation or precipitation of the virus. Attention should be given not only to the ions of the buffer but also to its pH and ionic strength (Diener, 1962; Scott, 1963). Some viruses require the presence of Mg or Ca (Steere, unpublished; Brakke, 1963) for the preservation of intact infectious particles, whereas others can be stored more satisfactorily in very dilute buffers or distilled water from which Mg or Ca have been eliminated (Scott,

1963; Steere, 1963). Some viruses will break up into subunits if the ionic strength of the buffer is reduced below 0.2 M (Steere, unpublished data), whereas others will fall apart as the ionic strength of the buffer in which they are suspended approaches or exceeds 0.2 M (Scott, 1963; Kelley and Kaesberg, 1962). Some viruses are extremely sensitive to high or low pH, whereas others are somewhat insensitive except at the extremes. For some viruses, specific ions are either advantageous (Brakke, 1963) or undesirable (Steere, 1963). Phosphate buffers have been used frequently in the purification and suspension of purified viruses ever since Stanley (Stanley, 1935) reported their use in his procedure for the purification of TMV. We now know that in some instances phosphate buffers are not only less useful than others but instigate aggregation, precipitation, or inactivation of viruses, including TMV (Scott, 1963; Steere, 1963). Therefore, one should not use phosphate buffers indiscriminately but should examine the effect of these and other buffers in preliminary tests on extraction and concentration. It is often important to include some sort of reducing agent such as ascorbic acid, sodium thioglycolate, cysteine hydrochloride, Na_2SO_3, or enzyme inhibitor such as sodium diethyl dithiocarbamate (Fulton, 1959) in the buffer used during maceration of tissues to prevent the loss of virus through oxidation, enzymatic action, or precipitation and to prevent adsorption of colored components to the virus. Additional proteins, including egg white and hide powder, have recently been employed to react with tannins during grinding of tissues infected with cocoa swollen shoot virus (Brunt and Kenten, 1963) and have been useful in the prevention of virus loss due to reaction with tannins. This and similar procedures may be very useful in preservation of other viruses during extraction and purification.

10–4. MACERATION OF INFECTED TISSUES AND JUICE EXTRACTION

The problem of grinding virus-infected plant tissue under the most favorable conditions for preservation of the infective virus presents little problem. Depending upon the availability of equipment and the desired purification procedure, the tissue may be ground, homogenized, squeezed, pressed, or squashed through any one of a number of hand- or motor-operated machines or tools. The various pieces of equipment which have been found more or less satisfactory for this purpose are: (a) blenders, (b) salad choppers, (c) food grinders, (d) juice extractors, (e) mortar and pestle, (f) presses, and (g) roller mills. There appears to be little advantage of one grinding tool over any other except for ease of operation, rapidity of extraction, thoroughness of extraction, and immediate contact of ground tissue with the desired buffer which can be difficult to maintain with some grinding systems. After the tissue has been ground or chopped, large tissue fragments and pulp are customarily removed by squeezing the juice through bandage gauze or cheesecloth or by forcing through cloth or filter paper bags in a special juice extracting centrifuge. The resulting extract, represented diagrammatically in Fig. 10–1, is usually a rather thick suspension of particulates of various sizes suspended in a solvent containing various salts, those from the ground tissues and those of the extracting buffer.

10–5. REMOVAL OF CONTAMINANTS

Having obtained an extract of the infected tissue, one faces the problem of (a) removing all nonvirus particles and undesired salts from the suspension in such a manner that the virus remains dispersed and unaffected in a buffer of known composition, or (b) removing the virus from the suspension and resuspending it in the desired buffer.

For a number of years attempts have been made to develop procedures whereby desired virus particles will remain in suspension throughout the processes involved in purification and concentration without ever being precipitated or closely packed by chemical or physical means. Little is known about what happens as virus particles are packed together tightly, precipitated, or adsorbed to other components as the result of chemical or physical treatments. It is well known, however, that resuspension is sometimes very difficult or impossible (Scott, 1963; Steere, 1956; Bennett, 1935) and that much virus may be lost during clarification after resuspension from pellets or precipitates.

What are the various means by which one can remove the different contaminants from an extract of virus-infected tissue? If we have as our objective the preparation of a monodisperse suspension of infectious virus in distilled water or in a known buffer, we must remove not only all noninfectious particulates but also all salts, sugars, and other soluble materials other than those we want. To do this we must examine the various natural properties of the virus and employ numerous physical or physicochemical procedures which allow separation of particulates on the basis of their natural properties. What are these procedures with which we must work? They are procedures based on the natural laws governing the movement and resistance to movement of

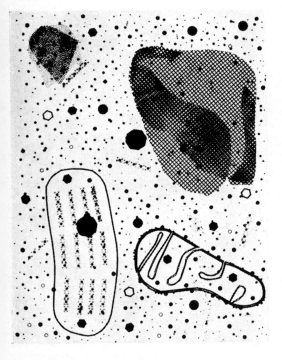

Fig. 10–1. Diagrammatic representation of crude juice extracted through a cloth bag.

suspended particles under the influence of various forces. The forces which one may apply are few in number, but variations in their application, singly or in combinations, are many, and one has a wide selection of applicable procedures from which to choose. Let us first consider the major properties of small suspended particles and the various physical mechanisms by which we may make use of these properties in separating one kind of particle from another or, more precisely, in removing all contaminants from the virus suspension. These properties and the physical or physicochemical mechanism or mechanisms which make use of each property for separation of particulates are shown below.

Property of particulates	Physical mechanism for sorting
1. Size	1. Filtration (Millipore,* Seitz,* and other microfilters, thin agar gel films)
	2. Restricted diffusion filtration (granulated agar gel or Sephadex* columns)
	3. Absorption. Dry agar gel or Sephadex* granules
	4. Sedimentation
2. Shape	1. Restricted diffusion filtration (agar gel or Sephadex* columns)
	2. Sedimentation
	3. Viscosity in density-gradient centrifugation
3. Chemical composition and internal structure "stability"	1. Heat denaturation
	2. Storage under various conditions
	3. Organic solvent denaturation or separation
	4. Ionic strength changes
	5. Changes in pH
	6. Use of specific ions, Ca, Mg, etc.
4. Surface charges	1. Electrophoretic mobility
	2. Isoelectric precipitation
	3. Aggregation
	4. Crystallization
	5. pH gradient electrophoresis
	6. Adsorption
	7. Chromatography
5. Density	1. Sedimentation
	2. Density-gradient separation
	3. Convection sedimentation
6. Color	1. None known
7. Surface configuration	1. Antibody reaction (precipitation)
8. Compressibility	1. Density-gradient centrifugation
9. Differential solubility	1. 2-phase polymer separation systems
	2. Salting-out procedures

* Mention of specific equipment, trade products, or a commercial company throughout this paper does not constitute its endorsement by the U.S. government over similar products or companies not named.

In attempting the purification of a virus for the first time, it is most important that samples be taken after every step in the procedure so that they may be assayed for infectivity to make certain that further efforts at purification are carried out with the appropriate fraction and that a rather high percentage of the virus is preserved.

A. CLARIFICATION OF THE EXTRACT

1. *Low-speed centrifugation.*—Customarily, large debris (large fragments of cells,

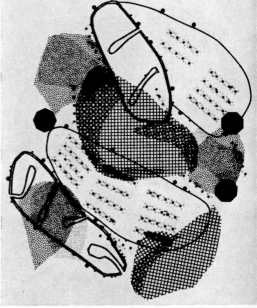

Fig. 10–2. Diagrammatic representation of the components of crude juice which are removed by low-speed centrifugation or filtration to yield a "clarified extract" (Fig. 10–3).

chloroplasts, nuclei, mitochondria, and any other components larger than the virus) (Fig. 10–2) is removed first by centrifuging the extract 10–30 min at 3000–10,000 G. This treatment yields a suspension of small particulates, represented diagrammatically in Fig. 10–3, in which the virus is generally the largest or one of the largest particulates remaining.

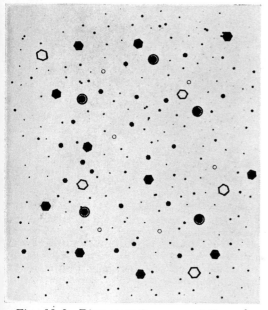

Fig. 10–3. Diagrammatic representation of a clarified extract. Hexagonal particles represent infectious virus—other hexagons represent empty protein shells.

2. *Filtration.*—As an alternate to centrifugal clarification, one might use simple filtration through several layers of filter paper or through fine fritted glass or ceramic filters. The resultant extract would contain essentially the same mixture of particulates as obtained with low-speed centrifugation (Fig. 10–3).

3. *Heating and freezing.*—If the infectivity of the virus is not altered by such treatment, it is sometimes advantageous to heat the crude juice to 50 or 60°C for 5–10 min or to freeze and thaw it before clarification. This causes the denaturation and aggregation of some proteins which are then removed by filtration or low-speed centrifugation. Suspensions resulting from such treatment usually contain less con-taminating material than suspensions obtained by centrifugation or filtration alone.

4. *Filtration with filter aids: charcoal, bentonite, diatomaceous earth, cellulose powder, and Celite.**–Filter aids which remove, in addition to the larger components, many of the small components may be employed in the initial steps for removal of contaminants. A simple procedure involves the addition of 5 gm activated charcoal (Merck 18351)* (Corbett, 1961) per 100 ml of extract (Steere, 1963). The mixture is shaken for ½ min and then 5 gm of diatomaceous earth, Celite*, or High-Flow Super Cell* is added. Shaking is continued for another ½ min and the mixture is poured onto a ¼-in. pad of the same diatomaceous earth in a Buchner funnel. If the diatomaceous earth is not added to the mixture, a thick layer of the large contaminants will soon cover the top of the filter cake and prevent or slow down the filtration of the remaining suspension. The same complication is to be expected with any other filtration procedure unless some fluffy or flocculent material is added to prevent formation of the sludge layer on top of the filter pad. When charcoal, Celite,* bentonite, cellulose powder, or some other filter aid is employed, one can expect the removal of more contaminants than when centrifugation or filtration alone is used. One can often remove all the colored components, some enzymes, and other components if the proper pH and ionic strength are maintained. Under some buffering conditions, one may lose most of the virus on the filter pad. If this happens, a change in the buffer should be tried. With TMV, it is important to use buffers of pH 7.5 or higher to prevent adsorption of the virus to the pad of diatomaceous earth. Ionic strength of 0.1 M or greater must be maintained if complete removal of all color is desired.

5. *Organic solvents: n-Butanol and chloroform (together or alone), ethanol, acetone, and freon.*–Some investigators prefer the use of organic solvents as an initial step in the removal of many contaminants from the virus suspension. Two alternatives to the procedure are employed: (a) The organic solvent is added to the crude juice

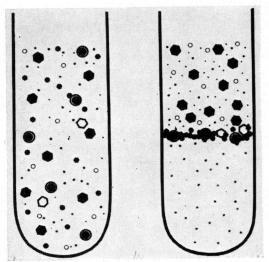

Fig. 10–4a (*left*). Diagrammatic representation of emulsion of clarified juice, n-butanol, and chloroform. All components are thoroughly mixed.

Fig. 10–4b (*right*). Diagrammatic representation of the separation of the emulsion of Fig. 10–5 into aqueous phase (containing the virus) top; interphase (containing precipitate) middle; and solvent phase (containing the chlorophyll) bottom.

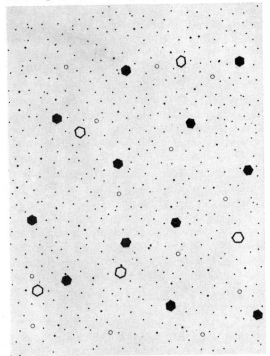

Fig. 10–5. Diagrammatic representation of clarified extract of Chinese cabbage infected with turnip yellow mosaic virus after treatment with ethanol and further centrifugation. Ethanol causes precipitation and removal of some components seen in Fig. 10–3.

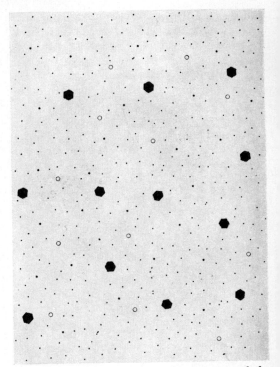

Fig. 10–6. Diagrammatic representation of the aqueous phase of an extract of turnip yellow mosaic-infected tissues. Note that most of the components removed by ethanol have been removed by this treatment and that the empty shells representing "top component" have also been removed (Fig. 10–5).

with rapid stirring to form an emulsion if the right solvents are used (Fig. 10–4a), and (b) buffer and solvent or solvents are mixed in a blender, the motor is started, tissue is added, and liquid is then extracted from the pulp by squeezing through cheesecloth. With either starting procedure, the mixture is often allowed to stand at room temperature, 20–23°C, or at 4°C for 14–20 hr and is then centrifuged at 10,000 G for 10–30 min. With some viruses, immediate centrifugation is employed and with still others the mixture is held at 4° for different periods of time. When emulsions are formed, they can be broken by centrifugation into aqueous phase (which usually contains the virus), interphase (containing mostly denatured proteins), and solvent phase (Fig. 10–4b). Different solvents and different procedures result in various degrees of contaminant removal. When an extract from turnip yellow mosaic virus-infected plants is treated with ethanol, a suspension containing infective nucleoprotein and noninfective protein shells as well as small contaminants is obtained (Fig. 10–5). Using the same starting material and a mixture of equal parts by volume of buffer, n-butanol, chloroform, and infected plant tissue, the final suspension contains infectious nucleoprotein and small contaminants but very few, if any, of the noninfectious protein shells (Fig. 10–6). Other combinations are often satisfactory for viruses which cannot survive treatment with both butanol and chloroform. Unfortunately, however, they usually remove fewer of the undesired contaminants.

B. FURTHER PURIFICATION OF CLARIFIED EXTRACTS

Now that we have a clarified extract, we must decide which of the available procedures could best be used to remove the remaining contaminants. The procedure used will certainly depend upon the properties of the virus and of the contaminants, and one may be forced to do considerable experimental work to find an acceptable procedure.

1. *Gel filtration: Agar, Agarose, Sephadex.*°—Gel filtration is one of the most satisfactory procedures for changing the buffer in a virus suspension; for removal of contaminants smaller than the virus; and for sorting viruses, large molecules, and cellular particulates according to size.

The principle involved in gel filtration, whether the gel involved is Sephadex°, agar, or some other gel, involves a process which might better be called "restricted diffusion filtration."

As shown graphically in Fig. 10–7, particles which are sufficiently large that they cannot enter the pores of the gel granules will flow down through the column around and between the gel granules with the movement of liquid through the column. Particles of another size may be sufficiently small that they can enter the surface pores of the gel by diffusion but sufficiently large that the strands of gel within the matrix offer enough resistance to diffusion that the particles very rarely move further into the gel. A third size of particle may be suffi-

Fig. 10–7. Diagrammatic representation of the principle involved in particle separation by gel filtration columns. Positions of subsequent particles of each size represent positions at equal periods of time. The largest particles are unable to enter pores of the gel and move down between gel grains. Successively smaller particles enter the gel by diffusion and meet less and less restriction to diffusion with a corresponding delay in appearance in effluent liquid.

ciently small that restriction to diffusion is considerably less than for the larger particles. Particles of this size may diffuse further into the gel but may still never reach the center of any gel grains. A series of particles of different sizes in this range may diffuse to different depths. Eventually, a size of particle is reached which is sufficiently small that the gel offers very little restriction to diffusion and we observe what approximates free diffusion within the gel for such particles. Superimposed upon the forces causing restrictive diffusion is the flow of liquid through the column. This exerts a positive flow on particles at any time they are in the free liquid surrounding the gel grains. Also, this positive flow of liquid around the gel grains establishes a positive, though slower, flow through the porous gel.

In Fig. 10–7, the subsequent positions of particles of the different sizes represent equal time distances. The twelfth time position of the large size particle is roughly twice as far down the column as the twelfth

Fig. 10–8. Diagrammatic representation of the sorting of rod-shaped particles through gel columns. If flow rate is sufficiently slow, particles are able to rotate by diffusion and Brownian motion and behave almost like spheres with a diameter equal to the length of the particles.

equal time position of the next largest particle, and four times the equal time position of the smallest particle shown.

In operation a sample sufficiently small that the column can be expected to separate the various components one from another is introduced into the column. As the sample flows into the column, buffer is added and a buffer level maintained above the surface of the packed gel grains. The column is allowed to flow slowly, and volumes equal to that originally placed on the column are collected and examined to determine what constituents of the original they contain.

When working with rod-shaped particles, if one maintains a flow rate sufficiently slow that the particles will rotate as they flow and diffuse through the column, one can then separate rod-shaped particles on the basis of length. Fig. 10–8 shows diagrammatically the separation of 300 mμ rods of tobacco mosaic virus from the 200 mμ and shorter length rods which always appear in purified preparations. By flowing

a TMV preparation through the column slowly enough, the particles behave as though they were spheres approximately equal in diameter to the length of the particle. Therefore, the 300 mμ rods have difficulty penetrating 1% gel made of Ionager #2* which has pore diameters of approximately 250 mμ. The 200 mμ and shorter rods, however, can enter these pores with little difficulty and will be retained in the column somewhat longer than will the 300 mμ particles. This method has been used to sort TMV according to length as shown in Fig. 10–9 (Steere, 1963).

In some instances the buffer most suitable for extraction needs to be eliminated as soon as possible and replaced with another buffer to avoid aggregation or decomposition of the virus. Sometimes enzymes, inhibitors, inactivators, colored components, or precipitating agents are present in the plant juices and are held in check only temporarily by antioxidants, enzyme-inhibitors, or other substances which have been added to the extraction buffer. These must be removed from the suspension as rapidly as possible. If the virus being purified does not adsorb specifically to agar or Sephadex*, one of the easiest and most rapid procedures to accomplish either or both of the tasks is to pass the suspension through a column of granulated 8% agar gel or G75 or G100 Sephadex* (Steere, 1963; Flodin, 1962). Because of their size, all viruses should come off such columns following the free liquid volume, whereas particulates smaller than about 15 mμ in diameter, salts, sugars, and other small molecules, should be delayed on passing through the column and will appear in later fractions of the effluent liquid. Prior to use, the column should be equilibrated with the buffer in which one wishes to have the virus suspended. As much as 200 ml of clarified juice can be passed through a column of 2-in. diameter and 20-in. length. The virus and other particles larger than 15 mμ will come off such a column suspended in the buffer with which the column was equilibrated (Fig. 10–10).

One of the simplest and cheapest instruments for further purification of a clarified virus suspension is a tube filled with granu-

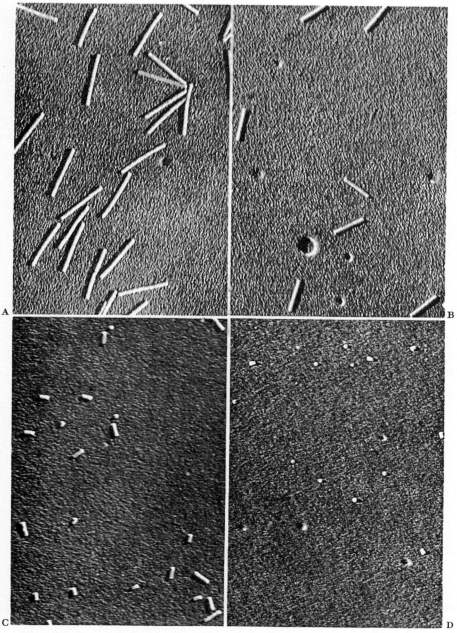

Fig. 10–9. Sorted TMV (Steere, 1963). TMV particles sorted according to length by two passages through agar-gel columns. A and B sorted on 1% agar column from fraction containing few short particles. C and D fraction containing few long particles and sorted by only one passage through 1% agar. Infectivity was found to be associated only with the longer particles (A).

lated agar gel or Sephadex* with pore diameters equal to or greater than the largest dimension of the virus. The procedure is essentially the same as that used with 8% agar gel; but by selecting the proper gel and using a long column, one can sort particles according to size or length and can obtain fractions such as those shown in Fig. 10–11 in which each fraction contains mostly particles of one size or

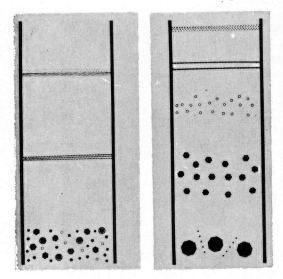

Fig. 10–10 (*left*). Diagrammatic representation of displacement of particulates of different sizes in an 8% agar-gel column. All particulates larger than about 15 mμ would leave column together and are shown near bottom. Smaller particulates are separated according to size.

Fig. 10–11 (*right*). Diagrammatic representation of agar-gel column (5–6%) in which only two components are larger than the gel pore diameter. Note the increased fractionation of particulates over that shown in Fig. 10–10.

length. One can select the best fraction and rerun it to improve the fractionation. This method works well as long as the desired particles do not adsorb to the agar or Sephadex* but do have a size sufficiently different from contaminating particles present in the suspension to be separated from them on the basis of restricted diffusion. For further details on the preparation of these columns see Section 10–9.

2. *Ionic-strength changes and salting-out or crystallization.*—By proper manipulation of the salt concentration, particularly with the addition of rather large quantities (up to 25% saturation with (NH_4)$_2SO_4$) many proteins can be caused to precipitate or to crystallize (Fig. 10–12). The virus, a contaminant, or both, may form the precipitate or the crystals and certain components may be removed with different salt concentrations and at different pH levels or different temperatures. The precipitate or crystals should be resuspended and the various

fractions should be tested for virus content to make certain where the virus is and that infectivity is retained. By proper manipulation of the conditions, a considerable degree of purification can often be obtained with this method. The method has found little use in recent plant virus purification procedures, however, because of the sensitivity of some viruses to the high ionic strengths involved and the difficulties sometimes encountered in dispersing virus from precipitates or dissolving the crystals.

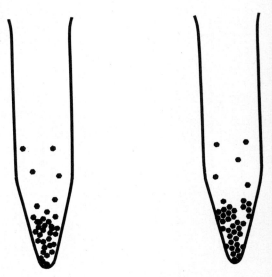

Fig. 10–12. Diagrammatic representation of precipitation (*left*) or crystallization (*right*) of virus or contaminants by salting out or isoelectric precipitation.

3. *Isoelectric precipitation.*—The isoelectric point of a virus or protein is that pH at which there is no net positive or negative surface charge. If the solubility of a particulate is much reduced at its isoelectric point, isoelectric precipitation will generally occur when the pH of a suspension containing that particulate is adjusted to its isoelectric point. A precipitate that forms can be removed by filtration or centrifugation and resuspended in a suitable buffer. Both fractions should be tested for infectivity to find out whether the virus, a contaminant, or both, formed the precipitate. Several ad-

justments of the pH may result in several precipitates. Possible results of this procedure with a virus suspension would be similar to those obtained by salting-out or crystallization. Another method involving the use of NaCl and polyethyleneglycol for the precipitation of viruses (Hebert, 1963; Venekamp and Mosch, 1963) may prove very satisfactory for viruses which can be resuspended after this treatment.

4. *Electrophoresis.*—Many adaptations of electrophoresis (Bier, 1959) may be em-

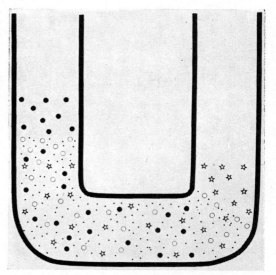

Fig. 10–14. U tube, as in Fig. 10–13, after voltage has been applied for some time. pH of suspension was at isoelectric point of one component (stars).

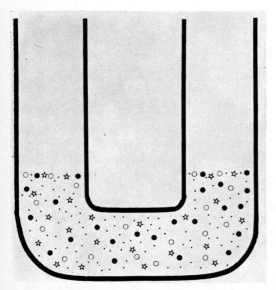

Fig. 10–13. Diagrammatic representation of a U tube containing 4 particulate components before operation.

ployed for further purification of the virus. The major principle involved in these procedures is the movement in an electrical field of suspended particles which have surface charges.

a. *Free or moving boundary electrophoresis.* Free (moving boundary) electrophoresis (Tiselius, 1937) in which the virus suspension is placed in a U tube (Fig. 10–13) may be used. A voltage is applied across the system and, depending on the nature of their net surface charges at the pH used, charged particles move toward the cathode or the anode. After several minutes to several hours of operation during which the sample must be kept cold to reduce convection, one can expect to see separation of

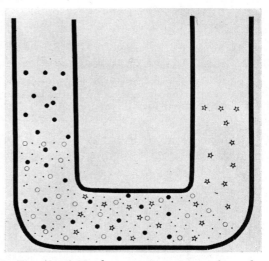

Fig. 10–15. U tube, as in Fig. 10–13, after voltage has been applied for some time. pH of suspension was below isoelectric point of one component (stars) but above isoelectric point of other components.

various components (Figs. 10–14 and 10–15). The separation obtained will depend on the pH of the buffer in which the samples are suspended, the voltage and amperage used, and the isoelectric points and electrophoretic mobilities of the included particles. Provided the particles are stable and remain suspended, each will move toward the cathode when its net charge is positive and toward the anode when its net charge is negative. If suspended in buffer of a pH equal to their own isoelectric point, particulates will remain stationary. It is possible that two different particulates may have the same isoelectric point and electrophoretic mobility. Therefore, even this method may not remove all contaminants from a virus preparation.

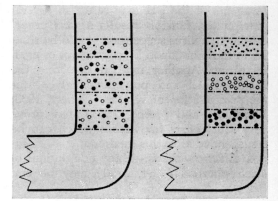

Fig. 10–18a (*left*). One side of U tube set up for pH-gradient electrophoresis before operation. Particulates mixed with buffer of various pH and sucrose to give a pH gradient stabilized by the sucrose gradient.

Fig. 10–18b (*right*). Same as (a) after operation. Particulates of each kind have migrated in both directions to reach isoelectric point.

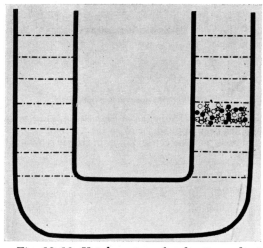

Fig. 10–16. U tube set up for density-gradient electrophoresis. Bands represent layers of sucrose of different concentration before operation.

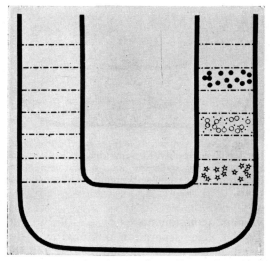

Fig. 10–17. Density-gradient electrophoresis as for Fig. 10–16 but after application of a voltage for several hours. Two components were at isoelectric point (center band) while the pH was above the isoelectric point of a third component and below that of a fourth.

b. *Density-gradient electrophoresis.* A concentrated virus suspension is layered in or on a sucrose gradient (Brakke, 1953, 1955) which has been prepared in the U tube (Fig. 10–16). After several minutes to several hours of operation, the components with different electrophoretic mobilities will have migrated to different zones (Fig. 10–17) and can be removed separately.

c. *pH-gradient electrophoresis.* Another modification for use of electrophoresis involves a gradient system in which the virus suspension is mixed equally throughout (Fig. 10–18a) but in which there is a pH gradient superimposed on the density gradient. The density gradient acts here only to help prevent convection and to stabilize the pH gradient (Kolin, 1955). In operation, each particulate component will move in both directions toward its own isoelectric point in the pH gradient. If the gradient is sufficiently broad and the particles all have different isoelectric points, one will theoretically obtain sharp banding of each component (Fig. 10–18b).

d. *Gel electrophoresis.* Another modification which may prove useful is gel electrophoresis (Consden *et al.,* 1946) in which agar, starch, gelatin, or some synthetic gel rather than a density gradient is employed as the stabilizing agent. Because of the 3-dimensional stability in such systems, it is possible to have the gels in horizontal troughs rather than vertical tubes as required in the above-mentioned methods (Fig. 10–19).

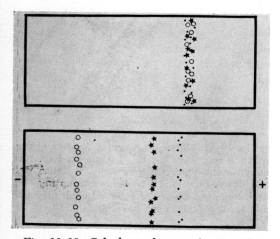

Fig. 10–19. Gel electrophoresis. (a, *upper*) A trough of gel with band of suspension to be separated. (b, *lower*) Same as (a) after application of a potential difference across cells for sufficient time to allow separation into components by migration of components at different rates.

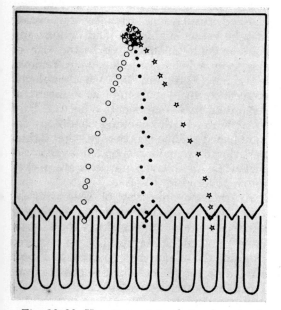

Fig. 10–20. Hanging-curtain electrophoresis. As particulates move down wet curtain from spot where they are applied continually, they are caused to flow straight down or to right or left by their charge and the potential difference applied across the curtain. Samples are collected in tubes.

e. *Hanging-curtain electrophoresis.* In the hanging-curtain procedure, the suspension is applied at one spot near the top of a vertical paper or cellulose curtain and moves downward (Grassmann and Hannig, 1953; DiCastro and San Marco, 1954). The potential difference across the curtain causes the various charged particulates to move toward one side of the curtain or the other as they flow down to the bottom. As various samples reach the bottom of the curtain, which is notched (Fig. 10–20), they drip off into separate tubes from which samples may be tested for activity and purity. Fractions obtained in this manner should be the same ones obtained by density-gradient electrophoresis with the possible exception that some additional separation may take place as a result of the physical properties of the curtain itself.

5. *Chromatography.*—Ion-exchange chromatography can be employed satisfactorily in the purification of viruses. Most likely this procedure involves the same surface charges as those employed in electrophoretic separation, but there may be some additional involvement of the chromatographic medium that will allow separation of some components which would not separate electrophoretically. Also, collection of the fractions may be much simpler. One feature which is often not necessary with other components but which must be kept in mind when using chromatography in virus purification is that the specimen must be kept moist at all times. Also selected solvents, preferably water solutions, must be employed. The object is to establish conditions under which the virus, the contaminants, or both, will adsorb to the column and other conditions where they will elute from the column separately. An ideal situation would be one in which the virus will move on through a column and leave all contaminants adsorbed to it. Some chromatographic work has been accomplished with plant viruses (Ragetli and van der Want, 1954; Shainoff and Lauffer, 1956, 1957), but much more work of this nature needs to be done. This system should prove to be one of the more valuable tools in virus purification as more people make use of various aspects of chromatography.

6. *Two-phase systems.*—Albertsson (Albertsson, 1958; Albertsson and Frick, 1960; Philipson *et al.*, 1960) established the usefulness of the 2-phase system involving large polymers for the concentration and purification of viruses. In this system two or more polymers and specific amounts of salt are mixed with the virus suspension. The mixture then separates by gravity or centrifugation into two phases, one of which contains most of the virus and the other most of the contaminants (Fig. 10–21). Repeated use of such fractionation could result in a concentrated purified virus suspension with only the polymers, which can be removed rapidly with agar gel or Sephadex* columns or by differential centrifugation as contaminants.

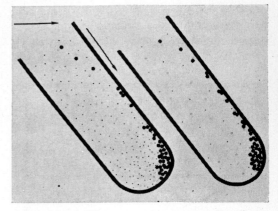

Fig. 10–22. Diagrammatic representation of preparative centrifugation in an angle-head rotor of an ultracentrifuge. Particles move to outer wall and down. Some small particles end up in pellet each time; but by use of repeated centrifuging at selected speeds, they can be diluted out.

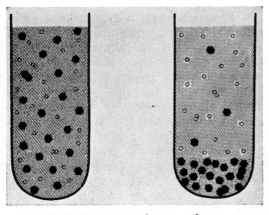

Fig. 10–21. Separation of virus and contaminant and concentration of virus by two-phase system. Most of the virus which is thoroughly mixed with the two polymers (a, *left*) is found in the polymer suspension of smallest volume which results from separation into two phases by centrifuging or gravity.

7. *Ultracentrifugation.*—When ultracentrifugation is employed in the purification of viruses it is used for two purposes: (a) to concentrate the virus, and (b) to separate the virus from the contaminants. Usually 2 or 3 cycles are used involving (a) ultracentrifugation, (b) resuspension of the resulting pellet, and (c) low-speed centrifugation to remove aggregated contaminants. Fig. 10–22 shows diagrammatically what happens in this procedure. The virus and other large particulates are pelleted

with small amounts of the smaller components. After resuspension, much of the non-virus protein of the pellet remains aggregated and can be removed by low-speed centrifugation. A second cycle leaves another fraction of the smaller components still suspended and packs more of the larger contaminants into pellets. The final clarified suspension, after several cycles, may be rather highly purified or may still contain contaminants close to the size of the virus which are difficult to remove. Markham (Markham, 1959) has employed convection in a centrifuge as a means of separating two components otherwise hard to separate. In this method conditions are established which encourage the lighter particles to remain suspended by convection while the heavier particles are packed into a pellet (Fig. 10–23).

Another possible way of separating by centrifugation particles which are otherwise hard to separate is to centrifuge for a longer period and at higher speed than required to pack the majority of particles of both kinds into the pellet. The object is to force the denser particles to the bottom of the pellet so that they will squeeze out the less dense particles. This should result in a double layered pellet (Fig. 10–24). The upper layer of such a pellet can be removed almost intact, leaving the lower layer in the tube to be resuspended.

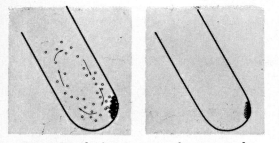

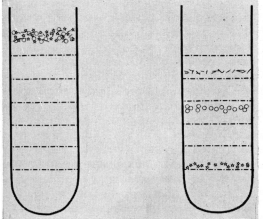

Fig. 10–23 (*left*). Separation of two particulates of same size but different densities on basis of convection in an angle-head rotor. Speed is selected so that most of the denser particles will sediment, whereas the less dense ones will remain suspended by convection forces.

Fig. 10–24 (*right*). Pellet resulting from long high-speed centrifuging of two components of same size but different densities. Heavier component squeezes out lighter one and forms dense pellet beneath a less dense pellet. Upper pellet can usually be resuspended with little disturbance of lower one.

Fig. 10–25. Rate zonal centrifugation in sucrose gradients (a, *left*) before centrifugation (b, *right*) after 10–16 hours' centrifugation. Particles have moved to different levels on basis of density and viscosity but not yet reached equilibrium positions.

8. *Density-gradient centrifugation.*—The use of density-gradient centrifugation in the study of viruses was introduced by Brakke (Brakke, 1951, 1960) and has become extremely useful in the purification of a number of viruses. Several modifications of the technique can be employed for specific separation problems. As initially used by Brakke, a sucrose density gradient is formed in a centrifuge tube, and the material to be separated is layered on top of the gradient (Fig. 10–25a). The gradient tubes are then placed in a special rotor which allows the tube to swing out into a horizontal position with the bottom farthest from the center of gravity. As the centrifuge is started, the tubes swing out; and when the centrifuge stops, the tubes swing back into an upright position so that the gradient remains undisturbed throughout the operation. If the centrifuge time and speed are such that the various components in the suspension are capable of moving to the position within the tube where the density of the sucrose solution is equal to the density of each particle, the particle will be unable to move farther down in the tube. The condition has been termed "equilibrium centrifugation" (Fig. 10–25b). Another application of this method involves the use of cesium chloride or some other heavy salt (Miselson *et al.*, 1957; Miselson

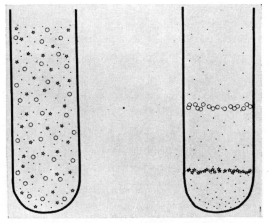

Fig. 10–26. Density-gradient centrifugation in cesium chloride in which particulates are mixed with salt solution at start. A density-gradient is formed as the salt is concentrated near bottom of tube by centrifugation. Particulates above their own density level sediment to that position; those below, float to the same level.

and Stahl, 1958). The salt is added to the material which is to be separated, and the centrifuge tube is filled with this mixture (Fig. 10–26a). As the mixture is centrifuged, the heavy salt molecules begin to move toward the bottom of the tube and a gradient becomes established during centrifugation. Particles in a solution of greater density will float to their own density level, whereas particles in a solution of lesser density than their own will sediment to their own density level (Fig. 10–26b, *right*).

a. *Rate zonal centrifugation.* If the gradients are established as described for equilibrium centrifugation and the centrifuge is stopped before the various components have reached their own density level, a more or less acceptable degree of separation is often obtained. In some instances, separation of components may even be better than that obtained by equilibrium centrifugation. This procedure has been designated "rate zonal centrifugation."

If the top level of a gradient consists of a 10–15% sucrose solution, the protein concentration which may be layered on it is limited to 5 mg/ml or less. If, however, the top of the gradient system contains 60–90% sucrose, as much as 15 mg/ml can be layered on top without undesirable convection (Figs. 10–27 and 10–28).

With sucrose gradients, at least two physical properties of the particles being sorted are employed for separation. As one would expect, the density of a particle is involved

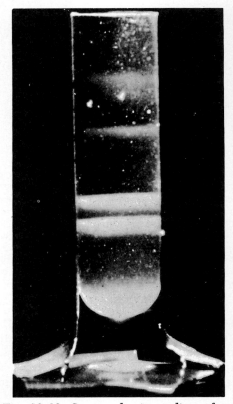

Fig. 10–28. Sucrose density-gradient after 16 hr at 35,000 g. Pod mottle virus of beans approximately 14 mg/ml. Virus components both separated and concentrated.

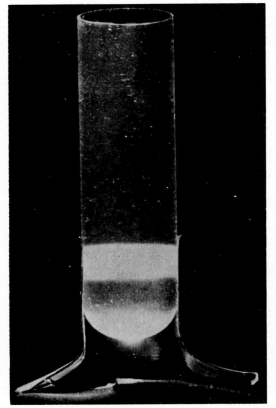

Fig. 10–27. Sucrose density-gradient after 16 hr at 24,000 g. Southern bean mosaic virus 14 mg/ml.

but, in addition, there is a viscosity effect due to the cold sucrose solution, and long flexuous rods which actually have a greater density than certain spherical components will sediment at a slower rate. The false impression will be gained on rate zonal centrifugation that the spherical particle has a greater density than the flexuous rod. Equilibrium centrifugation of the same components would show, however, that the spherical particle is actually less dense.

9. *Serological methods.*—It is possible to use serological methods in the purification of plant viruses if one develops the proper skills. One can obtain antiserum to partially purified virus, purify the gamma globulin fraction (Jager and Nickerson, 1948), and use this to precipitate virus from a partially purified preparation from another host. By dilution in the proper buffers and by digestion or degradation of the antibodies with enzymes and organic solvents, one can re-

move most of the antibodies from the virus and obtain a cleaner virus preparation than that available initially. Another approach is to prepare antibodies against healthy plant material and use these to precipitate the nonvirus proteins present in a partially purified preparation. This system would have the advantage that it would not be necessary to remove specific antibodies from attachment to the virus. A disadvantage, however, is that it may be very difficult or impossible to obtain good antibodies to all the unwanted proteins.

10. *Dry gels.*—A procedure which may be useful in certain instances is the use of dry agar or dry Sephadex* for the concentration and purification of viruses (Flodin *et al.*, 1960; Steere, 1962). The procedure involved is to add the dry gel to the clarified extract. As the gel takes in water, swells, and regains its original shape, contaminants so small that they can enter the pores of the gel will move in with the liquid and be removed from the suspension surrounding the gel granules. The suspension which contains virus particles too large to enter the gel pores is separated from the gel layer by centrifugation or is forced out of a column by being replaced with buffer. If one starts with a dark brown clarified extract containing southern bean mosaic virus and adds sufficient gel to take up all the liquid at each step then adds more buffer (as needed) to keep the virus in liquid suspension, essentially all contaminants and color can be removed by 3 or 4 applications of the dry agar.

11. *Microfilters.*—Still another procedure which may be useful for the removal of particulates that differ appreciably in size from the virus being purified is the use of microfilters. Depending on the pore sizes within the filters and the size of virus and contaminants to be separated, the filtration may be accomplished by use of a pressure system or by diffusion alone. Under some circumstances, a pressure system will cause the pores of the filter system to become clogged, whereas one can often get the virus or contaminants to pass rapidly through the membrane by diffusion and avoid clogging the membrane. In a simple procedure shown graphically in Figs. 10–29

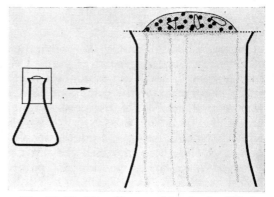

Fig. 10–29. Microfilter used in simple diffusion procedure for removal of salts and small contaminants from virus preparation.

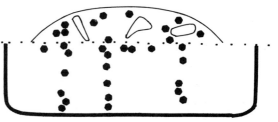

Fig. 10–30. Microfilter used in simple procedure for diffusion of virus through filter to remove larger contaminants.

and 10–30, the receiving vessel is filled with buffer or H_2O and capped with a microfilter. As the virus concentrate diffuses or flows through the filter, a denser layer forms just beneath the filter. Because of its greater density, this solution streaks down to the bottom of the reservoir and then starts diffusing upward. The process is allowed to continue until little or no virus is left above the filter. This diffusion filtration method is a simple and rapid method for removing particles larger than the virus, particularly those much larger such as a few remaining bacteria. To remove particulates smaller than the virus, the same procedure may be used but with a filter through which the virus will not pass and a large reservoir of buffer into which the contaminants can diffuse. Thin agar gel membranes (Ackers and Steere, 1962) can be employed in place of the microfilters, but longer time for equilibration should be expected because the pores in agar gels do not pass straight through the membrane as do those of the commercial ultrafilters.

227

10–6. CONCENTRATION PROCEDURES

At various stages during the preparation of a concentrated suspension of purified virus, it may become necessary or worth while to concentrate the suspension in one way or another. For this, two categories of procedures may be used: (a) those in which solvent is removed from the suspension, and (b) those in which the virus is removed from the suspension or concentrated beyond the level at which it will be stored for future use and is subsequently diluted or resuspended in the desired solvent. Depending on the stability or instability of the virus and equipment available for concentration, one may wish to use one method or another. A virus which is hard to resuspend should probably be concentrated by use of a method by which it will never be concentrated beyond the level desired. If, however, the virus resuspends freely and possesses a high degree of stability, it may be simpler to concentrate by high-speed centrifugation or precipitation and resuspend to the desired concentration.

A. REMOVAL OF SOLVENT FROM THE SUSPENSION

1. *Absorption of water by dry gels.*—Dry gel granules are added directly to the virus suspension and water, salts, and small particulates move into the pores of the gel leaving the virus, which is too large to enter the pores, in the free water surrounding the gel particles. This water may be removed by centrifuging through a sieve or basket centrifuge or by establishing a column with the mixture of gel suspension and flushing the virus concentrate out of the bottom of the column by adding buffer at the top.

2. *Ultrafiltration.*—Several modifications of ultrafiltrators are available commercially. However, one may wish to make a very simple one himself (Hofsten and Falkbring, 1960) or like that described below. Ultrafiltration depends on the porosity of the dialysis tubing and the air pressure against a vacuum to force water and salts out through the tubing against the osmotic pressure of the virus concentrate on the inside. A 24-in. long sack of $5/16$ in. dialysis

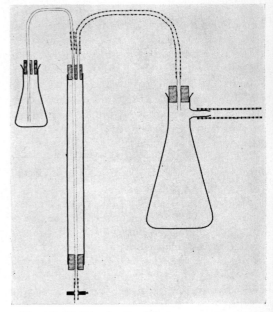

Fig. 10–31. Simple ultrafiltrator.

tubing will remove up to 24 ml per hour if the system is properly sealed and connected to a suitable vacuum pump. Either an oil pump or a water pump will do. One fault of this system, as with any system employing dialysis tubing, is that a certain amount of virus will adsorb irreversibly to the inside wall of the dialysis tubing. A simple ultrafiltrator (Fig. 10–31) can be made as follows.

Select two rubber stoppers which will fit tightly in the ends of a 24-in. length of 1-in. diameter glass tubing. One of the stoppers should have two $3/16$-in. holes drilled or bored into it, one near the center and the other near the edge. The other stopper should have one hole or none. Soak the dialysis tubing in water or buffer and thread one end through center hole of the 2-hole stopper. Moisten fire-polished end of a 2-in. piece of $3/16$-in. glass tubing and insert it into the short end of the dialysis tubing which should extend about 1 in. out of the top of the stopper. Force the glass tubing into the dialysis tubing and into the rubber stopper, making certain that the dialysis tubing is not twisted or torn. This will form a seal to prevent leakage. A single holed or plain stopper may be used at the bottom of the 1-in. diameter glass tubing. If a single hole stopper is used, the dialysis tubing is stretched through the glass tubing and threaded through the single hole in the bottom stopper. The stopper is pushed into the end of the tube and the dialysis tubing stretched and cut to leave about 1 in. extended. A 2-in. length of $3/16$-in. glass tubing with ends fire-polished is moistened and forced into the dialysis tubing and stopper as was done for the upper stopper. Care should be taken again to prevent twisting or tearing of the dialysis tubing and to be certain that it is stretched tightly between the two stoppers. The unit is now held upright on a ringstand, and the chamber outside the dialysis tubing is filled with water or the desired buffer. A third 2-in. length of $3/16$-in. glass tubing is inserted into the second hole at the top of the unit. A short length of rubber tubing is forced onto the $3/16$-in. glass tubing at the bottom and that end closed with a hose clamp. A longer length of rubber or plastic tubing is used to connect glass tubing at the upper end of the dialysis tubing to a reservoir. A third piece (thick-walled tubing) connects the outer chamber to a vacuum flask through a short piece of $3/16$-in. glass tubing in a single-holed stopper at top of the flask. The final step is to connect the vacuum flask to a vacuum source using thick-walled rubber tubing and to fill the reservoir with the suspension which is to be concentrated. A vacuum is applied to the unit and the dialysis tubing immediately expands forcing water from the outer chamber into the vacuum flask. At the same time, some of the suspension to be concentrated is forced into the dialysis tubing. There will still be some air inside the dialysis tubing; therefore, one must release the vacuum and reapply it 2 or 3 times to remove all air from dialysis tubing and the hose to reservoir. If the suspension to be concentrated is a purified virus, the density of the partially concentrated suspension just inside the wall of the dialysis tubing will be greater than elsewhere and will cause the more concentrated suspension to settle toward the bottom of the unit. After an hour or so, a few ml of the concentrated suspension may be removed from the bottom by opening the hose clamp briefly.

Another arrangement of the ultrafiltrator is to tie a knot in the lower end of the dialysis tubing, making the sack short enough to fit inside the 1-in. glass tubing and to seal the bottom with a solid stopper. This is particularly useful where one wants to reduce 100 ml or so to 1 ml. When the reservoir becomes empty, the upper stopper is removed and the concentrate is worked back up from the sack into the reservoir. A new knot is then tied to shorten the sack. Shortening of the sack can be repeated until it holds a final volume of 1 ml or less. With either variant of the technique, it is important to maintain liquid on both sides of all parts of the dialysis sack at all times. Drying and consequent denaturation may occur if the inside or outside level drops below the level of the upper stopper. Also, if one makes such a concentrator with a dialysis tubing 4 ft in length, the dialysis tubing will usually break. It is far better to make 2 or more 2-ft concentrators if faster concentration is desired.

3. *Dialysis.*—Dialysis against sucrose, concentrated proteins, polyethylene glycol, silica gel, Aquacide,* or some other substance which will pass through dialysis tubing slowly compared with water or not at all is a rapid and often a very satisfactory concentration method. The usual procedure is to place the virus suspension inside a bag of dialysis tubing and sink it in a concentrated suspension or surround it with the dry powder of whatever substance is to be used. The osmotic conditions which prevail will cause water and salts to move out into the dry substance or the concentrated suspension and result in a concentration of the virus on the inside of the bag. The amount of dialysis tubing normally used in this system is usually much greater in proportion to volume concentrated than with an ultrafiltrator. Therefore, one can expect a larger percentage loss from adsorption than with ultrafiltration. With small samples, this system may prove to be more rapid; one must be careful, however, not to allow the sample to become denatured by surface drying beyond the limits required for virus stability.

4. *Pervaporation.*—Pervaporation also involves the flow of water through dialysis

tubing bags but with evaporation from the outside rather than pressure or the use of some solute. The bags are often hung in a cold room with a fan blowing air past them to remove water. Local drying of the concentrate above the liquid level after some water has been removed may denature some virus. Also, salts are concentrated and may present problems.

5. *Freezing out.*—Freezing out involves the removal of water by freezing. If the conditions are properly established, water will freeze slowly from the outside of a container toward the inside, and the virus which is excluded slowly from the formed ice crystals will become more and more concentrated as the ice forms and the volume of the unfrozen suspension thus decreases (Shapiro, 1961).

6. *Two-phase systems.*—As described under "purification," the 2-phase system concentrates if the phase into which most of the virus will go is the one with the smallest volume. With the right system for a given virus, one ought to be able to obtain nearly any desired degree of concentration after several cycles.

7. *Surface evaporation.*—Under some circumstances, one may wish to concentrate by evaporation only. For instance, when one wishes to crystallize a small sample, it is often useful to let slow evaporation from the surface aid in the concentration of the sample until conditions are ideal for crystal formation. Also, use of a fan to blow air over a shallow container or placing the container in a vacuum system will remove water rapidly by surface evaporation. Three possible complications of this procedure are: (a) degradation of the virus on the walls of the container as liquid level drops, (b) surface denaturation of virus, and (c) concentration of salts.

B. Removal of Virus from Suspension

1. *Ultracentrifugation.*—The use of ultracentrifugation for the concentration of viruses is probably the most common procedure in use today. This method requires the use of a high-speed centrifuge capable of packing a reasonable amount of virus into a pellet within a reasonable length of time.

One simply fills the centrifuge tubes with the virus suspension, caps them, and places them in the proper rotor, which is then placed in the centrifuge, the centrifuge is turned on and operated at the desired rpm. The virus moves down in the tube and forms a jelly-like pellet at the point farthest from the center of gravity. The pellet is resuspended in the desired amount of selected buffer.

2. *Density-gradient centrifugation.*—Equilibrium centrifugation in density gradients will cause the virus to be concentrated into a pellet at its own density level. The "pad" which forms can be removed and resuspended in the desired amount of the selected buffer.

3. *pH-gradient electrophoresis.*—In the pH-gradient electrophoresis procedure, the virus is concentrated at its isoelectric point by migration in both directions. If the system is properly set up, one should obtain considerable concentration.

4. *Density-gradient electrophoresis.*—If a gradient which will not allow the virus to move below the level at which it is layered is established and the pH and electrodes are properly adjusted to move the virus toward the denser sucrose, the virus will layer out on top of the sucrose at a position where its buoyancy and electrophoretic mobility balance each other.

5. *Crystallization.* — Many viruses will crystallize out of suspensions if the concentration of virus is proper and the right buffer or salt solution is employed. $(NH_4)_2SO_4$ may be helpful in crystallization of viruses (Markham and Smith, 1949), but other salts including phosphates (Steere, 1956) are satisfactory for some viruses.

6. *Precipitation.*—Both isoelectric precipitation (Bawden and Pirie, 1943a) and precipitation with high concentrations of $(NH_4)_2SO_4$ (Stanley, 1936) or lower concentrations of other salts (Steere, 1956) have been used in the concentration of viruses. Sometimes there is a tendency for viruses aggregated in this manner to remain aggregated and to lose infectivity. These procedures are, therefore, less commonly employed now than in the past. An additional precipitation procedure which may prove to be very useful for concentration

of some viruses is the use of polyethylene glycol and NaCl mixture (Vanekamp and Mosch, 1963; Hebert, 1963).

7. *Chromatography.*—Ion-exchange chromatography may prove to be very useful for the concentration of viruses if the right system can be established for the adsorption of virus from a large volume of buffer onto a small column of resin followed by elution in a small volume of the proper buffer.

8. *Microfiltration.*—Several makes of microfilters which will prevent passage of virus are available. By forcing water out of a suspension through such a filter, virus can be concentrated into a jelly-like mass which can be resuspended in the desired amount of selected buffer. A difficulty of this procedure is that the pores of the filter get clogged up easily when pressure is applied and the virus concentrates on the filter pad. This can be partially avoided by slowing down the process sufficiently to allow the virus particles to keep moving in suspension by Brownian motion.

10–7. STORAGE OF PURIFIED VIRUS

Once a suspension of virus particles has been purified, there arises the problem of how it can be stored most effectively to retain its integrity and infectivity. The buffer employed for initial extraction may be unsuitable for storage. Occasionally the presence of additional salts and proteins in the plant sap will make a virus less sensitive to a given buffer than it is when partially or more completely purified. It is well, therefore, to examine the survival of purified virus upon storage in a series of buffers. One must not confine his tests to various ionic strengths and pH values of a single buffering system but should test samples in many different buffers. Also, since some viruses are much less stable when highly purified than they are in relatively crude extracts, it may prove advantageous to add a certain percentage of some protein (preferably one which is sufficiently different in size from the virus that it can be removed easily when desired) to the purified virus suspension to improve virus stability.

Some purified viruses can be stored for months or even years at 4°C. Others are unstable even at that temperature but may retain infectivity if kept frozen. Freezing all purified virus suspensions is not recommended, however, because some lose infectivity when frozen and thawed (Bawden and Pirie, 1943b). An additional procedure which might be useful if properly carried out is to freeze-dry the purified virus. It may be necessary to add some other protein to the virus suspension before it is freeze-dried if retention of infectivity is required. Organic solvents such as butanol or toluene are sometimes added to the purified virus preparation to cover the surface and help prevent bacterial contamination.

10–8. DETECTION OF IMPURITIES

When one has finally obtained what he believes to be a purified virus suspension, there is always the question of what impurities may be present. If one wishes to remove the salts required for storage, that can usually be accomplished easily by dialysis or by pelleting the virus in an ultracentrifuge and resuspending the pellets in distilled water or in the desired buffer. The critical contaminants would be proteins or nucleoproteins, free nucleic acid, or some other substances such as phenolic compounds or chlorophyll probably adsorbed to the virus. Usually these impurities can be detected in quantities equal to or greater than 1% of the total dry weight of the suspension if the sample is sufficiently large to permit examination by all the methods available. It is not unusual to find in an infected plant two components which have at least one property in common and which would appear as a single component if tested for purity by use of one method only. It is not likely that all known methods of testing for impurities would fail to detect a contaminant present at a concentration of 1% or more. However, if one fails to detect impurities by one method, he should test the material by other possible methods until he has found impurities or exhausted his means of detecting them. If he finds impurities by any method, he can use the information gained from the test in determining how he should purify the sample further. It is conceivable, but not very probable, that a virus suspension with a large amount of impurities would appear as a single component by all methods available for testing. In fact, one has no physical method of differentiating infectious from noninfectious virus nucleoprotein particles of the same kind. Also, physical methods are not capable of distinguishing many strains of virus from others. With this in mind and with the knowledge that viruses are continually mutating and that a purified virus suspension usually contains more than a billion particles per ml, one must assume that any purified virus suspension must contain contaminants in the form of other strains.

Methods for detecting impurities and comments regarding their use follow.

A. Electrophoresis

Impurities which differ from the virus on the basis of surface charge, isoelectric point, or electrophoretic mobility can be detected by use of one or more of the methods involving electrophoresis. They will appear as separate bands by density-gradient or pH-gradient electrophoresis or as partially separated suspensions if examined by moving boundary methods.

B. Electron Microscopy

The electron microscope can be used to detect impurities on a morphological basis. One may detect differences in size, shape, or ability to withstand flattening or distortion by specific preparative procedures.

C. Ultracentrifugation

The ultracentrifuge can detect contaminants on the basis of their sedimentation coefficients which are affected by size, shape, hydration properties, partial specific volume, and viscosity of the particles in solution (Schachman, 1958).

D. Density-gradient Centrifugation

If glycerol or sucrose is employed, both density and viscosity are important in the separation of mixtures of particulates. On the other hand, when cesium chloride is used for the gradient, final separation is on the basis of density alone.

E. Chromatography

Chromatography has been employed to detect and remove impurities in virus suspensions (Shainoff and Lauffer, 1956, 1957). One can collect fractions and test them to find out if more than one component can be detected.

F. Agar-gel Filtration

The agar-gel method separates particles on the basis of size, whereas ion-exchange methods work on the basis of difference in adsorption and elution of the virus and contaminants.

10–9. SAMPLE PROCEDURE FOR PURIFYING VIRUS PARTICLES AND KEEPING THEM IN SUSPENSION THROUGHOUT PURIFICATION AND CONCENTRATION

Prepare agar suspensions (1 and 8% by weight) using Ionager #2* (Consolidated Laboratories, Inc., P. O. Box 234, Chicago Heights, Ill.) and distilled water. Autoclave for 15–30 min, remove, and if the agar is not thoroughly dissolved, stir and repeat autoclaving. Remove agar from autoclave and allow it to solidify at room temperature. Break or cut into cubes 1 in. or smaller; shape does not matter. Fill a blender or rotary food cutter bowl ⅓ full of cold water (cold 0.01 M EDTA for 1% agar). Start motor and add agar blocks. Operate blender no longer than 30 sec at one cycle for 8% agar or 10 sec for 1% agar. (Food cutter can be operated for 2–3 min on 1% agar; 30 min or longer for 8% agar). Pour chopped agar into sieves (40-mesh on top of 60-mesh). Hold under strong tap to force smaller fragments through the 40-mesh into the 60-mesh sieve. Separate sieves and wash agar on 60-mesh sieve with a strong tap to wash through all fragments smaller than 1/60 in. in diameter. Pour agar-gel fragments from 60-mesh sieve into beaker using light stream on bottom of upside-down sieve to wash them out. Return all fragments larger than 40-mesh to blender or cutter, start motor (never run blender for more than 30 sec at a time). Repeat this cycle until most of the agar has been cut to the 40–60-mesh size. Be sure final suspension of 1% agar is in 0.01 M EDTA adjusted to pH 7.5. In order to remove air trapped in the agar by washing, pour chopped agar into vacuum flask and apply vacuum, or let stand 24 hr, then stir gently to make air bubbles rise to the surface. Prepare glass or plastic columns of desired length; 1.5–2 cm $\times$ 110 cm for 1% agar is satisfactory and 5–10 $\times$ 110 cm for 8% agar. One can use commercially prepared columns with cintered glass filters or make his own columns by cutting discs of porous polyethylene* (Porex Materials Corp., 348 Bay St., Fairburn, Ga.) with a sharp cork borer which will just fit inside a selected length of glass tubing. We customarily place a porous polyethylene disc on top of a single hole rubber stopper in the bottom of the column. A 2-in. length of $\frac{3}{16}$-in. glass tubing is inserted into the rubber stopper and a rubber hose with hose clamp is forced over the glass tubing to provide a flow control mechanism. To fill a column, the settled de-gassed agar chips are suspended in the liquid by stirring, and the suspension is poured into the column. As the agar settles, excess water or buffer runs out the bottom and additional agar suspension is added until the settled agar level is 5–10 cm above the desired level. Columns are then washed thoroughly by flowing 0.01 M EDTA, pH 7.5 through them (approximately 500 ml for the 1.5 or 2 $\times$ 110 cm column and 1–2 liters for the other). This washing removes unattached agar strands and other unbound contaminants from the agar and leaves the 1% column equilibrated with its proper buffer. The 8% agar column should then be equilibrated with 0.001 M EDTA, pH 7.5.

Source material should be tobacco plants systemically infected with TMV for one to three weeks. The leaves (one volume by weight) should be soaked for 10 min in two volumes of 0.05 M EDTA, 0.3 M NaCl, pH 9.5, and then ground in a regular meat grinder, the extra buffer is added to the mash, and juice is pressed from the pulp by squeezing through cheesecloth. The pH of the extract should be about 7.5 but should be adjusted to this level as rapidly as possible by addition of 1 N NaOH if it is lower (this adjustment is important only if one wants to prevent end-on aggregation of the TMV rods). As soon as the adjustment has been made, charcoal (Activated Charcoal, Merck 18351* 5 gm per 100 ml) is added. The mixture is shaken briefly 15–30 sec, and 5 gm of diatomaceous earth (Celite,* High Flow Super Cell*) per 100 ml is added. Shaking is continued for another 15–30 sec; then the mixture is filtered through a Buchner funnel with a well-washed ¼-in. Celite* pad. To avoid more dilution than necessary, the first liquid which comes through the Celite* pad is discarded. The liquid is retained as soon as the presence of considerable virus can be detected by light scattering. The virus-containing filtrate should be clear to milky white and should be passed immediately through the 8% agar to replace the high salt content with the 0.001 M EDTA to prevent end-to-end aggregation. A sample containing 200–300 ml of TMV extract can be moved through the column in one charge. The flow rate on the 8% agar column can be as high as 10 ml per min. When the virus comes out, it will be suspended in the 0.001 M buffer and free of most contaminants. It can then be concentrated by use of an ultrafiltrator, dry agar, or Sephadex* or one of the other concentration procedures. Further purification and size sorting are easily accomplished by passing the concentrate through the 1% agar-gel column. Flow rate this time should be no greater than 5 ml per hr. If proper precautions have been taken to prevent end-on aggregation, the first fractions from this column which contain virus should have rods only 300 mμ long and should be free of contaminants. For storage and prevention of aggregation, these should be pooled and re-run through a clean 8% agar column equilibrated with 0.001 M EDTA, pH 7.5, or dialyzed against this same buffer. They could be further concentrated at this time by ultrafiltration if that is desired.

* Mention of specific equipment, trade products, or a commercial company throughout this paper does not constitute its endorsement by the U.S. government over similar products or companies not named.

10–10. LITERATURE CITED

Ackers, G. K., and Steere, R. L. (1962). Biochim. Biophys. Acta **59**, 137.

Albertsson, P. A. (1958). Biochim. Biophys. Acta **27**, 378.

Albertsson, P. A., and Frick, G. (1960). Biochim. Biophys. Acta **37**, 230.

Bawden, F. C. (1950). Plant Viruses and Virus Diseases. 3d ed. Chronica Botanica Co., Waltham, Mass.

Bawden, F. C., and Pirie, N. W. (1943a). Biochem. J. **37**, 66.

Bawden, F. C., and Pirie, N. W. (1943b). Biochem. J. **37**, 70.

Bennett, C. W. (1935). J. Agr. Res. **50**, 211.

Bier, M. (1959). Electrophoresis, Theory, Methods, and Applications. Academic Press, New York.

Black, L. M. (1955). Phytopathology **45**, 208.

Brakke, M. K. (1951). J. Am. Chem. Soc. **73**, 1847.

Brakke, M. K. (1953). Phytopathology **43**, 467.

Brakke, M. K. (1955). Arch. Biochem. Biophys. **55**, 175.

Brakke, M. K. (1960). Advan. Virus Res. **7**, 193.

Brakke, M. K. (1963). Virology **19**, 367.

Brunt, A. A., and Kenten, R. H. (1963). Virology **19**, 388.

Burnett, F. M., and Stanley, W. M. (1959). The Viruses. Academic Press, New York.

Consden, R., Gordon, A. H., and Martin, A. J. P. (1946). Biochem. J. **40**, 33.

Corbett, M. K. (1961). Virology **15**, 8.

DiCastro, G., and San Marco, M. (1954). J. Chem. Soc. **54**, 4157.

Diener, T. O. (1962). Virology **16**, 140.

Flodin, P. (1962). Dextran Gels and their Applications in Gel Filtration. Pharmacia, Uppsala, Sweden. Meijels Bokindustri, Halmstad.

Flodin, P., Gelotte, B., and Porath, J. (1960). Nature **188**, 493.

Fulton, R. W. (1959). Virology **9**, 522.

Grassman, W., and Hannig, K. (1953). Z. Physiol. Chem. **292**, 32.

Hebert, T. T. (1963). Phytopathology **53**, 362.

Hofsten, B., and Falkbring, S. (1960). Anal. Biochem. **1**, 436.

Jager, B. V., and Nickerson, M. (1948). J. Biol. Chem. **173**, 683.

Kelley, J. J., and Kaesberg, P. (1962). Biochim. Biophys. Acta **55**, 236.

Kolin, A. (1955). Proc. Nat. Acad. Sci. U.S. **41**, 101.

Lauffer, M. A., and Smith, K. (1953, 1954, 1955, 1956, 1957, 1958, 1959, 1960, 1961, 1962). Advan. Virus Res. Academic Press, New York.

Markham, R. (1951). Discussions Faraday Soc. **11**, 221.

Markham, R. (1959). In Burnett and Stanley (eds.), The Viruses. **2**, 41. Academic Press, New York.

Markham, R., and Smith, K. (1949). Parasitology **39**, 330.

Miselson, M., and Stahl, F. W. (1958). Proc. Nat. Acad. Sci. U.S. **44**, 671.

Miselson, M., Stahl, F. W., and Vinograd, J. (1957). Proc. Nat. Acad. Sci. U.S. **43**, 581.

Philipson, L., Albertsson, P. A., and Frick, G. (1960). Virology **11**, 553.

Ragetli, H. W. J., and van der Want, J. P. H. (1954). Proc. Koninkl. Ned.

Ross, A. F. (1941a). Phytopathology **31**, 394.

Ross, A. F. (1941b). Phytopathology **31**, 410.

Schachman, H. K. (1958). Ultracentrifugation in Biochemistry. 13. Academic Press, New York.

Scott, H. (1963). Virology **20**, 103.

Shainoff, J. R., and Lauffer, M. H. (1956). Arch. Biochim. Biophys. **4**, 315.

Shainoff, J. R., and Lauffer, M. H. (1957). Virology **4**, 418.

Shapiro, J. (1961). Science **133**, 2063.

Smith, K. M. (1957). A Textbook of Plant Virus Diseases. Little, Brown and Co., Boston.

Stanley, W. M. (1935). Science **81**, 644.

Stanley, W. M. (1936). J. Biol. Chem. **115**, 673.

Stanley, W. M. (1939a). J. Biol. Chem. **129**, 405.

Stanley, W. M. (1939b). J. Biol. Chem. **129**, 429.

Steere, R. L. (1956). Phytopathology **46**, 60.

Steere, R. L. (1959). Advan. Virus Res. **6**, 1. Academic Press, New York.

Steere, R. L. (1962). Phytopathology **52**, 29.

Steere, R. L. Unpublished work on pod mottle virus.

Steere, R. L. (1963). Science **140**, 1089.

Tiselius, A. (1937). Trans. Faraday Soc. **33**, 524.

Venekamp, J. H., and Mosch, W. H. M. (1963). Virology **19**, 316.

11

ELLEN M. BALL

Serology: Techniques used in plant virus research

11–1. INTRODUCTION[1]

When warm-blooded animals are exposed to certain proteins, profound physiological changes take place which so alter the state of the animal that it is never again the same as it was prior to the exposure. One of the main characteristics of this change is an increase in and an alteration of the globulins found in the serum portion of the blood. The altered globulins are called *antibodies*. They are characterized by being able to combine with the proteins used in their production to form some visible reaction. In the animal body, the combination causes a *neutralization* type of reaction or an *anaphylaxis* or shock type of reaction. In the test tube, the combination causes a precipitation or agglutination type of reaction or a *binding of complement* which indirectly reveals the presence of the reactants.

The substances producing the alteration in the globulin of the blood are called *antigens*. Generally, antigens are *protein* in nature. A few complex lipids and carbohydrates have been shown to be capable of producing antibodies, but the majority of antigens contain protein of relatively *high molecular weight*. For a good immune response, molecular weights of 10,000 or more

are required; blood proteins of 60,000 and egg albumin of 40,000 molecular weights are good antigens. *Haptens* are incomplete antigens which have the ability to combine with antibody *in vitro* but do not have the ability to produce antibodies *in vivo*. The surface area of the antigen is important in its ability to produce antibody since some nonantigenic, low molecular weight substances have been made antigenic when absorbed to charcoal, glass, aluminum hydroxide, or collodion. Antigens must be *foreign* to the animal being immunized. On occasion, isoantibodies (from similar species) and autoantibodies (from similar individuals) have been described. Under special conditions, an animal can be made to produce antibodies to its own organs. The best antigens, however, are those complex proteins isolated from a source that is unrelated to the animal being immunized. Antigens must reach the antibody producing sites in the animal in a relatively *unaltered* state. This means that the antigens are introduced parenterally into the animal, that is, by any route except intestinal. The intravenous and intramuscular routes are used most generally but intraperitoneal, intracardial, or intracerebral can be employed also.

The reaction between antigen and antibody is highly *specific*, and therein lies the main advantage of using serological techniques for the identification of proteins or

[1] Published with the approval of the Director as Paper No. 1379, Journal Series, Nebraska Agricultural Experiment Station.

other antigenic substances. The specificity of the reaction is based on the nature, size, and number (valency) of certain determinate groups found on the surface of the antigen. The counterpart of these groups is located on the surface of the antibody molecule. The homologous reaction, that is, the reaction between an antiserum and the antigen that caused its production, resembles the fit between a lock and key. The tumblers of the lock and the notches on the key resemble the closeness of the fit between the antigen and antibody. The heterologous reaction, that is, the reaction between an antiserum and an antigen closely resembling but not identical to the one causing the production of the antibody, resembles the fit between a lock and a master key. Some of the tumblers of the lock and notches of the key fit so as to turn the lock, and some of the determinant groups of the antigen fit their counterpart on the antibody so as to cause the formation of a precipitate. However, the magnitude of the heterologous reaction never is as great as the homologous reaction. The extent of the reaction can be measured in terms of *titer*, the amount of dilution an antigen or antiserum can be subjected to and still produce a desired reaction. How much antibody is formed in the blood is determined by the concentration of the antigen, the stability of the antigen in the body of the animal, and the method and route used in the immunization procedure. The physiological state of the animal is involved also, since some individuals produce more antibody than others when the immunizing conditions are standardized.

The above paragraphs present a very brief concept of the science of immunology. The terms that are used generally in a discussion of this science have been mentioned. For more details of theory and procedure, the reader's attention is drawn to the textbooks listed following Literature Cited.

Serological methods were first applied to plant viruses by Dvorak (1927) when it was shown that antiserum prepared to mottled Triumph variety of potato reacted more strongly to the homologous antigen than to antigen made from nonmottled po-

tato. Strong cross reactions were observed with both antigens, "healthy" and diseased, and the antisera. The specificity of the serological reactions of plant viruses was established by Purdy (1928, 1929) and by (Purdy-) Beale (1931) using precipitin and complement fixation tests. Virus antiserum that was completely absorbed with extract from healthy plants still produced strongly positive reactions with tobacco mosaic virus (TMV) antigen. Birkeland (1934) was the first investigator to demonstrate that strains of plant viruses contained specific antigens which differentiated them from other members of the group. He also showed that membrane filters which would retain the virus removed the antigenic components from the solution. This contributed to the solution of the question as to whether the virus or some product of virus activity in the plant was indeed the antigen. Chester (1934) applied the neutralization test to plant viruses and demonstrated that antiserum reduced the infectivity of TMV more than did healthy plant sap, milk, and ovalbumin. In 1935b, he correlated the gradual loss in infectivity, due to treatment of the virus with heat and chemicals, with a dimunition of antigenic activity. Chester (1936) applied the Schultz-Dale modification of the anaphylaxis test to the detection of healthy plant components in purified virus preparations. Beale and Lojkin (1944) were the first to apply the quantitative precipitin test to plant virus studies in the United States, though the test had been used in Germany earlier (Schramm and Friedrich-Freksa, 1941). Generally, throughout this period of investigation the precipitin test performed in tubes was the principal technique. The complement fixation, neutralization, anaphylaxis, and quantitative precipitin procedures were applied less frequently. More details of the early serological studies can be found in a review by Chester (1937c) and in Bawden's text, Chapter 7 (1950).

One of the earliest suggestions for applying serology to the testing of field samples described the use of 2 ml of expressed sap and 3 ml of diluted antiserum (Chester, 1937a). The amount of precipitate was read after 15 min and again after 1 hr. In

Europe, serological testing became an integral part of the potato and bulb industries and more refined tests were developed (Stapp and Bercks, 1948; and van Slogteren, VIII, 1955). The procedures for maintaining virus-free seed stocks of potatoes as they were performed in Great Britain, in Germany and the Netherlands, in South Africa, and in Canada were reviewed by Munro (1954). In most cases, the tests or the control methods for maintaining the stocks were under the supervision of government agencies. More details of the serological tests for the early and precise diagnosis of viruses in vegetatively propagated plants have been reviewed by E. van Slogteren (1955) and again by him and D. H. M. van Slogteren (1957). The main advantages of using serology were described as (1) the sera could be stored for years, eliminating the need for continuous propagation of infected plants as a source for material for identification purposes, (2) the tests were rapid, permitting the roguing of infected plants from the field during the same day of testing, (3) plants harboring symptomless viruses could be eliminated, and (4) unknown viruses could be detected and described.

Chester (1935a, 1937b) used serological results to aid in the classification of plant viruses. His list was expanded somewhat by Bawden (1950, p. 271). Additional lists of antisera have appeared in Matthews' text (1957, pp. 36–41), in Bercks' review on plant virus serology (1958, p. 166), and in the previously mentioned review by the van Slogterens (1957). More recently, the Committee on Virus Type Culture Collection, American Phytopathological Society (1960) compiled a list of antisera available in the United States and Canada.

The purpose of this review is to present the current procedures in plant virus serology and to illustrate their applications. The research methods applied by investigators in the United States and Canada will be emphasized.

11–2. IMMUNIZATION TECHNIQUES

The most generally applied procedure for immunizing animals has been a series of intravenous injections. Adjuvants have been employed recently, and antisera of much higher titers have been obtained. In some cases, antisera have been produced by using adjuvants where other methods failed.

A. INTRAVENOUS INJECTION

With the intravenous method of immunization, graded doses of virus suspended in physiological saline are injected into the ear vein of the rabbit. The ear may be rubbed with an irritant or treated with a hot compress to dilate the vein and make the insertion of a needle easier.

Bagnall et al. (1959) used injections at 4-day intervals of 4 graded doses of potato viruses M and S and carnation latent virus. Three weeks later 2 more injections of 2 ml each were given, making a total of 9 ml per rabbit. Antisera to melon mosaic and squash mosaic viruses were prepared by giving a total of 5 doses of 1 ml each at 3-day intervals (Lindberg et al., 1956). Even though many injections were administered, the use of infectious sap resulted in a relatively low titer of immune serum, and antibodies to plant proteins were present in rather high proportions.

Few investigators presented data on the actual weight of virus injected into rabbits. Malkiel and Stanley (1947) injected 10 mg of TMV intraperitoneally and followed this with 2 consecutive intravenous injections; the procedure was continued for 20 weeks for a total of almost 300 mg. Weaver and Price (1952) used an intraperitoneal and repeated intravenous injections for 85 days to immunize rabbits with 7 strains of TMV. The total amount of antigen injected into the rabbits varied from 8.6 to 134.7 mg, and the complement fixing titers of the sera ranged from 1 : 256 to 1 : 640. Bancroft et al. (1960a) gave rabbits doses of 5 mg of alfalfa mosaic virus on 1, 4, 8, and 10 days and obtained a maximum response in 2 weeks. In studies with white clover mosaic virus, Bancroft et al. (1960b) injected rabbits 3 times at intervals of 4 days with 0.4 to 0.8 ml of a solution containing 4 mg protein/ml. Wright (1963) injected graded doses of solution containing 1 mg/ml of virus, i.e., 1, 1, 2, 2, 3, and 3 ml, for complement fixation studies on strains of potato virus X, TMV, and clover yellow mosaic virus. These sera gave tube precipitin titers of 1 : 640 and complement fixation titers of 1 : 2560.

B. Intramuscular Injection in Freund's Adjuvant

The use of this adjuvant is based on the research of Freund (1947). A paraffinic base mineral oil is mixed with a specific surface active agent, mannide monooleate, at a ratio of 9 parts to 1 part, respectively. (The "incomplete" adjuvant as described or the "complete" oil containing *Mycobacterium butyricum* is available commercially.) Equal volumes of the oil mixture and suspension of virus are emulsified. The formation of a thick, creamy solution is evidence of complete emulsification. The emulsion can be formed by repeatedly forcing the solution from a syringe through an 18-gauge needle into a serum vial (Salk and Laurent, 1952), by the rather violent motion of a commercial paint-mixing apparatus (Desjardins and Wallace, 1962), by using a Waring[2] blender (Commoner and Rodenberg, 1955), by stirring with a modified beater directly in the barrel of a syringe (Tremaine and Willison, 1961a), or by mixing with a syringe and needle in a polyethylene tube (suggested by R. W. Fulton). The last 2 methods permit the complete removal of all emulsified virus, whereas the other methods leave considerable emulsion adhering to the walls of the vial, a distinct disadvantage when only small amounts of purified virus are available for the immunization. Also helpful in preparing adjuvants that are particularly hard to emulsify is the addition of 0.1–0.2 ml of 1 M neutral phosphate buffer to a total volume of 2–5 ml of the mixture (personal observation).

Generally, less virus can be injected with comparable results when the Freund adjuvant is used than when virus is injected intravenously. Also, viruses that are ob-

tained pure in very small amounts can be used efficiently with the adjuvant. The first use of Freund's adjuvant in plant virology was with southern bean mosaic virus (Moorhead and Price, 1953). Black and Brakke (1954) prepared an immune serum to the leafhopper-transmitted, but nonmechanically transmitted, wound-tumor virus by this method. An antiserum was made to psorosis virus of citrus by 4 injections of adjuvant given at weekly intervals (Desjardins and Wallace, 1962). Tremaine and Willison (1961a, 1962a) and Willison *et al.* (1961) obtained antisera to several of the stone-fruit viruses by a single injection of the virus in adjuvant. More recent evidence of the success of this adjuvant has been reported in the preparation of antisera to the following viruses: tobacco mosaic (Moorhead, 1961), and its X-protein (Takahashi and Gold, 1960), common bean mosaic (Scott, 1962), barley stripe mosaic and brome mosaic (Moorhead, 1956), wheat streak mosaic (Moorhead, 1959), potato virus X (Govier, 1958), tobacco ringspot (Kahn *et al.*, 1962), and the viruses listed in the Committee on Virus Type Culture Collection publication (1960), to mention a few.

C. Comparative Studies and Combinations of Routes of Injection

Many investigators have found that a combination of intravenous and intramuscular injections, in saline and Freund adjuvant, respectively, have produced better results than only intramuscular injections. Pirone *et al.* (1961) reported that the antiserum titer for purified cauliflower mosaic virus could be increased significantly if a dose was divided between intramuscular and intravenous injections rather than given entirely in intravenous injections. In this case, volumes of 1 ml of virus were used for each injection, and the interval between injections was 10–14 days. Cadman and Lister (1961) also reported increases in antibody titer from 1 : 16 to 1 : 256 when intramuscular injections were supplemented by intravenous injections of tomato ringspot and peach yellow bud mosaic viruses. Anticucumber mosaic virus serum

---

[2] Any mention herein of trade-name products does not constitute endorsement by the U.S. government over similar products not named.

was obtained when virus in Freund's adjuvant was administered subcutaneously rather than intramuscularly (Grogan and Kimble, 1962). When 6 graded intravenous injections were given at intervals of 4 days and 2–4 intramuscular injections were given at intervals of 2 weeks, an antiserum was obtained for beet ringspot virus but not for celery yellow vein virus. Only when the latter virus was inactivated with formaldehyde was a successful attempt made to produce this antiserum (Hollings and Stone, 1962). Van Regenmortel *et al.* (1962) obtained an antiserum for watermelon mosaic virus with homologous titers of 1 : 16,000 by using a combination of intravenous and intramuscular injections.

These methods of injection as well as subcutaneous routes were studied extensively by Bercks (1960) and by Wetter (1960, 1961). Sera were analyzed by a drop test on a slide with incubation at 45°C in a moist environment, and the results were read in a dark-field microscope at 100× magnification. A summary is presented in Table 11–1 of the results of several investigators, who reported data from intravenous and from intramuscular methods of immunization. In some cases, intravenous injections were administered for the primary response and intramuscular injections for the anamnestic, or secondary, response; the most striking increase in antibody titer occurred with this procedure. It should be mentioned that data from immunization studies showed that the booster (secondary) dose was not effective until the antibody titer from the primary response had decreased more than four-fold from the maximum level.

D. Adjuvants Other Than Freund's Oil Emulsion

The properties of phosphorylated hesperidin in immunization were investigated in a search for other adjuvants that would be more efficient than Freund's emulsion (Moorhead, 1961). The viruses used were those of southern bean mosaic, tobacco mosaic, brome mosaic, and barley stripe mosaic. Since virologists are becoming more interested in viruses that are extremely hard to purify or obtain concentrated in

quantity, minimum amounts of these relatively stable viruses were injected into the rabbits. Intramuscular and subcutaneous injections were made at weekly intervals or in alternate weeks. While some of the antisera end points were the same as those obtained with the oil adjuvant, none of the titers exceeded these end points. Recently, studies were concluded on the use of 4% sodium alginate as an adjuvant for immunization with these viruses. Similar results were obtained as with hesperidin (publication in preparation). However, it should be emphasized that only 1.2–2.6 mg of virus per injection were used, and the adjuvant effect might have been much superior' if larger doses had been employed.

Allen and Tremaine (1962) reported on agar as an adjuvant. Carnation ringspot virus was doubly diffused in agar, precipitin zones were cut from the agar, and a suspension of the agar-precipitate was injected intramuscularly into rabbits. Serum titers from samples taken 7–8 weeks later showed an increase of eight-fold over the antibody level obtained when a saline suspension of the virus was injected intramuscularly. The authors suggested that the virus was bound to agar and released in the animal in an antigenically active form. More recently, Tremaine (personal communication) reported that additional data showed a less significant rise in titer with the agar-adjuvant than with saline.

E. Acquisition of Blood Samples

Intravenous bleeding of rabbits is recommended generally (Bawden, 1950; Smith, 1951; Matthews, 1957). Instead of using a syringe and needle, it is suggested that the ear vein be slashed near the base and the blood collected directly into a tube. Pressure and a collodion solution can be used to stop the flow of blood. It has been reported that a total of 100 ml of blood can be collected by this procedure over several days. Many investigators believe that the cardiac puncture is the most convenient and efficient method of obtaining blood. The heart can be punctured without anesthetizing the animal, and 10–20 ml samples can be withdrawn sterily in a minute. This is an excellent procedure to use in the ex-

TABLE 11–1. RECIPROCALS OF THE DILUTION END POINTS OF ANTISERA RESULTING FROM INTRAVENOUS, INTRAMUSCULAR, OR COMBINATIONS OF ROUTES OF IMMUNIZING RABBITS WITH SEVEN PLANT VIRUSES

(Arrows indicate one route of immunization followed by a second route in the booster series of injections. The number over the arrow indicates the interval in weeks between the injections series.)

Test Method	Virus System and Mode of Dose	Immunization Route		Investigator
		Intravenous	Intramuscular	
Tube Precipitin	Potato X			Govier (1958)
	Single	256	4096	
	Multiple	8192 512		
Ring Interface	Alfalfa Mosaic Multiple	4096	2048	Bancroft et al. (1960a)
Slide Precipitin	Carnation Latent			Wetter (1960)
	Single	2048 →[18]	16384	
	Multiple	2048 →[9]	16384 32768	
	Pea Streak			
	Single	2048 →[14] 2048 ↘[26]		
	Multiple		65536 →[28] 65536	
	Potato S			
	Single	2048 →[32] 4096 ↘[4]	→131072	
	Multiple		65536 –[26] ↗	
	Single		32768 →[24] 32768	
	Multiple		↖[10] 16384	
	Potato S			Wetter (1961)
	Single 2*	1024 →[8]	→32768	
	Multiple 4,4			
	Multiple 2,2		8192 ⎫	
	4,4		4096 ↙ ⎬ 8	
	Multiple 1.3, 1.3, 1.3		16384 ⎫ 8	
	4,4		8192 ↙ ⎭	
Complement Fixation	Alfalfa Mosaic Multiple	256	256	Bancroft et al. (1960a) Moorhead (1956)
	Brome Mosaic Multiple	64 →[8]	8192 →[15] 16384	
	Barley Stripe Multiple	256 →[16]	1024	

* mg of virus/injection

sanguination of the animal when the serological test period is finished.

Rabbits are usually the animals chosen for plant virus serology. Miller and Thornberry (1958) reported on the use of chickens and guinea pigs. The use of pigs and frogs has been reported, also (van Slogteren and van Slogteren, 1957). In the Netherlands, horses were used for the production of large volumes of immune serum, though some difficulty was observed in getting the proper precipitin test reaction; this result was due to the formation of incomplete antibodies (van der Veken, 1961).

11–3. SEROLOGICAL TECHNIQUES

The details of performing 6 serological tests for the identification of plant viruses are presented in a brochure by Ball (1961) and will be mentioned only briefly in this review. Included in the brochure are the chloroplast agglutination, microprecipitin, ring interface, agar single diffusion, and 2 modifications of agar double diffusion tests. These tests can be used readily, require relatively little equipment, and the results of the tests are not too difficult to interpret when the investigator has obtained a little experience. Other serological procedures that are being used to study the characteristics and relationships of plant viruses will be discussed in some detail.

A. DILUTION END-POINT PROCEDURES

1. *Chloroplast agglutination test.*—Chloroplast agglutination is the simplest procedure applicable to plant virus serology and requires only a drop of extract from an infected leaf and a drop of serum. Potatoes are frequently assayed for virus X in this manner (D. H. M. van Slogteren, 1955). Alfieri and Stouffer (1957) reported that virus S could not be identified by this test procedure after grafting scions of USDA line 41956 onto plants of Saco variety of potatoes. In other grafting studies, scions susceptible to potato virus X were grafted on plants of resistant USDA line 41956, and the chloroplast agglutination test was used to show absence of virus below the graft (Benson and Hooker, 1960). Scott (1962) diagnosed common bean mosaic virus 1–5 weeks after inoculation and found that the concentration of the virus was higher in the primary than in the trifoliolate leaves. Storm and Streets (1962) found that psorosis disease of citrus could be identified if 1 drop of extract from infected leaves and 2 drops of antiserum were mixed on a slide coated with Formvar.

Chloroplast agglutination is quick and requires little or no treatment of the infectious sap. However, at best, the procedure is crude and gives only a rough estimate of the presence of a virus. The test is most successful when the virus concentration in the leaves is relatively high.

2. *Microprecipitin test.*—More and more, the reaction of drops of clarified infectious sap and antiserum under oil, the van Slogteren test (1955, VIII), is being applied to plant viruses. Desjardin and Wallace's (1962) preparation of psorosis virus revealed cross precipitation with plant proteins with this method, though specific virus antibodies were also present. This procedure was employed to check plants being assayed for clover yellow mosaic and white clover mosaic viruses for contamination with alfalfa mosaic virus (Agrawal *et al.*, 1962). The procedure was used also to show that tobacco ringspot virus was associated with internal cork in a sweet potato disease complex (Hildebrand and Kehr, 1961), that pod mottle and red node viruses were not related (Scott *et al.*, 1961) and to prove the identity of a virus isolated from eucharis as a strain of tobacco ringspot virus (Kahn *et al.*, 1962). Takahashi and Gold (1960) found a cross reaction between tobacco mosaic virus and its X-protein by this method. They observed that a greater precipitation with X-protein could be obtained if the pH of the solution was 5.3. Presumably this acidity caused the polymerization of the protein and made it less soluble and easier to precipitate.

The microprecipitin test detected contaminating plant proteins in cauliflower mosaic virus preparations, whereas the ring interface test did not (Pirone *et al.*, 1961). Shepherd and Fulton (1962) applied microprecipitin and tube precipitin tests to the identification of southern bean mosaic virus in a seed-borne disease of cowpea. Homologous and heterologous tests with southern bean mosaic virus showed strong reactions; no cross-absorption studies were possible since the absorbing virus removed nearly all the antibody from the solution.

The microprecipitin test is widely used in Europe. A rather unique application of the procedure should be mentioned. Van Soest and de Meester-Manger Cats (1956) obtained 2–10 drops of exudate from the stylet cut from an aphid that was feeding on tobacco leaves infected with TMV, mixed this material with antiserum, incubated the drops under oil, and showed that no virus passed through the stylet. Both infectivity and electron microscope examinations confirmed the serological data.

3. *Tube precipitin test.*—The combination of antigen and antiserum in equal volumes, incubation of the tubes in a water-bath at 37°C, and reading the results with a background light in a dark room is the general procedure of the tube precipitin test, the oldest serological test. It is a relatively sensitive test compared to the 2 that have been mentioned, but it can be made much more accurate by the quantitative procedure discussed in the next section.

Using this technique and cross absorption, Knight *et al.* (1962) found group differences among 2 strains of TMV isolated from tomato and 5 additional strains. They also found great differences in the amino acid content of the various strains. Black and Brakke (1954) used this test, as well as complement fixation and neutralization, to confirm the presence of specific antibodies to wound-tumor virus. They noted the presence of a soluble antigen and presumed it to be a breakdown product of the virus. This antigen will be discussed further in the section on the ring interface test. Commoner and Yamada (1955) showed association between nonvirus proteins free of nucleic acid and infectious TMV antigen by this test. They isolated only 10–150 μg of protein per gm of tissue but were able to calculate a precipitin value per protein concentration in a dilution and to derive a quotient of relative antigen content that could be used for comparative purposes. Shepherd and Pound (1960) applied this procedure to the identification of turnip mosaic virus and showed that it was unrelated to cauliflower mosaic, turnip yellow mosaic, and turnip crinkle viruses. Thirteen viruses that infect the cucurbits were separated into 2 groups by this techique (Lindberg *et al.,* 1956). Other studies include those by Bagnall *et al.* (1959) on the relation of potato viruses S and M and carnation mosaic virus, the assay for potato virus X in plants doubly infected with viruses X and Y by Rochow *et al.* (1955), and the cross-absorption studies by Thomson (1961) to verify that a new strain with

properties unlike either parent strain could arise from a mixed infection of 2 strains of potato virus X. Tomlinson and co-workers (1959) obtained relatively high serum dilution end points using the procedure with purified cucumber mosaic virus, 1 : 512 or 1 : 1024. Cross reactions of 1 : 16 were obtained with plant protein. Such differences in the dilution end point in cross reactions make absorption of the serum with plant protein unnecessary.

4. *Quantitative precipitin test.* — The quantitative precipitin test, based on the work of Heidelberger and Kendall (1935), is an extremely sensitive procedure for studying the antigen : antibody reaction. A constant volume of antiserum is reacted with increasing amounts of antigen; constant antigen combinations can also be used. The precipitate formed after extended incubation is removed by centrifugation. The amount of precipitate is determined by dry weight, by total nitrogen, or by the Folin-phenol or some similar test for the measurement of protein by optical density. The supernatant fluids are also analyzed by adding antiserum or antigen to aliquot portions to determine the regions of excess antibody or excess antigen. The equivalence zone, the range in which there is no excess of either reactant in the supernatant fluid, is characteristic of a given antigen : antibody system and is an important point of comparison. The antibody : antigen ratio of the complex, in this range which can be calculated from the results, is also an important point of comparison. Generally, the equivalence range for plant viruses is broad, whereas for uncomplex antigens, like egg albumin, the range is narrow.

Kleczkowski (1941), Schramm and Friedrich-Freksa (1941), and Malkiel and Stanley (1947), who used the quantitative precipitin test, estimated that 70, 300, and 100 molecules of antibody, respectively, combined with a virus particle in the equivalence zone. The major reason for the discrepancies apparently was the difference in methods used to analyze the supernatant fluids. Nevertheless, Malkiel and Stanley found a curvilinear relation between the antibody : antigen ratio and the amount of antigen precipitated, but they could not apply the equations of Heidelberger and Kendall (1935). Rappaport and Siegel (1954) noted that the addition of antiserum in ranges of 10^{-3}–10^{-5} reduced the infectivity of TMV by the law of multiple proportions. Using the quantitative precipitin test (Rappaport and Siegel, 1955), they explained the curve characteristics on the basis of steric hindrance. They found greater than a 2–10-fold change in the antigen : antibody ratio from the equivalence range compared to that from the range of excess antibody. Later, Rappaport (1959) reported that the antigen : antibody reaction was reversible. The complex dissociated when ultraviolet, or heat, inactivated virus was added. The largest change in the antigen—antibody complex and surviving virus relation was observed in the region of excess antibody. This presumably was due to incomplete saturation of the antigen sites. The surviving antigen was measured by infectivity. Additional studies will be discussed in the section on the neutralization test.

Strains of TMV were studied by Aach (1957) using this procedure. (The rabbits in these experiments received 300–400 mg of virus in the immunization process.) He was able to relate his strains in such a way that the end strain of a series possessed minute but clearly demonstrable antigenic changes from the preceding mutant and in exchange lost some antigenic component of the original. The group specific antigens remained unchanged from the original. Commoner and Rodenberg (1955) used the quantitative precipitin test to study TMV and 3 proteins of low molecular weight that were associated with the infectious process. One of these soluble proteins, B8, was characterized as a noninfectious, polymerized protein isolated from TMV infectious sap after high-speed centrifugation and acid treatment. Using virus and B8 protein antisera in cross reactions, they found that serum to B8 protein produced a greater precipitate with the virus antigen than with the homologous antigen. All the soluble proteins reacted with the virus antiserum. Kleczkowski (1958) employed the quantitative precipitin test and the Tiselius electrophoresis apparatus to study the antigen—antibody complex of TMV to understand more fully the characteristics of the precipitin reaction. Recently, Matthews (1960) used this technique to measure the nucleoprotein content of turnip yellow mosaic virus after centrifugation in density-gradient columns of cesium chloride. He isolated 5 virus-like fractions and computed their combining rates with virus immune serum. Zaitlin et al. (1954) used this test as well as the Oudin single diffusion and ring interface tests to study the virus in cattleya orchids. The immunizing virus was purified by differential centrifugation and electrophoresis until homogenous. No serological reaction was obtained with healthy plant proteins. Quantitative precipitin analysis showed that more than one antibody was present in the sera; both antigen and antibody were present in the supernatant fluid, a situation that is observed when an antigen—antibody system is complex. The authors concluded that the antigen must have contained 2 viruses.

5. *Serological chromatographic test.*— Matthews (1957) and Lyttleton and Matthews (1958) devised a modification of the precipitin reaction, employing a chromatographic procedure, to determine the amount of precipitate. The precipitate is removed in the quantitative test. After being washed and dried, the precipitate is digested with alkali and chromatographed to measure ribonucleotides associated with the virus. The range of the precipitation reaction of antigen and antibody was adjusted so that the reaction took place in the equivalence zone or on the excess antibody side of equivalence (Matthews and Lyttleton, 1959). Physical, chemical, and serological data (chromatographic test) showed that heated turnip yellow mosaic virus was not different from normal virus, but its infectivity was reduced. Quantitative precipitin tests proved that the 2 types of virus bound the same antibody. Recently, studies were reported in which S^{35} was used to label the nucleic acid (Matthews et al., 1963). The results of isolation and separation of the protein constituents of the turnip yellow mosaic virus in cesium chloride gradients indicated that the protein formed

reversibly and the nucleoprotein irreversibly from the same pool of precursors in the plant.

6. *Ring interface test.*—The ring interface procedure increases the sensitivity of the precipitin test because it is easier to observe a thin line or zone of reaction at midpoint in a tube than an amount of precipitate. Whitcomb and Black (1961a) suggested modifications of this procedure to make it more sensitive. The modifications included using 10% glycerin for the diluent of serum to permit the use of higher dilutions of serum to support the antigen layer and give a clear interface, coating the microtubes (2 mm inside diameter) with mineral oil, and reading the test in a dark room with a strong beam from a microscope light focused on the interface, the heat from the lamp being removed by a water barrier in a lucite box. The test was used for the assay of the wound-tumor virus content of individual leafhoppers. Crushed tumor tissue was also assayed. The detection of the soluble antigen from the infection instead of the virus proved to be a reliable diagnostic method. With a 1 : 50 or 1 : 100 dilution of serum in the underlayer, the soluble antigen end point was 1 : 400 and that of the virus was 1 : 1600. The purified virus can be obtained by density-gradient centrifugation and zonal electrophoresis. Whitcomb and Black (1961b) further improved the accuracy of the ring interface test by devising a time recording of results based on the procedure described in Matthews' (1957) text. The time of appearance of the visible ring in grid titrations was plotted on semilog paper against the dilutions. A linear relation existed within certain ranges of concentration of the antigen, and the position of the line was directly related to the antibody concentration. Relative concentration of the antigen could be estimated from the horizontal distance between 2 lines.

The ring interface procedure has been used for the identification of tulare apple mosaic (Mink and Bancroft, 1962), cucumber mosaic (Tomlinson *et al.*, 1959), sweet potato strain of tobacco mosaic (Sill *et al.*, 1960), and white clover mosaic (Bancroft *et al.*, 1960a) viruses. In the last study, the

antiserum at 1 : 50 produced a tube precipitin end point of 1 : 128 with purified virus and 1 : 4 with plant protein, whereas in the ring test the antiserum at 1 : 128 gave end points of 1 : 512 and 1 : 8, respectively, for the 2 antigens. Bancroft (1962) used the ring interface test to associate bean pod mottle virus with the proteins isolated in density-gradient columns of sucrose. Three components were observed, and all reacted with the virus antiserum. Cross-absorption studies showed that the middle and bottom components were composed of the same antigens. In the test, the serum was diluted to 1 : 256 and the antigen was used at 0.04 mg/ml.

7. *Complement fixation test.*—Since the combination of antigen and antibody in the complement fixation test is in the range of a soluble complex, the extent of the reaction can only be determined by an indicator system. This system is composed of an antigen (sheep red blood cells) and antibody (amboceptor, or hemolysin, which is antisheep red blood cell serum made in rabbits) combined in a ratio that is sensitive to lysis by complement. Another property of complement is that it can be bound by an antigen—antibody complex. The test is designed so that an exact amount of complement will be bound by the virus antigen and its antibody when they are in the range of optimum ratios. The complement will not be bound unless the concentrations of the antigen and antibody are within this range, and therefore it will be free to lyse the sensitized cells of the indicator system. The test involves more than just the dilution of antigen and antibody as described in the previously mentioned serological tests. It is extremely sensitive and can be made quantitative as well as qualitative for the analysis of an antigen—antibody complex. The effort extended in performing the test is not greater than that required for the quantitative precipitin test or the serological chromatographic test, and the information obtained is more than worth the effort.

Tall *et al.* (1949) applied a modification of complement fixation, adequate for the Rickettsial diseases, to the plant viruses. This modified test was used for the study of the relation between tobacco ringspot and tomato ringspot viruses. Later the technique was applied to TMV, to the relationship among strains of TMV (Weaver and Price, 1952; Moorhead, 1953), to barley stripe mosaic virus and brome mosaic viruses (Moorhead, 1956), wheat streak mosaic virus (Moorhead, 1959), alfalfa mosaic virus (Allington et al., 1960; Bancroft et al., 1960a), southern bean mosaic virus (Moorhead, 1961), and the analysis of the sera in the study by the Committee on Virus Type Culture Collection, American Phytopathological Society (1960). Recently, Reichmann and Stace-Smith (1959) applied complement fixation to the characterization of ribonucleic acid isolated by treatment of potato virus X with 2.5 M guanidine and 0.005 M versene. The isolated material showed the correct ratio of absorption at 260 mμ to that at 280 mμ for nucleic acid and showed some infectivity on *Chenopodium amaranticolor* Coste and Reyn, which could be destroyed by ribonuclease. However, the reactions with this nucleic acid and the virus antiserum were negative by complement fixation and the tube precipitin techniques. Wright (1963) applied a quantitative complement fixation technique to the study of strains of TMV, clover yellow mosaic virus, and 12 strains of potato virus X. All the strains of the viruses could be distinguished except those of potato virus X; only one of its strains was serologically distinct. Antibody at 4 different dilutions was mixed with 25 μg virus/ml. The range of dilutions of the serum was chosen so that 85–100% of the complement was absorbed at 1 or more dilutions. Complete absorption of the low titer serum by heterologous antigen occurred at 1 : 50 whereas the higher titered sera were absorbed at 1 : 200 or 1 : 400. In earlier work without the absorption procedure, Wright and Hardy (1961) were unable to differentiate among the 12 strains of potato virus X.

8. *Neutralization test.*—The most recent and successful application of the neutralization test procedure to plant viruses has been the work of Rappaport (1957) and Rappaport et al. (1957) on TMV. The antibody had to be used at dilutions greater than 10^{-3} since normal serum at dilutions

more concentrated than this neutralized the virus. Dilutions of 5×10^{-4} mg of virus per ml were used with a series of antiserum dilutions. After 1 hour of incubation, the dilutions were assayed on *Nicotiana glutinosa* L. leaves, and the logarithm of the percentage of surviving virus activity was plotted against the logarithm of the antiserum concentration. Antisera were prepared against 3 strains—common, mild, and Holmes' ribgrass. Serological reactions of homologous and heterologous strains, including two additional strain antigens, were established. By this method common and masked strains were distinguished, whereas with the quantitative precipitin test they were similar. The strains were categorized into 2 groups. In more recent studies, which applied information from quantitative precipitin reactions, antibody : antigen molecular ratios of 0.5–1.0 were used to compare two methods of infecting *N. glutinosa* leaves—the rub method and the dip method (Furumoto and Wildman, 1963). A 50% loss of infectivity occurred at antibody : antigen ratios of 0.5 by the dip method, whereas no loss was measured by the rub method. The authors continued the analysis of the information derived from these neutralization experiments to estimate that at least 1 virus particle in 10 was infectious.

B. Agar Diffusion Procedures

These procedures represent the newest of the techniques used in the analysis of the antigen : antibody reaction. The tests were conceived in their present form by Ouchterlony (1958, 1962) and Oudin (1952), with modifications by Grabar (1958). The impetus of the technique on the study of the antigen : antibody reaction can be illustrated by the reviews of Ouchterlony; one in 1958 had 255 references whereas one in 1962 had 1,185 references. Many adaptations of the original techniques have appeared. The use of the procedures as they have been applied to plant virus serology in the United States and Canada will be reported here.

1. *Single diffusion test of Oudin.*—Commoner and Rodenberg (1955) applied a tube test of the single diffusion type to tobacco mosaic virus. The internal reactant

was virus antigen mixed with 0.4% agar. After this mixture formed a gel, 0.2 ml of antiserum was added as the external reactant, and the tubes were sealed. Both the intact infectious particle and a soluble fraction designated B8 were tested at concentrations of 92 μg/ml. The position of the leading edge of the precipitate that formed in the antigen-agar column was proportional to the square root of time; a plot of these 2 functions gave a straight line. Using the equation devised by Oudin,

$$R = D \log A$$

in which R = distance in mm/(time in hours)$^{1/2}$, D = diffusion constant of antibody, and A = concentration of antibody, the authors found that the slopes of R vs. log A were identical for the 4 combinations in homologous and heterologous reactions and concluded that the same antibody was reacting with both TMV and B8 antigen.

2. *Double diffusion test.—*

a. *Tube test of Oakley and Fulthorpe* (1953). In the report on the commercial production of antiserum (Committee on Virus Type Culture Collection, 1960), a modification of the test was used to analyze the sera for antigenic components and for contaminating plant proteins. The antisera were the internal reactants. Only tobacco ringspot virus and potato virus X failed to produce precipitation zones. Presumably this failure was due to the aggregation of the antigen since relatively old preparations were tested. Scott (1961) described a microprocedure for testing individual seeds infected with barley stripe mosaic virus. Using the commercially prepared antiserum mentioned previously, he performed the test in 0.2 cm diameter glass tubing containing 0.05 ml of serum at 1 : 10 dilution at one end and the extract from a single seed at the other end of the tube; these solutions were separated by 0.05 ml of 0.6% agar in phosphate buffer. A band of precipitate was observed in 24 hours. Tremaine and Willison (1961b) used the technique to estimate the diffusion constant of a stone fruit virus. With serum at a constant dilution, they observed that various dilutions of antigen not only formed a band that increased in distance from the antigen

meniscus with time, but also sharpened as the concentration of the antibody became optimum and then appeared diffuse. Using the position and concentration which formed the sharpest band, the diffusion coefficient was

$$X_g^2/X_b^2 = D_g/D_b$$

where X_g = distance between zone and antigen meniscus, D_g = diffusion coefficient of antigen, and X_b and D_b represent the same characters for the antibody. Polson (1958) used the same procedure with special measuring devices and obtained an agreement of 5% with the diffusion values determined by optical measurements.

These represent only a few of the manipulations possible with this technique.

b. *Plate test of Ouchterlony.* Van Slogteren (1955, VII) was the first to apply this procedure to plant viruses. He employed buffered saline in the agar solution and used methyl orange to aid in reading the position of the precipitate. Steel blocks were used to form wells in the agar before it hardened. Positive results were reported for TMV, tobacco necrosis virus, alfalfa mosaic virus, strains of cucumis virus I from chrysanthemum, and the unresolved virus complex of carnation mosaic. In another study, D. H. M. van Slogteren (1955) excised the precipitation zones formed by TMV and its antiserum, extracted the virus by freezing and thawing the agar piece, and observed typical rods in the electron microscope.

The double diffusion technique has been applied to a great number of plant viruses since the work of van Slogteren. A few of the applications reported since 1960 will be mentioned. Tremaine and Willison (1961a and 1962a) and Willison et al. (1961) used the procedure for the isolation, identification, and relationship of stone fruit viruses. A component with 72 S sedimentation coefficient was identified as the infectious virus and was observed to form a zone 1–3 mm from the antigen well. Another component with 22 S or 35 S value was contributed by the plant but was not present in extracts of healthy plants. This antigen formed a zone 4–5 mm from the antigen well. A third component was present in some virus preparations and was considered to be a contaminating plant protein that produced a zone 1 mm from the antigen well. These antigens were designated V, Q, and P, respectively. The V antigen was in all preparations except that of latent necrotic ringspot virus. Q antigen was present in 2 yellows preparations, latent and recurrent necrotic ringspot, 2 green ring mottle preparations from sour cherry, prune dwarf, 2 tatter leaf preparations of sweet cherry, and preparations from latent infections of plum and peach. The P antigen was in all preparations including latent necrotic ringspot from peach and plum but not in latent necrotic ringspot from other sources. Tremaine (1961) applied the procedure to give the evidence that a column of basic ion-exchange material could separate virus and plant proteins.

This technique has been used to identify psorosis virus of citrus (Desjardins and Wallace, 1962), tulare apple mosaic virus (Mink and Bancroft, 1962), southern bean mosaic as the seed-borne virus of cowpea (Shepherd and Fulton, 1962), and eucharis virus as tobacco ringspot virus (Kahn *et al.*, 1962). Scott *et al.* (1961) differentiated pod mottle and red node viruses, proving that each gave distinct lines of precipitation. Grogan and Kimble (1962) related 30 isolates of cucumber mosaic virus, and Allen (1962) did the same with stone fruit virus isolates from New York, Pennsylvania, and West Virginia. The multiple zones appearing in sucrose density-gradient columns after centrifugation of brome mosaic virus (Hamilton, 1961) and of bean pod mottle virus (Bancroft, 1962) were related by this serological test. Bean pod mottle virus would not produce precipitation zones if the merthiolate preservative was incorporated in the agar. Sodium azide had no inhibitory effect on the reaction. A mention should also be made of the appearance of a nonspecific plant protein-induced precipitate in agar, which could be eliminated by using sodium azide or by partial purification of the antigen (Tremaine and Willison, 1962b).

3. *Immunoelectrophoresis.* — The technique of immunoelectrophoresis was designed by Grabar (1958) and co-workers. It is based on the electrophoretic migration of a protein in a convection-preventing medium (starch, cellulose acetate, or agar) and on the subsequent location of the protein components by precipitation with antiserum. After electrophoresis in an agar medium, a trough for the antiserum is usually cut into the agar parallel to the flow of the current. Antigens and antiserum diffuse toward each other and precipitate where they meet in optimum proportions. The laws which apply to the tube or plate methods of diffusion also apply to immunoelectrophoresis.

Hamilton (1961) applied immunoelectrophoresis to the soluble antigens associated with brome mosaic virus. A 1 x 3 inch glass plate was coated with Formvar[2]. Agar (1%) in buffer was poured onto the plate to a depth of 3 mm. The buffers used were 0.016 M veronal-sodium veronal, pH 8.0, and 0.01 M potassium phosphate, pH 7.0, both with an ionic strength of 0.03. A well, cut in the agar, was filled with antigen and a current was permitted to flow through the agar for 18–20 hours at 3°C. A trough was cut in the agar and filled with antiserum, and the plate was incubated in a moist environment. Usually, zones began to appear in 24 hours, but the plates were observed for 1–2 weeks. Data from experiments with virus from infectious sap and with purified virus from differential and from density-gradient centrifugation suggested that the multiple zone precipitation was due to dissociation of the virus. Further studies with brome mosaic virus and barley stripe mosaic virus are being prepared for publication (Ball and Hamilton, 1963). The technique is excellent for resolving the total numbers of zones developing in a virus-antiserum system.

C. CONJUGATED ANTIBODY PROCEDURES

The procedure of Coons (1956) found wide application in the fields of medical diagnosis of animal virus diseases. The procedure is based on the conjugation of gamma-globulin with a fluorescent dye. In the "direct" procedure, conjugated antiserum is flooded over tissue containing the antigen, the antibody adheres, and the area glows under ultraviolet light. Nagaraj *et al.*

(1961) applied the technique to identify leafhoppers carrying wound-tumor virus. Antiserum was conjugated with fluorescein isothiocyanate, and the specificity of staining was improved when the conjugate was passed through DEAE-cellulose columns. Individual insects were crushed on a microscope slide, and the remaining parts were extracted with saline. The extract was clarified by centrifugation and tested for virus by the ring interface test. The tissue on the slide from the crushed insect was dried, stained with conjugated serum, washed, and observed in a microscope fitted with an ultraviolet light source. Very good agreement for presence of the virus was observed between the test methods.

The "indirect" method employs conjugated antirabbit serum prepared by immunizing sheep, goats, or any other animal with whole rabbit serum or with rabbit gamma-globulin. The sections of tissue are flooded with virus immune serum prepared in rabbits, washed, and flooded with the conjugated antirabbit serum, washed, and observed. The antivirus serum adheres to the tissue where the virus is located, and in turn the antirabbit serum adheres to the rabbit serum. Observations are made as described previously. Using the direct and indirect technique, Nagaraj and Black (1961) observed that wound-tumor virus was concentrated in pseudophloem and rarely in the thick-walled cells and xylem. Dye was never found in the epidermis, cortex, or in most of the xylem, ray, and pith cells. Sinha and Black (1962) reported much more satisfactory results with the indirect than with the direct technique; less nonspecific staining occurred in the tissue. One difficulty encountered in using the direct technique was the loss of antibody through each step in preparing the conjugate. Samples taken throughout the conjugation procedure and titrated in the ring interface test revealed an original titer of 1 : 2560 and a final titer of the conjugate at 1 : 80. Prolonged staining with more dilute serum did not give as brilliant a stain in the ultraviolet light as the more concentrated serum.

Worley (1962) reported on the successful use of the technique in tracing the development of southern bean mosaic virus in bean leaves. The virus was distributed widely in the epidermal cells of inoculated leaves in 24 hours, then it was located in the adjacent mesophyll cells, and finally it was observed in all cells in the area. On the opposite, uninoculated leaf, the distribution of virus was more uniform due to the systemic invasion of the virus.

Another procedure utilizes electron dense ferritin conjugated with serum. The antiserum adheres to the antigen particles making a dense area when viewed in the electron microscope. Borek and Silverstein (1961) prepared conjugated southern bean mosaic virus antiserum and characterized the serum by agar diffusion and immunoelectrophoresis. Extensive studies on the characterization of the reaction between TMV and ferritin conjugated antiserum were reported by Singer and Schick (1961). The specific combination of antigen and antibody was determined by chemical analyses for nitrogen and iron in the precipitate, by electron microscopy for the formation of aggregates of virus particles, and by electrophoresis for the separation of component parts of the system. The ferritin conjugated serum technique should be effective in locating virus accumulation areas *in vivo*.

11–4. APPLICATION

One of the most practical applications of serology has been in the diagnosis of the virus diseases of potato. Mention has been made of the conditions used in field testing in Europe, Africa, and Canada (Munro, 1954). Reviews, which describe the test procedure used in the Netherlands (E. van Slogteren, 1955; van Slogteren, IV, 1955; and van Slogteren and van Slogteren, 1957), stated that over a million plants were tested for potato virus X and S every year by the agglutination or microprecipitin technique. All these tests were done in 3–4 weeks with substations performing 21,000 tests a day during the period. Approximately 160 liters of immune sera were used each year.

Wide-scale serological testing of field material for the maintenance of virus-free potato seed stocks has not been reported in

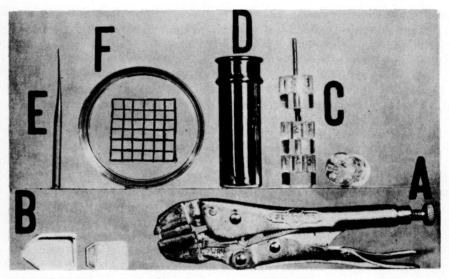

Fig. 11–1. Equipment used in the microprecipitin test for potato virus X in seed potato stocks in Nebraska. A. Vise-grip pliers modified to hold micropresses. B. Spoon and plate assembly of the micropresses. C. Lucite microcentrifuge tubes. Each section contains 8 wells of 0.5 cm diameter and 1.8 cm height. Four sections can be stacked for centrifugation. D. Fifty ml bucket for centrifuge tubes. E. Micropipette. F. Formvar treated Petri dish with grid drawn for testing individual samples.

the United States. Apparently, Nebraska is the only state with such a program, though the effort in this state is small compared to that of the Netherlands. In 1962, the seventh consecutive year of this program, 4000 individual serological tests were performed by the microprecipitin procedure. Approximately 14 ml of concentrated potato virus X antiserum was used; the serum could be diluted 1 : 7 in the test. "Mother" tubers, second, and third year progeny were tested individually, whereas older stocks in the fourth or fifth year of increase were tested by combining leaves from 5 plants. (Serological tests showed that 1 part of infected leaf could be detected in 4 parts of healthy leaf samples.) Of the 4000 separate tests, only 274 were positive for the presence of the virus. The majority of the positive reactions were found in fourth and fifth year stocks that were in the hands of growers and not under close experimental control.

The equipment used for the serological testing of potatoes for virus X is shown in Fig. 11–1. The micropresses and microcentrifuge tubes were developed under the supervision of William B. Allington. The microagglutination test (van Slogteren, VIII,

1955) was not applicable to testing in Nebraska, because some element, probably calcium, contributed to the plant from the soil caused nonspecific precipitation. It was necessary to clarify the sap by heating and by the addition of an equal volume of 0.1 M neutral phosphate buffer. The microcentrifuge tubes handle 8 samples in a block (section), and a stack of 4 sections can be placed in one centrifuge bucket. It is possible to centrifuge 128 samples in one run of the small "clinical" type centrifuge.

Serological methods have been applied to studies of the relationships among strains of other viruses in addition to those of potato. A great many of these studies have been cooperative efforts involving investigators within the United States and in various other countries. Waterworth and Fulton (1962) examined 50 isolates from necrotic ringspot disease of sour cherry and proved that the isolates were not related to prune dwarf virus. Oswald and Bowman (1958) used antiserum from the Netherlands to diagnose rattle virus in California. In another study (Oswald et al., 1955), antisera to the California and to the Netherlands isolates of alfalfa mosaic virus and aucuba mosaic virus from potato were compared. These viruses appeared similar on potato, but serological techniques and cross-protection tests showed that they were not related. Bercks (1962) reported on the study of 5 isolates of tomato black ring virus obtained from Scotland, England, and Germany. These isolates could be placed in 2 groups, and their relationship with each other was found to be independent of their geographical locations.

Perhaps one of the most striking cooperative studies was made with the legume viruses. Bancroft *et al.* (1960a) established the relationship of 12 isolates of alfalfa mosaic virus obtained from the Netherlands, California, Maryland, Indiana, Wisconsin, and Oregon. White clover mosaic isolates from Canada (Alberta and British Columbia), California, Idaho, and Washington were compared with the yellow mosaic virus. The former virus was not found east of the continental divide (Pratt, 1961). This was disputed by Agrawal *et al.* (1962), who studied isolates in 7 western states and 13 eastern states and found

clover yellow mosaic virus in Oklahoma and Kentucky. Bos *et al.* (1960a) described a commendable example of a cooperative study in which antisera as well as virus isolates were exchanged, thereby enabling the investigators to study the relations under their own conditions of growing and testing. A suggested procedure for the international identification of legume viruses has been made available (Bos *et al.*, 1960b). This approach to the problem of virus identification will aid tremendously in establishing the relation of viruses studied under vastly different conditions.

One statement by Bos *et al.* (1960a) can be applied appropriately to conclude this review. "Serology is the most informative and objective single method by which virus relationship may be determined."

❊ ❊ ❊

Acknowledgement. The author expresses appreciation to Myron K. Brakke for the helpful suggestions and comments made during the preparation of the manuscript.

11–5. LITERATURE CITED

Aach, H. G. (1957). Z. Naturforsch. **12b,** 614.

Agrawal, H., Bos, L., and Chessin, M. (1962). Phytopathology **52,** 512.

Alfieri, S. A., and Stouffer, R. F. (1957). Phytopathology **47,** 1.

Allen, W. R. (1962). Phytopathology **52,** 922.

Allen, W. R., and Tremaine, J. H. (1962). Phytopathology **52,** 721.

Allington, W. B., Moorhead, E. L., and Staples, R. (1960). Phytopathology **50,** 627.

Bagnall, R. H., Wetter, C., and Larson, R. H. (1959). Phytopathology **49,** 435.

Ball, E. M. (1961). Serological Tests for the Identification of Plant Viruses. Amer. Phytopath. Soc., Ithaca, N.Y.

Ball, E. M., and Hamilton, R. I. (1963). Bact. Proc. 132.

Bancroft, J. B. (1962). Virology **16,** 419.

Bancroft, J. B., Moorhead, E. L., Tuite, J., and Liu, H. P. (1960a). Phytopathology **50,** 34.

Bancroft, J. B., Tuite, J., and Hissong, G. (1960b). Phytopathology **50,** 711.

Bawden, F. C. (1950). Plant Viruses and Virus Diseases. 3d ed. Chronica Botanica Co., Waltham, Mass.

Beale, H. P. (1931). Contrib. Boyce Thompson Inst. **3,** 529.

Beale, H. P., and Lojkin, M. E. (1944). Contrib. Boyce Thompson Inst. **13,** 385.

Benson, A. P., and Hooker, W. J. (1960). Phytopathology **50,** 231.

Bercks, R. (1958). In M. Klinkowski (ed.), Pflanzliche Virologie. 162. Akademie-Verlag, Berlin.

Bercks, R. (1960). Virology **12,** 311.

Bercks, R. (1962). Phytopathol. Z., **46,** 97.

Birkeland, J. M. (1934). Botan. Gaz. **95,** 419.

Black, L. M., and Brakke, M. K. (1954). Phytopathology **44,** 482.

Borek, F., and Silverstein, A. M. (1961). J. Immunol. **87,** 555.

Bos, L., Maat, D. Z., Bancroft, J. B., Gold, A. H., Pratt, M. J., Quantz, L., and Scott, H. A. (1960a). Tijdschr. Plantenziekten **66,** 102.

Bos, L., Hagedorn, D. J., and Quantz, L. (1960b). Tijdschr. Plantenziekten **66,** 328.

Cadman, C. H., and Lister, R. M. (1961). Phytopathology **51,** 29.

Chester, K. S. (1934). Phytopathology **24,** 1180.

Chester, K. S. (1935a). Phytopathology **25,** 686.

Chester, K. S. (1935b). Phytopathology **25,** 702.

Chester, K. S. (1936). Phytopathology **26**, 715.

Chester, K. S. (1937a). Phytopathology **27**, 722.

Chester, K. S. (1937b). Phytopathology **27**, 903.

Chester, K. S. (1937c). Quart. Rev. Biol. **12**, 19, 165.

Committee on Virus Type Culture Collection, Amer. Phytopath. Soc. (1960). Phytopathology **50**, 428.

Commoner, B., and Rodenberg, S. D. (1955). J. Gen. Physiol. **38**, 475.

Commoner, B., and Yamada, M. (1955). J. Gen. Physiol. **38**, 459.

Coons, A. H. (1956). Histochemistry with Labeled Antibody. 1–23. Intern. Rev. Cytol. Vol. V. Academic Press, New York.

Desjardins, P. R., and Wallace, J. M. (1962). Virology **16**, 99.

Dvorak, M. (1927). J. Infect. Diseases **41**, 215.

Freund, J. (1947). Ann. Rev. Microbiol. **1**, 291.

Furumoto, W. A., and Wildman, S. G. (1963). Virology **20**, 53.

Govier, D. A. (1958). Scottish Plant Breeding Station Report. 77–81.

Grabar, P. (1958). Advan. Protein Chem. **13**, 1.

Grogan, R. G., and Kimble, K. A. (1962). Phytopathology **52**, 734.

Hamilton, R. I. (1961). Virology **15**, 452.

Heidelberger, M., and Kendall, F. E. (1935). J. Exptl. Med. **62**, 697.

Hildebrand, E. M., and Kehr, A. E. (1961). Phytopathology **51**, 833.

Hollings, M., and Stone, O. M. (1962). Nature **194**, 607.

Kahn, R. P., Scott, H. A., and Monroe, R. L. (1962). Phytopathology **52**, 1211.

Kleczkowski, A. (1941). Brit. J. Exptl. Pathol. **22**, 44.

Kleczkowski, A. (1958). Immunology **1**, 36.

Knight, C. A., Silva, D. M., Dahl, D., and Tsugita, A. (1962). Virology **16**, 236.

Lindberg, G. D., Hall, D. H., and Walker, J. C. (1956). Phytopathology **46**, 489.

Lyttleton, J. W., and Matthews, R. E. F. (1958). Virology **6**, 460.

Malkiel, S., and Stanley, W. M. (1947). J. Immunol. **57**, 31.

Matthews, R. E. F. (1957). Plant Virus Serology. Cambridge Univ. Press, Cambridge.

Matthews, R. E. F. (1960). Virology **12**, 521.

Matthews, R. E. F., and Lyttleton, J. W. (1959). Virology **9**, 332.

Matthews, R. E. F., Bolton, E. T., and Thompson, H. R. (1963). Virology **19**, 179.

Miller, P. M., and Thornberry, H. H. (1958). Phytopathology **48**, 665.

Mink, G. I., and Bancroft, J. B. (1962). Nature **194**, 214.

Moorhead, E. L. (1953). Ph.D. Thesis, Univ. of Pittsburgh.

Moorhead, E. L. (1956). Phytopathology **46**, 498.

Moorhead, E. L. (1959). Phytopathology **49**, 151.

Moorhead, E. L. (1961). Virology **13**, 249.

Moorhead, E. L., and Price, W. C. (1953). Phytopathology **43**, 73.

Munro, J. (1954). Am. Potato J. **31**, 73.

Nagaraj, A. N., and Black, L. M. (1961). Virology **15**, 289.

Nagaraj, A. N., Sinha, R. C., and Black, L. M. (1961). Virology **15**, 205.

Oakley, C. L., and Fulthorpe, A. J. (1953). J. Pathol. Bacteriol. **65**, 49.

Oswald, J. W., and Bowman, Tully. (1958). Phytopathology **48**, 396.

Oswald, J. W., Rozendaal, A., and van der Want, J. P. H. (1955). Proc. 2d Conf. Potato Virus Diseases, 1954, 137. Veenman and Zonen, Wageningen.

Ouchterlony, O. (1958). In Progr. Allergy. **5**, 1. S. Karger, Basel/New York.

Ouchterlony, O. (1962). In Progr. Allergy. **6**, 30. S. Karger, Basel/New York.

Oudin, J. (1952). In Methods in Medical Research. **5**, 335. The Year Book Publishers, Inc.

Pirone, T. P., Pound, G. S., and Shepherd, R. J. (1961). Phytopathology **51**, 541.

Polson, A. (1958). Sci. Tools **5**, 17.

Pratt, M. J. (1961). Can. J. Botany **39**, 655.

Purdy, H. A. (1928). Proc. Soc. Exptl. Biol. Med. **25**, 702.

Purdy, H. A. (1929). J. Exptl. Med. **49**, 919.

Rappaport, I. (1957). J. Immunol. **78**, 256.

Rappaport, I. (1959). J. Immunol. **82**, 526.

Rappaport, I., and Siegel, A. (1954). Phytopathology **44**, 503.

Rappaport, I., and Siegel, A. (1955). J. Immunol. **74**, 106.

Rappaport, I., Siegel, A., Owen, R. D., and Wildman, S. G. (1957). J. Immunol. **78**, 259.

Regenmortel, M. H. V. van, Brandes, J., and Bercks, R. (1962). Phytopathol. Z. **45**, 205.

Reichmann, M. E., and Stace-Smith, R. (1959). Virology **9**, 710.

Rochow, W. F., Ross, A. F., and Siegel, B. M. (1955). Virology **1**, 28.

Salk, J. E., and Laurent, A. M. (1952). J. Exptl. Med. **95**, 429.

Schramm, G., and Friedrich-Freksa, H. (1941). Hoppe-Seylers Z. Physiol. Chem. **270**, 233.

Scott, H. A. (1961). Phytopathology **51**, 200.

Scott, H. A. (1962). Phytopathology **52**, 166.

Scott, H. A., Vincent, M., and Zaumeyer, W. J. (1961). Phytopathology **51**, 755.

Shepherd, R. J., and Fulton, R. W. (1962). Phytopathology **52**, 489.

Shepherd, R. J., and Pound, G. S. (1960). Phytopathology **50**, 797.

Sill, W. H., Jr., Lal, S. B., and del Rosaria, M. S. E. (1960). Phytopathology **50**, 709.

Singer, S. J., and Schick, A. F. (1961). J. Biophys. Biochem. Cytology **9**, 519.

Sinha, R. C., and Black, L. M. (1962). Virology **17**, 582.

Slogteren, D. H. M. van. (1955). Acta Botan. Neerl. **4**, 474.

Slogteren, D. H. M. van. (1955). IV. Proc. 2d Conf. Potato Virus Diseases, 1954, 35. Veenman and Zonen, Wageningen.

Slogteren, D. H. M. van. (1955). VII. Proc. 2d Conf. Potato Virus Diseases, 1954, 45. Veenman and Zonen, Wageningen.

Slogteren, D. H. M. van. (1955). VIII. Proc. 2d Conf. Potato Virus Diseases, 1954, 51. Veenman and Zonen, Wageningen.

Slogteren, E. van. (1955). Ann. Appl. Biol. **42**, 122.

Slogteren, E. van, and Slogteren, D. H. M. van. (1957). Ann. Rev. Microbiol. **11**, 149.

Smith, K. M. (1951). Recent Advances in the Study of Plant Viruses. 2d ed. Blakiston, Philadelphia.

Soest, W. van, and de Meester-Manger Cats, V. (1956). Virology **2**, 411.

Stapp, C. and Bercks, R. (1948). Phytopathol. Z. **15**, 47.

Storm, L. W., and Streets, R. B. (1962). Phytopathology **52**, 754.

Takahashi, W. N., and Gold, A. H. (1960). Virology **10**, 449.

Tall, M. G., Price, W. C., and Wertman, K. (1949). Phytopathology **39**, 288.

Thomson, A. D. (1961). Virology **13**, 507.

Tomlinson, J. A., Shepherd, R. J., and Walker, J. C. (1959). Phytopathology **49**, 293.

Tremaine, J. H. (1961). Can. J. Botany **39**, 1705.

Tremaine, J. H., and Willison, R. S. (1961a). Can. J. Botany **39**, 1387.

Tremaine, J. H., and Willison, R. S. (1961b). Can. J. Botany **39**, 1843.

Tremaine, J. H., and Willison, R. S. (1962a). Can. J. Botany **40**, 361.

Tremaine, J. H., and Willison, R. S. (1962b). Phytopathology **52**, 179.

Veken, J. A. van der. (1961). Proc. 4th Conf. Potato Virus Diseases, 1960, 153. Veenman and Zonen, Wageningen.

Waterworth, H. E., and Fulton, R. W. (1962). Phytopathology **52**, 32.

Weaver, E. P., and Price, W. C. (1952). Proc. Soc. Exptl. Biol. Med. **79**, 125.

Wetter, C. (1960). Arch. Microbiol. **37**, 278.

Wetter, C. (1961). Proc. 4th Conf. Potato Virus Diseases, 1960, 164. Veenman and Zonen, Wageningen.

Whitcomb, R. F., and Black, L. M. (1961a). Virology **15**, 136.

Whitcomb, R. F., and Black, L. M. (1961b). Virology **15**, 507.

Willison, R. S., Tremaine, J. H., and Weintraub, M. (1961). Can. J. Botany **39**, 1447.

Worley, J. F. (1962). Phytopathology **52**, 757.

Wright, N. S. (1963). Virology **20**, 131.

Wright, N. S., and Hardy, M. (1961). Virology **13**, 414.

Zaitlin, M., Schechtman, A. M., Bald, J. G., and Wildman, S. G. (1954). Phytopathology **44**, 314.

11–6. SUPPLEMENTARY READING

Boyd, W. C. (1956). Fundamentals of Immunology. 3d ed. Interscience Publishers.

Carpenter, P. L. (1956). Immunology and Serology. W. B. Saunders, Publishers.

Kabat, E. A., and Mayer, M. M. (1961). Experimental Immunochemistry. 2d ed. C. C. Thomas, Publishers.

C. E. HALL

Electron microscopy: Principles and application to virus research

12–1. INTRODUCTION

IN 1873 Ernst Abbe showed that the minimum separation between small objects that could be distinguished with a microscope was limited by the half-angle of the cone of rays accepted by the objective lens (aperture) and by the wavelength of the light employed. Resolution increases with aperture but this is eventually limited as the angle approaches 90 degrees. The final limitation then is in the wavelength and the smallest distance between distinguishable points in an object is about one-half the wavelength, which in the case of visible light is about ¼ micron (μ) or 2500 Angstrom units (Å) [$1 \mu = 10^{-3}$ mm = 10,000A 1A = 10^{-8} cm].

With the discovery of X-rays of very short wavelength around the turn of the century hopes were raised that microscopes using X-rays might be built to overcome the limitations of optical microscopy. However no effective way of focusing X-rays has been found to exploit effectively the short wavelength they possess. Magnified pictures can be made with X-rays from contact radiographs and by other methods, but these have about the same resolution as the optical microscope. It was not until about 1926, when L. de Broglie showed that streams of electrons had associated with them a very short wavelength and H. Busch showed that electrons could be focused, that the physical basis for electron microscopes was established. The potentiality was not recognized immediately, but by 1932 M. Knoll and E. Ruska described the first crude prototype of modern electron microscopes, and by 1940 electron microscopes were being made with resolving powers far exceeding those of optical microscopes.

The de Broglie wavelength, λ, associated with an electron beam which has been accelerated from rest through a difference of V volts is

$$\lambda = \frac{12.3\text{Å}}{\sqrt{V}}. \qquad (12\text{–}1)$$

If we put V = 50,000 volts the wavelength is about 0.05A, which is much smaller than the diameter of single atoms. Unfortunately all electron lenses suffer from spherical aberration, which causes rays at larger distances from the lens axis to be too strongly bent compared to those passing through the lens closer to the axis. This produces a disc of confusion such that the diameter d_{sph} of the smallest object that can be sharply defined is:

$$d_{sph} = C_s a^3 \qquad (12\text{–}2)$$

where a is the aperture angle in radians and C_s is the spherical aberration constant, which has values from about 0.02 to 1 cm. To attain high resolution, a must then be very small. The wavelength limitation or diffraction error results in a disc of confusion, or Airy disc corresponding to a diameter d_{diff}:

$$d_{diff} = \frac{0.6\lambda}{a}. \qquad (12\text{--}3)$$

Thus at small angles the wavelength limitation becomes large. We have to strike a balance between spherical aberration and diffraction, which gives us our best resolution attainable as:

$$d_o \doteq C_s{}^{1/4} \lambda^{3/4} \qquad (12\text{--}4)$$

with aperture angles of 10^{-3} to 10^{-2} radian. The best resolving powers obtainable with current instruments is 5–10Å, which is much larger than the wavelength but is some 500 times better than the best optical microscopes.

As a consequence of the very small aperture of the imaging pencil the depth of field (i.e., the distance along the axis in object space over which parts of an object appear to be in satisfactory focus) is large compared to that of a high resolution optical microscope. This distance is approximately:

$$D \doteq \frac{d}{a} \qquad (12\text{--}5)$$

where d is the resolution limit and a is the aperture angle. The depth of field in image space is also correspondingly large, being M^2D where M is the lateral magnification. This means that when photographic plate and observation screen are not at the same plane the image can be in good focus at both simultaneously.

After the introduction of manufactured electron microscopes in some quantity about 1940 there followed a period of about 10 years when the main progress was due to the development of special specimen techniques to prepare and process materials so that they could be effectively examined with the high resolution that the instruments possessed. To some extent this is still going on but the major problems which appeared formidable in the beginning have been successfully overcome. Structure of a specimen is seen in an electron image (electron micrograph) by virtue of: (1) the scattering of beam electrons by atoms in the specimen, (2) by diffraction of the beam, and (3) alterations in phase of the electron beam as it passes through the specimen. The specimen must be very thin, usually 100 to 1000Å. It is inserted into a vacuum where it may suffer damage or alterations as a result of electron irradiation. Thus, specimens have to be prepared in a special way and interpretation of what is recorded in the image may not always be easy. It is the purpose of this brief discussion to present the principles of the instrument and the processes of image formation in simple terms and to show a few examples of application in virus research. Extensive coverage of each of the various aspects touched on here may be found expanded in the general references (Hall, 1953; Kay, 1961; Klug and Caspar, 1960; Williams, 1954).

12–2. THE ELECTRON MICROSCOPE

Electron lenses consist of electrostatic or magnetic fields in space having an axis of symmetry. Electrostatic lenses may consist of parallel metallic plates with coaxial circular holes through which electrons pass. Voltages are applied to the plates so that electrons are accelerated and decelerated, and as a result their paths are bent as they pass through the system close to the axis. Magnetic lenses consist of a cylindrically symmetrical gap in a magnetized iron circuit. Electrons passing through the gap close to the axis are deflected by the lines of force, experiencing a net deflection toward the axis. The same lens equations apply as in classical optics. In particular we have for a glass lens of focal length f in air producing a real image of an object placed a distance x_o to the left of the first focal point, the relation:

$$x_o x_i = f^2 \qquad (12\text{--}6)$$

where x_i is the distance of the image to the

right of the second focal point. The magnification is:

$$M = \frac{x_i}{f}. \qquad (12\text{-}7)$$

For a high magnification f must be small and x_i relatively large. For electron microscope lenses the minimum f is about 2–3 mm. Under these circumstances x_o is very small and the object is very close to the first focal point.

A schematic diagram of an electron microscope is shown in Fig. 12–1. Electrons from the tip of a hairpin tungsten filament are accelerated through a high positive field gradient produced between cathode and anode. A circular hole in the shield which carries a negative potential acts as an electron lens so that an image of the tip (crossover) is formed in the vicinity of the anode. The focal length of the condenser lens can be set so that an image of the crossover can be produced at the object plane under which circumstances the electron intensity (or intensity of illumination) and the aperture of illumination are a maximum and the area illuminated is a minimum. If the focal length of the condenser is made shorter or longer than this critical setting, intensity and aperture angle decrease and area illuminated increases. Frequently two condenser lenses are employed in series to obtain a very small illuminated area, which decreases specimen damage.

Part of the electrons pass through the specimen relatively unscattered but those that pass close to the nuclei of atoms will be deflected and prevented from reaching the image by being intercepted by the objective aperture which may have a diameter of 20–50 μ. In the absence of an objective aperture spherical aberration prevents widely scattered electrons from contributing to the meaningful image, though they appear at the final image plane as a background "fog." The objective lens is the most important component of the instrument and produces a magnified image of the object as indicated. Projector lenses (usually two) remagnify this image to produce the final image on a fluorescent screen, where it may be observed with a binocular viewer. When the viewing screen is moved

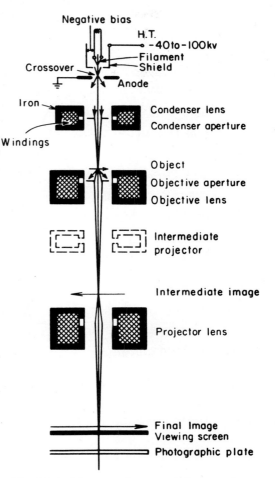

Fig. 12–1. Schematic diagram of the optical system of a magnetic electron microscope.

out of the way, electrons strike a photographic plate which is later processed to produce a recorded image. Magnifications on the plate may be anywhere from a few hundred to 200,000×, and after final enlargement on photographic paper the magnifications may be as high as a million or more.

The entire path of the electron beam is contained in a column which is kept evacuated by vacuum pumps. Object and photographic plates may be inserted through air locks or may be exchanged by isolating the pumps and letting atmospheric air into the column. Precisely regulated power supplies provide a stable high voltage (i.e., a monochromatic beam) and provide lens currents which can be varied by potentiometers to

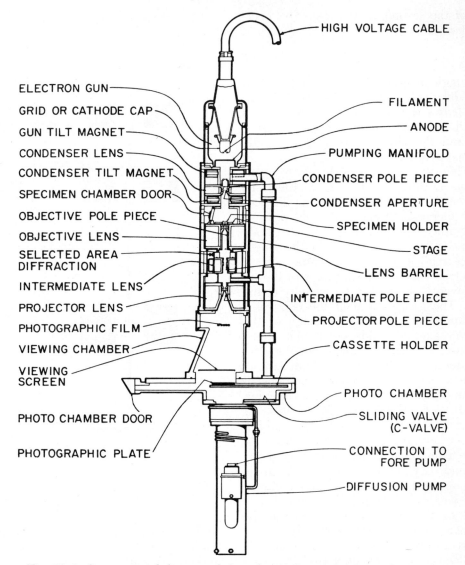

Fig. 12–2. Cross-sectional diagram of the column of an RCA Series EMU3 electron microscope (courtesy Radio Corporation of America).

alter the focal length of the lenses. In Fig. 12–2 is shown a cross-sectional diagram of the column of the RCA EMU3 electron microscope. Not shown are electrical supplies, forepump, valving systems, or operating controls.

12–3. IMAGE CHARACTERISTICS

In electron microscopes the object is kept in a fixed position and the focus of the final image is effected by adjusting the current through the objective lens winding which controls the focal length of the lens.

A. Focus

An initial experiment in learning the operation of electron microscopes and also a routine procedure for checking image quality consists of recording a through-focus series of some simple object, such as circular holes in a thin film or spherical particles on a thin supporting film. In Fig. 12–3 are shown diagrammatically the principal phe-

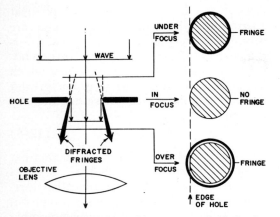

Fig. 12–3. Diagrams showing, on the left, the occurrence of anomalous Fresnel fringe at the edge of a hole in a thin film and, on the right, the appearance of this fringe when the objective lens is focused above, at, and below the plane of the film.

nomena occurring in connection with the imaging of a hole in an "opaque" film. Essentially what we observe are diffraction fringes close to the edge. In classical optics the analogous phenomena are called Fresnel diffraction. We use the same terminology in electron optics, though there are important differences in the appearance of the fringes close to focus. In the electron optical case, the most prominent feature is the anomalous fringe of high intensity scattered into the shadow of the edge as shown in Fig. 12–3, which does not occur in classical optics. If we focus on a plane below the hole we see a shadow outline of the hole with a high intensity halo inside the shadow as indicated in the figure. If we focus above the film we see the fringe in the virtual position produced by projecting the rays backwards, and the fringe appears outside of the edge or inside the hole. In exact focus no fringe is seen and at greater levels of defocusing secondary fringes appear. The terms "underfocused" and "overfocused" signify lens currents too weak and too strong, respectively. In Fig. 12–4 are micrographs showing the phenomena sketched in Fig. 12–3. In this case the film is not opaque but the essential features are the same close to focus. If the lens field is not absolutely symmetrical about its axis a condition will appear close to best focus where the fringe will be overfocused at opposite edges of the hole and underfocused at edges at 90° to this direction. This is astigmatism and is corrected by a "stigmator," which introduces a cylindrical field of proper magnitude perpendicular to that producing the defect.

In Fig. 12–5 is shown the edge of a spherical carbon particle supported on a thin microcrystalline film. The fringes in a and c near the edge of the particle show that a is underfocused and c is overfocused. Absence of a fringe in b shows it is in focus. Note that the image shows structure in the out-of-focus frames and no structure in focus. This is due to the fact that the microstructure of the film does not scatter sufficient electrons out of the beam to produce observable gradations of intensity in the in-focus image. The structure does, however, produce distortion in the wave front beyond the specimen, which shows as fluctuations in intensity in the out-of-focus frames. Details appearing as dark

Fig. 12–4. Electron micrographs of a hole in a test film showing appearances left to right corresponding to the sketches in Fig. 12–3 top to bottom. Magnification 110,000×.

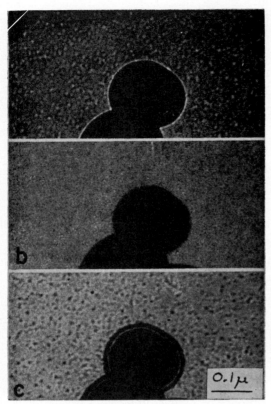

Fig. 12–5. Through focus series showing edge of a carbon particle suspended on a thin film. Film structure is visible in out-of-focus frames but not in focus. Magnification 115,000×.

ture of the lens as limited by spherical aberration or by a limiting diaphragm are subtracted from the imaging beam. If I is the intensity at the image plane corresponding to a small area of the specimen which has a mass per unit area w g/cm² greater than the adjoining area where the intensity is I_o, then

$$I = I_o e^{-Sw} \qquad (12-8)$$

where S is the scattering cross section per gram of the substance involved. S varies with beam potential, size of objective aperture, and spherical aberration constant but is relatively independent of atomic number of the atoms involved. For a given set of conditions it is then an instrumental constant which can be determined readily by measuring I_o/I photographically for a test object of known w, such as a measurement through the center of a polystyrene sphere (Hall and Inoue, 1957). The photographic density D is closely proportional to the electron intensity producing it up to $D \doteq 1.5$. Subsequently then with the same apertures, etc., one can measure unknown masses of particles on a substrate by measuring the photographic density at the image of the particle and in the adjacent area. This technique has been used to measure the amount of various stains taken up by virus particles (Hall, 1955).

The scattering equation discussed above holds for amorphous materials or regions consisting of many randomly oriented crystallites, but when crystals large enough to be resolved are observed contrast may be affected by the occurrence of discrete crystalline diffractions (Bragg reflections). When crystals are properly oriented for these to occur, anomalous high intensity pencils are scattered in discrete directions and contrast becomes a function of crystal orientation and of the relative perfection of the lattice. These effects are of the upmost importance in the electron microscopy of metals but are of much less consequence in biological materials, though they may occur.

C. GENERAL CONSIDERATIONS

Factors discussed above affect contrast in the image, that is to say, the visibility

spots in a appear as bright spots in c. This is phase contrast and is important for very small or very thin objects. Pictures are usually recorded at a slightly underfocused setting to take advantage of phase contrast and to enhance the definition of edges through the occurrence of the first Fresnel fringe. For example, electron micrographs of the protein capsomeres of virus particles are invariably recorded considerably underfocused. Underfocused micrographs can be misleading; but if regularity of structure is present, the regularity can be preserved in the out-of-focus image and contrast is considerably enhanced for these settings.

B. SCATTERING

Strong scattering of electrons occurs mainly very close to nuclei of atoms and in a thin specimen a large component is transmitted without appreciable scattering. Electrons scattered beyond the effective aper-

of structures or the differentiation of one part of a structure from another. Since the mass per unit volume for biological materials is low, obtaining sufficient contrast has always been a major problem. For this reason we use methods for enhancing contrast and must use very thin or special substrates whose structure does not intrude into the picture. In order to produce very thin substrates a large coherent component is transmitted which enhances phase and Fresnel phenomena.

Electron irradiation can produce damage through production of heat and chemical effects and dessiccation can be injurious. Stabilization of biological structures is therefore usually necessary. Electron bombardment of a specimen also causes a contamination deposit to build up consisting of breakdown products of the residual pump oils and other vapors in the vacuum. These deposits can cause rapid loss of contrast if contaminating oils and greases are excessive or if irradiation is prolonged.

12–4. TECHNIQUES

The peculiarities of electron microscope image formation require that the specimens be prepared in special ways to preserve their structure and to render it visible through interaction with the electron beam. Specimens should be thin (100–1000Å), capable of withstanding the effects of vacuum and of electron irradiation, and they usually have to be processed in some way to render structural features visible as sharp variations of intensity in the final image (i.e., to produce "contrast"). The student is referred to standard works for a survey of techniques in general (Hall, 1953; Kay, 1961). Remarks here will be confined to procedures that have been important in the electron microscopy of viruses. Three principal techniques are employed to enhance the visibility of viruses and their components in electron micrographs: shadow casting, positive staining, and negative staining.

A. Shadow Casting

This technique introduced by Williams and Wyckoff (1944) is an exceptionally

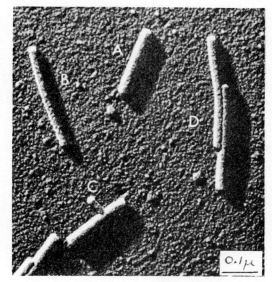

Fig. 12–6. Shadowed tobacco mosaic virus (TMV) showing various shadowing artifacts as described in the text. Magnification 125,000×.

effective method for enhancing the visibility of isolated particles on a substrate. The process consists of depositing at an oblique angle vaporized metals such as platinum (Pt) and uranium (U) on the specimen in a vacuum prior to examination with the electron microscope. The metal outlines the particles and the particles cast a "shadow," as seen in Fig. 12–6, which shows tobacco mosaic virus (TMV) treated in this way. The shadowing angle or shadow to height ratio being known, particle heights can be calculated from a measurement of shadow lengths. Pictures such as this figure are usually displayed as negative prints, having been put through an intermediate transparency in order to make the shadows black, although these are actually regions of high electron transmission since they are devoid of metal. The substrate should, of course, be structureless in order for dimensions of the particles to be examined. For viruses conventional films such as collodion or carbon are satisfactory. For smaller macromolecules the surface of freshly cleaved mica has proved to be an ideal substrate (Hall, 1956). Macromolecules suspended in volatile buffers are sprayed onto the mica surface from an atomizer, shadow-cast with Pt, and backed with an evaporated film of C or silicon monoxide (SiO) in the same vacuum chamber. After removal from the vacuum the layer is backed with a film of collodion. The resulting film is scored into 3-mm squares which float off onto the surface of water, from which they can be picked up over the usual metal screens with 200 openings per linear inch.

Although shadow casting is very effective in increasing contrast of particles down to about 10A in diameter, it has some drawbacks. What is seen in the image is the metal cap which exaggerates the dimensions of small objects. Under standardized conditions an estimate of the distortions can be obtained and a correction made to the apparent size of objects, as has been done for spherical protein molecules (Hall, 1960). Occasionally controversies have been raised regarding the true size of shadowed objects and in particular the width of the TMV rod which has generally been accepted to be 150Å as measured through electron microscopy by Kahler and Lloyd (1950). The shadowed TMV rods in Fig.

12–6 illustrate some of the features and artifacts inherent in the method. At A is a rod oriented approximately at 45° to the shadow direction, while at B we have a rod almost parallel and at C a small rod fragment closely parallel in contact with another that is perpendicular. Note the apparent difference in the widths according to their orientation and also at D as well as C the apparent intrusion of one particle into another, which is, of course, just intrusion into the metal. An interesting method for overcoming the distortion factor in measuring widths of rods such as TMV has been demonstrated by Ohad *et al.* (1963) and is shown in Fig. 12–7. The apparent width due to the cap of metal of shadowed TMV will depend on the azimuth of the rods with respect to the shadowing direction, being largest when the axis is perpendicular and approaching the true value when the rods are parallel to the shadow direction. The horizontal thickness of the metal is proportional to the sine of the angle (β) between rod axis and shadowing direction. Ohad *et*

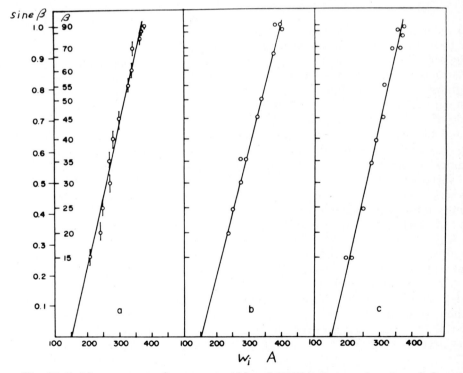

Fig. 12–7. Measurements of apparent widths of TMV rods as a function of the angle between rod axis and shadow direction. Extrapolation to zero angle gives the true width (Ohad *et al.*, 1963).

al. measured the apparent widths from several preparations (a, b, c, Fig. 12–7) and plotted the results as a function of sin β. As can be seen when the plot is extrapolated to $\beta = 0$ the true width is obtained, which is 150A in excellent agreement with Kahler and Lloyd.

Sometimes objects being shadow-cast have been continously rotated during metal evaporation which coats them evenly on all sides. Frequently it is advantageous to shadow from two directions in order to elucidate the shape of objects. An example of this is shown in Fig. 12–8 where the wound-tumor virus (WTV) has been double shadowed. An analysis of the pairs of shadows produced by particles in various azimuths leads to the conclusion that they have the shape of an icosahedron, that is, a regular polyhedron having 20 equilateral triangular faces. Steere (1958) has used a silhouette technique to show the projected outline of virus particles with good effect. He evaporates metal perpendicular to the specimen surface and subsequently removes the virus and its adhering metal.

The projected outline of the virus remains in the metallized substrate. In Fig. 12–9 are shown virus particles (bacteriophage ϕ X-174) extruding their DNA core. This specimen was made by the mica technique.

B. STAINING

Success in observing the structure of biological materials has to a large extent been due to the judicious use of heavy reagents to outline, combine with, or penetrate into elements of structure. Positive electron stains are those which combine chemically with the specimen, and negative stains (or negative contrast) consist of surrounding a particle or infiltrating its pores or interstices with a heavy unreactive compound. These two effects are shown on tomato bushy stunt virus (TBSV) in Fig. 12–10a and b. It is seen that the visibility of light particles is well enhanced by either method. Negative contrast has certain advantages for some things and has been one of the most important techniques for the elucidation of virus structure in recent years. By avoiding chemical reactivity, possible alterations in

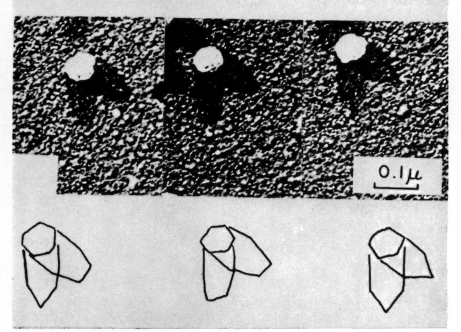

Fig. 12–8. Wound-tumor virus (WTV) double shadowed. The polygonal shape of the shadows is consistent with the assumption that the virus particles are icosahedrons (Bils and Hall, 1962).

morphology are avoided. Also the particles are embedded in a matrix which tends to protect them from distorting forces during drying. Some objects do not take positive stains well because of their chemical nature and tend to disintegrate under the effects of active stains. For example, there are fibrillar objects about 30–40Å wide in the negative contrast example of Fig. 12–10b which were not seen in preparations such as Fig. 12–10a. Either they did not combine with the positive stains or they disintegrated when so treated. Common positive stains are phosphotungstic acid, osmium tetroxide, uranyl compounds, lead ions, and numerous other compounds containing heavy elements. Negative contrast is usually achieved with phosphotungstates adjusted to neutrality or uranyl compounds near neutrality. In negative contrast we require compounds of high density, low reactivity, and amorphous structure. It is not always possible to predict which type of contrast is being produced as both effects may appear simultaneously and a positive effect may occur in one part of a specimen and a negative effect in another. A typical preparation for virus in negative contrast would be a mixture of 0.005 ml of 10^{12} titer virus with 0.02 ml of 1% PTA at pH 6.7. This mixture is sprayed from an atomizer onto filmed grids.

Fig. 12–9. Particles of bacteriophage ∮ X-174 extruding the DNA core as a result of mild heat. Magnification 112,000× (Maclean and Hall, 1962).

C. Other Techniques

The techniques discussed have been of the most consequence in the elucidation of virus morphology and structure and are mainly applied to isolated particles or components. Replica techniques (involving usually preshadowing) have been employed with considerable success to elucidate the structure of plant virus crystals (Labaw, 1959). Ultrathin sectioning is employed for the study of intracellular virus material, but the highly aqueous nature of plant material

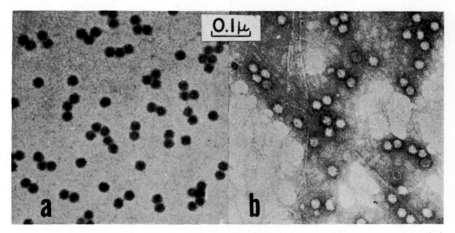

Fig. 12–10. Tomato bushy stunt virus (TBSV) in positive contrast (stain) in (a) and in negative contrast (stain) in (b) (Hall, 1955).

Fig. 12–11. TMV in negative contrast with phosphotungstate. Note the central core 40Å in diameter filled with stain. At (A) is a fragment seen end on. At (B) is an anomalous particle in which the protein molecules are stacked as discs in distinguishable pairs. Magnification 650,000× (micrograph by H. S. Slayter, MIT).

presents the difficulty that included virus is easily washed out in the various immersions necessary in the fixation and embedding procedures. Quantitative methods of virus particle assay have been developed in the spray drop technique of Backus and Williams (1950) and in the sedimentation technique of Sharp (1949).

12–5. MICROSCOPY OF PLANT VIRUSES

From the foregoing discussion it may be seen that electron microscopy is capable of giving information on virus particles of the following kinds: (1) particle size, (2) shape, (3) internal and external structure, (4) states of aggregation or crystallization, (5) quantitative particle assays, and (6) densitometric mass analysis. An adequate discussion of virus structure in general should properly include X-ray diffraction results as well as electron microscopy, since the two methods overlap and complement each other. Such a review has recently been made by Klug and Caspar (1960) and an earlier review devoted to electron microscopy of viruses has been made by Williams (1954). We shall here confine the discussion to a few examples illustrating the kind

of contributions obtained from electron microscopy.

A. TOBACCO MOSAIC VIRUS

One of the most thoroughly investigated plant viruses is, of course, TMV and the details of its structure have been worked out mainly by X-ray diffraction. The analysis provides a model wherein protein subunits are arranged helically around a hollow core about 40Å in diameter with a pitch of 23Å. The RNA is wound helically inside the protein. In Fig. 12–11 are shown rods of TMV in negative contrast with phosphotungstate showing the hollow center filled with stain, first demonstrated by electron microscopy by Huxley (1956). A fragment at A is seen on end. The 23Å period can be distinguished in places, and at B there is an anomalous rod consisting apparently of pairs of stacked plates 23Å thick producing a periodicity of twice this value. This appears to be the variant structure discussed by Klug and Caspar (1960) and is like repolymerized TMV protein. The length of TMV from electron microscopy is very close to 3000Å (Williams and Steere, 1951; Hall, 1958) and the width from electron microscopy is 150Å though X-ray diffraction gives a greater diameter.

B. SPHERICAL VIRUSES

The first evidence of the remarkable regularity existing in these so-called spherical viruses came from an X-ray diffraction study of tomato bushy stunt virus by Caspar (1956) and from the electron microscope observations of Williams (1954) and Kaesberg (1956), who noted that certain plant viruses had a polyhedral form. Since then the two methods have established that numerous spherical viruses, animal and bacterial as well as plant, have icosahedral symmetry. Electron microscopically this can be deduced from the shape of shadows in shadowed preparation as indicated in Fig. 12–8. In Fig. 12–12a is shown a micrograph of wound-tumor virus (WTV) in negative contrast where the number of protein units (capsomeres) can be counted along some edges. Examination of other similar pictures strongly suggest that the number is 4. In Fig. 12–12b is seen what

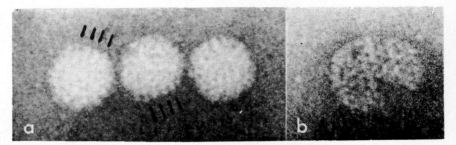

Fig. 12–12. WTV in negative contrast with phosphotungstate showing in (a) particle edges with 4 capsomeres and in (b) a ruptured protein envelope. Magnification 350,000× (Bils and Hall, 1962).

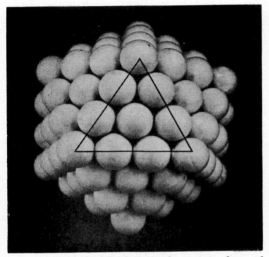

Fig. 12–13. Model of WTV showing packing of the capsomeres with icosahedral symmetry. The particle is about 550Å in diameter.

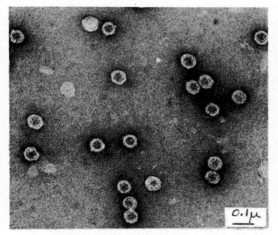

Fig. 12–14. WTV stained with uranyl acetate showing a positively stained core and the protein envelope in negative contrast. Magnification 81,-000× (Bils and Hall, 1962).

appears to be a ruptured protein shell. In Fig. 12–13 is shown a model icosahedron to represent the WTV. We have 20 equilateral triangular faces with 4 capsomeres on each edge to make a total of 92 capsomeres in all.

In Fig. 12–14 is shown WTV treated with uranyl acetate to produce a positive staining of the nucleic acid (or nucleoprotein) core while the residual stain around the particles produces a negative contrast for the protein envelope. For Fig. 12–15 the wound tumor virus has been broken down by mild heating, releasing strands of nuclei acid or nucleoprotein.

One of the smallest viruses, some 250Å in diameter, is bacteriophage ϕ X-174 shown in Fig. 12–16. The external structure is quite "knobby," appearing in this micrograph as a central peak knob surrounded by 5 others in pentagonal symmetry. A model of the structure is shown in Fig. 12–17 where there are 11 knobs visible and one directly below, making 12 in all. By joining the apexes, 20 equilateral triangles are formed. In order to have 5-fold symmetry as suggested by the morphology each knob would have to consist of 5 asymmetric units and there would thus be 60 such subunits in all. This is a DNA virus, and DNA strands from it are shown in Fig. 12–9.

Other viruses do not give quite so prominent a "knobby" structure. TBSV for example in negative stain and shadowed gives indication of icosahedral shape but the capsomeres have not been well resolved and the particle is more spherical. Turnip yellows mosaic virus (TYMV) on the other hand appears "knobby" and it is at first

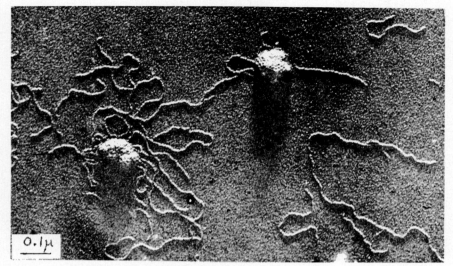

Fig. 12–15. Disintegrating WTV showing extruded RNA strands from the core. Magnification 100,000× (Bils and Hall, 1962).

glance similar to φ X-174. Steere (1957), Huxley and Zubay (1960), and Nixon and Gibbs (1960) have examined TYMV and suggest that there are 32 morphological subunits and suggest structures that are more complex than the regular icosahedron. These questions undoubtedly are to be resolved by combining results from both electron microscopy and X-ray diffraction.

Fig. 12–16. Bacteriophage φ X-174, shadowed with Pt at an angle of 45°. Magnification 200,000× (Hall *et al.*, 1959).

Fig. 12–17. Model of the knobs on φ X-174.

12–6. LITERATURE CITED

Backus, R. C., and Williams, R. C. (1950). J. Appl. Phys. **21**, 11.

Bils, R. F., and Hall, C. E. (1962). Virology **17**, 123.

Caspar, D. L. D. (1956). Nature **177**, 475.

Hall, C. E. (1953). Introduction to Electron Microscopy. McGraw-Hill, New York.

Hall, C. E. (1955). J. Biophys. Biochem. Cytol. **1**, 1.

Hall, C. E. (1956). J. Biophys. Biochem. Cytol. **2**, 625.

Hall, C. E. (1958). J. Am. Chem. Soc. **80**, 2556.

Hall, C. E. (1960). J. Biophys. Biochem. Cytol. **7**, 613.

Hall, C. E., and Inoue, T. (1957). J. Appl. Phys. **28**, 1346.

Hall, C. E., Maclean, E. C., and Tessman, L. (1959). J. Mol. Biol. **1**, 192.

Huxley, H. E. (1956). F. Sjöstrand and J. Rhodin (eds.), Proc. Stockholm Conference on Electron Microscopy. 260. Academic Press, New York.

Huxley, H. E., and Zubay, G. (1960). J. Mol. Biol. **2**, 189.

Kaesberg, P. (1956). Science **124**, 626.

Kahler, H., and Lloyd, B. J., Jr. (1950). J. Appl. Phys. **21**, 699.

Kay, D. (1961). Techniques for Electron Microscopy. Blackwell, Oxford.

Klug, A., and Caspar, D. L. D. (1960). Advan. Virus Res. **7**, 225.

Labaw, L. W. (1959). J. Ultrastruct. Res. **3**, 58.

Maclean, E. C., and Hall, C. E. (1962). J. Mol. Biol. **4**, 173.

Nixon, H. L., and Gibbs, P. J. (1960). J. Mol. Biol. **2**, 197.

Ohad, I., Danon, D., and Hestrin, S. (1963). J. Cell. Biol. **17**, 321.

Sharp, D. G. (1949). Proc. Soc. Exptl. Biol. Med. **70**, 54.

Steere, R. L. (1957). J. Biophys. Biochem. Cytol. **3**, 45.

Steere. R. L. (1958). Fourth International Conference on Electron Microscopy. **2**, 629. Springer, Berlin.

Williams, R. C. (1954). Advan. Virus Res. **2**, 183.

Williams, R. C., and Steere, R. L. (1951). J. Am. Chem. Soc. **73**, 2057.

Williams, R. C., and Wyckoff, R. W. G. (1944). J. Appl. Phys. **15**, 712.

13

D. L. D. CASPAR

Structure and function of regular virus particles

13–1. INTRODUCTION

THE ESSENTIAL function of a virus particle is to transmit the infectious nucleic acid to a susceptible host. The nucleic acid of all the stable well-characterized viruses is contained in a protective package and the design of these packages is related to the way in which the particles are assembled. Our ideas on the structure of viruses are based on Crick and Watson's (1956) suggestion that the protective coats of small virus particles are each built up of identical protein molecules packed together in a regular manner. It might appear, at first sight, that there are many various ways in which subunits can be assembled judging by the range of morphological variation found in viruses. On the contrary, it has been shown (Caspar and Klug, 1962) that there are only a few efficient designs for a biological container that can be constructed from a large number of identical molecules.

A biological argument for construction out of subunits is that production of the coat protein in the form of small identical molecules is an efficient use of the limited information contained in the virus nucleic acid (Crick and Watson, 1957). A more general argument, which applies to mass production of any kind of structure (Crane, 1950), is that it is more efficient to construct a large structure out of smaller preformed structures, rather than directly from raw

material. The components of a virus or parts of a living cell can be synthesized separately by a subassembly process and then associated, following definite rules, to form a complete system. The advantage of such a process is that biological control can be exercised at each level of organization, and even if mistakes occur at the various stages, the defective components can be rejected. The net result is that very complex systems can be built up with high efficiency.

The recognition that a virus particle can be constructed by a subassembly process implies that the building rules by which it is constructed can be deduced from the properties of the finished product. From structural studies it is possible to determine what a particular virus looks like. However, even a detailed model which illustrated the arrangement of the component parts would not, in itself, be sufficient to describe the functional organization of the particle. The dynamic properties of any organized structure are determined by the distribution of energy. A geometrical model for any structure is only physically significant insofar as it represents the energetic relations between the parts. Attempts to describe the nature of the design of virus particles in terms of static symmetry concepts are not likely to account for the physical organization. In order to understand why only certain types of designs are used, it is necessary to consider how the particles are assembled.

A production line is an apt analogy for some stages of the subassembly process used by a living cell. The synthesis of a polypeptide chain from amino acids is an example of such a process. However, once the peptide bonds of a protein are formed, the simple analogy of a production line breaks down. No template or other external direction appears to be needed to fold up many proteins; the stable configuration is evidently determined by the amino acid sequence and thus, ultimately, by the genetic code. Moreover, some proteins are capable of assembling themselves into highly organized structures. The assembly process of a living cell is different in principle from those of a factory in that the directions for constructing many complex biological structures are built into the constituent components. These biological structures are thus constructed by a self-assembly, and not merely a subassembly process. One of the clearest examples of self-assembly is provided by the simple viruses, in particular tobacco mosaic virus (TMV), where the self-assembly process has been reproduced *in vitro* (Fraenkel-Conrat and Williams, 1955).

13–2. DESIGN PRINCIPLES AND SELF-ASSEMBLY

Self-assembly is a process akin to crystallization and is governed by the laws of statistical mechanics. A system of units with equivalent bonding properties will condense to form an ordered structure or set of ordered structures if the free energy of the ordered state is less than that of all other possible states. The most stable ordered structure will be that in which the maximum number of most stable bonds are formed between the units. The necessary physical condition for the stability of any structure is that it be in a state of minimum free energy. Changing the environmental conditions of any ordered structure in such a way as to weaken the bonds between the units will favor its dissociation. If dissociation can proceed without altering the integrity of the constituent components, then

changing the environment back to the conditions which favor bond formation will lead to the re-formation of the organized structure. This is what happens when a crystal is dissolved and then recrystallized, or when TMV is dissociated and its components reconstituted. However, a simple virus particle is distinct from a crystal in that it has a finite, well-defined size and consists of two chemically and structurally different components. It is in the transition from a state in which protein subunits and nucleic acid chains are randomly arranged in space to a state in which they are highly ordered that the self-assembly of a virus particle resembles crystallization. The important features are that the design of the organized structure is determined by the specific bonding properties of its components, and the stability of the ordered state is determined by the condition of minimum energy.

Any ordered structure built of identical units, whether it is a crystal or a virus particle, will have some type of well-defined symmetry. Specific bonding between the units necessarily leads to a symmetrical structure since there will be only a limited number of ways in which any unit can be connected to its neighbors to form the maximum number of most stable bonds. The simplest situation is that in which each unit is equivalently related to its neighbors. A crystal, by definition, is a three-dimensionally periodic lattice built up of equivalently related units. All the 230 possible designs for crystals were mathematically enumerated in the nineteenth century (see *International Tables for X-ray Crystallography*, 1952) by analysis of the ways in which symmetry elements can be combined in a periodic lattice. No assumptions need be made regarding the chemical nature of the units, or the bonding between them in order to describe the designs for crystal lattices. Crystallography can thus be formulated in what may appear to be purely geometrical terms. All the possible designs for crystals can be represented by a set of symmetry groups. The relevance of these abstract geometrical constructs to the physical nature of crystals is that the 230 space groups represent all the possible minimum energy designs for three-dimensionally periodic lattices.

Crystals are not the only types of symmetric structures. Any array which is symmetric about a point, along a line, or in a surface, is also a possible minimum energy design for a physical structure. The necessary energetic relationships between the structure units in such regular systems can be implicitly represented by the geometrical formalism of strict equivalence. However, many minimum energy designs for structures built of equal units cannot be represented using the abstraction of strict equivalence. It is often possible to form a stable ordered structure in which the bonds between equal units are deformed in a number of slightly different ways. If each unit forms the same types of bonds with its neighbors, then all the units will be quasi-equivalently related. Introducing this physical concept of quasi-equivalence, Caspar and Klug (1962) have shown that a number of minimum energy designs can be deduced which do, in fact, occur in nature. The decision as to what constitutes quasi-equivalence cannot be expressed in absolute mathematical terms but is dependent on the physical analysis of the energetically allowable variation in the bonding of the system. These physical considerations have led to an extension of traditional concepts of symmetry, more specifically applicable to highly organized biological structures.

The possible designs for biological structures are limited by the physical principle of minimum energy. The actual designs which are used for a particular purpose are determined by the biological principle of natural selection. A characteristic of many biological structures is that they have a finite, well-defined size. It is evident that the regular crystalline lattices, which are capable of indefinite extension without change in their local properties, are generally unsuitable for the functional requirements of a living system. The possible types of regular finite structures are limited, thus similar designs may be selected by nature for different functions.

Studies of small virus structure by X-ray diffraction, electron microscopy, and chemical analysis have all borne out the hypothesis that these particles have regular substructure. In fact, many of the larger virus particles also appear to have regular substructure. The feature to be stressed is that virus particles built of identical subunits by a self-assembly process will have uniform size and regular shape. The regularly constructed protein coat of a virus particle has been defined as the *capsid* (Lwoff *et al.*, 1959), and the primary package of nucleic acid in its protein coat is called the *nucleocapsid* (Caspar *et al.*, 1962).

If we start with the postulate that a virus capsid (as in the case of TMV) is built of identical units which can assemble themselves, then it is possible to predict the types of design which allow self-assembly. The function of the capsid is to provide a protective container for the nucleic acid. A container made up of regularly bonded units can be represented by a surface lattice which is connected back on itself. The problem of enumerating the possible designs for a virus capsid can thus be analyzed in terms of the ways in which a plane lattice can be regularly connected into some type of container. This type of structure, which is periodic only in a surface, can be classed as a surface crystal as distinct from a three-dimensionally periodic crystal. It has been shown (Caspar and Klug, 1962) that the most probable minimum energy designs for surface crystals constructed of a large number of units are tubes with helical or cylindrical symmetry and closed shells with icosahedral symmetry. The helical and icosahedral designs have been selected for the construction of many different capsids since they provide efficient ways to package the nucleic acid chain. Quasi-equivalent bonding is a geometrical necessity in an icosahedral shell constructed from a large number of identical units. However, there is no geometrical requirement for quasi-equivalent bonding in helical structures but, as shown by studies on TMV structure, it may allow the formation of a more stable structure than strictly equivalent bonding. Even though the morphologies of helical and icosahedral viruses are very different, it appears that the principles applied in their construction are the same.

13–3. STRUCTURAL CLASSIFICA-
TION AND INTERRELATIONS
OF VIRUSES

Viruses can be classified according to the morphology of the particles which transmit the infection, by the biochemical and physical nature of their infectious nucleic acids, by the host-virus relationship and the nature of the virus replication, as well as all other properties characteristic of the viral life-cycle. It is clear from consideration of the design principles involved in virus particle construction that the use of morphology or symmetry as a basis for classifying biological interrelation must be regarded with caution. Although it is quite likely that closely related viruses will be morphologically similar, the converse is not true. The design of crystals provides an analogy. Since there are only 230 types of lattices, it is not surprising that chemically unrelated compounds can form crystals with identical symmetry. The structure of biologically unrelated viruses—for example, poliovirus and turnip yellow mosaic virus—may be based on very similar designs. The reason for this is that there are only a limited number of efficient designs possible for a virus capsid. Thus, the same kind of molecular packaging may be used for the RNA or DNA of unrelated viruses infecting plants, animals, or bacteria. Moreover, it is possible that closely related viruses may have significant differences in their morphology. For example, the bacteriophage T-3 which has a very short tail will give rise to mutants with long tails (Eisenstark *et al.*, 1961) which are thus morphologically more different from the wild type than many less closely related phages. A more extreme situation is observed with some defective mutants of TMV (Siegel *et al.*, 1962) which are not transmissible under the usual conditions of virus infection. These mutants produce no morphologically recognizable virus particles. The difficulty in transmission thus appears to be a result of a defect in the packaging but not in the replication of the viral nucleic acid.

A structural classification is helpful in analysing the organization of virus particles but is unlikely to provide information about properties which are not related to the structure. A significant feature of biological structures is that they are built up at levels of organization of increasing complexity. As we have seen, these grades of organization are a consequence of the sub- and self-assembly processes used in biological systems. The essential component of all viruses is the infectious nucleic acid. This may be a single- or double-stranded RNA or DNA molecule. The double-stranded DNA of many bacterial and animal viruses may be regarded as a transmissible piece of cellular chromosome which can undergo autonomous replication. The single-stranded RNA of many other viruses appears to correspond to a cellular messenger RNA which has acquired the ability to replicate itself. The single-stranded DNA and double-stranded RNA found in some viruses may have no normal cellular analogue, and they presumably represent stages in the nucleic acid replication which have become stabilized. The virus nucleic acid has the capacity of redirecting the synthetic machinery of the host cell to the production of more virus. This control over the host cell metabolism can be exerted at a number of different stages of normal biosynthesis. The ultimate classification of viruses may be primarily in terms of their biochemical and evolutionary relation to their hosts.

It is not merely a matter of labeling viruses as DNA- or RNA-containing, but also of distinguishing them in terms of the amount of information carried by the nucleic acid. On the assumption of a universal coding ratio between nucleic acid and protein (Crick *et al.*, 1961), the amount of information transmitted by a virus would depend on the size of its nucleic acid component. Large DNA viruses contain several hundred times as much nucleic acid as the very small DNA and RNA viruses. The RNA of a small bacterial virus (Loeb and Zinder, 1961) consists of only about 1600 nucleotides (molecular weight 500,000) which, if the coding ratio is 3 : 1, could specify perhaps only three different protein molecules. The comparably small tobacco necrosis virus particles (Kassanis and Nixon, 1960, 1961) do not appear to carry complete enough information for their own multiplication, and can reproduce only as satellites in association with another, larger tobacco necrosis virus.

Isolated nucleic acid molecules are very labile, particularly in an intercellular environment containing nucleases. The capsid provides a protective container for transmitting the nucleic acid. The use of helical and icosahedral designs in the capsids of many different viruses is an indication that the basic physical principles previously described apply to their construction. Some virus particles are naked nucleocapsids; others consist of a nucleocapsid contained in an envelope which may be derived from the cellular membrane. Complex viruses may consist of a number of distinct parts besides the nucleocapsid carrying the genetic information. These components may include normal cellular components, such as the envelope of some viruses, which are incorporated during the final maturation. In addition, there may be protein components that have attachment and enzymatic functions necessary for invasion of the cell. The large bacteriophages have a differentiated and specialized anatomy with separate components for attachment to their host, penetration of the cell wall, and injection of the nucleic acid. However, the substructure of the parts of their capsids appears to be similar to that of simpler viruses (Kellenberger, 1961). The individual components may be ble to assemble themselves, though additional control mechanisms may be required to insure the correct assembly of all the parts. Some large animal viruses, such as vaccinia, are comparable in size, and perhaps in complexity to the smallest, free-living cells. This wide range of variation from infectious nucleic acid and simple nucleocapsids to complex viruses and the smallest organisms is concrete evidence of the levels of organization in biological systems.

The more complex viruses are not necessarily more highly evolved forms of simpler ones. Viruses mutate and presumably evolve, but the direction of change may equally well be from a semiautonomous form to a highly efficient simple form, as from the simple to the complex. In fact, since viruses could not possibly exist before cells, the simple nucleocapsids might be a highly evolved form. The biological relationships between viruses are determined by their genesis and evolution, but this is a subject where it is only possible to speculate at present. If the genesis of a virus is an extremely improbable event, then many very different viruses may be descended from a single prototype. Although such a possibility cannot be ruled out, independent genesis of biologically distinct viruses might better account for the differences among them and the intimate nature of their relation to their hosts. The chemical similarities between viruses with very different host ranges could result from the unique role of DNA and RNA in the transfer of genetic information in all organisms. The morphological similarities between unrelated viruses can be accounted for by the universal nature of the design principles involved in organized molecular structures.

The simple virus particles, which are naked regular nucleocapsids, are a select class and are by no means representative of the range of variation that is possible among virus particles. They do, however, possess the fundamental properties of being able to reproduce within a living cell, and of being able to persist in an inert extracellular form until they encounter other cells they can infect. Detailed structural studies can be carried out on these viruses because of their relative simplicity. These studies provide a picture of the way in which the viral nucleic acid is packaged for transmission and, moreover, illustrate some of the general principles which govern the molecular organization of biological structures.

13–4. VIRUS SUBSTRUCTURE AND THE X-RAY DIFFRACTION METHOD

The essential concepts for understanding the self-assembly mechanism—the concepts of symmetry, equivalence, and quasi-equivalence—are clearly illustrated by the X-ray diffraction studies on the structure of regular virus particles. Although X-ray analysis can provide more detailed information about the three-dimensional molecular organization of viruses than any other technique, it is not likely to become a routine tool for the virologist because of the experimental problems involved in obtaining detailed diffraction patterns and the theoretical problems of interpretation. The experimental results of X-ray studies on TMV and some of the small icosahedral viruses have been reviewed in detail by Klug and Caspar (1960). It will only be relevant here to survey some aspects of method and to point out how the structural concepts involved in X-ray analysis are fundamentally related to the functional organization of virus particles.

As a method for studying the structural organization of virus particles X-ray analysis is complemented by other physical and chemical methods. Electron microscopy provides pictures which directly show the morphological features of viruses that have been either dehydrated or treated in some special way. Information about over-all size, shape, and hydration can be obtained by physicochemical studies of virus solutions. Biochemical studies are providing a wealth of information about the chemistry of viruses, but even knowledge of the amino acid sequence of the protein subunit and the chemical nature of the nucleic acid does not elucidate how the protein and nucleic acid are folded and assembled. Investigations of the thermodynamics and kinetics of virus degradation and the reaggregation of subunits, together with knowledge of the packing relations of the parts determined by X-ray analysis can provide a basis for describing the mechanics of the particle assembly.

X-ray diffraction is at present the only method available for studying the internal three-dimensional configuration of viruses and other highly organized biological structures in the hydrated biologically-active state. However, since the diffraction pattern of a single particle is so extremely weak, it cannot be measured. In order to record a measurable diffraction pattern from particles with a molecular weight about 10^7, a minimum of about 10^9 particles must be examined at one time. The observed pattern will thus represent an average for the population. To be able to relate this pattern to the structure of a single particle, all the particles must be regularly arranged in space, either in a crystal for the icosahedral viruses, or in an orientated gel for the rod-shaped particles. Moreover, to be able to interpret this pattern in terms of the structure of a single particle all the particles in the sample must have the same, or at least very nearly the same, structure.

Rod-shaped virus particles such as TMV form small true crystals in infected plants (Bawden and Sheffield, 1939) and have occasionally been observed to form unstable three-dimensionally periodic aggregates in purified preparations (Oster, 1950). The nature of the TMV structure makes it unlikely that any large stable crystals could be grown for X-ray work, but the very well-orientated gels or paracrystals which can be prepared from this virus serve equally well, if not better, than true crystals, as indicated by the detailed X-ray results already obtained with TMV. The techniques for orientating TMV have been described by Bernal and Fankuchen (1941). In the orientated gels of TMV the particles are all aligned parallel but are not otherwise fixed relative to one another. Since the individual particles are arranged in all possible rotational orientations about their long axes and there are no long-range regularities in their side-to-side packing, the diffraction patterns from such orientated gels correspond to the pattern of a single particle which has been cylindrically averaged about the particle axis. This type of situation is also typical of the long-chain molecules of a fiber. The diffraction pattern of a paracrystalline fiber or gel can be recorded simply by placing the sample in an X-ray beam and giving it a sufficient exposure. In general the axis of the specimen is arranged perpendicular to the X-ray beam, but sometimes it is necessary to tilt the axis to record spots which would otherwise not be observed. With high-resolution X-ray cameras, the exposure times to record the diffraction patterns from TMV gels are of the order of 100 hours. The large number of spots in such a detailed diffraction pattern (Fig. 13–1) represents a considerable amount of structural information.

The experimental problems in growing crystals of isometric viruses and in record-

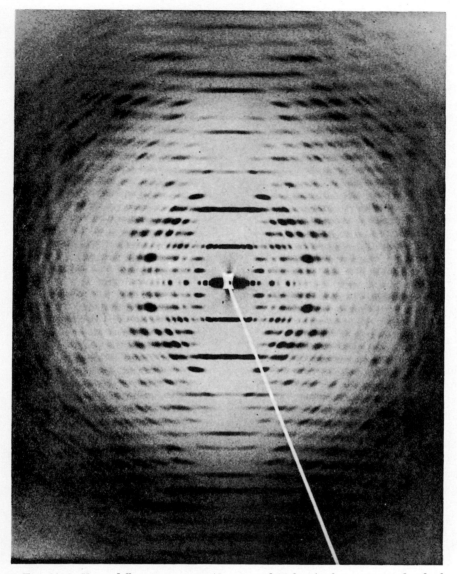

Fig. 13–1. X-ray diffraction pattern (Caspar and Holmes) of an orientated gel of the common strain of TMV, taken with a high-resolution camera and crystal-monochromatized Cu Kα-radiation.

The virus particles are all orientated with their long axis in the vertical direction, and the pattern represents the cylindrically averaged intensity diffracted by a single particle. The horizontal stratification (layer-lines) corresponds to the axial repeat of 69Å in the virus particle. High angle reflections can be observed in the X-ray pattern corresponding to spacings as small as 1.5Å which indicate that the regularity in the virus particle structure extends down to atomic dimensions.

ing their diffraction patterns have been described by Klug and Caspar (1960). There is nothing unusual about the ability of viruses to crystallize. This is only an indication of the high degree of regularity and equivalence of the individual particles produced by a particular virus infection. Crystallization occurs when a large number of structurally equivalent particles or molecules are present in solution under conditions of limiting solubility. Of all the possible interactions between particles there will

273

be a certain set of contacts which will represent a state of minimum energy under the particular solvent conditions. If the contact points are directed in three dimensions, the result of regular aggregation will be a three-dimensionally periodic crystal. Some virologists have expressed surprise that icosahedral virus particles can form true crystals, since five-fold symmetry is not possible in the repeating pattern of crystals. However, it is no more surprising that particles with noncrystallographic symmetry can form crystals than it is that protein molecules with no symmetry can crystallize. The symmetry of a crystal may be related to that of the units from which it is built, but there is no necessary physical relation.

Virus particles arranged in a three-dimensional crystal lattice have either all the same orientation or, at most, a small number of fixed orientations. There is nothing random about the arrangement of particles in a crystal. The regularly repeating pattern of a crystal produces a corresponding regularity in the diffraction pattern. The X-ray beam can be diffracted in only certain directions determined by the periodicity of the crystal, and the directions of all the possible diffracted beams can be defined by a reciprocal lattice which is uniquely determined by the real lattice. Spacings in reciprocal space are inversely related to spacings in real space. When the unit cell is very large, as in a virus crystal, many very closely spaced diffracted beams can be produced. If the crystal is stationary, only a small fraction of the possible diffracted beams can be recorded, and these produce spots in the pattern arranged in sets of circles and ellipses characteristic of the lattice type (Fig. 13–2). In order to record a section of the reciprocal lattice of diffraction spectra it is necessary to move the crystal in some systematic way in relation to the X-ray beam. The usual technique is to precess the crystal, since this gives an undistorted view of a section of the reciprocal lattice, and also allows the systematic recording of the diffraction pattern. Each precession photograph (Fig. 13–3) records only a fraction of the reciprocal lattice, thus many such pictures must be taken to record the whole diffraction pattern. The positions

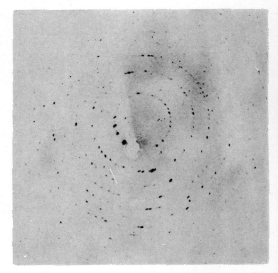

Fig. 13–2. X-ray diffraction photograph ("still") of a stationary bushy stunt virus crystal. Similar patterns are produced by all virus crystals. The positions of the rings of spots determine the orientation of the crystal and provide an accurate measure of the unit cell dimensions.

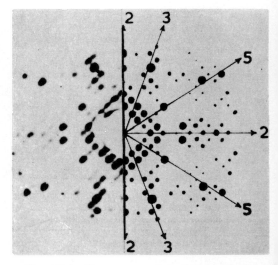

Fig. 13–3. X-ray precession photograph (Caspar, 1956b) of the central portion of the basal reciprocal lattice plane normal to the cube edge of a bushy stunt virus crystal (left). Drawing of the weighted reciprocal lattice net (right) showing the correlation between the "spikes" of strong reflections and directions of 2-, 3-, and 5-fold symmetry axes of the icosahedral point-group which lie in the plane of the photograph. The set of 2-fold axes are parallel to the cube edges of the unit cell, but these 3- and 5-fold symmetry axes of the virus particle lie in noncrystallographic directions.

of the spots in these patterns is characteristic of the symmetry and dimensions of the lattice, and the intensity distribution is determined by the structure and symmetry of the individual particles.

X-ray diffraction is particularly useful for studying any structure which repeats regularly in space. The scale of structure which can be investigated ranges from a few angstroms, as in crystals of small molecules, to hundreds of angstroms, as in virus crystals. X-rays pick out the ordered part of the structure in such a way that the diffraction diagram of a substance is directly related to the structural regularity within it. Disorganized material or impurities will not contribute to the ordered part of the pattern and thus will not directly affect its interpretation. The order in a structure arises from the regular arrangement of smaller parts (asymmetric units), and it is this arrangement that determines the position of the reflections in the X-ray diagram. The intensities of the reflections are determined by the detailed internal structure of the asymmetric unit. The asymmetric unit of a virus particle is related to the structure units from which it is constructed. In a stable particle all the structure units will be equivalently or quasi-equivalently related. The well-defined symmetry to be expected for virus particles is very favorable for X-ray analysis since the symmetry of the particle is indicated in a relatively direct way by the X-ray diagrams. Determination of the symmetry does not indicate what the asymmetric unit looks like. It does, however, determine how many there are and how they are packed together, and thus gives an indication of the size of the structure unit, and the over-all appearance of the virus particle. Moreover, since the order in the structure is a consequence of the regular bonding of the parts, the symmetry detected by the X-rays is related to the way in which the particles are constructed.

The basic problem in X-ray structure analysis is that the diffraction pattern itself does not contain all the information necessary to determine completely the structure which gave rise to it. The ultimate goal of a structure analysis is to determine the three-dimensional electron density distribution,

but there is no standard or direct method by which this can be done. Each X-ray reflection or spot on the photograph corresponds to a diffracted wave which is characterized by three quantities: direction, magnitude, and phase. Of these three, the first two can be directly measured, but in taking the photograph all information about the phase angle is lost. In order to reconstruct the electron density of the diffracting structure, this phase angle must somehow be determined. The isomorphous replacement method, which is based on measurement of the intensity changes produced in the diffraction pattern by regularly bound heavy metal atoms, provides a means to determine the phase, but with viruses this method has so far been successfully applied only to TMV (Caspar, 1956a; Franklin and Holmes, 1958). However, even without knowledge of the phase, the symmetry of the ordered structure and dimensions of the periodic structure can be determined from the positions of the spots and intensity distribution in the diffraction pattern.

13–5. SYMMETRY AND MOLECULAR MORPHOLOGY OF TOBACCO MOSAIC VIRUS

A. Helical Arrangement of Subunits

The interpretation of virus diffraction patterns can be briefly illustrated from the X-ray studies on TMV. To a trained eye, the helical symmetry is evident from the pattern shown in Fig. 13–1.

In describing the diffraction pattern of a helix, it is necessary to refer to two coordinate directions: the meridian, which is the vertical axis in Fig. 13–1 (parallel to the helix axis) and the equator which is the horizontal axis (perpendicular to the helix axis). The diffraction pattern is symmetrical about both these directions. It is necessary to remember that small spacings in the diffraction pattern correspond to large distances in the structure. The horizontal stratification (layer lines) corresponds to an axial repeat distance of 69Å in the virus particle. The near-meridional diffraction on third-order layer lines corresponds to a helix of 23Å pitch. Since only every third layer line has near-meridional reflections,

Fig. 13–4. Arrangement of two-dimensional units on a cylindrical surface illustrating equivalence in an array with helical symmetry. The packing relation between the units in this surface is similar to that in the TMV helix (see Fig. 13–6). The significant features are that each unit has six nearest neighbors and each unit is identically related to its neighbors.

there must be approximately an integral number of units distributed over three turns of the helix, to give the 69Å axial repeat. Watson (1954) was able to show that the number is $3n + 1$, but direct determination of the value of n proved very difficult. The value of n is now known to be 16 (Franklin and Holmes, 1958); thus there are 49 subunits in three turns. Franklin and Klug (1955) were able to show that the number of units in three turns is not an exact integer. The actual number is $49.02 \pm .01$, but since the difference between this value and an integer is so small, the integral value of 49 is sufficiently accurate for most purposes. The identification of the structure unit detected by X-rays with the chemical subunit which was first recognized by end-group analysis (Harris

and Knight, 1952) has been well established (Klug and Caspar, 1960).

The determination of the helical parameters establishes the packing relations between subunits in the particle. Since the packing is periodic only in a surface it can be schematically represented by a plane net rolled up into a tube with helical symmetry (Fig. 13–4). The shape of the units shown is arbitrary and is only intended to indicate that the units which build the helix are asymmetric. The significant features of this surface lattice are that each unit has six nearest neighbors and each unit is related to its neighbors in the same way. Thus all the units in the helix (except those on the ends) are in equivalent environments. Each unit can be regarded as having six bonding sites, but there are only three classes of "bonds," namely AD, BE, and CF. Specifying the bonds between the units is sufficient to define the structure. Therefore, such units with specific bond sites can assemble themselves in an unambiguous way to form the ordered structure.

Different strains of TMV give very similar X-ray diffraction patterns (Bernal and Fankuchen, 1941; Franklin, 1956a) which indicate that all the strains examined have the same basic helical structure. However, from the small differences in the diffraction patterns of the common strain, the U2 strain, and cucumber virus 4 (CV4) Franklin and Klug (1955) found that each of these viruses has a slightly different number of subunits per turn of the helix. Whereas the common strain has 16.34 subunits per turn, the U2 strain has 16.35, and CV4 has 16.33. The largest difference, that between CV4 and U2, corresponds to a change in the distance between the outside ends of neighboring subunits in these two helices of only about 0.04Å. The measurement of such a small difference in distance would normally be a challenge to the precision of the X-ray diffraction method applied to such large structures, but it can be detected because it produces a recognizable change in the symmetry parameters. Since the protein molecules which build these three viruses are chemically different, it is not surprising that their packing should be different. What is surprising is that the differences in the bonding arrangement are so small. Moreover, within the sensitive limits of the X-ray measurements, the subunits in each of these strains are equivalently related.

B. INTERNAL STRUCTURE

In order to analyze the internal structure of the subunit it is necessary to determine the phases of the X-ray reflections. Application of the isomorphous replacement method generally requires at least two, and preferably more, heavy atom derivatives to determine phase angles unambiguously. However, for the central part of the equator of the TMV diagram (Fig. 13–1), which corresponds to the cylindrically averaged electron density, the phase angles

are either 0° and 180°. In this case each reflection is characterized by a sign, either plus or minus, and a single heavy atom substitution is sufficient to determine the sign. The signs of the equatorial diffraction maxima were determined by Caspar (1956a) using a lead derivative, and these results were confirmed by Franklin and Holmes (1958) using mercury-substituted TMV. From these results, the cylindrically averaged radial electron density distribution, shown in Fig. 13–5, was calculated. Franklin (1956b) followed the same procedure to calculate the radial density distribution in TMV protein repolymerized in the same helical packing arrangement as in the intact virus, and this is also shown in Fig. 13–5. Comparison of these two curves demonstrates that the RNA is located at a radius of about 40Å, since the prominent maximum at this radius in the density map of the intact virus is replaced by density minimum in the RNA-free protein polymer.

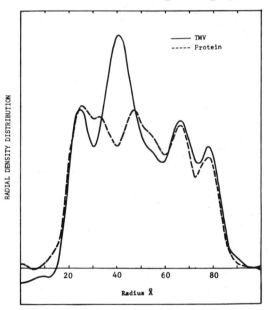

Fig. 13–5. The cylindrically averaged radial electron density distribution in the common strain of TMV (full curve) (Caspar, 1956a) and in re-polymerized nucleic acid-free TMV protein (dotted curve) (Franklin, 1956b). The curves show the difference between the electron density of the particles and that of water, plotted as a function of radial distance from the particle axis. The high density peak at 40Å in the intact virus is absent in the polymerized protein and must, therefore, be due to the RNA in the virus.

The arrangement of the RNA chain in the virus has been established by analysis of the X-ray diagrams of the intact virus and the RNA-free helical protein polymers (Franklin, 1958; Franklin *et al.*, 1959). The RNA is coiled as a single chain between the turns of the protein helix of 23Å pitch. There are 49 nucleotides in each turn of the 23Å pitch RNA helix; thus, there are 3 nucleotides associated with each protein subunit.

The radial density maps (Fig. 13–5) show that there is a hole of diameter about 40Å along the axis of the helix, and the maximum diameter of the particle is about 180Å. From the inside and outside dimensions of the helix, the length of the protein subunit is about 70Å, and its average thickness, from the pitch of the helix, is about 23Å. The maximum width at any radius can be calculated from the 22° angle subtended by a subunit. The subunits appear to be in close contact with each other out to a radius of about 55Å, where the width is about 21Å. At larger radii the average width does not appear to increase appreciably, and must eventually taper down at the outside end. Thus, to a first approximation the subunit can be represented by a prolate ellipsoid of a length 70Å and diameter about 20–25Å. The well-defined maxima and minima in the radial density map indicate that the subunit is not a smooth ellipsoid. There must be a notch in the subunit at 40Å radius to accommodate the RNA chain which packs in a very compact way with the protein. Furthermore, the subunit appears to be relatively thin at 55–60Å from the particle axis (Klug and Caspar, 1960), and the single cysteine residue is located in this crevice at a radius of 56Å (Franklin and Holmes, 1958). There is still much work to be done before a detailed picture of the conformation of the protein subunit can be delineated. Nevertheless, from the present knowledge of the packing relation of the protein subunits and nucleic acid chain, it is possible to analyze the way in which the virus particle is constructed (Caspar, 1963).

The results of the X-ray structure studies on TMV are summarized in Fig. 13–6, which illustrates the way in which the com-

Fig. 13–6. A drawing representing the structure of the common strain of TMV based on X-ray studies on the native hydrated virus particles (Klug and Caspar, 1960). The 6-turn segment shown corresponds to about ½₀ the length of the intact virus. The RNA chain is coiled between the turns of the 23Å pitch helix of protein subunits, and the coil has a diameter of 80Å. There are very nearly 16⅓ subunits in one turn of the protein helix and 49 nucleotides in one turn of the RNA helix. The hole down the axis has a diameter of 40Å, and the maximum diameter of the particle is 180Å. The shape of the protein subunits is rather schematic, and each nucleotide is represented by a flat disc. Each protein subunit is equivalently related to its neighbors (cf. Fig. 13–4).

ponent parts are organized. It should be pointed out that although the packing in the helix can be accurately characterized, it is not yet possible, from the X-ray analysis, to distinguish between a right- and left-handed helix. The reason for this is that mirror-image structures normally give indistinguishable X-ray patterns. High-resolution electron microscopy may provide a more direct way to determine the "hand" of the helix. However, since the nature of the assembly process would be the same for the mirror-image helices, ignorance of the hand does not affect the interpretation of the functional organization.

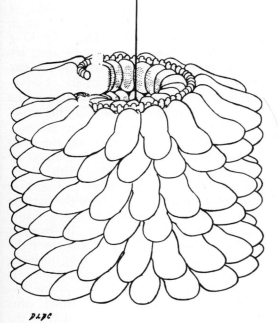

ᴘ↓ᴊᴄ

Fig. 13–7. A drawing representing the structure of the dahlemense strain of TMV based on X-ray diffraction studies (Caspar and Holmes, to be published). The structure and packing of the subunits of the dahlemense strain is very similar to that of the common strain (Fig. 13–6), but there is a periodic perturbation of the positions of ends of the subunits which brings turns of the helix near the outside surface alternately closer together and farther apart. The magnitude of these displacements has been exaggerated in this drawing for clarity. The net result of these periodic distortions is that chemically identical subunits in the dahlemense strain are packed in 98 symmetrically distinct but quasi-equivalent environments.

C. Deformed Helical Structures

A regular helical structure can be transformed into one in which the units are no longer all equivalently related by deforming the intersubunit bonds in slightly different ways. For example, if the bonds BE and CF between the turns of the helix in Fig. 13–4 could be easily stretched, the helix could be made flexible like a coiled spring. Although the TMV helix is quite rigid, there are a number of flexible filamentous virus particles. These sinuous structures are undoubtedly helical, but they differ from TMV in that they are not held rigid by strong interactions between successive turns of the helix. Strict helical

symmetry requires a straight axis; thus, the subunits of a sinuous helix cannot all be equivalently related. Nevertheless, since the local bonding pattern would not be changed very greatly when the helix axis is slightly bent, the subunits can remain quasi-equivalently related.

There is no long-range regularity in the departures from equivalence in a randomly flexed helix. However, even in a highly ordered structure, identical units need not be packed in exactly identical environments. X-ray diffraction studies on the dahlemense strain of TMV (Caspar and Holmes, to be published) indicate that there is a periodic perturbation in the packing of the subunits near the outside surface of the helix which leads to a small regular deformation of the helix in the axial direction. The nature of this periodic perturbation is illustrated in Fig. 13–7, where the magnitude of the displacements has been exaggerated. This structure is very similar to that of the common strain shown in Fig. 13–6. From the X-ray studies it has been found that there is very little difference in the over-all conformation of the subunits of the common and dahlemense strains. Sarkar's (1960) observation that the protein subunits of these two strains can copolymerize also indicates a close structural similarity. The packing in the interior of the helix is almost indistinguishable for these two viruses, and it is only near the outside surface that there is a significant structural difference which can be detected from the X-ray patterns. In the common strain each subunit is equivalently bonded to its neighbors, but in the dahlemense strain the outer end of a subunit can bend up or down into slightly different positions so that chemically identical parts of different molecules are packed in quasi-equivalent environments. The maximum up or down displacement from the position of equivalence is only about 1Å, and the displacements are coordinated in such a way that there is a minimum change in the side-to-side bonding. The net effect, as can be seen on the right side of the helix in Fig. 13–7, is that turns of the helix are brought alternately closer together and farther apart.

The energy for this periodic deformation comes from a weak interaction between the outside ends of the subunits. In order to form these bonds, chemically identical parts of neighboring molecules must be brought closer together than the pitch of the helix determined by the close packing of the subunits in the interior of the helix; thus, there is no strictly regular way in which all these possible bonds can be formed. Since this periodically deformed helix is more stable than a regular helix, it is evident that the decrease in free energy on forming some of the possible additional bonds is greater than the increase in free energy required to bend the subunits into the slightly different but quasi-equivalent positions. Under some solvent conditions a similar, though less ordered, helical perturbation is observed in the structure of the common strain of TMV. These results demonstrate that the protein subunit is not completely rigid, but the range of energetically possible deformations is, nevertheless, quite small.

A different type of regular perturbation in the helical structure of the common strain of TMV has been inferred by Mattern (1962) from electron microscope studies. He observed transverse and longitudinal striations in the surface of the virus particles with periodicities larger than those known from the X-ray studies of the virus in solution. The observed periodicities can be accounted for by a clustering of the structure units in groups of seven (six-around-one), and this clustering is presumably a result of the local surface-tension forces on dehydration. This periodically deformed structure is illustrated in an idealized fashion in Fig. 13–8, but it is unlikely that the clustering would be as regular as indicated since the surface forces on drying would tend to be nonuniform. Moreover, this type of clustering does not occur under all conditions of TMV specimen preparation for electron microscopy. Hart (1961) has shown that a surface structure corresponding to that known for the virus in solution (cf. Fig. 13–6) can sometimes be revealed in electron micrographs.

When TMV is dried in oriented gels (Bernal and Fankuchen, 1941) it is clear from X-ray diffraction studies that there are no ordered changes in the packing of the subunits in the helix such as those in Fig. 13–8. However, Franklin and Klug (1956) have shown that neighboring helices in these closely packed dry gels can intermesh, which accounts for the observation that the interparticle separation in the dry state is significantly less than the maximum diameter of the particle in solution. This indicates that, in solution, the ends of the subunits are normally separated by relatively large spaces filled with water. Although the clustering shown in Fig. 13–8 may not invariably occur when the particle is dried, it does represent an energetically plausible deformation since it requires only relatively small departures from the normally uniform helical packing to bring the ends of neighboring units together. It should be noted that even though the low-resolution appearance of the dried virus may seem quite different from that of the virus in solution (Fig. 13–6), the bonding relation between the subunits is very similar in the two cases.

D. Symmetry and Structure of Polymerized Protein

Rod-shaped particles of TMV protein without RNA, which physically resemble the intact virus in many ways, can be prepared by polymerizing the A-protein isolated from degraded virus (Schramm, 1943, 1947; Schramm and Zillig, 1955) or the X-protein present in infected cells (Takahashi and Ishii, 1952). The protein alone can polymerize either in the same helical arrangement as in the intact virus (Franklin, 1955; Rich et al., 1955) or in a variant stacked-disc structure (Franklin and Commoner, 1955). The rod aggregates are stable in the pH range 3–6.5 and are electrophoretically indistinguishable from the intact virus (Kramer and Wittmann, 1958). Although the conditions for rod formation have been studied in detail (Schramm and Zillig, 1955; Lauffer et al., 1958), the specific conditions which favor the formation of the helical or stacked-disc structures have not been determined. However, it appears that the helix may be the more stable structure at low ionic strength (Caspar, unpublished). In any case, it is clear that the energetic difference between these two structures is not great.

1. *Native helical structures.*—The analysis of the way in which the single strand of RNA is coiled between the turns of the protein helix in the intact virus, which has already been mentioned (see Fig. 13–6), was based on the X-ray studies on polymerized protein in the native helical structure (Franklin, 1955, 1956b, 1958; Franklin *et al.*, 1959). The symmetry of the protein helix, as indicated by the X-ray pattern, is indistinguishable from that of the intact virus, but the intensities of the X-ray reflections differ from those in the pattern from the intact virus because of the absence of the RNA chain. Not only are the subunits arranged in a helix of the same pitch with the same number per turn as in the virus particle, but the conformation of the protein subunit appears to be effectively unchanged. There is somewhat more disorder in the protein helix than in the virus helix, and there may be some slight local conformational changes in the protein, but these differences are small. A more marked difference is observed when the polymerized protein is dried. The distance between turns of the helix shortens from 23Å in the wet gel to about 20.5Å in the dry gel, and the structure becomes more disordered. In contrast, the pitch of the helix for the intact virus is maintained at 23Å on drying and only slight disordering occurs. Presumably, in solution the space normally occupied by RNA in the intact virus is replaced by water and anions to make up for the missing phosphate groups of RNA in the polymerized protein. This structure is stable, but when the water is removed by drying, the particle shrinks and becomes partially disordered. The RNA thus has a considerable stabilizing effect on the protein packing in the dry state, but can be replaced, at least structurally, by water and anions when the polymerized protein is in solution.

2. *Stacked-disc structure.*—The unusual X-ray patterns obtained by Franklin from polymerized TMV protein isolated from infected plants (Franklin and Commoner, 1955) provided the first indication of a protein packing arrangement different from

DLDC

Fig. 13–8. Drawing representing the structure of a 15-turn segment of a dried, isolated TMV particle as inferred from electron microscope studies (Mattern, 1962), and the known structure of the virus in solution. It is probable that the clustering which actually occurs is more disordered than indicated, because of the local variation that might be expected in the drying forces. The dimensions are the same as for the native hydrated virus shown in Fig. 13–6.

that of the virus. These patterns show that there is considerably more disorder in this variant structure than in the TMV or helical protein structure. The approximate correspondence of the strong meridional reflections in the pattern of the variant structure to the pitch spacing of TMV indicates that both structures are built up of units of the same thickness. Franklin pointed out that the presence of additional meridional reflections implies that the variant structure is built up of a stacked-disc arrangement of subunits. The position of the additional meridional reflections shows a repeat every two turns, which suggests the discs may be grouped in pairs. Unlike TMV, and to a much greater extent than repolymerized protein in the native helical packing arrangement, the stacked-disc structure is very sensitive to water content. The axial repeat distance increases by more than 20% in going from the dry to the wet gel. This is a change of about 5Å in the distance between layers of subunits; in the wet gel the subunits are about 3.5Å farther apart than in virus. Such reversible swelling and shrinking indicates that the forces between the layers are quite weak.

The X-ray patterns obtained from the stacked-disc structure are not, in themselves, detailed enough to define the packing relation between the subunits, but because of the correspondence of the diameter and axial spacing of this aggregate to that of the helical structure it is very likely that the arrangement of the subunits is similar in both structures. Moreover, X-ray patterns obtained from polymerized A-protein (Caspar, unpublished) have shown that both structures can coexist in solution, which suggests that there may be an equilibrium between the two forms. It is evident from Fig. 13–4 that the helical structure can be transformed into an array with cylindrical symmetry without very great changes in the local bonding of the units. This transformation corresponds to two different ways of connecting the same plane net into tubes with approximately the same number of units per turn. The TMV helix has 16.34 units per turn; thus, connecting the same units into discs of 16 units each would require only a very small change in the bond angles between neighboring units. Klug and Caspar (1960) pointed out that the electron micrographs obtained by Nixon and Woods (1960) of polymerized protein rods appeared to show the subunits arranged in the stacked-disc structure deduced from the X-ray studies. More recent electron microscope studies by Markham *et al.* (1963) have provided a detailed confirmation of this stacked-disc structure with 16 subunits in each layer. The possible nature of the grouping of the discs in pairs is suggested by the X-ray studies on the structure of the dahlemense strain (see Fig. 13–7). Displacement of the ends of the subunits in the discs toward each other in pairs would allow the formation of additional bonds, and more of these additional bonds can be formed in the disc arrangement than in the helical structure. Although the stability of the stacked-disc array may be comparable to that of the helix, it will not accommodate the nucleic acid chain; thus, it is the helical structure which is selected by the nucleic acid.

13–6. ASSEMBLY OF THE TOBACCO MOSAIC VIRUS PARTICLE

The assembly of protein subunits and RNA chains in the infected cell to produce intact virus particles cannot be directly observed. The purified virus particles can, however, be disassembled under controlled conditions *in vitro* (Schramm, 1943, 1947; Harrington and Schachman, 1956), and the isolated components can be reassembled (Fraenkel-Conrat and Williams, 1955) to produce virus particles indistinguishable from those assembled *in vivo*. In a sense, a virus particle can be considered as a finite sized crystal. Like a crystal it can be "dissolved" into its constituent parts, and these parts can be "recrystallized." The design for the virus structure is embodied in the protein subunits since they can assemble themselves into the same helical structure as in the complete virus without the RNA chain. The interactions with RNA, however, contribute significantly to the stability of the complete particle. The same self-assembly mechanism observed *in vitro* can work *in vivo;* thus, no external organizer is needed to put the parts together once they have been synthesized. A detailed analysis of the assembly process for TMV has recently been presented (Caspar, 1963), and only the conclusions from that study will be summarized here.

Starting with the postulate that the packing relations in any stable aggregate of

TMV protein are similar to those in the completed helix, it has been possible to account for the stable intermediates observed in solution. The smallest well-defined aggregate of TMV subunits is the 4–4.6S A-protein. From measurement of the sedimentation and diffusion constant, Schramm and Zillig (1955) concluded it had a molecular weight about 90,000, and consisted, therefore, of 5 or 6 subunits. However, this molecular weight measurement is inaccurate because of the difficulties in measuring the diffusion constant in this system of associating protein molecules. The A-protein aggregate is, in fact, a cyclic trimer in which each unit is bonded to both neighbors using the same type of bonds as in the helix. The next larger stable aggregate is a cyclic heptamer with a sedimentation constant about 8S, and this is followed by two- and three-turn disc aggregates with sedimentation constants about 20 and 30S, respectively. The two-turn disc apparently consists of 32 units arranged in 2 rings of 16 units, each of which is stabilized by displacement of the outside ends of the subunits toward each other in pairs. This two-turn disc is the precursor of the stacked-disc polymer. The stable three-turn aggregate may consist of a 49-subunit helical segment with a similar perturbation in the packing of the outside ends of the units, and it would presumably represent a precursor of the helical aggregate (Klug and Franklin, 1957).

The equilibria between the possible stable aggregates can be thermodynamically described in terms of their equilibria with monomers. Although any particular aggregate may not be formed directly from monomer, it is possible, in principle, to evaluate the free energy difference between monomer and n-mer, and thus to evaluate the free energy difference between any pair of aggregates. It has been shown that the process of rod polymer formation is a condensation phenomenon, analogous to the condensation of a gas into a liquid. Very small changes in the environmental conditions (e.g., temperature or pH) can lead to a large change in helix stability.

Although the assembly of the protein polymers can be described in terms of the aggregation of preformed intermediates, it is unlikely that protein molecules could be added in preformed clusters when protein and RNA are copolymerized to form the virus helix. Since the RNA chain must be wrapped between successive turns of the protein helix, the growth of the nucleoprotein helix will proceed by stepwise addition of subunits, following the basic helical path. However, the stable aggregates of TMV protein which can occur in the absence of RNA must be determined by the specific bonding between subunits, and the equilibria in their formation will, therefore, be related to the mechanics of virus particle assembly.

From studies of the thermodynamics of TMV protein association (Lauffer et al., 1958) it can be concluded that hydrophobic bonding contributes a large measure of the stabilization energy for the orderly close packing of the subunits in the polymers. The hydrophobic bond (Kauzmann, 1959) does not represent a specific affinity of nonpolar groups for each other, but rather, as its name implies, it results from an aversion of these groups for water. The hydrophobic bond is formed when nonpolar groups of the protein are transferred from an aqueous to a hydrocarbon environment by juxtaposing nonpolar surfaces, since this will lead to an increase in entropy of the water, and thus a decrease in free energy for the whole system.

Carboxyl-carboxylate bonding in the virus protein (Caspar, 1963) provides a specific electrostatic control mechanism for the protein association. Protons are bound to these carboxylate pairs when the protein is polymerized, but when the protein is depolymerized at a pH above 6 these protons are dissociated. These critical groups serve to prevent the polymerization of the protein alone at a pH above about 6.5, but in the presence of RNA copolymerization will occur because of the additional stabilization of the protein-RNA bonds.

The observations on the dissociation of the intact virus in alkali (Harrington and Schachman, 1956) and urea (Buzzell, 1962), and on the reconstitution of TMV protein with viral and nonviral RNA (Fraenkel-Conrat and Singer, 1957, 1959;

Holoubeck, 1962) have been interpreted (Caspar, 1963) to indicate that there is specificity in the RNA-protein association. It has been suggested that the nucleotide sequence in certain segments of the virus RNA is such that strong bonds can be formed with the protein subunits. Specificity in the RNA-protein combination would result if some segments of the RNA chain have exceptional affinity for the protein. The essential specificity is that for initiating the formation of the helical aggregate since once a stable segment of the helix has formed more subunits can be successively added at the screw dislocation which represents a favorable bonding site. In this way the RNA would be enfolded between the turns of the protein helix until it is completely covered. The protective coating of the RNA would be most effective if the end of the RNA molecule which is first synthesized is that which combines specifically with the protein subunits. Thus assembly of the nucleoprotein helix *in vivo* could start as soon as the end of the growing RNA chain becomes accessible to protein subunits, and assembly could proceed in sequence with RNA synthesis.

The process of virus particle construction can be considered to be divided into two phases: first, the biosynthetic stage in which the covalent bonds of the polypeptide subunit and RNA chain are formed; and second, the assembly stage in which the polypeptide chains are folded into globular units which pack together with the RNA chain to form the organized virus particle structure. The sequence of amino acids in the protein and of the nucleotides in the RNA is controlled by an external template (the RNA), but the assembly process which involves the formation of noncovalent bonds can proceed, as described here, without external control. A basic postulate in this description of the sub- and self-assembly mechanisms is that, although the synthesis of the parts and their assembly into the organized structure may proceed in a coordinated fashion, the various processes are not necessarily synchronous and interdependent.

The clearest evidence that coat-protein synthesis can be uncoupled from that of

RNA in TMV infection is provided by the studies of Siegel *et al.* (1962) on an unusually defective mutant produced by nitrous acid treatment. This PM1 mutant produces no physically or serologically detectable coat protein, but the nucleic acid will multiply. Although the RNA is very labile in its "undressed" state, under carefully controlled conditions, it can be isolated and propagated. Siegel *et al.* (1962) isolated another defective nitrous acid-produced mutant (PM2) which is of particular interest in relation to the mechanics of virus particle assembly. This mutant produces a protein which is serologically related and physically similar to TMV protein, but it does not combine with the virus RNA. The infectious agent of the PM2 mutant is therefore as labile as that of the PM1 mutant. The PM2 protein alone aggregates reversibly under similar conditions to TMV protein, and although the packing of the protein in these polymers has not yet been investigated in detail it is likely to be related to that of TMV protein aggregates. These observations indicate that the mutant protein subunits can combine together to form an ordered structure, but they cannot be combined with the RNA to form a virus particle. It is thus clear that the assembly of the component parts can be uncoupled from the synthesis of these parts.

A plausible picture of the virus reproduction is that protein subunits and RNA chains are synthesized at independent sites in the cell. As the concentration of free protein subunits builds up, they may form small aggregates (A-protein), but as soon as a small pool of subunits is built up they will aggregate with the RNA chains being synthesized. This follows since there is some specificity in the protein-virus RNA interaction and the negative free energy change for the copolymerization is greater than for polymerization of protein alone.

Once the TMV particle has formed it is very stable. This stability is due to the coordinated arrangement of a number of weak noncovalent interactions. The protein-protein bonding which determines the architecture of the virus particle is of such a nature that extensive association of the protein alone will not take place under normal physiological conditions. It would obviously be a biological misfortune for the virus RNA if its coat protein could form a stable structure without it. However, it is the additional energy of the protein-RNA interaction which insures the formation of the stable helical aggregate in the infected cell. This very stable package provides an efficient way of transmitting the nucleic acid, but if the virus is to multiply when the particle encounters a susceptible host, the nucleic acid must be unwrapped. On the assumption that disassembly, like assembly, does not require the mediation of a specific external agent, knowledge of the forces which hold the particle together can suggest the nature of the environment which is likely to favor dissociation.

The analysis presented here of the functional properties of the protein subunit would require that for optimum design: (1) the subunits combine specifically with the viral RNA by a self-assembly process; (2) the protein subunits form a stable coat structure which protects the nucleic acid from inactivation under a wide variety of environmental conditions; and (3) the organized structure becomes unstable in the special cellular environment where the exposed nucleic acid can function. Certain segments of the polypeptide sequence may be essential in order to form a subunit which can package the nucleic acid. However, considering the delicate balance of forces necessary to meet these three functional requirements it is plausible that every part of the protein subunit may have some functional role.

13–7. DESIGN OF ICOSAHEDRAL VIRUS PARTICLES

The amount of experimental information available regarding the molecular substructure of icosahedral viruses is much more limited than for TMV. However, on the assumption that the construction of regular isometric virus particles is governed by the same physical principles as have been shown to apply to TMV, it has been possible to show (Caspar and Klug, 1962) that there is only one kind of efficient design for their protein shells. The first experimental evidence for icosahedral symmetry in a virus came from the X-ray diffraction studies of Caspar (1956b) on tomato bushy stunt virus (see Fig. 13–3), soon followed by that of Klug et al. (1957) on turnip yellow mosaic virus. Shortly thereafter, electron microscope observations (see Horne and Wildy, 1961) showed that a number of isometric virus particles have icosahedral morphology. Crick and Watson (1956) pointed out that only regular bonding of identical units using one of the three types of cubic symmetry (tetrahedral, octahedral, or icosahedral) was likely to lead to an isometric particle. When icosahedral symmetry was established for quite unrelated viruses, it was recognized (Finch and Klug, 1959) that its occurrence was not a matter of chance selection, and the suggestion was made that there were other structural principles involved in addition to those put forward by Crick and Watson.

Icosahedral symmetry requires that the capsid consist of 60 geometrically equivalent parts. Chemical studies on two small icosahedral viruses (Harris and Hindley, 1961; Yamazaki and Kaesberg, 1961) have shown that the capsid is built of identical protein molecules but the number is greater than 60. In addition, electron microscope studies have revealed (see Horne and Wildy, 1961) that a number of viruses with icosahedral morphology consist of a regular surface array of morphological units and the number is often greater than 60 but not generally a multiple of 60.

These observations raised two structural problems: (1) Why is icosahedral symmetry preferred in the design of isometric virus capsids? (2) How can a capsid be constructed by regular bonding of a multiple of 60 structure units to have the type of morphology seen in the electron microscope? The answers we have found (Caspar and Klug, 1962) to these two questions were inspired by the geometrical principles applied by Buckminster Fuller in the construction of geodesic domes (see Marks, 1960). Fuller's dome designs involve the subdivision of the surface of a sphere into quasi-equivalently related triangular facets which are arranged with icosahedral symmetry (Fig. 13–9).

Fig. 13–9. A Fuller geodesic dome. Note that the surface is made up of quasi-equivalent triangular facets and that they are grouped in hexamers and pentamers about the small rings of the dome (reproduced by permission of R. Buckminster Fuller).

The device of triangulating the sphere with icosahedral symmetry represents the optimum design for a closed shell built of regularly bonded identical structure units. No other subdivision of a closed surface can give a comparable degree of quasi-equivalence, and thus the icosahedral surface crystals are minimum-energy structures. This answers the first question as to the selection advantage of icosahedral designs for closed containers.

The next problem was to enumerate all ways in which this subdivision could be carried out. The systematic way to do this is to consider the triangulation of the sphere to be derived from the folding up of a plane equi-triangulated net into a polyhedron with icosahedral symmetry. These polyhedra with icosahedral symmetry and triangular facets are called icosadeltahedra. The icosahedron itself has 20 triangular facets and any icosadeltahedron has 20 T facets, where T is the triangulation number given by the rule: $T = (H^2 + HK + K^2)$ where H and K are any pair of integers. The series of triangulation numbers, represented on an equilateral-triangular net in Figure 13–10, was first derived by Goldberg (1937) in connection with a similar type of geometrical problem. Figure 13–11 shows models of icosadeltahedra (constructed from Geodestix components, designed by Buckminster Fuller, and available from Geodestix, Spokane, Washington) representing the first five possible triangulation numbers ($T = 1, 3, 4, 7, 9$). The total number of connectors in each model is $10T + 2$, corresponding to 12 pentamers and 10 ($T - 1$) hexamers. The structure unit implicitly associated with each model can be visualized as a single sleeve of a connector, and the total number is 60T.

The triangulation numbers can be factored into classes by writing $T = Pf^2$ where $P = h^2 + hk + k^2$ (h and k any integers having no common factor), and f is any

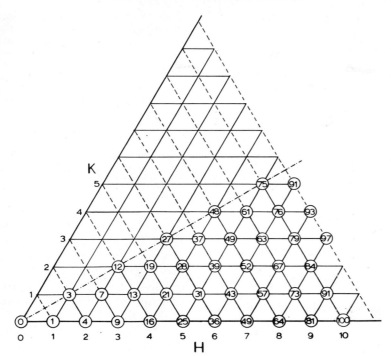

Fig. 13–10. Triangulation numbers $T = (H^2 + HK + K^2)$ represented on an equilateral-triangular net. An icosadeltahedron (see Fig. 13–11) with a 5-fold vertex at the origin of this net and a neighboring 5-fold vertex at the lattice point of index H, K will have $10T + 2$ vertices (12 five and $10(T - 1)$ six-connected vertices) and $20T$ triangular facets.

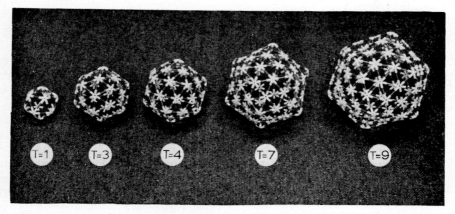

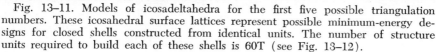

Fig. 13–11. Models of icosadeltahedra for the first five possible triangulation numbers. These icosahedral surface lattices represent possible minimum-energy designs for closed shells constructed from identical units. The number of structure units required to build each of these shells is $60T$ (see Fig. 13–12).

integer. Each value of P represents a particular class of icosadeltahedra. The classes $P = 1$ and 3 have been used by Fuller in his geodesic dome designs and have been recognized in the structure of some icosahedral viruses (see Caspar and Klug, 1962).

Models for icosahedral virus shells corresponding to any of the icosadeltahedra surface lattices can be constructed from 60T identical structure units. Figure 13–12a shows a spherical surface array of 540 structure units arranged in a lattice correspond-

287

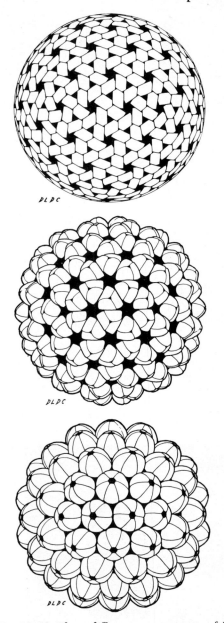

(a) Two-dimensional structure units on the surface of a sphere. (Compare with the helical array of two-dimensional units shown in Fig. 13–4 and the T = 12 icosahedral surface lattice of the Fuller dome shown in Fig. 13–9.) Note that each unit is connected to its nearest neighbors in the same way, but not all the environments are exactly alike. There are actually 9 symmetrically distinct, but quasi-equivalent environments.

(b) Clustering of 540 three-dimensional structure units into 180 trimers.

(c) Clustering of 540 three-dimensional structure units into 12 pentamers and 80 hexamers (92 morphological units).

Fig. 13–12. Three different arrangements of 540 identical structure units in the T = 9 icosahedral surface lattice (see Fig. 13–11). Similar models consisting of 60T structure units can be constructed for any of the geometrically allowed triangulation numbers.

The geometrical relation between the structure units in (b) and (c) is identical to that in (a) although the shape and physical bonding of the units is different in these three models. The coordination of the morphological units observed in electron micrographs of a number of icosahedral viruses corresponds to that shown in (c), but other coordination patterns, such as that shown in (b), can and *do* occur.

ing to the T = 9 icosadeltahedron of Figure 13–11. Protein molecules arranged in an icosahedral shell will have radial extent and may aggregate in symmetric clusters. Figure 13–12b shows the clustering of the 540 structure units into 180 trimers, and Figure 13–12c the clustering into 12 pentamers and 80 hexamers (92 morphological units). Any icosahedral shell of triangulation number T can be built up of 12 pentamers and $10(T-1)$ hexamers (i.e., $10T + 2$ five- and six-coordinated morphological units) or 20T trimers or 30T dimers or 60T monomers.

Clustering of the structure units provides a way of maximizing the contacts between them, but the particular clustering pattern observed in dried and stained virus particles in the electron microscope may not represent the most stable arrangement in solution. Some of the problems of identifying the underlying geometry of the particle substructure from electron micrographs have been pointed out previously (Caspar and Klug, 1962). It should be noted that the geometrical relation between the structure units in Figures 13–12a, b, and c are the same even though their physical appearances are different. The counting which is structurally relevant to describe the design of these shells is not the number of morphological units but, rather, the number of local symmetry axes and this can be represented by the icosahedral triangulation number.

The important point about these minimum-energy surface lattices is that the number of identical units which can be regularly bonded in a closed shell is quantized.

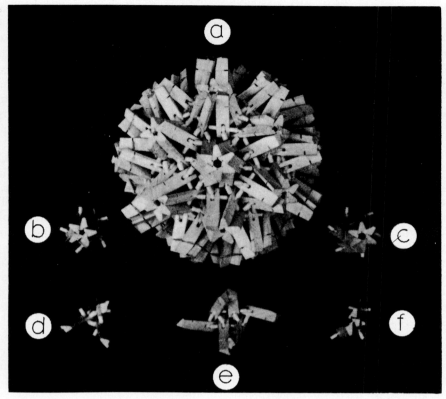

Fig. 13–13. A "self-assembly" model of an icosahedral capsid. The model (a) is built of 180 identical structure units bonded in the T = 3 icosahedral surface lattice. The units have been so designed that they can assemble in only one way to form a stable shell. The arrangement of the 32 clusters (12 pentamers and 20 hexamers) corresponds to that of the 32 morphological units observed in turnip yellow mosaic virus (Huxley and Zubay, 1960; Nixon and Gibbs, 1960).

Various small aggregates of the units are also shown: (b) pentamer; (c) hexamer; (d) trimer; (e) two trimers bonded together; (f) part of a hexamer or pentamer.

Moreover, the structure units designed to build a particular icosahedral shell can assemble themselves in a relatively unambiguous way. Just as with helical structures, mistakes in assembly can occur, but for the structure units of an isometric capsid one of the possible icosahedral shell designs will represent the most stable bonding arrangement.

We have shown (Caspar and Klug, 1962) how a model for a structure unit can be designed which can be assembled into only one of the possible icosahedral shells. Figure 13–13 shows a model for the shell with triangulation number T = 3, which is built of 180 asymmetric shaped wooden structure units. The structure unit has bonding sites on it which, purely geometrically,

tend to form a plane hexagonal lattice, but which, at the same time, require that the units aggregate in a curved surface. It is this built-in curvature which requires the formation of 12 pentamers. The unique feature of this model is that the subunits can be assembled in only one way to form a stable shell. If the bonds were represented by magnets, for example, these structure units could assemble themselves.

Although no icosahedral virus has yet been degraded into subunits which can be reassembled *in vitro* (as in the case of TMV), we would predict that such *in vitro* reassembly is in principle possible, and that the mechanism of icosahedral virus construction *in vivo* is the self-assembly process described here. Self-assembly leads automatically to these symmetric, minimum-energy structures, and no external organizer or other guiding principle is necessary to account for the economy, efficiency, and simplicity of these designs.

Even if the protein shell can form without the virus-specific nucleic acid, this does not mean that the nucleic acid has no structural function in forming the virus particle. We have already noted that the nucleic acid chain of TMV can select the "correct" helical form and reject the alternate stacked-disc packing arrangement of the protein structure units. Moreover, the RNA-protein interactions in TMV contribute significantly to the stability of the intact virus (Caspar, 1963). The properties of the empty shells and intact particles of the icosahedral papilloma virus (Breedis *et al.*, 1962) show similarities to the properties of nucleic acid free and intact TMV particles. Here again, the nucleic acid (DNA)-protein interactions may prevent "mistakes" in assembly and help to stabilize the correctly assembled nucleocapsid.

The fact that the same type of icosahedral shell design is used by viruses containing double-stranded or single-stranded DNA or RNA is convincing evidence that the icosahedral design is dependent on the packing properties of the protein subunits and not on the chemical nature of the nucleic acid. However, the ways in which a nucleic acid chain may be folded up inside an icosahedral capsid are not as obvious as in helical capsids. A flexible RNA molecule could be rolled up like a ball of string inside the shell, but the limited X-ray evidence (Klug and Finch, 1960) indicates that the RNA folding is, in fact, related to the structure of the capsid though it is not as highly organized as the protein packing. A double-helical DNA molecule, on the other hand, cannot easily be rolled up, and is more likely to be sharply folded at sequence-determined bending points. In either case, there appears to be no way in which a long-chain molecule (double- or single-stranded) can be wrapped so that it makes the same kind of contacts all along its length with the protein subunits of an icosahedral shell. In contrast, the helical design, such as the TMV nucleocapsid, allows maximum regular interaction between the single RNA strand and the protein subunits.

* * *

The investigations described here have been supported by Grant CA-04696 from the National Cancer Institute.

13–8. LITERATURE CITED

Bawden, F. C., and Sheffield, F. M. L. (1939). Ann. Appl. Biol. **26**, 102.

Bernal, J. D., and Fankuchen, I. (1941). J. Gen. Physiol. **25**, 111.

Breedis, C., Berwick, L., and Anderson, T. F. (1962). Virology **17**, 84.

Buzzell, A. (1962). Biophys. J. **2**, 223.

Caspar, D. L. D. (1956a). Nature **177**, 928.

Caspar, D. L. D. (1956b). Nature **177**, 475.

Caspar, D. L. D. (1963). Advan. Protein Chem. **18**, 37.

Caspar, D. L. D., and Klug, A. (1962). Cold Spring Harbor Symp. Quant. Biol. **27**, 1.

Caspar, D. L. D., Dulbecco, R., Klug, A., Lwoff, A., Stoker, M. G. P., Tournier, P., and Wildy, P. (1962). Cold Spring Harbor Symp. Quant. Biol. **27**, 49.

Crane, H. R. (1950). Sci. Monthly **70**, 376.

Crick, F. H. C., and Watson, J. D. (1956). Nature **177**, 473.

Crick, F. H. C., and Watson, J. D. (1957). Ciba Found. Symp. Nature Viruses, 5. Churchill, London.

Crick, F. H. C., Barnett, L., Brenner, S., and Watts-Tobin, R. J. (1961). Nature **192**, 1227.

Eisenstark, A., Maale, O., and Birch-Anderson, A. (1961). Virology **15**, 56.

Finch, J. T., and Klug, A. (1959). Nature **183**, 1709.

Fraenkel-Conrat, H., and Singer, B. (1957). Biochim. Biophys. Acta **24**, 540.

Fraenkel-Conrat, H., and Singer, B. (1959). Biochim. Biophys. Acta **33**, 359.

Fraenkel-Conrat, H., and Williams, R. C. (1955). Proc. Natl. Acad. Sci. U.S. **41**, 690.

Franklin, R. E. (1955). Biochim. Biophys. Acta **18**, 313.

Franklin, R. E. (1956a). Biochim. Biophys. Acta **19**, 203.

Franklin, R. E. (1956b). Nature **177**, 929.

Franklin, R. E. (1958). In A. Neuberger (ed.), Symposium on Protein Structure. 271. Wiley, New York.

Franklin, R. E., and Commoner, B. (1955). Nature 175, 1076.

Franklin, R. E., and Holmes, K. C. (1958). Acta Cryst. 11, 213.

Franklin, R. E., and Klug, A. (1955). Acta Cryst. 8, 777.

Franklin, R. E., and Klug, A. (1956). Biochim. Biophys. Acta 19, 403.

Franklin, R. E., Caspar, D. L. D., and Klug, A. (1959). In C. S. Holton (ed.), Plant Pathology-Problems and Progress, 1908–1958. 447. Univ. of Wisconsin Press, Madison.

Goldberg, M. (1937). Tohoku Mathematical J. 43, 104.

Harrington, W. F., and Schachman, H. K. (1956). Arch. Biochem. Biophys. 65, 278.

Harris, J. I., and Hindley, J. (1961). J. Mol. Biol. 3, 117.

Harris, J. I., and Knight, C. A. (1952). Nature 170, 613.

Hart, R. G. (1961). J. Mol. Biol. 3, 701.

Holoubeck, V. (1962). Virology 18, 401.

Horne, R. W., and Wildy, P. (1961). Virology 15, 348.

Huxley, H. E., and Zubay, G. (1960). J. Mol. Biol. 2, 189.

International Tables for X-ray Crystallography. (1952). Vol. 1. Symmetry Groups (N. F. M. Henry and K. Lonsdale, eds.).

Kassanis, B., and Nixon, H. L. (1960). Nature 187, 713.

Kassanis, B., and Nixon, H. L. (1961). J. Gen. Microbiol. 25, 459.

Kauzmann, W. (1959). Advan. Protein Chem. 14, 1.

Kellenberger, E. (1961). Advan. Virus Res. 8, 1.

Klug, A., and Caspar, D. L. D. (1960). Advan. Virus Res. 7, 225.

Klug, A., and Finch, J. T. (1960). J. Mol. Biol. 2, 201.

Klug, A., and Franklin, R. E. (1957). Biochim. Biophys. Acta 23, 199.

Klug, A., Finch, J. T., and Franklin, R. E. (1957). Biochim. Biophys. Acta 25, 242.

Kramer, E., and Wittmann, H. G. (1958). Z. Naturforsch. 13b, 30.

Lauffer, M. A., Ansevin, A. T., Cartwright, T. E., and Brinton, C. C., Jr. (1958). Nature 181, 1338.

Loeb, T., and Zinder, N. D. (1961). Proc. Natl. Acad. Sci. U.S. 47, 282.

Lwoff, A., Anderson, T. F., and Jacob, F. (1959). Ann. Inst. Pasteur 97, 281.

Markham, R., Frey, S., and Hills, G. J. (1963). Virology 20, 88.

Marks, R. W. (1960). The Dymaxion World of Buckminster Fuller. Reinhold, New York.

Mattern, C. F. T. (1962). Virology 17, 76.

Nixon, H. L., and Gibbs, P. J. (1960). J. Mol. Biol. 2, 197.

Nixon, H. L., and Woods, R. D. (1960). Virology 10, 157.

Oster, G. (1950). J. Gen. Physiol. 33, 445.

Rich, A., Dunitz, J. D., and Newmark, P. (1955). Nature 175, 1074.

Sarkar, S. (1960). Z. Naturforsch. 15b, 778.

Schramm, G. (1943). Naturwissenschaften 31, 94.

Schramm, G. (1947). Z. Naturforsch. 2b, 112, 249.

Schramm, G., and Zillig, W. (1955). Z. Naturforsch. 10b, 493.

Siegel, A., Zaitlin, M., and Sehgal, O. P. (1962). Proc. Natl. Acad. Sci. U.S. 48, 1845.

Takahashi, W. N., and Ishii, M. (1952). Nature 169, 419.

Watson, J. D. (1954). Biochim. Biophys. Acta 13, 10.

Yamazaki, H., and Kaesberg, P. (1961). Biochim. Biophys. Acta 53, 173.

14

Structural biochemistry of plant viruses

C. A. KNIGHT

14-1. INTRODUCTION

THE BIOCHEMICAL era of virology began less than 30 years ago when Stanley published his classic paper describing the proteinaceous nature of crystalline tobacco mosaic virus (TMV) (Stanley, 1935). At that time, the proposal that a crystalline, macromolecular substance could be the cause of an infectious disease was received by many with incredulous astonishment. Adherents to traditional concepts of the distinctions between organisms and molecules were confused by the new discovery, and the pioneer virologist, Dr. Thomas Rivers, quipped that there was concern whether plant viruses should be called "organules or molechisms." This question has never been settled, but in the ensuing years vast progress has been made in understanding the chemical and physical nature of viruses and their interactions with cells. Plant viruses have from the beginning played a leading role in the major advances, and some of the basic features of plant virus chemistry as they now appear will be outlined in the following review. The subject has been more extensively treated elsewhere (Knight, 1963).

14-2. COMPOSITION OF VIRUSES

Shortly after Stanley's crystallization of TMV, Bawden and Pirie and associates (1936) presented evidence that three strains of TMV (common, aucuba, and enation mosaics) contained ribonucleic acid (RNA) which could be released from the viruses by heat denaturation. This observation was soon confirmed and extended by Stanley and colleagues. Thus protein and nucleic acid were marked as important constituents of plant viruses. The importance of RNA tended to be underestimated for many years, because of general engrossment with the obviously vital functions of proteins in biological systems. Moreover, most of the viruses analyzed proved to consist predominantly of protein, and Stanley and others had shown that infectivity of TMV was intimately associated with the integrity of the protein. All of this was placed in a new perspective with the discovery of infectious nucleic acid, as will be discussed later.

A. GENERAL FEATURES AND RELATIONS AMONG THE MAJOR CLASSES OF VIRUSES

Over the years, analytical chemists have been alert to the possibility that viruses might contain bizarre constituents which would set them apart from other biologically active agents, but nothing truly distinctive has yet been found. In fact, if current analytical and functional points of view are combined, it now appears that the simplest viruses, whether plant, bacterial, or animal, may be composed solely of nucleic acid in which uniqueness is achieved not by bizarre constituents, but simply by virtue of

TABLE 14–1. APPROXIMATE COMPOSITION OF SOME PLANT VIRUSES

Virus	% RNA	% Protein	Particle weight $\times 10^6$	Reference
Alfalfa Mosaic	20	80	7.4	a, b
Broad bean mottle	22	78	5.2	c
Bromegrass mosaic	21	79	4.6	d
Cucumber 3 (and 4)	5	95	39	e
Potato X	6	94	35	f, g
Southern bean mosaic	21	79	6.6	h, i
Squash mosaic	35	65	6.9	j
Tobacco mosaic	5	95	39	e, k
Tobacco necrosis	18	82	6.3*	l, m
Tobacco rattle	5	95	73	n
Tobacco ringspot	35	65	5	o
Tomato bushy stunt	17	83	8.9	p, q
Turnip yellow mosaic	37	63	5	r
Wild cucumber mosaic	35	65	7	s

* An estimate from the sedimentation coefficient given by Kassanis and Nixon, 1961.

(a) Frisch-Niggemeyer and Steere, 1961, (b) Kelley and Kaesberg, 1962a; (c) Yamazaki et al., 1961; (d) Bockstahler and Kaesberg, 1962; (e) Knight and Stanley, 1941, and Knight and Woody, 1958; (f) Bawden and Pirie, 1938; (g) Reichmann, 1959a; (h) Miller and Price, 1946; (i) Lauffer et al., 1952; (j) Mazzone et al., 1962; (k) Boedtker and Simmons, 1958; (l) Bawden and Pirie, 1945; (m) Kassanis and Nixon, 1961; (n) Harrison and Nixon, 1959; (o) Steere, 1956; (p) de Fremery and Knight, 1955; (q) Hersch and Schachman, 1958; (r) Markham, 1959; (s) Yamazaki and Kaesberg, 1961a.

proper nucleotide sequences. However, the more prevalent and hence familiar form of simple viruses is that of particles consisting almost exclusively of nucleic acid encased in a characteristic protein shell (polyamines, trace elements, and other minor constituents are briefly discussed in later sections). More complex viruses, notably certain animal viruses, may contain, in addition to protein and nucleic acid, lipid, polysaccharide, and a variety of miscellaneous constituents. However, protein and nucleic acid comprise the bulk of most stable virus particles, and are the only constituents common to all.

B. PLANT VIRUSES

Plant virus diseases probably number in the hundreds, but only about 15 of the causative agents have been isolated in sufficient purity for chemical work. Careful analyses show protein and RNA and very little else. There is a priori no good reason to account for the absence of deoxyribonucleic acid (DNA) in plant viruses. The fact that both types of nucleic acid have been observed in bacterial, animal, and insect viruses suggests that DNA will some day be found in some virus of higher plants, but this has not yet occurred.

1. *Proportions of major components.—* The proportions of RNA and protein are given for some purified plant viruses in Table 14–1. The values for protein range from 63 to 95%, which indicates that the mass and morphology of the virus particles are dominated by the protein components. Conversely, the RNA contents for different viruses vary from 5 to 37%. This seems at first to represent a large range, but when expressed in terms of mass of RNA per virus particle, it is seen that the RNA contents of all the viruses listed fall in the range of 1 to 3×10^6 avograms (molecular weight units) per particle.

Bromegrass mosaic virus is the smallest independent plant virus studied thus far. However, an interesting case of a "satellite virus" which seems to multiply only in the presence of a tobacco necrosis virus has been reported (Kassanis, 1962). The satellite virus is about 17 mμ in diameter and has a particle weight of about 1.9×10^6, of which about 20% is RNA.

2. *Carbohydrates.*—All plant viruses contain ribose in their RNA components, but other carbohydrates seem so far to be excluded from these viruses. Occasionally, in partially or imperfectly purified preparations, some carbohydrate appears which upon hydrolysis yields glucose. Presumably this is a bit of starch or some similar plant polysaccharide. A notable instance of contamination with polysaccharide occurs in the purification of potato virus X if the usual salts are used in the differential centrifugation procedure. The long, sinuous particles of this virus tend to aggregate badly in the presence of salts and presumably adsorb and occlude extraneous components in the process. If the preparations are made in the absence of salts, using distilled water to dissolve the virus pellets, glucose-yielding products are no longer detected (Knight, unpublished observations). Other methods for reducing aggregation of potato virus X have been reported (Reichmann, 1959b; Corbett, 1961), but the effect of these procedures on the elimination of extraneous carbohydrate has not as yet been tested.

3. *Enzymes.*—Viruses are isolated from cells which throng with enzymes which are more or less sticky and are active in low concentrations. Hence it is difficult to evaluate the significance of enzymatic activities demonstrable in highly purified preparations of viruses. However, the fact that nucleic acid alone is sufficient to initiate infection and that infection in some systems at least is marked by activation of cellular enzymes or even synthesis of new enzymes (Cohen, 1961) supports earlier conclusions that plant viruses depend on the host for enzymatic functions, and that the enzymatic activities associated with purified viruses are probably present as adsorbed impurities. For example, early preparations of TMV and tomato bushy stunt virus were reported to contain phosphatase which Stanley (1942) showed to be adventitiously derived from plant tissues.

An instance of considerable practical importance for some types of experiments is the association of variable traces of ribonuclease, perhaps in the form of ribosomal particles, with highly purified viruses such as TMV (Pirie, 1956; Fraenkel-Conrat *et al.*, 1961).

4. *Polyamines.*—Many cells appear to contain appreciable amounts of polyamines such as putrescine, $H_2N-CH_2-CH_2-CH_2-CH_2-NH_2$, and spermidine, $H_2N(CH_2)_4NH(CH_2)_3NH_2$ (Tabor *et al.*, 1961). These cations are strongly attracted to the phosphoryl anions of nucleic acids and appear to become a part of mature virus particles in those cases where permeability of the protein envelope and other factors prevent their exchange for simpler cations. While enough polyamine to neutralize about half of the charge on the viral DNA is found in some phages under certain conditions, only amounts equivalent to about 1–2% of the P of the RNA are found in TMV, cucumber virus 4, and tomato bushy stunt virus (Ames and Dubin, 1960). Johnson and Markham (1962) also reported traces of polyamine in TMV and identified the product as 3,3'-diaminodipropylamine. This same compound was found in larger amounts (sufficient to neutralize about one-seventh of the phosphate groups) in turnip yellow mosaic, turnip crinkle, and broadbean mottle viruses. Johnson and Markham were unable to demonstrate 3,3'-diaminodipropylamine in healthy plants and hence suggest that there might be some relationship between plant viruses and polyamines more specific than charge neutralization. However, this suggestion is a little vague and, in the light of the phage-polyamine relationship, which seems to be quite unspecific (Ames and Dubin, 1960), the plant virus polyamines can also probably be considered as adventitious.

5. *Metallic elements.*—Loring and associates have called attention to the presence in TMV, in a rather tightly bound form, of iron, calcium, magnesium, and probably copper and aluminum (see Loring *et al.*, 1959). The iron was found to occur in an amount equivalent to about 10-11 atoms per mole of virus, and upon dissociation of the virus, was found almost entirely in the nucleic acid fraction. However, the RNA of TMV was shown by Haschemeyer *et al.* (1959) to have a high affinity for metal ions, but these could be very greatly reduced in quantity by treatment with the

chelating agent, versenate (sodium ethyl-enediaminetetraacetate), without appreciably affecting the infectivity of the free RNA or the infectivity subsequently achievable by reconstitution with viral protein. Hence there is considerable doubt that these metallic ions are anything but adventitious elements.

6. *Functions of major components.*—A general conclusion that may be drawn from the preceding discussion is that protein and nucleic acid are the only essential components of plant viruses and that other constituents need be considered only insofar as they may modify the function of the major components. What are the respective functions then of protein and RNA?

Beginning with the experiments of Gierer and Schramm (1956a,b) and of Fraenkel-Conrat (1956), the claim was made that TMV-RNA alone is sufficient to cause infection of tobacco plants. Since the consequences of such an infection seemed identical to those caused by infections with whole virus, it was concluded that the RNA constituted the genetic material of the virus. Infectivity was ascribed to the TMV-RNA alone on the following grounds: (1) Infectivity of the RNA preparations is destroyed by the enzyme, ribonuclease (RNase), under conditions scarcely affecting whole virus. (2) Antiserum to whole virus abolishes infectivity of intact virus without greatly reducing the infectivity of RNA (serum usually contains RNase, so some reduction of infectivity occurs when RNA is treated with antiserum. This effect is eliminated by using just the gamma globulin fraction of the serum). (3) At about 100,000 g, the infectivity of whole virus is sedimented quantitatively while the infectivity of RNA preparations remains unsedimented. The relatively small size of the infectious unit in RNA preparations, demonstrated by its nonsedimentability in water or dilute salt, is confirmed by the lack of electron microscopically detectable particles which resemble virus in these preparations. (4) The infectivity of RNA preparations is more labile than whole virus to destruction by heat, ultraviolet light, and numerous chemicals. (5) In mixed reconstitution (see Section 14–3H), the hybrids produced always show the properties of the nucleic acid donor. (6) In the ultraviolet, the absorption spectrum and the inactivation spectrum coincide and are those of nucleic acid rather than protein. (7) The target volume for inactivation of TMV by X-rays corresponds fairly well with the nucleic acid volume. (8) The amount of protein found in the most highly purified preparations of RNA is equivalent to only one protein subunit (MW 17,500) per 22 strands of RNA, and this protein has an amino acid content unlike that of TMV-protein. Since there are no observations which indicate that this trace of protein or peptidic material is essential for the infectivity of the RNA whereas there is much evidence to show that biological activity depends on the integrity of the RNA, the most reasonable conclusion at present is that the RNA alone is infectious and possesses the genetic activity of the virus.

The protein of TMV, and of other viruses, can be viewed as a protective sheathing for the RNA, but protein and nucleic acid are also related more specifically in this scheme, for the protein is considered to be an expression of the genetic activity of the RNA. Some details of this relationship will be summarized in a later section.

14–3. STRUCTURE OF VIRUSES

Examination of purified plant viruses in the electron microscope shows that some viruses have rod-like particles, some have sinuous forms, while others are roughly spherical or polyhedral. The architectural features of the virus particles are discussed in chapters 12 and 13. Therefore, attention will be focused here on the detailed chemical characteristics of plant virus structures.

A. Subdivisions of Protein Structure

In the early years of chemical virology the term "virus protein" was commonly used to designate whole virus, that is, the nucleoprotein. Presently, however, the term is restricted to the protein component alone.

There are several aspects to protein structure and it is often convenient to consider them separately and then to combine the findings to form an integrated picture.

To this end four categories of protein structure have been proposed (Kendrew, 1959) as follows: (1) Primary structure: the number of peptide chains, S-S bridges if any, and particularly, the sequence of amino acid residues. (2) Secondary structure: the geometric configuration of the peptide chain or chains with special reference to the presence or absence of helical structure and associated hydrogen bridges. (3) Tertiary structure: the folding pattern of the peptide chain or chains. (4) Quaternary structure: the number and spatial arrangement of repeating subunits when these are present.

B. Preparation of Viral Proteins

Some of the structural features of viral proteins, such as protein end-groups, can be determined on whole virus, but many others cannot. The amino acid analysis of a virus, for example, is better done on the isolated protein component than on whole virus, because such analyses are usually made on acid hydrolysates, and acid-degraded nucleic acid components interfere with the analyses. Therefore, a basic problem is the disruption of the virus particles in such a way that the protein subunits (or small aggregates of these) are obtained without breaking primary valence bonds or irreversibly changing secondary or tertiary structural features. The protein is not dissociated from all viruses with equal facility and hence a variety of treatments have been developed to accomplish this. These include treatment with an alkaline buffer (Schramm et al., 1955) or an amino alcohol (Newmark and Myers, 1957); cold 67% acetic acid (Fraenkel-Conrat, 1957); warm molar sodium chloride (Kelley and Kaesberg, 1962b); cold calcium chloride (Yamazaki and Kaesberg, 1963); and phenol (Anderer, 1959a,b). All of these procedures operate on the principle of breaking hydrogen bonds or other secondary linkages. Detailed procedures for these methods have been collected in the review by Knight (1963).

C. Some Properties of Viral Proteins

Probably all methods of preparing viral proteins cause some denaturation (unfolding of peptide chains, oxidation of —SH, etc.). Some of these changes are reversible and others not. From the point of view of structural chemistry, an essential condition is that carbon to carbon bonds have not been broken. The occurrence of such breaks can usually be detected by end-group analyses, since new terminal endings appear at the point of breaks. For certain experiments, such as in digestion by enzymes, it is advantageous to have the protein soluble at neutrality and for a couple of pH units on each side of neutrality. Furthermore, if the protein becomes insoluble immediately upon disaggregation from the virus particle, substantial amounts of nucleic acid are often occluded with the protein precipitate. In the application of the acetic acid method to turnip yellow mosaic virus, insoluble aggregates were obtained apparently as a consequence of oxidation of SH groups to form S—S bridges between protein subunits released from the virus particles (Harris and Hindley, 1961). This difficulty was overcome by converting the SH groups to carboxymethyl—S with iodoacetate before treating the virus with acetic acid.

Anderer (1959b) has proposed four criteria for judging the nativity of preparations of TMV-protein: native TMV-protein (1) is soluble in neutral aqueous media, (2) aggregates to virus-like rods at pH 5–7, (3) reconstitutes to infectious virus with appropriate viral RNA, and (4) resembles the protein in the undegraded virus in capacity to bind specific TMV antibody. Since only TMV and its strains have been reconstituted so far, points (2) and (3) would not apply to other plant viruses and the main general criteria for judging the native state of viral proteins are solubility and serological activity, that is, points (1) and (4).

Another useful property of viral proteins is their absorbancy in the ultraviolet. As shown in Figure 14–1, TMV-protein has a maximum absorption at about 280 mμ and a minimum at about 250 mμ. In contrast, the maxima for TMV and its RNA are 265 and 258, respectively. The ratio of absorbancies, 280/250, is about 2.4 for common TMV-protein when it is essentially free of RNA. This ratio may vary for other strains of TMV and for other viruses, for absorbancy at 280 mμ is due mainly to tryptophan and to a lesser degree to tyrosine. In general, however, the 280/250 ratio should be 2 or higher, unless the protein contains more than traces of nucleic acid. A small tryptophan bump will be noted at about 290 mμ on the curves shown in Fig. 14–1 for TMV and for TMV-protein. Such a feature regularly occurs if tryptophan is present to the extent of 1 or 2 moles per 100 moles of total amino acid, and is apparent in ultraviolet absorption curves for whole virus only when the virus contains less than 10% nucleic acid.

D. PRIMARY STRUCTURAL CHARACTERISTICS OF SOME VIRAL PROTEINS

From the particle weights (sometimes called molecular weights) and compositions of viruses such as those listed in Table 14–1, it is clear that the protein components of plant viruses would be incredibly large if they consisted of single, or even a few, peptide chains. For example, the protein component of TMV would have a molecular weight of about 38×10^6. However, it now appears that the protein components of all viruses are composed of repeating subunits ranging in molecular weight for different viruses from about 17,000 to 60,000.

1. *Size of protein subunits and nature of terminal groups.*—Several lines of evidence, such as degradation in detergents, urea, and alkali (Sreenivasaya and Pirie, 1938; Stanley and Lauffer, 1939; Schramm, 1947), and X-ray scattering studies (Bernal and Fankuchen, 1941), suggested that TMV possessed a substructure. However, direct chemical evidence for such viral architecture came later from the attempt to determine the number and nature of the peptide chains in TMV by using the enzyme, carboxypeptidase (Harris and Knight, 1952, 1955). This enzyme catalyzes the hydrolysis of carboxyl-terminal (C-terminal) amino acid residues from protein or peptide chains. When TMV was treated with carboxypeptidase, the only amino acid which appeared in the digest was threo-

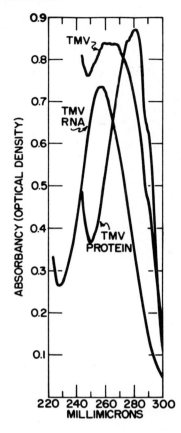

Fig. 14–1. Ultraviolet absorption spectra of tobacco mosaic virus (TMV) and its protein and ribonucleic acid components. (From Knight, 1963.)

nine. The quantity of threonine appearing was somewhat over 2300 per mole (40×10^6 avograms) of TMV. This is equivalent to a molecular weight for the protein subunit of about 17,000. Such a size was also consistent with a minimum molecular weight calculated on the basis of one cysteine residue per subunit, and the nature and approximate numbers of the C-terminal residue were also soon confirmed by an independent method involving hydrazinolysis (Braunitzer, 1954; Niu and Fraenkel-Conrat, 1955). In the hydrazinolysis reaction, all of the amino acids in a peptide chain are converted to hydrazides except the C-terminal one, which comes out as free amino acid and is readily separated from the amino acid hydrazides on the basis of solubility.

TABLE 14–2. PLANT VIRUS PROTEIN SUBUNITS

Virus	Subunits per particle	M.W. of subunit	N-terminal amino acid	C-terminal amino acid	Refer- ence
Alfalfa mosaic	156	38,000	*	*	a
Cucumber 4	2100	18,000	N-acetyl- alanine	alanine	b, c, d
Potato X	650	52,000	*	proline	e
Tobacco mosaic	2200	17,538	N-acetyl- serine	threonine	f
Y-TAMV†	2200	17,531	N-acetyl- serine	serine	g
Tomato bushy stunt	123	60,000	*	leucine	h
Turnip yellow mosaic	150	21,300	N-acetyl- methionine	threonine	i
Wild cucumber mosaic	212	21,500	*	*	j

* Not reported.

† A prototype of some natural and chemically induced mutants of TMV characterized by having C-terminal serine rather than threonine.

(a) Kelley and Kaesberg, 1962b; (b) Tsugita and Knight, unpublished; (c) Niu *et al.*, 1958; (d) Narita, 1959; (e) Reichmann, 1960; (f) Knight, 1960; (g) Knight *et al.*, 1962; (h) Hersch and Schachman, 1958; (i) Harris and Hindley, 1961; (j) Yamazaki and Kaesberg, 1961b.

Another means of checking the number of peptide chains in a protein is by determining the number of amino-terminal (N-terminal) amino acid residues using either the Sanger fluorodinitrobenzene method or the Edman phenylisothiocyanate procedure (see Fraenkel-Conrat *et al.*, 1955). However, application of these methods to TMV-protein showed no free N-terminal groups. This was eventually explained by the discovery that there was N-acetyl serine at the N-terminus of this protein (Narita, 1958). Since then, other viruses have been found to have acylated N-termini and this is now considered the usual structure in viral and several nonviral proteins. The approximate number and molecular weight of the subunits together with the nature of the terminal residues of some plant viruses are given in Table 14–2.

On the basis of present data it appears that the size of the subunits and the nature of the terminal amino acid residues are characteristic for a given virus and its strains. However, it should be noted that common TMV and turnip yellow mosaic virus both have C-terminal threonine and that, conversely, there are some strains of TMV which have serine rather than threo-

nine as the C-terminal amino acid residue.

2. *Amino acid contents.*—Like other proteins, viral proteins are characterized to a considerable extent by their amino acid contents. Amino acid analyses are usually made on acid hydrolysates of the proteins by means of ion exchange chromatography using an automatic analyzer of the type developed by Stein, Moore, and associates (Spackman *et al.*, 1958). The details of this and other procedures are reviewed by Knight (1963).

Some results of amino acid analyses made on plant virus proteins are summarized in Table 14–3. The results are expressed in terms of grams amino acid residue per 100 grams of protein. (An amino acid residue is represented by the usual formula for that amino acid less the H_2O lost in the formation of peptide bonds.) Examination of the figures of Table 14–3 reveals no unusual quantities of any of the amino acids. It will be noted that histidine, methionine, and cysteine are not universally present, whereas the other amino acids are.

3. *Amino acid sequences.*—The most important primary structural feature of a protein is the sequence of its amino acids. This

TABLE 14–3. THE AMINO ACID CONTENT OF SOME PLANT VIRUSES

Amino Acid	Virus					
	Tomato bushy stunt[a]	Cucumber 4[b]	TMV[c]	Turnip yellow mosaic[d]	Wild cucumber mosaic[e]	Potato virus X[*,f]
	Grams amino acid residue per 100 grams virus					
Alanine	4.7	4.9	5.6	2.8	3.4	10.1
Arginine	5.7	8.3	8.9	1.3	2.5	5.3
Aspartic acid	9.2	11.3	11.7	3.6	5.1	9.2
Cysteine	0.6	0.0	0.5		0.6	
Glutamic acid	5.0	5.7	11.2	4.6	4.3	7.8
Glycine	4.0	1.1	1.8	1.9	1.7	2.4
Histidine	1.2	0.0	0.0	0.9	1.3	1.0
Isoleucine	2.7	4.0	5.3	4.2	4.7	4.5
Leucine	8.9	8.1	7.7	4.8	8.5	4.1
Lysine	3.1	2.1	1.3	2.9	3.8	5.3
Methionine	0.7	0.0	0.0	1.2	0.5	3.4
Phenylalanine	3.7	8.7	6.2	2.1	3.9	6.2
Proline	2.8	4.8	4.0	6.4	6.0	5.7
Serine	5.6	7.8	8.3	3.6	6.4	5.0
Threonine	8.1	5.9	9.0	7.4	3.8	11.1
Tryptophan	0.6	0.5	2.5		1.1	
Tyrosine	3.1	3.3	3.3	0.8	2.1	1.2
Valine	7.3	7.5	7.3	3.4	4.3	4.9
Total	77.0	84.0	94.6	51.9	64.0	87.2
% Nucleic acid	17	5	5	37	35	6

[*] Ringspot strain.

The data included here were taken directly, or recalculated to gms. residue per 100 gms. virus, from the following sources: (a) de Fremery and Knight, 1955; (b) Knight, 1947; (c) Ramachandran, 1958; (d) Fraser and Cosentino, 1957; (e) Yamazaki and Kaesberg, 1961c; (f) Shaw et al., 1962.

is the characteristic which determines the specificity of a protein, and is presumably dictated by the genetic material. Secondary, tertiary, and even quaternary structures may all depend on amino acid sequence.

In general, proteins are too large to allow direct determination of amino acid sequence. Therefore, the procedure employed is to split the protein into smaller fragments, usually by use of such proteolytic enzymes as trypsin, followed by determination of the amino acid sequences of the smaller pieces. The latter is done by stepwise degradation procedures employing enzymatic and/or chemical treatments and many amino acid analyses. (See Knight, 1963, for detailed examples.) After determination of the amino acid sequences in the peptides obtained by one type of treatment, such as tryptic digestion, different fragments are obtained by treatment

with other enzymes. Sequence determinations enable recognition of the new peptides, some of which prove to be "bridge" peptides, that is, contain sequences which overlap those of two of the peptides first analyzed. By such means the relative positions of the first peptides are fixed to give the total amino acid sequence of the protein.

Partial sequences have been determined for the proteins of several viruses, but a complete sequence has been determined only for TMV-protein. This was accomplished at about the same time at the Virus Laboratory in Berkeley and at Tübingen, Germany (Tsugita et al., 1960; Anderer et al., 1960). Except for some relatively minor discrepancies, such as location of amide groups (permitting the distinction between aspartic acid and asparagine, for example), the total sequences obtained in

TABLE 14–4. SEQUENCES OF THE 158 AMINO ACID RESIDUES IN THE PROTEIN
SUBUNIT OF TOBACCO MOSAIC VIRUS

(From Knight, 1963, but compiled from Tsugita *et al.*, 1960,
with emendations by G. Funatsu)

5	10	15
N-Acetyl-Ser-Tyr-Ser-Ileu-Thr-Thr-Pro-Ser-GluNH₂-Phe-Val-Phe-Leu-Ser-Ser-		

N-Acetyl-Ser-Tyr-Ser-Ileu-Thr-Thr-Pro-Ser-$GluNH_2$-Phe-Val-Phe-Leu-Ser-Ser-

Ala-Try-Ala-Asp-Pro-Ileu-Glu-Leu-Ileu-$AspNH_2$-Leu-CySH-Thr-$AspNH_2$-Ala-

Leu-Gly-$AspNH_2$-$GluNH_2$-Phe-$GluNH_2$-Thr-$GluNH_2$-$GluNH_2$-Ala-Arg | Thr-

Val-$GluNH_2$-Val-Arg | $GluNH_2$-Phe-Ser-$GluNH_2$-Val-Try-Lys-Pro-Ser-Pro-

$GluNH_2$-Val-Thr-Val-Arg | Phe-Pro-Asp-Ser-Asp-Phe-Lys | Val-Tyr-Arg | Tyr-

$AspNH_2$-Ala-Val-Leu-Asp-Pro-Leu-Val-Thr-Ala-Leu-Leu-Gly-Ala-Phe-Asp-Thr-

Arg | $AspNH_2$-Arg | Ileu-Ileu-Glu-Val-Glu-$AspNH_2$-$GluNH_2$-Ala-$AspNH_2$-Pro-

Thr-Thr-Ala-Glu-Thr-Leu-Asp-Ala-Thr-Arg | Arg-Val-Asp-Asp-Ala-Thr-Val-Ala-

Ileu-Arg | Ser-Ala-Ileu-$AspNH_2$-$AspNH_2$-Leu-Ileu-Val-Glu-Leu-Ileu-Arg | Gly-

Thr-Gly-Ser-Tyr-$AspNH_2$-Arg | Ser-Ser-Phe-Glu-Ser-Ser-Ser-Gly-Leu-Val-Try-

Thr-Ser-Gly-Pro-Ala-Thr

Note: Vertical lines indicate the bonds broken by trypsin.

the two laboratories agree. The Berkeley sequence, as recently amended by the work of G. Funatsu, is given in Table 14–4.

As may be noted from Table 14–4 there are 158 amino acid residues in the TMV-protein subunit, and these add up to give a molecular weight of 17,531. The N-terminal portion of the protein is marked by the absence of basic amino acids, none occurring until the 41st residue. Ten pairs of amino acid doublets and one triplet occur in the 158 amino acid sequence. These repetitions should prove useful markers in working out codes which relate amino acid sequences to nucleotide sequences.

E. SECONDARY, TERTIARY, AND QUATERNARY STRUCTURES

Little is yet known about the secondary (amount of helical structure) and tertiary (folding) structural features of TMV-protein, or of other plant virus proteins. There is some preliminary evidence to indicate that the TMV-protein contains the alpha helical configuration rather common to proteins, but more data are required to establish this point. Likewise, consideration of atomic dimensions and the size and shape of the TMV-particle indicates that the subunit protein chain must be folded to fit in the allotted space. However, the precise nature of this folding remains to be demonstrated.

The quaternary structure (relation of subunits to one another and to the RNA) of TMV has been rather well deduced from a combination of chemical, electron microscope, and X-ray analyses. The results are summarized in the model shown in Figure 14–2, which is like the one first devised by Franklin and associates (1959).

In the case of spherical plant viruses, the results of detailed X-ray analyses indicate that the structures of these viruses show icosahedral symmetry. This implies that the viral particles consist of 60, or some multiple of 60, asymmetric units. These units may be formed from one or a few peptide chains (chemical subunits). There are several slightly different ways in which such units can be arranged but if the assumption is made that the crystallographic subunits (structures deduced from the X-ray studies) are approximately spherical in shape and form a structure as compact as possible, the model shown in Figure 14–3 results.

Much more detail concerning the quaternary structures of viruses can be found in the reviews by Klug and Caspar (1960), Knight (1963), and by Caspar in Chapter 13 of the present volume.

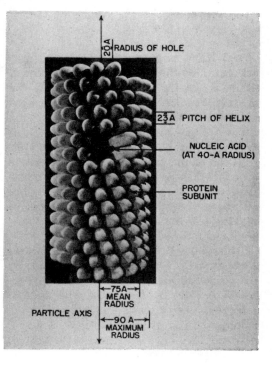

Fig. 14–2. Model of a portion (about a tenth) of the tobacco mosaic virus particle. The protein subunits are schematically illustrated in a helical array about the long axis of the particle. The structure repeats after 69 A in the axial direction, and the repeat contains 49 subunits distributed over three turns of the helix of 23 A pitch. Some of the subunits have been removed to show the location of the ribonucleic acid, which is represented as a smooth, black strand. (From Knight, 1963.)

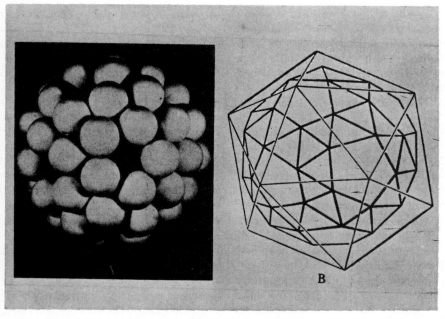

Fig. 14–3. (A). A schematic model illustrating a way in which 60 subunits may be packed according to icosahedral symmetry to form the protein shell of a spherical virus. The subunits are arranged at the vertices of a snub dodecahedron (B), which has the same rotational symmetry as the icosahedron in which it is shown inscribed. (From Franklin *et al.*, 1959.)

F. METHODS FOR PREPARING PLANT VIRUS NUCLEIC ACIDS

Viral RNA as it occurs in mature virus particles may be thought of as encased within a protein shell (especially in the spheroidal viruses) or as deeply embedded in a protein matrix (rod-like viruses such as TMV). In either case the extrication of RNA requires partial or complete disaggregation of the protein subunits. No single procedure has proved consistently successful in such an operation, although in general those reagents which are capable of breaking salt linkages and hydrogen bonds have been most effective.

Extraction of protein with water-saturated phenol, coagulation of protein by heating in the presence of salt, disaggregation of protein by treatment with sodium dodecyl sulfate or guanidine hydrochloride, or combinations of some of these, have all been employed with success with certain plant viruses. Success is usually judged by infectious capacity, which usually amounts to from 0.1 to 10% of the infectivity of an equivalent amount of RNA in the mature virus particle. Infectivities, directly measured, are usually of the lower order, and a fairly accurate gauge of the preservation of infectious capacity during isolation of RNA from the virus can be obtained only with TMV and its strains. This is accomplished by reconstituting virus particles using the isolated RNA and preparations of viral protein.

In media of moderate acidity or alkalinity (pH 5–9) RNA is fairly stable even at temperatures up to $60°$–$70°$. The greatest cause of instability seems to be traces of ribonuclease which have a great affinity for RNA and cause significant degradation even when present in submicrogram amounts. Early reports of instability of RNA in salt solutions are now viewed not as indication of lability of RNA in salt but rather as reflection of the enhanced activity of contaminant RNase with increasing ionic strength of the medium. For example, extraction of TMV-RNA by phenol in the presence of bentonite (an adsorbent earth with a strong affinity for nucleases) yields preparations which are demonstrably more stable upon storage in salt solutions than most preparations made without the addition of bentonite (Fraenkel-Conrat *et al.,* 1961; Singer and Fraenkel-Conrat, 1961).

G. SUBDIVISIONS OF NUCLEIC ACID STRUCTURE

To some extent the subdivisions facilitating consideration of protein structure can be applied to nucleic acid structure. Thus, the primary structure of RNA involves the sequence of nucleotides in the polynucleotide chain, or chains, should there prove to be more than one chain. Secondary structure of RNA is defined by the degree of helicity of the RNA strands. Tertiary structure is the folding of the polynucleotide chain, and quaternary structure deals with the presence or absence of polynucleotide subunits in the RNA strand.

1. *Primary structural features of viral RNA.*—As indicated earlier (see Table 14–1) the RNA component of all plant viruses thus far studied falls in the range of 1–3×10^6 avograms per particle of virus. In the case of the TMV particle, using a particle weight of 40×10^6 avograms and an RNA content of 5%, the RNA amounts to 2×10^6 avograms. It can be calculated that a polynucleotide chain of this molecular weight would have an extended length of 33,000 A (Hart, 1958), but if coiled to follow the helical pitch of the protein subunits at the radius indicated by X-ray data would just fit in a rod of 3000 A, the most common length of the TMV particle (Franklin *et al.,* 1959; Schuster, 1960). In experiments on isolated TMV-RNA, several workers, employing sedimentation or light-scattering methods, have reported calculated molecular weights of about 2×10^6. Furthermore, the rate of loss of infectivity of the TMV-RNA upon treatment with ribonuclease was found to be consistent with the random splitting of a single-stranded structure (Gierer, 1957). Application of end-group methods to TMV-RNA indicated that both ends of the RNA strand are unphosphorylated, and treatment of ^{14}C-labeled RNA with alkali or with appropriate nucleases released about 1 mole of adenosine per 2×10^6 avograms of RNA

STRUCTURAL BIOCHEMISTRY

TABLE 14–5. PROPORTIONS OF NUCLEOTIDES IN SOME PLANT VIRUS RNA'S

Virus	Adenylic Acid	Guanylic Acid	Cytidylic Acid	Uridylic Acid	Reference
	Moles per 100 moles total nucleotide				
Broad bean mottle	27.3	24.6	19.4	28.7	a
Cucumber 4	25.7	25.7	18.7	30.2	b
Potato X	32.2	21.8	23.8	22.2	c
Tobacco mosaic	28.0	24.0	20.0	28.0	d
Tobacco necrosis	28.0	25.5	22.0	25.7	e
Tobacco ringspot	23.9	24.7	23.2	28.2	f
Tomato bushy stunt	25.7	27.9	20.8	25.7	g
Turnip yellow mosaic	22.6	17.2	38.1	22.1	h
Southern bean mosaic	24.3	25.8	24.0	26.3	i
Wild cucumber mosaic	18.3	15.9	40.0	25.8	j

(a) Yamazaki *et al.*, 1961; (b) Knight, 1954; (c) Dorner and Knight, 1953, emended by Knight, 1959; (d) Cooper and Loring, 1954; (e) Markham, 1953; (f) Kaper and Steere, 1959; (g) de Fremery and Knight, 1955; (h) Markham and Smith, 1951; (i) Dorner and Knight, 1953; (j) Yamazaki and Kaesberg, 1961c.

(Fraenkel-Conrat and Singer, 1962; Sugiyama, 1962; Whitfeld, 1962). These findings, coupled with those outlined above, comprise strong evidence that the total RNA of a TMV particle occurs in a single strand of about 2×10^6 avograms. The sedimentation coefficients of RNA isolated from several other plant viruses are also compatible with a molecular weight of the order of 2×10^6. Hence, it is generally assumed that plant virus RNA is a single-stranded molecule representing the total charge of nucleic acid in the virus particle.

The compositions of plant virus RNA's are characterized by a variety of nucleotide proportions as shown in Table 14–5. No unusual purine and pyrimidine bases have yet been found in these nucleic acids, but some lopsided porportions of nucleotides have been observed. Notable among these are turnip yellow and wild cucumber mosaics, both of whose RNA contain unusually large proportions of cytidylic acid. Similarly, potato virus X-RNA has a greater proportion of adenylic acid than the other RNA's.

However, the crux of the problem of primary structure of RNA is the precise sequence of nucleotides in the polynucleotide chain. No method is yet available for determining the complete sequence of an RNA molecule, even of the small transfer RNA ("soluble RNA") of cells, to say nothing of TMV-RNA with its approximately 6400 nucleotides. However, approaches have been made along the lines of those used to elucidate the primary structures of proteins, namely, splitting the RNA into oligonucleotides (small polynucleotide fragments), separating these and determining the compositions and sequences of the pieces. Such analyses seem certain to fall short of completeness because of the enormity of the task and because of the lack of sufficient character in the pieces to permit bridging and reconstruction of the total structure. However, as a means for determining the kinds and frequencies of short polynucleotide segments the method has already been very fruitful. The procedure has been especially useful in pointing out similarities and differences among the nucleic acids of mutants of TMV (Rushizky and Knight, 1960; Rushizky *et al.*, 1961, 1962a,b). Some oligonucleotide sequences found in TMV-RNA are summarized in Table 14–6.

One of the outstanding findings from sequential analyses of TMV-RNA, and of other plant virus RNA's, is the common oc-

TABLE 14–6. SOME OLIGONUCLEOTIDE SEQUENCES FOUND IN TMV-RNA[*]

(The table is from Knight, 1963, and was compiled from Rushizky and Knight, 1960, and Rushizky et al., 1961, 1962a,b).

Dinucleotides	Trinucleotides	Tetranucleotides	Pentanucleotides
ApAp	ApApAp[†]	ApApApCp	(ApApApGp)Up
ApCp	ApApCp	ApApApGp	(ApApGpGp)Up
ApGp	ApApGp	ApApApUp	
ApUp	ApApUp	CpCpCpGp	
CpAp[†]	ApCpCp	UpUpUpGp	
CpCp	ApCpGp	(ApApCp)Gp	
CpGp	ApGpCp	(ApApGp)Cp	
CpUp	ApGpGp	(ApApGp)Up	
GpAp[†]	ApGpUp	(ApApUp)Gp	
GpCp	ApUpGp	(ApGpGp)Cp	
GpGp[†]	ApUpUp	(ApGpGp)Up	
GpUp	CpApGp	(ApCpCp)Gp	
UpAp	CpCpCp[†]	(ApCpUp)Gp	
UpCp	CpCpGp	(ApUpUp)Gp	
UpGp	CpUpGp	(CpCpUp)Gp	
UpUp	CpUpUp	(CpUpUp)Gp	
	GpApCp		
	GpApUp		
	GpGpCp		
	GpGpUp		
	GpUpUp		
	UpApGp		
	UpCpCp		
	UpCpGp		
	UpGpGp		
	UpUpGp		
	UpUpUp[†]		

[*] The abbreviations are those adopted by *The Journal of Biological Chemistry*, in which, for example, ApCpGp stands for the trinucleotide adenylyl-($3' \to 5'$)-cytidylyl-($3' \to 5'$)-guanylic acid. Where the composition is known but the sequences are not, parentheses are used.

[†] These sequences were deduced from higher oligonucleotides, whereas most of the compounds listed were actually isolated and identified as such after enzymatic digestion of TMV-RNA.

currence of clusters (two or more) of the same nucleotide. This provides a sensitive point for distinguishing between mutants and has implications for coding.

2. *Secondary, tertiary, and quaternary structures.*—The term "secondary structure" is used here as it was in the case of proteins to mean the helical, hydrogen-bonded structure present. Two phases of this question are apparent: (1) the structure of the RNA in solutions after extraction from the virus, and (2) the configuration of the RNA in the virus particle.

Three configurational states are obvious for a single-stranded fibrous RNA molecule in solution: (1) a highly helical structure with hydrogen bonds between adjacent bases in loops of the polynucleotide chain, (2) a randomly oriented fiber with no or very few hydrogen bonds ("random coil"), or (3) something intermediate to the first two types, namely a structure containing areas of hydrogen-bonded helix interspersed with segments of random coil. As might be suspected, the actual situation applying to RNA in solution is a dynamic one in which all of the possibilities may occur depending upon the primary structure of the RNA and the environmental conditions (ionic strength of the medium, temperature, and presence or absence of hydrogen-bond-breaking chemicals) (Haschemeyer *et al.*, 1959; Boedtker, 1959; Doty *et al.*, 1959; Gierer, 1960).

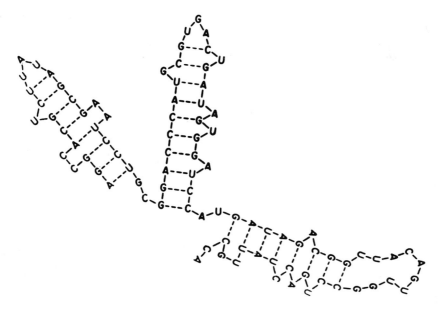

Fig. 14–4. A possible model for a segment of viral RNA in dilute, neutral salt solution at low temperature. The letters A, C, G, and U are used as abbreviations for the nucleotides, adenylic, cytidylic, guanylic, and uridylic acids, respectively. (From Doty, 1961.)

In summary, it appears that TMV-RNA, and probably other plant virus RNA's, have at low temperature and in dilute salt solution some secondary structure in the form of imperfect helical loops such as illustrated in Figure 14–4.

The problem of secondary structure of RNA as it occurs within virus particles is somewhat different and more difficult to examine. In the case of TMV, the RNA is held in a helical configuration by the protein helix in which it is embedded. Therefore, there is no question in rod-like viruses of this sort, but what secondary structure is there in the RNA contained in the spheroidal viruses? The case of tomato bushy stunt virus, a spherical virus about 30 mμ in diameter containing about 17 per cent RNA, has been examined by Bonhoeffer and Schachman (1960). They used ultraviolet absorption, taking advantage of the fact that helical forms absorb less than random coils at 260 mμ because of stacking of the bases. The ultraviolet absorption spectra of tomato bushy stunt virus before and after treatment with sodium dodecyl sulfate (which disaggregates the protein releasing the RNA) were compared with the spectrum obtained by heating the degradation mixture. Upon degradation of the bushy stunt virus, a slight decrease in absorbance was noted, but heating the degraded virus (which ruptures hydrogen bonds) caused a 23% increase in absorbance. From these facts it was concluded that the RNA within bushy stunt virus has partial secondary structure, possibly of the sort that TMV-RNA has in dilute salt solution (Figure 14–4).

Little attention has been paid as yet to the possibility of tertiary structure (specific folding) in RNA's as they exist in the spheroidal virus particles (it is unnecessary to consider the case of TMV and similar viruses because the RNA is held in a fixed position by the protein superstructure). If the RNA existed in an extended strand, it would, of course, be too long to fit into spheroidal viruses without folding. However, the formation of secondary structure, as in the case of tomato bushy stunt virus-RNA, results in a more compact form which may or may not be folded as well.

The possibility of quaternary structure in

viral RNA seems eliminated by considerations of the other types of structure. However, the possibility that the single strand of RNA, which seems characteristic of plant viruses, might be composed of subunits joined perhaps by hydrogen bonds was considered in early studies on TMV-RNA. Gierer (1960) found that TMV-RNA could be heated at 70° for 10 minutes or at 40° in 36% urea for 30 minutes without breaking down the RNA strands. Hence, in line with other evidence, it can be concluded that there are no hydrogen-bonded subunits in the TMV-RNA structure.

H. Reconstitution of Virus from Its Components

Reconstitution is defined as the mixing of protein and nucleic acid components of a virus under conditions such that they combine to yield characteristic particles possessing most, if not all, of the properties of the mature virus as it occurs in nature. The component parts for reconstitution are generally obtained by degrading the virus, although the protein may also be available as a product of infection which can be isolated as such and used in reconstitution. Reconstitution has been accomplished as yet only with TMV and its strains. Mixed reconstitution can be accomplished with components from mutants of TMV, sometimes with about the same yields as in the homologous reaction, but in others with reduced success (Fraenkel-Conrat and Singer, 1959; Holoubek, 1962).

The TMV reconstitution reaction as currently employed (Fraenkel-Conrat *et al.*, 1959) may be summarized as follows:

$$\text{A-Protein} + \text{RNA} \xrightarrow[\text{pH 7.3}]{\text{0.1 M pyrophosphate}} \begin{array}{c}\text{Reconsti-}\\\text{tuted}\\\text{TMV}\end{array}$$

M.W. 52,593 non-infectious	M.W. 2×10^6 slightly infectious	6 hr at 30°	M.W. 40×10^6 very infectious

A-protein is the quasi-stable polymer of the TMV protein subunit, which is the usual form in which isolated TMV-protein exists in neutral solution. The infectivity of reconstituted virus usually ranges from 50 to 80% of that shown by a standard virus preparation.

14–4. VIRUS MUTANTS

A plant virus mutation may be defined as a change in the RNA reflected by a new heritable characteristic in the progeny (provided that the mutation is not lethal) which distinguishes them from the parent virus. The product of mutation is called a mutant, variant, or strain. Most commonly, mutants are recognized by differences in host or tissue specificity, disease symptoms, and serological specificity. Some criteria for strain relationship among plant viruses as recently summarized (Knight, 1963) are as follows:

1. Positive serological cross reactions
2. Positive cross-protection tests
3. Similarity in host range
4. Similarity in method of transmission
5. Similarity in response to genetic change in host
6. Similar resistance to destruction of infectivity by chemical and physical agents such as heat, desiccation, hydrogen ion concentration, irradiations, pressure, chemicals, etc.
7. Coincidence of specific chemical and physical properties:
   (a) Same size and shape of particles
   (b) Same proportions of protein and nucleic acid
   (c) Same proportions of nucleotides in nucleic acid components
   (d) Same nucleotide sequences except for mutationally introduced differences
   (e) Same kind of N-terminal and C-terminal residues in protein subunits (some exceptions to this rule are now known)
   (f) Same number of terminal residues and, hence, same number of subunits in protein
   (g) Same number of amino acids in protein subunit and the same sequences of amino acids except for mutationally introduced differences.

Most reliance over the years in affirming strain relationship has been placed on the serological and cross-protection tests. These tests are always positive when applied to two strains one of which by circumstances has almost certainly arisen by mutation of the other. Then, by intensive study of such strains and comparison of the data with those on serologically unrelated viruses, additional criteria, such as 5–7 above, have developed.

From the biochemical point of view, a key question is what precisely is the nature of the chemical change or changes occurring in the mutation process? This problem has been approached mainly by comparing the proteins and nucleic acids of standard strains with those of spontaneous and chemically induced mutants.

A. Spontaneous Mutants

Much of the chemical investigation of virus mutation has been made on strains of TMV because there are many distinctive strains of this virus and they can often be isolated in sufficient quantities and adequate purity for good chemical analyses. Hence the examples used here will be taken from the many studies made on TMV and strains.

Some of the strains used as illustrations were obtained from natural diseases of crops or other plants (usually tobacco or tomato, but occasionally some other host such as Plantago), while others were obtained during experimentation in greenhouses. The specific origins of the strains most discussed here are described in reviews by Knight (1959, 1963).

1. *Strain proteins.*—Very early after the discovery of the chemical nature of TMV, Stanley (1937) obtained a clue that the protein components of spontaneous mutants might differ in amino acid content. It was found that a yellow mosaic strain, when isolated from tobacco by the same methods used to obtain TMV, had general chemical, physical, and serological properties very similar to those of TMV. Nevertheless, this yellow aucuba strain was less soluble than TMV in mildly acid solutions and had a higher isoelectric point. This suggested that yellow aucuba, and other strains as well, might differ from TMV in protein composition. It was difficult to test this postulate at first because accurate methods for amino acid analysis were not available. However, a series of studies was begun (Knight and Stanley, 1941; Knight, 1942, 1943) the results of which immediately showed that there were demonstrable differences in the amino acid contents of strain proteins. The first stage in this investigation was finished with the complete amino acid analysis of several strains of TMV (Knight, 1947). Some of the conclusions which were drawn from the results of these analyses, and which have been confirmed by recent more accurate analyses, are as follows: (1) The proteins of strains often differ from one another in proportions of some of their constituent amino acids, the rest of the amino acids appearing to be present in the same proportions. (2) In some strains, certain amino acids are present which are completely lacking in others (notable examples are histidine and methionine). (3) Strains which have arisen from a common strain presumably by few mutational steps are very similar in protein composition and, at the extreme, may in fact be identical. (4) Differences in strain proteins, when they occur, may involve almost any of the constituent amino acids. (5) The observation that strains arising from few mutational steps have correspondingly few amino acid changes suggests that in some cases at least mutation involves stepwise changes in amino acid content.

With the development of ion exchange chromatography it was possible to reanalyze the old strains of TMV as well as new ones, and the results could now be expressed in terms of numbers of amino acid residues per protein subunit, thus sharpening the comparisons of strain proteins. The generalizations derived from the earlier results were confirmed and are illustrated by the data given in Table 14–7.

A comparison of strain proteins in more detail than that provided by amino acid data such as those in Table 14–7 is dependent on knowledge of amino acid sequences in the protein subunits. The potentialities of this approach were first demonstrated by an indirect procedure in which the proteins were hydrolyzed by trypsin and the resulting tryptic peptides were separated by a two-dimensional process of paper electrophoresis and paper chromatography

TABLE 14–7. Amino Acid Content of Some Strains
of Tobacco Mosaic Virus[*]

(Moles amino acid residue per mole of protein subunit)

Amino Acid	Strain[†]								
	TMV	M	J14D1	YA	GA	D	Y-TAMV	G-TAMV	HR
Ala	14	14	14	14	14	11	11	18	18
Arg	11	11	11	12	12	9	9	8	11
Asp	18	18	17	19	19	17	18	22	17
Cy-SH	1	1	1	1	1	1	1	1	1
Glu	16	16	15	16	16	19	19	16	22
Gly	6	6	6	6	5	6	6	4	4
His	0	0	0	0	0	0	0	0	1
Ileu	9	9	9	8	8	7	7	8	8
Leu	12	12	12	12	12	13	13	11	11
Lys	2	2	3	2	2	2	2	1	2
Met	0	0	0	0	0	1	1	2	3
Phe	8	8	8	8	8	8	8	8	6
Pro	8	8	8	8	8	8	8	10	8
Ser	16	16	17	14	15	16	15	10	13
Thr	16	16	16	17	17	17	17	19	14
Try	3	3	3	3	3	3	3	2	2
Tyr	4	4	4	4	4	5	5	6	7
Val	14	14	14	14	14	15	15	12	10
Total	158	158	158	158	158	158	158	158	158
Number of exchanges[‡]		0	2	3	3	8	8	17	17

[*] From Knight, 1963, but compiled from Tsugita, 1962; Knight *et al.*, 1962; and Knight, unpublished.

[†] The strains are TMV, common tobacco mosaic virus; M, masked; J14D1, Jensen's derivative No. 1 from his No. 14 strain; YA, yellow aucuba GA, green aucuba; D, dahlemense; Y-TAMV, yellow tomato atypical mosaic virus; G-TAMV, green tomato atypical mosaic virus; HR, Holmes' ribgrass. See Knight, 1959 and 1963, for descriptions of these strains.

[‡] The number of exchanges is equal to the sum of the numbers of amino acid residues which are in excess of those found in TMV (or the converse, since gains in one amino acid or more are balanced by equal losses in others).

(called "mapping" or "fingerprinting") (Knight, 1957; Woody and Knight, 1959). The maps obtained with tryptic peptides from several strain proteins were remarkably similar, the extreme case being complete identity between common TMV and the M strain. Next, the peptide maps obtained from such strains as YA and J14D1 appeared to have the same pattern as TMV except for two to five differences. The HR strain, in accordance with its many differences in amino acid composition gave a peptide pattern vastly different from that of TMV. The more direct procedure, which has been used much in recent studies (Wittmann, 1960, 1961; Tsugita, 1962), is to separate the tryptic peptides on the ion exchange column and to determine by analysis whether or not an amino acid has been exchanged, and if so which one. Since the complete amino acid sequence is known for TMV-protein, it is often possible with the simpler peptides to locate an exchange at a specific amino acid residue without making further analyses. If more than one exchange occurs in a given peptide, or if the exchange involves a residue which occurs multiply, it is necessary to subject the peptide to stepwise degradation procedures in order to assign each of the exchanges to a specific locus. In all of this, it is assumed that the unexchanged portions of the peptide have maintained their original sequences without inversions.

A point of potential importance emerging from sequence studies is the finding (Tsugita, 1962) that strains representative of four different groups of TMV mutants, while differing markedly in some areas, have the same amino acid sequence in residues 113 to 122 (numbering the 158 amino acid chain from the N-terminus), as well as the same sequence in two other smaller areas, residues 69 to 71, and 90 and 92.

Perhaps the greatest interest in amino acid sequence lies in its relationship to the viral genetic apparatus, or more specifically to the sequence of nucleotides in the viral RNA. Little specific information is yet available on this subject, but some current ideas will be mentioned in the section on The Coding Relationship.

B. Chemically Induced Mutants

1. *General features.*—For many years, attempts to produce mutants by treating plant viruses with chemical reagents appeared to be fruitless. With the discovery of infectious RNA, new efforts were made in this direction. Schuster and Schramm (1958) showed that TMV-RNA was oxidatively deaminated by treatment with nitrous acid and that the reaction consisted mainly in the deamination of adenine, guanine, and cytosine to produce hypoxanthine, xanthine, and uracil, respectively. Loss of infectivity with time is exponential, indicating that one deamination ("one hit") is sufficient to inactivate. However, instead of inactivating, the reaction with nitrous acid could conceivably produce mutation, and this in fact was first reported in experiments with TMV (Gierer and Mundry, 1958; Mundry and Gierer, 1958). Subsequently, production of mutants by treatment of TMV with hydroxylamine (Schuster, 1961; Schuster and Wittmann, 1963), dimethyl sulfate (Fraenkel-Conrat, 1960), and N-bromosuccinimide (Tsugita and Fraenkel-Conrat, 1962a) has been claimed.

Attention will be directed here mainly to the mutants induced by treatment with nitrous acid since these have been studied most. More importantly, the principle is presumed to be the same for all cases of chemically induced mutations, namely, a mutation may occur whenever a purine or pyrimidine base is altered in such a way that it pairs with a different base than originally in the replicative process.

2. *Nitrous acid mutants.*—A variety of mutants appear in the reaction mixture following treatment of TMV or of TMV-RNA with nitrous acid at about pH 4.2. A convenient method for following the rate of mutant production with TMV is to score only those mutants which give local lesions on a variety of tobacco (such as "Java" or *Nicotiana sylvestris*) in which TMV causes a systemic disease. The rate of appearance of lesions on Java as a function of time of treatment with nitrous acid was found to fit moderately well a theoretical one-hit curve (Gierer and Mundry, 1958). Roughly fitting expectations, a maximum number of mutants was observed at about the one-hit (one-deamination) level, and the number of mutants, as a percentage of the surviving particles (measured by ratio of lesions on Java to lesions on Xanthi), increased linearly with time.

It has been argued (Bawden, 1959) that common TMV may inhibit the symptom expression of spontaneous mutants already present in TMV preparations, but that upon reducing the infectivity of TMV by nitrite, those spontaneous mutants which were more resistant to inactivation by nitrite than common TMV would then cause symptoms and hence be detected. Thus, the mutants obtained would represent selection rather than mutation. However, there is no evidence to show that removal of inhibition follows first order reaction kinetics as described above, and it is difficult to explain by inhibition effects an observed increase in absolute numbers of mutants of at least 20 times the number present before nitrite treatment, while the infectivity is being reduced to only 50%. Moreover, the selection hypothesis requires that the mutants have substantially greater resistance to inactivation by nitrite than the wild type (common TMV), and no such resistance has been demonstrated. Finally, Mundry (1959) has shown that theoretical curves allowing for different degrees of resistance to inactivation by nitrite than shown by TMV, and which also are corrected for inhibition effects, do not at all agree with the actual curve describing the rate of appearance of mutants with time. Thus, at present, the evidence strongly favors the production of mutants of TMV by treatment of either TMV or its RNA with nitrous acid in the test tube.

The types of mutants resulting from nitrous acid treatment of TMV and strains have been classified as symptom mutants (altered symptoms in Turkish or Samsun tobacco), host response mutants (change from systemic effect to local lesions or vice versa), and altered lesion size mutants (Siegel, 1960).

Among the outstanding characteristics of nitrous acid mutants of TMV as observed thus far are the following: (1) All the altered lesion size mutants observed by Siegel (1960) gave smaller lesions on *Nicotiana glutinosa* than the parent strain. Similar observations have been made by the author (unpublished data) using *N. tabacum* L. var. Xanthi, nc or *N. sylvestris* as test plants. Therefore, if this trend continues, the class will be more appropriately called "reduced lesion size mutants." (2) Some strains of TMV, like the masked or symptomless (in Turkish tobacco) strain, give markedly fewer nitrous acid mutants than TMV (Siegel, 1960). (3) Many of the mutants arising from nitrous acid treatment of TMV appear to be defective. This defectiveness is apparent in the difficulty in passing the infection from some local lesions. This has been observed by numerous workers, but the nature of the defectiveness was demonstrated most clearly by Siegel *et al.* (1962) in detailed studies on two selected strains designated PM 1 and PM 2. The infectivity of these strains can be extracted from the leaf tissue with water-saturated phenol (as demonstrated by tests on a local lesion host), but little or no infectivity can be recovered when extraction is made with $M/15$ phosphate buffer at pH 7. The infectivity of PM 1 and PM 2 was found to be very labile to heat ($55°–60°$) in tissue extracts, and the infectivity was largely destroyed by pancreatic ribonuclease at 0.1 μg per ml. Hence it appears that these nitrous acid mutants occur in

plants in the form of infectious RNA which is lacking in the ability to form complete virus particles. PM 1 was distinguishable from PM 2 in that no viral protein could be detected by serological means in clarified homogenates from infected plants, whereas viral protein was readily detected in extracts of PM 2-infected tissues even though, remarkably, it appears not to get built into viral particles.

The chemical investigation of nitrous acid mutants has centered almost exclusively on the proteins of these new strains. Methods are not yet available for detecting the small changes (minimally, one nucleotide) which presumably occur in the RNA during mutation, whereas the exchange of a single amino residue in the viral protein can be detected and precisely located. Some noteworthy aspects concerning the proteins of nitrous acid mutants of TMV are as follows: (1) Numerous nitrous acid mutants were found to have no changes at all in the primary structure of their protein components and thus resemble the spontaneous mutant, M, earlier described (Wittmann, 1961; Tsugita, 1962; Siegel, 1960). (2) Mutants of TMV which give systemic symptoms on *N. sylvestris* seldom showed amino acid exchanges whereas those giving local lesions on this host (in contrast to the systemic effect of wild type) almost always had amino acid changes (Tsugita and Fraenkel-Conrat, 1962b; Tsugita, 1962). (3) In most of the mutants with altered proteins, 1–3 amino acid residues have been found to be exchanged, but a few cases were found in which 8–17 changes were detected. (4) Some of the amino acid exchanges have been specifically located in the peptide chain of the protein subunit, and, so far, appear to be scattered over the entire sequence. (5) At least 8 pairs of amino acids have been involved in the exchanges observed, and these exchanges have so far been in one direction, e.g., aspartic acid to alanine, but not alanine to aspartic acid. This is consistent with the expectation that the primary mutagenic action of nitrous acid depends on the conversion of cytosine to uracil, the reverse change being impossible with this reagent. (6) Some exchanges have been observed more frequently than others. Examples are aspartic acid to alanine, proline to leucine, serine to phenylalanine, and threonine to isoleucine.

C. THE CODING RELATIONSHIP

It is now generally assumed that the sequence of nucleotides within a certain area (cistron) in plant viral RNA determines the sequence of amino acids in the viral protein. This is commonly called coding. The possible nature of the code has been arrived at partly on theoretical grounds (Crick et al., 1957) and partly from certain experimental findings. Outstanding among the latter are the crucial experiments in which synthetic polynucleotides were shown to direct incorporation of amino acids into proteins in *Escherichia coli* ribosomal systems (Nirenberg and Matthaei, 1961). A great body of literature has developed in this area, and various steps in the development of a code will not be reviewed here, but the interested reader is referred to such papers as those by Jones and Nirenberg (1962), Nirenberg et al. (1963), Ochoa (1963), and Crick (1963a,b). The general properties which the genetic code appears to have at present can be summarized as follows: the code is a triplet one (the coding unit, called a "codon," consists of three adjacent nucleotides); it is degenerate (more than one codon can code for a given amino acid); it may be ambiguous (the same triplet may code for more than one amino acid); it is nonoverlapping, being read in groups of three nucleotides from a fixed starting point. Whether or not the code is universal is not yet clear. Preliminary findings suggest that it may be. For example, it has been reported that something very similar to rabbit hemoglobin was synthesized in a cell-free system, part of which was derived from *E. coli* and part from rabbit reticulocytes (von Ehrenstein and Lipmann, 1961). Likewise, something similar to TMV-protein, though not identical, appeared to be synthesized in an *E. coli* ribosomal system (Tsugita et al., 1962; Nirenberg et al., 1963). Support for the universal nature of the code seems to come from the analysis

TABLE 14–8. NUCLEOTIDE TRIPLET CODES
FOR AMINO ACIDS
(Compiled from Wahba et al., 1963, and Jones and Nirenberg, 1962)

Amino Acid	Nucleotide Code*
Alanine	CGU, CCG, ACG
Arginine	CGU, CCG, AAG
Aspartic Acid	AGU, ACA, ACG
Asparagine	AAU, ACU, AAC
Cysteine	GUU
Glutamic Acid	AGU, AAC, AAG
Glutamine	AAC, AGG
Glycine	GGU, AGG, CGG
Histidine	ACU, ACC
Isoleucine	AUU, AAU
Leucine	CUU, AUU, GUU
Lysine	AAU, AAA, AAC, AAG
Methionine	AGU
Phenylalanine	UUU
Proline	CCU, CCC, ACC, CCG
Serine	CUU, GCU, ACG
Threonine	ACU, AAC, ACC, CCG
Tryptophan	GGU
Tyrosine	AUU
Valine	GUU

* Except in the cases of phenylalanine, one of the sequences for proline, cysteine, and tyrosine, the sequences are not known. Arbitrary sequences, mostly alphabetical, are used here for cases other than the exceptions just mentioned.

of the proteins of TMV nitrous acid mutants, for, as will be noted below, the code deduced from *E. coli* ribosome incorporation experiments fits the exchanges observed with the nitrous acid mutants fairly well.

It is difficult to keep pace with the developments on coding, but a list of some triplets which have been deduced for the various amino acids is given in Table 14–8.

The application of the proposed triplet code letters for amino acids (Table 14–8) to the analytical data showing amino acid exchanges in nitrous acid mutants of TMV permits a testing of the applicability of the code. The types of changes in the code resulting from deamination of RNA bases should be mainly cytosine $\rightarrow$ uracil, or possibly adenine $\rightarrow$ guanine. The data for some comparisons of this sort are given in Table 14–9.

As seen from the table, it is possible to select from the several groups of code

Table 14–9. Amino Acid Exchanges Observed After Treatment of TMV
with Nitrous Acid

(Compiled from Wittmann, 1961; Tsugita and Fraenkel-Conrat, 1962a;
Tsugita, 1962)

Amino Acid Exchange	Cases Observed	Nucleotide Transition (from triplets listed in Table 14–8)	Type of Change
Arginine → Glycine	2	AAG → AGG	A → G
Aspartic Acid* → Alanine	6	ACA → ACG	A → G
Aspartic Acid* → Glycine	4	AGU → GGU	A → G
Aspartic Acid* → Serine	1	ACA → ACG	A → G
Glutamic Acid* → Glycine	3	(AGU → GGU)	A → G
		(AAG → AGG)	A → G
Glutamic Acid* → Valine	2	no fit	
Leucine → Phenylalanine	1	CUU → UUU	C → U
Proline → Leucine	3	CCU → CUU	C → U
Proline → Serine	1	CCU → CUU	C → U
Serine → Leucine	1	GCU → GUU	C → U
Serine → Phenylalanine	5	CUU → UUU	C → U
Threonine → Isoleucine	7	(ACU → AUU)	C → U
		(AAC → AAU)	C → U
Threonine → Methionine	3	no fit	
Threonine → Serine	2	ACU → GCU	A → G

* Not certain in all cases in the protein analyses whether aspartic acid or
asparagine is involved, and the same uncertainty applies to glutamic acid and
glutamine. In selecting code letters above, the free acids rather than the
amides were assumed.

letters available for each amino acid combinations which lead to the observed amino acid exchange if either a cytosine to uracil change or an adenine to guanine transition occurs as a result of treatment with nitrous acid. In the cases selected, only two failures are apparent, but it must be admitted that the degeneracy of the present code provides considerable latitude for finding results compatible with the theory.

Two general conclusions may be drawn with respect to codes and the amino acid analyses of nitrous acid mutants. The large number of cases observed in which no change in protein composition appears to have accompanied the mutation indicates that only a portion of the viral RNA is coding for the viral protein. This segment of RNA would minimally be about 7% (474 out of about 6400 nucleotides) of the total RNA chain on the basis of a triplet code. If the assumption is made that deamination along the viral RNA strand is a random process, the numbers of mutants showing changes in protein composition should have the same relation to the total number of

mutants produced as the size of the protein-coding segment of the RNA has to the whole RNA strand. In a group of 25 mutants examined by Siegel (1961), 3 showed altered proteins. Other protein analyses made on much larger numbers of nitrous acid mutants by Wittmann (1961) and by Tsugita and Fraenkel-Conrat (1962a), but with less attention to random selection from the total population of mutants, showed that less than half of them had altered proteins. These experimental data are not suitable for a precise quantitative deduction, but they are definitely consistent with the general idea that only a portion of the polynucleotide chain is involved with coding for viral protein. Another rather clear point is that the protein analyses on nitrous acid mutants have not yet shown clusters of adjacent amino acid exchanges. In fact, as mentioned earlier, a single amino acid exchange is often observed. These findings eliminate the possibility of an overlapping triplet code, for this would bring about more than one amino acid exchange for each deamination.

14–5. LITERATURE CITED

Ames, B. N., and Dubin, D. T. (1960). J. Biol. Chem. **235**, 769.

Anderer, F. A. (1959a). Z. Naturforsch. **14b**, 24.

Anderer, F. A. (1959b). Z. Naturforsch. **14b**, 642.

Anderer, F. A., Uhlig, H., Weber, E., and Schramm, G. (1960). Nature **186**, 922.

Bawden, F. C. (1959). Nature **184**, B. A. 27– B. A. 29.

Bawden, F. C., and Pirie, N. W. (1938). Brit. J. Exptl. Path. **19**, 66.

Bawden, F. C., and Pirie, N. W. (1945). Brit. J. Exptl. Path. **26**, 277.

Bawden, F. C., Pirie, N. W., Bernal, J. D., and Fankuchen, I. (1936). Nature **138**, 1051.

Bernal, J. D., and Fankuchen, I. (1941). J. Gen. Physiol. **25**, 111.

Bockstahler, L. E., and Kaesberg, P. (1962). Biophys. J. **2**, 1.

Boedtker, H. (1959). Biochim. Biophys. Acta **32**, 519.

Boedtker, H., and Simmons, N. S. (1958). J. Am. Chem. Soc. **80**, 2550.

Bonhoeffer, F., and Schachman, H. K. (1960). Biochem. Biophys. Res. Communications **2**, 366.

Braunitzer, G. (1954). Z. Naturforsch. **9b**, 675.

Cohen, S. S. (1961). Federation Proceedings **20**, 641.

Cooper, W. O., and Loring H. S. (1954). J. Biol. Chem. **211**, 505.

Corbett, M. K. (1961). Virology **15**, 8.

Crick, F. H. C. (1963a). Science **139**, 461.

Crick, F. H. C. (1963b). In J. N. Davidson and W. E. Cohn (eds.), Progress in Nucleic Acid Research. Academic Press, New York.

Crick, F. H. C., Griffith, J. S., and Orgel, L. E. (1957). Proc. Natl. Acad. Sci. U.S. **43**, 416.

De Fremery, D., and Knight, C. A. (1955). J. Biol. Chem. **214**, 559.

Dorner, R. W., and Knight, C. A. (1953). J. Biol. Chem. **205**, 959.

Doty, P., Boedtker, H., Fresco, J. R., Haselkorn, R., and Litt, M. (1959). Proc. Natl. Acad. Sci. U.S. **45**, 482.

Fraenkel-Conrat, H. (1956). J. Am. Chem. Soc. **78**, 882.

Fraenkel-Conrat, H. (1957). Virology **4**, 1.

Fraenkel-Conrat, H. (1960). Biochim. Biophys. Acta **49**, 169.

Fraenkel-Conrat, H., and Singer, B. (1959). Biochim. Biophys. Acta **33**, 359.

Fraenkel-Conrat, H., and Singer, B. (1962). Biochemistry **1**, 120.

Fraenkel-Conrat, H., Harris, J. I., and Levy, A. L. (1955). Methods of Biochem. Analy. **2**, 359.

Fraenkel-Conrat, H., Singer, B., and Tsugita, A. (1961). Virology **14**, 54.

Fraenkel-Conrat, H., Staehelin, M., and Crawford, L. V. (1959). Proc. Soc. Exp. Biol. Med. **102**, 118.

Franklin, R. E., Caspar, D. L. D., and Klug, A. (1959). In Plant Pathology—Problems and Progress, 1908–1958. 447–61. Univ. of Wisconsin Press, Madison.

Fraser, D., and Cosentino, V. (1957). Virology **4**, 126.

Frisch-Niggemeyer, W., and Steere, R. L. (1961). Virology **14**, 83.

Gierer, A. (1957). Nature **179**, 1297.

Gierer, A. (1960). Progress in Biophysics **10**, 299.

Gierer, A., and Mundry, K. W. (1958). Nature **182**, 1457.

Gierer, A., and Schramm, G. (1956a). Nature **177**, 702.

Gierer, A., and Schramm, G. (1956b). Z. Naturforsch. **11b**, 138.

Harris, J. I., and Hindley, J. (1961). J. Mol. Biol. **3**, 117.

Harris, J. I., and Knight, C. A. (1952). Nature **170**, 613.

Harris, J. I., and Knight, C. A. (1955). J. Biol. Chem. **214**, 215.

Harrison, B. D., and Nixon, H. L. (1959). J. Gen. Microbiol. **21**, 569.

Hart, R. G. (1958). Biochim. Biophys. Acta **28**, 457.

Haschemeyer, R., Singer, B., and Fraenkel-Conrat, H. (1959). Proc. Natl. Acad. Sci. U.S. **45**, 313.

Hersch, R. T., and Schachman, H. K. (1958). Virology **6**, 234.

Holoubek, V. (1962). Virology **18**, 401.

Johnson, M. W., and Markham, R. (1962). Virology **17**, 276.

Jones, O. W., and Nirenberg, M. W. (1962). Proc. Natl. Acad. Sci. U.S. **48**, 2115.

Kaper, J. M, and Steere, R. L. (1959). Virology **7**, 127.

Kassanis, B. (1962). J. Gen. Microbiol. **27**, 477.

Kassanis, B., and Nixon, H. L. (1961). J. Gen. Microbiol. **25**, 459.

Kelley, J. J., and Kaesberg, P. (1962a). Biochim. Biophys. Acta **61**, 865.

Kelley, J. J., and Kaesberg, P. (1962b). Biochim Biophys. Acta **55**, 236.

Kendrew, J. C. (1959). Federation Proc. **18**, 740.

Klug, A., and Caspar, D. L. D. (1960). Adv. Virus Res. **7**, 225.

Knight, C. A. (1942). J. Am. Chem. Soc. **64**, 2734.

Knight, C. A. (1943). J. Biol. Chem. **147**, 663.

Knight, C. A. (1947). J. Biol. Chem. **171**, 297.

Knight, C. A. (1954). Adv. Virus Research **2**, 153.

Knight, C. A. (1957). In G. E. W. Wolstenholme and E. C. P. Millar (eds.), The Nature of Viruses. Ciba Found. Symp. 69–78. J. and A. Churchill, Ltd., London.

Knight, C. A. (1959). In F. M. Burnet and W. M. Stanley (eds.), The Viruses. **2**, 127–56. Academic Press, New York.

Knight, C. A. (1960). Brookhaven Symposia in Biology **13**, 232.

Knight, C. A. (1963). Protoplasmatologia **IV**, 2, 1.

Knight, C. A., and Stanley, W. M. (1941). J. Biol. Chem. 141, 39.

Knight, C. A., and Woody, B. (1958). Arch. Biochem. Biophys. 78, 460.

Knight, C. A., Silva, D. M., Dahl, D., and Tsugita, A. (1962). Virology 16, 236.

Lauffer, M. A., Taylor, N. W., and Wunder, C. C. (1952). Arch. Biochem. Biophys. 40, 453.

Loring, H. S., Fujimoto, Y., and Eng, L. F. (1959). Proc. Natl. Acad. Sci. U.S. 45, 287.

Markham, R. (1953). In P. Fildes and W. E. Van Heynigen (eds.), The Nature of Virus Multiplication. 85–95. Cambridge Univ. Press.

Markham, R. (1959). In The Viruses. 2, 33–125. Academic Press, New York.

Markham, R., and Smith, J. D. (1951). Biochem. J. 49, 401.

Mazzone, H. M., Incardona, N. L., and Kaesberg, P. (1962). Biochim. Biophys. Acta 55, 164.

Miller, G. L., and Price, W. C. (1946). Arch. Biochem. 10, 467.

Mundry, K. W. (1959). Virology 9, 722.

Mundry, K. W., and Gierer, A. (1958). Z. Vererbungslehre 89, 614.

Narita, K. (1958). Biochim. Biophys. Acta 28, 184.

Narita, K. (1959). Biochim. Biophys. Acta 31, 372.

Newmark, P., and Myers, R. W. (1957). Federation Proc. 16, 226.

Nirenberg, M. W., and Matthaei, J. H. (1961). Proc. Natl. Acad. Sci. U.S. 47, 1588.

Nirenberg, M. W., Matthaei, J. H., Jones, O. W., Martin, R. G., and Barondes, S. H. (1963). Federation Proc. 22, 55.

Niu, C.-I., and Fraenkel-Conrat, H. (1955). Biochim. Biophys. Acta 16, 597.

Niu, C.-I., Shore, V., and Knight, C. A. (1958). Virology 6, 226.

Ochoa, S. (1963). Federation Proc. 22, 62.

Pirie, N. W. (1956). Biochem. J. 63, 316.

Ramachandran, L. K. (1958). Virology 5, 244.

Reichmann, M. E. (1959a). Can. J. Chem. 37, 384.

Reichmann, M. E. (1959b). Can. J. Chem. 37, 4.

Reichmann, M. E. (1960). J. Biol. Chem. 235, 2959.

Rushizky, G., and Knight, C. A. (1960). Proc. Natl. Acad. Sci. U.S. 46, 945.

Rushizky, G., Knight, C. A., and Sober, H. A. (1961). J. Biol. Chem. 236, 2732.

Rushizky, G., Knight, C. A., Roberts, W. K., and Dekker, C. A. (1962a). Biochim. Biophys. Acta 55, 674.

Rushizky, G., Sober, H. A., and Knight, C. A. (1962b). Biochim. Biophys. Acta 61, 56.

Schramm, G. (1947). Z. Naturforsch. 2b, 112.

Schramm, G., Schumacher, G., and Zillig, W. (1955). Z. Naturforsch. 10b, 481.

Schuster, H. (1960). In E. Chargaff and J. N. Davidson (eds.), The Nucleic Acids. 3, Ch. 34. Academic Press, New York.

Schuster, H. (1961). J. Mol. Biol. 3, 447.

Schuster, H., and Schramm, G. (1958). Z. Naturforsch. 13b, 697.

Schuster H., and Wittmann, H. G. (1963). Virology 19, 421.

Shaw, J. G., Reichmann, M. E., and Hatt, D. L. (1962). Virology 18, 79.

Siegel, A. (1960). Virology 11, 156.

Siegel, A. (1961). Virology 15, 212.

Siegel, A., Zaitlin, M., and Sehgal, O. P. (1962). Proc. Natl. Acad. Sci. U.S. 48, 1845.

Singer, B., and Fraenkel-Conrat, H. (1961). Virology 14, 59.

Spackman, D. H., Stein, W. H., and Moore, S. (1958). Analytical Chemistry 30, 1190.

Sreenivasaya, M., and Pirie, N. W. (1938). Biochem. J. 32, 1707.

Stanley, W. M. (1935). Science 81, 644.

Stanley, W. M. (1937). J. Biol. Chem. 117, 325.

Stanley, W. M. (1942). Arch. Ges. Virusforsch. 2, 319.

Stanley, W. M., and Lauffer, M. A. (1939). Science 89, 345.

Steere, R. L. (1956). Phytopathology 46, 60.

Sugiyama, T. (1962). Ph.D. Thesis. University of California, Berkeley.

Tabor, H., Tabor, C. W., and Rosenthal, S. M. (1961). Ann. Rev. Biochem. 30, 579.

Tsugita, A. (1962). J. Mol. Biol. 5, 293.

Tsugita, A., and Fraenkel-Conrat, H. (1962a). In J. H. Taylor (ed.), Progress in Molecular Genetics. 477–520. Academic Press, New York.

Tsugita, A., and Fraenkel-Conrat, H. (1962b). J. Mol. Biol. 4, 73.

Tsugita, A., Fraenkel-Conrat, H., Nirenberg, N. W., and Matthaei, J. H. (1962). Proc. Natl. Acad. Sci. U.S. 48, 846.

Tsugita, A., Gish, D. T., Young, J., Fraenkel-Conrat, H., Knight, C. A., and Stanley, W. M. (1960). Proc. Natl. Acad. Sci. U.S. 46, 1463.

Von Ehrenstein, G., and Lipmann, F. (1961). Proc. Natl. Acad. Sci. U.S. 47, 941.

Wahba, A. J., Gardner, R. S., Basilio, C., Miller, R. S., Speyer, J. F., and Lengyel, P. (1963). Proc. Natl. Acad. Sci. U.S. 49, 116.

Whitfeld, P. P. (1962). J. Biol. Chem. 237, 2865.

Wittmann, H. G. (1960). Virology 12, 613.

Wittmann, H. G. (1961). Naturwissenschaften 48, 729.

Woody, B. R., and Knight, C. A. (1959). Virology 9, 359.

Yamazaki, H., and Kaesberg, P. (1961a). Nature 191, 96.

Yamazaki, H., and Kaesberg, P. (1961b). Biochim. Biophys. Acta 53, 173.

Yamazaki, H., and Kaesberg, P. (1961c). Biochim. Biophys. Acta 51, 9.

Yamazaki, H., and Kaesberg, P. (1963) (in press).

Yamazaki, H., Bancroft, J., and Kaesberg, P. (1961). Proc. Natl. Acad. Sci. U.S. 47, 979.

WILLIAM N. TAKAHASHI

The biochemistry of virus infection

15–1. INTRODUCTION

THE BIOCHEMISTRY of virus infection in a sense is synonymous with the biochemistry of virus synthesis. Without synthesis, infection cannot become established, abnormal changes in host metabolism cannot take place, nor will external symptoms of disease usually appear. The typical plant virus has been shown to consist of two chemical components, the infectious ribonucleic acid (RNA) and virus protein. This RNA and protein do not occur in uninfected tissue. The protein has not exhibited any known enzymic activity, cannot by itself initiate infection, and appears to serve only as the protecting coat for the more delicate RNA. The RNA on the other hand possesses the capability of causing infection that results in the formation of typical virus particles. It therefore appears to carry the genetic information to reproduce not only itself but also the virus protein.

Briefly, in the normal plant it is generally accepted that the nucleus or the nuclear DNA, the genetic material of the cell directs the synthesis of RNA. The RNA in turn, in association with ribosomes that are found in the cytoplasm, forms protein by a multistep process. Does the biosynthesis of virus, an anomalous substance, follow this same host pattern or by virtue of its being a disease entity plot its own course of self-duplication?

15–2. CONCEPTS OF NATURE OF PLANT VIRUS MULTIPLICATION

A. OLD CONCEPT

Most early workers believed that the multiplication of viruses did not differ essentially from that of microorganisms, that is, the mechansim of reproduction resided within the virus particles and, given the proper medium, new progeny would arise from the parent. The final step of reproduction could be longitudinal or transverse fission followed by growth to maturity. When appreciable quantities of TMV particles shorter than the characteristic 300 mμ lengths were isolated by Bawden and Pirie (1945) from specially prepared infected tobacco tissue, there was some question as to whether these were infective or whether they were immature noninfective particles, the progeny of transverse fission of the parent. It was shown later by Takahashi and Rawlins (1949) that the shorter than 300 mμ particles were not infective. All or most of the infectivity was associated with the longer particles. It is possible to cause end-to-end aggregation of some of the short particles to form particles of longer length but the increased length is not correlated with increased infectivity.

B. NEW CONCEPT

The current view is that virus protein and nucleic acid are formed by two separate systems, the protein and nucleic acid then combine to form the stable, complex nucleoprotein particle. This concept is based on 3 pertinent findings:

(1) Anomalous protein, formed *de novo* within virus-diseased cells, has been detected, isolated, and positively characterized as viral in nature (Takahashi and Ishii, 1952; Commoner *et al.*, 1953; Jeener and Lemoine, 1953).

(2) Virus stripped of its protein, i.e., naked nucleic acid, has been shown to be infectious. The product of the infection is the complete nucleoprotein virus particle (Gierer and Schramm, 1956; Fraenkel-Conrat and Singer, 1957).

(3) A suspension of virus protein and nucleic acid *in vitro* can be made to reconstitute into stable, fully infectious virus identical in all respects with the native virus (Fraenkel-Conrat and Williams, 1955).

C. Bipartite Synthesis of Virus

There appears to be no alternative at present but to consider the biochemistry of virus multiplication to be intimately associated with two separate but interrelated biosynthetic mechanisms of the host; the RNA mediated by the activity of the nucleus or its immediate environment and the protein through the ribosomal system.

In more specific terms, we are faced with these two questions:

(1) Does the virus influence or alter the genetic coding of the nuclear DNA to make an obviously foreign RNA or given the proper substrates, energy, and enzymes, does viral RNA serve as its own template?

(2) How does the viral RNA participate in the synthesis of yet another foreign product, virus protein?

To virologists these are questions of paramount importance for in their solution may well be the answer to the direct control of virus diseases. Then again, in the language of the pathologist, intelligent disease control requires a clear knowledge of the "life cycle" of the offending agent. In the following discussion an attempt will be made to keep these two questions in mind as we examine the mass of related literature we have on hand today.

15–3. INFECTION PROCESS

A. Adsorption Phase

The logical starting point of this discussion is the process of infection, particularly the early stages of it. We know of no plant virus that can enter the susceptible plant unaided by man, animal, or fungi. It must be introduced into the cell or enter through an abrasion. The cell may be injured but must not be killed. This implies that the virus makes intimate contact and union with the living substance of the cell. Furthermore, the union is instantaneous; washing inoculated tissue immediately with water will not reduce infection. The evidence for the former is attributed to Siegel (unpublished) quoted by Wildman (1959). When infectious TMV-RNA was inoculated on *N. glutinosa* leaves and then immediately dipped into a solution of RNase sufficient to destroy RNA, no reduction in local lesions was observed. This process is instantaneous and irreversible. This union, then, is the first physical or chemical event attributable to the invading virus. This stage is usually called adsorption.

B. The Infectious Entity

Neither the X protein (free native TMV protein) nor the A protein (protein separated from purified TMV by chemical methods) has been found to be infectious or even to bring about local response when inoculated onto host plants. On the other hand, RNA separated from the virus is fully infective. It then appears that this RNA carries within its structure the information necessary not only for its own replication but also for the synthesis of its protein counterpart. These two important functions are believed to be inherent in the orderly sequence of the four nucleoside phosphates of adenine, cytidine, guanine, and uracil that compose the RNA. In other words, virus RNA serves an indispensable dual role. According to Franklin *et al.* (1959), the structure of TMV, e.g., is such that 2200 units of identical protein are arranged in a helix along the long axis of the particle, and embedded within it and following the line of the helix is the single strand of RNA. Can the RNA tightly encased in its coat of protein carry out its functions? Most workers do not think so.

C. Shedding of Protein Coat

There is some evidence that immediately following the adsorption or penetration phase the protein of the virus particle is unravelled by some means in order to free the bound strand of RNA. It is believed that if this does not occur infection will not become established. The mechanism by which the stripping is accomplished in the living cell is not known. Enzymes of the host that are capable of degrading native virus protein have not been found. When detached mosaic leaves were cultured on distilled water in darkness, abundant inclusion bodies that were present in epidermal cells showed no sign of dissolution even while the tissue was degenerating from starvation (Takahashi, 1941). Judging from the ease with which TMV virus protein alone can be formed or reconstituted with RNA into the characteristic rod-shaped particles, the unravelling process is most likely accomplished by breaking the secondary bonds that hold the protein units together. In the laboratory several methods of separating protein units from the nucleic acid of purified virus are used: detergent (Sreenivasaya and Pirie, 1938); mild alkali (Schramm et al., 1955); 67% acetic acid (Fraenkel-Conrat 1957); and warm salt (Kelley and Kaesberg, 1962).

One line of evidence has been presented by Hamers-Casterman and Jeener (1957), who showed that if mosaic-inoculated leaves are infiltrated with RNase, within 2 hr virus will not multiply. This has generally been interpreted to mean that approximately 2 hr are required to free the RNA from its protein mantle and during this time it is vulnerable to the action of the infiltration enzyme. However, if the infiltration takes place after 2 hr the liberated RNA will have become protected either by its association with the host or polymerization with virus protein.

In another type of experiment Siegel et al. (1957) used as a measure the ultraviolet sensitivity of the infectious centers on Nicotiana glutinosa. It is believed that once the infective material (RNA) becomes intimately associated with the infection center of the cell, increased resistance to irradiation results. Two strains of intact TMV showed a $2\frac{1}{2}$ and 5 hr lag in infection while their respective RNA showed little or no lag in resistance. It required, then, $2\frac{1}{2}$ and 5 hr to free the RNA from the protein coat and make the necessary contact with the infection site. Other workers with TMV, Fraenkel-Conrat et al. (1958), and Kassanis (1960), show that virus is detected sooner and local lesions appear earlier when test plants were inoculated with the RNA than with the intact virus. In another type of experiment Engler and Schramm (1959) inoculated a parallel series of local-lesion test plants with intact TMV or TMV-RNA. The infectious material that was synthesized during different time intervals was assayed. The extrapolation of the curves of infection showed that the latent period was 10 hr less with RNA than for the virus.

D. Hyperactivity of the Nucleus

In the normal cell the synthesis of RNA is directed by the DNA or the genetic substance of the nucleus. It is thought that all of the RNA emanates from this source. Whether virus RNA is so directed or whether the correct milieu for virus RNA synthesis resides within the confines of the nucleus has not yet been proven. The best evidence that virus RNA is synthesized in or about the nucleus is found in the experiments of Zech and Vogt-Köhne (1955). In their experiments a microscope equipped with ultraviolet penetrating optics and a sensitive microspectrometer were used to record the behavior of a single nucleus in situ. They found that 4–20 hr after infection the nucleus became coated with a UV absorbing substance, presumably RNA. This was later followed by an increase of UV absorption in the cytoplasm and the diffusion of like material around the nucleus. Although by this method it is not possible to distinguish between normal and viral RNA it is at least a good indication of hyperactivity of the nucleus brought about by virus infection. Abnormal activity in and about the nuclei of TMV-infected cells was also observed by Bald and Solberg (1961) by means of a phase contrast microscope.

On infection, a denser than normal material was seen to flow from the nucleus to structures that appeared to be virus inclusion bodies. Contrary to the present concept they concluded that the final step of virus multiplication took place in the nucleus and not some distance away from it in the cytoplasm. They also noted that this activity occurred in bursts as though the virus multiplied in cycles.

From studies utilizing fluorescent TMV antibodies on infected tissue sections Schramm and Röttger (1959) report that virus protein is synthesized in the cytoplasm. In early infection the protein was found in a zone around the nucleus. Later the virus protein appeared throughout the cell. No virus protein was detected in the nucleus or the chloroplast.

Infrared spectrophotometry was used by Cochran (1960) to study the infection process of cucumber infected with cucumber mosaic. This unique method is based on the theory that spectrophotometric changes at certain wave lengths reflect the increase or decrease of chemical reactions involved in the formation of peptide bonds and nucleic acid. For example, high absorption at wave lengths 3–6 μ denotes nucleic acid and protein, 6.1 to 6.5 μ peptide bonds, and 9–9.5 nucleic acid. Whether this theory is tenable when applied to these substances in a mixture or even to purer systems has been questioned by some workers. Whatever the cause, the experimental results obtained by the above worker should be examined and evaluated. The upper surface of the cotyledons of young cucumber plants was inoculated with virus, and after varying periods of time the lower epidermis was stripped, dried, and analyzed by means of an infrared spectrophotometer. The corresponding epidermis of buffer inoculated control cotyledons was taken as the reference point. Increase in absorbance over the control was taken to mean synthesis, and decrease as degradation. He reported that absorption at 3–6 μ and 9–9.5 μ (nucleic acid) increased in 2 days, dropped markedly at 3, 4, and 5 days, then rose at 6 and 7 days. Conversely, the band at 6.5 μ (peptide bonds) increased on the 3d, 4th, and 5th days, then dropped on the 6th and 7th days. Like Bald and Solberg, he also reported that cyclic variation occurred. Without considerably more work with pure and mixed systems one cannot even hazard an interpretation of these results.

15–4. VIRUS PROTEIN

A. MACROMOLECULAR NONINFECTIOUS PARTICLES

Before the detection, isolation, and the positive identification of the X protein from extracts of TMV diseased tissue, now considered the protein unit of TMV, was accomplished, others have reported the presence of noninfective particulates in extracts of diseased tissue. A small form of TMV nucleoprotein was found by Bawden and Pirie (1945) in especially milled preparations of diseased tissue.

B. TOP COMPONENT OF TURNIP YELLOW MOSAIC VIRUS PREPARATION

An anomalous particle identical in size and shape to the virus was found by Markham and Smith (1949) in Chinese cabbage plants infected with turnip yellow mosaic. They were first detected by them in preparations purified by an alcohol-ammonium sulfate method. When this was studied by means of an analytical ultracentrifuge two distinct components were detected. The denser component was composed of protein and 38% nucleic acid and was infectious, while the top component, although identical in physical appearance with the former, contained no nucleic acid. It was not infectious. In plant virus work this perhaps was the first indication that the nucleic acid moiety of the virus was responsible for its infective property. For some reason this important discovery in 1949 was not fully appreciated until the work of Gierer and Schramm (1956) and Fraenkel-Conrat and Singer (1957), who separated the nucleic acid from TMV and demonstrated that the nucleic acid alone was capable of causing infection.

It was further found that as much as 20–35% of the total virus protein of turnip yellow mosaic occurred as the top component. It is now known that the structure of both top and bottom components is composed of smaller protein units that have polymerized in a definite pattern. An obvious conclusion is that, whatever the mechanism, normal or abnormal, the rate of virus protein synthesis exceeded that of the RNA.

C. Anomalous Protein of TMV Infection

The present discussion deals with the anomalous, unpolymerized, simple protein that is found free in extracts of TMV diseased tissue. Is this the virus protein unit? How and where in the cell is it synthesized? When formed, how does it combine with virus nucleic acid to construct the stable infectious macropolymer? These are the questions that concern us today.

The protein of TMV designated as the X protein (Takahashi and Ishii, 1952), soluble antigen 1 (Jeener and Lemoine, 1953), and B6 (Commoner et al., 1954) is now generally believed to be the same protein. In this paper it will be referred to hereafter simply as virus protein. This was originally detected in semipurified and crude extracts from mosaic leaves by electrophoresis and by serology. Similar proteins resulting from virus infections other than TMV have also been reported (Takahashi and Ishii, 1953). A simple method of detecting them is by means of Ouchterlony's (1958) gel diffusion. The virus and the virus protein share antibodies in common. In a test the virus protein being much smaller than the virus will diffuse more rapidly toward the antibody containing cell and form its antigen-antibody complex in a position different from that of the slower moving virus.

D. Some Properties of the Virus Protein

Like Markham and Smith's (1949) top component, fully polymerized virus protein is not infectious. This is to be expected, as it too contains no essential nucleic acid. Identical virus proteins were isolated from some common infected hosts of TMV, tobacco, *Nicotiana tabacum*, tomato, *Lycopersicon esculentum*, and *Phlox drummondi*. This shows clearly that the host is unable to

exert any influence in altering the composition of virus protein. On the other hand, different strains of TMV and their proteins have exhibited different rates of migration when tested by electrophoresis (Takahashi, 1955). The amino acid composition of the protein particle is often reflected in the charge density on its surface. This protein then is virus specific.

Isolated virus protein will polymerize into rod-shaped particles with ease. These particles, however, are of varying lengths and their population does not nearly approach in uniformity that of the virus. When reconstitution with an RNA preparation of high infectivity is effected, rods of exceedingly uniform lengths, 300 mμ, are formed (Fig. 15–1). Such preparations show infectivity as high as, and in some cases somewhat higher than, that of the native virus. There is no doubt that the length of the virus particle is determined by the length of the RNA strand. It is believed today that an infective single strand of TMV-RNA is composed of 6400 nucleotides arranged in a specific sequence.

E. The Role of This Protein in the Biosynthesis of Virus

With the purification and reconstitution of the anomalous protein that is present in extracts of virus-diseased tissue into the stable, highly infectious virus particle, the positive role of this protein in the biosynthesis of virus has been unequivocally established. However, early workers suggested the possibilities that the protein could be (a) a degeneration product of the virus, (b) a rejected, imperfect virus protein, (c) an accessory protein not necessarily concerned with virus biosynthesis, (d) some sort of a protective reaction against the invader, or (e) actually the virus protein.

In an effort to solve this problem a great deal of careful work was done. It was agreed by Commoner et al. (1953) and Jeener (1954) that a large pool of the protein did not appear before the virus could be detected. It was some 200 hr after infection that Commoner et al. detected the protein. Jeener, however, found the protein in 72 hr. In agreement with Zech and Vogt-Köhne, Bald, and Cochran, Engler

319

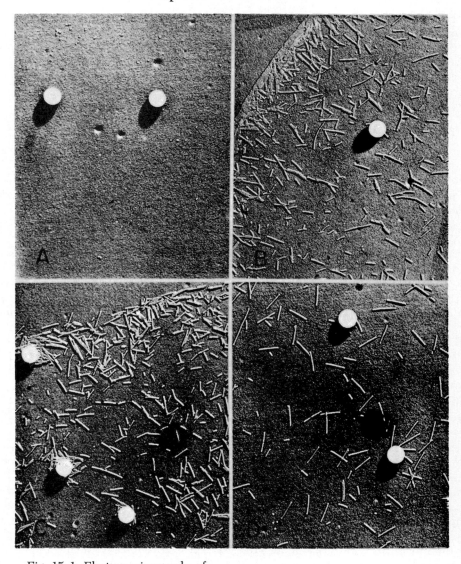

Fig. 15–1. Electron micrographs of:
A. X protein, pH 7.3; B. X protein polymerized, pH 5.3; C. Reconstituted TMV;
D. TMV.

and Schramm (1959) report that in the early stage of infection a large amount of RNA was synthesized in the nucleus. The latter workers claim this RNA to be infectious. The RNA then was poured out of the nucleus into the cytoplasm. Soon after this, the synthesis of virus protein was initiated. They further point out that the rate of protein units synthesis was 2000 times that of the nucleic acid. In the cell the two components of the virus probably combine in much the same manner as they were shown to reconstitute *in vitro* by Fraenkel-Conrat and Williams (1955). In a short time the supply of protein exceeded that of the RNA and the excess protein accumulated. This, today, appears to be the most plausible explanation of their observations.

15–5. PROTEIN SYNTHESIS

A. STRUCTURE OF PROTEIN

Before we are able to discuss how and where virus protein is formed it is necessary to obtain a basic understanding of the manner in which normal protein is synthesized in the cell. First, we should bear in mind that a protein is a polypeptide of definite composition. The backbone of the polypeptide is constructed of 20 common amino acids all of the L series joined together by peptide (−CO−NH−) bonds. The individuality of the protein is reflected in the number and ordered sequence of the amino acids and the manner in which it is folded into a three-dimensional structure. In the case of TMV protein the sequence of the 158 amino acids of a subunit has been worked out by Anderer *et al.* (1960) and Tsugita *et al.* (1960).

B. SYNTHESIS IN NORMAL CELLS

In the normal cell the synthesis of a specific protein is controlled by the genetic substance, DNA, of the nucleus. This means that the sequence of the amino acids in a sense is an image of a gene. DNA does not participate directly in the synthesis of protein but transmits the essential code to an RNA of complementary composition, called the messenger, which in turn becomes associated with the ribosomes.

C. RIBOSOMES

The ribosomes, subcellular particles, are found in abundance in the cytoplasm of most cells. Ribosomes from various sources —yeast, pea, tobacco, *Azotobacter vinelandii*, and *E. coli*—are nearly spherical particles with a sedimentation constant of 80 S and a molecular weight of about 4.5×10^6. They are composed of about 40% RNA and 60% protein. The molecular weight of the RNA has been estimated to be from 1.7 to 2.0×10^6. *In vivo* experiments have shown that the intensity of protein synthesis is directly related to the numbers of ribosomes present in the tissue. Numerous studies with ribosomes from different sources, in cell free systems, with and without the aid of radioactive amino acid tracers, have demonstrated ribosomes to be indispensable for protein synthesis. It is now thought that a loose cluster of 80 S ribosomes together with the messenger RNA is the essential part of the protein synthesizing system. Comparatively few workers have reported findings with ribosomes of plant origin. Many of the early studies were carried out with animal tissues. More recently ribosomes from *E. coli* are favored.

D. MECHANISM OF PROTEIN SYNTHESIS

The importance of this problem to biologists in general is reflected in the vast amount of literature that has accumulated in recent years. From the combined efforts of many workers from several fields the following mechanism of protein synthesis has been accepted by most workers.

(1) Each amino acid is activated by an activating enzyme in the presence of ATP (adenosinetriphosphate). The ATP serves not only as a source of chemical energy but also forms a complex of amino acid-acyladenylate-enzyme (AmAc-AMP-Enz). In this reaction, pyrophosphate (PP) is released. This reaction can be expressed thus: Amino acid + Enzyme + ATP $\leftrightarrows$ (AmAc-AMP-Enz) + PP.

(2) The amino acid-acyladenylate-enzyme transfers the amino acid to an RNA known as the soluble RNA (SRNA). This RNA is composed of from 50 to 80 nucleotide residues and is so named because it is found free in the soluble fraction of cell extracts. SRNA is more or less specific for each amino acid and there appear to be at least 20 different ones. RNA separated from the body of ribosomes does not accept activated amino acids, showing that it is not a template and does not take a direct part in the synthesis of polypeptides.

(AmAc-AMP-Enz) + SRNA →
(AmAc-SRNA) + AMP + Enz.

(3) The complex, amino acid-SRNA is then transferred to the messenger RNA-ribosome cluster where the SRNA bearing the amino acid finds its proper place on the messenger RNA. This RNA carries the code that determines the character of the protein. Whether peptide bonds are formed in this one operation is not known. It is believed that a transfer enzyme and a poly-

peptide synthetase of some kind are most likely involved.

$$n(\text{AmAc-SRNA}) \xrightarrow{\text{messenger RNA}} \text{Polypeptide} + n \text{ SRNA.}$$

(4) How the polypeptide is released from the messenger RNA template-ribosome complex is not well understood. GTP seem to be a necessary agent. Because messenger RNA is usually short-lived some believe that it is destroyed by an RNase, thus freeing the newly-formed polypeptide. It is believed that the folding of this free polypeptide occurs spontaneously.

E. REACTION MIXTURE

The reaction mixture of cell-free systems for synthesizing protein is based on the above 3 main reactions. They contain the following ingredients.

(1) Ribosomes—usually prepared from fresh material by one cycle of low- and high-speed centrifugation similar to the method commonly used to purify viruses.

(2) Amino acids—20 of the L-series one or more of which is tagged with C^{14} or acid hydrolysates of radioactive algal protein.

(3) ATP and its regenerating system, e.g., pyruvate and pyruvate kinase.

(4) Activating and transfer enzymes prepared from the supernatant liquid after the ribosomes have been pelleted by the high-speed centrifugation. The enzymes are precipitated at pH 5.0.

(5) SRNA—prepared from an aliquot of the same supernatant liquid as in (4) by the phenol method.

(6) Magnesium ions to preserve the integrity of the ribosomes. In the absence of magnesium 80S ribosomes tend to break up into nonfunctional smaller particles.

(7) Messenger RNA—natural or synthetic polynucleotides.

Early workers used no messengers. It must be assumed that these were present in the natural mixture or that partially synthesized polypeptides were completed.

The complete reaction mixture is buffered with either 0.05–0.1 M phosphate or Tris (hydroxymethyl) amino methane at pH values between 7.0 and 7.8. Most experiments are incubated at 37°C for 10–90 min.

F. PROTEIN SYNTHESIS WITH ISOLATED PEA RIBOSOMES

A working system has been firmly established. To several virologists, almost at the same time, it appeared to be a relatively simple task to utilize this system by adding isolated TMV-RNA as messenger. The final product would be expected to be the protein of this virus. It could then be identified positively by serology, reconstitution with RNA, or analyzed by peptide mapping. Encouraged also by the claims of Webster (1959) and Raacke (1959) that isolated ribosomes of pea seedlings were able to synthesize not only tracer amount protein but also as much as 40% of the amino acid input, biologists in many parts of the world commenced work with pea seedlings. To this day, however, no confirmation of their work has appeared in the literature. Moreover, neither Webster nor Raacke has been able to repeat the work of the other. Recently, Webster *et al.* (1962) have concluded that it is not the general characteristic of pea ribosomes to synthesize measurable amounts of protein. Only Alaska peas probably grown under a certain set of conditions contain "active" ribosomes that possess extraordinary synthetic ability. The chance delivery of successive batches of peas led to the erroneous assumption that pea ribosomes in general synthesize milligram quantities of protein in a cell-free system.

In our experiments (Lett and Takahashi, 1962) with ribosomes of Alaska pea and using Webster's or Raacke's system, no net increase of protein was detected. An increase in soluble protein was noted but these originated from the ribosome particle. Compared to controls kept at 0°C in mixtures incubated at 37°C as much as 20% of the total protein was destroyed. It was concluded that the pea system contained RNase that tended to disintegrate the ribosome; and then proteases, also present, degraded the protein.

G. PROTEIN SYNTHESIS WITH ISOLATED RIBOSOMES OF E. coli

A greater measure of success has been obtained by workers using *E. coli* as source material. A more elaborate system of *E.*

coli ribosomes was devised by Matthaei and Nirenberg (1961). They (Nirenberg and Matthaei, 1961) found that when TMV-RNA or RNA from yeast was used as messenger the incorporation of labelled amino acids was stimulated by as much as 75 times.

H. Synthesis of TMV Protein Using TMV-RNA as Messenger

In cooperation with Nirenberg and Matthaei the identification of the expected virus protein was attempted by Tsugita *et al.* (1962). When protein synthesized by the aid of TMV and yeast RNA messengers were treated with anti-TMV serum, both gave positive results. The reaction with TMV-RNA synthesized protein, however, was three times greater than that with protein synthesized with yeast RNA. No record of the usual control with normal serum is given.

Although the type TMV protein does not contain histidine or methionine (Knight, 1947) as much or more of these two amino acids was incorporated by systems containing TMV-RNA messenger than that of Holmes' Ribgrass (HR) strain RNA. Both histidine and methionine are components of HR protein. They postulate that one strand of TMV-RNA is composed of some 6400 nucleotide residues. According to the triplet code of Crick *et al.* (1961) only 474 of these (a cistron) are required to form virus protein composed of 158 amino acids. (See discussion, Section 15–6,B.) The balance of the nucleotides could code for other polypeptides including the protein of HR or other protein composed of histidine and methionine.

When TMV protein is digested with trypsin, 12 well-defined peptide fragments of known amino acid content can be separated out by chromatography. If labelled protein from reaction mixtures of ribosomes with TMV-RNA messenger is so treated, a qualitative and quantitative examination of the peptide can be made. Such a study was carried out by them with protein separated from the mixture by a method considered to be specific for virus protein (isoelectric precipitation and column chromatograph). In experiments with C^{14} phenylalanine and tyrosine the bulk of the label was associated with typical TMV peptides and contained these two amino acids in roughly the expected proportion. However, one of the peptides—N-acetyl-seryl-tyrosine—which marks the N-terminal of the virus protein carried almost no label. The digest also showed several peptides that are foreign to TMV virus protein which interfered with the separation of the 12 peptides. It is unfortunate that the purity of the protein fraction used in this important study is questionable. TMV-RNA, these investigators conclude, directed the synthesis of a virus-like protein.

So far ribosomes of plant origin isolated by the traditional method and incubated in mixtures including ATP, ATP regenerating system, activating enzymes, amino acids, SRNA, messenger RNA, $MgCl_2$, KCl, and mercaptoethanol have exhibited little or no response. The negative response has been attributed to the presence of RNase and proteases in or about the ribosomes. How these can be eliminated from the system without destroying the integrity of the ribosome seems to be the immediate problem.

I. Failure to Form TMV Protein with Ribosomes of Plant Origin

The protein synthesizing systems of Matthaei and Nirenberg were duplicated as closely as possible by the authors (1961) with ingredients from Alaska pea seedlings. Although some incorporation of C^{14} labelled algal protein hydrolysate, arginine, and leucine was achieved, in no experiment did the addition of TMV-RNA stimulate their incorporation or show any net increase of protein. In some cases, a decrease was noted. Similar experiments with ribosomes from bean seedlings, mustard leaves, and healthy and mosaic tobacco leaves gave uniformly negative results.

15–6. INFECTIOUS VIRUS NUCLEIC ACID

A. Integrity of Infectious RNA

Indirect evidence for the stripping of the protein coat of the virus before infection could be initiated by the RNA was presented earlier. Does the stripping process

323

take place in the cytoplasm not only where RNase abounds, but also where the concentration of this enzyme has been found to increase during early infection (Reddi, 1959; and Diener, 1961)? If virus RNA serves as messenger for the synthesis of viral protein, what is to prevent its immediate association with the large numbers of ribosomes that are present in the cytoplasm? The stepwise degradation of the RNA chain was studied by Gierer (1957, 1958). He concluded that the integrity of the entire 6400 nucleotide chain must be preserved. When a few (or possibly only one) phosphate bonds were cleaved the infective power of TMV-RNA was destroyed. It does seem more logical to expect the virus to enter into the nucleus and there shed its coat in a more favorable medium where most of the cellular nucleic acid is known to be synthesized.

Whether DNA or RNA, the sequence of the bases in their chain is of utmost importance in determining not only its own character, but also the sequence of amino acid in a polypeptide chain.

In this discussion we are concerned mainly with the RNA of TMV. Briefly, it is a polynucleotide composed of 4 different nucleotides of adenine, guanine (purine base), cytosine, and uracil (pyrimidine base), each linked together by phosphate in diester linkage from the 3' hydroxyl of one ribose molecule to the 5' hydroxyl of the next ribose. It has been pointed out before that there are 6400 nucleotides arranged in a single strand.

B. TMV-RNA

To biologists who are involved in synthesizing infectious TMV-RNA in a cell free medium no less than 6400 nucleotides must be condensed in a definite sequence in order to duplicate the infectious macromolecule. To others who seek to form the protein, cistrons responsible for the proper arrangement of 158 amino acids must be kept intact in the face of RNase activity.

According to the recent degenerate, nonoverlapping triplet code of Crick *et al.* (1961) one codon consists of 3 nucleotides, e.g., UUU = phenylalanine, CGU = arginine, and AUU = tyrosine. A cistron for virus protein then is 158 amino acids $\times$ 3 = 474 nucleotides, or only 7.5% of the length of the RNA. If the cistrons are similar in size the entire length of the chain could accommodate at least 13 of them. However, from studies of the amino acid sequence of protein unit of TMV mutants induced by chemical means, Wittman (1961) and Tsugita and Fraenkel-Conrat (1962) concluded that less than 50% of the nucleotides of the RNA could be involved in virus protein synthesis. From physical consideration TMV-RNA, compared with a chromosome, is a relatively simple entity and can carry only a few genetic units. At most then, the RNA could carry only 5 or 6 virus protein cistrons. Innumerable strains of TMV are found in nature. Their hosts range from Solanaceae, Leguminoceae, Orchidaceae, to even Cactaceae. The code for these characteristic proteins could not possibly be found latent in a single strand of RNA.

C. REPLICATION OF RNA

It is not known how many genetic units are carried by one messenger RNA. In the normal nucleus the double-stranded DNA of the entire chromosome does not serve as a single multiple coded messenger. There is good evidence (Hurwitz *et al.*, 1961) that the mechanism of RNA messenger synthesis takes place in the following manner: (1) A short segment of the DNA double strand partially unwinds. (2) Nucleotides in triphosphate form pair off against the nucleotides of one strand (complementary pairing). An enzyme, RNA polymerase, is believed to be involved in this reaction. (3) The nucleotides link up into an RNA polymer. Phosphate groups are lost and the messenger pulls away from the DNA matrix.

Is the entire infectious TMV-RNA a multiple messenger for virus protein as well as for other accessory enzymes, etc., that are concerned in infection and other changes of the host? At present most workers think so. Yet, as in DNA, perhaps several simple units of messenger, e.g., for virus protein only, are replicated by a similar process from the RNA template.

The actual synthesis of infectious TMV-

RNA in cell free systems has been claimed by four separate groups of workers almost at the same time: Cochran *et al.* (1962), Kim and Wildman (1962), Karasek and Schramm (1962), and Cornuet and Astier-Manifacier (1962). These studies, no doubt, were prompted by the recent discoveries of enzymes that condense nucleotides in chains of polynucleotide similar in structure to that of native RNA.

D. RNA POLYMERASES

Before discussing the results obtained by these from workers, a few words should be said about the types of RNA polymerizing enzymes that are found in impure fractions of cellular material.

(1) The first of these is the polyribonucleotide phosphorylase of Grunberg-Manago and Ochoa (1955), that is capable of synthesizing a polynucleotide from nucleoside diphosphates. It was isolated from *Azotobacter vinelandii*. Since no template or primer is required for the reaction, nucleotides are bonded at random so specificity is not conferred on the product. Curiously enough, however, it will reconstitute with TMV-A protein to form noninfective rod-like particles (Hart and Smith, 1956).

(2) The RNA polymerase of Weiss and Gladstone (1959) requires substrate nucleoside triphosphates and a DNA primer. This polymerase fits the role of the enzyme that completes the formation of messenger RNA in the presence of nucleoside triphosphates and the unwound section of the double helix of DNA. Host DNA can hardly be expected to be burdened with cistrons for a foreign protein nor does it seem possible for virus RNA to alter the base sequence of the DNA. At present it does not seem possible that this type of mechanism could be applied to the replication of viral RNA or to its protein.

(3) An RNA polymerase that is stimulated by an RNA primer was isolated from chick embryo by Chung *et al.* (1960). The substrates in this reaction were the triphosphonucleosides. In a recent work Nakamoto and Weiss (1962) isolated a similar enzyme from *Micrococcus lysodeikticus*. The enzyme, the 4 nucleoside triphosphates, one tagged (ATP^{32} and CTP^{32}) in two separate experiments, and a primer of turnip yellow mosaic virus RNA were incubated. In the controls one nucleoside was withheld. They report appreciably more tagging in the complete system compared to the controls. *De novo* synthesis of RNA is claimed by them. Unfortunately, infection tests were not included in the experiments.

E. EXPERIMENTS REPORTING SYNTHESIS OF INFECTIOUS RNA

There are a number of elements in common in the experiments of the four groups of investigators. To simplify the discussion these will be listed together before the individual experiments are examined.

(1) In most experiments tissue infected with TMV for 1–20 days was used as the source of the polymerases, primer TMV-RNA, and in some cases the substrates. The purity of material was not tested. Appreciable residual virus activity was exhibited in all preparations.

(2) Nucleotide triphosphates—ATP, CTP, GTP, and UTP—were added to the reaction mixture. In tracer experiments the P carried the label. All were aware of the danger of RNase to their system. Some used RNase inhibitors such as bentonite and polymethacrylic acid. TMV-RNA primer was not always used.

(3) Increase in infectivity was measured on local lesion forming hosts, Pinto bean, *Nicotiana glutinosa, N. tabacum* var. Xanthi, nc. The rise in infectivity was from negligible to about 4-fold.

All four reports of successful synthesis of infectious RNA appeared in 1962, showing that these experiments were carried out independently and simultaneously. The first of these to appear was that of Cochran *et al.* (1962). Their basic experiment was performed as follows:

In order to reduce the concentration of RNase in their preparation the crude crushed tissue that had been infected for 14–52 hr was passed through a column of 2% crushed agar. The first effluent fraction consisting of greenish particulate material including some intact nuclei was collected and centrifuged lightly. The greenish residue was resuspended in buffer. **To an** aliquot of it the 4 nucleoside triphosphates were added; another was kept as control. After both were incubated at 25°C for 10–60 min they were inoculated on local lesion-forming test plants. Forty to 400% more local lesions developed on leaves inoculated with the complete mixture than on those with the control. These results are interpreted by them as indicating the *de novo* synthesis of infectious RNA.

In later experiments Cochran (1963) separated nuclei and chloroplasts from mosaic tissue by means of density-gradient centrifugation. These were disrupted by sonication and then incubated with the usual nucleotides. Chloroplasts as well as nuclei were able to synthesize new infectious viral RNA from the added substrates, Cochran reports. Still further, a polymerase containing fraction was separated from chloroplasts of mosaic leaves by continuous flow electrophoresis and fractionation on a Sephadex 75 column. A mixture of this fraction, the four nucleotides, and a primer of either phenol prepared TMV-RNA or disrupted chloroplasts of mosaic leaves when incubated for varying times showed an increase in local lesions.

An enzyme preparation of untested purity was used by Karasek and Schramm (1962) in a similar experiment. Their enzyme was prepared in this manner:

To the extract from mosaic leaves, bentonite was added; then the mixture was ultracentrifuged. The proteins of the supernatant liquid were precipitated with ammonium sulfate. The four nucleotides were added to this impure fraction and incubated. The increase in the number of local lesions with increasing time of incubation was considered by them to be significant. The infectivity at 0 time was high (574 local lesions); at 4 hr the greatest number was obtained (718). When RNase was added the number was still 619.

A recent group of workers, Cornuet and Astier-Manifacier (1962), were concerned with nuclei of mosaic tissue. According to their method the nuclei, 40-hr infected, were isolated by a method described by Alfrey and Mirsky (1957). The nuclei were ground in alumina and fractionated by centrifugation. The polymerase was precipitated with protamine sulfate and then resuspended in a succinate buffer. The polymerase with the four nucleotides and TMV-RNA was incubated. Like the former workers, they used the increase of local lesions with time of incubation as a measure of synthesis. In experiments where the local-lesion counts were low, 0 time 26 and 60 min 71, the per cent increase was high, 174%; but where the counts were higher, 594 and 618, the increase was only 4%.

The fourth group was interested in the DNA fraction that was isolated from the nuclei of the mesophyll cells. In this work Kim and Wildman preferred to use tobacco leaves that had been infected for many days. When the lower mesophyll cells were rubbed with a KOH-Maleate buffer, 0.5M pH 6.9, a viscous substance, mostly DNA was exuded. An RNA polymerase is contained in it and can be released from it, they report. In incubation mixtures similar to those described above without primer, a time course experiment showed at; 0, 15, 30, 60 min; 476, 609, 658 and 820 local lesions, respectively. In this experiment the relatively high residual activity of 476 local lesions should be noted.

A different interpretation has been given to the work of Kim and Wildman by Ralph and Matthews (1963). These investigators report that TMV in a phosphate buffer of pH 9.5 containing sodium chloride and glycine tended to become RNase sensitive. Presumably the protein coat was stripped from the particle. Some of the altered infective material was occluded with the DNA fraction and was carried with it. On heating or incubation the occluded material was dispersed and when samples were inoculated onto test plants an apparent increase in infectivity was observed.

That deoxyribonucleic acid is not likely to participate in the formation of TMV-RNA was reported by Reddi and Anjaneyalu (1963). They found that DNA isolated from healthy and mosaic-infected tobacco leaves has similar purine and pyrimidine composition. There was no difference in the uptake of P^{32} into DNA obtained from check or infected leaves, showing that the synthesis of new DNA was not stimulated by infection. They believe that if viral RNA is formed continuously by means of cellular DNA it should be possible to isolate a DNA-RNA hybrid in cells actively engaged in virus synthesis. Such a hybrid was not found. On the basis of these findings they concluded that cell DNA is not involved in the synthesis of viral RNA.

More direct evidence that the replication of TMV-RNA is not dependent upon a DNA template has been furnished by Sänger and Knight (1963). Actinomycin D, a known inhibitor of DNA-dependent RNA synthesis, was used and its effect on viral RNA synthesis was followed by infectivity tests, absorbence at 260 mμ, and the incorporation of Uracil-2 C[14]. Density-gradient ultracentrifugation runs of normal TMV and infected tobacco leaf RNA showed 3 components with sedimentation coefficients of 28 S, 17 S, and 4 S. The infectivity was found to be associated with the 28 S fraction. When leaves were treated with Actinomycin D little or no Uracil-2 C[14] was incorporated into the 28 S and 17 S components. RNA from virus tissue showed appreciable incorporation into the 28 S infective fraction, showing that the TMV-RNA was not inhibited.

In more recent experiments, Cochran (1963) claims the synthesis of infectious RNA using nuclei and chloroplasts of normal tissue. Nuclei from normal Pinto bean tissue were isolated by repeated centrifugation in a sucrose density gradient. These were sonically ruptured in the presence of bentonite and polymethacrylic acid. The mixture was primed with TMV-RNA and then incubated. Aliquots tested after about 3 hr of incubation showed local lesions when tested on Pinto bean. Sonically ruptured chloroplasts from normal bean or tobacco primed with sonically treated chloroplasts from diseased tissue showed as much as 100–1000-fold increase in infectivity. TMV-RNA, however, was not effective. Cochran suggests that the RNA polymerase present in nuclei may differ from that of chloroplasts.

15–7. DISCUSSION

When only the positive results of the above 4 experiments are collected and studied there is a suggestion that some infectious RNA could have been synthesized. In the normal living tissue the complete system is no doubt present. Whether that of diseased tissue differs from it is not known. The work so far hints of it. In view of our present knowledge it appears to be a relatively simple reaction in contrast to the more complicated multiple step, multiple enzyme-requiring process of protein synthesis.

Save those of Cochran's, in experiments where infectious RNA was believed to have been synthesized, the source of the enzyme has been mosaic-infected tissue. Others have not succeeded when enzyme from normal tissue was used. A single high-speed centrifugation does not usually free the supernatant of all virus particles. It should be noted that in some trials (Karasek and Schramm, 1962) treatment with RNase failed to abolish the infectivity from the mixture. This can be considered as evidence for the presence of intact virus particles. Where crude material was used (Cochran *et al.*, 1962) it is important to determine the total residue virus content of it. Some years ago Bawden and Crook (1947) showed that much virus was tightly adsorbed to tissue residue and could be released from it only by special treatment such as milling and by snail crop enzymes.

The enzyme containing fraction has not been fully characterized. It cannot be said with confidence that it contains only the one RNA-dependent polymerase. It is obvious that this could have a bearing on experiments where tracers are used.

Since much reliance is placed on the results of local-lesion assay more emphasis could be placed on its proper use. Many workers in this field feel that the method cannot be used for exacting analyses unless local-lesion counts fall within the straight line segment of the infection curve. Differences of less than 15% are not always significant.

Factors other than the actual number of infective units often influence the susceptibility of the local-lesion forming host and the infectivity of the agent; some of these are the presence or absence of inhibitors and especially certain additives. For example, as much as a hundred-fold increase in the number of local lesions on Pinto beans by the addition of phosphate to the inoculum has been clearly demonstrated by Yarwood (1952). Given the same RNA inoculum, considerably more local lesions develop on Pinto bean than on *N. glutinosa*. Recently, Sarkar (1963) has shown that the use of a buffer of high pH value favors by many times the infectivity of TMV-RNA on *N. glutinosa*. His most effective buffer was composed of 0.05 *M* Tris and 0.05 *M* Na$_2$HPO$_4$ adjusted with HCl to pH 8.5–9.0.

Where incorporation of radioactive tracers was used, the values obtained were low and did not parallel the observed increase in infectivity. This does not support the *de novo* synthesis of infectious material.

Although it is premature to claim unequivocal proof of synthesis in a cell-free medium of virus protein or virus RNA, a promising start has been made in what appears to be the right direction.

15–8. LITERATURE CITED

Alfrey, V. G., and Mirsky, A. E. (1957). Proc. Nat. Acad. Sci. U.S. **43**, 589.

Anderer, F., Uhligh, H., Weber, E., and Schramm, G. (1960). Nature **186**, 922.

Bald, J. G., and Solberg, R. A. (1961). Nature **190**, 651.

Bawden, F. C., and Crook, E. M. (1947). Brit. J. Expt. Pathol. **28**, 403.

Bawden, F. C., and Pirie, N. W. (1945). Brit. J. Expt. Pathol. **26**, 277.

Chung, C. W., Mahler, H. R., and Enrione, M. (1960). J. Biol. Chem. **235**, 1448.

Cochran, G. W. (1960). Nature **187**, 1049.

Cochran, G. W. (1963). Paper presented in 17th Annual Symp. of M. D. Anderson Hosp. and Tumor Inst., Houston, Texas. (In press.)

Cochran, G. W., Dhaliwal, A. S., Welkie, G. W., Chidester, J. L., Lee, M. H., and Chandrasekhar, B. K. (1962). Science **138**, 46.

Commoner, B., Yamada, M., Rodenberg, S. D., Wang, T. Y., and Basler, E. (1953). Science **118**, 529.

Cornuet, P., and Astier-Manifacier, S. (1962). Compt. Rend. Acad. Sci. **255**, 3076.

Crick, F. H. C., Barnett, L., Brenner, S., and Watts-Tobin, R. J. (1961). Nature **192**, 1227.

Diener, T. O. (1961). Virology **14**, 177.

Engler, R., and Schramm, G. (1959). Nature **183**, 1277.

Fraenkel-Conrat, H. (1957). Virology **4**, 1.

Fraenkel-Conrat, H., and Singer, B. (1957). Biochim. Biophys. Acta **24**, 540.

Fraenkel-Conrat, H., and Williams, R. C. (1955). Proc. Nat. Acad. Sci. U.S. **41**, 690.

Fraenkel-Conrat, H., Singer, B., and Veldee, S. (1958). Biochim. Biophys. Acta **29**, 639.

Franklin, R. E., Caspar, D. L. D., and Klug, A. (1959). Plant Pathology–Problems and Progress, 1908–1958. Univ. of Wisconsin Press, Madison.

Gierer, A. (1957). Nature **179**, 1297.

Gierer, A. (1958). Z. Naturforsch. **13b**, 477.

Gierer, A., and Schramm, G. (1956). Nature **177**, 702.

Grunberg-Manago, M., and Ochoa, S. (1955). J. Am. Chem. Soc. **78**, 3165.

Hamers-Casterman, C., and Jeener, R. (1957). Virology **3**, 197.

Hart, R. C., and Smith, J. D. (1956). Nature **178**, 739.

Hurwitz, J., Furth, J. J., Anders, M., Ortiz, P. J., and August, J. T. (1961). Cold Spring Harbor Symp. Quant. Biol. **26**, 91.

Jeener, R. (1954). Biochim. Biophys. Acta **13**, 307.

Jeener, R., and Lemoine, P. (1953). Nature **171**, 935.

Karasek, M., and Schramm, G. (1962). Biochem. Biophys. Res. Commun. **9**, 63.

Kassanis, B. (1960). Virology **10**, 353.

Kelley, J. J., and Kaesberg, P. (1962). Biochim. Biophys. Acta **55**, 236.

Kim, Y. T., and Wildman, S. G. (1962). Biochem. Biophys. Res. Commun. **8**, 394.

Knight, C. A. (1947). J. Biol. Chem. **171**, 297.

Lett, J. T., and Takahashi, W. N. (1962). Arch. Biochem. Biophys. **96**, 569.

Markham, R., and Smith, K. M. (1949). Parasitology **39**, 330.

Matthaei, J. H., and Nirenberg, M. W. (1961). Proc. Nat. Acad. Sci. U.S. **47**, 1580.

Nakamoto, T., and Weiss, S. B. (1962). Proc. Nat. Acad. Sci. U.S. **48**, 880.

Nirenberg, M. N., and Matthaei, J. H. (1961). Proc. Nat. Acad. Sci. U.S. **47**, 1588.

Ouchterlony, O. (1958). Progr. Allergy **5**, 1.

Raacke, I. D. (1959). Biochim. Biophys. Acta **34**, 1.

Ralph, R. K., and Matthews, R. E. F. (1963). Biochem. Biophys. Res. Commun. **12**, 287.

VIRUS INFECTION

Reddi, K. K. (1959). Biochim. Biophys. Acta **33**, 164.

Reddi, K. K., and Anjaneyalu, Y. V. (1963). Biochim. Biophys. Acta **72**, 33.

Sänger, H. L., and Knight, C. A. (1963). Biochem. Biophys. Res. Commun. **13**, 455.

Sarkar, S. (1963). Virology **20**, 185.

Schramm, G., and Röttger, B. (1959). Z. Naturforsch. **14b**, 510.

Schramm, G., Schumacher, G., and Zillig, W. (1955). Z. Naturforsch. **10b**, 481.

Siegel, A. W., Ginoza, W., and Wildman, S. G. (1957). Virology **3**, 554.

Sreenivasaya, M., and Pirie, N. W. (1938). Biochem. J. **32**, 1707.

Takahashi, W. N. (1941). Phytopathology **31**, 1117.

Takahashi, W. N. (1955). Virology **1**, 393.

Takahashi, W. N. (1959). Plant Pathology—Problems and Progress, 1908–1958. Univ. of Wisconsin Press, Madison.

Takahashi, W. N., and Ishii, M. (1952). Nature **169**, 419.

Takahashi, W. N., and Ishii, M. (1953). Am. J. Botany **40**, 85.

Takahashi, W. N., and Rawlins, T. E. (1949). Phytopathology **39**, 672.

Takahashi, W. N., and Ruchti, J. (1961). Fourth Plant Virus Conference Report Czech. Acad. Sci. (In press.)

Tsugita, A., and Fraenkel-Conrat, H. (1962). J. Mol. Biol. **4**, 73.

Tsugita, A., Fraenkel-Conrat, H., Nirenberg, M. W., and Matthaei, J. H. (1962). Proc. Nat. Acad. Sci. U.S. **48**, 846.

Tsugita, A., Gish, D. T., Young, J., Fraenkel-Conrat, H., Knight, C. A., and Stanley, W. M. (1960). Proc. Nat. Acad. Sci. U.S. **46**, 1463.

Webster, G. C. (1959). Arch. Biochem. Biophys. **85**, 159.

Webster, G., Whitman, S. L., and Heintz, R. L. (1962). Exp. Cell Res. **26**, 595.

Weiss, S. B., and Gladstone, L. (1959). J. Am. Chem. Soc. **81**, 4118.

Wildman, S. G. (1959). Burnet and Stanley (eds.), The Viruses. **2**, Ch. 1. Academic Press, New York.

Wittmann, H. G. (1961). Reprint No. 72. Symposium No. 1. 5th Intern. Congr. Biochem., Moscow.

Yarwood, C. E. (1952). Phytopathology **42**, 137.

Zech, H., and Vogt-Köhne, L. (1955). Naturwissenschaften **11**, 337; **42**, 327.

L. BROADBENT

Control of plant virus diseases

16–1. EPIDEMIOLOGY

BEFORE MEASURES to control a disease can be formulated and applied it is usually necessary to know the identity of the virus causing it and of the vectors spreading the virus, as well as the sources of both virus and vectors. If this knowledge is not available attempts at control can be very "hit or miss."

A. IDENTITY OF VIRUS

As disease symptoms in the plant are often not diagnostic for the causal virus, correct identification of the virus is essential. Two examples of the confusion that can arise by different viruses causing similar symptoms in the host are: (1) Lettuce mosaic virus is seed-borne in lettuce but virus-free seed can be produced by growing plants for seed in areas that are too hot during part of the year for the aphids that normally colonize lettuce and spread mosaic. Early attempts to do this in Australia, however, were confused because many plants were infected with other viruses brought from nearby weeds by vagrant insects, and which caused symptoms similar to lettuce mosaic but were not seed-borne in lettuce (Stubbs and O'Loughlin, 1962). These viruses have since been recognized as tomato spotted wilt and a new one called necrotic yellows. (2) Several strains of tobacco mosaic virus (TMV) can infect both tobacco and tomato; most crops of these plants are infected, and consequently so is most cured smoking tobacco. It was thought, therefore, that smoking tobacco was one of the commonest sources of TMV for tomato, but recent surveys in Canada (MacNeill, 1962) and Britain (Broadbent, 1962) and unpublished ones in the Netherlands and France have shown that the strains of TMV common in tomato are different from those in tobacco.

B. SOURCE OF VIRUS

Different control measures will be required if a virus is normally present in some of the plants of a crop from the beginning than if the virus is introduced later from outside. Plants are infected and act as sources of virus within crops because (1) they grow from infected seeds, as with lettuce mosaic and barley false stripe viruses; (2) they are infected in a seedbed and are transplanted when the crop is set out, as with cauliflower mosaic in brassicas; (3) they grow from infected tubers or other vegetative organs, as with potato leaf roll; (4) they are infected early by incoming vectors, as with sugar-beet yellows virus; or (5) they are the infected remains of a previous crop, i.e., "volunteers" or "self-sets." Doncaster and Gregory (1948) found that almost a full crop of volunteer potatoes grew under wheat following the potato crop, and that occasionally some were still left after six years of arable cultivation. The potatoes in the cereal crops were rarely aphid-infested, and the incidence of disease remained steady; but when another crop of potatoes was grown the volunteers were infested by aphids and those that were infected became important sources of virus. For instance, a healthy stock of the variety Majestic was planted two years after Up-to-Date potatoes had been grown. In the ensuing crop 23% of the plants were Up-to-Date, and of these 55% showed rugose mosaic and 27% leaf roll. As a result, 97% of the Majestic plants were infected the following year, in contrast to 9% of the same stock lifted from an uncontaminated part of the field.

When infected plants within a crop are the only source, the ultimate incidence of disease may be directly proportional to the initial incidence; thus two lettuce crops which initially contained 0.5% and 3% infected seedlings finally had 14% and 85% of the plants infected (Broadbent et al., 1951). More often, however, spread is complicated by multiple infections, caused by viruliferous insects feeding on plants already infected, and, in experiments, spread from one plot to another. Thus Zink et al. (1956) obtained in eight trials the mean final percentages of 3.4, 7.6, and 29.5 from seed stocks with 0, 0.1, and 1.6% infection, respectively.

If virus is introduced from outside it can come either from other cultivated crops or from weeds and other uncultivated plants. Viruses are often spread from one crop to another when arthropod vectors leave old infected crops to seek alternative hosts. Crops near to a virus source usually become more infected than those further away because insects or mites tend to be dispersed by wind and the greater the distance between crops, the greater is the dispersion. Serious losses occur often in lettuce crops in Britain, for lettuce is usually grown successively in small plots and aphids spread mosaic virus from the old plants to the nearby young ones (Broadbent et al., 1951). Sometimes the spread is from one crop species to another, as when the pea aphid, after overwintering on alfalfa and clover fields, moves to peas and carries pea mosaic virus

with it (Huckett, 1945). The susceptible crop need not be colonized by the vectors, as when vagrant pea aphids carry yellow bean mosaic virus from red clover to beans (Crumb and McWhorter, 1948). Hewitt et al. (1946) showed that when vineyards adjoined alfalfa fields steep gradients of infection developed, either of Pierce's disease in the vines or of dwarf in the alfalfa, depending on which was the young crop, and whether the leafhoppers were transmitting the virus from alfalfa to vine or vine to alfalfa.

Probably most economically important viruses have moved from wild plants to cultivated ones when new crops have been planted in an area. This subject was discussed by Bennett (1952), and he concluded that as most epidemics of virus disease have occurred in the newer agricultural regions, the viruses existed locally and spread into the crops. Several records of such spread support this thesis, e.g., tristeza of citrus, swollen shoot of cacao, peach mosaic, and sugar-beet yellow wilt. Posnette et al. (1950) listed seven species of plants indigenous to West Africa that were susceptible to viruses from cacao. They are usually symptomless carriers of virus or show transient symptoms, are more difficult to infect, and are poorer sources of virus for the mealybug vectors. Trees of Ceiba pentandra Gaertn. and Cola chlamydantha K. Schum. were found naturally infected and have been important sources of virus for cacao. Thresh (1958a,b) reviewed these and later studies by other workers and concluded that although such forest trees were the original sources of cacao viruses, the viruses are now so widespread in cacao that the native sources are relatively unimportant.

Schlösser (1952) suggested that sugar-beet yellows and mosaic viruses originated in the wild Beta maritima L. which grows on the British coasts and then spread into the sugar-beet crops, first in England and then on the continent of Europe. Certainly wild beets are often infected in southern Britain (Blencowe, 1956; Gibbs, 1960) and may sometimes be sources of virus for commercial crops, especially of mosaic, but in sugar beet, as in many other crops, it is not

possible now to know if the viruses originated in the wild or in cultivated plants.
Bennett (1952) stressed that there is no
evidence as to how "new" viruses originate
and suggested that most originated in uncultivated plants, in which natural selection
tended to a development of tolerance. Severe disease develops only in "unusual" host
plants and the increase of such diseases
during this century is probably due to the
recent mobility of man and the development of new areas of mass agriculture.
There is little doubt that many unknown viruses exist and that further "escapes" into
cultivated crops may be expected in the
future. Perennial uncultivated plants are
much more dangerous than annual ones because once they are systemically infected
they remain potential sources of virus.

Wild plants often become infected with
viruses that are introduced into an area
with cultivated plants and then form a permanent reservoir of virus for further cultivated crops. Such a sequence occurred in
New York State during the late 1930's when
"X"-disease of peach infected chokecherries
(*Prunus virginiana* L.). The virus apparently did not spread from peach to peach,
but it spread rapidly to peach from chokecherries when these were within 200 ft of
the orchards (Hildebrand and Palmiter,
1942). A more recent instance occurred in
Florida when potato growing was started in
a new area in 1956. Potato virus Y soon
spread from the potatoes to weeds, especially nightshade (*Solanum gracile* Link
and *S. nigrum* L.) around the fields, from
where it was carried to pepper and tomato
crops, causing considerable losses in 1959
(Simons *et al.*, 1959). *S. gracile* is semi-
perennial in Florida and is also the main
source of vein-banding mosaic virus in pepper fields (Simons, 1956).

Some aphid-transmitted viruses are
thought to depend on weeds for their survival. Thus celery yellow spot virus could
not be transmitted by nine species of aphids
from celery to celery, but *Rhopalosiphum
conii* (*Hyadaphis xylostei* Schrank) collected from infected but symptomless
poison hemlock (*Conium maculatum* L.)
transmitted virus to celery and hemlock
(Freitag and Severin, 1945). Recently sev-

eral of the soil-borne, nematode-transmitted
viruses have been shown to commonly invade weeds, and to be seed-borne in some,
so ensuring the survival of viruses that have
relatively immobile vectors (Noordam,
1955; Lister, 1960).

The frequency with which some of the
wild plants that have been studied are infected with viruses suggests that more surveys of the type made by MacClement and
Richards (1956) in Canada would be worth
while. They tested the sap from five species
of wild plants from six different areas of the
Royal Botanical Gardens, Ontario, inoculating a range of test plants every two
weeks. Although this method severely limited the number of viruses that might be
recorded, about 10% of all the plants were
infected, often with more than one virus,
sugar-beet curly top, cucumber mosaic, and
tomato spotted wilt being among those
identified. In a similar survey near Berlin,
augmented by exposure of test plants for
fortnightly periods, Schwarz (1959) found
that cucumber mosaic, cabbage black ring
spot, lucerne mosaic, and potato Y viruses
were common. Thirty of 69 plants were potential hosts of cucumber mosaic when inoculation tests were made, 33 of cabbage
black ring spot virus; and in 1956, 95% of
exposed tobacco plants became infected
with cucumber mosaic virus. Other useful
papers on this subject have been published
by Hein (1957), and in Italy, by Lovisolo
and Benetti (1960), who found cabbage
black ring spot virus in several wild plants,
including *Diplotaxis erucoides* (L). DC.,
42% of which were infected.

Although wild plants are sometimes the
principal source of a virus, often they are
of little importance in the epidemiology of
crop diseases. Beet yellows virus is reported to often infect species of *Chenopodium* in beet and spinach fields, but
rarely spreads from them to the cultivated
plants (Bennett and Costa, 1954). Wiesner
(1959) infected 10% of 294 plants (34
species) with yellows virus but passage
through some, e.g., *Capsella bursa-pastoris*
(L.) Medic. and *Thlaspi arvense* L., resulted in loss of virulence, and he concluded that weeds were of very minor importance for overwintering compared with

the beet seed crop. In Britain, also, there is no evidence that common susceptible weeds play a significant part in the epidemiology of potato, lettuce, and brassica virus diseases (Doncaster and Gregory, 1948; Broadbent et al., 1951; Broadbent, 1957a), although in view of the results quoted above, weeds may be a common source of cabbage black ring spot virus.

C. Host Susceptibility

Whether virus is spread within, or brought into crops, the amount of spread will depend not only on the numbers of sources but on the availability of the virus in them and on the susceptibility of the uninfected plants. Both these can differ with age and environment. Susceptibility to infection often decreases with increasing age of plants; consequently, other things being equal, incidence of a disease may be influenced by the age of the plants when infective vectors are active. Even a few days' difference in age greatly affects the susceptibility of sugar beet to yellows virus (Hansen, 1950). Beet is also more susceptible to, and intolerant of, curly-top virus when in the cotyledon stage than later (Wallace and Murphy, 1938). Similarly, Oswald and Houston (1953) found that cereal yellow dwarf virus caused a severe disease only if plants were infected when young, so that it was usually of economic importance in barley, but not in wheat and oats, which were sown earlier. An extreme instance was cited by Storey and Nichols (1938): Bemisia spp. infect only immature cassava leaves with mosaic virus, although they feed as well on mature ones.

Temperature may influence both plant resistance and vector infectivity. Thus when Myzus persicae (Sulzer) were reared on potato infected with leaf roll virus at 22° or 27°C and were transferred singly to Physalis floridana Rydb. grown also at these temperatures, 58% transmitted at 27°C but only 26% at 22° (Webb, 1956).

Sometimes viruses can be transmitted to a plant species but not be acquired from them again by similar vectors. A contrary state of affairs was found by Frazier and Posnette (1957) when forms of Euscelis plebejus (Fall.) transmitted green petal virus from clover to clover and from, but not to, strawberry. In England the vector of green petal virus in strawberry crops is Aphrodes bicinctus (Schrank) (Posnette and Ellenberger, 1963). Watson (1956) pointed out that the transmissibility of a virus by aphids was determined partly by the host in which it was multiplying. Potato virus C was not transmissible from potato in 1945 by aphids but after manual inoculation in Nicotiana glutinosa L. and N. tabacum L. for 10 years it was transmissible by M. persicae. However, after passage through potato back to tobacco it again ceased to be aphid transmitted.

Not only are older healthy plants usually less susceptible to infection and better able to tolerate infection than young ones, but vectors often have difficulty in acquiring virus from older infected plants, probably because the virus content of the sap decreases. Young leaves were better sources of three cacao viruses than mature leaves for the vector Pseudococcus njalensis Laing, and sometimes the mealybugs failed to acquire virus from petioles or stems, suggesting that the virus was not completely systemic (Posnette and Robertson, 1950). Similar examples were found by Kassanis (1952) with leaf roll virus in potato, and by Hollings (1955a) with viruses in chrysanthemum.

Evans (1954) found that the groundnut variety Mwitunde was field resistant to rosette virus partly because. although it was as susceptible as other varieties in laboratory tests, the proportion of aphids able to acquire virus was less than on other varieties. With virus Y, also, different potato varieties differed in the ease with which they became infected and in the extent to which virus multiplied in them and hence in the readiness with which aphids became infective when feeding on them (Bawden and Kassanis, 1946). Resistance to infestation by the insect vectors can also affect virus spread. Varieties of lettuce and celery which, experimentally, were all equally susceptible to yellows virus, contracted the disease to different extents in the field because of differential feeding by the leafhopper vectors (Linn, 1940; Yamaguchi and Welch, 1955). Even the colour of a plant may affect disease incidence: three times as many aphids alighted on green or yellow lettuce plants as on brown ones, and Müller (1956) found the brown variety was infected with mosaic virus less frequently than the others.

Different cultural practices affect plant susceptibility to viruses. Janssen (1929) was one of the first to investigate the connection between plant nutrition and the incidence of virus diseases, and like most subsequent workers, he found that the better plants were fed and grew the more likely they were to become infected: increasing nitrogen increased both aphid numbers per plant and the susceptibility of potato plants to infection with leaf roll and Y viruses; a deficiency of potash also favoured aphid reproduction and spread of virus Y. Ross *et al.* (1947) suggested that fertilizers affected potato diseases by increasing plant susceptibility because they found no effect on aphid populations. Heavy nitrogen dressings increased susceptibility of cauliflower to mosaic virus and, especially when given as dung or hoof and horn meal, decreased the tolerance of the plants to infection (Broadbent, 1957a).

Plant spacing can have a considerable effect on disease incidence. Close planting of groundnuts greatly reduced the incidence of rosette (Storey, 1935) and, with delayed weeding, usually practised by the peasant cultivators in East Africa, the disease was harmless. As van der Plank (1947, 1948a) has shown, most insects that bring virus into a crop land at random, so a greater proportion of plants will be visited when they are widely spaced than when they are crowded together. This was demonstrated by sticky traps in place of potato plants (Broadbent, 1948), and also by counting aphids on the potato plants and on sugar beet that were differently spaced (Steudel, 1953).

D. IDENTITY AND EFFICIENCY OF VECTORS

It is relatively easy to find if a virus is spread mainly by man, but most plant viruses are spread by insects, and only occasionally by birds or other animals, and then it is often difficult to find which of the many species of insects that infest or feed transiently on plants is spreading a virus. It took, for example, over 8000 tests with more than 150 species of insects and mites during many years to incriminate *Eriophyes insidiosus* Keifer and Wilson as the vector of peach mosaic virus in California (Wilson *et al.*, 1955). When several species can transmit a virus it is often even more difficult to assess their relative importance. The principal vector is sometimes the least prevalent insect, as in the citrus orchards of California where *Aphis gossypii* (Glover) is the main vector of tristeza virus but forms only about 3% of the aphids visiting trees. Even this species is an inefficient vector, for over 5000 aphids were required to cause each infection. However, it was calculated from trap catches that about 35,000 *A. gossypii* visited each tree per year, and the disease incidence roughly doubled in this time (Dickson *et al.*, 1956). Similarly, yellow vein mosaic virus causes an important disease in bhendi (*Hibiscus esculentus* L.) in India; two jassids and an aphid commonly infest the plants but the virus is spread by *Bemisia tabaci* Genn., a whitefly pest of cotton that is seldom seen on bhendi (Capoor and Varma, 1950). Some of the viruses of narcissi are spread by aphids, which do not normally infest spring-grown plants in western Europe, and it is often difficult to persuade growers and advisory officers that a non-pest species is a virus vector. Sometimes, however, the colonizing species are the main vectors, as with *M. persicae* and *Brevicoryne brassicae* (L.) which infest and transmit cauliflower mosaic virus in many brassica crops; at least 20 other species of aphids could transmit the virus in experiments, but played little part in field spread (Broadbent, 1957a).

More work has been done on the spread of leaf roll and Y viruses of potato than on any others transmitted by aphids. *M. persicae* has long been known as the principal vector of these viruses in western Europe, and this was confirmed by trapping aphids in potato crops in different parts of England and statistically correlating the catches with the increases in incidence of disease. Almost all the spread of leaf roll virus within the crop could be attributed to winged *M. persicae,* which was also responsible for much of the spread of virus Y (Broadbent, 1950; Hollings, 1955b). Evidence that *Aphis nasturtii* (Kltb.) and *Macrosiphum solanifolii* (Ashm.) are important vectors of virus Y, but not of leaf roll virus, was obtained in Sweden and Norway where *M. persicae* is confined to the southern coastal areas, as is the spread of leaf roll virus; the other aphids occur further north and in Finland, and virus Y spreads in these areas also (Björnstad, 1948; Jamalainen, 1948; Lihnell, 1948). In central Poland, too, *A. nasturtii* and *Doralis frangulae* (Kltb.) are the commonest aphids, and alates of these are responsible for most of the spread of virus Y (Gabriel, 1960).

The subject of specificity among virus vectors was reviewed by Day and Bennetts (1954), and recently Kennedy *et al.* (1962) have compiled and discussed a most useful list of aphid vectors and non-vectors. Even under reasonably standard feeding conditions, when different species of aphids were allowed only single probes on plants infected with potato virus Y and on healthy plants, *M. persicae* infected 55%, *A. nasturtii* 31%, *M. solanifolii* 9%, and *Aulacorthum solani* (Kltb.) 4% of them (Bradley and Rideout, 1953).

Races or strains of aphids exist which are morphologically similar or indistinguishable, but which differ in their ability to transmit specific viruses and may frequent different hosts. Hille Ris Lambers (1955) found that the winged forms of three *Myzus* species that did not infest potatoes were almost indistinguishable from *M. persicae,* the main vector of potato leaf roll virus. They were occasionally very numerous in the Netherlands and could have confused those identifying trapped aphids in relation to the potato virus control programme. Even within a species strains differ in their ability to transmit virus: Stubbs (1955) sorted out several strains of *M. persicae* with different abilities to transmit a yellows virus of spinach, and Björling and Ossiannilsson (1958) isolated 85 strains of this aphid capable of transmitting sugar-beet yellows virus with different degrees of efficiency ranging from 10 to 80%. Several

other workers have described similar results with other viruses and insects, and Simons (1959) showed that such variation applied also to stylet-borne (non-persistent) viruses, potato virus Y, and southern cucumber mosaic, and also that a strain efficient at transmitting one virus will not necessarily be efficient at transmitting others.

It is obvious from the above figures that not all the potential vectors that feed on infected plants become infective. This subject of virus-vector relations has been dealt with earlier in the course, and was recently very ably reviewed by Maramorosch (1963), but the time taken for insects to become infective after feeding on a virus source has to be taken into account when planning control measures, especially those that include insecticides. Thus it should be much easier to limit the spread of circulatory (persistent) viruses, vectors of some of which take several days to become infective after feeding on infected plants, than to control stylet-borne viruses which can be acquired and transmitted within a few minutes. It is also useful to know how long the virus is likely to persist in a feeding or in a fasting vector. Most of the information on the proportion of insects that become infective is based on laboratory experiments and we know little of the numbers of infective insects within crops. Experiments under cages in the field indicated that between 15 and 20% of winged aphids bred on cauliflowers infected with cauliflower mosaic virus were infective when they left the plants (Broadbent, 1957a).

E. ACTIVITY OF VECTORS

There has long been controversy about the relative roles of winged and wingless aphids as virus vectors and much more field experimentation is needed before final conclusions can be drawn. Obviously virus is carried from one crop to another by alatae, and virus spread by non-colonizing aphids must also be by them. The only point at issue is which forms of colonizing aphids spread virus from sources within the crop to nearby plants. Many workers believe that such spread must be by walking aphids, but I have seen no evidence additional to that reviewed earlier (Broadbent and Martini, 1959) to make me change my opinion that, with many species and many viruses, alatae are also responsible for some of the plant to plant spread, and that in some instances the evidence suggests that alatae are mainly responsible. It may be that the different aphid forms differ in their capacity to transmit viruses, but few adequately careful tests have been made: one such was by Sylvester (1955) who found that under similar conditions and from the same source of lettuce mosaic virus, winged *M. persicae* transmitted to 6/49 plants, apterae to 15/42, and nymphs to 15/46. Simons (1954) found that first instar nymphs of *Acyrthosiphum pisum* (Harris) acquired pea enation mosaic virus more readily than did adults, and infected six times as many plants as did apterous adults. Female *Bemisia tabaci* infected about twice as many plants with euphorbia mosaic virus as males (Costa and Bennett, 1950).

Having found which species of insects or other vectors are transmitting a virus, it is necessary to obtain information about their numbers and times of activity if control measures are to be applied effectively. Weather affects insect flight, but the main factor is the number capable of flight (Johnson, 1956). Some insects have well-defined periods of movement, others move frequently during a long season. Some aphid species form dense colonies of apterae, e.g., *Aphis fabae* Scop. and *B. brevicoryne*, whereas others disperse more readily, but more important for virus spread is the period before the aphid's wing muscles atrophy after its initial flight (Johnson, 1953). *A. fabae* and *B. brevicoryne* quickly lose the power to fly, which is another reason why these species form dense colonies, in contrast to *M. persicae* which deposits nymphs in ones or twos in different parts of a plant and on different plants, and remains active for several days. Most virus transmission, especially of the stylet-borne viruses occurs during the initial flights, for Kennedy (1950), Müller (1953), and others have shown that during this active flight phase host plants are visited and abandoned several times, during which visits short probes are made. The more suitable the host the sooner the aphids settled, reproduced, and lost the power to fly, so that more spread of non-circulatory viruses might be expected when the host plants were not in a very suitable condition for colonization. This may often be in mid-summer when the aphids are most numerous, for mature leaves are not as acceptable as young or senescing ones (Kennedy et al., 1950), but this is counteracted in most crops by the increased resistance to infection that develops with age.

Control of a vector is made easier if its alternative host plants are known with certainty, for geographical and seasonal variations occur with most widely distributed insects. Thus in England, the aphid *M. persicae* overwinters on many herbaceous hosts, and only about 1% of the spring migrants develop from eggs, whereas in the areas of North America and Europe that have cold winters it overwinters mainly as eggs on species of *Prunus* (Gorham, 1942; Hille Ris Lambers, 1955; Broadbent and Heathcote, 1955).

It is necessary to know when the vectors are active, but such information must be linked with knowledge of when the virus is being spread. In England, for example, most spread of potato leaf roll and Y viruses is from plants within the crop during the spring when a few winged aphids are colonizing the plants; the large summer apterous and alate populations are less important (partly because the plants are less susceptible to virus then), except that it is at this time that a few plants in healthy crops become infected by aphids that have come from infected ones (Doncaster and Gregory, 1948; Broadbent et al., 1960). The strawberry aphid, *Pentatrichopus fragaefolii* (Cockerell), has a different cycle, which depends on the age of the plants. Winged forms are numerous only when the population is maximal, which is in late summer on first year plants but is in late May or June on older ones (Dicker, 1952). Most virus spread coincides with these maximum populations (Posnette and Cropley, 1954).

Finally, if an attempt to control a disease by killing the vectors with insecticides is contemplated, the chemicals must be tested to make sure they will kill the insects quickly and not stimulate them to more activity than usual before they die. The problem of killing insects as pests is simple compared with preventing them from spreading viruses, for it is easy to keep their numbers below the level at which their feeding will cause economic damage, but difficult to kill them quickly enough to prevent them—especially winged forms—from infecting healthy plants. This applies particularly to the stylet-borne viruses which can be acquired and transmitted within minutes, but also to insects already infective with circulatory viruses when they arrive on the treated healthy plants.

16–2. EXCLUSION AND PROTECTION—I. INTRODUCTION OF VIRUSES INTO CROPS BY MAN, MAMMALS, AND BIRDS

A. VIRUSES SPREAD BY CONTACT

Few viruses are easily spread by contact but some of these are of great economic importance, particularly tobacco mosaic virus (TMV) in tobacco and tomato, and potato viruses X and spindle tuber. TMV is unique, as far as we know, in remaining so long infective outside living cells or within dead ones. Clothing contaminated with infective tomato sap has remained infective for nearly four years when kept in darkness, and for several months in daylight (Broadbent, 1963a) and dried tobacco leaf has remained infective for 24 years (Caldwell, 1959). The ease with which infective clothing can contaminate plants is not always realised by advisory officers and others who visit one crop after another, although it was stressed as long ago as 1929 by Johnson and Ogden. One of our workers, in an overall worn for two days in an infected tomato crop, walked between two rows of potted tomato plants for 10 minutes, so that only his overall brushed the plants, and 19 of 20 were infected.

Most spread of TMV in tomato crops is by the hands, for the plants, at least under glass, are tended at frequent intervals when they are young and again when fruit is being picked. Potato virus X is not quite so persistent but it can be carried for some weeks on clothing; and machinery, dogs, and other animals that pass through potato crops help to disseminate it (Todd, 1958). In reviewing the spread of plant viruses in 1959 I postulated that if man and mammals could spread such viruses, birds also were likely to do so on their feathers and beaks, and occasionally might introduce virus into healthy stocks. We have now proved such transmission of TMV in tomatoes.

Potato virus X is not spread by cutting knives unless the blade passes through young sprouts, though it may spread by contact among sprouting tubers in sacks (Bawden *et al.*, 1948), but potato spindle tuber virus is spread by knife and, like virus X, is also readily spread by machinery (Merriam and Bonde, 1954). Other viruses spread by harvesting knives, etc., are tulip breaking virus (van Slogteren and Ouboter, 1941), cymbidium mosaic (Jensen and Gold, 1955), and bean yellow mosaic, cucumber mosaic, and tobacco ringspot in gladiolus (Brierley, 1962).

Controlling the spread of such easily transmitted viruses is not easy but can be achieved in the following ways (B-F).

B. PROTECTED CROPPING

This may be achieved under glass, but occasionally under wire or cloth cages to exclude birds and mammals, including men who are not conversant with the precautions needed.

C. HYGIENE MEASURES

Workers should never visit a healthy crop after a diseased one without washing well and changing their outer clothing. For tomato crops under glass, clean overalls can be kept in each house, to be donned by worker or visitor before moving among the plants. Workers should be discouraged from wearing the same clothing for tending successive crops unless it has been cleaned. Trousers and shoes are especially liable to carry potato viruses; plastic overleggings are useful garments for potato inspectors and are easily cleaned.

Most workers have thought that washing hands with soap and water will remove virus, but Berkeley (1942) stated that washing in a pail may be ineffective and that running water was essential. He found that washing in a solution of tri-sodium ortho-phosphate was usually effective. We have done several tests recently and found it very difficult to free sap-engrained hands from TMV. The best way was to wash in a 3% solution of tri-sodium orthophosphate (tsop) and then to scrub well with soap and water, but this did not always free virus from under the nails (Broadbent, 1963b).

The best way to free contaminated tools is heat sterilisation but this is not always possible; and, if not, the next best treatment that we have found is to dip in tsop but not to wash the solution off because it is a virus inhibitor, not an inactivator. Mul-holland (1962) also used tsop to stop the spread of TMV on trimming knives. Knives with hollow handles were filled with tsop solution which slowly trickled over the blades. Similar knives might well be tried to limit the spread of gladiolus, tulip, cym-bidium, and other viruses when harvesting the blooms.

Workers should be forbidden to smoke when tending tobacco or tomato plants, and especially when grafting young tomato plants, although TMV is seldom trans-mitted from tobacco to tomato (Broadbent, 1962).

When machinery has to be driven through infected crops during cultivations or spraying there is little hope of prevent-ing the spread of such viruses as potato X and spindle tuber within those crops, but the same machinery should not be taken into a healthy crop without being washed with water containing an inhibitor like tsop or inactivating detergents.

D. Virus Inhibitors and Inactivators

In 1954 Bawden wrote that "it is surpris-ing that no experiments have been re-ported to test whether inhibitors of infec-tion have any practical value in protecting crops from virus diseases, for their potenti-alities have long been obvious." Much more work had been done on the inhibition of virus increase, but after reviewing this Bawden concluded that there would be more hope for successful chemotherapy if there were evidence that viruses such as

TMV possessed any independent metabo-lism, but all the evidence suggested that they depended on the synthetic systems of the host cells. He considered that the chances of developing prophylactic sprays were quite good because particles of even the most stable viruses are often easily inactivated on first entering healthy cells.

The use of tri-sodium orthophosphate as an inhibitor of infection has been described above, but apart from this no other treat-ment has been found wholly satisfactory. Stoddard and Dimond (1949) watered tomatoes in sand culture with a 1/4000 aqueous solution of malachite green on 10 successive days and then inoculated them with TMV. One month later fewer plants were infected than in the control series, but Howles (1957) found that neither mal-achite green nor 2-chlorphenoxyacetic acid affected susceptibility, although both de-layed symptom appearance. Following Ful-ton's (1943) demonstration that cow's milk contained virus inactivators, a test in Eng-land apparently prevented the spread of TMV in glasshouse tomatoes, but no control plants were left unsprayed (Newell, 1954). Since then, several workers have done ex-periments but with conflicting results. Har-rison (1957), Crowley (1958), and Fry and Coleman (1960) reported that sprayed crops tended by workers whose hands were wet with the milk solution were as readily infected as unsprayed plants handled with-out precautions. However, Hare and Lucas (1959) found that only 10% of young to-matoes became infected when sprayed and allowed to dry before being inoculated with TMV-infected tomato sap, in contrast to 60% when sprayed just after inoculation and 90% when unsprayed, and Hein (1962) also obtained satisfactory control, only 4/400 plants being infected in four trials, compared with 11–39% of unsprayed plants. Hagborg and Chelack (1960) found that both skim milk and whey reduced field spread of barley stripe mosaic when sprayed weekly, one application of 100% whey, for instance, decreasing the percent-age of mosaic from 33 to 15.

Lucas and Winstead (1958) tested the antibiotic cytovirin by atomizing it over young tomato plants and one hour later inoculating one leaf of each with TMV. All the control plants showed symptoms after 14 days but 70% of treated plants showed no symptoms 30 days later. Wittmann (1958) showed that this chemical affected the symptom incubation period but completely inhibited virus multiplication only at a concentration near the toxic level. Both cytovirin and thiouracil adversely affect growth as well as virus production so are unlikely to be of practical value, especially as cytovirin is highly toxic to man. The work reported during the 10 years since Bawden's review has been discussed in greater detail earlier in this course, but I know of none which holds out any hope of preventing virus spread in practice.

E. Cultural Modifications

Cultural modifications may sometimes help to prevent the spread of viruses transmitted by contact. Bawden *et al.* (1948) stressed the importance of isolation from infected crops and freedom from volunteer plants in the fields where potatoes free from virus X were being grown, and Hansen (1957) showed that the incidence of this virus increased progressively with delay in lifting from early July onwards. Changing a variety may help to limit this type of spread; for instance, when Bonde and Merriam (1951) contaminated young potato sprouts with spindle tuber virus, 50% of the variety Kennebec were infected but only 5% of Katahdin.

F. Infection with Mild Virus Strains

Bennett (1951) reviewed work on interference between plant viruses. It was thought earlier that a mild strain of any particular virus would protect infected plants against related but more severe strains, but there are many instances where this is not so. Bennett concluded that the method and site of introduction of the challenging virus, environmental conditions, and species of host plant may determine whether the challenging virus will infect a plant or not. If the initial virus is not completely systemic it is possible to establish the second one in uninvaded tissues.

Inoculation of potatoes with mild virus X has been used in some countries to protect varieties from more severe virus strains which cause much greater loss, and also to show up more readily plants infected with virus Y, for the two viruses together cause a synergistic reaction. It is then easier to rogue the Y-infected plants. However, workers elsewhere, including Britain, prefer not to use this method, for virus X occurs in many strains and it is likely that mild ones will sooner or later mutate into severe ones, especially if widely disseminated in millions of plants. For this reason cross protection should be used only if a disease is impossible to eradicate by other means, and if the losses caused by the severe strains of virus are such that they outweigh those from the widespread use of the milder strains.

G. Viruses Introduced in Vegetatively Propagated Plant Parts

Man has been responsible for taking many viruses into new areas in budwood, scions, rootstocks of trees and shrubs, and in tubers, rhizomes, corms and bulbs, etc., of herbaceous plants, as described earlier. A good example is tristeza virus of citrus trees, originating probably in China, and introduced into South Africa by 1900, and probably at times into the USA, but lack of a vector and the use of tolerant varieties masked its presence. During 1930–31, however, many sweet orange trees on lemon rootstocks were imported into South America from South Africa, and later into California, and were probably carrying the virus symptomlessly. The presence of millions of trees on sour orange and other non-tolerant rootstocks, and an abundant vector, *Aphis citricides* Kirk., led to the serious epidemic that occurred during the next few years in South America, but the disease was never so serious in California because there was no efficient vector there (Wallace *et al.*, 1956). To prevent new introductions of infected material into the USA, only seed was allowed in for a time, but this was followed later by an indexing programme in quarantine, in which imported budwood is propagated and then indexed in several susceptible varieties under glass. Most countries discriminate against some vegetatively propagated material from another country

339

where diseases they fear are known to occur, or insist on certificates of health (Klinkowski, 1959). Many of the quarantine regulations promulgated by different countries have failed because it is not possible to rely on visual symptoms and much of the material that is imported is dormant. Relatively few countries grow imported plants in quarantine or index to test plants under insect-proof conditions. Thresh (1960), discussing quarantine arrangements for intercepting virus-infected cacao, commented that only viruses causing mild symptoms are likely to be encountered in such work because severely affected material would not normally be collected for export. He suggested that the movement of rooted cuttings should be restricted and the use of budwood encouraged now that it can be transported quickly by air. Healthy test plants should be top-worked with this material, which would be considered healthy after three or four symptomless flushes had been produced.

There are many schemes for distributing healthy material, such as the potato seed certification regulations, Nuclear Stock Scheme for strawberries and other soft fruits, and the Mother Tree Scheme for top-fruit trees in England. The latter scheme was adopted to reduce the risk of the wrong variety being supplied, to reduce the risk of bud-sports being perpetuated in scions and to provide virus free or tested material (Posnette, 1962). It provides propagators with the best scion wood of commercial varieties that is available, and stocks are continually being tested and replaced as better material becomes available. Stout (1962) described similar schemes for seven crops in California—potato, citrus, strawberry, cherry, grape, avocado, and garlic. He warned against "the urge to take unwise short cuts for what at the time appears to be expediency," which plant pathologists often meet from commercial interests when trying to set up or operate such schemes.

Undoubtedly most work has been done on potatoes, a staple food plant of many nations, because such disastrous losses result from infection, particularly with leaf roll and Y viruses. Although infected tubers are transported by man, the plants become infected with most of the viruses by insects,

so control methods will be discussed in the next section. The certification schemes in Britain depend upon visual inspection, the three common grades being Stock Seed (fewer than 4 plants infected per acre), A certificate with less than 0.5% infected plants, and H certificate with less than 1%. The Scottish certification scheme was started in 1932, and no epidemic of aphid-borne virus has developed since 1945, probably because of the decrease in virus sources and growth of the better crops in areas where aphids arrive late and the seed crops are lifted early (Todd, 1961). Measures to limit spread of viruses within crops will be discussed later. Tobacco veinal necrosis was first discovered in Scotland in 1953, most stocks of the variety Craigs Royal, which had recently been introduced, being infected, some to the extent of 20%. Control was achieved through the certification scheme, and this virus has been eliminated from most stocks of Craigs Royal and the few outbreaks in other varieties have been contained (Todd, 1960). Such high standards cannot be maintained in some countries where seed has to be produced in what the British would call "degeneration" areas. In the USA and several other countries a proportion of stocks to be certified are either grown under glass after breaking tuber dormancy, or in southern areas where potatoes will grow outside during the winter (such as Florida), so that the health of the stocks can be assessed before they are planted (Folsom, 1952). It is essential to have representative samples for these tests, and to use land free from volunteers. For foundation and breeders' stocks, tuber indexing is often used, and roguing is made easier by planting in tuber units, i.e., growing together all the cut pieces from one tuber or all the tubers from one plant. The West Germans use field inspection, a callose colour test for leaf roll, serological tests where possible, e.g., for viruses X and S, and single eye cultures under artificial light, but even so they cannot maintain very high standards, stock seed having a limit of 4% leaf roll, Y, A, X, and S viruses, and certified seed for ware crops not more than 10% tubers infected with these viruses (Kabiersch, 1962). The Igel-Lange test and similar callose tests for leaf roll are now widely used in Europe; they are helpful tools but are not wholly reliable and have not been adopted in Britain (Sardina *et al.*, 1958; Broadbent and Heathcote, 1960; Horvath, 1962; Govier, 1963). Where vegetatively propagated plants such as bulbs or potato tubers are stored for a period they may sprout and are then very susceptible to infection if they should become infested with aphids or other virus vectors, especially as the stored stock will often contain some infected units. Doncaster and Gregory (1948) drew attention to the rapid spread of leaf roll and Y viruses among "chitting" potatoes, and Smith and Brierley (1948) to the spread of cucumber mosaic, mottle, and rosette viruses among lilies.

H. Seed Infection

Lister (1960) has shown that some of the soil-borne or nematode-transmitted viruses, viz., arabis mosaic, tomato black ring, and raspberry ringspot, are readily seed-borne in several wild plants, and it would appear that this is their normal method of spread, for their nematode vectors are rather restricted in range. Despite these recent additions, the number of seed-borne viruses is still small, and most of the known ones are in food or ornamental plants and thus are disseminated by man. In areas where lettuce is grown in large fields and most spread of mosaic is within the crop, as in California, the use of virus-free seed effectively controls mosaic (Grogan *et al.*, 1952); in experiments, plots with virus-free seed had 2% of the plants infected at harvest whereas adjacent plots sown with commercial seed had 12%. In England lettuce is usually grown in smaller areas and much spread is from older infected crops into young ones, but nevertheless the cycle is started by seed infection (Broadbent *et al.*, 1951). When plots were isolated, those sown with seed with fewer than 0.1% infected varied at harvest from 0 to 0.5% infected plants, but those with 2.2 to 5.3% infected seeds varied from 25 to 96% at harvest (Tomlinson, 1962).

With insect-borne viruses the methods of preventing infection in the seed crop are the same as in the main crop, and will be dealt with later. Seldom is it possible to distinguish between infected and healthy seeds, but Middleton (1944) found that light, poorly filled squash seeds gave a mean of 1% diseased plants, whereas heavy well-filled ones gave only 0.1%, so that winnowing decreased disease incidence slightly. Virus concentration decreases rapidly in some seeds and storage is a means of freeing them from virus; seed is the most important source of cucumber green mottle virus but the virus is in or on the testa, not in the embryo, and seed saved for a year is free from virus (van Koot and van Dorst, 1959). TMV is similarly situated in tomato seeds but we have found some batches of seed still infective after 7-years' storage. There has long been debate, following many conflicting experimental results, as to whether or not TMV is seed-borne in tomato. We have recently confirmed the findings of several past workers—particularly Crowley (1957) and Taylor *et al.* (1961)—that virus is not in the embryo and that infection is caused when the seed coat is pressed against the seedling during pricking out. Gol'din and Yurchenko (1958) controlled the disease in field tomatoes by direct sowing to eliminate such infection, obtaining only five infected plants in a field directly sown but 71% infected when plants were transplanted. In some crops different varieties differ in the extent to which seed transmission occurs, and those with the least should be chosen when possible (Quantz, 1955; Anderson, 1957). Even within a variety, however, the percentage of infected seeds varies greatly, depending mainly upon the time of infection.

Some viruses do not enter the seed if infection occurs during flowering, e.g., lettuce mosaic (Couch, 1955), and others, e.g., bean mosaic and barley stripe mosaic, infect embryos only during their early development (Fajardo, 1930; Quantz, 1955; Crowley, 1959), so measures to delay spread, such as roguing out infected plants until the crop flowers, are worth while (van Velsen, 1961). A seed certification programme to obtain barley seed free from barley stripe mosaic virus was begun by growing samples of seed under glass during late autumn and winter to select those

341

most free for further propagation (Hampton *et al.*, 1957). As with all such glasshouse tests, symptoms varied with light and temperature, and it was necessary to try several combinations to find that which gave the best results.

16–3. EXCLUSION AND PROTECTION—II. INTRODUCTION OF VIRUSES INTO CROPS BY INSECTS AND MITES

A. PROTECTED CROPPING

This is not so easy when insects and mites have to be excluded from glasshouses, for if adequate insect-proof screening is fitted, ventilation and cooling are usually inadequate. Air then has to be drawn in or out by fan and elaborate measures taken to prevent insects from being sucked in at the same time. Even if an adequate system is devised, there is always the danger of insects being carried into the houses on workers' clothes.

In the field, cloth or plastic fibre cages are sometimes used to exclude insects from valuable plants. Large cages were used by Jones and Riker (1931) to protect asters from aster yellows, and Linn (1940) protected lettuce and endive seedlings from yellows virus in cloth-covered cold frames or screened glasshouses prior to transplanting, obtaining a delay of 14 days in the appearance of disease in the crop and decrease in incidence of yellows from 36% in field sown crops to 7%. This type of protection is expensive, however, and has not been widely used, although one commercial firm in England uses Tygan cages for rearing virus-free lettuce seed plants and screened houses are used in Arkansas for increasing virus-free clones of strawberries (Fulton and Seymour, 1957).

B. BARRIER AND COVER CROPS

Insect-transmitted viruses usually spread faster into and within a pure stand of susceptible hosts than in mixed ones and use has been made of non-susceptible cover crops to screen the undersown susceptible plants in sugar-beet seed production. The first-year plants (stecklings) make little growth before the barley cover is cut, but

rapid growth afterwards, and Hull (1952) reported 12% plants with beet yellows compared with 100% in open beds. Hansen (1950) obtained similar results when beet rows were alternated with rows of barley, and he recommended growing cereals on areas where beet had been clamped to isolate any volunteers that emerged. No protection was obtained when the distance between barrier rows was about 7 yards. Radish mosaic affected the widely grown radish crops in Japan, spreading rapidly in newly sown crops during August, but catch cropping the radish between rows of rice or trefoil greatly reduced its incidence (Shirahama, 1957). Viado and Matthysse (1959) found that a cover crop of *Centrosema plumieri* decreased the incidence of abaca mosaic from 33 to 12%, giving better control than insecticidal sprays applied both to the crop and to the nearby weed hosts.

However, more use has been made of narrow barrier rows at intervals than of cover crops. Early work with barriers used mostly meshes of wire or cloth, and Kunkel (1929) was one of the first to report that 4–8-ft-high screens of wire around plots of asters 10×25 ft, cut the incidence of yellows from 80% in unfenced plots to 20%. Jones and Riker (1931) at the same time and for the same purpose were experimenting with cloth screens 6-ft-high, but found complete cages more effective. Yellows virus is carried to the crop plants by leafhoppers coming from weeds and Linn (1940) found that 6-ft-high cloth screens delayed the onset of disease in lettuce by 9 days and decreased final incidence from 35 to 12%.

Single rows of plant barriers were perhaps first used by the French, who latticed their sugar-beet steckling beds with rows of oats, maize, hemp, or sunflowers about 1-yard-wide around beds 20×5 yards (Hull, 1952). In a recent paper Bonnemaison (1961) reported that the percentage of plants with yellows in plots screened with 2 rows of maize and 3 of sunflower was 21 when the unscreened plots had 56% in September. In another experiment on size of plots the unscreened had 54%, those with barriers every 5m 28%, every 10m 31%, and every 15m 36% plants with yellows. The same idea was used to protect brassica seedbeds from cauliflower mosaic virus; rows of barley, which is non-susceptible and not colonized by the aphid vectors, proved more effective than barriers of beans or other brassicas and decreased disease incidence in several experiments by about 80%. It was recommended that a 3-row band of barley should be sown between every 12 rows of seedbed, with single cross-rows of cereal at intervals in long seedbeds; the barriers were effective when sown at the same time as the cauliflower seeds (Broadbent, 1957a). Keener (1956) found barrier or trap crops of alfalfa or corn around tomato crops effective in preventing *Circulifer tenellus* (Baker) from carrying beet curly-top virus into tomato fields, but only in seasons when the leafhoppers were few.

A considerable amount of work on the effectiveness of plant barriers has been done in Florida by Simons (1957–60). Several viruses, such as pepper veinbanding mosaic and potato Y, have become prevalent in weeds, from which they are carried into pepper, celery, tomato, and other crops by aphids. In experiments sunflower barriers around pepper plots 150 ft from the source had 63% of the pepper plants infected in the fifth week, compared with 95% of unprotected plants. Barriers delayed infection by about 10 days but eventually all plants were infected, those in the centre of the plots much earlier than those near the sunflowers (1957). A low single barrier 1.5-ft-high was nearly as effective as a single 10-ft barrier, but most effective were 50-ft-wide strips of non-susceptible crops such as beans, corn, or cucumber around the fields, especially when the barriers were also sprayed with parathion (1958). The primary spread of potato virus Y from *Solanum nigrum* to pepper was decreased 50% by one row of sunflower around three sides of the plots, 70% by a 50-ft barrier of beans and by 85% when the beans were sprayed weekly with parathion. After six weeks all plants within sunflower barriers were infected, as before, but those within bean barriers had one-third less diseased and those within sprayed barriers had only half as many as in unprotected plots (1960).

It must not be forgotten that barriers to insect flight, such as trees, tall hedges, and buildings, can cause insects to land on the windward side (Taylor and Johnson, 1954) and infective ones may spread more disease than in the open parts of fields (Broadbent *et al.*, 1951). In effect, the edges of fields are barriers to flight, which is why edge-rows are often more infected than others, but this point will be discussed in Section 16–3D.

C. Isolation

Obviously isolation is the best way of preventing virus spread from one crop to another, for the greater the distance between crops, the greater will be the dispersion of the vectors leaving the diseased one. Overlapping of crops in time frequently occurs in market gardening, and isolation is difficult under these conditions, but with some viruses even isolation over short distances can be most effective. Successive lettuce crops are usually planted in England in small areas wherever an area of market garden is vacant, and often adjacent to old crops. Lettuce mosaic spreads from the old to the new crops successively throughout the year, reaching epidemic proportions when aphids are numerous. One grower was persuaded to concentrate all his early crops in one area, and the next series in another about half a mile away, not returning to the first area until all the plants had been used or destroyed. Disease incidence in these crops averaged about 3%, whereas the general level of disease in the area was about 60% (Broadbent *et al.*, 1951).

A minimum distance cannot be stipulated as adequate isolation for healthy crops because so much depends on chance. Although aphids are sometimes blown hundreds of miles, they would cease to be infective with stylet-borne viruses during prolonged flight, or during occasional probes on non-susceptible plants. When susceptible crops are separated from each other by immune plants, virus spread is greatly retarded, especially if the intervening plants are suitable hosts for the vectors.

The production of seed of biennial crops usually entails the overlapping of crops and consequently a high incidence of disease. Pound (1946) successfully raised cabbage seed plants at distances of 7 or 20 miles from the seed fields, obtaining 0.2 to 1% of infected seed plants after transplantation into the seed fields compared with 47% and 73% of those raised 1100 or 110 yards, respectively, from old seed crops. He (1947) was not quite as successful with raising beet stecklings free from mosaic virus, possibly because this virus might occur in wild plants, although he found none infected; nevertheless, control was good when steckling beds were more than 5 miles from diseased fields but poor when less than 1 mile. Much of the work of isolation has been done on sugar beet; Hansen (1950) and Hull (1952) found most early attacks of yellows virus in the root crop near seed fields (and occasionally near root clamps), and vice versa; the percentage infection fell with increasing distance from these sources. Since 1940 all the seed for the British crop has been grown in Britain, and at first much of it was produced in the root-growing areas. Watson et al. (1951) found that the distance from a seed crop within a seed area had a pronounced effect on the incidence of mosaic, which was usually confined to fields within 100 yards. Yellows virus persist much longer in the aphid vectors and spread much further. In England stecklings are now raised in areas isolated from beet and mangold crops, but even so, some become infected by aphids carrying virus from weeds, volunteers, and mangold clamps, and efforts are made to persuade farmers to clear these before sowing. Stecklings grown in isolation or under cover crops are taken into the seed-growing areas, which often coincide with the root-growing areas, but the incidence of disease is kept down by the steckling certification scheme, whereby only beds with fewer than 1% yellows-infected plants are used (Hull, 1952). Szirmai (1957) in Hungary found a distance of 1.5 km between seed and root crops prevented most virus spread.

The value of isolation for the control of stylet-borne viruses was demonstrated by Simons (1957). Pepper veinbanding mosaic virus, carried mainly by A. gossypii, infected 90% of pepper plants 6 ft from rows of infected nightshade (Solanum gracile) but only 10% at 50-ft distance. Extrapolation of this distance suggested that infective flights might extend to 400 ft, but removal of nightshade from an area up to 700 ft from the pepper plants showed that virus was carried further, probably to about 1000 ft. The virus spread much further during the spring than during the autumn, probably because the warmer weather encouraged flight and the aphids were more numerous during the spring. Simons et al. (1959) concluded that most aphid flights are shorter than 100 ft but as the insects can often remain infective for an hour, longer flights followed by infective probes are occasionally possible. Wellman (1937) found that southern celery mosaic virus was transmitted by aphids from weeds to 85–95% of celery plants in plots 3–30 ft away, but only to 12% at 75 ft and 4% at 120 ft. Distances differed from year to year but no plant was infected during three years in plots 240 ft away from the source. Another successful instance of isolation was reported by Martin and Kantack (1960) who found that the aphid-transmitted internal cork of sweet potato, which was a serious problem in Louisiana, could be controlled by isolating plantings at least 100 yards from infected crops. Incidence in isolated crops averaged 1% at harvest and 3–9% after storage, compared with 11–23% and 18–58%, respectively, for non-isolated ones. Thus the amount of isolation to be recommended for virus control will depend on the type of virus, the vectors, and the prevalence and distribution of host plants; it is often a very effective control measure, especially for stylet-borne viruses, and is usually insisted upon in certification schemes for virus-free clonal material, for instances, strawberries (Fulton and Seymour, 1957) and potatoes (Münster and Mayor, 1953). Unfortunately, like all the other methods of control, it may occasionally break down.

Raisers of new varieties of perennial plants, such as flower bulbs, are often insufficiently aware of the need for isolating the new seedlings from their old stocks and from clones that must be propagated vegetatively. Thus a high proportion of narcissi, lilies, etc., are infected by the time they reach the market (Haasis, 1939; Smith and Brierley, 1948; Broadbent *et al.,* 1962a).

D. FIELD SIZE

A gradient of infection from a high incidence in outer rows to a low one within a crop is diagnostic of spread from a nearby source outside the crop. Storey and Godwin (1953) found that most plants infected with cauliflower mosaic virus occurred in the first 50 rows adjacent to diseased crops, and in potato crops gradients of leaf roll or rugose mosaic usually ceased between the 10th and 20th rows from the edge (Doncaster and Gregory, 1948). Incoming aphids and other insects usually congregate around the edges of fields and so more plants become infected there; observations of aphid colonies (Taylor and Johnson, 1954) and the incidence of circulatory viruses like potato leaf roll, show that the insects sometimes stay in the area where they first land, but the degree of further movement depends on the age of the insects and their species, those like *M. persicae* distributing themselves through the crop more than species like *A. fabae* and thus spreading more virus. The greater activity of insects near the borders of fields may lead to more virus disease there, even if the source is within the crop (Zink *et al.,* 1956), but the evidence from brassica and lettuce fields in Britain suggests that when spread is from sources within, the incidence of disease is greater within the crop than near the edges (Broadbent *et al.,* 1951; Broadbent, 1957a). Van der Plank (1948b, 1949) pointed out that the heavily infected outer zone formed a greater proportion of a small than of a large field, the amount of infection entering per acre from nearby sources being approximately inversely proportional to the square root of the field area. He stated: "If disease entering fields can easily be controlled by isolation, it can also be controlled by making the fields larger and proportionally fewer," unless the rate of subsequent spread of virus within the field is rapid; and he quoted how maize streak virus often destroyed the whole crop in small fields in the Transvaal, whereas many plants in large ones escaped infection. This view has been challenged recently by Waggoner (1962), who showed that van der Plank's single-dimensional analysis was not as realistic as a two-dimensional one, according to which the chance of a pathogen being introduced into a field increased with increasing size of field.

E. PLANT SPACING

Storey (1935) was one of the first to show that close planting would reduce disease incidence, in his case rosette of groundnuts, if virus were being brought into a crop by insects, because the more plants there are per unit area, the smaller will be the proportion infected by the same number of insects. A'Brook (*in litt.*) has recently confirmed this in Nigeria. The virus was introduced by alate *Aphis craccivora* Koch., and there was little subsequent spread. Spacing had little effect on yield with plants sown early, which usually escaped infection, but had a pronounced effect with late planting because of the incidence of disease. The actual number of aphid-infested and rosetted plants decreased as the plant population was increased from 10,000 to 160,000 per acre, probably because the increased ground cover with higher plant populations deterred aphids from landing. Thus ten times as many aphids landed in traps in the 10,000 plants/acre plots as in the 160,000 ones, in which no *A. craccivora* were caught. This effect of spacing applies particularly if there is little subsequent spread of virus within the crop, as when spotted wilt virus is carried by thrips into tobacco crops; van der Plank and Anderssen (1944) calculated that if the incidence of disease were 50% with single plant spacing, it would be decreased to 9% by transplanting two plants per hill, and to 1% by three, without altering the spacing between hills and when the surplus and infected plants were removed later, and they found this to be a satisfactory method of control in practice. A similar practice was adopted in Utah where curly-top virus often more than halved the number of tomatoes planted per acre. Shapovalov *et al.* (1941) planted two plants per hill and planted the hills closer together. When four times the number were planted per acre, disease decreased by up to 30%. Linford's (1943) data with thrips-transmitted spotted wilt virus in pineapple confirms those quoted, 718 and 755 plants per acre being infected at 12 and 18 in. spacing, giving percentages of 3.3 and 5.2, respectively.

Blencowe and Tinsley (1951) and Broadbent (1957a) experimented with different row widths and distances between plants in the row in sugar-beet crops and brassica seedbeds, respectively, finding much less disease in the more densely grown crops. High seeding rates also reduced the incidence of oat blue dwarf and aster yellows in flax (Frederiksen, 1962) and barley yellow dwarf (Slykhuis *et al.*, 1960).

Van der Plank (1948a) also stated that more aphids were likely to be found on large than on small plants, and gave examples from counts on potatoes. Larger plants might be older than smaller ones, and the effect of age on susceptibility to infection will be discussed later, but experiments with cauliflower seedbeds support van der Plank's thesis that large plants will be infected more readily than small ones, and therefore those in seedbeds should not be transplanted (Broadbent, 1957a).

F. Elimination of External Sources of Virus or Vector

Attempts have been made in many parts of the world to limit the spread of viruses by eliminating alternative hosts either of the virus or the vector. Tomato spotted wilt virus was introduced into the Rhodesian tobacco-growing areas in dahlia tubers, commonly grown in town gardens. Quarantine restrictions were placed on nurseries and, as the result of appeals, most growers destroyed all their dahlias. Despite this, the virus became established in several other hosts and continued to infect tobacco crops (Hopkins, 1943). In the Sudan three species of *Hibiscus* are susceptible to cotton leaf curl virus, but only the favoured food plant *H. esculentus* is widely grown. Quarantine laws forbid the importation of all Malvaceous planting material and the culture of *Hibiscus* is forbidden in the Gezira cotton area during two months before and one month after cotton is sown (Tarr, 1951).

Posnette *et al.* (1950) found seven species of trees indigenous to West Africa that were often symptomless carriers, and probably the original hosts, of cacao swollen shoot viruses, and recommended that *Ceiba pentandra* and *Cola chlamydantha* near cacao plantations should be destroyed. In some parts of Europe the culture of peaches is forbidden because the trees are the principal overwintering host of *M. persicae*, the main vector of potato, sugar-beet, and many other viruses (Kabiersch, 1962).

Most work on weed hosts has been done in the USA, where some of the economically important diseases are carried from them to cultivated crops by leafhoppers. One of the most studied diseases is beet curly top, which affects beet, tomato, cucumber, beans, and spinach in western USA. The virus is transmitted by *Circulifer tenellus*, often during transient feeding, when the leafhoppers move from overwintering wild hosts in the desert or foothills, or weeds in the cultivated valleys. The insects breed on the susceptible Russian thistle on open range land and on several wild mustards, and the proportion of infective hoppers varied from 4 to 67% in the springs of different years (Wallace and Murphy, 1938). Most of the efforts at control have been insecticidal and will be referred to later, but Keener (1956) found the elimination of weeds and volunteer crop plants, such as sugar beet, among cantaloupes useful in limiting the spread of the virus. The best form of control would undoubtedly be that advocated by Piemeisel (1954), who pointed out that the weed hosts were largely concentrated on open range grazing land that had been overstocked and otherwise mismanaged. The rehabilitation of these areas to productive grass grazing would eliminate the weeds and so decrease both the sources of virus and leafhopper populations.

Macrosteles fascifrons (Stål) moved into lettuce fields from weed borders where aster yellows virus overwintered, chiefly in *Plantago major* L., or were driven into the weeds during harvesting and later moved back into new crops. Eradication of weeds within 100 ft of prospective beds led to considerable decreases in incidence in the ensuing crops compared with nearby un-treated beds, e.g., from 11 to 2%, 44 to 4%. Wellman (1937) also obtained satisfactory control of southern celery mosaic by eradicating all weeds, especially *Commelina nudiflora*, for 75 ft around seed beds and from around fields before transplanting and about five times during the growing season. Anderson (1959) found 21 species of plants growing near pepper fields in Florida infected with viruses to which *Capsicum* is susceptible, and Simons *et al.* (1959) found their elimination, by spraying with herbicides before planting the peppers, more effective than spraying them with aphicides at intervals during the crop's growth. They stressed the need for co-operation between neighbours in this work so that whole areas could be cleared. Mangold clamps are an important source of sugar-beet viruses in some countries, and if they are not close-trimmed before being clamped, the mangold shoots may remain infested with the aphid vectors throughout the winter; the aphids then carry virus to beet crops in the spring (Broadbent *et al.*, 1949). Spraying the plants with maleic hydrazide before harvest inhibited sprouting in the clamps (Cornford, 1955).

Eradication of alternative hosts is a most useful control measure, but it is to be hoped that a wider appreciation of virus disease problems will prevent a repetition of some of the serious mistakes in planting such hosts that have been made in the past. A considerable increase in the numbers of *M. persicae* occurred after the last war in the Netherlands after millions of *Prunus serotina* Ehrh. were planted in the north as forest shade trees; they proved to be excellent winter hosts for the aphid in an area where peach is scarce (Hille Ris Lambers, 1955).

G. Breaking in Crop Cycles

Many viruses are not commonly found in wild plants and are spread from one cultivated crop to the next successively. The simplest way of controlling this type of spread is to break the cycle and have a gap between crops, but this will be successful only if the farm is rather isolated or if growers in an area agree to co-ordinate breaks. This practice was applied by Hopkins (1932) for tobacco leaf curl; the whitefly vectors bred on infected suckers from the previous year's tobacco crop, but a 3-week fallow after the destruction of all crop remains effectively controlled the disease. A celery-free period of 3–5 months during the summer, adopted by agreement with the growers, successfully controlled western celery mosaic (Severin and Freitag, 1938); all the fields in the restricted area were fallowed and no celery was imported. The summer crop had been unprofitable, anyway, because when the weeds withered enormous numbers of aphids flew into celery fields and spread virus. Flock and Deal (1959) found that a beet-free period in July or August decreased the numbers of beet leafhoppers, although small populations were maintained on several weeds, especially in irrigated areas of California, and so they advocated summer weed control as well.

Wheat streak mosaic virus is spread by the eriophyid mites *Aceria tulipae* Keifer, all stages of which can survive the winter on wheat and can live long enough on leaves, buried or on the surface, to attack wheat of the next crop if sown within 6 days of ploughing. The disease could be almost eliminated by delaying sowing winter wheat until nearby spring wheat had been harvested and by destroying early volunteer wheat which, germinating before or immediately after harvest, favours a big increase in mites and virus (Slykhuis, 1955; Staples and Allington, 1956). Regrowth of cut cotton plants when the field was irrigated for the next crop was important for the seasonal carry-over of cotton leaf curl virus, and Tarr (1951) recommended the grubbing of old cotton plants by hand, as ploughing or grazing did not eliminate them. Fields should be left fallow, or at least not irrigated, for at least one season after a cotton crop.

Breaks in the cycles of the biennial seed and annual food crops of plants such as sugar beet and brassicas have been discussed under Isolation (Section 16–3.C). It is important not to let old crops linger on when the bulk of the plants have been harvested. This is often done with market garden crops such as lettuce and brassicas, and with tuberous or perennial crop plants infected "volunteers" may remain in soil, forming sources of viruses and vectors.

H. Avoidance of Vectors

Potato seed production is traditionally based on avoidance of vectors, for until recently it was not possible to limit spread with insecticides. Isolation, practised in Scotland, Ireland, Switzerland, and other countries, has already been mentioned, but in the better seed areas of Scotland, for instance, the low incidence of leaf roll and rugose mosaic is due to the lateness of the aphid infestation rather than to complete freedom (Fisken, 1959). Consequently it is possible to rogue infected plants before any or many aphids visit the crop, and the fairly healthy crops in most other parts of Scotland ensure that few of the incoming aphids are infective, even if they have come from earlier planted potatoes. In England most spread of virus is early, by the colonizing aphids, and crops seldom become greatly infected by those dispersing in summer (Doncaster and Gregory, 1948; Broadbent et al., 1960) because stocks are renewed frequently and most crops contain few diseased plants. Trap catches of aphids and counts of them on potato plants have been used in Britain to determine areas suitable for seed production; the best way of estimating whether degeneration is likely to occur or not was developed by Hollings (1955b; 1960), based on the earliness and spread of aphid infestation.

In other parts of Europe, however, diseased crops are plentiful and seed production is based partly on early haulm destruction to avoid the dispersing aphids, as in Maine (Schultz et al., 1944). In most countries chemical or mechanical destruction of the haulms must be completed within 3–5 days of a warning issued by the certifying authority and there must be no regrowth (because young shoots are very susceptible to infection)—the particular time differs with variety and aphid activity (Münster, 1958; Kabiersch, 1962). Effective haulm killing lowered leaf roll incidence from 19 to 5% (Keller and Baltensperger, 1961). The most elaborate system of aphid avoidance is that developed in the Netherlands. Hille Ris Lambers (1955) pointed out that Friesian seed potato growers realised the advantages of lifting early to minimize leaf roll as long ago as 1810, and today the best four grades are not certified unless lifted by a fixed date, determined according to variety, grade, and region. The aphid forecast which determines the date is based on overwintering data, the time of spring flight from *Prunus* spp. and on trap catches. Catches from 2 traps per field from many localities (220 traps in all in 1955) are examined daily and a report on the presence of *M. persicae* sent to the Regional Inspection Services, enabling them to prescribe lifting dates when aphids have invaded an area but before virus can pass to the tubers, which takes longer the later infection occurs (Beemster, 1961). This allows the maximum growth possible and is better than lifting on a fixed date as was done in Maine, USA, where lifting each year on 14 August enabled several susceptible varieties to be grown near diseased ones since 1932 (Anon., 1955).

In some of the more arid parts of eastern Europe aphids are few during the hot summer weather and healthier crops have been grown by planting potatoes late. Reports of this led to a considerable amount of experimentation in other parts of Europe, but with little success, for the young plants were often infected by the aphids which are usually most numerous in the summer further west, or if planted so late as to avoid these, gave extremely poor yields (Wartenberg, 1954; Wenzl, 1955; Münster, 1956; Broadbent et al., 1957; Birecki et al., 1961). The optimum temperature for aphid reproduction is about 26°C, and van der Plank (1944) found that when the mean daily maximum temperature reached 32°C, *M. persicae* ceased to infest potatoes in Africa and virus spread became negligible, but it does not seem to have been reported if this has been exploited for seed production. Advantage has been taken of the adverse effect of hot climates on aphid numbers to produce healthy lettuce seed in Australia and parts of California (Stubbs, 1954; Stubbs and O'Loughlin, 1962; Grogan et al., 1952).

Rain has a considerable effect on insect populations, which may be greater during wet periods in arid climates because wild plants survive longer (Winkler, 1949), but one of the few instances in which lack of rain prevents a disease from establishing itself is in Mauritius, where chlorotic streak of sugar cane, probably caused by a soil-borne virus, occurs only in areas with more than 50 in. of rain per year (Antoine, 1959). Uninfected canes from the dry areas could be used to replant the wet ones instead of heat-treated canes.

Some insects have fairly well-defined dispersal periods, including *Cavariella aego-podii* (Scop.), the vector of carrot motley dwarf virus, which almost caused the abandonment of early carrot production in parts of Australia. Stubbs (1948) found that delaying sowing until the spring aphid dispersal was over resulted in healthy crops. Similar success was reported by Harpaz (1961) in controlling maize rough dwarf virus, which is spread by *Calligypona marginata*, a hopper which breeds on grasses. Withering of the grasses at the end of the rainy season induces the insects to move to the irrigated maize fields where they infect the young seedlings, although it is not known where they acquire the virus. As they do not breed on maize they do not spread virus within the crop and they remain scarce during the hot weather from late May until September. Delaying maize sowing until late May controlled the disease, incidence being less than 3% in contrast to 45% in early sown crops.

I. Infection with Mild Strains of Virus

The protection of plants by a mild strain of a virus against more virulent related strains is described in Section 16–2, F. The same arguments apply to cross-protection of insect-borne viruses as to contact-transmitted ones and were discussed by Posnette and Todd (1955), who protected cacao against the most prevalent virus in Ghana, usually virulent, by previous infection with mild strains. During three years only 35 of 416 trees infected with the mild strain developed severe symptoms in contrast to 273 of 387 previously uninfected trees, and the

yield from the "protected" trees was much higher than from those infected with the virulent strain. Despite this, the dangers of deliberate infection with a mild strain were such that more research on its consequences was recommended.

Mild strain protection of *Passiflora edulis* Sims. against the aphid-transmitted woodiness virus has been used successfully in Queensland. The selected strain remained mild during successive transfers over a period of five years. Only 4% woodiness occurred in plants infected with the mild strain in contrast to 68% in those infected with the severe (Simmonds, 1959).

J. Killing Vectors Before They Enter the Crop

Insecticides can be used to kill the insect vectors either on the old crop plants or on wild plants before they leave to infest the crop that needs protection, or now that persistent insecticides are available, this crop can be treated to kill infective vectors as they arrive. Killing them before they acquire virus from plants within the crop will be dealt with later, although in many instances it is difficult to separate these two aspects of virus spread. Work on the control of plant virus spread by insecticides was reviewed in 1956 (Broadbent, 1957b) and the only change of any significance since has been the development of systemic soil-applied insecticides.

The best-known attempt to control vectors away from the crops it was desired to protect is that against *C. tenellus*, the vector of beet curly-top virus in southwestern USA. From 1931 onwards the sugar-beet companies in California financed a large-scale control programme, spraying pyrethrum in diesel oil in the foothill desert areas where the insects congregate in the autumn and winter, and on Russian thistle, one of their chief summer and autumn hosts. Cook (1943) attempted to evaluate the control programme but found it difficult as he could not assess the potential damage in the absence of spraying. Later attempts by the State Department of Agriculture were made by spraying DDT in diesel oil from aeroplane or ground machines during the first three weeks of October (Armitage,

1952); 141,000 acres were sprayed in 1950; 150,000 in 1951. Curly-top incidence in early tomatoes was near 100% in 1950 but was reduced to below 10% in the same area in 1951 after the first season of large-scale spraying. Douglass *et al.* (1955) also attacked the leafhoppers in their breeding grounds in Idaho, spraying soon after the nymphs had hatched because these are more susceptible than adults to DDT. After spraying 15,000 and 11,350 acres of the worst infested breeding areas in 1950 and 1953, they estimated that curly top in snap beans was reduced in 1953 from an expected 11% to 2%.

Hoffman (1952) sprayed lettuce with parathion in June and July and the edges of the field, where infective leafhoppers came from, with parathion, DDT, or both, from May to August. More than half the lettuces in a nearby field with no border control were infected with aster yellows virus in contrast to 7% (sprayed) and 11% (unsprayed) in the field with border control. Spraying the borders was more effective than spraying the crop. Parathion, TEPP, and BHC were used successfully to control strawberry yellows, which was the limiting factor in strawberry production in the Pacific northwest of the USA. Migrant *P. fragaefolii* were produced mainly on mature plantings during the fruiting season, and dusting at the start of blossoming prevented them from developing. New plantings were dusted every two weeks from setting out until after harvest, and this together with roguing kept them healthy, whereas similar fields in other areas showed 75% infected plants. The treatment of new plantings alone was insufficient, because the insecticide did not prevent incoming alatae from introducing virus.

K. Killing Vectors After Arrival

Insecticidal treatment of crops to prevent incoming infective vectors from infecting the plants has usually failed to decrease disease incidence to a worthwhile extent because all insecticides take a fairly long time to inactivate insects unless the chemicals are sprayed directly on to them (Huckett, 1945; Stubbs, 1948; Michelbacher *et al.*, 1950; Swenson *et al.*, 1954). Aphids

carrying stylet-borne viruses can infect a plant within a few seconds or minutes, and insects carrying circulatory viruses can often infect at least one plant before being affected; however, the insecticide may prevent them from moving on and may thus decrease the number of plants infected by each insect. McClean (1957) found that *M. persicae* infective with sugar-beet yellows virus, when transferred successively at 20-min intervals to plants treated with phorate, demeton, methyl parathion, parathion, or malathion were not killed in less than 80 to 100 min and some still transmitted virus in the fifth period.

Several workers have reported that spraying sugar-beet crops with systemic insecticides, or using the newer granular insecticides, at the beginning of aphid colonization delayed the onset of yellows and thus increased yield, presumably because the incoming aphids were prevented from moving so much from plant to plant (Hull, 1958; Steudel and Thielemann, 1962). In England, a second spray with demeton-methyl brought little extra benefit except when plants were recolonized later and there was late spread. Now much of the beet crop is sprayed either before or soon after the issue of regional warnings that the aphid attack has begun, delaying but not preventing infection, but increasing yield considerably (Hull, 1958). Thus in 1958 the incidence of yellows averaged 2.5 times more in unsprayed than in sprayed crops in the same area, and a single spray increased yields by 7–8% (Hull, 1959). In Switzerland spraying beet with morpho-thion, at the first appearance of *M. persicae*, and again 6–12 days later, reduced yellows incidence from 67 to 7%, and from 40 to 6% in two years (Münster and Joseph, 1959).

That insecticides may sometimes limit the introduction of virus is suggested also by the work of Strong and Rawlins (1959), who caged *M. fascifrons*, infective with lettuce yellows virus, over lettuce plots within 1 hr, 2 hr, 3, 6, or 10 days of spraying the plants with DDT, demeton, malathion, or parathion, and then removed the cages and disinfested the plants after 3 days, assessing yellows after one month. The plots recently sprayed had much less disease (32–45%) than the unsprayed ones (89%), but not those sprayed 3 days or more before being infested.

16–4. ERADICATION OF VIRUS

A. ERADICATION FROM SOIL

Very few viruses can persist free or in debris in soil like TMV, and many of the other so-called "soil-borne" viruses may eventually prove to be transmitted by nematodes or other soil organisms. Doolittle (1928) found that TMV remained active in glasshouse soils for at least 70 days, and Johnson (1937) found that free virus leached into soil could remain active for 1–2 years if not dried or frozen. We have recently found old tomato root debris to be still infective 2 years after the soil was covered with polythene so that crops could be grown in peat and sand above it. TMV in soil is an important, if not the most important, source of virus for ensuing tomato crops under glass, and Johnson found 15 times more infections in tobacco grown in infected than in uninfected soil. Crop rotation is probably the only satisfactory way of freeing soil from TMV because the root debris and virus are eventually destroyed by fungi and bacteria in cultivated soil; thus tomatoes planted under glass within 5 weeks of clearing diseased plants became infected, whereas those planted after other crops had been grown for 6 months between tomato crops remained healthy (Jones and Burnett, 1935). Growing in peat and sand above polythene, as mentioned above, also enabled healthy crops to be grown in houses with a long history of TMV and other root-borne diseases (Wheeler, 1962).

TMV in soil and plant debris can be destroyed by steaming, but this as practised by many glasshouse growers is inadequate, for the virus can survive in dried debris much longer than the 10 min needed to inactivate it in tobacco sap at 93°C (Bartels, 1955). Moist soil needs to be held at nearly 100°C for 10–20 min to be sure of inactivating TMV, and then the treatment is only effective in the top 1–2 ft. Tomatoes become infected later when their roots penetrate below this level.

Most of the chemical soil sterilants have little or no effect on TMV. Limasset (1957) found 3% and 6% formalin ineffective, and we have recently tested this—chloropicrin, metham-sodium, methyl isothiocyanate, and methyl bromide—by treating glasshouse soils, soils in small closed containers, or mixing the chemical with infective tomato sap when possible; only formalin at five times the usual concentration effectively decreased TMV concentration, and this would be uneconomic and, again, only affect the top few inches of soil. Metham-sodium and chloropicrin prevented the breakdown of TMV by soil organisms and more plants became infected earlier after their use than in untreated soil. This confirms McKeen's (1962) observation that metham-sodium or methyl isothiocyanate plus chlorinated hydrocarbons did not affect TMV in leaves buried in treated soil; 98% methyl bromide plus 2% chloropicrin only halved TMV infectivity; but several other viruses, including tobacco necrosis and tomato ringspot, were inactivated.

B. ERADICATION FROM SEEDS

Most of the attempts to free seeds from virus have been made with TMV in tomato as it is known that virus does not enter the embryo, but many of the results are conflicting because some workers considered virus to be an external contaminant, others that it was also present inside the seed, as was demonstrated by Taylor et al. (1961). To try to clear up this confusion, we recently tested all the recommended methods of freeing tomato seeds from virus, either during or after extraction, and found that success depended on whether or not virus was inside or only on the outside of the testa. Extracting seeds by fermentation or by adding an equal volume of 10% sodium carbonate solution to the pulp for 18 hr had little effect on virus concentration but hydrochloric acid extraction eliminated virus from the outsides of seeds (see Chamberlain, 1947); the best method was to treat pulp with one quarter its volume of concentrated hydrochloric acid for 30 min. Soaking extracted seeds in a 10% solution of Teepol for 2 hr effectively eliminated TMV from the outsides of seeds (see Crowley, 1957), and soaking in a 10% solution of tri-sodium orthophosphate inhibited infection if the solution were not washed off, but prolonged rinsing restored infectivity (see John and Sova, 1955). The only treatment that affected virus within the seeds was dry heat. Howles (1957) found that even 22 days at 72°C did not eliminate all virus, but further work has shown that it is eliminated from most seeds during 1–3 days at 70°C, and that this does not affect germination, while Vovk (1961) found that TMV was eliminated after 2 days at 50–52°C followed by 1 day at 78–80°C.

C. ERADICATION FROM VEGETATIVELY PROPAGATED MATERIAL BY HEAT

Heat treatment for freeing plants from virus has been reviewed and discussed several times during recent years (Kassanis, 1957; Kassanis and Posnette, 1961; Hollings, 1962; Baker, 1962). Heat is used to free clonal material from viruses and is applied either by soaking the plants in hot water or keeping them in hot air. Kunkel (1936) used both methods in his pioneering work with peach, curing dormant trees by soaking them for 10 min in hot water (50°C) and trees in growth by keeping them at 34–36°C for 2–4 weeks. Later (1937) he also freed infective leafhoppers from aster yellows virus by keeping them at 32°C for 12 days or longer.

Posnette (1953) and others have shown that plants survive much longer in hot air than in hot water, so the water treatment is of less general application. It is widely used to cure sugar-cane setts from ratoon stunting virus in most sugar-cane growing countries. The setts are immersed for 2 hr at 49–50°C, which has to be carefully maintained because higher temperatures do considerable damage (Hughes and Steindl, 1955; Chu and Lin, 1956). In Louisiana hot air treatment (at least 5 hr at 58°C) is used instead because the cane is more immature than in tropical countries at the time of treatment and is severely injured by hot water (Steib, 1958). De Fluiter and van der Meer (1955) eliminated rubus stunt virus from raspberry by immersing rootstocks for 1.5–2 hr in water at 45°C, but apart from this, hot air treatment is used

commerically on strawberries, raspberries, fruit trees, and some ornamental plants.

Strawberry is cured from mottle, the most prevalent virus, in 1–2 weeks at 37°C, but only a small proportion of plants from crinkle or yellow edge in 4–7 weeks (Posnette and Cropley, 1958). Until recently no virus-free plants of any raspberry variety were known, but Chambers (1961) was able to free some by heating dormant plants at 32° or 35°C for 5–35 days. Most plants were freed from leaf mottle, but not from veinbanding, vein chlorosis and yellows viruses, and the varieties differed in their response to the treatment. Apple plants were cured from apple mosaic in 4 weeks at 37°C (Posnette and Cropley, 1956), and cherry and peach plants from stone fruit ringspot virus in 2 weeks and 3 weeks, respectively (Nyland, 1960). Nyland (1959) also used short periods (5–15 min) in hot water at 50° or 52°C to cure sweet cherry budsticks from necrotic rusty mottle virus in 50–70% of those immersed.

Hollings and Kassanis (1957) freed chrysanthemum plants from aspermy, one strain of stunt and ring pattern viruses, but not from vein mottle and several others. Among other ornamental plants freed by heat are carnation from ringspot virus (Hollings, 1962) and rose from mosaic virus (Holmes, 1960). Kassanis (1950) freed potato tubers from leaf roll virus in 25 days at 37°C, and later Thirumalachar (1954) pointed out that tubers stored in thatched huts in Bihar for 6 months at average maximum temperatures between 29° and 36°C were freed from leaf roll, whereas others kept in cold stores were all infected.

The workers who have used these methods with growing plants stress the necessity for using well-established potted plants with ample carbohydrate reserves, cutting the tops back slightly a week or two before treatment starts to increase the root to shoot ratio, raising the temperature gradually during a preliminary week from c.24° to 37°C or whatever temperature is to be maintained, and maintaining adequate light and water at the same temperature as the plants. Baker (1962) points out that very little work has been done on preconditioning plants before treatment. Instead of the usual "hot-box" Brierley and Lorentz (1960) used a less accurately controlled glasshouse chamber open to natural daylight, and some chrysanthemum plants withstood an average of 35°C for a year, whereas Hollings and Kassanis (1957) stated that chrysanthemum could be treated only in summer.

Not all viruses are eliminated by heat treatment, and Kassanis and Posnette (1961) postulated that degradation and synthesis of virus take place continuously; that multiplication of some viruses is completely inhibited at 36°C while inactivation still continues, so that ultimately the plant is freed. Other viruses, however, continue to multiply, most more slowly but a few even faster than at lower temperatures. They suggest that inactivation is not a direct effect of temperature on virus, but that some system in the plant takes part in the inactivation. Whatever the mechanism, heat treatment does not eliminate most viruses from the entire plant but is a useful method when used in conjunction with tip or bud culture. Only a proportion of plants is usually freed with either method, and neither heat treatment nor tip culture should be used without subsequent testing by one means or another, except when dealing with very distinctive diseases that show in the treated material. Commercial firms in several countries now heat treat chrysanthemums and carnations, but few adequately test afterwards before selling "virus-free" cuttings.

D. Eradication by Tip Culture

Many viruses are not completely systemic in plants, often failing to invade the tips of new shoots, and sometimes healthy plants can be raised by cutting off these tips and rooting them (Holmes, 1955; Baxter and McGlohon, 1959). Sometimes the virus invades the tip except the actual meristem, and some viruses even invade this. To take meristems only is difficult (Morel and Martin, 1955), and they often fail to root, so most workers include the first leaf primordia and enhance their chances of obtaining virus-free material by subjecting the plants to heat treatment first (Stone, 1963). Brierley (1957) has freed several clonal varie-

ties in this way, including *Hydrangea macrophylla* (Thunb.) DC after 12–19 weeks at 35°C and chrysanthemums after 2–8 months (Brierley and Lorentz, 1960). Quak (1957, 1961) obtained some carnation plants free from virus by tip culture after 6–8 weeks at 40°C, and tried other methods than heat to inhibit virus multiplication in the growing tip, either spraying substances such as thiouracil or 2,4-D on to the plants or adding them to the nutrient medium in which the plants were growing; some potato plants free from viruses X and S were obtained. Potato virus Y was eliminated from 13 of 27 surviving plants when sprouted tubers were kept in darkness at 30, 35, or 38°C for up to 23 days and tips of new shoots were taken, but these treatments did not eliminate virus X (Thomson, 1957).

A modification of tip culture, the raising of plants from axillary buds from heated plants, was used by Posnette and Jha (1960) to free strawberry plants from crinkle and vein chlorosis viruses, and apple rubbery wood virus was eliminated in 22 of 27 buds from shoots heated for three weeks at 37°C (Posnette *et al.*, 1962). Similar techniques using shoot tips or budwood have freed several kinds of fruit trees from viruses, for example, plums from bark split, line pattern, and peach green mottle (Ellenberger, 1960), apples from mosaic (Hunter *et al.*, 1959) and three latent viruses (Campbell, 1962), and citrus from tristeza and psorosis viruses (Grant, 1958).

E. Eradication by Roguing

Roguing is a useful term signifying the removal of infected plants either before or after they are planted out to crop. Roguing of plants such as lettuce or brassicas in seedbeds has long been practised by commercial growers when they reject stunted or "poor" seedlings during planting out from seedbeds. Roguing of infected plants from the field is the traditional way of maintaining healthy potato stocks in good seed-growing areas, as in parts of Scotland and Ireland, and is based solely on visual symptoms. To establish virus-free stocks in some countries roguing follows "indexing," whereby a stock is grown under glass and the infected plants are rejected either because they show symptoms or their sap infects test plants or reacts serologically with antisera (van Slogteren, 1955; Orad and Roman, 1960). In Maine about 1400 tubers were indexed under glass each year, then the healthy ones were increased in isolation for distribution to seed growers (Anon., 1955). Larson (1959) advised growers to eliminate purple top wilt virus by chitting their tubers at 68–72°F for two weeks before planting and rejecting those with many weak sprouts. Early roguing is essential before virus has been spread from the infected to healthy plants within crops, and as most spread is to adjacent plants some workers recommend removing these as well, even though they are symptomless (Bagnall, 1953). In many potato growing areas, however, such as southern England, the aphids arrive before symptoms are obvious, much of the season's spread of virus is early and by the colonizing alatae, and roguing is then useless unless spread is limited by using insecticides (Broadbent, et al., 1950; Broadbent et al., 1961).

Roguing is also not worth while when viruses are very easily spread by handling or machinery, e.g., TMV in tobacco and tomato crops, unless it can be done early before such spread occurs (Wolf, 1933). With some contact-transmitted viruses, however, such as barley stripe mosaic, early roguing was effective, reducing incidence in two varieties from 85 to 12%, and 46 to 0% (Inouye, 1962). Zink et al. (1957) found that roguing lettuce mosaic infected plants once soon after thinning had no effect on disease incidence at harvest, presumably because much spread had already occurred, but roguing twice or thrice decreased disease, e.g., from 73 to 45 and 36%; and 17 to 9 and 6%, respectively, in two experiments. Roguing by spraying the plants with diesel oil and parathion was slightly more effective than hoeing. Rogued plants should always be removed from fields and be destroyed so that any vectors on them cannot move to healthy plants.

Roguing has proved a very successful method of limiting virus diseases in several perennial crops. Adam (1962) described the efforts in Honduras to eliminate banana mosaic, caused by strains of cucumber mosaic virus. Each farm is inspected three times a year and any infected plant is sprayed with nicotine, together with the 25 acres around it. Then the infected plants and the 80 nearest to them are dug out, chopped into small pieces and sprayed with malathion. The 25 acres are sprayed again 20 and 40 days later, the cleared area checked for regrowth and not replanted for at least 6 months. In addition, plantains, which are an alternative host of the virus, have been eradicated from within and near all banana farms. This programme has reduced the incidence of disease on a 14,000-acre plantation from about 21 infected plants per 1000 acres in 1956 to 0.1 in 1960 and prevented its introduction on to any newly-established farms. Bunchy top of bananas also has been controlled by roguing in Australia (Cann, 1952). By 1925 over 90% of the area in N.S. Wales producing bananas in 1922 had gone out of production because of this disease, so in 1927 the Department of Agriculture destroyed all plantations, then permitted replanting with virus-free suckers in 1928. The movement of plants in and between all banana areas is strictly regulated and frequent inspections are made, any infected plant being sprayed with kerosene to kill the aphid vectors, then dug up and destroyed.

In tree crops the best-known roguing programmes are those for peach diseases in the USA and cacao in West Africa. Large-scale elimination programmes were started in the early 1930's to control peach mosaic and phony peach diseases (Persons, 1952; List et al., 1956). Phony peach disease was found in 17 of the 26 States surveyed, but it was not widespread in most and was soon eliminated from six. Wild plum was shown to be an alternative host and was included in the roguing programme, which, coupled with isolation regulations, proved successful in preventing serious outbreaks. Trees affected with peach mosaic have been rogued in Colorado since 1934, 36% of the total removed to 1955 being taken out in the first two years, which shows how effective the programme was. In total, 1% of the trees were removed but the incidence of disease did not decrease after the first four years and List *et al.* (1956) stressed the need to find when the virus was spreading and if there were symptomless carriers, so that roguing could be done at the most opportune time.

Thresh (1958b, 1959) and Hammond (1958) have reviewed the progress of swollen shoot control in Nigeria and Ghana, where most new outbreaks were grouped around infected trees because of the movement of immature mealybugs through the foliage canopy. Spread is slow and so theoretically it can be controlled by eradication, but the job was tremendous because of the high incidence of disease when the programmes started; for instance 1.5 million trees were destroyed in Nigeria between 1946 and 1950. Naturally this was unpopular with the farmers and so eradication was abandoned in two areas but this led to further increases in disease. It is difficult to recognize recently infected and tolerant trees and those infected with mild strains of virus, and where roguing was continued between 1950 and 1955, not only the infected trees but all those within 30 yards were removed also. However, coppicing experiments showed that young growth soon showed symptoms and that the 30-yards clearance was too drastic; Thresh (1959) recommended the removal of trees within 5, 10, or 15 yards of outbreaks of fewer than 6, 6–50, or 50–200 trees, respectively, followed by regular inspection of the peripheral trees. At that time in Ghana all swollen shoot outbreaks were treated within 4–6 weeks of discovery, the infected trees only being removed, although attempts were being made to persuade farmers to eliminate one ring of trees in contact with the infected one to increase the chances of control. All outbreak areas were examined every two months until no further infected trees were found during a period of two years. During the 2.5 years 1955-57, over 28 million trees were removed, 68% after the first inspection. A total of 63 million had been cut down since 1946.

F. Eradication by Chemical Treatments

Virus inactivators, antibiotics with antiviral properties, and virus inhibitors that might prevent multiplication while allowing normal virus decay to continue have been dealt with earlier in the course, and I can find little in the literature to suggest that they have as yet any practical application. Kooistra (1959) reported that many substances had been screened and tested in the field for therapeutic activity without phytotoxicity, especially against TMV in tobacco, yellows in sugar beet, common yellow mosaic in bean, either by spraying the foliage or watering the roots two days before inoculation. Some extended the incubation period by about 13% and slightly increased yield, but none was of economic importance. Bobyr (1961) also reported a high preventative and some therapeutic effect against TMV when field tomato and tobacco plants were sprayed before inoculation and after the appearance of symptoms with imanin, arenarin, gramicidin, and milk whey.

Bhatt and Verna (1958) quoted one practical result from India, namely, mixed virus streak usually killed field-grown tomatoes within a month of infection, but plants sprayed with weak solutions of β-3-indolpropionic acid or α-naphthalene acetic acid recovered in two weeks.

16–5. ERADICATION OF VECTORS

A. Eradication of Vectors Within Crops by Insecticides

The chances of being able to control virus spread from sources within crops by killing the vectors before they can become infective with circulatory viruses are very good. It is sometimes possible to limit stylet-borne virus spread also but this will depend upon the speed with which the aphid vectors are incapacitated before they have made as many flights as they might otherwise have done.

A great deal of work has been done in England on the control of leaf roll and Y viruses in potatoes, spread of which is mainly within the crop. Any efficient aphicide proved effective, and after several years' experiments four sprays of DDT emulsion at 2 lb active ingredient per acre, applied fortnightly at either high or low volume, were recommended (Broadbent et al., 1956; 1958). It was essential to start spraying as soon as the potato foliage emerged above ground, for aphid attack and virus spread were usually early. Other experiments, not yet published, have shown that the first two sprays were the most important ones. In 1956 leaf roll increased by a factor of 7.4 and virus by 4.9 in plots each of which contained initially 0.8% of each disease; spraying with DDT four times at low volume (25 gal/acre) limited spread to 1.4 and 1.9 times, respectively. Insecticides often halved the spread of virus Y but were not so effective in years when aphids were numerous and very active. These methods were tried out commercially in several parts of England and sprayed potato stocks were kept for four years or longer in many areas where they had previously been replaced every one or two years (Broadbent et al., 1960). One stock which was rogued as well as sprayed was kept for eight years in an area where other experiments suggested that it would have become entirely infected in three years, and was finally discarded when disease incidence reached 10% (Broadbent et al., 1961; Broadbent et al., 1962b).

The necessity for frequent spraying, and the damage to the plants and soil compaction from the passage of machinery, led to experimentation with soil-applied granular insecticides such as dimethoate, phorate, and disulfoton when they became available, or with menazon sprayed on the tubers before planting. A single application at planting effectively kept aphids from colonizing the plants for three months and was as effective as DDT in limiting virus spread (Burt et al., 1960; Broadbent and Burt, 1962).

Since spraying or dusting of potatoes with DDT became general in Maine, most of the virus spread between crops has been curtailed and the position is similar to that in England (Simpson and Shands, 1949; Simpson et al., 1951). The considerable amount of work done by these workers and their collaborators during the last two decades has allowed Maine potato seed growers to reduce virus diseases to negligible proportions during recent years. These results have been more striking in Maine and Washington (Stitt and Breakey, 1952; King, 1952) than in England because growers in the USA appear more willing to cooperate with each other in insecticidal programmes applied over a large area, no doubt because insect populations are very much larger and insecticides are necessary to prevent feeding damage to the crop, apart from virus spread. Insecticides are now used in potato seed production in most countries, and recently there has been much experimentation with soil-applied insecticides, often incorporated with the fertilizers. Results are similar to those obtained previously, i.e., good control of leaf roll but often poor control of virus Y (Bonnemaison, 1962; Hoyman, 1958; Küthe, 1961; Simpson and Shands, 1961, 1963). There is one major fault with granular fertilizers when used on tuberous plants like potatoes; the shoots develop and emerge above ground before the roots absorb the chemical, and if the aphid attack is early much spread can occur before the insecticide takes effect. In these circumstances tuber applied systemic insecticides, such as menazon, are more effective but may not be as long lasting. Systemic insecticides in general are more effective than contact ones because the new foliage produced between applications is usually invaded by the chemical. Useful as present insecticides are, however, it is to be hoped that further research will provide others which will inactivate insects more quickly.

Other examples of insecticides effectively controlling the spread of viruses within crops were given by de Fluiter (1958), who stopped the spread of strawberry viruses with demeton-methyl, and Davis et al. (1961), who reported that three parathion sprays at weekly intervals decreased pea enation mosaic in peas from 54 to 9%; they also stressed that the first application should be soon after emergence. Demeton-O-methyl was successfully applied from aircraft to rice, 20, 50, and 78 days after germination, decreasing "hoja blanca" disease from 23 to 4% (Malaguti and Angeles, 1957).

CONTROL

B. Eradication by Predators and Parasites

Examples of effective biological control of virus vectors are few. Stubbs (1956) reported that carrot motley dwarf is widespread but not epidemic in California, where vectors are few on carrots, in contrast to Australia and Britain, where enormous numbers of the vector *C. aegopodii* occur. In California there is considerable parasitism of this aphid by a braconid wasp which does not occur in the other countries and it may be for this reason that the virus spreads less readily.

Another complex situation was unravelled by Evans (1954): the groundnut variety Mwitunde is field resistant to rosette virus, although as susceptible as other varieties in laboratory tests, mainly because the vector, *A. craccivora*, breeds more slowly on Mwitunde than on others and so predators and parasites were able to eliminate the aphids quickly.

The relationships between vectors and their enemies are complex and not easily elucidated. They help to determine the ultimate size of an insect population on a crop, and in several parts of Europe they tend to establish a biennial rhythm in aphid numbers on potato, a year with many aphids often being followed by one with few (Blattný, 1925; Hille Ris Lambers, 1955). Because of more complex overwintering conditions and weather in Britain such a rhythm does not occur, although predators and parasites do play a large part in controlling aphid populations (Doncaster and Gregory, 1948; Broadbent and Heathcote, 1961). Thus parasites and predators can be said to play a part in limiting virus spread by limiting insect populations, but they seldom or never stop it because, inevitably, they arrive after the insects, and with most viruses it is the early colonizing aphids that are the principal vectors. In West Africa, attempts to introduce fungal, hymenopterous, and other parasites of the mealybug vectors of swollen shoot viruses failed to control them, even though the vectors are relatively immobile (Thresh, 1958a).

C. Eradication of Vectors in Soil by Chemicals

Several tests have been done on the elimination of soil-borne viruses and their vectors, but often in containers, and these may bear little relation to sources in the field, for chemicals often penetrate only a few inches whereas roots and vectors may inhabit lower soil layers. Wheat and oat mosaic viruses were eradicated by formaldehyde, chloropicrin, carbon disulphide, D.-D., and ethyl alcohol (McKinney *et al.*, 1957); and several similar soil fumigants and steam eradicated peach yellow bud mosaic virus (Wagnon and Traylor, 1957), all from soil in containers. With the peach virus, infection occurred in untreated soil from a depth of 4–14 in. but not in the top 4 in. Miyamoto (1961) obtained effective field control of soil-borne mosaic of barley with pyroligneous acid applied to the soil several days before sowing or with a flamethrower giving heat penetration of 40–60°C to a depth of 15 cm for several minutes, which suggests that the virus was only in the upper layers. However, in discussing raspberry virus diseases, Cadman (1961) considered that control would be easier to achieve by eliminating sources of infection and the use of tolerant varieties rather than by attempting to kill nematodes in the field by chemicals.

16–6. PLANT IMMUNITY AND TOLERANCE

A. Use of Immune or Tolerant Varieties of Plants

Breeding for resistance to, or tolerance of, viruses in plants is, or has been, attempted for almost all the economically important diseases, sometimes with considerable success, but at other times with little result of practical importance. Work up to 1953 was reviewed by Holmes (1954), who commented that in most instances single genes conferred effective resistance, although in others two or more genes in association were required. Several kinds of resistance were described: (1) immunity, (2) resistance to infection, (3) hypersensitivity, i.e., prompt death of invaded tissues, (4) tolerance, i.e., failure to show disease even though infected, and (5) resistance to insect feeding. It is important that plant breeders should aim at achieving immunity, but if this proves impossible, then at hypersensitivity or resistance to infection. Tolerance should be accepted only as a last resort, because its use necessarily involves the growing of many infected plants; and there is the possibility, perhaps even the probability, that any genetic form of virus control will ultimately be overcome by a genetic change in the host plant. To minimize the chances of such changes, resistant varieties should be grown in isolation where possible, and every precaution be taken to prevent viruses coming into contact with them.

Some examples of effective resistance are quoted by Carter (1963), who stated that the development of sugar-beet varieties resistant to curly-top virus has saved the beet industry in many parts of western USA from extinction, and some bean varieties are also resistant to the same virus. In East Africa, varieties of cassava, a staple food plant of the peasants, have been bred resistant to mosaic and brown streak viruses, and sugarcane varieties immune or resistant to several viruses have been bred in different parts of the world. Tolerant varieties of cotton are grown in the areas of the Sudan where leaf curl is epidemic, although they do not provide such good quality cotton as some susceptible varieties (Tarr, 1951). Some varieties are resistant to infection by the whitefly vectors rather than to the virus: thus the variety Lambert is a field-resistant selection of the variety Domain Sakel, but is equally susceptible in graft transmission tests. This type of resistance was found also by Bagnall and Mackinnon (1960) with potato virus A in the variety Katahdin; however, aphids readily acquired virus from graft-infected Katahdin, so the mechanism of the resistance is not clear. Bagnall and Bradley (1958) pointed out the importance of doing field trials for resistance in plants normally grown outside, because some varieties of potatoes were hypersensitive to virus Y there but not under glass. Immunity to nematode-transmitted arabis mosaic virus fortunately exists in some varieties of raspberry, e.g., Malling Jewel, for there is little possibility of avoiding the disease by other means on land infested with the vector (Harrison and Winslow, 1961).

In breeding for resistance to sugar-beet yellows virus, Russell (1960) found no resistance in 100,000 seedlings, so further efforts were to be concentrated on trying to achieve tolerance. Similar lack of success was reported by Simpson et al. (1952) who were able to obtain some resistance to potato leaf roll among the 51,000 seedlings they tested, but this was lost again as crosses were made to produce commercially acceptable varieties. However, Mackinnon et al. (1960) reported that although no immunity to leaf roll had been found, despite breeding since 1937, there was hope of obtaining an acceptable variety resistant to infection.

B. Plant Age at the Time of Infection

In Section 16–1,C, examples were given of the increased resistance to infection with virus often shown as plants age. Instances where early planting decreased disease incidence because the plants were older and more resistant when insect vectors invaded the crop are given by Smartt (1961) for groundnut rosette, Wallace and Murphy (1938) for sugar-beet curly top, and Bennett (1960) for sugar-beet yellows. Cadman and Chambers (1960), experimenting with Majestic potatoes, found that susceptibility to infection with leaf roll virus decreased sharply within 6–8 weeks after emergence, from about 80% of plants infected during late June to about 6% in mid-August. Older sugar beets also were less susceptible to yellows virus, 38% of plants sown on 1 April becoming infected, in contrast to 53% of those sown on 15 April and 70% of those sown on 1 May (Hansen, 1950). Similar data were obtained by Steudel (1952), who found that the number of aphids per plant, as well as the incidence of yellows, increased with successively later sowings. With sugar-beet seed crops, also, plants (stecklings) sown at the end of August usually had one-quarter to two-thirds as many diseased plants as those sown at the end of July (Hull, 1952). Fajardo (1930) stressed that beans should be sown so that the period of maximum vegetative growth did not coincide with the period of maximum aphid activity, because plants infected when flowering or podding suffer less than those infected when younger. This interaction of age with time of insect activity was shown when beans were sown between 20–25 May and 0–40% of the different plots developed mosaic, whereas 50–100% of those sown during the period 6 June to 15 July became infected.

Tolerance to virus may also differ with age; Webb (1927) found severe wheat mosaic was almost limited to the early seedling stage, plants infected then usually being rosetted, but those six weeks old or more at the time of infection usually being only mottled.

C. Control by Altering Nutrition

There is little prospect of affecting significant control of virus spread by altering nutrition without seriously affecting crop yields, despite the influence of fertilizers on susceptibility described in Section 16–1,C. Fertilizer treatments that greatly influenced the growth of tobacco and potato under glass had little effect on the number of plants infected with potato virus Y (Bawden and Kassanis, 1950), and Hull and Watson (1947) obtained similar results in field experiments with sugar beet. Much work has been done on the influence of fertilizers on potatoes but, in general, manuring for maximum yields increases virus disease incidence (Broadbent et al., 1952).

16–7. CONCLUSION

It is not easy to summarize in a few words so many different methods of achieving a measure of control. It must be stressed again that most diseases cannot be eliminated, but their incidence can be decreased, usually by the use of several different methods. Many people will consider the most promising is the development of immune, or resistant or tolerant varieties, or the inclusion of such resistance in the gene structure of existing varieties. Considering the effort involved, the plant breeders have not been too successful as yet, but their continuing and expanding work augurs well for the future. We can only hope that the viruses are not quite as variable as some of the fungi, so that resistant varieties remain so. The widespread occurrence of symptomless tolerance to viruses in wild plants suggests that they may.

There is certain to be an expansion of quarantine, certification, and nuclear stock schemes, especially to control seed-borne viruses and those vegetatively propagated. These will be based on material freed from viruses by indexing and roguing or selection, or heat treatment and tip culture, and will rely on isolation, insect vector control, and other hygiene measures for their maintenance.

The recent interest in viruses in wild plants may result in greater efforts to prevent virus spread from them. Bennett (1952) expressed the opinion that there are still many viruses in weeds waiting to escape into cultivated plants, and there are still many in cultivated plants, especially ornamentals, waiting to be discovered! Quarantine, still in its infancy as regards virus diseases, may delay but cannot prevent the spread of viruses around the world (see also Kahn et al., 1963), and to quote Bennett again, ultimately viruses will achieve maximal distribution, determined by the geographical distribution of their hosts and vectors. When this occurs, natural selection and the plant breeders may have ensured the continuance of tolerant plant varieties only, but man may, or may not still dominate the scene.

Until that time, control can best be achieved by obtaining a thorough knowledge of disease epidemiology and using this to devise schemes which attack the virus or its vector at as many vulnerable points as possible.

16–8. LITERATURE CITED

Adam, A. V. (1962). Plant Disease Reptr. **46**, 366.

Anderson, C. W. (1957). Phytopathology **47**, 515.

Anderson, C. W. (1959). Phytopathology **49**, 97.

Anon. (1955). Rep. U.S.D.A. Potato Advisory Committee, Maine Agr. Expt. Sta.

Antoine, R. (1959). Rep. Sug. Ind. Res. Inst. Mauritius, 1958, 55.

Armitage, H. M. (1952). J. Econ. Entomol. **45**, 432.

Bagnall, R. H. (1953). Can. J. Agr. Sci. **33**, 509.

Bagnall, R. H., and Bradley, R. H. E. (1958). Phytopathology **48**, 121.

Bagnall, R. H., and Mackinnon, J. P. (1960). European Potato J. **3**, 331.

Baker, K. F. (1962). Phytopathology **52**, 1244.

Bartels, W. (1955). Phytopathol. Z. **25**, 72; 113.

Bawden, F. C. (1954). Advan. Virus Res. **2**, 31.

Bawden, F. C., and Kassanis, B. (1946). Ann. Appl. Biol. **33**, 46.

Bawden, F. C., and Kassanis, B. (1950). Ann. Appl. Biol. **37**, 46.

Bawden, F. C., Kassanis, B., and Roberts, F. M. (1948). Ann. Appl. Biol. **35**, 250.

Baxter, L. W., and McGlohon, N. E. (1959). Phytopathology **49**, 810.

Beemster, A. B. R. (1961). Proc. 4th Conf. Potato Virus Dis., Braunschweig, 1960, 60.

Bennett, C. W. (1951). Ann. Rev. Microbiol. **5**, 295.

Bennett, C. W. (1952). Plant Disease Reptr. Supplement **211**, 43.

Bennett, C. W. (1960). Tech. Bull. U.S. Dep. Agric. **1218**.

Bennett, C. W., and Costa, A. S. (1954). Proc. Am. Soc. Sugar Beet Technologists **8**, 230.

Berkeley, G. H. (1942). Sci. Agric. **22**, 465.

Bhatt, J. G., and Verna, S. S. (1958). Sci. and Cult. **23**, 610.

Birecki, M., Gabriel, W., and Piechowiak, K. (1961). Roczniki Nauk Rolniczych **82-A-3**, 739.

Björling, K., and Ossiannilsson, F. (1958). Socker **14**, 1.

Björnstad, A. (1948). Nord. Jordbrugsforskn. 1948, 586.

Blattný, C. (1925). Tijdschr. Plantenziekten **21**, 139.

Blencowe, J. W. (1956). Rep. Rothamst. Expt. Sta. 1955, 99.

Blencowe, J. W., and Tinsley, T. W. (1951). Ann. Appl. Biol. **38**, 395.

Bobyr, A. D. (1961). Rep. Acad. Sci. Ukr., 1961, 678. (Rev. Appl. Mycol. **41**, 60.)

Bonde, R., and Merriam, D. (1951). Am. Potato J. **28**, 558.

Bonnemaison, L. (1961). Ann. Epiphyties **12**, 155.

Bonnemaison, L. (1962). Phytiat. Phytopharm. **11**, 85.

Bradley, R. H. E., and Rideout, D. W. (1953). Can. J. Zool. **31**, 333.

Brierley, P. (1957). Plant Disease Reptr. **41**, 1005.

Brierley, P. (1962). Plant Disease Reptr. **46**, 505.

Brierley, P., and Lorentz, P. (1960). Phytopathology **50**, 404.

Broadbent, L. (1948). Ann. Appl. Biol. **35**, 379.

Broadbent, L. (1950). Ann. Appl. Biol. **37**, 58.

Broadbent, L. (1957a). Investigations of Virus Diseases of Brassica Crops. A.R.C. Report Series No. 14. Cambridge Univ. Press.

Broadbent, L. (1957b). Ann. Rev. Entomol. **2**, 339.

Broadbent, L. (1962). Ann. Appl. Biol. **50**, 461.

Broadbent, L., and Fletcher, J. T. (1963a). Ann. Appl. Biol. **52**, 233.

Broadbent, L. (1963b). Ann. Appl. Biol. **52**, 225.

Broadbent, L., and Burt, P. E. (1962). Proc. Brit. Insecticides and Fungicides Conf. 1961, **1**, 81.

Broadbent, L., and Heathcote, G. D. (1955). Plant Pathol. **4**, 135.

Broadbent, L., and Heathcote, G. D. (1960). Plant Pathol. **9**, 126.

Broadbent, L., and Heathcote, G. D. (1961). Entomol. Exp. Appl. **4**, 226.

Broadbent, L., and Martini, C. (1959). Advan. Virus Res. **6**, 93.

Broadbent, L., Burt, P. E., and Heathcote, G. D. (1956). Ann. Appl. Biol. **44**, 256.

Broadbent, L., Burt, P. E., and Heathcote, G. D. (1958). Proc. 3rd Conf. Potato Virus Diseases, Lisse-Wageningen, 1957, 91.

Broadbent, L., Green, D. E., and Walker, P. (1962a). Daffodil Tulip Yearbook. 1963, 154.

Broadbent, L., Gregory, P. H., and Tinsley, T. W. (1950). Ann. Appl. Biol. **37**, 640.

Broadbent, L., Gregory, P. H., and Tinsley, T. W. (1952). Ann. Appl. Biol. **39**, 509.

Broadbent, L., Heathcote, G. D., and Burt, P. E. (1960). European Potato J. **3**, 251.

Broadbent, L., Heathcote, G. D., and Wright, R. C. M. (1962b). Exp. Hort. **7**, 4.

Broadbent, L., Cornford, C. E., Hull, R., and Tinsley, T. W. (1949). Ann. Appl. Biol. **36**, 513.

Broadbent, L., Heathcote, G. D., Brown, P. H., and Wheeler, G. F. C. (1961). Exp. Hort. **4**, 8.

Broadbent, L., Heathcote, G. D., McDermott, N., and Taylor, C. E. (1957). Ann. Appl. Biol. **45**, 603.

Broadbent, L., Tinsley, T. W., Buddin, W., and Roberts, E. T. (1951). Ann. Appl. Biol. **38**, 689.

Burt, P. E., Broadbent, L., and Heathcote, G. D. (1960). Ann. Appl. Biol. **48**, 580.

Cadman, C. H. (1961). Hort. Res. **1**, 47.

CONTROL

Cadman, C. H., and Chambers, J. (1960). Ann. Appl. Biol. **48**, 729.

Caldwell, J. (1959). Nature (London) **183**, 1142.

Campbell, A. I. (1962). Nature (London) **195**, 520.

Cann, H. J. (1952). Agric. Gaz. N. S W. **63**, 73.

Capoor, S. P., and Varma, P. M. (1950). Indian J. Agr. Sci. **20**, 217.

Carter, W. (1963). Insects in Relation to Plant Disease. Interscience Publishers, New York.

Chamberlain, E. E. (1947). Bull. N. Z. Dept. Agr. **281**, 1.

Chambers, J. (1961). J. Hort. Sci. **36**, 48.

Chu, H. T., and Lin, P. (1956). Rep. Taiwan Sug. Expt. Sta. **14**, 83.

Cook, W. C. (1943). J. Econ. Entomol. **36**, 382.

Cornford, C. E. (1955). Plant Pathol. **4**, 89.

Costa, A. S., and Bennett, C. W. (1950) Phytopathology **40**, 266.

Couch, H. B. (1955). Phytopathology **45**, 63.

Crowley, N. C. (1957). Australian J. Biol. Sci. **10**, 449.

Crowley, N. C. (1958). J. Australian Inst. Agr. Sci. **24**, 261.

Crowley, N. C. (1959). Virology **8**, 116.

Crumb, S. E., and McWhorter, F. P. (1948). Plant Disease Reptr. **32**, 169.

Davis, A. C., McEwen, F. L., and Schroeder, W. T. (1961). J. Econ. Entomol. **54**, 161.

Day, M. F., and Bennetts, M. J. (1954). Australian C.S.I.R.O. Div. Entom. Monograph. 172 pp.

Dicker, G. H. L. (1952). J. Hort. Sci. **27**, 151.

Dickson, R. C., Johnson, M. McD., Flock, R. A., and Laird, E. F. (1956). Phytopathology **46**, 204.

Doncaster, J. P., and Gregory, P. H. (1948). Agr. Res. Counc. Rep. 7, London, H.M.S.O.

Doolittle, S. P. (1928). Phytopathology **18**, 155.

Douglass, J. R., Romney, V. E., and Jones, E. W. (1955). Circ. U.S. Dep. Agr. 960.

Ellenberger, C. A. (1960). Rep. E. Malling Res. Sta. 1959, 99.

Evans, A. C. (1954). Nature (London) **173**, 1242.

Fajardo, T. G. (1930). Phytopathology **20**, 469.

Fisken, A. G. (1959). Ann. Appl. Biol. **47**, 264; 274.

Flock, R. A., and Deal, A. S. (1959). J. Econ. Entomol. **52**, 470.

de Fluiter, H. J. (1958). Mededel. Landbouwhogeschool Gent **23**, 745.

de Fluiter, H. J., and van der Meer, F. A. (1955). Mededel. Landbouwhogeschool Gent **20**, 419.

Folsom, D. (1952). Am. Potato J. **29**, 229.

Frazier, N. W., and Posnette, A. F. (1957). Ann. Appl. Biol. **45**, 580.

Frederiksen, R. A. (1962). Dissertation Abstr. **22**, 3800.

Freitag, J. H., and Severin, H. H. P. (1945). Hilgardia **16**, 375.

Fry, P. R., and Coleman, B. P. (1960). N.Z. Comm. Grower **16**, 25.

Fulton, J. P., and Seymour, C. (1957). Plant Disease Reptr. **41**, 749.

Fulton, R. W. (1943). Phytopathology **33**, 674.

Gabriel, W. (1960). Proc. 4th Conf. Potato Virus Dis. Braunschweig, 1960, 126.

Gibbs, A. J. (1960). Ann. Appl. Biol. **48**, 771.

Gol'din, M. I., and Yurchenko, M. A. (1958). Plant Protect., Moscow 1958, 36. (Rev. Appl. Mycol. **38**, 338.)

Gorham, R. P. (1942). Rept. Entomol. Soc. Ont. **72**, 18.

Govier D. A. (1963). Virology **19**, 561.

Grant, T. J. (1958). Florida State Hort. Soc. **70**, 51.

Grogan, R. G., Welch, J. E., and Bardin, R. (1952). Phytopathology **42**, 573.

Haasis, F. A. (1939). Mem. Cornell Agr. Expt. Sta. **224**, 3.

Hagborg, W. A. F., and Chelack, W. S. (1960). Can. J. Botany **38**, 111.

Hammond, P. S. (1958). Rept. Cocoa Conf., London, 1957, 110.

Hampton, R. E., Sill, W. H., and Hansing, E. D. (1957). Plant Disease Reptr. **41**, 735.

Hansen, H. P. (1950). Trans. Danish Acad. Techn. Sci. **1**, 1.

Hansen, S. E. (1957). Tidsskr. Planteavl. **61**, 277.

Hare, W. W., and Lucas, G. B. (1959). Plant Disease Reptr. **43**, 152.

Harpaz, I. (1961). FAO Plant Protect. Bull. **9**, 144.

Harrison, B. D. (1957). Rept. Scottish Hort. Res. Inst. 1956-57, 31.

Harrison, B. D., and Winslow, R. D. (1961). Ann. Appl. Biol. **49**, 621.

Hein, A. (1957). Phytopathol. Z. **28**, 205; **29**, 79; **29**, 204.

Hein, A. (1962). Rhein. Mschr. Gemüseb., 1962, No. 3, 2 pp.

Hewitt, W. B., Houston, B. R., Frazier, N. W., and Freitag, J. H. (1946). Phytopathology **36**, 117.

Hildebrand, E. M., and Palmiter, D. H. (1942). N.Y. State Agr. Soc. Proc. 1942, 34.

Hille Ris Lambers, D. (1955). Ann. Appl. Biol. **42**, 355.

Hoffman, J. R. (1952). Quart. Bull. Mich. Agr. Exp. Sta. **34**, 262.

Hollings, M. (1955a). Ann. Appl. Biol. **43**, 86.

Hollings, M. (1955b). Plant Pathol. **4**, 73.

Hollings, M. (1960). Plant Pathol. **9**, 1.

Hollings, M. (1962). N.A.A.S. Quart. Rev. **57**, 31.

Hollings, M., and Kassanis, B. (1957). J. Roy. Hort. Soc. **82**, 339.

Holmes, F. O. (1954). Advan. Virus Res. **2**, 1.

Holmes, F. O. (1955). Phytopathology **45**, 224.

Holmes, F. O. (1960). Plant Disease Reptr. **44**, 46.

Hopkins, J. C. F. (1932). Rhodesia Agr. J. **29**, 680.

Hopkins, J. C. F. (1943). Rhodesia Agr. J. **40**, 47.

Horvath, J. (1962). Novenytermeles **11**, 257.

Howles, R. (1957). Plant Pathol. **6**, 46.

Hoyman, W. G. (1958). Am. Potato J. **35**, 708.

Huckett, H. C. (1945). N.Y. State Agr. Expt. Sta. Bull. **713**, 1.

Hughes, C. G., and Steindl, D. R. L. (1955). Bur. Sugar Expt. Sta. Queensland Tech. Comm. 2. (quoted by Kassanis and Posnette, 1961).

Hull, R. (1952). J. Roy. Agr. Soc. Engl. **113**, 86.

Hull, R. (1958). Agriculture, Lond. **65**, 62.

Hull, R. (1959). Plant Pathol. **8**, 145.

Hull, R., and Watson, M. A. (1947). J. Agr. Res. **37**, 302.

Hunter, J. A., Chamberlain, E. E., and Atkinson, J. D. (1959). New Zealand J. Agr. Res. **2**, 945.

Inouye, T. (1962). Ber. Ohara Inst. Landwirtsch. Biol. Okayama Univ. **11**, 413.

Jamalainen, E. A. (1948). Nord. Jordbrugsforskn. 1948, 568.

Janssen, J. J. (1929). Tijdschr. Plantenziekten **35**, 119.

Jensen, D. D., and Gold, A. H. (1955). Phytopathology **45**, 327.

John, C. A., and Sova, C. (1955). Phytopathology **45**, 636.

Johnson, B. (1953). Nature (London) **172**, 813.

Johnson, C. G. (1956). Rept. Rothamst. Expt. Sta. 1955, 191.

Johnson, J. (1937). J. Agr. Res. **54**, 239.

Johnson, J., and Ogden, W. B. (1929). Wisconsin Univ. Agr. Expt. Sta. Bull. 95.

Jones, L. K., and Burnett, G. (1935). Wash. State Univ. Agr. Expt. Sta. Bull. 308.

Jones, L. R., and Riker, R. S. (1931). Wisconsin Univ. Agr. Expt. Sta. Res. Bull. 111.

Kabiersch, W. (1962). Outlook Agr. **3**, 268.

Kahn, R. P., *et al.* (1963). Plant Disease Reptr. **47**, 261.

Kassanis, B. (1950). Ann. Appl. Biol. **37**, 339.

Kassanis, B. (1952). Ann. Appl. Biol. **39**, 157.

Kassanis, B. (1957). Advan. Virus Res. **4**, 221.

Kassanis, B., and Posnette, A. F. (1961). Recent Advan. Botany 1961, 557.

Keener, P. D. (1956). Ariz. Univ. Agr. Expt. Sta. Bull. 271.

Keller, E. R., and Baltensperger, H. (1961). Mitt. Schweiz. Landw. **9**, 93.

Kennedy, J. S. (1950). Proc. 8th Int. Congr. Entomol. 423.

Kennedy, J. S., Day, M. F., and Eastop, V. F. (1962). A Conspectus of Aphids as Vectors of Plant Viruses. Comm. Inst. Entomol., London. 114 pp.

Kennedy, J. S., Ibbotson, A., and Booth, C. O. (1950). Ann. Appl. Biol. **37**, 651.

King, L. W. (1952). Am. Potato J. **29**, 53.

Klinkowski, M. (1959). Nachrbl. Deut. Pflanzenschutzdienst (Berlin) **13**, 41.

Kooistra, G. (1959). Acta Botan. Neerl. **8**, 373.

Kunkel, L. O. (1929). Phytopathology **19**, 100.

Kunkel, L. O. (1936). Phytopathology **26**, 809.

Kunkel, L. O. (1937). Am. J. Botany **24**, 316.

Küthe, K. (1961). Z. Pflanzenkrankh. **68**, 209.

Larson, R. H. (1959). Am. Potato J. **36**, 29.

Lihnell, D. (1948). Nord. Jordbrugsforskn. 1948, 571.

Limasset, P. (1957). Expos. Act. Biol. Cell. **6**, 175.

Linford, M. B. (1943). Phytopathology **33**, 408.

Linn, M. B. (1940). Cornell Univ. Agr. Expt. Sta. Bull. 742.

List, G. M., Landblom, N., and Sison, M. A. (1956). Colo. Agr. Expt. Sta. Tech. Bull. 59.

Lister, R. M. (1960). Virology **10**, 547.

Lovisolo, O., and Benetti, M. P. (1960). Boll. Staz. Patol. Veg. **17**, 61.

Lucas, G. B., and Winstead, N. N. (1958). Phytopathology **48**, 344.

McClean, D. M. (1957). Phytopathology **47**, 557.

MacClement, W. D., and Richards, M. G. (1956). Can. J. Botany **34**, 793.

McKeen, C. D. (1962). Phytopathology **52**, 742.

McKinney, H. H., Paden, W. R., and Koehler, B. (1957). Plant Disease Reptr. **41**, 256.

Mackinnon, J. P., Rankin, D. F., and Young, L. C. (1960). Am. Potato J. **37**, 373.

MacNeill, B. H. (1962). Can. J. Botany **40**, 49.

Malaguti, G., and Angeles, N. (1957). Agron. Trop. (Maracay, Venezuela) **7**, 161.

Maramorosch, K. (1963). Ann. Rev. Entomol. **8**, 369.

Martin, W. J., and Kantack, E. J. (1960). Phytopathology **50**, 150.

Merriam, D., and Bonde, R. (1954). Maine Farm Res. **1** (4), 7.

Michelbacher, A. E., Gardner, M. W., Middlekauff, W. W., and Walz, A. J. (1950). Plant Disease Reptr. **34**, 307.

Middleton, J. T. (1944). Phytopathology **34**, 405.

Miyamoto, Y. (1961). Ann. Phytopath. Soc. Japan **26**, 90.

Morel, G., and Martin, C. (1955). C. R. Acad. Agr. **41**, 472.

Mulholland, R. I. (1962). Commonwealth Phytopath. News **8**, 60.

Müller, H. J. (1953). Beitr. Entomol. **3**, 229.

Müller, H. J. (1956). S.B. Dtsch. Acad. Landw. Wiss. Berl. **5**, 1.

Münster, J. (1956). Rev. Rom. Agric. **12**, 53.

Münster, J. (1958). European Potato J. **1**, 31.

Münster, J., and Joseph, E. (1959). Ann. Agr. Suisse, N. S. **8**, 579.

Münster, J., and Mayor, G. (1953). Rev. Rom. Agric. **9**, 1.

Newell, J. (1954). Grower, Lond. **41**, 1409.

Noordam, D. (1955). Mededel. Dir. Tuinb. **18**, 639.

Nyland, G. (1959). Phytopathology **49**, 157.

Nyland, G. (1960). Phytopathology **50**, 380.

Orad, A. C., and Roman, F. P. S. (1960). Inst. Nac. Invest. Agron. **9**, 215.

Oswald, J. W., and Houston, B. R. (1953). Phytopathology **43**, 308.

Persons, T. D. (1952). Phytopathology **42**, 286.

Piemeisel, R. L. (1954). Botany Rev. **20**, 1.

Posnette, A. F. (1953). Nature (London) **171**, 312.

Posnette, A. F. (1962). Rept. E. Malling Res. Sta. 1961, 125.

Posnette, A. F., and Cropley, R., 1954. Rept. E. Malling Res. Sta., 1953, 154.

Posnette, A. F., and Cropley, R. (1956). J. Hort. Sci. **31**, 119.

Posnette, A. F., and Cropley, R. (1958). J. Hort. Sci. **33**, 282.

Posnette, A. F., and Ellenberger, C. E. (1963). Ann. Appl. Biol. **51**, 69.

Posnette, A. F., and Jha, A. (1960). Rept. E. Malling Res. Sta. 1959, 98.

Posnette, A. F., and Robertson, N. F. (1950). Ann. Appl. Biol. 37, 363.

Posnette, A. F., and Todd, J. M. (1955). Ann. Appl. Biol. 43, 433.

Posnette, A. F., Cropley, R., and Wolfswinkel, L. D. (1962). Rept. E. Malling Res. Sta. 1961, 94.

Posnette, A. F., Robertson, N. F., and Todd, J. M. (1950). Ann. Appl. Biol. 37, 229.

Pound, G. S. (1946). Phytopathology 36, 1035.

Pound, G. S. (1947). J. Agr. Res. 75, 31.

Quak, F. (1957). Tijdschr. Plantenziekten 63, 13.

Quak, F. (1961). Proc. 15th Int. Hort. Cong. Nice, 1958, 1, 144.

Quantz, L. (1955). Lehrg. gärtn. Pflanzenz. Samenb., Göttingen 21–24 Juni, 1955, 18.

Ross, A. F., Chucka, J. A., and Hawkins, A. (1947). Maine Agr. Exp. Sta. Bull. 447, 97.

Russel, G. E. (1960). Brit. Sugar Beet Rev. 28, 163.

Sardina, J. R., Orad, A. G., and San Roman, F. P. (1958). Proc. 3rd Conf. Potato Virus Dis., Lisse-Wageningen, 1957, 59.

Schlösser, L. A. (1952). Phytopathol. Z. 20, 75.

Schultz, E. S., Bonde, R., and Raleigh, W. P. (1944). Maine Agr. Expt. Sta. Bull. 427.

Schwarz, R. (1959). Phytopathol. Z. 35, 238.

Severin, H. H. P., and Freitag, J. H. (1938). Hilgardia 11, 495.

Shapovalov, M., Blood, H. L., and Christiansen, R. M. (1941). Phytopathology 31, 864.

Shirahama, K. (1957). Agricultural Improvement Extension Work Conference (Tokyo, Japan).

Simmonds, J. H. (1959). Queensland J. Agr. Sci. 16, 371.

Simons, J. N. (1954). Phytopathology 44, 283.

Simons, J. N. (1956). Abst. 10th Int. Congr. Entomol. (Canada) 1023.

Simons, J. N. (1957). Phytopathology 47, 139.

Simons, J. N. (1958). Florida Univ. Agr. Expt. Sta. Ann. Rept., 1957, 251.

Simons, J. N. (1959). Virology 9, 612.

Simons, J. N. (1960). Phytopathology 50, 424.

Simons, J. N., Orsenigo, J. R., Stall, R. E., and Thayer, P. L. (1959). Mimeo Rept. Everglades Expt. Sta. Univ. Fla. 59–31, 11pp.

Simpson, G. W., and Shands, W. A. (1949). Maine Agr. Expt. Sta. Bull. 470.

Simpson, G. W., and Shands, W. A. (1961). Maine Farm Res. 9, 3.

Simpson, G. W., and Shands, W. A. (1963). Maine Farm Res. 11, 19.

Simpson, G. W., Shands, W. A., Cobb, R. M., and Lombard, P. M. (1951). Maine Agr. Expt. Sta. Bull. 491, 50.

Simpson, G. W., Bonde, R., Merriam, D., Akeley, D. F., Manzer, F. E., and Hovey, C. L. (1952). Maine Agr. Expt. Sta. Bull. 502.

Slykhuis, J. T. (1955). Phytopathology 45, 116.

Slykhuis, J. T., Zillinsky, F. J., Young, M., and Richards, W. R. (1960). Plant Disease Reptr. Supp. 262, 317.

Smartt, J. (1961). Empire J. Exp. Agr. 29, 79.

Smith, F. F., and Brierley, P. (1948). Phytopathology 38, 841.

Staples, R., and Allington, W. B. (1956). Nebraska Univ. Agr. Expt. Sta. Res. Bull. 178.

Steib, R. J. (1958). Sugar Bull. 36, 303.

Steudel, W. (1952). Nachrbl. Deut. Pflanzenschutzdienst (Stuttgart) 4, 40.

Steudel, W. (1953). Zucker 4, 69.

Steudel, W., and Thielemann, R. (1962). Zucker 15, 261, 286.

Stitt, L. L., and Breakey, E. P. (1952). Mededel. Landbouwhogeschool Opzoekingssta. Gent 17, 94.

Stoddard, E. M., and Dimond, A. E. (1949). Phytopathology 39, 24.

Stone, O. M. (1963). Ann. Appl. Biol. 52.

Storey, H. H. (1935). E. African Agr. J. 1, 206.

Storey, H. H., and Nichols, R. F. W. (1938). Ann. Appl. Biol. 25, 790.

Storey, I. F., and Godwin, A. E. (1953). Plant Pathol. 2, 98.

Stout, G. L. (1962). Phytopathology 52, 1255.

Strong, R. G., and Rawlins, W. A. (1959). J. Econ. Entomol. 52, 686.

Stubbs, L. L. (1948). Australian J. Sci. Res. 1, 303.

Stubbs, L. L. (1954). J. Dep. Agric. Vict. 52, 259.

Stubbs, L. L. (1955). Australian J. Biol. Sci. 8, 68.

Stubbs, L. L. (1956). Plant Disease Reptr. 40, 763.

Stubbs, L. L., and O'Loughlin, G. T. (1962). Australian J. Expt. Agr. 2, 16.

Swenson, K. G., Davis, A. C., and Schroeder, W. T. (1954). J. Econ. Entomol. 47, 490.

Sylvester, E. S. (1955). Phytopathology 45, 357.

Szirmai, J. (1957). Ann. Inst. Prot. Plant. Hung. 7, 393.

Tarr, S. A. J. (1951). Leaf Curl Disease of Cotton. Commonwealth Mycol. Inst. 55 pp.

Taylor, C. E., and Johnson, C. G. (1954). Ann. Appl. Biol. 41, 107.

Taylor, R. H., Grogan, R. G., and Kimble, K. A. (1961). Phytopathology 51, 837.

Thirumalachar, M. J. (1954). Phytopathol. Z. 22, 429.

Thomson, A. D. (1957). N.A.J. Sci. Tech. (A) 38, 482.

Thresh, J. M. (1958a). Tech. Bull. W. Afr. Cacao Res. Inst. 5, 1.

Thresh, J. M. (1958b). Tech. Bull. W. Afr. Cacao Res. Inst. 4, 1.

Thresh, J. M. (1959). Trop. Agr., Trin. 36, 35.

Thresh, J. M. (1960). F.A.O. Plant Prot. Bull. 8, 89.

Todd, J. M. (1958). Proc. 3rd Conf. Potato Virus Dis., Wageningen-Lisse, 1957, 132.

Todd, J. M. (1960). Proc. 4th Conf. Potato Virus Dis. Braunschweig, 1960, 82.

Todd, J. M. (1961). European Potato J. 4, 316.

Tomlinson, J. A. (1962). Plant Pathol. 11, 61.

van der Plank, J. E. (1944). Nature (London) 153, 589.

van der Plank, J. E. (1947). Ann. Appl. Biol. 34, 376.

van der Plank, J. E. (1948a). Ann. Appl. Biol. 35, 45.

van der Plank, J. E. (1948b). Empire J. Expt. Agr. 16, 134.

van der Plank, J. E. (1949). Empire J. Expt. Agr. 17, 18; 17, 141.

van der Plank, J. E., and Anderssen, E. E. (1944). S. African Agr. Dep. Sci. Bull. 240.

van Koot, Y., and van Dorst, H. J. M. (1959). Tijdschr. Plantenziekten 65, 257.

van Slogteren, E. (1955). Ann. Appl. Biol. 42, 122.

van Slogteren, E., and Ouboter, M. P. de B. (1941). Mededel. Landbouwhogeschool, Wageningen 45, 1.

van Velsen, R. J. (1961). Papua New Guinea Agr. J. 14, 38.

Viado, G. D., and Matthysse, J. G. (1959). Philippine Agriculturist 42, 364.

Vovk, A. M. (1961). Tr. Inst. Genet. Akad. Nauk. S.S.S.R. 1961, 28, 269.

Waggoner, P. E. (1962). Phytopathology 52, 1100.

Wagnon, H. K., and Traylor, J. A. (1957). Phytopathology 47, 537.

Wallace, J. M., and Murphy, A. M. (1938). U.S. Dep. Agr. Tech. Bull. 624.

Wallace, J. M, Oberholzer, P. C. J., and Hofmeyer, J. D. J. (1956). Plant Disease Reptr. 40, 3.

Wartenberg, H. (1954). Deut. Landwirtsch. 5, 578.

Watson, M. A. (1956). Ann. Appl. Biol. 44, 599.

Watson, M. A., Hull, R., Blencowe, J. W., and Hamlyn, B. G. M. (1951). Ann. Appl. Biol. 38, 743.

Webb, R. E. (1956). Phytopathology 46, 470.

Webb, R. W. (1927). J. Agr. Res. 35, 587.

Wellman, F. L. (1937). U.S. Dep. Agr. Tech. Bull. 548.

Wenzl, H. (1955). Bodenkultur 8, 274.

Wheeler, G. F. C. (1962). Grower 57, 819.

Wiesner, K. (1959). Wiss. Z. Martin-Luther-Univ. 8, 577.

Wilson, N. S., Jones, L. S., and Cochran, L. C. (1955). Plant Disease Reptr. 39, 889.

Winkler, A. J. (1949). Hilgardia 19, 207.

Wittmann, H. G. (1958). Phytopathol. Z. 34, 221.

Wolf, F. A. (1933). Phytopathology 23, 831.

Yamaguchi, M., and Welch, J. E. (1955). Plant Disease Reptr. 39, 36.

Zink, F. W., Grogan, R. G., and Bardin, R. (1957). Proc. Am. Soc. Hort. Sci. 70, 277.

Zink, F. W., Grogan, R. G., and Welch, J. E. (1956). Phytopathology 46, 662.

17

F. C. BAWDEN

Speculations on the origins and nature of viruses

17–1. INTRODUCTION

MY SUBJECT was allotted to me and had the choice been left to me, I would have chosen otherwise. I do not say this to disclaim responsibility, for I gave those who allotted it good reason to think it would be acceptable by making it the subject of the last chapter of my book *Plant Viruses and Virus Diseases*. They were not to know I have changed, as indeed has the last chapter of the book. In the first two editions, the chapter heading began with the word "Discussion," which I changed to "Speculations" in the third edition, so that unwary readers were better warned about the dubious nature of its contents. The fourth edition, now being printed, contains no such chapter.

The omission is a fact; interpreting it is speculative. It is also factual that I am older than I was, but I hesitate to interpret the omission as evidence that I am also wiser. Loss of imagination is an equally plausible explanation and, although less attractive to me, I have little doubt will be fully acceptable to most other people. Perhaps a partial explanation is that so much more is now known about viruses, for there is no better curb on speculation than a few facts. Perhaps another part is my increasing awareness of the futility of much past speculation, which was indeed what can be aptly described as "second-order" speculation, for the supposed facts used as bases

or as evidence for the ideas developed were often proved false by later work. It is the bounden duty of scientists, as of newspaper editors, to distinguish between facts and comments on them, but even the most conscientious sometimes unwittingly fail in their duty. It is not only that constant repetition of interpretations invest them with an air of reality that ultimately gets accepted as truth, but the way in which factual results are described, often with no other intent than to achieve a brevity that would be commendable if it were consistent with accuracy, can translate them into interpretations. Should anyone doubt this, his doubts ought to be dispelled by simply contemplating the many viruses for long described as "not transmissible mechanically" but that have been so transmitted during the past few years. When a worker has tried not only every known way of transmitting, but also every new way he can devise, and still failed to transmit a virus mechanically, he may well conclude that it is "not transmissible mechanically." However, this is his conclusion, not necessarily a statement of fact and certainly not what he has established.

Speculation in science, as in the Stock Market, can be profitable, but unless it is based on sound information it can also be extremely hazardous. Again, as in the Stock Market, where shares in different kinds of industries change greatly in popularity from time to time, science also has its changing fashions for prime subjects of speculation. Currently, only nucleic acids are fashionable, whereas proteins were the favourites in 1939 when the first edition of *Plant Viruses and Virus Diseases* was written. Before now speculating any further, it will be salutary to consider the fate of some speculations in that edition. To do this, and to show to what extent ideas and fashions have changed, it is necessary to try to recall something of the atmosphere of the period.

17–2. CHANGING IDEAS ABOUT VIRUSES

Knowledge about the nature of viruses began to accrue in the 1930's, that is, some 40 years after their existence was first demonstrated by the discovery that seemingly sterile fluids could be infective. This discovery came only shortly after the germ theory of disease had become generally accepted and was by itself not enough to change the fruitful new creed of pathologists that infectious diseases were the result of one kind of organism preying on another. It is true that there was no lack of speculation about the nature of viruses, with suggestions ranging from Beijerinck's well-known description of tobacco mosaic as a *contagium vivum fluidum,* through toxins, enzymes, autocatalysts, and free genes to degenerate microbes that had increasingly lost structures and functions as a result of long continued parasitism. With no compelling reason for adopting any of these other ideas, however, most pathologists were content to assume that viruses were essentially similar to bacteria. They could always point to the obvious similarities between pathogenic bacteria and viruses, of which the most significant biologically were the ability of both to multiply in host organisms and, while doing so, occasionally to vary and produce offspring with new characters. Neither the inability of viruses to multiply saprophytically nor their invisibility was a telling argument against the organismal theory, because it was possible to point to some undoubted organisms, both fungi and bacteria, that had also failed to grow on nutrient media and to some or-

ganisms that did grow saprophytically but were only just large enough to be seen through a microscope.

Differences of opinion were understandable enough when nothing was known about the composition or structure of viruses, but it is less understandable that they grew larger rather than smaller as information began to be gained. This information came by applying to extracts of infected plants the methods of fractionation whereby some enzymes had been isolated and crystallised. It led to the isolation of crystalline or liquid crystalline nucleoproteins from plants infected separately with several different viruses, and much evidence was gained relating these nucleoproteins with the viruses. With the amount of attention now being given to nucleic acids, those not fully familiar with the literature will fail to appreciate to what extent proteins then dominated thinking about specificity in biological reactions and that Pirie and I had considerable difficulty in persuading some people to our view that nucleic acid was an integral and essential part of tobacco mosaic virus (TMV). However, as a footnote to page 157 of the first edition of *Plant Viruses and Virus Diseases* shows, Stanley not only described his first preparations as globulin but for some years afterwards maintained that the nucleic acid was a contaminant, inessential for infectivity.

Although, from 1939 onwards, there was no disagreement about tobacco mosaic and the other viruses that had been purified being nucleoproteins, the nucleic acid still got scant attention. For many years the proteins were considered to be the prime determinants of biological specificity and, indeed, many results with viruses were advanced as evidence that they were. In explanation of then current thinking, it must be remembered not only that viruses were first characterised as nucleoproteins soon after it had become generally accepted that enzymes were proteins, but when nucleic acids were thought to be so small that their four components seemed quite inadequate to allow for the extensive isomerism necessary to determine biological specificity. It is true that early work with nucleic acid from TMV showed that this was much larger than yeast nucleic acid as usually prepared, but this pointer was not sharp enough to shift attention from the proteins, which with their 20 or so different amino acids and large size obviously provided opportunities for isomerism more than enough to explain any number of specific structures and activities.

In seeking the minimal infective units, the ultimate may have been reached in the nucleic acids. Certainly there is much evidence now being accumulated indicating that infectivity depends on the integrity of the nucleic acid. However, as a warning about the need for scepticism in interpreting this evidence, it must be pointed out that similar evidence was advanced over many years to show that it depended on the integrity of the protein. It is a particularly valuable and salutary exercise now, when infections are being made experimentally almost as often with preparations of virus nucleic acids as with whole virus particles, to read the many papers that presented evidence purporting to show such things as that the nucleoprotein was the minimal infective unit, that infectivity depended on the integrity of the protein, that reversible changes in the protein destroyed and restored infectivity, and that mutations were caused by changes in the amino acid composition.

It may be, too, that the four nucleotides yet identified in preparations of virus nucleic acids are their only components, but before assuming that this is certainly so it is well to remember the size of these nucleic acids and the chances of their containing quantitatively minor components that may be biologically important. One nucleotide is only about 0.016% of the weight of the nucleic acid from TMV and a substance with molecular weight of 2000 would be only 0.1%. It would be vain to pretend that knowledge is precise enough to exclude the possibility of one or two bizarre nucleotides or other substances of similar sizes and it is to be hoped that it will not too readily be accepted that the nucleotides making up the bulk of the nucleic acid necessarily represent the total.

During the 1930's and 1940's the widening conflict in opinions about the nature of viruses is amply evidenced by the fact that while some people unhesitatingly called them organisms others equally unhesitatingly called them molecules. This conflict seemed irreconcilable but was not, for it was unreal in that it had no factual basis but arose from prejudices and the use of emotive words with no relevance to viruses. The word organism demands a wealth of independent activities there was never any reason to attribute to viruses, whereas molecule implies a precise and unchanging chemical composition that is not only impossible to demonstrate with such large particles but that also fits ill with the mutability of viruses. Viruses could be put into either category only by speculation, which rested less on factual information than on subjective decisions about the significance of such things as apparent ability to multiply and apparent homogeneity when subjected to some physico-chemical tests. To use these categories also posed a false antithesis, because it postulated that viruses must be either organisms or molecules and overlooked the fact they might be neither. That they are a distinct category is now generally recognised, and even those most bigoted in calling viruses organisms or molecules gave up the practice after the great complexity of the bacteriophage particles was revealed and after it was shown that disrupted virus particles could be infective.

Indeed, to show their distinctiveness new words are now being coined, such as *capsid, capsomere, nucleocapsid,* and *virion,* to identify either different parts of the virus particles or different stages in their development (Caspar *et al.,* 1962). In this proposed terminology *virus* applies generally to all phases of development; *virion* is the mature virus particle, which may be synonymous with *nucleocapsid* or may be the *nucleocapsid* in an envelope. The *capsid* is the closed shell or tube containing the nucleic acid and perhaps other components, such as polyamines, whose occurrence has only recently been recognised (Johnson and Markham, 1962), although they amount to as much as 0.7% of the weight of turnip yellow mosaic virus; the *capsid* is composed of small structural units aggregated into morphological units, the *capsomeres,* which are large enough to be resolved by electron microscopy. I shall not be much concerned with the morphology of virus particles and shall not need to adopt this terminology, but I summarise it because it indicates current ideas about virus structure and composition, and shows how far these ideas are removed from earlier ones.

17–3. THE ORIGINS OF VIRUS

There were in 1939 several things known about some of the plant viruses that separated them sharply from even the simplest microorganisms. First, there was their chemical simplicity; secondly, as shown by X-ray crystallography, their structural units were arranged with a three-dimensional regularity that conflicts strikingly with the continuously changing composition of cells; thirdly, the uniformity of particle sizes seemed to deny multiplication by a process of binary fission. In composition, structure, and manner of production they seemed to resemble components of cells more nearly than whole cells, and their nearest analogues seemed to be the nucleoproteins of normal cells. As a possible theory for the origin of viruses, I therefore suggested in the first edition of *Plant Viruses and Virus Diseases* that viruses might have arisen as accidents in the protein metabolism of organisms, perhaps by faulty synthesis in the hosts the viruses now affect or perhaps by the accident that a normal nucleoprotein from one organism had got introduced into another where it could multiply.

A. The Irrelevance of Potato Paracrinkle

As possible evidence that normal components of one plant might become viruses in another, I described what was then known about potato paracrinkle virus. This now provides an excellent example of what earlier I referred to as "second-order" speculation, and as a cautionary tale is worth telling. Salaman and Le Pelley (1930) gave the name paracrinkle to a disease produced when some other potato varieties were grafted with scions from seemingly normal plants of the variety King Edward. They failed to cause the disease by inoculating susceptible potato varieties with sap from King Edward. All the many King Edward plants tested in the next few years proved to be infected with paracrinkle virus and it became increasingly probable, though obviously impossible to prove, that every plant of this clonal variety was infected. King Edward is one of the most widely grown potato varieties in the United Kingdom, yet paracrinkle was not reported occurring naturally in susceptible varieties growing near to King Edward. It seemed reasonable to infer that paracrinkle virus had no natural method of spread, which in turn implied that the virus was present in the original seedling from which the clone was derived and that it had survived only because it was in a vegetatively propagated plant.

When drawing attention to the inferences possible from the then known occurrence and behaviour of paracrinkle virus, I pointed out that, had the original seedling been infected from some external source, it seemed necessary to assume that the virus then had some method of spread since lost. I suggested it seemed equally plausible (it did at that time, though it seems ridiculous when several viruses have been found to lose or gain the ability to be transmitted by a given insect) that the virus had arisen endogenously in the variety, but I stressed the fact that nothing was known about the origin or early history of the clone and the highly speculative nature of any interpretations. The warnings went unheeded, and for some years paracrinkle virus featured prominently in discussions on the origins of viruses, seemingly without any doubts that it was intrinsic to King Edward. No further work was done on it and its chemical nature was quite unknown, but this did not prevent Darlington (1944) writing "What is a stable and presumably useful cell protein with one genotype acts as a destructive agent with another." He concluded that "the virus must have arisen by grafting" and to stress its origin from a normal plant constituent he (Darlington, 1949) separated it from other plant viruses in a group he called "provirus," of which the distinguishing character was transmissible by grafting.

It was fun while it lasted, but it only needed some facts to show what nonsense it all was. Let us summarise present knowledge about paracrinkle virus. It is transmissible by inoculation and some strains have been transmitted by aphids. King Edward plants contain specific particles, long filaments, indistinguishable from those in experimentally infected plants, either other potato varieties or tomatoes, whether infected by grafting or inoculation. It is serologically related to two other potato viruses—leaf rolling mosaic and S—and to carnation latent virus, which is aphid-transmitted. Although every King Edward plant yet examined has been virus-infected, some contain virus S and not paracrinkle virus. Many contain both viruses, but these plants look similar to those with paracrinkle virus only. So far from being a useful component of King Edward plants, it is harmful, for a virus-free clone produced by culturing an excised apical meristem is more vigorous, has darker green and less wavy leaves, and has out-yielded infected clones in field trails (Bawden *et al.*, 1950; Kassanis, 1956, 1957, 1961; Bagnall *et al.*, 1959).

The origin and history of paracrinkle virus will probably always remain uncertain, but there is now obviously no reason to consider it to be intrinsic to King Edward potatoes. On current knowledge, it seems likely that it and the three other viruses to which it is distantly related serologically, and which have particles of similar sizes and shapes, have evolved from a common stock, an aphid-transmitted virus. This virus may well have existed in variants that were virulent towards King Edward but any such would have been eliminated by the selection practised by potato-seed growers, whereas while it has been maintained in a vegetatively propagated host selection for transmissibility by aphids has not been operating and many of the variants avirulent to King Edward now seem to have lost this ability.

Paracrinkle is not the only virus that has been considered to provide evidence of viruses arising endogenously in higher plants (Smith, 1952), but it is now obvious that most of these others are soil-borne and could have been contracted from infested soil, something not suspected when seemingly spontaneous infections occurred in plants growing in conditions then assumed to be proof against accidental infections. Similarly, the idea that viruses arise *de novo* in lysogenic bacteria is no longer compelling since the demonstration that lysogeny is a state that can be induced by infection with appropriate bacteriophages. However, the knowledge that the potentiality to produce virus particles can be long perpetuated without becoming a reality, and that the genetic material of a virus can multiply without causing the concomitant virus proteins to be produced may be significant not only in explaining apparently spontaneous productions of viruses but also in speculating on the origin of viruses. May not a normal nucleic acid undergo a series of inherited changes ultimately leading to a state where it can induce a transmissible nucleoprotein? Or may not a nucleic acid that somehow manages to spread from one organism to another perhaps find conditions such that it is not only perpetuated but can produce proteins able to combine with it and make it stable and transmissible?

B. Changes in the Behaviour of Nucleic Acids

That there is no longer any example that can be pointed to as evidence for the idea of plant viruses arising as accidents in the metabolism of organisms does not mean that the idea must be abandoned. Accidents in the protein metabolism, which was my speculation in 1939, would not now be acceptable as the primary cause, but accidents in the nucleic acid metabolism not only fit better into current thinking but are less open to some of the objections brought against viruses arising from nucleoproteins.

Perhaps the main objection when the nucleoprotein particles seemed to be the minimal reproductive units was the morphological differences between virus particles and any components of normal plants. This objection could be partly countered by postulating what is almost certainly true, namely that the viruses currently studied have undergone large evolutionary changes and now differ greatly from their forebears, which were probably much less well equipped for transmission and survival outside cells when they first acquired some virus-like behaviour. However, morphological differences become less important when it is accepted that virus morphology is determined by the composition and arrangement of the protein, but that protein synthesis is a secondary feature of virus multiplication and although dependent on the composition of the nucleic acid is not an essential concomitant of nucleic acid replication. That the last is true has long been evident with viruses of lysogenic bacteria and there is increasing evidence that it may be so with plant viruses. Variants of viruses as different morphologically and in other ways as are tobacco rattle (Cadman, 1962), tobacco mosaic (Siegel *et al.*, 1962), and tobacco necrosis (Babos and Kassanis, 1962) have been described that seem to have lost the ability to form the nucleoprotein particles characteristic of their parent viruses; these variants presumably multiply as nucleic acid only, although this is not established unequivocally, and unlike prophage in lysogenic bacteria, are pathogenic. If the ability to produce nucleoprotein particles can be lost, it could presumably be restored by reversing whatever change in the nucleic acid led to the loss. So far the change noted in plant viruses has always been the loss of the ability to produce stable nucleoprotein particles, and it is commonplace that the great majority of genetic changes are losses of characters and not their acquisition, but the prophage in lysogenic bacteria apparently readily regains its ability to produce mature bacteriophage particles.

How then in the light of present knowledge can a virus be pictured as originating? The only essential component of a virus seems to be its nucleic acid, and the purpose of the protein seems largely to protect the nucleic acid during the hazards of transmission. However, the bacterial transforming factors provide examples of nucleic acids that are transmissible, and with current methods for stabilising nucleic acids

in vitro it is likely that some conditions previously thought not to be caused by transmissible agents will be found to be so. Till now, transmission of viruses has largely depended on the infectivity of their nucleic acids being preserved by being contained in a protective package of protein. These packages are of two basic designs, helical tubes and icosahedral shells made by the linking together in a regular manner of similar, perhaps identical, small protein units (Caspar and Klug, 1962). One step in producing a conventional virus, therefore, is the acquisition of potential infectivity by a nucleic acid and another acquiring the ability to affect protein synthesis of a cell so that protein units are made that can condense into protective shells. According to a hypothesis advanced by Belyavin and Rowatt (1963) a stable protein shell can be formed from random collision between protein units that are held together by specific bonds when they meet in the right orientation, and units with 4 or 6 bonds will form hollow cylinders, whereas units with 3 or 5 bonds will generate polyhedra. On this hypothesis, then, a virus with one or other of the common particle shapes will develop when a potentially infective nucleic acid finds itself in an environment where it can stimulate the synthesis of stable protein units of a given size and with the required number of specific bonds.

It is perhaps worth stressing the need for the protein units to be stable. With the current emphasis on the primary role of nucleic acids in determining protein structure by the sequence of nucleotides coding for sequence of amino acids, it is apt to be overlooked that coding alone is not adequate to ensure that a protein will be produced, even though all the necessary amino acids and synthesising systems are present. The protein for which the nucleic acid may be coding must also resist proteases and other disruptive agents in the environment, for otherwise as soon as a link is forged that can be broken it will be. The variants of tobacco rattle, mosaic, and necrosis viruses that seem to multiply without producing the nucleoprotein particles characteristic of their parent strains have been described as defective in their ability to synthesise protein. The defect, though, may be less in their ability to direct protein synthesis than in their ability to ensure that conditions in infected cells are such that the synthesis they are directing ends in a stable product.

Even the multiplication of strains that do produce characteristic nucleoprotein particles does not proceed uniformly to produce a single end product. Extracts from plants infected with type TMV have long been known to contain a range of particles differing in size, composition, and infectivity (Bawden and Pirie, 1945b; Takahashi and Ishii, 1953), and it becomes increasingly evident that infections with other viruses also lead to a mixture of products, of which only a minority may be infective. Particles consisting of protein only need not concern us here, for these can be regarded as protein that condenses into polyhedral shells or partial hollow cylinders without enclosing nucleic acid. However, there is also a range of nucleoprotein particles only some of which are infective. Particles of the rod-shaped viruses like tobacco mosaic and rattle are not infective unless they exceed a minimum length. As infectivity of the longer particles is not destroyed by removing the protein (Gierer and Schramm, 1956; Fraenkel-Conrat, 1956), it seems that infectivity depends on the nucleic acid thread containing about 6000 nucleotides. One explanation for the variable lengths of the individual particles may be that particle length is determined by the length of the nucleic acid along which the protein units condense, and the particles of various lengths in extracts from plants infected with TMV may be formed by protein condensing along incomplete threads or pieces of broken threads. However, this seems inadequate to account for the lengths of specific particles present in extracts from plants infected with tobacco rattle virus. In addition to small rods, which may be produced in such a way or by large rods fragmenting, there are two main lengths, 75 mμ and 185 mμ, such as could not be derived from one another either by aggregation or fragmentation (Harrison and Nixon, 1959). The shorter are the more abundant; they are not infective, but as they are the major part of the specific material present, they can hardly be regarded as anything other than an end product of synthesis. If, then, lengths of particles are determined by the length of the nucleic acid thread, it seems that the nucleic acid must be made in two different but definite lengths. Rods of both lengths contain the same ratio of nucleic acid to protein, but whether the nucleic acid in the two differs in ways other than amount is unknown. If it does, one of the many possible explanations for the different behaviour of the rods of the two specific lengths could be that infectivity and ability to synthesise a given protein are properties conferred by different parts of the longer thread, with the shorter rods containing the part able to code for the protein but lacking the part that confers infectivity.

Except that the shorter rods are the major component of preparations of tobacco rattle virus and it is therefore plausible to assume that they have some biological significance, there is no impelling reason to attribute any specific activity to the nucleic acid they contain; their protein seems to be the same as in the longer rods, so its synthesis could be controlled directly by the infective nucleic acid of the longer particles. Work with the Rothamsted culture of tobacco necrosis virus perhaps provides stronger reasons for suggesting that ability to direct the synthesis of protein and the assembly of a protein shell can occur without the ability to be infective, which perhaps means the ability of the nucleic acid to reproduce. This culture has long been known to yield specific components with three different sedimentation constants, 50, 116, and 240S, of which the smallest were readily obtained crystalline but not infective and behaved as though they were side products of the multiplication of the larger ones (Bawden and Pirie, 1945a, 1950). Recent work (Kassanis and Nixon, 1961) indicates another explanation. The components with the two extreme sedimentation constants prove to be essentially the same material, the larger consisting of 12 of the smaller particles aggregated regularly; when inoculated to bean or tobacco, preparations containing only these components

371

do not produce lesions and there is no evidence that they infect and multiply; they are serologically unrelated to the 116S particles, preparations of which are infective and produce necrotic lesions in bean and tobacco. Plants infected with inoculum containing only 116S particles produce only particles of this type, whereas plants inoculated with mixtures of these and 50S particles contain them both, in proportions that reflect the proportions of the two in the inoculum. In the presence of the 50S particles, the 116S particles produce smaller necrotic lesions than when inoculated on their own. Kassanis and Nixon interpret their results as indicating that the Rothamsted culture contains two unrelated viruses, one a conventional, fully functioning tobacco necrosis virus, and the other, which Kassanis has called the satellite virus, defective in some respect and able to multiply only when the deficiency is made good by some activity supplied by the 116S particles.

More than one of the tobacco necrosis viruses can activate the satellite virus, but tobacco mosaic and several other viruses tested did not. What the activators do to allow the satellite virus to multiply to detectable amounts is not known, but it has the smallest particles of any known plant virus and contains only about one quarter as much nucleic acid, so Kassanis and Nixon suggest that its nucleic acid is inadequate to function independently and needs to borrow activities from the activating virus. This is plausible in the light of current theories about the sequence of nucleotides coding for the sequence of amino acids (Crick *et al.*, 1961), for with the suggested universal coding ratio of three successive nucleotides for each amino acid, the 1500 or so nucleotides in the nucleic acid of the satellite virus might well be able to do little more than code for its structural protein. If the suggestion is correct, it also implies that the part of the nucleic acid thread responsible for infection and nucleic acid multiplication is specific and separate from parts that code for the structural protein, for if the satellite virus does borrow any activity from the tobacco necrosis viruses, it does not show in the constitution of its protein.

There is no call to labour the point that, if sequences of nucleotides represent information able to determine the course of syntheses, the more total nucleic acid a virus contains the more are the specific syntheses it is likely to be able to direct and the more are the proteins it is likely to produce, for use either in its own structure or for other purposes. As evidence, all that is needed is to contrast the simplicity of the small plant viruses that contain about 6000 nucleotides with the complexity of the tadpole-shaped bacteriophages which can engender their own transmission, have particles containing several different kinds of protein, and possess more than 50 times as much nucleic acid, though deoxy and not ribose. However, attractive as it is to speculate about possible relations between the size of nucleic acids and their ability to show virus-like qualities, the uncertainties are too many for the speculation to proceed profitably. Certainly, it is not safe to assume that increase in amount of nucleic acid necessarily leads to morphological complexity or that the satellite virus provides evidence of a minimum size. For example, the iridescent virus from *Tipula paludosa* contains as much deoxyribose nucleic acid as do the coliphages, but although much larger than the icosahedra of the small plant viruses it has essentially the same morphology (Williams and Smith, 1957; Thomas, 1961).

Further, although the satellite virus has not been detected multiplying in any host yet studied unless aided by a tobacco necrosis virus, this does not necessarily mean that it wholly fails to multiply; not only does multiplication have to be considerable before it becomes detectable, but also there may be hosts as yet untested in which it multiplies detectably. At present, however, its seeming ability to multiply only when accompanied by another virus makes its behaviour unique, although some analogies for it can be found in the behaviour of some plant viruses whose multiplication is stimulated by infection with another virus. Potato virus X, for example, reaches larger amounts in tobacco leaves simultaneously infected with potato virus Y than in leaves infected with it alone (Stouffer and Ross, 1961; Close, 1962). The concentration of virus X depends greatly on the temperature at which infected plants are kept and decreases as the temperature increases above about 24°. The proportional effect of simultaneous infection with virus Y increases with increasing temperature, and around 34° virus X may multiply detectably only in leaves also infected with virus Y. Should this also be interpreted as showing that the nucleic acid of virus X carries enough information to multiply in plants below 30° but has to borrow some from the nucleic acid of virus Y to multiply above 30°? In the ultimate analysis, perhaps it should, but the interpretation is little help in explaining the chain of mechanisms involved. A less remote explanation and one more open to study is that increasing temperature makes conditions in tobacco cells increasingly unfavourable for either the synthesis or survival of virus X and that infection with virus Y disturbs the cell metabolism so that whatever system is inimical to virus X does not develop fully. Similarly, there are many examples of phenotypic changes in plants affecting their ability to act as hosts for viruses. We need consider only beans and the tobacco necrosis viruses that activate the satellite virus. These viruses readily infect young leaves, but leaves rapidly lose their susceptibility as they mature; within a week during summer, leaves may change from being excellent hosts to seeming immunity, although partial susceptibility can often be restored by keeping the plants for a day or two in darkness or at temperatures around 36°. This also could be interpreted as indicating that the nucleic acid of the viruses is inadequate to multiply in old leaves and does so in young leaves by borrowing information from the host nucleic acid. But again, it is not very helpful to do so and it is likely to be more rewarding to seek an explanation in changes in the metabolism of the host plant with age that are inimical to the survival of the tobacco necrosis viruses.

The relevance, if any, of the various phenomena described above to a discussion of the origins of viruses is that they provide examples illustrating that the extent to which a nucleic acid behaves like a virus, that is, whether it multiplies, whether it produces specific nucleoprotein particles, and whether it is pathogenic, often depends only on the environment in which it finds itself. They suggest that each of these properties can be evinced independently of the others and so imply that they may be acquired independently, either by a change in the nucleic acid or by a change in its environment. They indicate a general origin of viruses but are of no value in seeking the origin of any individual virus. The problem here is not the lack of sources, but the plethora. Every living cell contains nucleic acids and can synthesise proteins, so every cell is a potential source for originating viruses.

Because viruses are the simplest-known reproducing systems and many are stable when outside cells, they often feature prominently in discussions on the origin of life, but whether they are relevant to such discussions is another matter. Outside cells, they are inert and they require such a complex and specific environment before they can multiply, it seems very improbable that entities closely resembling viruses existed in the pre-biotic world. Rather than stages leading to the development of cellular organisms, they are more likely late evolutionary forms, representing the equivalent of errors in copying the complex information needed to direct the activities of an elaborate biological system. In terms of information theory, they can be regarded as pieces of misinformation that are perpetuated in and confuse the information service on which the metabolism of cells depends.

That viruses are late products of evolution is no novel concept; it has for long been implicit both in the "free-gene" hypothesis and in the idea that they derived by degenerative evolution from pathogenic microbes. How do these ideas stand now? The free-gene concept has little appeal as the origin for plant viruses that contain ribose nucleic acid, and it is obvious that viruses have too many independently inherited characters to be regarded as single genes, but the deoxy nucleic acids of bacteriophage can aptly be regarded as pieces of the bacterial chromosomes that become fully operative only when they become free (Luria, 1959). The idea of viruses evolving through the loss of form and function by parasitic microbes in essence postulates that some reproducing part of the microbe now manages to reproduce in the host cells rather than in the microbe. There is no reason to exclude this as a possible origin, but there is equally no reason to think it applies at all generally. The only reason for selecting pathogenic microbes as origins of viruses is that they are obviously in a favoured position for introducing potential viruses into other organisms. However, all other cells also contain nucleic acids, and it is this generality of nucleic acids that precludes conclusions about the initial origins of current viruses. Whether any virus that today infects flowering plants, originated in a flowering plant, a bacterium or fungus, an insect or some other animal, is likely always to remain in doubt. It may be tempting to assume that viruses originated in the kinds of hosts they now infect, but any such assumption is clearly unwarranted when some viruses can use as hosts organisms that are phylogenetically so remote as flowering plants and insects.

Nor need viruses that resemble one another morphologically or in their ratios of protein to nucleic acid be considered necessarily to be closely related phylogenetically. To be a virus, a nucleic acid must be stable in an environment where it is an alien. To reach a foreign environment, it must be stable enough to be transmissible; in general this seems to require packing the nucleic acid in protein and there seem to be only a few ways in which this can be done. Similar morphology, then, may come from convergent evolution, a feature determined by physical requirements rather than reflecting similar phylogeny. The only common ancestry for currently existing viruses may lie very far back, in whatever was the successful precursor of nucleic acids that allowed them to be selected as the materials responsible for genetic continuity and for directing biological syntheses. On current knowledge it is reasonable to seek origins for plant viruses in ribosomal or messenger rather than chromosomal nucleic acid, but to speculate beyond this and try to identify the kind of accidents that lead to these acquiring virus-like characters is idle until more is known both about these and their differences from virus nucleic acids.

17–4. INFECTION AND MULTIPLICATION

If viruses ever originate spontaneously from normal nucleic acids changing in ways that leave them still able to reproduce but make them transmissible and pathogenic, such happenings can be expected to be rare. Most accidents during the assembly of nucleic acids normal to cells will be trivial; though they may lead to some local and temporary imbalance of syntheses, the aberrant forms are likely either to be unstable or, if stable, unable to reproduce. Also, even when an accident or series of accidents creates a virus, this will be significant only in the organism where it happens, unless the virus manages to spread from this organism to others in which it can also multiply. Although the creation of viruses will be a rare event, it may be commoner than is evident, because viruses may often have arisen only to disappear on the death of the organism in which they arose. Even the most stable of viruses inactivate slowly *in vitro* and survival demands the infection of a continued succession of susceptible cells. The vast majority of cells that contain viruses do so because of exogenous infection, and the immediate origin of most virus particles is to be sought not in the nucleic acids of their hosts but in virus that has invaded them from outside.

The viruses that infect flowering plants spread in two ways, (1) from one individual organism to another, which may or may not be of the same species, and (2) from cell to cell within one individual. They do the second unaided, but not the first, because uninjured plants seem immune from infection and some second agent, usually an organism that acts as a vector and also moves the virus through space, is needed to make a wound through which the infecting virus can enter. Different viruses differ greatly in the kind of agent that spreads them between individuals and in the readiness with which they can be transmitted. They also differ greatly in the extent to which they spread from cell to cell, for whereas some infect and multiply in only a small volume of cells around their initial entry points, others can spread systemically, some to invade all the tissues including cells that result from meiosis, but most falling short of a true systemic infection by failing to enter the pollen or egg cells and some by failing to enter the apical meristems.

These differences in behaviour are far from wholly determined by the identity of a virus, for the same virus may be localised in one host, cause a near systemic infection in a second, and be seed-transmitted in a third. However, even to speak of what any given virus does in any given host is to generalise beyond what is justified, because what it does in any one host can be determined by the physiological condition of the host at that time. Whether or not a plant can be a host for a given virus is presumably determined primarily by its genetical constitution, but phenotypic changes can determine whether a potential host will become infected by a given inoculum, how it reacts should it be infected, and the extent to which the virus will multiply in it.

Many phenomena could be described illustrating that the establishment of infection and continued virus multiplication depend on the condition of the host, but unfortunately there is little information on which to base any adequate explanations of the phenomena. For infection to occur and virus to be produced in a cell, both the infecting inoculum and the products of its activities must be stable, and the simplest explanation of increasing resistance to infection is an increase in the scavenging powers of the cells to get rid of aberrant nucleic acid or protein, but there are many other possible explanations. If cells contain specific infectible sites to which infecting virus must attach itself, or components that it must enter, changes in their composition or structure might complicate or prevent infection. Or, if the nucleic acid must be freed from its accompanying protein as a preliminary step in the infection process, this is presumably done by some host system and infection would depend on this system acting. The idea that susceptibility to infection depends on such a system is implicit in the claim that *Rhoeo discolor* is insusceptible to infection by intact TMV particles but becomes infected by inocula of its nucleic acid (Gordon and Smith, 1960). However, although unequivocal virus multiplication in this intrinsically resistant host is more readily demonstrated with inocula of nucleic acid, because subsequent assays are not complicated by residual infectivity from the inoculum, intact particles can infect (Bawden, 1961). The idea that increasing resistance to infection reflects the increasing failure of some host system able to separate virus nucleic acid from its protecting protein loses its attractiveness when, in all other hosts yet tested, changes that increase resistance do so proportionally much more when the inoculum is nucleic acid than when it is intact virus particles.

Changes in resistance to infection are usually measured either by differences in numbers of local lesions or in differences in amount of virus present in leaf extracts made at different times after inoculation. Differences are usually attributed to differences in the numbers of sites at which the inoculum established infection. This may be justified, but it is by no means certain that it is. It is well to remember that, from what is known about the virus content of single leaf cells and the minimum amount of virus that can currently be detected, infection of and virus multiplication in single cells would most likely pass undetected. That a virus needs to infect many cells at each site to cause a visible lesion is obvious enough, but it is less obvious that the same is true before multiplication can be detected by infectivity assays. Whether the initial inoculum infects more than one cell at each site is uncertain, but many mesophyll cells are infected by the time multiplication is evident in leaves in which the inoculum probably infects only the epidermis, and this presumably means that virus produced in the epidermis has moved to and infected the mesophyll. Apparent changes in susceptibility to infection may be less in the changed ability of inoculated cells to deny infection than in the changed ability of virus to spread from these cells to their neighbours. Similarly, the seeming intrinsic immunity of some plants to infection may not mean that individually their cells cannot support the multiplication of the virus, but that the virus cannot spread between cells. A corollary to this is that infection and virus multiplication can be studied only in hosts in which a virus does move between cells, and the study is thereby complicated by the fact that it is rarely possible to distinguish between increases in virus content because of virus increasing in already infected cells and because of additional cells becoming newly infected. At all times except soon after inoculation, the system being studied consists of cells in different stages of the full infection cycle.

Presumably the establishment of infection in a cell is basically similar whether it happens directly from an exogenous inoculum or indirectly by virus produced in another cell of the same plant. The end result is the same whether the extraneous inoculum is nucleic acid or intact virus particles, so it matters not that, when the inoculum is intact virus particles, there may be the difference that spread between cells may be by nucleic acid, perhaps moving along the plasmodesmata that link leaf cells, which travels between cells like the messenger ribose nucleic acid of uninfected cells is thought to travel between nucleus and ribosomes. The likelihood of infection between cells being by nucleic acid is perhaps indicated by the fact that variants of viruses such as tobacco rattle and tobacco necrosis that differ in their ability to form stable nucleoprotein particles, all produce similar local lesions. That the nucleoprotein particles may be better able than nucleic acid to move over long distances through the vascular system, however, is suggested ·by the fact that variants of tobacco rattle virus seemingly defective in their ability to form such particles take much longer than other strains to infect plants systemically.

There is no evidence that any plant virus possesses any enzymic activity, and the fact that infections with inocula of nucleic acid can lead to the formation of nucleoprotein particles suggests that they need not introduce any specific enzymes to aid their multiplication. In other words, host cells must not only supply the nucleotides and amino acids that form the substance of a virus, but also provide the polymerases able to join these together in the specific sequences and final sizes characteristic of the virus. Whether they need to contain these enzymes ready-made, or whether it is part of a successful infection process to cause them to be made, is unknown. However, that biological systems unable to support virus multiplication may contain enzymes able to string amino acids together in an order determined by virus nucleic acid is suggested by the report that nucleic acid from TMV stimulates a cell-free system from *Escherichia coli* to produce protein that reacts specifically with virus antiserum (Tsugita *et al.*, 1962). Hence, in accordance with expectations from the coding hypothesis, the mere presence of a nucleic acid in a protein-synthesising system influenced the sequence in which amino acids were joined together, but the protein formed differed in many ways from virus protein and did not combine to form virus-like rods, so it seems that how the code is translated does depend on the environment where it is translated. If this report is confirmed and it is further found that nucleic acid from TMV produces different proteins when added to cell-free, protein-synthesising systems from different sources, it will obviously have implications when seeking explanations for the failure of some virus variants to produce stable nucleoprotein particles.

In general terms it is simple to state that infection primarily entails the survival of the virus nucleic acid in a cell and its ability to direct the metabolism of the cell so that virus nucleic acid is produced in addition to the nucleic acids normal to the cell. This in turn will affect protein synthesis, but may not lead to the formation of the protein sub-units. If it does, these will condense around the nucleic acid to form either the hollow tubes or polyhedra characteristic of virus particles. As particles of TMV can be re-formed *in vitro* simply by acidifying disaggregated virus protein and free nucleic acid (Fraenkel-Conrat and

Williams, 1955), this last obviously calls for no very specific environment, though whether this is also true of other viruses has yet to be demonstrated.

These general terms, however, give no idea of what actually goes on during the establishment of infection. Nor do they account for the differences between the behaviour of different viruses, such as the changes in the phenotype of a potential host denying infection by one virus but not by another. Nor indeed what limits the host range of any one virus. How is it that a virus able to multiply in such diverse organisms as a leafhopper and a flowering plant may be able to do so in only a few species of either leafhoppers or plants? How is it that two viruses may have a dozen common hosts, but then each fails to multiply in plants that support the multiplication of the other? To these and to all other questions of specificity, the generalities of nucleic acids being templates both for their own replication and for the stringing together of amino acids return only dusty answers. On present knowledge of the composition of nucleic acids of plant viruses, there is nothing except differences between the ratios and sequences of their four nucleotides to distinguish them from one another or from other nucleic acids; similarly, their proteins seem not to contain any distinctive amino acids. Hence, for virus multiplication there is no need to invoke any mechanisms additional to those that produce other nucleic acids and proteins, but while accepting this and before proceeding to discuss the infection process, it is well to stress that there must be some distinctive quality that allows viruses to be viruses; also that individual viruses have specific limitations and they are far from able to multiply in all cells that contain their known components.

A. Establishing Infection

Knowledge about the events concerned in the initiation of infection is restricted to infection by extraneous inocula, and is all indirect. There is evidence that nucleoprotein particles inoculated to leaves become unstable and, from differences between the behaviour of inocula of intact and disrupted virus, it is possible to piece together a story of the nucleic acid from virus particles becoming free from its protective protein and finding a safe haven in some cell component, rich in nucleic acid, where it is preserved from inactivation. The story, though, is woefully incomplete, for if the nucleic acid does shed its protein shell, whether it does it at cell walls or at the boundaries of such cell components as the nuclei or ribosomes, is unknown. For the safe haven, obvious suspects are the nucleus or ribosomes, with the nucleus perhaps the first choice because it is thought to be the origin of the messenger nucleic acids that determine the identity of proteins synthesised by the ribosomes, and messenger nucleic acids seem perhaps the nearest analogues to virus nucleic acids.

Many phenomena can be instanced in support of the idea that an initial step in the process of infection is for the nucleic acid of infecting particles to become freed from its protein. Indeed, this now is often spoken of as though it were established unequivocally, so it is perhaps well to point out that it is a plausible interpretation rather than necessarily true, and that not all the evidence advanced in its support has been consistent or demands this explanation. For instance, that virus retained by leaves thoroughly washed after inoculation becomes unstable is evidenced by the fall in infectivity of successive extracts made until virus multiplication becomes evident. However, virus can inactivate without separating into protein and nucleic acid, and whether the inactivation has any relevance to the infection process is uncertain because it continues for many hours after there is good reason to think that infecting particles have already undergone their initial changes. Also, although the fact that pancreatic ribonuclease inhibits infections when present in inocula, or when applied to leaves shortly after they are inoculated, is plausibly explained by postulating that it hydrolyses the nucleic acid when it becomes free (Casterman and Jeener, 1955), the explanation becomes rather less compelling with the knowledge that inhibitors without any nuclease activity behave similarly, that leaf ribonucleases, although equally able to hydrolyse virus nucleic acids *in vitro,* do not inhibit infections to the same extent, and the ability of pancreatic ribonuclease to inhibit depends much on the species of host plant.

Experiments with ultraviolet radiation provide further evidence for infecting virus particles changing their state and becoming unstable. With inocula of suitably irradiated potato virus X, three states can be identified: first the damaged virus is not photoreactivable; a few particles change within 15 minutes from this state to the second, in which they are photoreactivable, but most take 30 and some more than 60 minutes; the second state lasts for an hour or so, when the particles pass into a state in which they are no longer reactivated by exposing the leaves to visible light. How inocula of nucleic acid from virus X would behave has not been determined, but irradiated nucleic acid from TMV becomes photoreactivable without any lag period. This again cannot be compared with the behaviour of intact TMV, for this does not undergo photoreactivable changes when irradiated. However, it may be relevant that virus nucleic acids inoculated to leaves seem to inactivate unless they establish infection within an hour or so. Comparisons between intact particles of one virus and the nucleic acid from another, are obviously suspect, but there is the implication not only that free nucleic acid becomes photoreactivable sooner than intact virus particles, but that the unstable state with virus X may be when the nucleic acid becomes free (Bawden and Kleczkowski, 1955, 1959, 1960).

Better evidence for nucleic acid changing its state sooner than intact virus particles comes from irradiating leaves at different periods after inoculation (Siegel and Wildman, 1956; Siegel *et al.,* 1957). After an interval that depends greatly on the ·temperature but otherwise seems characteristic of individual viruses and virus strains, infection sites initiated by intact virus start to increase in their resistance to inactivation by ultraviolet radiation. By contrast, infection sites initiated by inocula of nucleic acid from several different viruses all start to increase their resistance

very soon after inoculation. On the assumption that the processes initiated by the two kinds of inocula coincide from when the resistance of the infection sites starts to increase, there is no better explanation of the extra time taken by the intact particles than that it represents their undressing period. However, if this assumption is unjustified, there is another possible explanation, namely that the nucleic acid inoculum acquires its initial resistance by doing something the intact particles do not, perhaps by clothing itself in some protective garment.

Other differences between the behaviour of the two inocula have also been described, such as that virus multiplication occurs sooner when the inocula are nucleic acid (Schramm and Engler, 1958; Kassanis, 1959, 1960) and that local lesions appear sooner (Fraenkel-Conrat *et al.,* 1958), but these are of doubtful significance. First, the intervals reported by different workers between when TMV begins to multiply in leaves inoculated with the two inocula differ greatly; secondly, the certainty with which multiplication can first be detected differs with the two inocula. Even the most concentrated inocula of nucleic acid leave no residual infectivity in leaf extracts, so assays start with the base line at zero, whereas the infectivity of successive extracts of leaves inoculated with intact virus falls before it begins to rise, and for a time the inactivation of the inoculum can obscure virus multiplication.

The statement that nucleic acid produces local lesions sooner is also inaccurate; when both kinds of inocula are inoculated to opposite halves of the same leaves in amounts that produce similar numbers of lesions, the first lesions appear on both halves simultaneously. The difference is that the halves inoculated with intact virus continue to produce lesions for much longer; in other words, the lesions produced by nucleic acid are much better synchronised. This does not demand the explanation that intact virus must shed its protein to infect, but rather suggests that whereas the nucleic acid must act quickly to act at all, intact particles can be more dilatory without being inactivated. Evidence supporting this difference comes from inoculating appropriately irradiated leaves; leaves inoculated while their capacity to support infection is being photoreactivated become infected by intact virus but not by nucleic acid (Bawden and Kleczkowski, 1960). This greater instability of the free nucleic acid may account for many of the differences between the behaviour of the two kinds of inoculum, but the fact that both can produce lesions equally quickly suggests that, if intact particles must shed their protein to infect, some do so almost immediately they enter the leaf.

What processes determine whether an active inoculum will infect a potential host are almost wholly unknown. The fact that resistance increases proportionally more to infection by nucleic acid than by intact virus suggests that lack of host systems able to separate virus protein from nucleic acid are rarely responsible. Obviously, if protein and nucleic acid must separate, the critical event may be whether the free nucleic acid survives. But to assume that the protein does no more than protect the nucleic acid during a hazardous journey to infection sites may be unjustified. Are there perhaps infection sites open to intact virus particles but debarred to free nucleic acid? An active role by the protein is perhaps suggested by its ability to inhibit infections by intact particles. However, this and the inhibition by virus antibodies are also explicable by postulating that free virus protein, and virus antibodies, act by interfering with the *in vivo* system that otherwise would have allowed the nucleic acid to become free.

Until much more is known about the infection process and the identity of infection sites, differences between the behaviour of the two kinds of inocula will remain largely uninterpretable. For example, how is the behaviour of red clover mottle virus in plants at different temperatures to be explained? Up to 28° increases in temperature shorten the lag period between inoculation and when infection sites start to increase their resistance to inactivation by ultraviolet radiation, but at 32° the infection sites keep their initial susceptibility for a day or more. The inoculum slowly inactivates at 32° and plants kept continuously at this temperature produce few or no lesions, but after a day at 32° leaves put at a lower temperature produce half as many lesions as when kept continuously at the lower temperature (Bawden and Sinha, 1961). Does this mean that the system freeing the virus nucleic acid from its protein works increasingly fast up to 28°, but fails at 32°? It may, but if so another factor is also needed to explain the failure of infection, because preparations of nucleic acid that infect at lower temperatures do not infect plants at 32°. Indeed, such inocula also fail to infect plants kept for only 4 hours at 32° and then put at a lower temperature. This contrast between the ability of the two kinds of inocula to survive in leaves at 32° suggests that, whatever may happen at lower temperatures, the nucleic acid probably does not become free at 32°. Other viruses will infect beans kept at 32°. Does this mean they use a different undressing system? Or are more readily undressed? Or have a more stable nucleic acid? Or use a different infection site? Or what? To try to explain all failures to infect on the basis of a single critical step in the infection process, particularly the separation of nucleic acid from protein, which although likely is unestablished, is probably vain. There may well be many critical stages, not only when the inoculum, whether nucleic acid or intact virus, is exposed to potential inactivating systems, but also later when steps in synthesis may depend on the host containing necessary metabolites or enzyme systems and being unable to destroy virus components as they are formed.

B. SYNTHESIS AND ASSEMBLY

The fact that infection sites continue to increase their resistance to inactivation by ultraviolet radiation with time, suggests that the infecting material, whether nucleic acid or intact virus, is in a region of the cell where it is stimulating the synthesis of purines and pyrimidines, and it is reasonable to suspect the nucleus or ribosomes. Although the first claims to have demonstrated that the synthesis of virus nucleic acid precedes protein were probably unjustified, there is now considerable evidence that this is true. It is plausible to think of nucleic acid multiplying in the nucleus and moving from there to the ribosomes, perhaps not only those in the same cell but also in nearby ones, where it changes the direction of protein synthesis. Presumably thiouracil (Commoner and Mercer, 1951, 1952) and other analogues of purines and pyrimidines that inhibit virus multiplication do so by confusing synthesis at the initial stage of assembling nucleotides. At what stage virus variants that fail to produce stable nucleoprotein particles behave differently from their parents is unknown, but inability to influence ribosomes to produce the customary protein units is an obvious choice.

Comparisons between a parent tobacco necrosis virus and one such variant show that their behaviour runs parallel early in infection and perhaps provide the strongest evidence that protein synthesis waits on the synthesis of nucleic acid. The parent strain is readily transmitted by inoculating leaves with sap, whereas the variant is not and is transmissible only when leaf extracts are made in ways that inhibit ribonuclease activity, of which the simplest is to grind leaves in the presence of bentonite and pH 8 phosphate buffer (Kassanis and Welkie, 1962). There is no doubt that the variant occurs in leaf extracts as free nucleic acid, and it seems likely that this is also its state *in vivo*, though this is unproven. Kassanis and Welkie inoculated leaves with either nucleic acid from the parent virus or the unstable variant and then assayed leaf extracts made at intervals of 2 hours by two ways, grinding in water and in alkaline bentonite. Inoculated plants were kept at 23° and with the inocula leaving no residual infectivity, the extracts at 2 and 4 hours were not infective, but those made with bentonite at 6 hours were, equally so whether from leaves inoculated with the parent virus or the variant. Water extracts of leaves with the variant never produced more than an occasional lesion, whereas water extracts of leaves with the parent virus were first infective at 8 hours, 2 hours later than the bentonite extracts, and for the first 12 hours were much less so than

the bentonite extracts. The difference then became less and after 24 hours both kinds of extract from leaves infected with the parent virus contained so much nucleoprotein that any proportion of infectivity in the bentonite extracts conferred by nucleic acid was too small to detect. Bentonite extracts made up to a week after inoculation contained about the same amount of virus nucleic acid whether from leaves infected with the parent virus or the variant. How the nucleic acid of the variant is stabilised can only be guessed at; when introduced into leaves as an inoculum, it has only a brief existence unless it establishes infection, yet it survives in the necrotic lesions for long periods. Clearly the leaves still contain ribonuclease and other systems able to inactivate it *in vitro,* for water extracts of leaves are not infective. In infected leaves it must be protected from these, either in some cell component, or by some covering less stable than the protein of the parent virus, or else the cells in which it is produced are unable to inactivate it.

It has been long known that virus protein free from nucleic acid occurs in extracts of plants infected with turnip yellow mosaic (Markham and Smith, 1949) and TMV (Takahashi and Ishii, 1952, 1953). With the first they take the form of protein shells, morphologically resembling virus particles, and with the second, aggregates of a few protein units, which will join together *in vitro* to form tubular particles. Such free protein has not been detected until leaf extracts already contain much nucleoprotein, and although its amount may fluctuate, it usually increases more or less in proportion to the nucleoprotein. Its occurrence probably means that the synthesis of nucleic acid and of protein are separately controlled and do not always run in step. If nucleic acid multiplication is a preliminary to protein synthesis in each infected cell, the first protein formed will always find nucleic acid to combine with, whereas later on protein may be in excess. The effect of thiouracil on the multiplication of turnip yellow mosaic virus perhaps provides evidence that, once the synthesis of virus protein has been initiated, it may continue without a balancing synthesis of nucleic acid (Francki and Matthews, 1962). Applying thiouracil to leaves already infected for some days increases the ratio of protein shells to nucleoprotein particles from the usual 1 to 2, to 4 to 1; as there is no corresponding increase in the total leaf nucleic acid, the changed ratio seems to happen because of failure to synthesise nucleic acid rather than because thiouracil prevents nucleic acid from being incorporated in protein. This, of course, carries the further implication that the protein synthesised is not necessarily determined by the presence of a nucleic acid thread with which it will later combine to form nucleoprotein particles, but that, once the ribosomes have been routed to form virus protein, they do so without needing a repeated stimulus.

Virus infection leads to a range of products—nucleic acid, protein, and nucleoprotein—only some of which are infective. Non-infective specific particles seem a constant feature of infections by many viruses. Their biological significance is unknown, but although unable to initiate new infections they may not be wholly inactive in the cells where they are produced. Not all may originate in the same way. Some may be examples of incomplete assembly, others of breakdown products; for in cells not killed by infection, viruses like other nucleoproteins are probably often changing in amount, with the concentration at any one time representing the balance between synthesis and degradation. Only exceptionally stable viruses, such as TMV, achieve and maintain large concentrations; many probably maintain themselves only by continued multiplication and some fail to maintain the concentrations they attain early on, but from a peak concentration diminish rapidly, presumably because they are broken down and their components return to the metabolic pool sustaining normal nucleoprotein synthesis.

17–5. GENETIC VARIABILITY

Variability in viruses has long been recognised, but only recently has its extent been appreciated or has it been possible to speculate on possible causes. The variations mostly recognised at first were in pathogenicity or host range, and with some viruses these are the only type yet described but with others there is evidence of variability in almost every character that has been examined; amino acid constitution, ability to form characteristic nucleoprotein particles or be transmitted by a given vector, crystal form, resistance to inactivating treatments, these and others can all change, and some seemingly independently of others. Viruses reach such immense populations that the great variability of some is no surprise. Evidence has been advanced suggesting variability by genetic recombination (Best and Gallus, 1955; Best, 1961; Watson, 1960), but random mutation alone could be expected to produce many variants. With a mutation rate of only 1 in 10^6, many thousands of aberrant types would be contained in one systemically infected tobacco plant.

The fact that inocula of nucleic acid produce the same results as inocula of nucleoprotein particles shows that the genetic specificity resides wholly in the nucleic acid, and until there is knowledge of components any other than the four nucleotides making up its bulk, the causes of variation can be sought only in the ways these four are arranged. With TMV nucleic acid containing 6000 or so nucleotides, there are obvious possibilities of many different sequences; also, producing a chain of this length in a required sequence will call for a remarkably close control to avoid errors. Most errors will not be stable, and variants can be regarded as errors in copying that manage to be perpetuated. Such errors may be the simple substitution of one nucleotide by another, but there could well be others, such as the omission of a short sequence of nucleotides or the rearranging of the order of oligonucleotides. In the same way as many sentences become meaningless when a word is omitted or its position changed, but some take on a completely new meaning, so omitting or moving an oligonucleotide will usually give an unviable result but may occasionally produce something with a new genetic specificity.

Until recently mutation was something that seemed to happen only *in vivo* while viruses were multiplying. It usually became evident when employing selected instead of bulk inoculum or when the conditions in which the virus was propagated were changed considerably. With unselected inoculum and a constant host plant grown in one environment, cultures long remain stable because natural selection then operates as a stabilising influence. Few variants will be better suited than their parents for conditions in which their parents have long been selected, and the more they depart from their parents the less likely are they to supersede their parents. When conditions change, however, they may be better fitted than their parents to survive and so show their existence. The ability to vary, indeed, has its main evolutionary significance in increasing the range of potential habitats and the likelihood that the line will survive when conditions change. All such variants are explicable on the basis of selecting aberrations occurring while the nucleic acid was being assembled, but recently there have been increasing claims that mutations can be produced *in vitro* by treating viruses or their nucleic acids with various chemicals.

The first such chemical was nitrous acid, and its action on TMV has also been advanced as evidence that the genetic specificity is determined by the sequence of nucleotides and can be changed simply by substituting one nucleotide with another. Nitrous acid is a deaminator and converts adenine, guanine, and cytosine, respectively, to hypoxanthine, xanthine, and uracil. It does this when it reacts with nucleic acid of TMV (Schuster and Schramm, 1958), and there is no doubt that, by replacing cytosine with uracil, it could alter the distribution of nucleotides normal to the nucleic acid. It inactivates viruses, and of those who have studied its action (Mundry and Gierer, 1958; Mundry, 1959; Bawden, 1959; Siegel, 1960; Tsugita and Fraenkel-Conrat, 1960; Rappaport and Wildman, 1962), only Bawden has questioned that it is also mutagenic, that is, able to produce changes in the nucleic acid that are perpetuated in the progeny. There is no doubt that nitrous acid alters the qualitative behaviour of inocula and that variants of TMV are much more easily isolated from

plants inoculated with partially inactivated than with untreated preparations. However, although many different variants have been isolated from treated preparations, none of these is distinctive, and it seems highly improbable that some of them could result from the single deamination that has been reported to be the mutagenic action. As with variants isolated without chemical treatments, some from preparations treated with nitrous acid are pathogenically different but have the same amino acid constitutions; others have different amino acid compositions from the parent strain and these fall into the same 2 groups as naturally occurring variants, 1 group with 3 or fewer differences and the other with about 16 differences, which are scattered throughout the peptide chain (Tsugita and Fraenkel-Conrat, 1962; Tsugita, 1962a,b).

Not only do the variants isolated after treatment with nitrous acid resemble those that already exist in untreated preparations of TMV, but similar ones have also been reported to be produced with N-bromosuccinimide and the alkylating agents methyl iodide, dimethylsulphate, and propylene oxide (Fraenkel-Conrat, 1961). If these chemicals, and nitrous acid, are producing mutations and not acting by allowing already existing variants to be preferentially selected, then clearly the chemical basis of mutation lies in something other than changing the order of customary nucleotides, because these other chemicals do not change cytosine to uracil, or change any other normal base to another. Indeed, the chemical changes they produce seem unlikely to be the kind that would be perpetuated when nucleic acid replicates. If they are mutagenic, and all produce the same kind of variants, then it seems they probably act by damaging specific segments of the nucleic acid thread so that they cannot reproduce and are eliminated when the nucleic acid replicates. Most variants from type TMV seem to lack some character of the type strain, and the fact that the type strain produces more variants than most other strains, or other viruses, may perhaps indicate that it has more dispensable characters.

The mutagenic action of these chemicals

is widely regarded as being established, so it is well to stress that none has produced any novel variant and when tested on tomato aucuba mosaic virus, a strain less variable than type TMV, nitrous acid gave no evidence of producing variants, though it was inactivating and so must presumably have been changing cytosine to uracil. The failure to get novel variants is no evidence that these chemicals are not mutagenic, because mutagens might be expected to produce the same kinds of variants that also occur most often spontaneously. However, when there is good reason to think that more than 1% of the particles in the preparations treated already differed from the type strain (1% of tomato aucuba mosaic virus can be added to preparations of TMV and go unnoticed unless it is specially sought), it is wise to suspect selection instead of mutation until there is evidence that the mutants obtained after chemical treatments have undergone some inheritable chemical change. The greater ease with which variants are isolated after chemical treatment may lie in effects on the type strain that make it less able than previously to dominate over variants at infection sites.

Whether or not chemicals produce mutations *in vitro*, it is obvious that variants can differ in pathogenicity but have the same amino acid constitution. This has two implications, (1) that the structural protein of the virus is not concerned in the causing of symptoms, and (2) that different nucleic acids can produce the same kind of protein. Whether the multiplication of the nucleic acid is directly responsible for the symptoms or whether it operates by producing other protein distinct from its structural ones, is unknown. With a coding ratio of three nucleotides to one amino acid, less than 10% of the nucleotides of TMV would be needed to code for its structural protein. Hence, there is nothing in conflict between the coding hypothesis and the existence of pathogenically different variants with the same amino acid constitution, because parts of the nucleic acid coding for the structural protein might be identical while parts responsible for other functions differed. However, there is conflict between the coding

hypothesis and the ideas advanced to explain the behaviour of chemical mutagens, for although again it is plausible that pathogenically distinct variants might occur from single changes in nucleotides, with or without single changes in the amino acid constitution, the occurrence of many scattered amino acid changes is incompatible with single substitutions of cytosine by uracil.

What kind of change happens to variants that cease to form customary nucleoprotein particles is wholly obscure, but the change seems to happen too often to equate it with other kinds of mutations. With some isolates of tobacco rattle virus more than half the lesions formed by preparations of nucleoprotein particles are defective variants (Cadman and Harrison, 1959), and 5% of the lesions produced by stable preparations of a tobacco necrosis virus contain only the unstable variant (Babos and Kassanis, 1962). It seems that, while the forms able to produce stable nucleoprotein particles are multiplying, their nucleic acid segregates into two types, both of which can become enclosed in protein shells to form stable nucleoprotein particles, but only one of which has the necessary structure to produce the required protein in infected cells. The defective variants seem not to revert to the parent types, but continue indefinitely unable to produce stable particles, behaving in a way analogous to the properties of pure recessives that result when heterozygotes are selfed. The nucleic acids from parent and variant types have yet to be compared, so it is unknown whether the ability to produce nucleoprotein particles depends on a major difference in the constitution or size of the nucleic acid.

Work on the variability of viruses promises to be rich in results significant not only to pathology but also to many other branches of biology, because virus strains currently seem to provide the most promising systems for seeking information about such general biological problems as nucleic acid replication, the relation between structure of nucleic acid and structure of protein, and the causes of genetic changes. However, there is need for caution and patience, for the subject is still in the state of disclosing phenomena rather than explaining them, and may well remain in this state for some time. Simple as viruses seem to be when studied *in vitro*, they are not then behaving like viruses; when they are, they become part of the functioning of a whole cell and there is as yet little more than a glimmering of how complex are the processes in which they become engaged. The only safe speculation is that the future, like the past, will bring plenty of surprises; only slightly less safe is to suggest that it will be more profitable to speculate on the likelihood that current hypotheses are wrong, than to try to adapt them to accommodate awkward facts.

17–6. LITERATURE CITED

Babos, P., and Kassanis, B. (1962). Virology 18, 206.

Bagnall, R. H., Wetter, C., and Larson, R. H. (1959). Phytopathology 49, 435.

Bawden, F. C. (1959). Nature (London) 184, 27.

Bawden, F. C. (1961). J. Biol. Chem. 236, 2760.

Bawden, F. C., and Kleczkowski, A. (1955). J. Gen. Microbiol. 13, 370.

Bawden, F. C., and Kleczkowski, A. (1959). Nature (London) 183, 503.

Bawden, F. C., and Kleczkowski, A. (1960). Virology 10, 163.

Bawden, F. C., and Pirie, N. W. (1945a). Brit. J. Expt. Path. 26, 277.

Bawden, F. C., and Pirie, N. W. (1945b). Brit. J. Expt. Path. 26, 294.

Bawden, F. C., and Pirie, N. W. (1950). J. Gen. Microbiol. 4, 464.

Bawden, F. C., and Sinha, R. C. (1961). Virology 14, 198.

Bawden, F. C., Kassanis, B., and Nixon, H. L. (1950). J. Gen. Microbiol. 4, 210.

Belyavin, G., and Rowatt, E. (1963). Biochem. J. 87, 45P.

Best, R. J. (1961). Virology 15, 327.

Best, R. J., and Gallus, H. P. C. (1955). Enzymologia 17, 297.

Cadman, C. H. (1962). Nature (London) 193, 49.

Cadman, C. H., and Harrison, B. D. (1959). Ann. Appl. Biol. 47, 542.

Caspar, D. L. D., and Klug, A. (1962). Cold Spring Harbor Symp. Quant. Biol. 27, 1.

Caspar, D. L. D., Dulbecco, R., Klug, A., Lwoff, A., Stoker, M. G. P., Tournier, P., and Wildy, P. (1962). Cold Spring Harbor Symp. Quant. Biol. 27, 49.

Casterman, C., and Jeener, R. (1955). Biochim. Biophys. Acta 16, 433.

Close, R. (1962). Ph.D. Thesis. London Univ.

Commoner, B., and Mercer, F. L. (1951). Nature (London) 168, 113.

Commoner, B., and Mercer, F. L. (1952). Arch. Biochem. Biophys. 35, 278.

Crick, F. H. C., Barnett, L., Brenner, S., and Watts-Tobin, R. J. (1961). Nature (London) 192, 1227.

Darlington, C. D. (1944). Nature (London) 154, 164.

Darlington, C. D. (1949). Colloq. Int. Cent. Nat. Rech. Sci. 8, 123.

Fraenkel-Conrat, H. (1956). J. Amer. Chem. Soc. 78, 883.

Fraenkel-Conrat, H. (1961). Biochim. Biophys. Acta 49, 169.

Fraenkel-Conrat, H., and Williams, R. C. (1955). Proc. Nat. Acad. Sci. Wash. 41, 690.

Fraenkel-Conrat, H., Singer, B., and Veldee, S. (1958). Biochim. Biophys. Acta 29, 639.

Francki, R. I. B., and Matthews, R. E. F. (1962). Virology 17, 367.

Gierer, A., and Schramm, G. (1956). Nature (London) 177, 702.

Gordon, M. P., and Smith, C. (1960). J. Biol. Chem. 235, PC28.

Harrison, B. D., and Nixon, H. L. (1959). J. Gen. Microbiol. 21, 569.

Johnson, M. W., and Markham, R. (1962). Virology 17, 276.

Kassanis, B. (1956). J. Gen. Microbiol. 15, 620.

Kassanis, B. (1957). Ann. Appl. Biol. 45, 422.

Kassanis, B. (1959). J. Gen. Microbiol. 20, 704.

Kassanis, B. (1960). Virology 10, 353.

Kassanis, B. (1961). Eur. Potato J. 4, 13.

Kassanis, B. (1963). J. Gen. Microbiol. 27, 477.

Kassanis, B., and Nixon, H. L. (1961). J. Gen. Microbiol. 25, 459.

Kassanis, B., and Welkie, G. (1962). Virology 21, 540.

Luria, S. (1959). The Viruses 1, 549. Academic Press, New York.

Markham, R., and Smith, K. M. (1949). Parasitology 39, 330.

Mundry, K. W. (1959). Virology 9, 722.

Mundry, K. W., and Gierer, A. (1958). Z. Vererbungslehre 89, 614.

Rappaport, I., and Wildman, S. G. (1962). Nature (London) 195, 1029.

Salaman, R. N., and Le Pelley, R. H. (1930). Proc. Roy. Soc. B. 106, 140.

Schramm, G., and Engler, R. (1958). Nature (London) 181, 916.

Schuster, H., and Schramm, G. (1958). Z. Naturf. 13b, 697.

Siegel, A. (1960). Virology 11, 156.

Siegel, A., and Wildman, S. G. (1956). Virology 2, 69.

Siegel, A., Ginoza, W., and Wildman, S. G. (1957). Virology 3, 554.

Siegel, A., Zaitlin, M., and Sehgal, Om. P. (1962). Proc. Nat. Acad. Sci. Wash. 48, 1845.

Smith, K. M. (1952). Biol. Rev. 27, 347.

Stouffer, R. F., and Ross, A. F. (1961). Phytopathology 51, 5.

Takahashi, W. N., and Ishii, M. (1952). Phytopathology 42, 690.

Takahashi, W. N., and Ishii, M. (1953). Amer. J. Bot. 40, 85.

Thomas, R. S. (1961). Virology 14, 240.

Tsugita, A. (1962a). J. Mol. Biol. 5, 284.

Tsugita, A. (1962b). J. Mol. Biol. 5, 293.

Tsugita, A., and Fraenkel-Conrat, H. (1960). Proc. Nat. Acad. Sci. Wash. 46, 636.

Tsugita, A., and Fraenkel-Conrat, H. (1962). J. Mol. Biol. 4, 73.

Tsugita, A., Fraenkel-Conrat, H., Nirenberg, M. W., and Matthei, J. H. (1962). Proc. Nat. Acad. Sci. Wash. 48, 846.

Watson, M. A. (1960). Virology 10, 211.

Williams, R. C., and Smith, K. M. (1957). Nature (London) 179, 119.

FRANK LANNI

Viruses and molecular taxonomy

18-1. INTRODUCTION

NOWADAYS, if you happen to see a virologist grow bacterial cultures for studies of viral replication, you can no longer be sure that the viruses engaging his interest are bacterial viruses. They may be typical plant viruses such as tobacco mosaic (Nirenberg and Matthaei, 1961; Tsugita *et al.*, 1962) and turnip yellow mosaic (Ofengand and Haselkorn, 1962; Haselkorn *et al.*, 1963), or typical animal viruses such as polio (Darnell, 1962; Warner *et al.*, 1963).

This does not mean that host range, giving the familiar primary division into plant, animal, and bacterial viruses, is completely useless in virus classification. It does mean that virology, advancing side by side with molecular biology and more often than not leading the way, has reached the stage where one can discern a fundamental unity of viruses at the molecular level, largely independent of host range and other venerable taxonomic characters. This unity stems from (a) the compositional similarity of mature virus particles (virions), which all contain nucleic acid and protein and often nothing else of interest, (b) the infectivity of mature virus particles and, more important for the breakdown of host-range barriers and tissue tropisms, the often demonstrated and the otherwise potential infectivity of the free viral nucleic acid, (c) the characteristic eclipse of mature virus particles, in which the nucleic acid becomes disengaged from other viral components and, acting as a template, governs the specificity of intracellular syntheses leading to mature viral progeny, (d) the fairly standardized machinery used by various hosts for their own macromolecular syntheses and made available on demand to intruding viral nucleic acids, and (e) the unified theory by which molecular biology attempts to explain the correspondence between genotype and phenotype in terms of the fine structure of nucleic acids and proteins.

In fact, if the major premises of contemporary molecular biology are correct, it is easy to see that taxonomic theories for viruses are of two main kinds, related by mutual implication and together redundant. *Classical taxonomy* leans heavily on ordinary phenotypic traits—host range, epidemiology, pathology, viral architecture, serology, etc.—more or less removed from the genome and variable in their reliability. How such criteria are to be selected, weighted, and applied are matters of continuing discussion and debate not only for viruses (Andrewes, 1962; Lwoff *et al.*, 1962; Pirie, 1962; Smith, 1962; Wildy, 1962) but also for bacteria and other organisms (see, for example, Ainsworth and Sneath, 1962; Floodgate, 1962; Liston *et al.*, 1963; Lockhart and Hartman, 1963).

Molecular taxonomy, in its purest form,

strikes to the theoretical source of the ordinary phenotypic traits in the fine structure, mainly the nucleotide sequence, of genetically active nucleic acids. One might say that molecular biology allows us to see through the phenotypic fog of organisms to certain fundamental laws (postulates, if one prefers) believed to be valid for all organisms. These are the elementary molecular laws of (a) the storage of genetic information in nucleotide sequences, (b) point-by-point replication of the information on a polynucleotide template, (c) eventual translation of the information into polypeptide chain sequences via a specific correspondence (coding relation) between particular sets of nucleotides (code words) and particular amino acids, and (d) variation in the genetic information via changes in nucleotide sequence. Molecular taxonomy accepts these laws as being universal (if they are not, we shall eventually find out) and sets itself the primary task of comparing the polynucleotide messages of actual organisms. By the principle of mutual implication, a bold molecular taxonomist would say that the message and the organism-minus-the-message are interchangeable.

Although molecular taxonomy has already taken giant strides, its future is much more glorious than its past. Our present concerns will be to outline the conceptual bases, exhibit some results, consider some compromises (genetics, protein structure) forced by technological realities, and speculate about prospects. The discussion will be illustrative, not exhaustive. Where possible we shall draw examples from viruses, but we shall not hesitate to call on other organisms, including man, any more than we should hesitate to call on viruses if our primary interest lay elsewhere. The fact is, viruses, with their simple architecture and shortage of useful ordinary traits, both facilitate and force a molecular approach to taxonomy.

Background material occurs in widespread deposits, e.g., *Advances in Genetics, Advances in Virus Research, Annual Review of Biochemistry, Annual Review of Microbiology, Cold Spring Harbor Symposia on Quantitative Biology, Journal of Molecular Biology, Proceedings of the National Academy of Sciences (U. S.), Virology*, Ainsworth and Sneath (1962), Burnet and Stanley (1959), Chargaff and Davidson (1955, 1960), Taylor (1963), and Vogel *et al.* (1963). A timely review by Marmur *et al.* (1963a), stressing bacteria, is the most recent and comprehensive treatment of molecular taxonomy presently available. For expediency, we shall frequently cite a recent review of the biological coding problem by Lanni (1963a).

18–2. CONCEPTUAL BACKGROUND OF MOLECULAR TAXONOMY

In attempting to explain the genetic control of ordinary phenotypic traits, including those of viruses, molecular biology stresses the (colinear) structural correspondence and the physiological interrelations of nucleic acids and proteins. The main ideas are no doubt familiar to everyone. The following discussion, relying on the reader's general knowledge, summarizes ideas that have special relevance to molecular taxonomy. For more complete discussion and references, see Lanni (1963a).

A. ORGANIZATION OF GENETIC INFORMATION: CODING RELATIONS

Viral genomes (Schuster, 1960; Schaffer, 1962; Lanni, 1963a; Thomas, 1963; see, however, Hirst, 1962; Joklik, 1962a) and very probably those of bacteria (Cairns, 1963; Nagata, 1963; Yoshikawa and Sueoka, 1963) generally appear to consist of a single, unbranched nucleic acid molecule. The type and molecular form of a viral nucleic acid depend on the virus and may be one or another of the following: double-stranded (duplex) DNA of the Watson-Crick type, made up of A-T and G-C complementary nucleotide pairs; single-stranded DNA; single-stranded RNA; or perhaps even double-stranded RNA (Gomatos and Tamm, 1963). So far as is known, the genomes of all other organisms, including bacteria, consist of Watson-Crick DNA duplexes. The single-stranded DNA of phage ϕX174 appears to have a covalently bonded ring structure (Fiers and Sinsheimer, 1962); and the "duplex" DNA of Shope papilloma virus (Watson and Littlefield, 1960), fowlpox virus (Szybalski *et al.*, 1963), and polyoma virus (Crawford, 1963; Weil, 1963) also seems to be structurally anomalous. The single-stranded RNA of phage R17 appears to exist in a highly ordered, perhaps helical, configuration in the virion (Mitra *et al.*, 1963). The important common feature of all these genetic nucleic acids is that, so far as is known, they consist of linear polynucleotide chains, in which the individual nucleotide residues (or the constituent bases) are the ultimate biochemical subunits of interest and also the ultimate units of information. The two strands of a duplex are regarded as equivalent in information content.

A whole viral or bacterial genome consists of a linear series of somewhat autonomously functioning segments, the genes, arranged in a definite order (*genetic map sequence*). An average gene comprises hundreds of nucleotides or nucleotide pairs. The best-known genes are of two main functional types:

1. *Structural genes*, stated briefly, specify the structure of proteins, apparently by specifying the amino acid sequence of polypeptide chains. (Operationally, structural genes are not quite equivalent to the so-called cistrons.) The qualitative correspondence between structural genes and polypeptide chains is one-to-one. For a few proteins, the evidence strongly suggests that the chain sequence of amino acids suffices to specify the folded native conformation. Pending further studies, we shall conveniently assume that this is generally true, and that aggregates of two or more chains, characterizing certain proteins, also arise spontaneously.

In bacteria, the respective structural genes for the enzymes of a metabolic pathway often are clustered in the genome, where their map sequence may follow that of the corresponding metabolic steps (Demerec and Hartman, 1959). In phage T4, the genes for various structural proteins and phage-induced enzymes are remarkably organized in the genome (R. S. Edgar, cited by Luria, 1962). The genetic map of phage T4 is circular (Streisinger *et al.*, 1963a; see Campbell, 1963), but the DNA

molecule (mol wt about 130 million) of the closely related phage T2 is open-ended and appears to be circularly permuted over a population of molecules (Thomas and Rubinstein, 1963). The classical approach to gene order is genetic recombination. Outside the bacterial viruses, recombination has so far been reported for a few animal viruses (Burnet, 1959a; Hirst, 1962; Ledinko, 1963) and no plant viruses. As indicated later, molecular biology already offers new approaches to gene order and intragenic structure, independent of recombination.

2. *Controlling genes* (operators, regulators) affect the rate of expression of structural genes in response to environmental conditions (Jacob and Monod, 1961). Controlling genes are best known in bacteria (Riley and Pardee, 1962), but they probably occur also in viruses, as suggested by phenomena of lysogeny and by the timing of macromolecular syntheses during viral reproduction (Luria, 1962).

The important *coding hypothesis* subdivides a structural gene into small sets of nucleotides, called *coding units* or *code words*, each one of which specifies the type of amino acid at one site (*target site*) in the corresponding polypeptide. The qualitative correspondence between code word and amino acid appears to be independent of position in the structural gene and the polypeptide; hence, these correspondences can be listed in a table, or *dictionary* (Section 18–2,E). The experimental evidence (reviewed by Lanni, 1963a) strongly suggests that each code word consists of at least three, and perhaps not more than three, nucleotide letters.

The subsidiary *colinearity hypothesis* recognizes the (topological) linearity of the structural gene (as given by fine-structure mapping), the polynucleotide chain segment (or complementary duplex of segments) constituting the gene, and the corresponding polypeptide chain; and the hypothesis asserts that the linear order of code words in the gene is the same as that of the corresponding target sites in the polypeptide. The point-by-point correspondence between code words (W) and amino acids (A) may thus be shown as:

Structural gene: $W_1 \cdot W_2 \cdot W_3 \cdot W_4 \cdots\cdots W_n$
Polypeptide: $A_1 \cdot A_2 \cdot A_3 \cdot A_4 \cdots\cdots A_n$

The colinearity hypothesis has long been a favored postulate, but has only recently found convincing experimental support in studies with the tryptophan synthetase of the bacterium *Escherichia coli* (Yanofsky, 1963). Certain structural features of the genetic message, such as code-letter spacing within a word, code-word overlap, and the demarcation of distinct genes, are still unsettled but need not detain us.

For molecular taxonomy, the important point is that the relation of mutual implication between genotype and phenotype, expressed in molecular terms, reduces to a similar relation, first, between structural gene and polypeptide, and second, between code word and amino acid. A fuller discussion (Lanni, 1963a) would temper the foregoing statement but not alter it significantly. Outside nucleic acids, polypeptide chains are the fundamental organized structures.

B. Hereditary Variation: Effects of Mutation

Mutations and other changes in structural genes may have a variety of effects on polypeptides, including replacement of amino acids at one or more polypeptide sites, deletion or insertion of one or more amino acids, and fusion of formerly distinct polypeptides or parts of polypeptides. Additional possibilities, not yet convincingly demonstrated, include inversion and translocation of chain segments. The simplest effects, immensely valuable for many purposes, are the single amino acid replacements, which dramatize the pinpoint control exercised by the genome over polypeptide chain sequences.

All of these phenotypic effects, except possibly inversion, are easily explained in terms of polynucleotide alterations. In particular, the single amino acid replacements (reflecting simple *missense mutations*) require nothing more than the replacement of a single nucleotide or nucleotide pair. Evidence that single nucleotide changes indeed occur and have the imputed effects is now very persuasive, even though it might

not satisfy a hard-boiled chemist. Much of this evidence (reviewed by Lanni, 1963a) comes from treatment of tobacco mosaic virus (TMV), either the whole virions or the purified RNA, with nitrous acid (Tsugita and Fraenkel-Conrat, 1963; Wittmann, 1963). Here, the deamination of adenine (A) to hypoxanthine (H), leading eventually to the replacement of adenine by guanine (G), and the deamination of cytosine (C) to uracil (U), leading directly to a natural RNA base, are believed to be the responsible chemical events.

In coding terms, a simple missense mutation, causing just one amino acid replacement, involves the replacement of one *sense word* (= word appearing in the dictionary) by another with a different meaning. Since most, perhaps all, of the 20 amino acids commonly found in proteins appear to be coded by more than one word (*degeneracy*), nucleotide replacements and word replacements may occur without affecting the polypeptide. Hence, a given polypeptide chain sequence would be compatible with many alternative sequences in the polynucleotide. This feature may limit, though perhaps not seriously (see Section 18–3,E), the value of polypeptide chain sequences in molecular taxonomy, and it is one reason why we spoke earlier of *pure* molecular taxonomy, with emphasis on polynucleotide sequences. It is important to realize, too, that missense mutations and grosser genetic changes may be *silent*, i.e., they need not obviously affect the function of a protein. This feature may be beneficial for phenotypic stability, but it helps weaken the force of classical taxonomy. More so does the well-known propensity of missense mutations to produce functionally defective proteins. Small molecular lesions, as small as one amino acid and one nucleotide, become immensely amplified biologically in the network of phenotype determination (they may mean the difference between life and death). Hence they tend to be grossly exaggerated by classical taxonomy, which often scores them as total absence of the traits mediated by the normal proteins.

Structural genes may also undergo *nonsense mutations*, in which a sense word is substituted by a *nonsense word,* i.e., one that is absent from the prevailing dictionary and therefore has no meaning in terms of amino acids. Such mutations, for which evidence is accumulating in phage (Benzer and Champe, 1962) and bacteria (Garen and Siddiqi, 1962), are believed to abort polypeptide chain synthesis by introducing an impassable gap at the target site corresponding to the nonsense word. Either nonsense or missense mutations could easily account for certain anomalous variants of tobacco necrosis and tobacco mosaic viruses, in which the viral nucleic acid replicates but no detectable structural protein seems to be made (Babos and Kassanis, 1962; Siegel *et al.,* 1962).

Mutations in controlling genes, altering the concentration of structural-gene products, likewise are known to have profound effects on phenotype (Jacob and Monod, 1961; Riley and Pardee, 1962). For discussion of other genes, e.g., suppressor genes, affecting polypeptide structure, see Lanni (1963a).

C. Information Transfer: Replication, Transcription, Translation

Structural genes have to replicate their information along with the rest of the genome, and they must directly or indirectly transfer their information to protein.

In the case of organisms, including appropriate viruses, with DNA genomes, the known pathways of information transfer are:

Replication: DNA → DNA
Transcription: DNA → mRNA (= Messenger RNA)
Translation: mRNA → protein

The arrows indicate the direction of information flow, generally assumed to be irreversible. The inductive role of antigen in antibody formation is occasionally proposed as an example of reverse flow from protein. Suggestions of reversal from RNA to DNA (e.g., Gershenshon *et al.,* cited by Smith, 1962) need thorough documentation before they can be accepted.

There seems little doubt that the replication of duplex DNA proceeds mainly or exclusively by a semiconservative mechanism more or less like that originally proposed by Watson and Crick (1953), utilizing DNA-directed DNA polymerase (Kornberg enzyme) (Bessman, 1963) as catalyst. Functioning as a molecular template, each of the two strands governs the synthesis of a complementary strand according to the following rules of information transfer from template to product nucleotides:

$$A \rightarrow T; \ T \rightarrow A; \ C \rightarrow G; \ G \rightarrow C$$

Barring mutation and recombination, this point-by-point mechanism replicates the original duplex twofold at each cycle, producing hybrid duplexes of one old and one new strand. Replication of the ϕX174 single-stranded DNA appears to involve the intermediate formation of a duplex replicative form (Sinsheimer *et al.,* 1962; Hayashi *et al.,* 1963a). Since the single DNA strands of ϕX virions are probably sequentially homogeneous (Section 18–3,D), an interesting but unsolved problem is how the second type of strand is excluded from the viral progeny.

Continuing with DNA organisms, the transcription from DNA to mRNA proceeds by a mechanism like that just described, but using DNA-directed RNA polymerase (Hurwitz-Stevens-Weiss enzyme) (Grunberg-Manago, 1962) and precursor ribonucleoside triphosphates instead of the deoxy analogues. The information transfer rules are:

$$A \rightarrow U; \ T \rightarrow A; \ C \rightarrow G; \ G \rightarrow C$$

Recent experiments with phage ϕX (Hayashi *et al.,* 1963b) and with pneumococcal DNA (Guild and Robison, 1963), supporting earlier indirect considerations, indicate that only one strand of duplex DNA functions as a template for mRNA *in vivo.* The suppression of the second strand is convenient and, once more, mysterious. Other brands of cellular RNA, such as the sRNA and rRNA mentioned shortly, appear also to be synthesized on DNA templates via the transfer rules for mRNA (see Section 18–2,D and Lanni, 1963a).

The translation from mRNA to protein (polypeptide) occurs on ribosomes, small structures consisting of (ribosomal) protein and (ribosomal) RNA (rRNA) (Roberts *et al.*, 1963). After the free amino acids have been coupled to small, amino acid-specific molecules of "soluble" RNA (sRNA) with the aid of amino acid-specific activating enzymes (*alias* aminoacyl-sRNA synthetases), the aminoacyl-sRNA complexes go to the ribosomes. Here, the attached host or viral mRNA sorts the incoming complexes and selects one for each polypeptide target site. The "read-out" process is linear, proceeding from the N-terminus to the C-terminus of the polypeptide chain, as successive code words are read in turn. Current conceptions (Noll *et al.*, 1963; Gilbert, 1963; Watson, 1963; Zubay, 1963) of this exquisitely regulated process, confirming early ideas of Crick *et al.* (1961), are fantastic and breath-taking, like much of molecular biology, but quite likely to be true in essential features. At this point we let the finished polypeptide chain find its own way off the ribosome and into its stable, folded conformation.

According to the Crick-Hoagland adaptor hypothesis, the sorting of aminoacyl-sRNA complexes by mRNA is mediated by direct chemical interaction between mRNA code words and a patch of (complementary) nucleotides in the sRNA moiety; at this stage, the attached amino acid has nothing to do with its own selection; and instead, the direct chemical recognition of the amino acid occurs earlier, during the attachment to sRNA by the appropriate activating enzyme. The hypothesis appears to be at least one-third correct (see Lanni, 1963a) and may well be closer to being three-thirds correct. But even the one-third suffices to create the interesting prospect that the genetic code is not precisely the same in all organisms. This happens because, to predict what amino acid will be selected for a certain target site, we should need to know not only the identity of the corresponding mRNA code word (or its counterpart in the structural gene), but also something about the appropriate sRNA and activating enzyme. Stated differently, the genetic dictionary would be at least partly dependent on (embodied in) sRNA and activating enzymes. Since both of these

structures are likely to be mutable, the genetic code need not be universal. The available evidence (Lanni, 1963a; Neidhardt and Fangman, 1963) suggests that the code is largely the same in all organisms but is indeed capable of hereditary variation. The possibility of code variation among naturally occurring organisms is, of course, what makes this discussion especially relevant to molecular taxonomy.

Organisms, i.e., certain viruses, with RNA genomes obviously have to do some things differently. The current view, with much to support it (see Lanni, 1963a), is that viral RNA is itself capable of functioning as mRNA in association with host-cell ribosomes. Here, by the processes just outlined, the RNA specifies the synthesis of a new RNA-directed RNA polymerase, needed for viral RNA replication, as well as other virus-specific proteins. The biochemical details of RNA replication are unclear. By analogy with DNA-directed mRNA formation, the transfer rules might prove to be:

$$A \rightarrow U; \quad U \rightarrow A; \quad C \rightarrow G; \quad G \rightarrow C$$

The complementary RNA strands implied by these rules have been looked for in the case of several viruses with single-stranded RNA, but not found (Darnell, 1962; Spiegelman, 1963). Possibly they do not exist, and information transfer proceeds by identity rather than complementarity. The example of reovirus RNA, which appears to consist of a complementary duplex (Gomatos and Tamm, 1963), suggests, however, that information transfer proceeds by complementarity at least for some RNA viruses. (It is not altogether excluded that reovirus RNA consists of a single strand with complementary halves, but this feature would still support the notion of transfer by complementarity.) There is no persuasive evidence that viral RNA ever induces a virus-specific DNA. What features of viral RNA allow this RNA to replicate, whereas various brands of ambient host RNA do not, is one more unsolved mystery (see Section 18–3,D; Dulbecco, 1962; Jacob and Brenner, 1963).

For molecular taxonomy, an important product of experiments on the synthesis and interrelations of crucial macromolecules is the discovery that certain subcellular components (e.g., ribosomes, sRNA, activating enzymes, polymerases) from diverse taxonomic sources often are interchangeable in reconstituted protein- or nucleic acid-synthesizing systems. Of course, viruses, by means of their infectivity, have long led the biochemists in probing the taxonomic limits of productive molecular interactions. But where viruses are largely restricted to testing pure hosts one at a time, and then only if conditions are favorable to viral eclipse, the biochemists can make the usual host-range barriers irrelevant, and they can mix subcellular and subviral components in all sorts of taxonomically improbable combinations. The present unity of molecular biology owes a good deal to this trick of combining taxonomically heterogeneous components in test tubes. More or less the same trick produced the first substantial progress in deciphering the genetic code (Section 18–2,E).

D. Molecular Basis of Genetic Homology

1. *Genetic homology, genetic recombination, and molecular homology.*—Like most scientific concepts, that of genetic homology in microorganisms (and elsewhere) has undergone progressive refinement in consequence of technological, experimental, and theoretical advances (see Ravin, 1963).

Genetic homology comes in degrees. Two organisms might be said to show complete genetic homology if all their genes are homologous, similarly grouped into linkage groups, and similarly ordered within the linkage groups; and they might be said to show incomplete homology if one or more of these conditions fail. From what we have said before, homology of polynucleotide chain sequences (by identity or complementarity) would be a chemical index of genetic homology.

Until a few years ago, the best available sign of genetic homology in microorganisms was genetic recombination. The molecular details of recombination are still obscure, although progress is being made (Luria, 1962; Ravin, 1961, 1963). The stability of the recombinational genetic map, and the

very fact that maps can be constructed, imply that genes know their place in relation to other genes. A simple and favorite hypothesis is that map position is recognized and conserved by specific point-by-point pairing between sequentially homologous polynucleotide chains or chain regions prior to recombination. Within certain limits discussed later, this very plausible notion rationalizes the use of recombination as an index both of genetic homology and of sequential homology in genetic polynucleotides. It also strengthens the expectation that tests of molecular homology, through studies on polynucleotide sequences and interactions, would be a valid index of genetic homology.

2. *Nucleic acid composition and genetic homology.*—The mean composition of bacterial and viral DNA ranges from about 25 to about 75% GC (molar percentage of guanine plus cytosine) depending on the microbial source. Yet for a given bacterium or virus the compositional heterogeneity of the extracted DNA is very small at the level of the DNA fragments usually studied (references in Marmur *et al.*, 1963a).

If our former reasoning is correct, these facts imply that genetic recombination should be observable only between organisms with DNA of closely similar composition; i.e., similarity of mean DNA composition would be a *necessary* condition for recombination. It would not be a *sufficient* condition since (a) DNA's of the same composition may differ widely in sequence and (b) irrelevant physiological barriers to recombination might exist. With one interesting type of exception, the facts accord with the expectations for all known examples of recombination in bacteria, phages, and also the RNA-endowed influenza viruses (Lanni, 1960; Marmur *et al.*, 1963a). The exception, first noted by Lanni (1960), has to do with certain bacterial genetic elements called episomes (Campbell, 1962). By way of cell conjugation, these anomalous elements are capable of transferring between bacteria of different mean DNA composition; but when they do, the episomal genes fail to integrate with the recipient chromosome, and the episomal DNA can be detected as a satellite peak in density-gradient centrifugation (Marmur *et al.*, 1963a). The exception is thus very useful, since it increases the conviction that intrachromosomal recombination, as opposed to mere mixing of genetic elements, requires and reflects sequential homology of genetic polynucleotides. It is interesting, and very useful for molecular taxonomy, that a seemingly crude measure such as whole DNA composition can reflect such subtle features as genetic homology. We shall later examine the value of nucleic acid composition in taxonomy.

3. *Molecular hybridization.*—One of the most exciting discoveries in recent years is the specific hybridization of polynucleotide chains *in vitro* (references in Marmur *et al.*, 1963a). This discovery promises to be the methodological backbone of molecular taxonomy for years to come.

When microbial duplex DNA is denatured ("melted") by heating at temperatures near 100°C, the strands separate. On slow cooling ("annealing"), duplexes closely resembling the original duplexes reform (renaturation). Under suitable conditions, experiments with heavy-isotope labels show that the choice of partners during renaturation is essentially random, provided that labeled and unlabled DNA specimens came from the same microbial source. In this case, density-gradient centrifugation in CsCl reveals three well-defined peaks: heavy-heavy, heavy-light (hybrid), and light-light, in a ratio approximating the theoretically expected $1:2:1$ for equal inputs. When differentially labeled DNA's from different sources are annealed in mixture, the result depends on the sources. Generally speaking, hybrid formation correlates closely with ability to undergo genetic recombination (for exceptions, see Marmur *et al.*, 1963a) and requires that the two DNA's be closely similar in base composition. There seems little question that hybrid formation reflects sequential homology of the interacting polynucleotides. For taxonomy, a valuable feature is that the process is not all-or-none: the size of the hybrid peak depends on the choice of DNA's and can be measured accurately.

The principle has now been used in a wide variety of fruitful studies (see Marmur *et al.*, 1963a), including the demonstration of specific hybrid formation between DNA and each of the three ordinary brands of cellular RNA (mRNA, sRNA, rRNA). The amount of DNA needed for hybrid detection is very small, and the sensitivity is truly remarkable. Thus, about 0.019–0.025% of the total DNA of *E. coli* is found capable of hybridizing with *E. coli* sRNA (Giacomoni and Spiegelman, 1962; Goodmann and Rich, 1962), and a total of about 0.32% of the DNA of *Bacillus megaterium* hybridizes with the 16S (0.14%) and 23S (0.18%) ribosomal RNA's of this organism (Yankofsky and Spiegelman, 1963). Other illustrative applications have led to the isolation of several RNA's (mRNA?) transcribed from ordinary genes of *E. coli* (Attardi *et al.*, 1962, 1963; Hayashi *et al.*, 1963c), to the isolation of an analogous RNA believed to correspond specifically to the *r*II genetic region of phage T4 (Bautz and Hall, 1962), and to the demonstration that the DNA molecules of T2 virions are not sequentially homogeneous, but circularly permuted (Thomas and Rubinstein, 1963). Applications to taxonomy are discussed in Sections 18–4 and 18–5,B.

It seems apparent that a radically new way of characterizing genes and gene action has emerged. In virology, the prospects seem especially intriguing for the many viruses that have not yet exhibited genetic recombination. Hybrid formation with viral RNA (that present in virions) has not yet, however, been reported.

E. The Nirenberg-Ochoa Codes

Nirenberg and Matthaei (1961) added polyuridylic acid, a synthetic RNA-like polymer, to a cell-free, mRNA-responsive extract from *E. coli* and noted the synthesis of polyphenylalanine. They suggested that one or more U's are the code (at the mRNA level) for phenylalanine. Exploitation of this discovery with a variety of U-rich polymers, containing other RNA bases in various proportions, quickly led to presumptive codes for all but one (glutamine) of the common amino acids. These

TABLE 18–1. THE PRIMARY (U-RICH) CODES OF NIRENBERG AND OCHOA*

Amino acid	Code word(s)	Amino acid	Code word(s)
alanine	(UCG)	leucine	(UUA), (UUC), (UUG)
arginine	(UCG)	lysine	(UAA)
asparagine	(UAA), (UAC)	methionine	(UAG)
aspartic acid	(UAG)	phenylalanine	UUU
cysteine	(UUG)	proline	(UCC)
glutamic acid	(UAG)	serine	(UUC), (UCG)
glutamine	—	threonine	(UAC), (UCC)
glycine	(UGG)	tryptophan	(UGG)
histidine	(UAC)	tyrosine	(UUA)
isoleucine	(UUA)	valine	(UUG)

* Compiled from Matthaei *et al.* (1962) and Speyer *et al.* (1962); see Lanni (1963a). Writing a code word in parentheses means that the correct order of code letters is not specified, but only one of the possible permutations is applicable.

codes, conveniently called the *primary* or *U-rich codes*, appear in Table 18–1. Writing the codes as triplets, rather than as the doublets got by deleting one U, formerly rested on unproved assumptions but now has strong experimental support (Lanni, 1963a).

Later studies with U-less polymers produced a variety of U-less triplet codes, frequently differing from the primary triplets only in the substitution of U by A or C. Adjustments of some former codes have been suggested, and additional codes are a likely prospect. In this fluid situation, we propose to base the discussion in this and later sections entirely on the primary codes (Table 18–1), fully realizing that backward glances will be in order when the situation has stabilized. There are sound reasons, however, for expecting that the chief conclusions reached from perusal and application of the primary codes are unlikely to be invalidated by a more comprehensive set of codes.

A large body of evidence (see Lanni, 1963a) leaves little doubt that the primary codes, or codes much like them, are the true codes in a variety of organisms ranging from viruses to man. To illustrate, consider amino acid replacements resulting from mutation. If it is correct to think that such replacements arise mainly from single nucleotide replacements (considered at the level of mRNA), valid codes for two interchanging amino acids should more often than not be related by a one-letter code change. In fact, *all* amino acid replacements in the polypeptides judged to be most suited for the analysis (Group I replacements; Lanni, 1963a) can be fitted by a one-letter change in the primary codes. Most of the replacements were compiled from tobacco mosaic virus, *E. coli* tryptophan synthetase, and the α and β chains of human hemoglobin. The probability that meaningless codes would exhibit the observed agreement is exceedingly small ($P = 10^{-5}$). (This calculation takes into account the fact that the code triplets are unordered internally and therefore afford extra freedom in fitting amino acid replacements.)

Nitrous acid-induced replacements in TMV are listed in Table 18–2. All 16 can be interpreted by one-letter code changes, as shown ($P = 0.002$). Eleven afford single code-letter changes of the types $A \to G$ and $C \to U$, compatible with the theory of nitrous acid mutagenesis ($P = 10^{-5}$). For any induced amino acid replacement $X \to Y$, in no case has nitrous acid been found to induce the reverse replacement $Y \to X$ at the same or a different polypeptide site. These facts support the following conclusions (Lanni, 1963a):

(1) The codes deduced in *E. coli* cell-free systems, using synthetic RNA messengers, are largely valid for the taxonomically distant TMV. (The five anomalous replacements in Table 18–2 can be rationalized in

TABLE 18–2. AMINO ACID REPLACEMENTS INDUCED IN TMV BY NITROUS ACID[*]

Replacement	Interpretation	Replacement	Interpretation
arg → gly[†]	C → G	pro → leu	C → U
asn → ser	A → U,G	pro → ser	C → U,G
asp → ala[‡]	A → C	ser → leu	C → A,G; C,G → U
asp → gly	A → G	ser → phe	C → U
glu → gly	A → G	thr → ilu	C → U
ilu → met[†]	U → G	thr → met[†]	C → G
ilu → val	A → G	thr → ser	A → U,G; C → U,G
leu → phe	A,C,G → U	tyr → phe[†]	A → U

[*] Adapted from Table 9 of Lanni (1963a); see this reference for sources. For degenerately coded amino acids (Table 18–1), all possible one-letter code changes are shown. Forms such as A → U,G indicate alternative interpretations.

[†] The five replacements so marked cannot be interpreted by C → U or A → G.

many ways. The more recent U-less codes already bring some of them into line.)

(2) The theory of base transitions inducible by nitrous acid is definitely on the right track. In support of the previous outline, the belief is justified that single base transitions (= single code-letter changes) suffice to cause single amino acid replacements. Many of the TMV mutants do, in fact, differ from the ancestor by just one amino acid replacement.

(3) The RNA of a population of tobacco mosaic virions is very probably sequentially homogeneous and not a mixture of complementary strands. Otherwise, amino acids X and Y would very likely exhibit replacements in both directions. The few relevant data from direct chemical analysis of the viral RNA (Sugiyama and Fraenkel-Conrat, 1961, 1963; Whitfield, 1962) accord with sequential homogeneity (see Section 18–3,D).

(4) During TMV replication, the role of mRNA (at least for the structural protein) is played directly by the viral RNA or an identical copy, not by a complementary copy (see Tsugita et al., 1962). Otherwise, the direction of amino acid replacements in Table 18–2 would be reversed (assuming only the codes in Table 18–1). This does not exclude the formation of complementary copies, serving some other function, but such complements have not yet been discovered for any virus with single-stranded RNA. Wittmann (1962) reached the present conclusion independently.

These results, plus many others on TMV (reviewed by Lanni, 1963a; Tsugita and Fraenkel-Conrat, 1963), illustrate the great power of chemical genetics, even in an organism where genetic recombination has not yet been observed. When chemical genetics, molecular hybridization, and other modern methods of studying nucleic acids and proteins are considered together, the prospects for a new taxonomy are truly enormous.

The results also illustrate the value of the Nirenberg-Ochoa codes as analytical tools. Here the application was to viral RNA structure, information transfer, and chemical mutagenesis. The application to code universality has been mentioned. In Section 18–6,B we describe an interesting application to the direction of molecular evolution.

18–3. GENERAL TAXONOMIC CONSIDERATIONS

The foregoing background allows us to view some aspects of taxonomy in seemingly reliable perspective. To repeat a previous contention, there are two and only two fundamentally different taxonomies—classical and molecular—connected by mutual implication, and reflecting the basic biological duality of phenotype and genotype (for a moderating discussion, see Sonneborn, 1960, 1963). The fact that, in taxonomic practice, the two taxonomies are frequently merged, if not confused, alters neither the distinction nor the relation. Ideally, we fully expect the two to validate each other, and from available comparisons (Sections 18–4 and 18–5,B) it is already apparent that they largely do. Let us begin by asking the inevitable question.

A. WHAT IS TAXONOMY?

The answer is elusive, but is being actively sought (see, for example, Ainsworth and Sneath, 1962). All workers seem to agree that taxonomy has to do with the theory and/or practice of organism classification (as opposed to "mere" identification, given an existing classification), but the purposes, premises, procedures, and interpretations are in dispute.

Is phylogeny a premise or a product of taxonomy? Is it, should it be, either? What is a character? Should all characters have equal weight? Is it necessary that any real organism display all the characters used in constructing a taxonomic group? In measuring similarity or affinity, should "negative" matches have the same value as "positive" ones? What is a species? Do species preexist, or are they myths made by taxonomists? Need a taxonomic scheme be hierarchical? Do various taxonomic categories (taxa) have the same significance throughout the biological world? And an ultramodern question: Should the raw data be fed to incompassionate electronic computers or sifted lovingly by warm intellect?

Questions such as these must, of course, be debated, and we look forward to an early consensus—because the particular assemblages created (or discovered) by classical taxonomy affect its mutual validation with molecular taxonomy. We shall conveniently leave the debate to the experts. The fact is, the microbial classifications derived by various approaches—whether alternative classical approaches, or molecular, or mixed —generally show a heartening over-all agreement. So far, this seems truer of bacteria than of viruses, but comparisons between the two domains are not easy. Interpreted optimistically, the agreement may reflect naturally existing "adaptive peaks" (like those postulated for higher organisms), as opposed to a more or less continuous spectrum of phenotypes.

We take the view that molecular taxonomy best serves taxonomy (and biology) by finding its own way, as free as possible of preconceptions and analogies. Let phylogeny, and the classical characters and taxa, fall where they may. Viruses practically force this freedom upon us.

Unity is one thing, but diversity feeds the taxonomic trees. All practical taxonomists want plenty of "good" differentiating characters—reliable and easy to score—since they want their classifications to be maximally stable when challenged with new organisms and characters. The next question is obvious.

B. WHAT IS A CHARACTER?

Here the major pitfalls of classical taxonomy are well known, and one has to be impressed by the over-all success nevertheless achieved. For cellular organisms, the network of phenotype determination—proceeding outward from the genome and subject to environmental modulation—is exceedingly complex, but may usefully and simply (oversimply, to be sure) be thought to have a crosstied hierarchical structure. Beginning with the simplest phenotypic elements, we might progressively recognize the peptide-bonded amino acid residue, the polypeptide chain, the multichain enzyme protein, the set of enzymes for a (linear) metabolic pathway, the whole enzyme complement of a cell, multicellular aggregates, clones, and mixed populations. Somewhere should be mentioned the cellular particulates, membranes, and other formed elements; the uni- and multivalent inhibitors, inducers, repressors; metabolic branchpoints; etc. The phenotype-determining role of the specific preformed organization of a cell (Sonneborn, 1960, 1963) also should be acknowledged.

To be useful at all for taxonomy, a character has to be more than an observable trait: it has to show variation somewhere in the biological domain of interest. Thus, the mere possession of cytoplasm or membranes is not a taxonomically useful character of cellular organisms, but is part of their definition.

Evidently a differentiating character (*differentia*) may reflect single or multiple differences at any one or more of our hierarchical levels, not to mention the crossties. Take, for example, the requirement (X^-) *vs.* lack of requirement (X^+) for the substance X as an exogenous nutrient for growth of bacteria in an otherwise fixed environment. X might be an amino acid, vitamin precursor, purine or pyrimidine, etc. Suppose that the sole observation is growth, or lack of it, in a medium lacking X but otherwise sufficient. For simplicity, assume that growth is absolutely dependent on an intracellular supply of X. The condition X^+ then will usually mean that the transport of appropriate precursors into the cell, the synthesis of X, and the utilization of X proceed, let us say, normally; i.e., the transport mechanisms both exist and function, and so do the enzymes needed for synthesis and utilization of X.

What does X^- mean? Somewhere in the chain of transport, synthesis, and utilization there exist one or more "blocks." The alternative possibilities are numerous: a single missing or defective enzyme, groups of missing or defective enzymes, membrane lesions, etc. Worse yet, X^- may reflect not a lesser, but a greater synthetic capacity, e.g., the synthesis of a new inhibitor, in which case the designations " $+$ " and " $-$ " are purely formal. In the simple case of a block at one enzymatic step, the enzyme might merely be defective, perhaps because just one amino acid residue is incompatible with activity; or the enzyme might be totally absent for any of a variety of genetic reasons (nonsense mutation, mutation in a control or suppressor gene, etc.). The physiological interpretation of X^+ is also ambiguous, since neither the relevant metabolic pathways, nor the corresponding genes, need be homologous; and even if they were, and if X^+ and X^- organisms were also homologous, the difference X^+/X^- might rest on a single nucleotide pair. Phenotypically silent genetic differences are, of course, completely overlooked.

The character X^+/X^- is a relatively simple character. Anxiety only increases when we turn to more complex characters whose physiology either is poorly defined or involves interactions at hierarchical levels closer to the "periphery" of the determinative network. Further, a single relatively centripetal lesion may have a set of diverse phenotypic manifestations (pleiotropy), which might erroneously be scored as distinct characters (redundancy). And how does one deal with quantitatively varying characters such as growth rate, metabolic rates, cell dimensions, content of various biochemical constituents, antibiotic sensitivity, virulence?

In short, if classical taxonomy has a universally accepted definition of *character*—we really mean *distinct* character—we have not seen it, and it would be easy to understand that none exists. Contrast this with (pure) molecular taxonomy, where *character* refers to the (variable) occupant at a certain nucleotide site in a genetic polynucleotide, and *distinct* refers to the sequentially distinct sites (see Section 18–3,C).

In this hostile terrain, classical taxonomy has armed itself with some effective weapons:

(1) Instead of relying on a few characters, it attempts to amass a large number and counts on the whole constellation to reduce the effect of "occasional" faulty judgments. Some exponents insist on the propriety of assigning weights to various characters. Others, e.g., the numerical taxonomists of recent years (see Sneath, 1962), accept the Adansonian principle that all characters should have equal weight, but this ideal is difficult to translate into practice, as partly evidenced by the existence of different schools of numerical taxonomy. In any case, wittingly or no, characters are selected and weighted, and a fine eye is very useful in demarking taxonomic groups.

(2) Keeping abreast of biochemistry and other developments, it has progressively refined its characters, moving steadily closer to the center of the network of phenotype determination. It now places increasing emphasis on well-characterized metabolic pathways, individual enzymatic processes, and the molecular character of individual proteins.

(3) It has generally been willing to supplement its materials with concepts and data emerging from genetics and genetic chemistry, and therefore properly belong-

ing to molecular taxonomy. For this reason we might say that there are no classical taxonomists in spirit, only classical taxonomy.

With slight adjustment, what we have been saying for nonviral organisms applies also to viruses, especially when the characters deal with gross aspects of virus-host interaction, including many properties of virus-infected cells (see Cooper, 1961). Take the progressive erosion of *host range* as a taxonomic character. We know, best with bacterial viruses, that one-step mutations in virus or host can increase or decrease host range. The physiological block might be located at the cell surface, preventing virus adsorption or penetration, or at any of a variety of intracellular steps necessary to viral growth and release of progeny into the medium (Adams, 1959). The familiar and very useful adaptation of animal viruses to laboratory hosts (and no doubt the natural evolution of host range) also involves mutational variation in the viruses. Several so-called plant viruses have been shown to multiply in their insect vectors (Black, 1959; Smith, 1962). The related character *tissue tropism,* usefully variable in avirulent vaccine manufacture, similarly deteriorates as viruses mutate or as formerly resistant host cells are cultured *in vitro* (Holland and Hoyer, 1962). Both host range and tissue range increase (only for one intracellular cycle, generally) when infection is initiated with free viral nucleic acid or modified virions instead of whole, normal virions (see, for example, Fraser *et al.,* 1957; Spizizen, 1957; Guthrie and Sinsheimer, 1960; Meyer *et al.,* 1961; Holland and Hoyer, 1962; Schaffer, 1962). Judged by host range, REO virus (animal) and wound-tumor virus (plant) seem very different; yet the respective virions have a remarkably similar architecture (Lwoff *et al.,* 1962), they appear to cross react serologically (Streissle and Maramorosch, 1963), and they are the only known carriers of an anomalous, apparently double-stranded RNA (Gomatos and Tamm, 1963). A former, seemingly fundamental correlation of host range with nucleic acid type—RNA in plant viruses, RNA or DNA in animal viruses, DNA in bacterial viruses

—was shattered with the discovery of the RNA phage f2 (Loeb and Zinder, 1961); a DNA plant virus would finish the interment. Finally, several typical plant and animal viruses have been shown to exercise at least some of their synthetic functions when the viral RNA is added to a bacterial extract (Nirenberg and Matthaei, 1961; Darnell, 1962; Ofengand and Haselkorn, 1962; Tsugita *et al.,* 1962; Haselkorn *et al.,* 1963; Warner *et al.* 1963). We do not mean to imply (although it may be true) that all viruses can grow in all cells with appropriate human assistance. It seems clear, however, that host range and tissue tropism have to be (and presently are) used very cautiously in taxonomy. Where the blocks to growth are intracellular, it would be very interesting to know whether they reflect variations in the genetic code.

Having seen some features, mostly drawbacks, of classical taxonomy, let us next consider some desirable features of molecular taxonomy. If this bias seems unsporting, remember that classical taxonomy is an elder discipline, whereas molecular taxonomy is a baby. Besides, like those of a baby, the present shortcomings of molecular taxonomy seem mostly technological.

C. Power of the Molecular Approach Through Nucleic Acids

The theoretical virtues of a taxonomy based on genetic polynucleotides are easy to identify and for the most part will appear self-evident.

(1) Such a taxonomy has a sound theoretical and experimental basis, which makes it pre-eminently a natural taxonomy.

(2) It affords a fairly straightforward definition of *unit character:* the nucleotide (base) at a given site in a genetic polynucleotide. Neglecting minor nucleotides, a unit character has five values: the four ordinary nucleotides (or nucleotide pairs, in a duplex) plus *void;* the latter value is useful when a site appears to be missing in one of two genomes under comparison. Two unit characters are *distinct* if they represent distinct polynucleotide sites. Definition of the fundamental concept of homology between polynucleotides, anticipating the variety of circumstances that might be en-

countered, is not easy. We leave this to another occasion or to someone else and rely here on intuition.

(3) Its unit characters, except when void, each tend to be represented by the same number of nucleotides in a sufficiently large, random sample of genetic nucleic acid. A factor of two in relative concentration would cover most of the known or suspected deviations from equality for the unit characters of a given bacterium (see, for example, Yoshikawa and Sueoka, 1963). In most viruses, one should not be surprised if the concentration were precisely or almost precisely the same for each character. This contrasts with the highly variable concentration of gene products such as proteins.

(4) It does not wittingly or unwittingly select characters but includes all that are present. For this reason, and because it tends to give all characters equal weight, it closely approximates the Adansonian ideal of the numerical taxonomists.

(5) It is *efficient* both because its characters are multivalued and because it avoids redundancy arising from pleiotropy. It is *sufficient* because it needs no information from other sources. The visible methodology, e.g., molecular hybridization, promises to make it practically, as well as theoretically, efficient.

(6) Using a large number of characters, it minimizes the importance of a small subset and is therefore stable. It does not admit the differential magnification of effects that plagues classical taxonomy.

(7) It affords objective, quantitative estimates of similarity (affinity) between organisms, and it affords a sound basis for predicting over-all phenotypic similarity. Its precision, accuracy, and sensitivity are limited only by its already highly refined and standardized instruments and techniques.

(8) It is capable of detecting trace homology "blind," i.e., without having to be informed of the associated phenotypic traits.

(9) It can deal effectively with organisms, such as viruses, whose paucity of useful ordinary traits makes them refractory to classical taxonomic approaches.

(10) It is capable of revealing and delineating ancestral relation even where auxiliary evidence is lacking or uncertain; hence, it should be especially useful in viral taxonomy. This accepts the truism that genetic homology reflects ancestral relation.

(11) Its (primary) working materials, nucleic acids, are notably stable during storage and shipment.

D. Homology Criteria Based on Nucleic Acids

Needless to say, we do not yet have the complete sequence formula for any genetic nucleic acid. The analytical task is formidable, since even the smallest known genetic nucleic acids, those of viruses, already contain at least 1000 nucleotide residues. To appreciate the difficulty, recall that the largest polypeptide of known sequence is that of TMV, with 158 residues (Tsugita and Fraenkel-Conrat, 1963); and that not one species of sRNA, with only about 70 residues, has yet been fully ordered. For a few RNA and DNA viruses, a good deal is known about the sequences of oligonucleotides split out from the viral nucleic acid with appropriate nucleases (discussed later in this section and in Section 18–5,B; see Scholtissek et al., 1962). For a few DNA viruses, the proportions of all the possible nearest-neighbor (dinucleotide) sequences are known (Josse et al., 1961; Swartz et al., 1962). Unfortunately, the value of nearest-neighbor sequences in microbial taxonomy is greatly limited by their strong correlation with the over-all base composition of nucleic acids (Kaiser and Baldwin, 1962), as a result of which the two measures are largely redundant.

There are, however, some immediately available homology criteria that are clearly related to sequences but do not require explicit sequence analysis. *Oligonucleotide fingerprints* (maps) and *oligonucleotide column chromatograms* are intermediate data along the way to sequence analysis and can just as well be a stopping point. The patterns in each case reflect both the sequence of the nucleic acid and the specificity of the nucleases or other splitting agents used. For other approaches to sequences, see Marmur et al. (1963a).

Molecular hybridization (see Sections 18–2,D, 18–4, and 18–5,B) is particularly valuable for taxonomic surveys. An ingenious technique, trapping a denatured DNA in agar and allowing it to interact with a second nucleic acid (DNA or RNA) at elevated temperature (Bolton and McCarthy, 1962), has greatly improved the applicability of the procedure and has been used in taxonomic surveys of bacteria by McCarthy and Bolton (1963) and Colwell and Mandell (unpublished). The technique will probably need modification for use with the small DNA genomes of some viruses. A procedure applicable to RNA viruses is not yet available.

Base composition (nucleotide composition) is a very useful first measure, since (a) extensive sequential homology necessitates close similarity in base composition, and (b) base composition varies widely among microorganisms. The use of DNA base composition in taxonomic surveys is best illustrated by the monumental pioneer studies of Lee *et al.* (1956) in bacteria. For a study in protozoa, see Schildkraut *et al.* (1962a). Heterogeneity of base composition, best seen in a CsCl density gradient, and unusual bases may afford additional compositional criteria.

A second group of properties or techniques, reflecting the amount, type, and/or organization of genetic information, includes molecular weight or length, number of molecules (not number of strands), circularity or open-endedness, hyperchromicity and other biophysical or physicochemical properties, acceptor ability for methyl groups (Srinivasan and Borek, 1963; Gold *et al.*, 1963), and possibly the profile of stimulated amino acid incorporation in cell-free protein-synthesizing extracts. The grosser structure (gene order) of suitable genetic nucleic acids might be tackled with the DNA-agar hybridization technique, as used by Thomas and Rubinstein (1963), and perhaps also by the linear replication of the nucleic acids (see Cairns, 1963; Nagata, 1963; Yoshikawa and Sueoka, 1963). Some of these procedures are too tedious for routine use but might illuminate special problems. We may rely confidently on the ingenuity of molecular biologists to

make today's impossible task tomorrow's routine and to expand the list of procedures.

From our point of view, compositional type (DNA vs. RNA) and strand number (one vs. two) may, but do not clearly, belong in the list. At present we have no secure reason to believe that total information content or sequential homology depends on either of these properties. The properties may, however, reflect the sequence, in the sense that appropriate subsequences may specify each of them. In this case, the properties should be mutable, but no such mutations have yet been observed.

Along a similar line, the information for RNA self-replicability, a property known for viral RNA but not for sRNA or rRNA, is very probably contained in the RNA sequence and therefore mutable (see Jacob and Brenner, 1963). RNA self-replication involves two physiologically distinct processes: (a) induction of an RNA-directed RNA polymerase, for which the structural information (let's call it *poly*) is very probably in the viral RNA, and (b) the actual polymerase-mediated RNA replication with the viral RNA acting as template (Section 18–2,C). Since the polymerase distinguishes viral from nonviral RNA (Spiegelman, 1963), viral RNA must also carry information (*tem*) marking it as a template for replication. An important question is whether *poly* and *tem* coincide. In any case, a study of mutual compatibility (cross reaction) of heterologous viral RNA's and polymerases, and perhaps also viral DNA's and their polymerases, may contribute useful taxonomic information. To illustrate an additional possibility for mapping information in viral nucleic acid, it is conceivable that careful digestion with exonucleases, accompanied by functional tests, would reveal the chain location of *poly* and *tem*.

If we can ask whether the information for certain ordinary properties of genetic nucleic acids is contained in special subsequences, we can also ask whether one subsequence has a determinative relation to another (see Lanni, 1960), in which case the sequence would be to some extent redundant. Here we run against well-founded dogma, and we might wish the answer to be negative, if only for simplicity.

So far there is no persuasive evidence that mutation at one point affects the sequence at another, but this is not to deny correlation in the mutual placement of nucleotides. Nearest-neighbor and other analyses clearly show that nucleic acid sequences are not random, a feature very probably arising at least in part from the functional grouping of nucleotides into code words (Lanni, 1962). The subdivision of polynucleotides into code words larger than one nucleotide evidently reduces the taxonomic value of single nucleotides (the unit characters), but code degeneracy (Section 18–2,B) makes up some of the loss. To play safe, it might be desirable to estimate total information content in terms of, say, nucleotide triplets rather than single nucleotides. Processes such as convergent evolution, operating on proteins and possibly leading to polypeptide sequence patterns (see, for example, Šorm and Keil, 1962; Lanni, 1963b), would also reduce the information content. But now we are looking at some of the baby's shortcomings.

In Section 18–2,E, discussing TMV, we noted evidence that the viral nucleic acid is sequentially homogeneous in the sense of not being a mixture of complementary strands. It is too early to feel secure about this conclusion or to extend it freely to other single-stranded nucleic acids. With the smaller viral nucleic acids, oligonucleotide fractionation plus a modicum of luck can yield the answer. Under suitable conditions, the molar yield and the nucleotide length of various oligonucleotides can be estimated without determination of their nucleotide composition or sequence. In such analyses, the phage R17 RNA (mol wt $= 1.2 \times 10^6$; about 3600 residues), after digestion with ribonuclease, yields at least 10 chromatographic peaks (on DEAE), including one 10-mer, two 9-mers, and three 8-mers (Kaesberg, 1963). The yields of these oligomers are very close to the theoretical values for sequentially homogeneous RNA. Similar studies by Hall and Sinsheimer (1963) with phage ϕX174 DNA (mol wt $= 1.7 \times 10^6$; about 5500 residues), stressing pyrimidine oligonucleotides and including analysis of composition, indicate that this DNA, too, is very probably sequentially homogeneous.

Although the experiments with R17 and ϕX argue against many kinds of heterogeneity, including a mixture of complementary strands, they do not rule out all imaginable forms of heterogeneity. In particular, those with the open-ended R17 nucleic acid do not rule out circular permutation. By the agar hybridization procedure, Thomas and Rubenstein (1963) found evidence that phage T5 DNA is not, but phage T2 DNA is, circularly permuted (for compatible genetic evidence, see Streisinger et al., 1963a, 1963b; Sechaud et al., 1963). The size of the permutation steps is essentially unknown and would have to be less than 2% of the T2 DNA molecule to approach the length of the R17 nucleic acid. At least with T2, circular permutation does not obviously preclude valid tests of homology, as evidenced by the fact that molecular hybridization was itself used to show the permutation. In conclusion, we have no reason at present to suspect that chemical homology tests will be insuperably complicated by sequential heterogeneity of viral nucleic acids.

A related question has to do with the stability of the various homology criteria under mutation. Apart from the observable taxonomic diversity, there seem to be very few signs of instability, perhaps because the criteria are fairly stable or because they have not been much used. The total DNA of a phage λ virion (Kellenberger et al., 1961) and the DNA molecular weight (Burgi, 1963) have been shown to decrease by mutation. Oddly, small deletions in the T4 genome shorten the map around the deletion (Nomura and Benzer, 1961) but appear not to shorten the total genome (Streisinger et al., 1963b), as if a "headful" of DNA is meted out to each virion. The missing section seems to be compensated by increased redundancy of the remaining genes. A few workers, most recently Weed (1963), have reported evidence of gross mutational changes in the mean composition of certain bacterial DNA's. The results are provocative (see Lanni, 1960) but require additional documentation and confirmation. Occasional reports of compositional changes in viral nucleic acids have been questioned by other workers (see Schaffer, 1962). In any case, heterogeneity with respect to a given molecular property need not invalidate the property for taxonomy and may enhance its usefulness.

E. Other Molecular Approaches: Genetics and Proteins

1. *Recombinational genetics.*—By hypothesis and experience, genetics is a way of studying nucleotide sequences, functional groupings of nucleotides and nucleotide subsequences, and polynucleotide interactions. The virtues and accomplishments of genetics are so evident that to allude to them seems discourteous. Given cooperative material, its resolving power is good enough to discern adjacent individual nucleotides, as best illustrated by the classical fine-structure studies of Benzer (1957), and its sweep covers whole systems of genetic polynucleotides. As to the various functional subdivisions of genetic polynucleotides (Section 18–2,A), it seems fair to say that for the most part genetics affirmed their existence, estimated their size, and anticipated crucial features of their physiology well in advance of biochemistry, although in recent years the interval between genetic prediction and biochemical verification has somewhat shortened and has occasionally taken a negative sign.

But genetics also has clear limits, especially when it tries to do certain biochemical and biophysical analyses in live organisms rather than test tubes. Although it can resolve adjacent nucleotides, the cost in concentration, energy, time, mutants, and no doubt money is large, and it appears to have performed this remarkable feat only a few times (Benzer, 1957; Yanofsky *et al.*, 1963), enough only to establish the principle. When genetics tries to pin chemical labels on nucleotides, the task, aided by chemical mutagens (Freese, 1963) and the Nirenberg-Ochoa codes (see Lanni, 1963a), is somewhat simpler. Here again (biochemical) genetics is to be congratulated for being the first and so far the only discipline to identify mutationally altered nucleotides, but the procedures hardly belong in handbooks of analytical biochemistry.

We could go on reviewing the brilliant achievements of genetics, but each time (or so we think) we should have to remark that for more routine analyses, of the type needed by taxonomy, we had better look to, or look forward to, biochemistry and biophysics. We might also remember that the Watson-Crick theory of DNA structure and replication, a theory on which genetics now leans to the point of envelopment, was the product not of genetics but of crystallography and model building. Genetics, of course, helped to pick out the right material.

Let us now quickly review some limitations of *in vivo* recombinational genetics in analyzing genetic homology, i.e., sequential homology of genetic polynucleotides. We refer mainly to microorganisms.

(1) Recombinational genetics cannot deal, except by indirection and analogy, with the vast majority of bacteria and viruses that are unknown to show genetic recombination.

(2) Where genetic recombination occurs, the possible involvment of episomes (see Section 18–2,D) or analogous structures has to be evaluated. This cause of ambiguity has not yet been met in viruses.

(3) Silent genes, i.e., genes that do not yield recoverable mutants, and inarticulate regions of noisy genes are precluded from analysis. Here the power of the direct molecular approach, using molecular hybridization, is perhaps best illustrated by its priority in discovering presumptive genes for sRNA and rRNA (Giacomoni and Spiegelman, 1962; Goodman and Rich, 1962; Yankofsky and Spiegelman, 1962) in an organism, *E. coli*, that had long been combed by mutational and recombinational methods.

(4) Representative sampling of appreciably long genomes, such as those of bacteria and large viruses, requires considerable effort, and only a handful of such genomes have been extensively explored. With the seemingly more advantageous small viruses, genetic mapping has barely begun, and the prospect of a map saturated as much as 5% is invisible. Moreover, recombinational geneticists are interested in many problems besides homology.

(5) Even in organisms reasonably ex-

pected to be genetically homologous, physiological barriers causing infertility often preclude analysis. The explicit molecular approach can often discard these barriers as impurities. Signs of intracellular molecular-pairing difficulties are valuable because they suggest incomplete homology (see Marmur *et al.*, 1963a; Ravin, 1963), but such difficulties, which might arise through deletions, duplications, translocations, etc., very likely produce underestimates of homology. The molecular approach is capable of reducing pairing restraints by using nucleic acid fragments obtained by sonication or other treatment. Such a device, together with hybridization in agar, is presently being used in taxonomic surveys by M. Mandel (personal communication) and McCarthy and Bolton (1963). Information about gene order is, of course, fractured along with the nucleic acid.

(6) Being essentially indirect, recombinational genetics often meets great difficulty in verifying molecular hypotheses of its fundamental phenomena, this in spite of considerable *in vitro* aid from molecular biochemistry and biophysics. In simple testimony, we do not yet have, in the current break-and-rejoin model of recombination (Meselson and Weigle, 1961), a reasonably authenticated picture of how polynucleotide chains are cut, reassorted, and glued back together (see Kozinski and Kozinski, 1963).

Although genetics may be unsuited to some investigations, we cannot hold with the opinion (no doubt intended only facetiously when occasionally heard of late) that genetics is outmoded, in particular by biochemistry. Such a view would only betray insensitivity to current periodicals and to the too visible limitations of contemporary biochemistry. As friend of the court and devil's advocate both, genetics will continue to supply data, leads, breakthroughs, concepts, hypotheses, penetrating analyses, illumination, verification, inspiration, and—not least in value—criticism. In this formative period of molecular taxonomy, not only have recombinational tests of homology already provided valuable data for checking the explicit molecular approach and the results of classical taxonomy (Sections 18–2,D, 18–4, and 18–5,B), but continuing tests are indispensable to a secure foundation.

2. *Proteins.*—By hypothesis and experience, the study of (coded) polypeptide chain sequences, best illustrated by those of TMV protein, hemoglobin, and tryptophan synthetase, is implicitly a study of certain sequences in genetic polynucleotides (Section 18–2). There is now strong evidence of a point-by-point correspondence (colinearity) between successive amino acids and successive groups of nucleotides (code words); but belief in the existence of a definite coding relation, apart from knowledge of its actual form, suffices to justify use of polypeptide chain sequences as a substitute for polynucleotide sequences in molecular taxonomy. Code degeneracy loosens the correspondence somewhat, since a given amino acid residue may reflect any one of several interchangeable code words. Convergent evolution may introduce spurious homologies between polypeptides. These influences are unlikely to be weighty, but only experience will make us sure.

A polypeptide chain of 150 amino acid residues corresponds to perhaps $3 \times 150 = 450$ nucleotides. This number is an appreciable fraction of the smaller viral polynucleotides, ranging upward from about 1000 residues, but it is a very small fraction of nucleic acids like that of a T-even phage, with about 2×10^5 nucleotide pairs. Nevertheless, demonstration of significant homology in one protein would be an excellent start in the taxonomic appraisal of any two viruses.

It is very important to appreciate that amino acid sequence formulas have, theoretically and very probably in fact, a taxonomic value vastly superior to that of the classical properties revealed by ordinary biochemical, biophysical, and physicochemical studies of proteins. To be sure, most or all of these properties reflect to a greater or lesser degree the sequence of amino acid residues in the chain(s) of a given protein; yet one is led to believe that the classical properties generally would be hard put to distinguish the actual chain(s) from a large number of others, both real and hypothetical. The difficulty often encountered in purifying proteins, and the seemingly primitive state of theories attempting to relate biological activity of proteins to molecular structure, support this belief.

On the other hand, for most or all polypeptides of interest, the chain sequence may well be the major or exclusive determinant of *all* other properties, including interaction with like or unlike chains in the assembly of multichain protein molecules and interaction with like or unlike molecules in the construction of multimolecular aggregates such as viral capsids (see Caspar and Klug, 1962; Lanni, 1963a; Tsugita and Fraenkel-Conrat, 1963). In the ideal case, we may say that chain sequence is related by mutual implication to the rest. This is not to say that classical protein characters are useless in taxonomy. Experience shows otherwise. But, having viral taxonomy specifically in mind, awaiting systematic analysis of the problem perhaps with the help of computers, and leaving aside complications from deletions, insertions, and other chain rearrangements, we venture to suggest that identification of the residues at some 20–40 randomly chosen but analogous sites in two polypeptides would generally have a taxonomic value greater than that of the combined classical information presently available for any single protein, including the extremely well-characterized hemoglobin (but perhaps not including properties, such as crystallographic properties, that relate closely to chain sequence). The "distinct" classical characters of proteins are largely redundant anyway (molecular pleiotropy).

For general taxonomy based on proteins, two "classical" approaches, serology and enzymology, stand out above the rest. For viral taxonomy, enzymology has not yet found wide application. Only a few viruses, mostly myxoviruses and phages, are known to possess virion-associated enzymes; however, intracellular virus-induced enzymes increase the imaginable scope.

On the other hand, serology based on virions (see, e.g., Burnet, 1959b; Porterfield, 1962) has found extremely wide application both in taxonomy and in diagnosis. Although the serological properties of a protein antigen can rarely be interpreted explicitly in terms of chain sequence (for interesting results with TMV, see Anderer, 1963), there seems little question that these properties indeed reflect various portions of the chain sequence, even though a given antigenic determinant may be composed of widely scattered amino acid residues that are brought together by the folding of a protein (see Levine, 1962). Hence, authentic serological cross reaction almost automatically is a display of at least partial sequential homology (this is probably why serology is so valuable), and we need feel no great reluctance in admitting serology to the fold of choice molecular-taxonomic procedures.

Serology is not, however, without hazard (see Porterfield, 1962). Nonprotein constituents such as polysaccharides, by virtue of their simpler composition, have an appreciable likelihood of producing taxonomically irrelevant cross reactions. Procedures purporting to measure specific neutralization—the primary serological observation on viruses—may in fact be measuring something else (see Lanni, 1959). Failure to show cross reaction does not necessarily mean absence of sequential homology (see Hummeler *et al.*, 1962). Mutation, perhaps involving only one nucleotide or nucleotide pair, may radically alter the serological reactivity and antigenic structure of a virus (see Lanni and Lanni, 1957; F. Lanni, 1958). All this assumes adequate attention to the serological purity of antigen preparations and antisera.

Attractive possibilities with denatured protein antigens, which may afford not just an alternative but a superior index of sequential homology, seem to have been almost completely overlooked (see Darnell, 1962; Levine, 1962).

Presently, amino acid sequence formulas, the first-choice data for molecular taxonomy based on proteins, are in exceedingly short supply. Understandably, mammalian proteins have so far been the most extensively studied, and Wilson and Kaplan (cited by Marmur *et al.*, 1963a) have been able to correlate sequential homology with previously deduced taxonomic relatedness in mammals. In viruses, most of the available information has come from studies of mutants and naturally occurring variants of TMV (Tsugita, 1962a, 1962b; Tsugita and Fraenkel-Conrat, 1963; Wittmann, 1963). These data are discussed in Section 18–5,B. The tail-associated lysozyme of phage T4 is also under study (Streisinger *et al.*, 1961).

Intermediate data on the way to full sequence analysis should, however, be very useful. With suitable polypeptides, e.g., that of TMV, the *amino acid composition* of the whole chain can now be analyzed very accurately and affords, incidentally, a very close approximation to *chain length*, another valuable criterion. Thus, Tsugita (1962b) was able to classify TMV variants according to the number of methionine residues; and the chain length is constant (158 residues) for all analyzed variants. In a study that might have seemed unpromising in advance, Sueoka (1961a, 1961b) analyzed the amino acid composition of *unfractionated* bacterial protein and compared the mole fraction of various amino acids with DNA base composition (% GC) for a variety of bacteria (plus *Tetrahymena*) covering the spectrum of base composition. In this way he discovered important correlations that not only support the postulated informational relation between DNA and protein and the usefulness of proteins in taxonomy, but also afford excellent confirmation of the Nirenberg-Ochoa codes (Lanni, 1963a). Protein-nucleic acid compositional correlations have been sought in viruses but have not yet been convincingly demonstrated.

Peptide fingerprints (maps) and *column chromatograms* yield information not only about chain length but also, implicitly, about the over-all chain sequence. Woody and Knight (1959) distinguished several naturally occurring TMV variants by their fingerprints. In an exemplary molecular-taxonomic study, Zuckerkandl *et al.* (1960) compared the hemoglobin fingerprints of a wide range of vertebrates. Peptide separation is, of course, a first step in localizing compositional differences between two polypeptides. *End groups* and *terminal subsequences* may be investigated directly on whole chains. Thus, Knight *et al.* (1962)

were able to show that Y-TAMV, a naturally occurring TMV variant, has C-terminal serine instead of the usual threonine. Narita (1958) found that the N-terminal amino acid of cucumber virus 4 protein is acetylated, like that of TMV *vulgare* protein; the respective N-terminal heptapeptides differ, however, in sequence (see Section 18–5,B for further comparison of these viruses). For multichain proteins, a recent paper by Herner and Riggs (1963), dealing with hemoglobin, illustrates the taxonomic possibilities of *molecular hybridization* with polypeptides (see Baglioni, 1963). For analogous studies with TMV, see Sarkar (1960).

In conclusion to this brief consideration of the taxonomic use of proteins, we may think of the individual polypeptide chain site as being here the unit character, with perhaps 21 values: one for each of the common amino acids, plus void. What we said previously about the power of the molecular approach through nucleic acids (Section 18–3,C) applies with appropriate modification also to proteins. Since microorganisms are capable of propagating asexually in mutual isolation and since the structural-gene polynucleotide sequences of two isolated strains may diverge without effect on the corresponding polypeptide sequences (this in consequence of code degeneracy), a hierarchical system might in some circumstances have to place polypeptide homology above polynucleotide homology. Proteins may well have a better memory of distant ancestry.

18–4. BACTERIA AND THE MUTUAL VALIDATION OF CLASSICAL AND MOLECULAR TAXONOMY

There are several reasons why, among the possible groups of organisms presently offering opportunities to compare the results of classical and molecular taxonomy, bacteria are perhaps the most favorable.

(1) In contrast to the taxonomy of many higher organisms, bacterial taxonomy developed to an advanced state (or states) with essentially no assistance from tests of genetic compatibility. Even today, genetic

recombination is known for relatively few bacterial genera.

(2) Similarly, bacterial taxonomy developed to an advanced state without reference to criteria based explicitly on nucleic acids. Although serology has, of course, been a taxonomic tool for many years, this tool seems to have been used chiefly to delineate the smallest branches of taxonomic trees, and then not routinely. The recent numerical taxonomists make minimal or no use of serology, or molecular-taxonomic procedures in general, in their initial appraisal of over-all affinity.

(3) Although there are some outstanding differences of opinion about how bacteria should be classified, the conclusions reached by various classical or mostly-classical taxonomists, including numerical taxonomists, generally show considerable agreement (Sneath, 1962), enough to afford relatively unambiguous comparisons with molecular-taxonomic data. Viruses afford fewer unbiased comparisons, largely because of the considerable use of serological criteria by viral taxonomists.

(4) The wide variation of DNA base composition in bacteria greatly enhances the value of this measure in taxonomy. Likewise, the near-homogeneity of bacterial DNA has facilitated studies based on molecular hybridization. In many higher organisms, the DNA has practically the same over-all composition and at the same time a given specimen shows gross compositional heterogeneity.

The volume of useful molecular-taxonomic data for bacteria is now large, and several studies, explicitly comparing these data with conclusions from classical taxonomy, have already appeared. All in all, the available comparisons leave no question that our two taxonomies stand in excellent, though by no means perfect, agreement. The comprehensive review by Marmur *et al.* (1963a) should be consulted for details. Here we shall briefly describe a few studies, illustrating both the agreement and the disagreement. Where bacteria are designated by their scientific name, the reader will understand that the name is a product of classical or mostly-classical taxonomy and means that (a) bacterial strains (iso-lates) exhibiting appropriate phenotypic similarity have been brought together under that name, and (b) bacterial strains not satisfying the criteria for inclusion will generally have been brought together under other names. It should be remarked that the characters used to construct given taxa, e.g., species, are by no means the same for all bacteria, and there is continuing debate between "lumpers" and "splitters." Further, most of the available comparisons of our two taxonomies involve the lowest taxa (species, genera, and families).

Catlin and Cunningham (1961) compared seven species (*meningitidis, perflava, flava, subflava, sicca, flavescens, catarrhalis*) of the genus *Neisseria* with respect to DNA base composition and mutual (interspecific) transformability by free DNA. (Transformation is one of several recombinational indices of genetic homology.) The first six of the above-named species resemble one another very closely in base composition (49.5–51.5% GC). Each of these six gave successful transformation with itself and with the other five. The ratio of interspecific to intraspecific transformation was usually, but not always, less than 1.0, in general agreement with the assignment to different species. In contrast, *N. catarrhalis*, whose DNA has about 40.7% GC, gave no significant transformation with any of the others. Catlin and Cunningham suggest that "the inclusion of *catarrhalis* strains in the genus *Neisseria* appears illogical from the evolutionary point of view."

Schildkraut *et al.* (1961) compared bacteria from close and distant genera by the procedure of DNA molecular hybridization, using heavy-isotope labels (N^{15} and deuterium) in one of the two DNA's and resolving the DNA peaks in a CsCl density gradient. *Bacillus subtilis* DNA (43% GC) formed hybrids with that of *B. natto* (43% GC) but not with that of *B. brevis* (42.5% GC), *Diplococcus pneumoniae* (39% GC), or *E. coli* (50% GC). Among other tests, many of them preliminary, *E. coli* DNA gave an intermediate result with that of *Shigella dysenteriae* (50% GC) but was negative with that of various *Salmonella* species (all about 50% GC). *Escherichia* shows definite but incomplete homology with both *Shigella* and *Salmonella* by the criterion of genetic recombination, and the three genera show strong phenotypic similarity. It was concluded that "equality of base composition and some genetic relation are necessary but not sufficient requirements for the formation of hybrid DNA molecules composed of strands from different organisms." This extended the previous conclusion (Lanni, 1960) that near-identity of base composition is necessary but not sufficient for genetic recombination. By the DNA-agar technique, McCarthy and Bolton (1963) obtained excellent hybridization with the DNA's of *E. coli* and *Salmonella typhimurium*. These two DNA's also contain very similar frequencies of pyrimidine sequences (Burton, 1962).

Marmur *et al.* (1963b) investigated representatives of 20 species of *Bacillus*, whose DNA composition ranged from 32.5% to 50.5% GC. All were compared with *B. subtilis* (43% GC) in transformation experiments. The five positive DNA's ranged from 42.5% to 44% GC. Two negative DNA's also fell in this composition range, but most of the negative DNA's (32.5–41% and 46–50.5% GC) fell outside. Two DNA's were tested for hybrid formation with *B. subtilis* DNA; a transformation-positive DNA (42.5% GC) formed hybrids, and a transformation-negative one (40% GC) did not. Evidently, the tolerance in base composition is very close. As in the experiments of Catlin and Cunningham with *Neisseria*, the ratio of interspecific to intraspecific transformation was sometimes very low. Marmur *et al.* suggest that shearing the DNA might improve both the transformation and the hybridization assays. They also state that "finding that a close relationship exists between [classical] taxonomy, transformability, and DNA hybrid molecule formation provides a precedent for the use of either transformation or hybrid band formation as a rational approach for studying the relatedness of microorganisms." Various assessments agree in regarding *Bacillus* as a very heterogeneous group. It is not surprising therefore that, over the group as a whole, the correlation between DNA base composition (Marmur *et al.*, 1963b) and affinity measured by numerical

taxonomy (Sneath, 1962) is less than one might like to see.

Independently of Giacomoni and Spiegelman (1962), Goodman and Rich (1962) showed that *E. coli* sRNA is capable of hybridizing *in vitro* with about 0.025% of the total DNA of *E. coli*. The same sRNA gave negative results with DNA from salmon sperm, calf thymus, and phages T2, T7, P22, and ϕX174. Goodman and Rich then tested the ability of *E. coli* sRNA to hybridize with DNA from a variety of bacteria, differing widely in their taxonomic relation to *E. coli*. The results were expressed as percentage of the hybrid formation observed with the homologous *E. coli* DNA. DNA's from various members of Enterobacteriaceae, the taxonomic family to which *Escherichia* belongs, gave values ranging from 30 to 70%, in evident correspondence to classically assessed taxonomic affinity. DNA's from representatives of four other families gave values ranging from 5 to 15%. The base composition of sRNA is practically constant throughout the bacterial world, in striking contrast to the highly variable composition of whole bacterial DNA. The inference from the hybridization experiments is that a very small fraction of the total DNA likewise has a fairly constant composition in various bacteria. It is as if the sRNA-specific DNA resisted the forces leading to compositional divergence of the remainder. In any case, the experiments of Goodman and Rich, together with the parallel experiments of Giacomoni and Spiegelman, not only afford an alternative way of assessing taxonomic relatedness, but they also embrace organisms whose homology is too weak to be perceived in experiments of the types described in the preceding paragraphs. Gene transfer via episomes (Section 18–2,D) likewise embraces a relatively broad range of bacteria (Marmur *et al.*, 1963a).

In a paper appearing when this article was practically complete, McCarthy and Bolton (1963) studied molecular homology in the major DNA fraction of Enterobacteriaceae by the DNA-agar hybridization technique. Appropriate DNA samples were melted, trapped in agar, and allowed to interact at 60°C with mRNA-like RNA, or with melted DNA that had first been sheared to a (duplex) molecular weight of about 500,000. RNA and melted, sheared DNA from the same source gave practically the same result, regardless of their taxonomic relation to the trapped DNA. In general, the greater the classically assessed affinity of two bacteria, and the more nearly identical their DNA base composition, the greater was the level of hybrid formation.

The McCarthy-Bolton data give a new picture of molecular homology in the Enterobacteriaceae. Whereas the Schildkraut-Marmur procedure of equilibrium centrifugation in a density gradient seems to detect homology only between very closely related bacteria, practically indistinguishable in DNA base composition, the DNA-agar procedure gives positive results (sometimes weak) over the whole family, even between bacteria differing greatly in base composition. In the usual Schildkraut-Marmur procedure, both of the interacting nucleic acids (DNA) have a high molecular weight (perhaps 10–20 million); a phosphodiesterase specific for denatured DNA (and probably active also on poorly matched ends of a hybrid duplex) is used to solubilize undenatured strands; and DNA's from the two sources compete actively for partner strands. In the DNA-agar procedure, the free nucleic acid (RNA or sheared DNA) has a low molecular weight; weak hybrids can and do contribute to the result; and competition is reduced by trapping one nucleic acid in agar and by using a low ratio of free to trapped nucleic acid. Thus it appears that the DNA-agar procedure would have the better chance of detecting weak, randomly distributed molecular homology, or localized regions of weak or strong homology. In fact, the McCarthy-Bolton data give direct evidence of localized molecular homology in the case of distantly related bacteria (see also Falkow et al., 1962). On the other hand, the Schildkraut-Marmur procedure would be expected to correlate more closely, as it does, with genetic recombination and to require, as it does, near-identity in DNA base composition.

We can see in the McCarthy-Bolton data, and in the results with sRNA and episomes, the prospect of a widely comprehensive molecular taxonomy and the beginnings of a massive taxonomic tree. Will viruses show similar phenomena?

18–5. VIRAL TAXONOMY

A. A Brief Orientation

Over the years, the sources of taxonomic characters for viruses have understandably reflected the main problems of virology, which might be listed as chemistry and architecture of the virion, virion-host interaction, growth, heredity and variation, pathogenesis, and epidemiology. Similarly, the visibly shifting character preferences have reflected the shifting experimental and theoretical orientation to the main problems. Although all three of the major subdivisions of virology have experienced a shift toward primary emphasis on chemistry and structure of the virion, the historical traditions, the motivation, and the kind of emphasis have been notably different. As everyone knows, the traditions were largely kept distinct by viral host range, and it is only recently, because of advances in molecular biology, that the traditions have really come together (see Luria, 1953, 1959; Cohen, 1955; Lwoff et al., 1962).

In one sense, plant virology, the first subdivision to become molecular, has been modern for years. Stanley's crystallization of TMV in 1935 started an uninterrupted devotion by him and his colleagues to the chemistry of the tobacco mosaic virion. Thanks largely to Stanley's group, but with recognition also of other plant virologists, our chemical knowledge of this virion exceeds that for any other. Good fortune gave TMV a relatively simple composition and structure: a single RNA molecule of some 6500 nucleotides, surrounded by a helical array of some 2100 apparently identical protein subunits, each a single polypeptide chain of 158 residues. As a consequence of continuing chemical studies over many years, the polypeptide sequence formula is essentially fully known (no other viral polypeptide can say the same), and much progress has been made in the sequential analysis of the RNA (but other viruses, with still simpler nucleic acids, may well reach the finish line first). With TMV usually leading the way, other plant viruses have met intensive analysis at the chemical bench. On the other hand, the biology of plant viruses, especially that part dealing with infection and growth, is an exceedingly difficult matter, and we know much less here than for other viruses. In short, if our view of plant virology is reasonably correct, it is easy to understand that plant-virus taxonomy has had access for many years to detailed chemical information about virions. This is not to suggest, however, that epidemiology, symptomatology, etc., especially where agricultural crops were involved, did not have their say.

With bacterial viruses, the germs of a modern tradition can be traced to one of the co-discoverers, d'Hérelle, almost 50 years ago, and to sporadic followers; but these viruses did not really acquire momentum until the 1940's, when Delbrück started the American school with its single-minded and highly productive allegiance to the T phages of *E. coli* strain B. Morphology and serology of the virion were quickly adopted as useful characters (serology had already found extensive use in phage taxonomy) and were soon backed up by genetic recombination. The T phage/*E. coli* system lent itself so well to precise kinetic and biochemical experiments on invasion and intracellular growth, and the workers were so attracted by the evident promise of their material for solving fundamental problems of heredity, that the virion took a back seat—but a comfortable one if we would recall only the famous physiological dissection of the T2 virion by Hershey and Chase, with demonstration of the independent functions of DNA and protein. The complex morphology of the favorite T-even virions—exquisite from one point of view but terrible to contemplate from another—and the large total of DNA did little to encourage detailed chemical studies on the virion itself. (Of course, the virion has lately come back into the front seat with the discovery of simpler phages such as ϕX174 and f2.) Moreover, in contrast to the many workers who are interested in the molecular biology of phages, relatively few are presently concerned with taxonomy as a serious enterprise. But we can hardly complain, since the phage workers and their intellectual offspring fashioned many of the basic concepts and tools of molecular taxonomy. The situation is obviously changing, and we may expect an increasing number of workers to be attracted by taxonomy. It is too early, however, to expect to find extensive data on the composition and sequence of phage nucleic acids and proteins, although some data of this kind of course exist. Since molecular taxonomy purports to deal with genetic homology, we could not leave bacterial viruses without alluding to the signs of phage-host homology in the phenomenon of lysogeny, which merits serious attention in discussions of the origin of viruses.

Understandably, the tradition of animal virology springs largely from age-old preoccupation with disease in man and domestic animals. Viruses were (and still are) sorted and named according to the chief host, the associated disease, geographic and seasonal incidence, favorite intrahost habitat, etc. (We might have made such a comment also for plant virology, but not for bacterial virology, where for the most part only the host contributed its name to the parasite.) In animal virology, more than its sister virologies, compelling problems of diagnosis, epidemiology, and immunity pre-empted attention and had to be met with simple and effective procedures. Convalescent human and animal sera were on tap. So were rabbits and other inducible antibody factories. The all-purpose answer was serology of the virion. This is why we know animal viruses down to their amino acid side chains (implicitly, of course) generally much better than we know plant and bacterial viruses, and it is one reason why serology has for many years played a major role in animal-virus classification, almost to the exclusion of chemistry and morphology. Lately, biochemistry also has begun to make significant contributions to many problems of animal virology. The explicit comparative molecular chemistry of virions is, however, barely underway, and the same might be said for mutational and recombinational genetics. Closing mention should be made of the enzyme neuraminidase, associated with myxovirus virions, and the property of hemagglutination associated with these virions and some others. Both of these properties have been used in animal-virus taxonomy and both appear to merit high esteem, along with serology.

In all three virologies, recent refinements in electron microscopy—especially the procedure of negative staining with phosphotungstic acid, which reveals very fine details of viral architecture—have greatly increased the value and use of morphological criteria (see Horne and Wildy, 1961; Bernhard and Tournier, 1962; Morgan *et al.*, 1962; Wildy and Watson, 1962).

If the foregoing sketches are not too blurred, it is easy to understand that, until about 10 years ago, communication among the three virologies was highly restricted and that taxonomists (and other virologists) generally confined their attention to the virology in which they had been weaned. The available data in all subdivisions were enormous, making it appear that nothing short of an international committee could cope with it all and come up with a system. Taxonomists did, however, generally agree on three points: (a) viruses are extremely heterogeneous, (b) viruses are not easy to classify, and (c) viruses have somehow evolved, though not necessarily from a single origin. The phenotypic heterogeneity is indisputable. A favorite trick in textbook and classroom is to calculate that the volumes of the largest and smallest virions differ by a factor in the order of 10,000. For the inquiring student, no one has been able to calculate what this means. How many one-step mutations would it take to go from the smallest to the largest, or vice versa? One can imagine how ancestral relation might be proved, but how does one go about proving independent origin?

Looking back, one senses that the unity of virology, and a fresh start in viral taxonomy, first quickened, not in a committee, but in the minds of a few individuals (one thinks of the likes of Burnet, Cohen, and Luria, named alphabetically) who, each in his own way, had the experience and insight needed to contemplate virology more or less as a whole, approaching it mostly from the viewpoint of general biology.

Then, about 10 years ago, the great desegregation of the three virologies began. A small conference at Pasadena in 1950 and larger symposia at Oxford in 1952 and at Cold Spring Harbor and Detroit in 1953 brought together plant, animal, and bacterial virologists from around the world. Luria's *General Virology* appeared in 1953. People trained in one of the virologies moved into another, in all directions. The word about the power of phage techniques and about the new knowledge they were revealing leaked not only to the other virologies, but perhaps more important, to host-rangeless disciplines such as biochemistry and biophysics. Meantime, bacteriology was experiencing a similar interchange with other disciplines. In our universe the result was inevitable. Virology, cellular biology, genetics, biochemistry, and biophysics quickly converged to a natural center where, with the blessing of structural chemistry, they merged and produced molecular biology as we know it today.

The question is, if we begin from the unifying characteristics of plant, animal, and bacterial viruses enumerated earlier (Section 18–1), can we find our way around in the so far incomprehensible heterogeneity? In the following sections, we review some recent studies of the kind that may eventually lead us through the maze.

B. SOME RECENT MOLECULAR-TAXONOMIC STUDIES

1. *The T phages.*—As originally defined, the set of T phages included seven independently isolated phages, all active on *E. coli* strain B. Their biological and chemical properties have been summarized by Luria (1953), Stent (1958), Adams (1959), and Sinsheimer (1960). The seven phages comprise four serological groups:

T1; T2, T4, T6; T3, T7; T5

such that serological cross reaction occurs within a group but not between groups. From time to time, other independently isolated phages have been added to each group. Many other criteria, including genetic recombination, confirm the serological groups. The basic classification can therefore be regarded with great confidence. By a number of "distinct" characters, T5 might be grouped with the T-evens (T2, T4, T6), and T1 with T3 and T7 (Adams and Wade, 1955; Y. T. Lanni, 1958; Stent, 1958). Many of these characters may be related pleiotropically (see Stent, 1958).

Schildkraut *et al.* (1962b) tested chemical homology among the seven T phages by the method of DNA-DNA molecular hybridization, using heavy-isotope labels and CsCl density-gradient centrifugation. T4 DNA hybridized with that of T2 and T6 (and T4), but not with that of T1, T3, T5, or T7. The T4-T2 and T4-T6 hybrid peaks were smaller than the control T4-T4 peak, suggesting that the base-sequence homology was incomplete. The DNA's of T3 and T7 gave excellent hybridization, suggesting "essentially complete" homology. The base composition of T1, T3, and T7 DNA resembles that of *E. coli* DNA, and it has been suggested that these three phages are somewhat homologous to the host. The DNA of T3 and T7 failed, however, to give detectible hybridization with *E. coli* DNA; T1 DNA was not tested. Schildkraut *et al.* indicate that negative results must be regarded cautiously until the sensitivity of their technique has been evaluated. More recently, the DNA of temperate (= lysogenizing) phages has been found to hybridize *in vitro* with the RNA transcribed from *E. coli* DNA (see Attardi *et al.*, 1962, 1963; Hayashi *et al.*, 1963c).

It is a curious fact that demonstration of genetic recombination between T3 and T7 has been long delayed. The T3-T7 hybridization suggested to Schildkraut *et al.* that recombination should occur between these phages *in vivo*. Schildkraut *et al.* were unaware that recombination had been reported a year earlier by Hausmann *et al.* (1961). The fact that the prediction was confirmed in advance detracts nothing from this demonstration of the power of molecular techniques. The power shows up in one more very important way. Mixed infections between T3 and T7, or between two of the T-evens, are characterized by partial exclusion, with one phage type outnumbering the other in the progeny. With T3 and T7, only a very small percentage of mixedly infected bacteria yields both types, and this may be why recombination escaped discovery for so long. In mixed infections between phages from different serological groups, an individual host cell produces one or the other of the two phage types, not both, and with some pairs of phages the whole culture produces only one type of phage. These exclusion phenomena are poorly understood, but they evidently restrict the opportunities to test homology *in vivo*. The *in vitro* molecular approach overcomes the partial or complete exclusion barriers.

A full tabulation would make it quickly apparent that molecular hybridization stands in complete agreement not only with genetic recombination and serology but also with other "hard" characters such as morphology, DNA base composition (including the replacement of cytosine by hydroxymethylcytosine in the T-evens), DNA dinucleotide sequences, and total DNA per virion, plus a number of "softer" characters dealing with inactivation of the virion by various agents and the physiology and biochemistry of infection. Host range, however, is not one of the concording characters.

In checking the specificity of DNA-RNA hybrids using the DNA-agar procedure, Bolton and McCarthy (1962) included tests with some of the T phages. T2 RNA (a new RNA appearing rapidly in T2-infected bacteria and reported earlier by other workers) was passed through agar columns loaded with denatured DNA from various sources. The RNA hybridized with DNA from T2 and T4, but not with the DNA of T7, *E. coli*, or *Proteus vulgaris*. Also using the agar-column technique, Thomas and Rubinstein (1963) observed DNA-DNA hybrid formation with T2-T2 and T5-T5, but not T2-T5. The results by various techniques thus stand in excellent agreement.

2. *The tobacco mosaic viruses.*—As discussed by Knight (1959), the classification of plant viruses—in particular, the decision whether two isolates should be regarded as distinct viruses or as strains of the same virus—formerly rested heavily on serological cross reaction and on cross protection in suitable hosts. Both of these criteria are still used widely, and others, such as host range, method of transmission, inactivation of the

TABLE 18–3. MOLAR PERCENTAGE OF BASES IN SOME VIRAL RNA's[*]

Virus	A	G	C	U	Reference
Tobacco mosaic	28.2	25.0	19.2	27.8	Knight (1959)
CV3 and CV4	24.2	25.5	19.5	31.2	"
Turnip crinkle	26.1	27.8	23.7	22.4	Symons *et al.* (1963)
WCMV	17.0	16.4	41.0	25.6	"
TYMV group 1	22.5	17.3	38.3	21.9	"
TYMV group 2	21.4	16.6	41.6	20.3	"
Bushy stunt	25.5	28.0	20.5	25.8	Knight (1959)
Polio type 1 (Mahoney)	28.5	24.8	21.8	25.0	Schaffer *et al.* (1960)
Polio type 2 (MEF1)	28.8	23.2	22.5	25.5	"
Polio type 3 (Saukett)	27.9	24.2	21.6	26.2	"
REO type 3	29.7	19.3	20.5	30.5	Gomatos and Tamm (1963)
Influenza A (PR8)	23.1	20.1	24.0	32.8	Ada and Perry (1956)
Influenza B (Lee)	23.0	18.4	23.0	35.6	"

[*] A = adenine, G = guanine, C = cytosine, U = uracil, CV = cucumber virus, WCMV = wild cucumber mosaic virus, TYMV = turnip yellow mosaic virus.

virion by various agents, and chemical and physical properties of the virion, have also come into use.

In agreement with the views expressed in previous sections, Knight considers that "the coincidence of specific major chemical and physical properties would seem to provide the best evidence for strain relationship." He would regard serological tests as "second only in specificity to the structural characteristics themselves," and "all of the other criteria," except possibly a certain test suggested by Holmes, would be "inferior to the physicochemical and immunological standards."

The naturally occurring strains usually included in the TMV group (we temporarily omit the arguable cucumber viruses 3 and 4, discussed shortly) show serological cross reaction, and their virions appear to be indistinguishable in morphology, over-all composition in terms of total RNA and protein, and RNA base composition. This seems to be fairly true of strains assigned to other groups of plant viruses; in contrast, two groups, set apart by lack of serological cross reaction, frequently differ widely in morphological and/or compositional properties. Restricting our attention here to the TMV group, about which most is known, we shall briefly review recent comparative

studies of the over-all amino acid composition of the viral polypeptide, the polypeptide chain sequence, and the RNA base sequence.

Careful comparisons of the masked TMV strain (M) with the common or type strain (*vulgare*) have failed to show differences in the composition of the whole polypeptide or of tryptic peptides derived therefrom (Tsugita, 1962b), peptide maps (Woody and Knight, 1959), or the composition of oligonucleotides obtained by digestion of the viral RNA with pancreatic ribonuclease (Rushizky and Knight, 1960) or ribonuclease T₁ (Rushizky *et al.*, 1962).

In contrast, strain HR differs decidedly from *vulgare* with respect to all of the properties just named. This result shows the importance of analysis of RNA subsequences in cases where the over-all base composition appears the same. Since the oligonucleotide analyses are tedious to discuss, we refer the reader to the original papers and to a paper by Staehelin (1961) comparing the very different oligonucleotide chromatograms of TMV and the unrelated turnip yellow mosaic virus. These two viruses differ greatly in RNA base composition (Table 18–3) and other properties.

Knight *et al.* (1962), looking to a correlation (still undiscovered) between biological properties and the chemistry of viral macromolecules, carried out an extensive chemical comparison of *vulgare* and two naturally occurring TMV variants, Y-TAMV and G-TAMV. The analyses included serological precipitation of the virions, over-all composition of the polypeptide (whose chain length proved to be constant), peptide maps, N-terminal and C-terminal amino acids, RNA base composition (same within 5%), and yield of various oligonucleotides liberated by digestion with ribonuclease. The results leave no question about the affinity of Y-TAMV and G-TAMV to each other and to *vulgare*, but they also show that all three strains differ considerably in nucleotide sequence and amino acid sequence.

Tsugita (1962b) and Wittmann (1963) analyzed the amino acid composition of the polypeptide of additional naturally occurring variants of TMV, and both workers have undertaken a detailed comparison of polypeptide chain sequences. As expected from the large differences often encountered in over-all amino acid composition, many differences in chain sequence are emerging. Thus, *vulgare* and *dahlemense* polypeptides differ by 27 amino acid replacements (Wittmann, 1963), and *vulgare* and Y-TAMV polypeptides differ by more than 30 (Tsugita, 1962b). It also appears that certain subsequences are relatively resistant to variation.

Only a careful perusal of the original papers would give the reader an adequate appreciation of the great significance and promise of these studies on TMV. At the same time that over-all fine-structure similarity in the viral macromolecules leaves no question about homology and ancestral relation, the fine-structure differences indicate that considerable evolutionary divergence has occurred. Hopefully, the TMV studies may be able to identify some rules of molecular evolution.

The cucumber viruses 3 and 4, whose properties have been summarized by Knight (1955, 1959) and Markham (1959), offer an interesting taxonomic challenge. On the one hand, these viruses show definite affinity to TMV, as indicated by morphological similarity of the virions, serological cross reaction, and mutual interference in infections of cucumber cotyledons. On the other hand, there is no known common host in which the respective viruses can multiply systemically, the respective viral polypeptides differ considerably in overall composition, and the respective RNA's also show significant compositional difference (Table 18-3). Knight believes that the cucumber viruses should not be classified with the TMV group, whereas Markham thinks that to exclude the cucumber viruses is "a matter of definition or even of personal taste" and that the reasons for exclusion "would seem rather arbitrary." We do not have to take a stand in the nomenclatural issue as such, but we do have to note the breakdown of the correlation between (a) near-identity in RNA base composition and (b) serological and other signs of affinity. Other examples follow shortly.

3. *Other plant viruses.*—Symons *et al.* (1963) compared six independently isolated strains of turnip yellow mosaic virus (TYMV), one strain of wild cucumber mosaic virus (WCMV), and one strain of turnip crinkle virus (TCV) with respect to polypeptide amino acid composition, RNA base composition (Table 18–3), and yield of various oligonucleotides liberated by ribonuclease digestion. The six TYMV strains segregated clearly into two groups, 1 and 2, each with three strains. Within each group, the strains were very similar, but slight differences occasionally were evident. Between groups, the differences were larger in all comparisons. The greatest differences emerged in comparisons of WCMV and TCV with each other and with TYMV strains. Although differences in RNA were associated with differences in amino acid composition, no close correlation could be discerned. Symons *et al.* were impressed by the ability of the oligonucleotide analysis to detect small differences. Their paper should be consulted for a discussion of the relevance of their results to the coding problem.

TYMV and WCMV are very similar morphologically, and their RNA's are unusual in having a very high content of cytosine, about 40% (Table 18–3), which is higher than that recorded for RNA from any other source. The two viruses are not known to have a common host, and until recently there was no serological evidence of relationship. Encouraged by the similarity in RNA base composition, Macleod and Markham (1963) proceeded to look for, and they found, serological cross reaction. These workers mention that other viruses have now been added to the TYMV-WCMV group, and that analogous experiments have revealed a second group of viruses that had not previously been connected and that lack a common host. It appears also that in a set of three viruses—A, B, and C—serological cross reaction may be positive for A-B and B-C, but negative for A-C (see also Adams and Wade, 1954). The implications for viral taxonomy are evident. Most important is the prospect that adequate comparison of strains formerly thought to be unrelated will reduce the apparent heterogeneity of viruses to more manageable proportions. Macleod and Markham believe that virion architecture and nucleic acid composition are the most important criteria for establishing relationships between viruses. It is not altogether clear why serology, properly performed, should be held much less important.

Kaesberg and coworkers have undertaken detailed biophysical and biochemical studies of a variety of plant viruses, including those of alfalfa mosaic (Kelley and Kaesberg, 1962), broad bean mottle (Yamazaki and Kaesberg, 1963), bromegrass mosaic (Bockstahler and Kaesberg, 1962), squash mosaic (Mazzone *et al.*, 1962), and wild cucumber mosaic (Yamazaki and Kaesberg, 1961), plus the RNA phage R17 (Enger *et al.*, 1963; Mitra *et al.*, 1963). Since the taxonomic relation, if any, of these viruses is presently unclear (at least to this writer), we shall not discuss the findings here. Systematic studies of this type (see also Knight, 1959; Markham, 1959) promise, however, to be exceedingly valuable as the list of analyzed viruses increases.

4. *Reovirus and wound-tumor virus.—* The reoviruses inhabit the respiratory and enteric tracts of man and animals. The wound-tumor virus infects a variety of plants and several species of leafhoppers.

The respective virions contain RNA and are very similar in size and architecture, the capsid in each case consisting of 92 capsomeres. Noting these facts, Lwoff *et al.* (1962) suggested that it might be "worthwhile to look for possible relationships . . . for example, for antigenic similarities."

Two other groups of investigators appear to have converged on the similarity independently. Streissle and Maramorosch (1963) found strongly suggestive evidence of serological cross reaction (complement fixation) between wound-tumor virus and each of three reovirus strains. They suggested that all these viruses should be classified in the same group.

Gomatos and Tamm (1963), struck by several resemblances between reovirus RNA and duplex DNA, examined the RNA structure in several ways. The mole fractions of A and U were nearly equal, as were those of C and G (Table 18–3); the melting transition at elevated temperature was very sharp; the reaction with formaldehyde was very poor; and the RNA resisted digestion by ribonuclease. Subject to verification by other analyses, these properties confirm the belief that the RNA is double-stranded. Preliminary studies suggested that wound-tumor RNA also is double-stranded. Independently, Black and Markham (cited by Streissle and Maramorosch, 1963) found evidence that the RNA of wound-tumor virus is double-stranded. No other viral RNA has been suggested to be double-stranded, but there is occasional evidence of extensive complementarity between parts of a single-stranded RNA (see, e.g., Mitra *et al.*, 1963).

Once again it appears that molecular criteria, guided by morphology and composition but neglecting host range, have helped to reduce the overwhelming heterogeneity of viruses.

5. *Some animal viruses.—*The influenza viruses include a large variety of strains resembling one another closely in virion architecture, over-all composition, and biological properties. The serological groups A, B, and C include strains that cross react within a group but not between groups. Genetic recombination has been demonstrated between several A strains, and sev-

eral B strains, but not between members of A and B (Burnet, 1955; Hirst, 1962). Ada and Perry (1956) found that strains of a given group, A or B, resemble one another closely in RNA base composition, but differ significantly, though slightly, from strains of the alternate group (examples in Table 18–3). The reliability of these data is somewhat uncertain (Schaffer, 1962).

The polioviruses likewise include strains that closely resemble one another in many ways. The three known serological types do not seem to cross react in neutralization or protection tests, but appear to cross react in complement fixation (Melnick, 1953). As seen in Table 18–3, strains representing the three types have practically the same RNA base composition. The RNA's of the Mahoney and MEFl strains differ significantly, however, in guanine content and in the ratio of $A + U$ to $G + C$ (Schaffer et al., 1960).

Ben-Porat and Kaplan (1962) confirmed the classically deduced affinity of herpes simplex and pseudorabies viruses by showing that the respective virions have a similar buoyant density, they both contain DNA, and their DNA's are almost identical in base composition, with an unusually high GC content (73–74%).

Joklik (1962b) found that the virions of four strains of poxvirus were indistinguishable in DNA/protein ratio and in DNA base composition (0.36–0.375% GC).

Woodroofe and Fenner (1960) had previously demonstrated genetic recombination between several poxvirus variants.

Andrewes (1962) and Porterfield (1962) cite several serological studies that confirmed previous groupings of animal viruses or brought together viruses which were formerly thought to be unrelated.

In a very recent report on human adenoviruses, Green and Piña (1963) noted a correlation between DNA base composition and tumorigenicity. The DNA of two nontumorigenic strains (serotypes 1 and 2) has 56–57% GC, whereas that of two tumorigenic strains (serotypes 12 and 18) has 48–49% GC. Remarkably, the DNA of polyoma virus and Shope papilloma virus, these being tumorigenic viruses of animal (i.e., nonhuman) origin, also has 48–49%

GC. The four adenoviruses presumably cross react serologically in complement fixation (Brandon and McLean, 1962). Both for the theory of tumorigenicity (see Green and Piña's paper) and for molecular taxonomy, further comparisons of the human and animal viruses will have great interest.

In conclusion to this section, it seems apparent that the molecular approach, whose power is coming to be widely recognized by virologists, has already afforded valuable taxonomic insights, but only enough to make us sure, as we said earlier, that the future of molecular taxonomy is much more glorious than its past.

C. A Neoclassical System of Viruses

With a few exceptions, the examples discussed in preceding sections have dealt with the grouping of virus strains into small groups designated by names such as T-even phages, tobacco mosaic viruses, turnip yellow mosaic viruses, reoviruses, etc. The strains assembled into one of these groups generally show such a strong resemblance that the problem of classification at this level is relatively simple. The larger problem of the interrelation of the primitive groups is not so easy. Many recent workers (e.g., Cooper, 1961; Andrewes, 1962; Pirie, 1962; Wildy, 1962) have been concerned with the choice of criteria for such a venture, and systems for some of the groups, for example, groups of animal viruses (Cooper, 1961; Andrewes, 1962), have been proposed. To the best of our knowledge, only Lwoff et al. (1962), expanding an earlier proposal by Horne and Wildy (1961), have so far suggested a definite system that includes representatives of all three subdivisions and is potentially capable of embracing all viruses. The system is not molecular, in our sense, because it makes no immediate use of the base composition or sequence of nucleic acids, the amino acid composition or sequence of polypeptides, serology, molecular tests of homology (e.g., hybridization), or genetic recombination. Lwoff et al. suggest that such properties (they do not list polynucleotide sequences, molecular hybridization, or genetic recombination) may be useful in further subdivision of the groups

TABLE 18–4. A NEOCLASSICAL SYSTEM OF VIRUSES BASED ON COMPOSITION AND ARCHITECTURE OF THE VIRION

(Adapted from Lwoff *et al.*, 1962)

I. RNA
  A. Helical symmetry
    1. Naked capsid. Diameter:
      (a) 100–130Å.   White clover mosaic, potato X, cactus, potato aucuba, Wisconsin pea-streak, wheat streak mosaic
      (b) 170–200Å.   TMV, cow-pea, cucumber green mottle
      (c) 250Å.   Barley stripe mosaic
    2. Enveloped capsid. Diameter:
      (a) 90–100Å.   Influenza, fowl-plague
      (b) 170Å.   Parainfluenza, mumps, sendai, NDV, rinderpest, canine distemper, measles
  B. Cubic symmetry
    1. Naked capsid. Number of capsomeres:
      (a) 32.   Turnip yellow mosaic
      (b) 60.   Bushy stunt, polio
      (c) 92.   Wound-tumor, REO

II. DNA
  A. Helical symmetry
    1. Enveloped capsid. Diameter:
      (a) 90–100Å.   Vaccinia, contagious pustular dermatitis
  B. Cubic symmetry
    1. Naked capsid. Number of capsomeres:
      (a) 12.   Phage øX174
      (b) 42.   Polyoma, warts, SV40
      (c) 252.   Adeno, infectious canine hepatitis, GAL
      (d) 812.   *Tipula* iridescent
    2. Enveloped capsid. Number of capsomeres:
      (a) 162.   Herpes, varicella, pseudorabies
  C. Binal symmetry
    1. Naked capsid. Form of head:
      (a) Prism.   Phage T2
      (b) Icosahedron.   Phage of *Bacillus megaterium*

they propose. We call the system *neo*classical because it stresses certain "hard" characters of the virion to the exclusion of "softer" characters and various biological properties.

The system is hierarchical, as shown in Table 18–4. In order of use, the primary characters ("essential integrants") are:

(1) Type of nucleic acid: RNA or DNA.

(2) Capsidal symmetry: Helical, cubic, or binal (binal indicating the dual symmetry exhibited by tailed bacteriophages).

(3) Exposure of the capsid: Naked or enveloped.

(4) In capsids with cubic symmetry: Number of capsomeres. In capsids with helical symmetry: Capsid diameter.

Lwoff *et al.* call attention to a few assignments that are in doubt for lack of information.

Other workers have used the same set of primary characters in comparing certain viruses. The particular contributions of Lwoff *et al.* are that (a) they did this for a large set of viruses simultaneously, and (b) they proposed a definite hierarchical relation of the characters.

The *particular selection* of primary characters has much in its favor, since viruses that have been brought together by other criteria generally exhibit the same set of primary characters. We saw, too, the serological and/or chemical confirmation of the affinity between reoviruses and wound-tumor virus, herpes and pseudorabies viruses, and (not listed by Lwoff *et al.*) turnip yellow mosaic and wild cucumber mosaic viruses.

The *hierarchy* of primary characters has to be considered separately. Reasonable though the proposed hierarchy may seem, it is apparent that the hierarchical order can be permuted arbitrarily without altering the ultimate subdivisions. For example, turnip yellow mosaic will be set off from bushy stunt plus polio, and from wound tumor plus REO, independently of the permutation of primary characters. How, then, can we assess the proposed hierarchy objectively? Macromolecular chemistry may prove very helpful and some tests can already be made. To illustrate, the RNA's of polio, bushy stunt (Lwoff *et al.* group these two viruses with reservation), turnip yellow mosaic, and REO viruses—all these viruses being RNA viruses with cubic capsidal symmetry and naked capsids—differ appreciably and sometimes considerably in base composition (Table 18–3). (Since reovirus RNA appears to be a complementary duplex, it would be appropriate to compare $A + U$, and $G + C$, rather than percentages of individual bases.) Unfortunately, we do not yet know how to interpret such differences in terms of homology except to say that they do not necessarily disprove homology, since significant compositional differences exist between the nucleic acids of certain viruses (e.g., TMV and cucumber viruses 3 and 4; turnip yellow mosaic and wild cucumber mosaic viruses; adenoviruses of various serotypes) whose affinity is less in doubt. Nor do we understand the taxonomic significance of single- vs. double-stranded RNA. The recently reported affinity between adenoviruses and the polyoma-papilloma group (Green and Piña, 1963) gives some limited support to the proposed hierarchy. It appears, however, that adequate confirmation of the hierarchy will have to await additional information.

18–6. PROSPECTS AND SPECULATIONS

A. Taxonomic Discrepancies and Viral Evolution

It is apparent, in the case of viruses, that base composition may diverge appreciably in spite of serological cross reaction and strong classical signs of affinity. Rationalization of the apparent discrepancies does not, however, seem difficult. Consider some of the relatively simple RNA viruses, many of which contain one molecule of single-stranded RNA, with a molecular weight of about 2×10^6 (corresponding to about 6000 nucleotides), and one kind of structural polypeptide, with a molecular weight of about 20,000 (corresponding to about 200 amino acids). TMV, poliovirus, and wild cucumber mosaic virus are examples already discussed in various connections. On the hypothesis of nonoverlapping triplet codes, about 600 nucleotides, or 10% of the total RNA, would have the task of coding the structural polypeptide. Especially from studies with TMV (Siegel, 1961; Gierer, 1962; Tsugita and Fraenkel-Conrat, 1963; Wittmann, 1963), we can be confident that the remaining 90% also has important functions, among which might be listed the coding of an RNA-directed RNA polymerase and possibly other proteins needed for viral replication. The likelihood

of a functional subdivision of viral RNA is indicated not only by the cited studies with TMV and by analogy with viruses amenable to detailed genetic analysis, but also by the peculiar properties of the tobacco necrosis satellite "virus" (SV), the smallest yet to be identified (Kassanis and Nixon, 1961; Kassanis, 1962; Babos and Kassanis, 1962). SV appears incapable of multiplying by itself, but can multiply in the presence of the serologically unrelated tobacco necrosis virus (TNV) and also certain defective TNV strains that seem not to produce viral polypeptide. The RNA of SV has a (maximum) molecular weight of about 394,000, corresponding to 1160 nucleotides. The polypeptide has a (minimum) molecular weight of about 25,000, corresponding to 240 amino acid residues (Kassanis, 1962; Reichmann et al., 1962). Coding this polypeptide very likely requires $3 \times 240 = 720$ nucleotides, or about 60% of the total RNA. A reasonable presumption is that SV contains enough RNA to code a specific polypeptide, but not enough to exercise other essential functions; for these extra functions, SV requires a compatible "helper" virus. (To this writer, it appears that explicit molecular-taxonomic comparisons might be very helpful in confirming the interpretation of SV as a virus.)

Given the subdivision of an ordinary viral RNA into functionally distinct segments or genes, each containing a few hundred nucleotides but only one of them coding viral polypeptide, it is not hard to imagine (a) evolutionary divergence of the various genes with respect to base composition, (b) evolution of different genes at different rates as a result of variable selection pressures, and (c) progressive loosening of the correlation between various molecular-taxonomic criteria (e.g., base composition and serology), and also between these criteria and classical ones, as two formerly identical viruses grow in mutual isolation. By obvious arguments, one can easily explain all the discrepancies illustrated in previous sections. Elsewhere in this volume Bawden discusses the origin and evolution of viruses. Here we shall stress only a few points.

(1) The taxonomic discrepancies ob-

served with viruses, in contrast to the seemingly superior correlations found with bacteria in many assays, may stem largely from the smaller size of viral genomes. As proposed by Freese (1962) and Sueoka (1962), the near-homogeneity of bacterial DNA (meaning the low compositional variance of ordinary DNA fragments with a molecular weight of about 10 million or greater) would tend to be maintained during compositional drift because (a) ordinary DNA fragments are so large that statistical variation in total mutational experience per fragment tends to be very small, and (b) the various sections of a bacterial DNA are exposed to a common mutagenic environment. (The small portions of DNA specifying the sequences of sRNA and rRNA must, of course, be excepted in this discussion.) As smaller and smaller DNA fragments are considered, the compositional variance must sooner or later increase, and the only question is that of the actual correlation between fragment size and variance. The few relevant experimental data (see, for example, Guild, 1963) indicate that the variance (σ^2) in GC content is approximately inversely proportional to fragment size and that DNA fragments with a molecular weight of 1–2 million already show appreciable variance. With the smaller genomes of viruses like TMV, the opportunity for "statistical buffering" of the base composition is somewhat reduced. Since each viral gene is a large fraction of the total genome, any special compositional tailoring of a single gene has a quantitatively important effect on the whole composition. When two ancestrally related viruses diverge in host range, the guarantee of a similar mutagenic environment becomes less secure. Finally, the experimental difficulty in demonstrating genetic recombination with the smaller viruses may reflect a natural disinclination to recombine. Absence of a quantitatively significant mechanism for interclonal sharing of mutational experience would, of course, increase the opportunity for compositional divergence of two strains even though their host range might be the same.

(2) These considerations might make it appear idle to contemplate a comprehensive molecular taxonomy of viruses. We must therefore temper the discussion by recognizing that (a) the "distressing" taxonomic discrepancies (e.g., the base-compositional differences between serologically crossreacting viruses) are somewhat small, and (b) conservative forces operate in virus evolution. Medical history suggests that certain diseases such as smallpox and polio have been caused by the "same" virus for thousands of years. In the notoriously labile influenza viruses, whose serological character changes from epidemic to epidemic, the range of serological variation nevertheless seems limited; and epidemiologists can use current strains in serological assessments of the childhood viral experience of our elderly contemporaries. Viruses closely resembling known strains of one or another virus have been isolated repeatedly from geographic areas around the world. For example, phages clearly related to T2 seem to occur in all fecally polluted waters. After all, preservation of the essential viral functions—self-replication, with the production of more or less precisely organized virions capable of infecting host cells that must be more or less immediately available—must impose severe constraints on viral evolution.

(3) Apart from the possibility of independent origin of certain viruses, taxonomic diversification has to work somewhere between the constraints and the freedom previously noted. By analogy with the sRNA and rRNA genes of bacteria (Section 18–2,D), a delightful prospect is that the freedom/constraint quotient, i.e., the evolutionary rate, will prove to be very different for different viral genes. Highly stable genes would afford the equivalent of fossils in identifying remote evolutionary branchpoints, whereas the more labile genes would be guides to recent divergence. A half dozen genes evolving at distinctly different rates might make it possible to delineate the ancestral relations of all the known viruses in a single scheme. The well-known serological or other differentiation of viruses that are unquestionably related by their whole aggregate of properties is strong presumptive evidence of gene-specific evolutionary rates. Serological

criteria, by themselves, suggest a similar conclusion. For example, the adenoviruses are brought together by a variety of properties including a soluble, group-specific complement-fixing antigen, but are differtiated into serotypes by one or more virion-bound antigens reacting with neutralizing antibody (Brandon and McLean, 1962). The outlook for a monolithic taxonomy of viruses is still speculative; but when it begins to seem hopeless, remember REO and wound tumor. Far from being a nuisance, taxonomic discrepancies should be greeted by taxonomists with open arms.

(4) There is also the clear prospect of differential evolutionary rates for various sections of a single gene. In viruses, the TMV group affords the best supporting evidence. Both Tsugita (1962b) and Wittmann (1963) have noted that the central portion of the viral polypeptide seems more resistant than the two ends to mutational variation. Wittmann suggests that amino acid replacements in the central portion might loosen the virion structure enough to expose the viral RNA to host ribonuclease in extracts. Mutants with such replacements would therefore perish in the virion phase. In any case, it is apparent that certain subsequences of a viral polypeptide may serve to measure near ancestral relations, whereas other subsequences may serve better for distant relations. Serology might be stable or labile, depending on the relation of antigenic determinants to the conserved conformational features of proteins and of multiprotein aggregates such as capsids.

(5) Certain important serological considerations have not been mentioned before. Since plants (and insect vectors of plant viruses?) are unknown to produce antibody, the serological properties of plant viruses are unlikely to have a direct influence on viral evolution. This would be true also of phages infecting free-living bacteria, and it might or might not be true of phages infecting bacteria that parasitize antibody-producing vertebrates. On the other hand, specific antibody, particularly virus-neutralizing antibody, is quite likely to play, or to have played, an important role in the evolution of those animal viruses that infect antibody-producing vertebrates, especially if the viral cycle includes, or included, viremia. With such animal viruses, serology has a somewhat circular significance: it is a convenient tool for analyzing taxonomic diversity that it helped to create.

Thus, there are good reasons for suspecting that the taxonomic correlation between serological specificity and other viral traits may vary greatly in stability depending on viral host range and on the serological procedure employed. With animal viruses, we would expect to find, and we find, that strains confidently grouped by a variety of criteria, including cross reaction in serological phenomena not evidently related to neutralization, often fail to show cross neutralization; this is, of course, the usual basis for the subdivision of animal viruses into serotypes. In contrast, with plant viruses, bacterial viruses, and perhaps also insect viruses (Smith, 1962), one has the distinct impression that strains brought together by other criteria generally show serological cross reaction; i.e., the tendency to serotypic differentiation is much reduced (for some apparent exceptions, see Adams and Wade, 1954; Gibbs et al., 1963; Macleod and Markham, 1963). In confirmation of this impression, Knight (1959; see p. 135), referring to plant viruses, comments that "viruses which are almost certainly strains by other criteria have thus far always shown positive serological cross-reactions." The discussion of phage taxonomy by Adams (1959; see p. 421 et seq.) confirms the impression for bacterial viruses.

Animal-virus taxonomy has leaned heavily on specific neutralization and complement fixation. Phage taxonomy has resorted almost exclusively to neutralization. Plant-virus taxonomy has made extensive use of specific precipitation, but has also used complement fixation and neutralization.

Evidently, breakdown of a taxonomic correlation involving serological cross reaction as one component may have a quite variable significance, depending on the type of virus, the serological procedure, and, we might add, the details of antigen and antiserum preparation (see, for example, Porterfield, 1962). We might speculate, too, that the serological properties of ani-

TABLE 18–5. AMINO ACID REPLACEMENTS IN HUMAN HEMOGLOBINS[*]

Variant	Site	Replacement	Triplet change	Letter change
I	α16	lys/asp	UAA/UAG	A/G
G-Honolulu	α30	glu/gln	UAG/ ?	?
Norfolk	α57	gly/asp	UGG/UAG	G/A
M$_B$	α58	his/tyr	UAC/UUA	C/U
G-Philadelphia	α68	asn/lys	UAC/UAA	C/A
S	β6	glu/val	UAG/UUG	A/U
C	β6	glu/lys	UAG/UAA	G/A
G-San José	β7	glu/gly	UAG/UGG	A/G
E	β26	glu/lys	UAG/UAA	G/A
Zürich	β63	his/arg	UAC/UCG	A/G
M$_S$	β63	his/tyr	UAC/UUA	C/U
M$_{M-1}$	β67	val/glu	UUG/UAG	U/A
O$_{Ar}$	β121	glu/lys	UAG/UAA	G/A
D-Punjab	β121	glu/gln	UAG/ ?	?

[*] Adapted from Table 6 of Lanni (1963a); see this reference for sources. The replacements show the "normal" amino acid (hemoglobin A) first. Parentheses around the triplets (from Table 18–1) are omitted for simplicity. In the G-Philadelphia replacement, the alternative triplet (UAA) for asparagine is identical in composition to that for lysine and is omitted from consideration. No other degenerately coded amino acids are involved.

mal (vertebrate) viruses are quite likely to reflect a natural selection for *lability*. From this viewpoint, the serological variability of the influenza viruses (see Edney, 1957; Francis, 1959) is no great surprise, and neither is the finding that polio-infected cells produce objects that resemble polio virions but show negligible serological cross reaction (Hummeler *et al.*, 1962).

(6) We have been speaking of viral evolution as an isolated process, whereas there can hardly be any question that viruses and their hosts evolve interdependently. Whether this coordinate evolution will simplify or complicate viral taxonomy remains to be seen. Virus-host molecular homology, of the type believed to characterize the genomes of temperate phages and their hosts in lysogeny, may reflect a fundamental taxonomic relation; and appropriate host polynucleotides may be useful reagents in viral taxonomy proper (see Attardi *et al.*, 1962, 1963; Hayashi *et al.*, 1963c). There are, however, clear and simple arguments for a viral taxonomy at least partly independent of host taxonomy. First, some viruses, e.g., the T-even phages (Section 18–5,B), show no sign of molecular homology with their usual hosts. Second, the host range of some viruses, e.g., those

infecting both plants and insects, encompasses taxonomically diverse hosts.

B. DIRECTION OF MOLECULAR EVOLUTION

Given a set of polynucleotide or polypeptide chain sequences and no auxiliary information about ancestral relations, it is one thing to deduce molecular homology and quite another to deduce the direction of molecular evolution. Examples from the human hemoglobins will serve to suggest how the writing of evolutionary arrows might be tackled.

The α and β chains of adult human hemoglobin A (the "normal" brand) respectively contain 141 and 146 amino acid residues, whose sequence is now fully known (Baglioni, 1963). Sequential analysis of a number of variant ("abnormal") hemoglobins has shown that each differs from hemoglobin A by a single amino acid replacement in the α or β chain. Purely for convenience, Table 18–5 lists these replacements in reference to hemoglobin A and shows also the corresponding Nirenberg-Ochoa codes (from Table 18–1). For the purposes of the present exercise, we start by regarding the α and β chains of hemoglobin A as variants in equal standing with the rest. What can we say about ancestral relations?

Consider first the α-chain variants. The "normal" variant differs from each of the others by one amino acid replacement. The five "abnormal" variants differ from each other by two replacements. A reasonable assumption, based on *a priori* considerations plus experience with mutants isolated in the laboratory, is that evolution is more likely to occur in steps of one replacement than in steps of two. Two ancestral hypotheses are equally economical in total single-replacement mutational steps:

(1) Write the "normal" α chain first and let it spawn each of the other variants.

(2) Choose one of the other variants arbitrarily, write it first, let it give rise to the "normal" variant, and let this variant produce the rest.

The β-chain variants yield a generally similar result, i.e., the "normal" β chain would be written first or close to first in the evolutionary diagram. However, the multiplicity of variants at each of three chain positions (β6, β63, and β121) calls for special discussion. Consider, for example, the three alternatives at β6. With equal economy, we might write nine alternative evolutionary diagrams (Table 18–6) using single amino acid replacements. Reference to the appropriate Nirenberg-Ochoa codes shows, however, that only three of these diagrams afford a one-letter code change for each of the two amino acid replacements. In these maximally economical diagrams, the "normal" β chain, containing *glu* at β6, appears either first or second.

The three alternatives at β63 produce an analogous result: the "normal" chain must be written first or second. This chain cannot, however, be written second for both the β6 and the β63 series of variants. The situation at β121 is indeterminate since there is no code for glutamine in Table 18–1 and we have decided to use only these codes in the analysis.

Pooling all of the information, we conclude that *both* the α and β chains of hemoglobin A should be written not later than second in their respective series and that these two chains have generated most or all of the "abnormal" variants. Although the

TABLE 18–6. ALTERNATIVE ANCESTRAL DIAGRAMS AT β6 IN THE HUMAN HEMOGLOBINS

Amino acid changes	Triplet changes[*]
lys ← glu → val	UAA ← UAG → UUG
glu → lys → val	UAG → UAA UUG
glu → val → lys	UAG → UUG UAA
glu ← lys → val	UAG ← UAA UUG
lys → glu → val	UAA → UAG → UUG
lys → val → glu	UAA UUG → UAG
glu ← val → lys	UAG ← UUG UAA
val → glu → lys	UUG → UAG → UAA
val → lys → glu	UUG UAA → UAG

[*] Parentheses around triplets are omitted for simplicity. Arrows are written only between triplets affording a one-letter change. Only three diagrams accommodate the data.

actual ancestry of the human hemoglobins is not yet firmly established by analysis of pedigrees, the conclusions just stated accord with the prevalent belief that the "abnormal" variants arose by mutation of hemoglobin A. For discussion of the evolution of human hemoglobin see Ingram (1962).

It will be very interesting to see how the present deductive procedure works out with the polypeptides of naturally occurring TMV variants, whose full sequence formulas have not yet been published.

Until we have more facts, who can say whether the molecular taxonomy of viruses will trace a tree, a forest, or a free-form doodle defying botanic metaphor?

18–7. SUMMARY

(1) It is proposed that there are two and only two fundamentally different taxonomies, classical and molecular, which are related by mutual implication and reflect the basic biological duality of phenotype and genotype. Molecular taxonomy uses primarily the nucleotide sequences of genetic polynucleotides but draws confidently on the nucleotide sequences of messenger and analogous RNA's, and on the amino acid sequences of coded polypeptides. Properties directly dependent on sequences, e.g., over-all base composition and amino acid composition, also belong to molecular taxonomy. Classical taxonomy uses the remaining properties. Serological specificity is a type of property that may be argued

into either category. In actual taxonomic practice, the two taxonomies are frequently merged, not always with explicit recognition of the redundancy thereby introduced.

(2) A description of the theoretical virtues of molecular taxonomy, in contrast to evident shortcomings of its classical counterpart, makes it appear that the power of molecular taxonomy is enormous. Enough results are at hand to show that estimates of the power are not grossly exaggerated. Although the molecular-taxonomic approach is not altogether new, its full theoretical justification and effective tools for taxonomic surveys have appeared only recently. The pace of molecular-taxonomic studies is noticeably quickening.

(3) Ideally, molecular and classical taxonomy should validate each other, not stand in conflict. Extensive studies with bacteria clearly support the mutual validation. With viruses, the opportunities for critical comparison are fewer, but the overall agreement is heartening. The somewhat confused state of classical viral taxonomy and the special characteristics of viruses (these characteristics being no doubt largely responsible for the confused state of classical viral taxonomy) suggest that molecular taxonomy is particularly suited to viruses, and vice versa.

(4) Some recent molecular-taxonomic studies of viruses are described. Certain discrepancies and other signs suggest that the respective genes of a given virus, and parts of a given gene, may evolve at distinctly different rates. If this is true, it may be possible to embrace all viruses in a single taxonomic scheme delineating ancestral relationships. Of course, independent viral origins, which should certainly not yet be taken for granted, might call for as many schemes as there are origins. A pleasant note is that molecular and classical assessments of affinity continue to shorten the list of "distinct" viruses.

(5) Ecological considerations suggest that serotypic differentiation should occur much more extensively with animal (vertebrate) viruses than with other viruses. The facts appear to accord with the expectation.

(6) Amino acid replacements in the human hemoglobins afford illustrations of how the direction of molecular evolution might be deduced in the absence of auxiliary information about ancestral relationships.

* * *

This paper is publication No. 635 from the Division of Basic Health Sciences; supported in part by grant E-857 from the National Institute of Allergy and Infectious Diseases, U.S. Public Health Service.

Time did not permit a systematic survey. The result therefore lies somewhere between an essay and a review, and the reader informed in any area of virology or microbial taxonomy will quickly perceive that some relevant data and considerations have been omitted. The discussion is based on literature appearing before August, 1963. Where suitable reviews are available, these are cited in preference to original articles. I apologize to all workers whose papers should have been cited but were omitted through inadvertence, ignorance, or expediency. I thank my wife and other members of the Molecular Biology Workshop of this University for stimulating discussions, and colleagues elsewhere for supplying manuscripts in advance of publication.

MOLECULAR TAXONOMY

18–8. LITERATURE CITED

Ada, G. L., and Perry, B. T. (1956). J. Gen. Microbiol. 14, 623.

Adams, M. H. (1959). Bacteriophages. Interscience Publishers, New York.

Adams, M. H., and Wade, E. (1954). J. Bacteriol. 68, 320.

Adams, M. H., and Wade, E. (1955). J. Bacteriol. 70, 253.

Ainsworth, G. C., and Sneath, P. H. A. (eds.). (1962). "Microbial Classification." Symp. Soc. Gen. Microbiol. No. 12. Cambridge University Press, London.

Anderer, F. A. (1963). Biochim. Biophys. Acta 71, 246.

Andrewes, C. H. (1962). Advan. Virus Res. 9, 271.

Attardi, G., Naono, S., Gros, F., Brenner, S., and Jacob, F. (1962). Compt. Rend. Acad. Sci. 255, 2303.

Attardi, G., Naono, S., Gros, F., Buttin, G., and Jacob, F. (1963). Compt. Rend. Acad. Sci. 256, 805.

Babos, P., and Kassanis, B. (1962). Virology 18, 206.

Baglioni, C. (1963). In J. H. Taylor (ed.), Molecular Genetics. Part I, 405. Academic Press, New York.

Bautz, E. K. F., and Hall, B. D. (1962). Proc. Natl. Acad. Sci. U.S. 48, 400.

Ben-Porat, T., and Kaplan, A. S. (1962). Virology 16, 261.

Benzer, S. (1957). In W. D. McElroy and B. Glass (eds.), The Chemical Basis of Heredity. 70. The Johns Hopkins Press, Baltimore.

Benzer, S., and Champe, S. P. (1962). Proc. Natl. Acad. Sci. U.S. 48, 1114.

Bernhard, W., and Tournier, P. (1962). Cold Spring Harbor Symp. Quant. Biol. 27, 67.

Bessman, M. J. (1963). In J. H. Taylor (ed.), Molecular Genetics. Part I, 1. Academic Press, New York.

Black, L. M. (1959). In F. M. Burnet and W. M. Stanley (eds.), The Viruses. 2, 157. Academic Press, New York.

Bockstahler, L. E., and Kaesberg, P. (1962). Biophys. J. 2, 1.

Bolton, E. T., and McCarthy, B. J. (1962). Proc. Natl. Acad. Sci. U.S. 48, 1390.

Brandon, F. B., and McLean, I. Wm., Jr. (1962). Advan. Virus Res. 9, 157.

Burgi, E. (1963). Proc. Natl. Acad. Sci. U.S. 49, 151.

Burnet, F. M. (1955). Principles of Animal Virology. Academic Press, New York. (See p. 414.)

Burnet, F. M. (1959a). In F. M. Burnet and W. M. Stanley (eds.), The Viruses. 3, 275. Academic Press, New York.

Burnet, F. M. (1959b). In F. M. Burnet and W. M. Stanley (eds.), The Viruses. 1, 525. Academic Press, New York.

Burnet, F. M., and Stanley, W. M. (eds.). (1959). The Viruses. Vols. 1–3. Academic Press, New York.

Burton, K. (1962). Brit. Med. Bull. 18, 3.

Cairns, J. (1963). J. Mol. Biol. 6, 208.

Campbell, A. (1963). Virology 20, 344.

Campbell, A. M. (1962). Advan. Genet. 11, 101.

Caspar, D. L. D., and Klug, A. (1962). Cold Spring Harbor Symp. Quant. Biol. 27, 1.

Catlin, B. W., and Cunningham, L. S. (1961). J. Gen. Microbiol. 26, 303.

Chargaff, E., and Davidson, J. N. (eds.). (1955, 1960). The Nucleic Acids. I (1955), II (1955), and III (1960). Academic Press, New York.

Cohen, S. S. (1955). Advan. Virus Res. 3, 1.

Cooper, P. D. (1961). Nature 190, 302.

Crawford, L. V. (1963). Virology 19, 279.

Crick, F. H. C., Barnett, L., Brenner, S., and Watts-Tobin, R. J. (1961). Nature 192, 1227.

Darnell, J. E. (1962). Cold Spring Harbor Symp. Quant. Biol. 27, 149.

Demerec, M., and Hartman, P. E. (1959). Ann. Rev. Microbiol. 13, 377.

Dulbecco, R. (1962). Cold Spring Harbor Symp. Quant. Biol. 27, 519.

Edney, M. (1957). Ann. Rev. Microbiol. 11, 23.

Enger, M. D., Stubbs, E. A., Mitra, S., and Kaesberg, P. (1963). Proc. Natl. Acad. Sci. U.S. 49, 857.

Falkow, S., Rownd, R., and Baron, L. S. (1962). J. Bacteriol. 84, 1303.

Fiers, W., and Sinsheimer, R. L. (1962). J. Mol. Biol. 5, 424.

Floodgate, G. D. (1962). Bacteriol. Rev. 26, 277.

Francis, T., Jr. (1959). In F. M. Burnet and W. M. Stanley (eds.), The Viruses. 3, 251. Academic Press, New York.

Fraser, D., Mahler, H. R., Shug, A. L., and Thomas, C. A., Jr. (1957). Proc. Natl. Acad. Sci. U.S. 43, 939.

Freese, E. (1962). J. Theoret. Biol. 3, 82.

Freese, E. (1963). In J. H. Taylor (ed.), Microbial Genetics. Part I, 207.

Garen, A., and Siddiqi, O. (1962). Proc. Natl. Acad. Sci. U.S. 48, 1121.

Giacomoni, D., and Spiegelman, S. (1962). Science 138, 1328.

Gibbs, A. J., Kassanis, B., Nixon, H. L., and Woods, R. D. (1963). Virology 20, 194.

Gierer, A. (1962). Biophys. J. 2, 5.

Gilbert, W. (1963). J. Mol. Biol. 6, 374 and 389.

Gold, M., Hurwitz, J., and Anders, M. (1963). Proc. Natl. Acad. Sci. U.S. 50, 164.

Gomatos, P. J., and Tamm, I. (1963). Proc. Natl. Acad. Sci. U.S. 49, 707.

Goodman, H. M., and Rich, A. (1962). Proc. Natl. Acad. Sci. U.S. 48, 2101.

Green, M., and Piña, M. (1963). Proc. Natl. Acad. Sci. U.S. 50, 44.

Grunberg-Manago, M. (1962). Ann. Rev. Biochem. **31**, 301.

Guild, W. R. (1963). J. Mol. Biol. **6**, 214.

Guild, W. R., and Robison, M. (1963). Proc. Natl. Acad. Sci. U.S. **50**, 106.

Guthrie, G. D., and Sinsheimer, R. L. (1960). J. Mol. Biol. **2**, 297.

Hall, J. B., and Sinsheimer, R. L. (1963). J. Mol. Biol. **6**, 115.

Haselkorn, R., Fried, V. A., and Dahlberg, J. E. (1963). Proc. Natl. Acad. Sci. U.S. **49**, 511.

Hausmann, R. L., Almeida Magalhães, E. P., and Araujo, C. (1961). Anais Microbiol. **9**, 511.

Hayashi, M., Hayashi, M. N., and Spiegelman, S. (1963a). Science **140**, 1313.

Hayashi, M., Hayashi, M. N., and Spiegelman, S. (1963b). Proc. Natl. Acad. Sci. U.S. **50**, 664.

Hayashi, M., Spiegelman, S., Franklin, N. C., and Luria, S. E. (1963c). Proc. Natl. Acad. Sci. U.S. **49**, 729.

Herner, A. E., and Riggs, A. (1963). Nature **198**, 35.

Hirst, G. K. (1962). Cold Spring Harbor Symp. Quant. Biol. **27**, 303.

Holland, J. J., and Hoyer, B. H. (1962). Cold Spring Harbor Symp. Quant. Biol. **27**, 101.

Horne, R. W., and Wildy, P. (1961). Virology **15**, 348.

Hummeler, K., Anderson, T. F., and Brown, R. A. (1962). Virology **16**, 84.

Ingram, V. M. (1962). Federation Proc. **21**, 1053.

Jacob, F., and Brenner, S. (1963). Compt. Rend. Acad. Sci. **256**, 298.

Jacob, F., and Monod, J. (1961). J. Mol. Biol. **3**, 318.

Joklik, W. K. (1962a). J. Mol. Biol. **5**, 265.

Joklik, W. K. (1962b). Virology **18**, 9.

Josse, J., Kaiser, A. D., and Kornberg, A. (1961). J. Biol. Chem. **236**, 864.

Kaesberg, P. (1963). Symposium talk at the Cleveland meetings of the American Society for Microbiology.

Kaiser, A. D., and Baldwin, R. L. (1962). J. Mol. Biol. **4**, 418.

Kassanis, B. (1962). J. Gen. Microbiol. **27**, 477.

Kassanis, B., and Nixon, H. L. (1961). J. Gen. Microbiol. **25**, 459.

Kellenberger, G., Zichichi, M. L., and Weigle, J. (1961). J. Mol. Biol. **3**, 399.

Kelley, J. J., and Kaesberg, P. (1962). Biochim. Biophys. Acta **61**, 865.

Knight, C. A. (1955). Virology **1**, 261.

Knight, C. A. (1959). In F. M. Burnet and W. M. Stanley (eds.), The Viruses. **2**, 127. Academic Press, New York.

Knight, C. A., Silva, D. M., Dahl, D., and Tsugita, A. (1962). Virology **16**, 236.

Kozinski, A. W., and Kozinski, P. B. (1963). Virology **20**, 213.

Lanni, F. (1958). Science **128**, 839.

Lanni, F. (1959). J. Immunol. **83**, 148.

Lanni, F. (1960). Perspectives Biol. Med. **3**, 418.

Lanni, F. (1962). Proc. Natl. Acad. Sci. U.S. **48**, 1623.

Lanni, F. (1963a). Advan. Genet. **12**. Publication scheduled for 1964.

Lanni, F. (1963b). J. Theoret. Biol. **4**, 1.

Lanni, F., and Lanni, Y. T. (1957). Federation Proc. **16**, 421.

Lanni, Y. T. (1958). Virology **5**, 481.

Ledinko, N. (1963). Virology **20**, 107.

Lee, K. Y., Wahl, R., and Barbu, E. (1956). Ann. Inst. Pasteur **91**, 212.

Levine, L. (1962). Federation Proc. **21**, 711.

Liston, J., Wiebe, W., and Colwell, R. R. (1963). J. Bacteriol. **85**, 1061.

Lockhart, W. R., and Hartman, P. A. (1963). J. Bacteriol. **85**, 68.

Loeb, T., and Zinder, N. D. (1961). Proc. Natl. Acad. Sci. U.S. **47**, 282.

Luria, S. E. (1953). General Virology. John Wiley & Sons, New York.

Luria, S. E. (1959). In F. M. Burnet and W. M. Stanley (eds.), The Viruses. **1**, 549. Academic Press, New York.

Luria, S. E. (1962). Ann. Rev. Microbiol. **16**, 205.

Lwoff, A., Horne, R., and Tournier, P. (1962). Cold Spring Harbor Symp. Quant. Biol. **27**, 51.

McCarthy, B. J., and Bolton, E. T. (1963). Proc. Natl. Acad. Sci. U.S. **50**, 156.

Macleod, R., and Markham, R. (1963). Virology **19**, 190.

Markham, R. (1959). In F. M. Burnet and W. M. Stanley, (eds.), The Viruses. **2**, 33. Academic Press, New York.

Marmur, J., Falkow, S., and Mandel, M. (1963a). Ann. Rev. Microbiol. **17**, 329.

Marmur, J., Seaman, E., and Levine, J. (1963b). J. Bacteriol. **85**, 461.

Matthaei, J. H., Jones, O. W., Martin, R. G., and Nirenberg, M. W. (1962). Proc. Natl. Acad. Sci. U.S. **48**, 666.

Mazzone, H. M., Incardona, N. L., and Kaesberg, P. (1962). Biochim. Biophys. Acta **55**, 164.

Melnick, J. L. (1953). Advan. Virus Res. **1**, 229.

Meselson, M., and Weigle, J. J. (1961). Proc. Natl. Acad. Sci. U.S. **47**, 857.

Meyer, F., Mackal, R. P., Tao, M., and Evans, E. A. (1961). J. Biol. Chem. **236**, 1141.

Mitra, S., Enger, M. D., and Kaesberg, P. (1963). Proc. Natl. Acad. Sci. U.S. **50**, 68.

Morgan, C, Rifkind, R. A., and Rose, H. M. (1962). Cold Spring Harbor Symp. Quant. Biol. **27**, 57.

Nagata, T. (1963). Proc. Natl. Acad. Sci. U.S. **49**, 551.

Narita, K. (1958). Federation Proc. **17**, 281.

Neidhardt, T. C., and Fangman, W. L. (1963). Federation Proc. **22**, 643.

Nirenberg, M. W., and Matthaei, J. H. (1961). Proc. Natl. Acad. Sci. U.S. **47**, 1588.

Noll, H., Staehelin, T, and Wettstein, F. O. (1963). Nature **198**, 632.

Nomura, M., and Benzer, S. (1961). J. Mol. Biol. **3**, 684.

Ofengand, J., and Haselkorn, R. (1962). Biochem. Biophys. Res. Commun. **6**, 469.

Pirie, N. W. (1962). Symp. Soc. Gen. Microbiol. 12, 374.

Porterfield, J. S. (1962). Advan. Virus Res. 9, 127.

Ravin, A. W. (1961). Advan. Genet. 10, 61.

Ravin, A. W. (1963). Am. Nat. 97, 307.

Reichmann, M. E., Rees, M. W., Symons, R. H., and Markham, R. (1962). Nature 195, 999.

Riley, M., and Pardee, A. B. (1962). Ann. Rev. Microbiol. 16, 1.

Roberts, R. B., Britten, R. J., and McCarthy, B. J. (1963). In J. H. Taylor (ed.), Molecular Genetics. Part I, 292. Academic Press, New York.

Rushizky, G. W., and Knight, C. A. (1960). Virology 11, 236.

Rushizky, G. W., Sober, H. A., and Knight, C. A. (1962). Biochim. Biophys. Acta 61. 56.

Sarkar, S. (1960). Z. Naturforsch. 15b, 778.

Schaffer, F. L. (1962). Cold Spring Harbor Symp. Quant. Biol. 27, 89.

Schaffer, F. L., Moore, H. F., and Schwerdt, C. E. (1960). Virology 10, 530.

Schildkraut, C. L., Marmur, J., and Doty, P. (1961). J. Mol. Biol. 3, 595.

Schildkraut, C. L., Mandel, M., Levisohn, S., Smith-Sonneborn, J. E., and Marmur, J. (1962a). Nature 196, 795.

Schildkraut, C. L., Wierzchowski, K. L., Marmur, J., Green, D. M., and Doty, P. (1962b). Virology 18, 43.

Scholtissek, C., Rott, R., Hausen, P., Hausen, H., and Schäfer, W. (1962). Cold Spring Harbor Symp. Quant. Biol. 27, 245.

Schuster, H. (1960). In E. Chargaff and J. N. Davidson (eds.), The Nucleic Acids. 3, 245.

Sechaud, J., Streisinger, G., Lanford, H., Reinhold, H., and Stahl, M. M. (1963). Manuscript not yet published.

Siegel, A. (1961). Virology 15, 212.

Siegel, A., Zaitlin, M., and Sehgal, O. P. (1962). Proc. Natl. Acad. Sci. U.S. 48, 1845.

Sinsheimer, R. L. (1960). In E. Chargaff and J. N. Davidson (eds.), The Nucleic Acids. 3, 187. Academic Press, New York.

Sinsheimer, R. L., Starman, B., Nagler, C., and Guthrie, S. (1962). J. Mol. Biol. 4, 142.

Smith, K. M. (1962). Advan. Virus Res. 9, 195.

Sneath, P. H. A. (1962). Symp. Soc. Gen. Microbiol. 12, 289.

Sonneborn, T. M. (1960). Proc. Natl. Acad. Sci. U.S. 46, 149.

Sonneborn, T. M. (1963). In J. M. Allen (ed.), The Nature of Biological Diversity. 165. McGraw-Hill, New York.

Šorm, F., and Keil, B. (1962). Advan. Protein Chem. 17, 167.

Speyer, J. F., Lengyel, P., Basilio, C., and Ochoa, S. (1962). Proc. Natl. Acad. Sci. U.S. 48, 441.

Spiegelman, S. (1963). Symposium talk at the Cleveland meetings of the American Society for Microbiology.

Spizizen, J. (1957). Proc. Natl. Acad. Sci. U.S. 43, 694.

Srinivasan, P. R., and Borek, E. (1963). Proc. Natl. Acad. Sci. U.S. 49, 529.

Staehelin, M. (1961). Biochim. Biophys. Acta 49, 27.

Stent, G. S. (1958). Advan. Virus Res. 5, 95.

Streisinger, G., Edgar, R. S., and Denhardt, G. H. (1963a). Proc. Natl. Acad. Sci. U.S. 51, 775 (1964).

Streisinger, G., Stahl, M. M., and Emrich, J. (1963b). Manuscript not yet published.

Streisinger, G., Mukai, F., Dreyer, W. J., Miller, B., and Harrar, G. (1961). J. Chem. Phys. 58, 1064.

Streissle, G., and Maramorosch, K. (1963). Science 140, 996.

Sueoka, N. (1961a). Proc. Natl. Acad. Sci. U.S. 47, 1141.

Sueoka, N. (1961b). Cold Spring Harbor Symp. Quant. Biol. 26, 35.

Sueoka, N. (1962). Proc. Natl. Acad. Sci. U.S. 48, 582.

Sugiyama, T., and Fraenkel-Conrat, H. (1961). Proc. Natl. Acad. Sci. U.S. 47, 1393.

Sugiyama, T., and Fraenkel-Conrat, H. (1963). Biochemistry 2, 332.

Swartz, M. N., Trautner, T. A., and Kornberg, A. (1962). J. Biol. Chem. 237, 1961.

Symons, R. H., Rees, M. W., Short, M. N., and Markham, R. (1963). J. Mol. Biol. 6, 1.

Szybalski, W., Erikson, R. L., Gentry, G. A., Gafford, L. G., and Randall, C. C. (1963). Virology 19, 586.

Taylor, J. H. (ed.). (1963). Molecular Genetics. Part I. Academic Press, New York.

Thomas, C. A., Jr. (1963). In J. H. Taylor (ed.), Molecular Genetics. Part I, 113. Academic Press New York.

Thomas, C. A., Jr., and Rubinstein, I. (1963). Biophys. J. 4, 93 (1964).

Tsugita, A. (1962a). J. Mol. Biol. 5, 284.

Tsugita, A. (1962b). J. Mol. Biol. 5, 293.

Tsugita, A., and Fraenkel-Conrat, H. (1963). In J. H. Taylor (ed.), Molecular Genetics. Part I, 477. Academic Press, New York.

Tsugita, A., Fraenkel-Conrat, H., Nirenberg, M. W., and Matthaei, J. H. (1962). Proc. Natl. Acad. Sci. U.S. 48, 846.

Vogel, H. J., Bryson, V., and Lampen, J. O. (eds.). (1963). Informational Macromolecules. Academic Press, New York.

Warner, J., Madden, M. J., and Darnell, J. E. (1963). Virology 19, 393.

Watson, J. D. (1963). Science 140, 17.

Watson, J. D., and Crick, F. H. C. (1953). Cold Spring Harbor Symp. Quant. Biol. 18, 123.

Watson, J. D., and Littlefield, J. W. (1960). J. Mol. Biol. 2, 161.

Weed, L. L. (1963). J. Bacteriol. 85, 1003.

Weil, R. (1963). Proc. Natl. Acad. Sci. U.S. 49, 480.

Whitfield, P. R. (1962). J. Biol. Chem. 237, 2865.

Wildy, P. (1962). Symp. Soc. Gen. Microbiol. 12, 145.

Wildy, P., and Watson, D. H. (1962). Cold Spring Harbor Symp. Quant. Biol. **27**, 25.

Wittmann, H. G. (1962). Z. Vererbungs. **93**, 491.

Wittmann, H. G. (1963). In H. J. Vogel, V. Bryson, and J. O. Lampen (eds.), Informational Macromolecules. 177. Academic Press, New York.

Woodroofe, G. M., and Fenner, F. (1960). Virology **12**, 272.

Woody, B. R., and Knight, C. A. (1959). Virology **9**, 359.

Yamazaki, H., and Kaesberg, P. (1961). Biochim. Biophys. Acta **53**, 173.

Yamazaki, H., and Kaesberg, P. (1963). J. Mol. Biol. **6**, 465.

Yankofsky, S. A., and Spiegelman, S. (1962). Proc. Natl. Acad. Sci. U.S. **48**, 1069 and 1466.

Yankofsky, S. A., and Spiegelman, S. (1963). Proc. Natl. Acad. Sci. U.S. **49**, 538.

Yanofsky, C. (1963). Symposium talk at the Cleveland meetings of the American Society for Microbiology.

Yanofsky, C., Henning, U., Helinski, D., and Carlton, B. (1963). Federation Proc. **22**, 75.

Yoshikawa, H., and Sueoka, N. (1963). Proc. Natl. Acad. Sci. U.S. **49**, 559 and 806.

Zubay, G. (1963). Science **140**, 1092.

Zuckerkandl, E., Jones, R. T., and Pauling, L. (1960). Proc. Natl. Acad. Sci. U.S. **46**, 1349.

MAX A. LAUFFER

Form and function: A problem in virology

A1–1. INTRODUCTION

MODERN VIRUS research laboratories are equipped with a formidable array of physical tools for isolating, purifying, analyzing, characterizing, and visualizing particles produced in infected tissues. The use of all of this equipment is relatively pointless, however, unless the particles being characterized have some specific relationship to disease. To be of any real interest, these particles must be the bearers of infectiousness or they must have some other specific role, perhaps in relation to the immunity mechanism or to the development of signs and symptoms of disease. The most fundamental question in modern virology, therefore, is the identification of the biological role of characteristic particles.

Thoughtful virologists have been aware of this since the beginning of the discipline of virology and have adduced what evidence they could to establish biological function of physical particles. In 1952, however, the author published an article in which a fresh point of view was presented with respect to the identification of the biological function of isolated and characterized virus particles (Lauffer, 1952). This article was entitled "Form and Function: A Problem in Biophysics." The word "form" was taken to mean "a physical body with recognizable shape and structure" and the word "function," "the natural, proper or characteristic action of anything; especially the normal and special action of any organ or part of a living animal or plant." Considerable emphasis was placed on the problem of establishing a relationship between the etiological agent of a virus disease and particles which can be isolated, analyzed, characterized, and pictured with the electron microscope.

Most virologists have employed methods comparable to those used by biochemists and physiologists to relate specific biological functions to purified preparations obtained either by extraction of biological material or by synthesis. In rough outline, this method consists of isolation or synthesis, purification, tests for purity, and finally, biological tests to determine presence or absence of biological function associated with the purified material. Additional biological tests are often performed to correlate loss of biological function with chemical or physical alteration of the purified substance. In general, this approach is reasonably satisfactory for most of the problems encountered by the biochemist. The greater the number of particles or molecules of the active substance required to produce the biological effect, the more reliable is this general approach. The virologist, however, is confronted with a special problem. In many instances, it can be demonstrated that infection can be caused by a single virus particle, and it is theoretically

427

possible, if not even probable, that, for a wide variety of virus diseases, infection results from the introduction of a single particle which multiplies in the host (Lauffer and Price, 1945). Since purity, however exhaustibly investigated, is only relative, there is great danger, in principle at least, that a minor contaminant present in amounts too small to be detected might be the actual infectious entity, and that the particles in the purified preparation might be only incidentally associated with the disease process. Therefore, it seems to the author that special techniques are mandatory for the identification of viral function with particles.

In very favorable circumstances, as, for example, in the case of certain bacteriophages, it is possible to show that there is an approximately 1 : 1 correspondence between the number of infections produced by and the number of particles of a certain size and shape in a given volume of a preparation. When this is the case and when, in addition, reasonably good evidence for the purity of the preparation is available, there is a very good case for believing that the particles are the actual bearer of infectiousness. In the more usual case, however, even though there is reason to believe that an infection or at least a local site of infection is caused by a single particle, the probability of any given particle actually causing infection is so low that, in practice, a large number must be supplied for each lesion initiated. In such examples, it isn't possible to demonstrate 1 : 1 correspondence between the number of particles and the number of sites of infection. Other methods must be utilized.

A1–2. THE OPERATIONAL APPROACH

The point of view presented in the publication referred to above (Lauffer, 1952) represents an operational approach to the problem. Operationally speaking, two kinds of experiments are done by investigators in virology. In one kind, susceptible hosts are used to determine what happens to material when it is given some experimental treatment. Operationally, such experiments provide information concerning biological activity, for example, infectiousness. In the terminology of the title of this paper, such procedures give us information about function. Since it is the universal experience of biologists that sooner or later someone finds a molecule or a particle or a structure to be responsible for function, the assumption is made almost automatically that biological activity is the property of some physical or material body. Thus, infectiousness is associated with a form; the infectious entity is, by assumption, a form, but a form the physical nature of which may be unknown.

Other kinds of experiment are done by virologists in which physical or chemical observations are employed to find out what happens to a material when it is treated experimentally. Operationally, such experiments provide information about a characteristic particle or molecule. This characteristic particle is, by definition, a form. Its physical nature is usually partially known because it is recognized, in the first place, by virtue of such physical characteristics as sedimentation rate and electron microscope image.

It is, therefore, consistent with operationalism to recognize that the experiments of virologists provide information about two entities, an infectious or biologically active entity and a physical entity or characteristic particle. The problem of associating function with form can, therefore, be described as a problem of investigating the identity of two forms, an operationally defined physical entity which can be characterized by physical observations and an operationally defined biological entity, by definition, the agent associated with the function, which can be observed by biological means.

If the infectious entity and the characteristic particle are identical, then all of the properties of the infectious entity as determined by biological means must be identical with the corresponding properties of the characteristic particles as determined by physical observation.

Before proceeding with a detailed discussion of the various methods of establishing coincidences between the properties of characteristic particles and infectious entities, two important issues must be raised. In a private communication, von Tavel emphasized that significant evidence of identity can be obtained only by methods which are able to discriminate active particles from contaminants. This limitation applies to all methods. When this power of discriminating is absent, a trivial coincidence must result. For example, the finding that characteristic particles and infectiousness are destroyed by incineration provides a coincidence, but it is trivial because it does not discriminate.

Another general point must also be considered. When it is shown that a physical particle, for example, the tobacco mosaic virus (TMV) nucleoprotein rod, is identical with the infectious entity, the possibility is not excluded that some specific portion of that particle, for example, the RNA, might be the infectious entity. In general, the only way to determine whether a subform contained as an integral part of a form identified as the infectious entity is, indeed, the infectious entity is to find a way of degrading the original form without losing biological activity. At this stage, one is confronted with a new problem; that of identifying one or more of the degradation products with the infectious entity. The intellectual process for doing this is the same. In principle, one can almost never be certain that the ultimate particle associated with biological activity has been found, for the possibility usually exists that someone at some future date will find a way of degrading that particle into components, one of which is sufficient to produce the biological effect. The best that one can do is to establish that a particular characteristic physical body either is or contains the ultimate biological entity. From a practical point of view, this, in itself, is a great achievement because it justifies one in subjecting the particle in question to exhaustive investigation with the assurance that the biologically active principle is contained within it.

A1–3. METHODS FOR IDENTIFYING FORM WITH FUNCTION

It is relatively easy to determine the physical properties of a characteristic particle, for, in this case, one uses purely physical (including chemical) methods of observing the results of experiments. For this reason, very little attention will be paid this aspect of the problem. It is much more difficult to determine the properties of an infectious or, more generally, a biological entity because, by definition, only biological methods of observation can be used to characterize such a particle. Some of the methods which have been used have the disadvantage that the precision of the characterization depends, in large measure, upon the precision of the biological test used to make the observation. In more favorable instances, experiments can be designed in such a way that the bioassay is used as an indicator rather than as a direct quantitative measure of the effect produced. In such favorable instances, one can obtain highly significant measurements of properties of the infectious entity even though the bioassay is relatively inaccurate from a quantitative point of view.

A. Correlation of Infectiousness with Characteristic Particle

Among the methods which depend upon precision of bioassay is the correlation of degree of infectiousness with amount of purified characteristic particle. If the characteristic particle and the infectious entity are, indeed, identical, then infectiousness must be proportional to the amount of the characteristic particle no matter where or when it is found. Such proportionality can be established only by making quantitative measurements of both, and the reliability of the proportionality as evidence of identity is strongly dependent upon both the physical method of measuring the amount of the characteristic particle and the biological method of measuring the number of infectious entities. When the infectious entity is highly unstable, this method is difficult to use. The most refined application, already mentioned, of this technique is the demonstration, in a few instances, of 1 : 1 correspondence between the number of characteristic particles of certain bacteriophages and the number of plaques produced upon bioassay.

B. FRACTIONATION

Another method depending upon the precision of bioassay involves fractionation of the virus material by physical, chemical, or biological methods followed by measuring the relative amounts of characteristic particle in the fractions and comparing them with the relative amounts of infectious entity in the fractions. Again, if the infectious entity and the characteristic particle are identical, then, within the limits of the errors of bioassay and physical assay, the ratios of numbers of characteristic particles to numbers of infectious entities must be identical from fraction to fraction. Where there are uncertainties in the bioassay of 10–50%, as is almost always the case, the reliability of a single identification is small. This disadvantage can be obviated, in part, by making an extremely large number of investigations. Stanley (1937, 1939) and his co-workers did assemble an exhaustive number of identifications of this sort to provide evidence for the identity of the infectious entity of TMV with the rod-like characteristic particle, isolated and crystallized and shown to be a ribonucleoprotein of molecular weight 40 million.

C. DIFFUSION COEFFICIENT

The method of diffusion can be used. The diffusion coefficient of characteristic particles can be measured with high precision, particularly by the method of free diffusion at an interface. In this case, a boundary is established between the solution of the characteristic particles and solvent, and the diffusion coefficient of the material is determined by optical observation of the gradual dispersion of the initially sharp boundary. The diffusion coefficient of the infectious entity can be determined by the method of Northrop and Anson (1928–29) involving diffusion through a porous plate, by the method of Schantz and Lauffer (1962) involving diffusion into a gel, or by the method of Polson (1947) involving free diffusion at an interface. In all cases, samples must be taken for bioassay after a certain time of diffusion. The precision with which the diffusion coefficient can be determined is dependent in large measure upon the precision of the bioassay. If the characteristic particle and infectious entity are the same, they must have the same diffusion coefficient. The reliability of an identification depends, therefore, upon the reliability of the method of observation in both cases and particularly upon the reliability of bioassay, since it is the least accurate.

D. DESTRUCTION OF INFECTIOUSNESS

A final method involving quantitative bioassay procedures is the comparison of the destruction of infectiousness by physical, chemical, or biological means with alterations in the characteristic particle brought about by these same means. In general, such methods do not provide particularly satisfactory evidence because some procedures which result in measurable changes in characteristic particles do not seriously affect infectiousness and other procedures which destroy infectivity do not result in easily detectable physical and chemical changes in the characteristic particle. However, under special circumstances, such procedures do yield significant results; for example, the action spectrum for destruction of TMV infectivity as determined by Hollaender and Duggar (1936) was found to coincide with the ultraviolet absorption spectrum of TMV nucleoprotein as determined by Lavin and Stanley (1937), a fact which provided strong evidence of the identity of the TMV characteristic particle with the infectious entity. Since the ultraviolet absorption spectrum and the action spectrum are strongly influenced by the nucleic acid, in retrospect this coincidence afforded evidence of the currently accepted, more refined identification, of TMV-RNA as the infectious entity.

E. ULTRAFILTRATION

Whenever an experiment can be designed in such a way that virus material moves from one position to another as a boundary or as a zone or through a restraining medium, the bioassay becomes a mere indicator to show where the infectious entity is at a given time. Such experiments are capable of yielding very accurate characterizations of the infectious entity even when the assay procedure has a high error from a quantitative point of view.

Among methods of this sort, one must consider ultrafiltration. In the main, the bioassay is used in such experiments to determine whether the infectious entity does or does not pass the filter. If the filters are standardized, one can obtain some estimate of the size of the infectious entity. This estimate, admittedly not very precise, can be compared with the size determined for the characteristic particle by such methods as ultracentrifugation, electron microscopy, etc., to determine whether there is a coincidence in property of the characteristic particle and the infectious entity. In principle, a more precise use of ultrafiltration is possible. If one examines the filtrate for characteristic particles by means of electron microscopy, for example, and for infectious entities by means of bioassay and finds with a graded series of filters that the characteristic particle just penetrates the same filter as does the infectious entity, one has a convincing identification. If filters were perfect, that is, if they had absolutely uniform pores, such experiments would be easy to perform. With filters having a distribution of pore sizes, however, the success of such an experiment depends on having bioassays and physical detection procedures of comparable sensitivity.

F. Ultracentrifugation

Ultracentrifugation experiments can be carried out on infectious entities in three different ways employing the bioassay as a detector of position of the material. The first and oldest of these techniques is to sediment for a given time and then take samples at various levels in the ultracentrifuge cell and, by means of bioassay, determine the position of the sedimenting boundary of the infectious entity. In this way, the distance moved in a given time of sedimentation under given circumstances can be evaluated with an accuracy depending more on the patience of the investigator than on the precision of the bioassay. Sedimentation experiments can be repeated in media of different densities and further information can be obtained. In this manner, the ratio of the mass to the friction coeffi-

cient and also the effective specific volume of the sedimenting unit, presumably hydrated infectious entity, can be measured. These physical properties can then be compared with those of the characteristic particle determined by similar experiments but involving optical or other physical observation procedure.

Density-gradient sedimentation experiments can also be carried out and, at the end of the experiment, the gradient can be examined by physical means to find the position of the band of characteristic particles and by biological means to detect the position of the infectious entity. If they coincide, this provides evidence that the effective specific volume of hydrated infectious entity is identical with the comparable property of the characteristic particle. One can also carry out zonal sedimentation experiments in density gradients. By a sampling technique, the position of the zone containing the infectious entity can be located through bioassays and this can be determined as a function of time and speed of the sedimentation and steepness of the gradient. Corresponding experiments on the characteristic particle involve the observations by optical or other physical procedures. If the zone bearing the infectious entity is always the same as the zone corresponding to the characteristic particle, this again will provide evidence that the ratios of mass to friction coefficient and the effective specific volumes of the characteristic particle and of the infectious entity are identical.

G. Electrophoretic Mobility

Electrophoretic mobility experiments can also be performed on infectious entities using bioassay merely as an indicator of position. These can be carried out by the moving boundary technique or by the zonal technique on paper or various kinds of gel. The position of the infectious entity boundary or zone can be determined after migration by sampling procedures followed by bioassay. Electrophoretic mobility experiments can be carried out under a variety of conditions of pH and ionic strength. Comparable experiments can be done on the characteristic particle, always using optical or other physical methods of observation. As will be shown in a later paragraph, as many pieces of information can be obtained from experiments of this sort as the number of arbitrary constants required to determine the shape of the electrophoretic mobility versus pH curve plus the number of additional parameters required to describe the variation of isoelectric point with ionic strength of specific electrolytes. In addition, pH gradient electrophoresis experiments can be done. In such a case, the material will collect in a zone where the buffer has a pH corresponding to the isoelectric point. Such experiments can be used to establish identity of isoelectric point of infectious entity and characteristic particle.

H. CHROMATOGRAPHY

Chromatography, whether carried out in columns, on paper or on plates, can also be used to identify characteristic particles and infectious entities. Here again, sampling followed by bioassay is used to detect a zone or an advancing front corresponding to the infectious entity, and physical methods of analysis are used to detect the zone or the advancing front of the characteristic particle. With appropriate solvents, counter-current distribution methods could also be used.

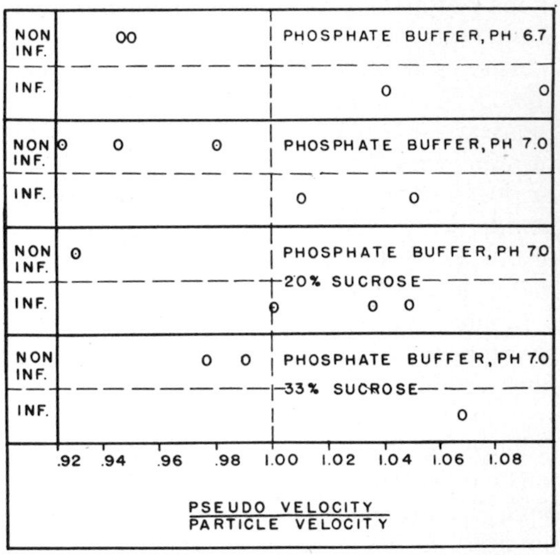

A1–4. SOUTHERN BEAN MOSAIC VIRUS

The author and his associates have carried out studies using the methods of ultracentrifugation, electrophoresis, and column chromatography on southern bean mosaic virus. The purpose was to investigate how much information can be obtained on a favorable material. Southern bean mosaic virus affords a good test. It is not too difficult to obtain in reasonable amounts, it is stable enough for practical purposes, and there is a convenient local-lesion bioassay procedure.

Epstein and Lauffer (1952) carried out sedimentation studies in a separation cell (Tiselius *et al.*, 1937) on southern bean mosaic virus (Section A1–3F). In studies carried out in phosphate buffer at pH 6.7, phosphate buffer at pH 7.0, phosphate buf-

Chart A1–1. A chart which shows whether inner compartment contents in separation cell experiments on southern bean mosaic virus in various media are infectious or noninfectious in relation to the ratio of the pseudo velocity, defined as the distance from the meniscus to the barrier divided by the time of sedimentation, to the sedimentation velocity of the characteristic particles. *From* Epstein and Lauffer (1952). Arch. Biochem. Biophys. 36, 371.

fer at pH 7.0 plus 20% sucrose, and phosphate buffer at pH 7.0 plus 33% sucrose, it was found that the sedimentation velocity of the infectious entity was in all cases within a few per cent of the values obtained for the characteristic particle by optical observation (Chart A1–1).

The determination of the sedimentation coefficient of the infectious entity was carried out by sedimenting the virus in the separation cell for varying periods of time, then stopping the centrifuge and removing the solution above the barrier in the cell. This material was then assayed on Kentucky Wonder or Early Golden Cluster bean plant. In this way, it is possible to determine the time of sedimentation at a given speed at which infectiousness disappears from the upper compartment of the cell. This time and the distance between the meniscus or original top of the virus solution and the barrier permit one to evaluate the velocity of sedimentation of the infectious entity. The infectivity measure-

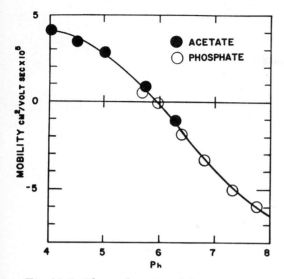

Fig. A1–1. Electrophoretic mobility at 0.02 ionic strength of southern bean mosaic virus as a function of pH. *From* Hartman and Lauffer (1953). J. Amer. Chem. Soc. **75**, 6205.

ment is merely an indicator. What one is actually measuring is time and distance and these can be determined as precisely as the patience of the investigator will allow.

Even though four experiments were carried out in which the sedimentation rate of the infectious entity and of the characteristic particle were found to be identical within a few per cent, for a hydrated particle, sedimentation coefficient is related to the density of the medium in accordance with the equation, $s = m/f(1 - V_h\rho)$, where "s" is the sedimentation coefficient, "m" is the hydrated mass, and "f" is the friction coefficient of the particle, "V_h" is the effective specific volume of the hydrated particle, and "ρ" is the density of the medium. To the extent that this equation is obeyed in detail, one should obtain a straight line when sedimentation coefficient corrected for viscosity is plotted as a function of density of the medium. From the slope and the intercept of this line, one can evaluate V_h and m/f. Lauffer *et al.* (1952) showed that the sedimentation behavior of southern bean mosaic virus characteristic particles in sucrose solutions very nearly obeys this equation. Therefore, the four

measurements, in reality, demonstrate that two physical properties of the characteristic particle and of the infectious entity of southern bean mosaic virus coincide; namely, the effective specific volume and the ratio of mass to friction coefficient.

Hartman and Lauffer (1953) applied electrophoresis to the problem of identifying biological activity of southern bean mosaic virus with the characteristic particle (Section A1–3G). In this case, mobility measurements were made by the moving boundary technique. The migration of the characteristic particles was followed by optical observation and that of the infectious entity, by sampling the cell at various depths and testing for biological activity. A large number of measurements were made in 0.02 ionic strength phosphate or acetate buffers covering the pH range from 4 to 7.8. Additional measurements were made in phosphate buffer at 0.1 ionic strength. In all cases, the boundary corresponding to the infectious entity was found to coincide with that of the characteristic particle. This means that the mobilities were the same in all cases within experimental error. The pH mobility curve in 0.02 ionic strength buffers was sigmoidal in shape (Figure A1–1). Over the range studied, the mobility could be described by an empirical equation involving four arbitrarily assigned constants. The curve was the same for the infectious entity and for the characteristic particle. Therefore, one can conclude that these data demonstrate four fundamental coincidences between properties of the characteristic particle and of the infectious entity. In addition to that, the experiments in 0.1 ionic strength phosphate buffers showed that the isoelectric point of both the infectious entity and the characteristic particles occurred at pH 5.10 as contrasted with the value of 5.9 in 0.02 ionic strength. This shift in isoelectric point with respect to ionic strength constitutes another fundamental coincidence between a property of the infectious entity and of the characteristic particle.

Shainoff and Lauffer (1957) employed a chromatographic procedure involving a strongly basic anion exchange resin to investigate the identity of the infectious en-

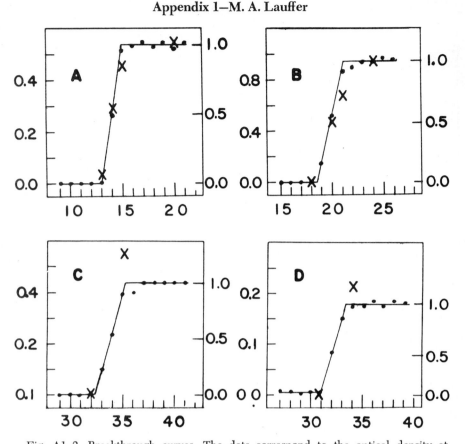

Fig. A1–2. Breakthrough curves. The dots correspond to the optical density at 260 mμ of diluted samples of effluent solution, and the optical density scale is the ordinate at the left of the diagrams. The points indicated by X correspond to the infectivity determinations, and the scale of infectivity, antilog 0.75 log (relative number of lesions), is the ordinate at the right. The abscissa of each diagram corresponds to effluent sample tube number. *Curve A:* pH = 5.80; μ = 0.08; C = 1 mg/ml; 0.40 ml/tube; retention volume (V) = 5.40 ml. *Curve B:* pH = 7.40; μ = 0.08; C = 1 mg/ml; 0.605 ml/tube; V = 11.8 ml. *Curve C:* pH = 7.80; μ = 0.08; C = 0.5 mg/ml; 0.637 ml/tube; V = 20.3 ml. *Curve D:* pH = 7.80; μ = 0.08; C = 1 mg/ml; 0.379 ml/tube; V = 13.5 ml. *From* Shainoff and Lauffer (1957). Virology 4, 418.

tity with the characteristic particle of southern bean mosaic virus (Section A1–3H). Virus was moved through the column until it emerged in the effluent material. The emerging front corresponding to the characteristic particles was detected by optical density measurements and that corresponding to the infectious entity by biological assay on Kentucky Wonder bean plants. Coincidences were observed in all experiments (Figure A1–2). Values of the retention volume, that is, the volume in milliliters of virus solution required to satu-

rate a column, were obtained from the effluent volume corresponding to the midpoint of the breakthrough curves. Retention volumes were found to depend upon virus concentration, ionic strength, and pH (Figure A1–3).

The curves showing the relationship between retention volume and pH are essentially sigmoidal in shape. To represent such a curve by a mathematical equation in the form of a power series requires at least four terms with coefficients adjusted to fit the data. Thus, a single pH versus retention

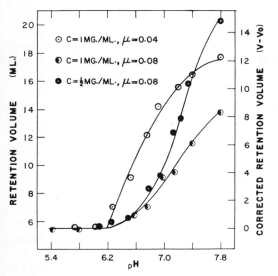

Fig. A1–3. The retention volumes of southern bean mosaic virus at various values of pH, ionic strength, and concentration. *From* Shainoff and Lauffer (1957). Virology 4, 418.

A1–5. TOBACCO MOSAIC VIRUS RNA

In 1956, two lines of evidence converged to focus attention on the RNA of TMV as the infectious center. Gierer and Schramm (1956a) and Fraenkel-Conrat (1956) announced essentially simultaneously that highly purified preparations of TMV-RNA are infectious and Lauffer *et al.* (1956) showed that the destruction of the infectivity of TMV by X-rays was correlated with depolymerizations of the RNA inside the virus rod. In the ensuing years, the hypothesis that TMV-RNA is a single nucleotide of molecular weight approximating 2 million, all of which is required for infectiousness, has gained general acceptance. We will attempt to examine critically the evidence in favor of this position.

The first line of evidence, of course, is the fact that RNA preparations are infectious (Section A1–3A). The evidence in the original publication of Gierer and Schramm indicated infectiousness approximating 1/10 of 1 per cent of that of TMV itself on an RNA basis. Singer and Fraenkel-Conrat (1961) found that when the RNA was tested on the leaves of host plants prerubbed with bentonite, there was a very considerable increase in the number of lesions produced and, under these circumstances, RNA preparations could be demonstrated to have infectivity titers 1 or 2% of TMV on an RNA basis. More recently, a value of 5% was reported (Sarkar, 1963).

The second line of evidence bears on the question of the purity of the RNA preparations. Ramachandran and Fraenkel-Conrat (1958) showed that phenol reagent can estimate with an accuracy of ± 5% amounts of protein ranging from 0.5 to 5.0 micrograms per milligram of RNA. They reported that their procedures for preparing TMV-RNA gave values for protein contamination ranging from 0.4 to 0.04%. If the lower value indeed represents protein contamination and if each RNA molecule of molecular weight 2 million has attached to it a small amount of protein, that amount would have a molecular weight of around a thousand. If the protein is undegraded TMV, then, according to Ramachandran

volume curve for which coincidences have been established at each experimental point implies at least four fundamental coincidences between the characteristic particle and the infectious entity. Additional coincidences are provided by the variation of retention volume with ionic strength.

Von Tavel (1959) investigated the extent to which chromatographic procedures are able to resolve closely similar virus characteristic particles. He investigated a preparation of TMV shown to be somewhat inhomogeneous by electrophoresis on ECTE-OLA-Cellulose using a salt gradient to elute the chromatograms. His results showed that the resolving power was not good. This finding demonstrates that one should exercise caution in interpreting chromatographic procedures. Actually, what one needs is a great backlog of experience to establish how widely chromatographic behavior varies from one macromolecule to another. This will enable one to assess the usefulness of information obtained from experiments such as those of Shainoff and Lauffer (1957) for the purpose at hand.

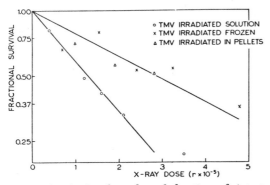

Fig. A1–4. Semilog plot of fraction of intact RNA to survive breakage after various X-ray doses. *From* Englander *et al.* (1960). Biochim. Biophys. Acta **40**, 385.

and Fraenkel-Conrat, it would account for only 0.01% of the infectivity of the RNA preparation. The evidence seems to be good that the RNA preparations are pure in the sense that they are not contaminated by a significant amount of protein. Further evidence of the lack of TMV contamination was obtained from serological studies. Gierer and Schramm (1956b) and later, Fraenkel-Conrat *et al.* (1957) showed that antiserum to TMV, which inactivates TMV completely, had no effect on the infectiousness of TMV-RNA preparations.

Gierer (1958b) carried out sedimentation experiments on the infectious principle of TMV-RNA (Section A1–3F). It had been previously established (Gierer, 1958a) that TMV-RNA preparations contain a principal component with a sedimentation coefficient extrapolated to infinite dilution and corrected to water at 20° of 31 Svedbergs plus considerable amounts of inhomogeneous, more slowly sedimenting material. For the determination of the sedimentation coefficient of the infectious material, Gierer (1958b) sedimented RNA at a concentration of 0.2% in 0.1 M phosphate buffer at pH 7.3 in an ordinary analytical ultracentrifuge cell. In one set of experiments, he sedimented until the principal component (S 31) had just reached the bottom. He then stopped the centrifuge and pipetted off the upper four-fifths of the supernatant fluid and tested this for infectivity on *Nicotiana glutinosa*. He found essentially none and concluded, therefore, that the sedimentation coefficient of the infectious entity must

be greater than four-fifths that of the principal component. In a second series of experiments, he sedimented the principal component four-fifths of the way to the bottom and then decanted the material above the pellet and measured for biological activity in the same way. In this experiment, he obtained very substantial infectiousness. He therefore concluded that the sedimentation coefficient of the infectious principle could not be greater than five-fourths that of the principal component. While this identification of the sedimentation coefficient of the infectious entity with that of the characteristic particle is much less precise than that described above for southern bean mosaic virus, it, nevertheless, does provide a coincidence with a rather large error between properties of the infectious entity and of the characteristic particle.

A considerable amount of evidence to identify the infectiousness of TMV with the RNA component with a sedimentation coefficient of 31 Svedbergs is afforded by X-ray studies carried out by the author and several colleagues (Section A1–3D). Englander *et al.* (1960) showed by ultracentrifugal analysis that the amount of the S 31 component contained in RNA isolated from TMV after irradiation decreased exponentially with the dose (Figure A1–4). When the material was irradiated in the frozen state or in very concentrated pellets, the dose corresponding to 37% change (D_o) was found to be 4×10^5 roentgens. The average value of D_o from a variety of experiments for inactivation of infectiousness was found to be 1.8×10^5 roentgens. The action of ionizing radiation is probably to break chemical bonds. It is conceivable that breaking any bond in an RNA molecule might lead to inactivation, but that depolymerization requires a break in the backbone. About 40% of the electrons in the RNA are associated with the backbone. These X-ray results, therefore, agree very well with the hypothesis that the S 31 RNA component is the infectious entity. Wohlhieter *et al.* (1960) obtained comparable but more complex results upon irradiation of isolated RNA.

Further conclusions can be deduced from the X-ray inactivation data. Biological activity of native TMV and of isolated RNA decrease exponentially with dose of X-rays (Buzzell *et al.*, 1956; Lea *et al.*, 1944; Gowen and Price, 1936; Ginoza and Norman, 1957; Englander *et al.*, 1960; Wohlhieter *et al.*, 1960). This means that inactivation, whether of RNA inside the intact virus particle or of isolated RNA, is the result of a single radiation induced event. It follows that each virus particle, and also each isolated infectious RNA particle, contains only one infectious target for X-rays and, in the case of the isolated RNA, this target must be a single physical unit. This conclusion is independent of any detailed theory concerning the nature of the effect of ionizing radiation on biological materials. Furthermore, D_o for inactivation of TMV ranges from 1.2 to 2.4 $\times$ 10^5 roentgens (Englander *et al.*, 1960) while that for inactivation of isolated TMV-RNA with X-rays of the same wave length is 1 $\times$ 10^5 roentgens (Wohlhieter *et al.*, 1960). Almost all viewpoints concerning the nature of the action of ionizing radiations relate the effect to the size of the target. This result indicates that the size of the infective target in isolated RNA preparations and in intact TMV are within experimental error the same or, at worse, differ by a factor of 2.

Other evidence indicates that the infectious target in case of the isolated RNA is all one physical piece. As found by Gierer (1958b), the number of lesions produced by infectious RNA is approximately proportional to the RNA concentration. In accordance with the theoretical considerations discussed by Lauffer and Price (1945), this eliminates the possibility that more than one particle either of the same or of different kinds must be present to initiate infection. Somewhat similar data obtained over a different concentration range by Cartwright in the author's laboratory are consistent with the same view.

Another line of evidence in the category of Method D (Section A1–3D) was presented originally by Gierer and Schramm (1956a) and confirmed by Fraenkel-Conrat *et al.* (1957). While the infectivity of TMV is essentially unaffected by pancreatic ribonuclease, that of the RNA preparations is very sensitive to the action of this enzyme.

If it is assumed that ribonuclease is absolutely specific for ribonucleic acid, then this result would constitute proof that the infectious principle is RNA and not some contaminant even if present.

Gierer (1958b) studied the decrease in infectivity and the decrease in mean molecular weight as measured by intrinsic viscosity of TMV-RNA under the influence of very small amounts of ribonuclease. Infectivity decreased much more rapidly than the mean molecular weight. Gierer interpreted this to mean that the molecular weight of the infective unit is higher than the mean molecular weight of the RNA in infectious preparations and thus identified it with the maximum molecular weight present.

We come now to the question of the actual size of the infectious RNA particle either in the intact virus or in the isolated state. From the known molecular weight of TMV of 40 million and the RNA content determined by chemical analysis, one knows that the entire RNA content of a virus particle weighs approximately 2 million times the hydrogen atom. There is some reason for believing that this is all in one physical piece, for the details of the TMV structure are such that a single chain of molecular weight 2 million would just fit a TMV particle in the arrangement suggested by X-ray diffraction data. This would account for the physical stability of particles of TMV with molecular weight of 40 million. Englander *et al.* (1960) showed that there is a correlation between the fraction of RNA in the S 31 component after isolation with the fraction of the original TMV particles of the basic size corresponding to 40 million molecular weight. This constitutes evidence that the S 31 component of the RNA has a molecular weight of about 2 million. Further evidence is the fact that when the sedimentation coefficient of 31 Svedbergs is combined with the intrinsic viscosity by the method of Mandelkern and Flory (1952), as was done by Gierer (1958a), a molecular weight of approximately 2 million is obtained.

X-ray inactivation data also provide some evidence. If one accepts the target theory of Lea (1955) as modified by Buzzell *et al.*

(1956), one can interpret the 37% inactivation dose (D_o) for TMV in terms of a target volume which fits reasonably well the total RNA content of the virus particles.

This paper is publication No. 107 of the Department of Biophysics. Work was supported by U.S. Public Health Service Grant No. GM 10403.

A1–6. LITERATURE CITED

Buzzell, A., Trkula, D., and Lauffer, M. A. (1956). Arch. Biochem. Biophys. **63**, 470.

Englander, S. W., Buzzell, A., and Lauffer, M. A. (1960). Biochim. Biophys. Acta **40**, 385.

Epstein, H. T., and Lauffer, M. A. (1952). Arch. Biochem. Biophys. **36**, 371.

Fraenkel-Conrat, H. (1956). J. Amer. Chem. Soc. **78**, 882.

Fraenkel-Conrat, H., Singer, B., and Williams, R. C. (1957). Biochim. Biophys. Acta **25**, 87.

Gierer, A. (1958a). Z. Naturforsch. **13b**, 477.

Gierer, A. (1958b). Z. Naturforsch. **13b**, 485.

Gierer, A., and Schramm, G. (1956a). Nature **177**, 702.

Gierer, A., and Schramm, G. (1956b). Z. Naturforsch. **11b**, 138.

Ginoza, W., and Norman, A. (1957). Nature **179**, 520.

Gowen, J. W., and Price, W. C. (1936). Science **84**, 536.

Hartman, R. E., and Lauffer, M. A. (1953). J. Amer. Chem. Soc. **75**, 6205.

Hollaender, A., and Duggar, B. M. (1936). Proc. Natl. Acad. Sci. U.S. **22**, 19.

Lauffer, M. A. (1952). Sci. Monthly **75**, 79.

Lauffer, M. A., and Price, W. C. (1945). Arch. Biochem. **8**, 449.

Lauffer, M. A., Taylor, N. W., and Wunder, C. C. (1952). Arch. Biochem. Biophys. **40**, 453.

Lauffer, M. A., Trkula, D., and Buzzell, A. (1956). Nature **177**, 890.

Lavin, G. I., and Stanley, W. M. (1937). J. Biol. Chem. **118**, 269.

Lea, D. E. (1955). Actions of Radiations on Living Cells. 2d ed. Cambridge Univ. Press, Cambridge, England.

Lea, D. E., Smith, K. M., Holmes, B., and Markham, R. (1944). Parasitology **36**, 110.

Mandelkern, L., and Flory, P. J. (1952). J. Chem. Phys. **20**, 212.

Northrop, J. H., and Anson, M. L. (1928–29). J. Gen. Physiol. **12**, 543.

Polson, A. (1947). Onderstepoort J. Vet. Sc. Animal Ind. **22**, 41.

Ramachandran, L. K., and Fraenkel-Conrat, H. (1958). Arch. Biochem. Biophys. **74**, 224.

Sarkar, S. (1963). Virology **20**, 185.

Schantz, E. J., and Lauffer, M. A. (1962). Biochemistry **1**, 658.

Shainoff, J. R., and Lauffer, M. A. (1957). Virology **4**, 418.

Singer, B., and Fraenkel-Conrat, H. (1961). Virology **14**, 59.

Stanley, W. M. (1937). Ergeb. Physiol. Biol. Chem. Exptl. Pharmakol. **39**, 294.

Stanley, W. M. (1939). Physiol. Rev. **19**, 524.

Tiselius, A., Pedersen, K. O., and Svedberg, T. (1937). Nature **140**, 848.

Von Tavel, P. (1959). Arch. Biochem. Biophys. **85**, 491.

Wohlhieter, J. A., Buzzell, A., and Lauffer, M. A. (1960). Biochim. Biophys. Acta **43**, 163.

KENNETH M. SMITH

Virus diseases of arthropods

A2–1. INTRODUCTION

INTENSIVE STUDY of the viruses affecting arthropods is of comparatively recent date; in consequence our knowledge of them is slight compared with what we know of other viruses. Arising out of this neglect is the fact that no viruses have yet been discovered in several of the insect orders, such as the Orthoptera and Hemiptera, or in some other members of the Arthropoda such as the Crustacea, although there are signs that suggest their existence.

This group of viruses is very suitable for fundamental study and it is difficult to understand why they have been neglected for so long. Insects are comparatively easy to rear in captivity, and fairly large quantities of virus are obtainable. Indeed, in the case of *Tipula* iridescent virus (TIV), in which 25 per cent of the dry weight of an infected insect is pure virus, the preparation of a gram of virus presents no difficulty.

Two methods of approach which have wide application in the study of other animal viruses, the serological and tissue culture techniques, have not yet been developed to any great extent in insect virology, but work has now been started along these lines.

It is hoped that the serological technique may help in the difficult task of differentiating the many viruses of the polyhedroses, especially of the cytoplasmic polyhedroses, some of which appear morphologically identical in the electron microscope.

Very little is known of the method of replication of insect viruses and here the growing of insect tissues in culture as pioneered by Grace (1958) and others will be of great value. A characteristic of insect virus diseases is the fact that, with a few exceptions, it is the larval stage which is susceptible to the virus. Imagos of butterflies and moths are occasionally found infected with polyhedra, and this usually means that the larva was infected at a late stage of its development.

A2–2. TYPES OF ARTHROPOD VIRUSES

The virus types are classified by the presence or absence of intracellular inclusions, morphology of the virus particles, site of multiplication in the tissues, and the kind of disease produced. Based on these criteria the insect viruses are arranged into *nuclear* and *cytoplasmic* polyhedroses, *granuloses*, and the "*free viruses,*" so called. This last is, so far as present knowledge goes, a very small group characterized by the absence of intracellular inclusions and with the virus particles free in the tissues as in the virus diseases of plants and the higher animals.

The polyhedroses, in which the tissues of the infected larvae are filled with many-sided (polyhedral) protein crystals, comprise the largest known group of insect viruses, and the nuclear type of polyhedrosis has been known for many years.

A. Nuclear Polyhedroses

The following are the characteristics of the nuclear polyhedroses; affected larvae, as a rule, continue feeding until a comparatively late stage of the disease. The virus attacks the skin, tracheae, and blood cells, and it is the effect of the virus on the skin which produces the somewhat dramatic aspect of the nuclear polyhedroses. The dead larvae hang head downwards from the food plant, remaining attached by the abdominal "feet"; it is from this characteristic feature and from the fact that the dying larvae climb to the highest point available, that the name "Wipfelkrankheit" or "tree-top" disease was derived. The skin, rendered extremely fragile, ruptures at a touch and the now liquefied body contents consisting mainly of millions of polyhedra are liberated, spreading the polyhedra far and wide.

So far as is known at present the virus particles, which are occluded in the polyhedra, are always rod-shaped, a point of difference, as we shall see later, from the cytoplasmic polyhedroses. In addition to being occluded in the polyhedral crystal the virus rods are enclosed within an outer capsule sometimes singly and sometimes two or three at a time. Finally, the material of the virus itself, the nucleoprotein, is contained within a thin envelope, the intimate membrane. As a general rule the virus rods are distributed haphazardly within the polyhedron, but in one particular case, to be described later, the virus rods appear to be arranged in a more regular manner.

For many years the nuclear polyhedra were a subject of much controversy, and they were for long thought to be some kind of organism and to be the cause of the disease. However, Komárek and Breindle (1924) demonstrated that there were particles of some kind inside the polyhedra, and some years later, in 1939, Paillot and Gratia dissolved the polyhedra with alkali and observed in the dark field by optical microscopy numerous highly refractive granules which they suggested were the causal virus. Then in 1947 Bergold demonstrated, by means of the electron microscope, the presence of rod-shaped particles; he dissolved the polyhedra with weak sodium carbonate and isolated the virus.

The reaction of the nuclear polyhedra to weak sodium carbonate differs considerably from that of the cytoplasmic polyhedra when similarly treated. The nuclear polyhedra with the exception previously noticed dissolve completely leaving behind a thin outer membrane containing the rod-shaped virus particles; the membrane is probably only the hardened outer layer of the polyhedron.

B. Chemical Composition of the Nuclear Polyhedrosis Viruses and their Polyhedra

One of the earliest attempts to make a quantitative study of the nucleic acid was made by Gratia *et al.* (1945), who found 0.48 per cent DNA but no RNA in the polyhedra of *Bombyx mori*. An analysis of purified virus particles from *B. mori* and *Porthetria dispar* revealed 13 and 16 per cent DNA, respectively (Bergold, 1947; Bergold and Pister, 1948). Smith and Wyatt (1951) and Wyatt (1952a) made an investigation of the bases of several insect viruses of the nuclear polyhedrosis type. They were found to contain the purines, adenine and guanine, and the pyrimidines, cytosine and thymine, but no 5-methylcytosine or uracil. According to Wellington (1951, 1954), who investigated the amino acid composition of several nuclear viruses, they all have a similar pattern of amino acid composition. This differs considerably, however, from the pattern of the surrounding polyhedral body protein.

That the amino acid composition of the intimate virus membrane differs from that of the contained virus was shown by Bergold and Wellington (1954), the virus membranes containing more aspartic acid and less arginine than the virus. For a more complete account of the chemical composition of the nuclear viruses and their polyhedra the reader is referred to Bergold (1963).

440

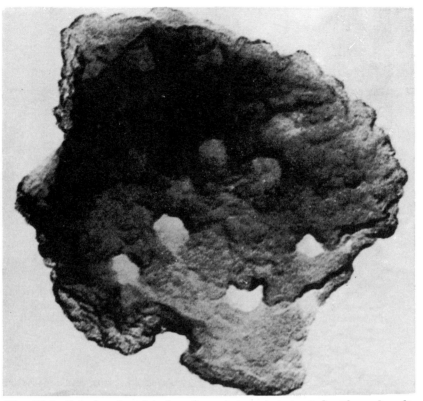

Fig. A2–1. Cytoplasmic polyhedron from *Automeris io* treated with weak sodium carbonate; note the polyhedral shape of the sockets which contained the virus particles. Magnification × 127,000.

C. Cytoplasmic Polyhedroses

The existence of a separate and distinct type of polyhedrosis virus which was near-spherical instead of the usual rod-shape was first demonstrated by Smith and Wyckoff (1950) in the larvae of *Arctia caja* (Linnaeus) and *A. villaca* (Linnaeus), and the differential staining properties of this new type of polyhedra later investigated (Smith *et al.*, 1953).

Previously, other workers had observed polyhedra in the cytoplasm of the midgut cells of lepidopterous larvae (Ishimori, 1934; Lotmar, 1941), but the facts that they were of an entirely different nature from the nuclear polyhedra and contained a different type of virus were not realized. In the decade, or so, since the first cytoplasmic polyhedrosis was described, the number of this type of disease recorded has become very large; no less than 80 have been re-corded from Cambridge alone. It is not known, of course, how far these numerous viruses differ from each other, and whether many of the cytoplasmic polyhedroses in the different insects may not be due to the same virus.

The first clue to the existence of the cytoplasmic polyhedroses was found during a routine examination of a larva of *Sphinx ligustri*, the privet-hawk moth. The usual method of testing for the presence of polyhedra in a larva is to make a blood smear on a microscope slide and stain with Giemsa's solution. This gives a stained background against which the *unstained* nuclear polyhedra stand out, and are easily seen with the oil-immersion lens. In this case, however, among the unstained polyhedra were numerous polyhedra which showed up darkly stained; when these were treated with dilute sodium carbonate and

Fig. A2–2. Two virus particles from the cytoplasmic polyhedron shown in Fig. A2–1; note the polyhedral contour of the particles. Magnification × 104,000.

observed under the electron microscope the reaction was seen to be of a different nature from that of the nuclear polyhedra. Instead of dissolving completely and leaving the rod-shaped virus particles enclosed in a membrane, the stained crystals dissolved only partially leaving a matrix containing many near circular holes which have now been shown to be hexagonal in outline (Fig. A2–1). Further investigation has shown that the virus particles are actually icosahedra (twenty-sided figures) as revealed by the 5- or 6-sided contour of the particle (Fig. A2–2).

The site of multiplication of this type of virus is the cytoplasm of the cells of the midgut, but in some cases, at least, as the disease progresses the polyhedra may be found in the cells throughout the whole length of the gut. As the skin is not attacked the symptoms of the cytoplasmic polyhedrosis differ considerably from those of the nuclear disease. The infected larvae lag behind the normal in their development; there is no outstanding symptom at first, but affected individuals can be recognized by their small size, loss of appetite, and, sometimes, disproportionately large head or long bristles. Later, the polyhedra developing in the gut can frequently be observed through the dorsal integument as a pale yellow or whitish area. Since the skin is not attacked, it does not rupture and thus distribute the polyhedra; instead, in late stages of the disease, polyhedra are frequently regurgitated or voided in large quantities with the feces.

On opening a larva which has died of a cytoplasmic polyhedrosis, the abnormal state of the alimentary canal, especially the midgut, is at once apparent. Instead of the translucent pale green organ of healthy larvae, the gut is opaque and pale yellow or milky in appearance owing to the huge numbers of polyhedra which often become liberated as a milky fluid if the gut is punctured during the dissection procedure.

So far, all the rod-shaped viruses of the nuclear polyhedroses have been shown to contain deoxyribose nucleic acid (DNA), but some of the near-spherical viruses from cytoplasmic polyhedroses contain ribonucleic acid (RNA). This, however, is not a fundamental difference between the rod-shaped and near-spherical viruses, since, as we shall see later, the *Tipula* iridescent virus (TIV), a cytoplasmic virus of polyhedral shape, contains only DNA.

Chromatographic and electrophoretic analyses of the nucleic acid content of the cytoplasmic virus from *Laothoe populi* Linnaeus showed that they contained 0.9% RNA and no DNA. Chromatographic analysis of five further viruses from cytoplasmic polyhedroses showed the presence of comparable quantities of RNA but no DNA (Xeros, 1962).

D. THE GRANULOSES

This type of disease was first described by Paillot (1926) in the larvae of the cabbage butterfly *Pieris brassicae* Linnaeus and again a few years later (Paillot, 1934) in the larvae of the cutworm *Agrotis segetum* Schiffermüller. In 1947 Steinhaus discovered a similar disease in the variegated cutworm *Peridoma margaritosa* (Haworth); and in 1948 Bergold demonstrated the presence of a rod-shaped virus in the granulosis of the fir-shoot roller, *Choristoneura murinana* (Hübner).

The name "granulosis" was given to the disease because of the presence in the tissues of infected larvae of large quantities of very small granules which are just at the limit of the resolution of the optical microscope. Actually these "granules" are minute protein crystals, probably similar in nature to the polyhedra but containing only a single rod, instead of hundreds as in the polyhedra. These inclusions have been called "capsules," but, in the writer's opinion, this is not very indicative of the crystalline nature of the inclusion body.

The symptoms of the granulosis disease are somewhat similar to those of the nuclear polyhedroses, especially in the final stages. Affected larvae cease to feed and change colour, usually on the ventral side; this colour change is due to the development of quantities of the "capsules" in the tissues and may vary in the different species. Larvae of *Pieris brassicae*, in the final stage of the disease, hang down in an inverted V and consist virtually of a fragile sack filled with "capsules." The skin is exceedingly thin and easily ruptures, liberating the liquefied internal tissues together with vast numbers of "capsules."

Diagnosis of the disease with the ordinary oil-immersion lens of the optical microscope is difficult, owing to the possible confusion of the "capsules" with small bacterial spores. Huger (1961) has developed a staining method for demonstrating the presence of a granulosis in *C. murinana*. An intense bright red staining of the capsules could be obtained by treatment of sections in 50 per cent acetic acid at room temperature for 5 min prior to staining with Heidenhain's iron haematoxylin and counterstaining with an aqueous solution of 0.5 erythrosin for 2 min.

The most certain diagnosis of the granulosis is, of course, made by means of the electron microscope. There are two standard methods, one is by dissolving the "capsules" in weak alkali, and the other by cutting ultrathin sections of the capsules. When treated with the appropriate strength of sodium carbonate the outer granule or "capsule" collapses partially dissolved leaving what the writer has called the "inner capsule" or, as Huger (1963) prefers it, the "outer membrane." Inside this structure again is the virus rod itself consisting of the nucleoprotein contained within the "intimate membrane." Further treatment with sodium carbonate dissolves away the nucleoprotein leaving only the "intimate membrane" as a straight narrow tube.

E. CHEMICAL COMPOSITION

Wellington (1951, 1954) has analyzed the "capsule" protein of *C. murinana* and the granulosis virus particles of *C. murinana* and *C. fumiferana*. The following amino acids were determined by paper chromatography from both purified virus rods and purified capsule protein: alanine, arginine, aspartic acid, cysteine, glutamic acid, glycine, histidine, leucine, lysine, methionine, phenylalanine, proline, serine, threonine, tyrosine, and valine. Although the amino acid values from the two granulosis viruses are similar, the respective nucleic acids differ in their composition. Wyatt (1952a,b) showed that both were DNA viruses and resembled the viruses of nuclear polyhedroses in that they only contain the purines adenine and guanine and the pyrimidines cytosine and thymine but no 5-methylcytosine or uracil.

So far as the pathology of the granuloses is concerned the fatbody is the main focus of virus development, although as the disease progresses the blood cells, skin, and tracheae are also affected. In the granulosis of *Pieris brassicae,* where the epidermis is regularly attacked, there do occur larvae with infection confined to the fatbody.

There has been some difference of opinion as to whether the granulosis virus develops in the cytoplasm or nucleus of the cell. Bird (1958, 1959) considers that the granulosis virus and "capsules" of *Choristoneura fumiferana, Eucosma griseana,* and *Pieris rapae* develop only in the cytoplasm of cells. On the other hand Smith and Rivers (1956) have observed the "capsules" in the nuclei of the fat cells in the granuloses of *Pieris brassicae* and *Melanchra persicariae* Linnaeus. Bergold (1948) and Steinhaus and Thompson (1949) have also observed "capsules" in the cell nuclei. Huger (1961) has developed a method of selective staining, and he considers that there is little doubt that the "capsules" of *C. murinana* develop in the nucleus as well as in the cytoplasm.

Granuloses have so far only been described in the larvae of the Lepidoptera.

F. The Free Viruses

Not very many diseases have been described in which the causative virus is free in tissues as in the virus diseases of the higher animals. This is probably due to the greater difficulty of diagnosis in the absence of the characteristic intracellular inclusions. In the Diptera there are two such viruses, the *Tipula* iridescent virus which is described in a later section and the so-called "sigma virus" of *Drosophila* sp. which is inherited and causes the fly to be sensitive to carbon dioxide; it has not been isolated or characterized under the electron microscope.

From a species of army worm *Pseudaletia unipuncta* (Haworth) [Lepidoptera], a small near-spherical virus measuring approximately 25 mμ has been isolated (Steinhaus, 1951; Wasser, 1952).

A Japanese worker, Yamazaki (1960),

and his co-workers (Yamazaki *et al.,* 1960) claim to have isolated a non-inclusion virus from silkworms, *Bombyx mori,* infected with the disease known as "flacherie" (Paillot, 1941).

Two non-inclusion viruses are known to attack the honey bee, *Apis mellifera* Linnaeus (Hymenoptera). One attacks the adult insect, causing bee paralysis (Burnside, 1945); this is a small near-spherical virus, morphologically somewhat similar to poliovirus. The second virus causes a disease in the larva known as sacbrood (White, 1917); very little is known of this virus, and the disease would well repay further study.

Another virus in this group has been recorded in the larvae of cockchafer grubs *Melolontha* spp. (Coleoptera); the disease has been called "Wassersucht" by Krieg and Huger (1960). It appears similar to the "histolytic disease" of *Oryctes* spp. (Surany, 1960). In the fatbody of infected larvae, the albuminoid spheres normally present are apparently transformed into virogenetic stroma and give rise to virus particles which appear to be spherical and contain RNA.

Two non-inclusion virus diseases, and a possible third, have been described in Arthropods outside the Insecta. These occur in the spider mites (Arachnida); in the citrus red mite, *Panonychus citri* (McGregor) (Smith *et al.,* 1959a); and in the European red mite, *Panonychus ulmi* (Koch) (Steinhaus, 1959).

The third possible mite virus is a transovarian factor which affects the morphology in spider mites, *Tetranychus* sp. It has not been isolated or characterized under the electron microscope (Boudreaux, 1959).

A2–3. ORDERS IN WHICH VIRUSES HAVE BEEN DESCRIBED

It has been mentioned earlier that distribution of viruses among the Arthropoda is very uneven, a phenomenon probably more apparent than real and reflecting the lack of investigation into this branch of virology.

By far the greatest number of viruses have been recorded from the larvae of the butterflies and moths (Lepidoptera); examples of all three types, the polyhedroses, the granuloses, and the non-inclusion or free viruses have been recorded from this Order, and in the case of the granuloses it is the only known susceptible group.

In the larvae of the true flies (Diptera) only two viruses are at present known, one causing a nuclear polyhedrosis and the other a cytoplasmic virus, the *Tipula* iridescent virus. Both are briefly described in a following section.

Sawfly larvae (Hymenoptera) are susceptible to a number of nuclear polyhedroses and two non-inclusion viruses attack the adult and larval honey bee, respectively.

In the beetles (Coleoptera) one non-inclusion virus is known to attack larvae of the chafer family.

All the above are natural infections; they do not include numerous artificial cross-transmissions with the *Tipula* iridescent virus (Smith *et al.*, 1961), nor the apparent artificial infection of Hemerobiid larvae (Neuroptera) with viruses from nuclear and cytoplasmic polyhedroses of other insects (Sidor, 1960; Smith *et al.*, 1959b; Smith, 1963a).

At the present time, therefore, no viruses have been recorded from some insect Orders containing many species of insects such as the Hemiptera, aphids, plant bugs, etc., and the Orthoptera, locusts, grasshoppers, etc.

Outside the Insecta we have mentioned two non-inclusion viruses with a possible third in the mites (Arachnida).

So far no virus has been discovered in the Crustacea, although there are suggestions of a possible virus disease in the common wood louse or sowbug (*Asellus* sp.).

A2–4. DESCRIPTION OF SOME VIRUS DISEASES OF ARTHROPODS

Although, as we have seen, only two virus diseases have so far been described in the larvae of Diptera, these two are sufficiently outstanding for a brief description to be given of each.

The first of these is the nuclear polyhedrosis of the larva of the crane fly *Tipula*

paludosa Meig., and it shows some interesting differences from the nuclear polyhedroses of caterpillars. The disease caused is purely a blood disease, and it seems to be accompanied by an increase in the number of blood cells; affected larvae are whitish in colour and they may live under laboratory conditions for long periods even longer than the normal larval life though they never reach the pupal stage.

The development of the disease seems to be as follows. There is first a concentration of chromatin in which the virus rods develop. As the disease progresses the virus rods accumulate in lines and the polyhedral protein crystallizes around them; the particles thus appear to be arranged regularly in lines following the shape of the crystal. This is a point of difference from other nuclear polyhedroses where the distribution of the virus particles in the polyhedra seems to be entirely haphazard. At first, the nucleus of an infected blood cell begins to increase in size and, as the polyhedra form, the nucleus almost completely fills the cell, which is itself greatly distended. The polyhedra are by this time arranged along the periphery of the nuclear membrane; shortly after this stage the cell bursts and the polyhedra are discharged. The polyhedra tend to be of a crescent or half-moon shape, rather different from the usual many-sided crystals.

Perhaps the most outstanding peculiarity of the *Tipula* polyhedra is their reaction with weak alkali. We have seen already how the nuclear polyhedra of lepidopterous larvae dissolve readily in dilute sodium carbonate leaving the virus rods enclosed within the hardened outer skin of the crystal. However, the behaviour of the *Tipula* polyhedra in the presence of different reagents is most unusual and differentiates them sharply from either of the other two groups of polyhedra. They are resistant to trypsin and to dilute and weak acids and alkalis. In 1 N sodium hydroxide they elongate to six or more times their length, becoming first biconvex spindles and then elongating into crescents or wormlike shapes. At about three times their normal length this elongation is completely reversible, and in water, at pH 5.8, they return to their original size and shape. After such treatment, however, the polyhedra are "activated"; in other words, they now respond in a similar manner in ammonia, 1–12% sodium carbonate, and hydrochloric acid, pH 1–4, but not to 1 N hydrochloric acid or 25% sodium carbonate. The elongation and contraction or return to normal shape, which take place along the same axis, can be repeated indefinitely in these solutions and take place as rapidly as the solutions can be alternated.

The polyhedra are not usually dissolved even after half an hour in 1 N sodium hydroxide at 20°C. In a solution of equal parts of 1 N sodium hydroxide and 1 N potassium cyanide, the response is speeded up enormously and the polyhedra elongate even further to reach their maximum length in 1½ min. They dissolve completely in 2–4 min.

It is not known what happens to the rod-shaped virus particles during the extension and retraction of the polyhedra. Electron micrographs of the extended polyhedra showed whitish, ghost-like bodies which might have been virus particles. However, the question as to whether virus particles were actually present inside the polyhedra, which could not be answered by dissolving the polyhedra, was answered by cutting ultrathin sections of the polyhedra and observing them under the electron microscope. By this method it was shown that the polyhedra did, in fact, contain rod-shaped virus particles morphologically similar to the virus rods of other nuclear polyhedroses.

We come now to the consideration of another insect virus, of the non-inclusion or "free" type, and affecting the same larva, *Tipula paludosa,* as does the nuclear polyhedrosis just described. It is curious that the only two viruses so far described from this fly larva should both be of such outstanding interest.

This virus, called the *Tipula* iridescent virus (TIV) for reasons to be given later, was disco /ered by the Virus Research Unit at Cambridge, England, during routine examinations of large numbers of *Tipula* larvae in a search for examples of the nuclear polyhedrosis.

There are many interesting and outstanding characteristics of this unusual virus, the particles of which are of large size and extreme uniformity. In a larva in an advanced stage of the disease the virus is present in such large quantities that 25% of the dry weight of the insect is pure virus. As a consequence of this high concentration spontaneous crystallization of the virus takes place within the living insect giving rise to Bragg reflections, the optical effect being the production of a blue or violet iridescence. The virus multiplies, in the first place, in the cytoplasm of the fatbody cells; later multiplication occurs in various other tissues such as the muscles and even in the head but always in the cell cytoplasm. In affected pupae there is a high concentration of virus in the wing buds with consequent brilliant iridescence.

The opinion was long held by some insect virologists that the viruses were strongly species-specific; in view of the large amount of work done on cross transmission this view is no longer tenable. However, TIV is unusual in the ease with which it can be transmitted to insects of widely separated orders as, for instance, from the Diptera to the Coleoptera and Lepidoptera and back again to the Diptera (Smith *et al.,* 1961).

When the fatbody of a larva infected with TIV is removed the iridescence shows up plainly and sections of such fatbody observed in the electron microscope have an unmistakable appearance. The cell cytoplasm is completely filled with virus particles which, in an advanced stage of the disease, will already be oriented into a crystalline pattern. It is these microcrystals formed in the living insect which produce the iridescence.

A. Chemical Composition

Studies on the chemical composition of TIV have been carried out by Thomas (1961), and the following facts are quoted from his work. The analyses of TIV indicate that it contains 12.4 per cent DNA and 5.2 per cent lipid, most of which is phospholipid. It does not contain any appreciable amount of polysaccharide nor any RNA; the remainder of the virus, 82.4 per cent, appears to be protein. The DNA of the virus contains only adenine, guanine, thymine, and cytosine; there is no methylcytosine or 5-hydroxymethylcytosine. The particle-weight of TIV, 1.22×10^9, is the largest so far determined among viruses that are highly uniform in size and shape.

Finally a short account is given of a non-inclusion virus affecting a member of the Arthropoda, but not an insect, the citrus red mite, *Panonychus citri* (McGregor). The disease is highly infectious and appears to attack the nervous system of the mite, since affected mites become paralyzed with the legs held in a stiltlike manner; in some cases diarrhoea is an accompanying symptom. A curious feature of the disease is the almost invariable appearance, in the body of the affected mite, of numerous birefringent crystals which are not virus crystals but appear to be the result of a disordered metabolism (Smith *et al.*, 1959a; Smith and Cressman, 1962). The virus from the citrus red mite measures about 35 mμ in diameter, has a six-sided contour, and is probably an icosahedron.

A2–5. ISOLATION AND PURIFICATION

In the purification of the polyhedrosis viruses, it must be remembered that the first step is the isolation of the virus-containing polyhedra, and the second the extraction of the virus. The isolation of the nuclear polyhedra is best done by grinding up the whole insects and filtering through fine muslin into boiled distilled water. By means of a short cycle of spins on an ordinary angle centrifuge a pure suspension of the inclusion bodies can be obtained. To liberate the virus particles from the polyhedra it is necessary to dissolve the latter in weak alkali; this is a highly critical operation since an incorrect alkali concentration will also dissolve out the virus particles. The procedure for the purification of the rod-shaped viruses from the nuclear polyhedroses and the granuloses is given in detail by Bergold (1958) and so will not be repeated here.

The isolation of the virus from the cytoplasmic polyhedra is a more difficult process, since the near-spherical viruses of this type of disease tend to dissolve in dilute alkali more readily than the polyhedral crystal itself. Hills and Smith (1959) have recently worked out a method for the purification of this type of virus. The method used for the extraction of the nuclear polyhedra is not recommended for use with cytoplasmic polyhedroses, since the polyhedra, which are confined to the gut, tend to get lost in the general debris. Futhermore, the polyhedra themselves show severe etching with consequent loss of the virus in the sockets near the surface of the polyhedra. A more successful method is to extract the guts intact, plunge them immediately into distilled water, and then extract the polyhedra; this gives undamaged polyhedra with the individual virus particles on the surface of the crystal covered with a layer of protein.

It is necessary by trial and error to find out what are the optimum concentrations of sodium carbonate and times of exposure for each species. It was found that for the isolation of the virus from a number of species the optimum conditions are as follows: 0.5% sodium carbonate for 1.25 min for the cytoplasmic polyhedra from *Arctia caja* L.; 1.0% for 2 min for *Antheraea pernyii* Guerin-Meneville; for 1.5 min at 1.0% for *Evanessa antiopa* L.; and 1 min at 1.0% for *Pyrameis cardui* L. and *Calophasia lunula* Hufnagel.

Undoubtedly the easiest of all insect viruses to isolate and purify, if not the easiest of all viruses, is the *Tipula* iridescent virus (TIV). The process is aided by the large quantity of virus present in each insect and by the absence of other particles of similar size in the tissues of the diseased host. To obtain the purified suspension the infected larvae are cut up in distilled water and allowed to stand for 24 hours; occasional shaking aids liberation of the virus. The suspension is then clarified by low-speed centrifugation and the virus obtained essentially pure by two cycles of high- and low-speed centrifugation. The virus can be further purified by centrifugation in a sucrose gradient.

When centrifuged down the virus crystallizes spontaneously and the pellets have fascinating optical properties. By trans-

Fig. A2–3. Particles of the *Tipula* iridescent virus (air-dried); note the 5- and 6-sided contour. Magnification × 56,000.

mitted light the pellet appears an orange or amber colour, but by reflected light it has an iridescent turquoise appearance. Within the pellet may be seen small regions reflecting the incident light quite brilliantly, giving the entire pellet the appearance of an opal (Williams and Smith, 1957).

When dealing with non-inclusion viruses affecting very small arthropods such as the citrus red mite, *Panonychus citri* (McGregor), cycles of low- and high-speed centrifugation can be used. An aqueous suspension of diseased mites, about 40 mg, is ground up in a hand homogenizer and spun on a clinical centrifuge to clear debris. The supernatant is then centrifuged on a Model L Spinco at 36,000 rpm (110,000g). The pellet is next taken up in 1 ml distilled water and given a low-speed spin to clear debris. Next the supernatant is run in a Model E Spinco centrifuge until the peak is about halfway down. The Spinco is stopped and the supernatant removed; this is mixed with potassium phosphotungstate and sprayed onto the grids for electron microscopy. An alternative method is to suspend the pellet, after sedimenting in the Model L Spinco, and purify on a sucrose gradient.

A2–6. MORPHOLOGY AND ULTRA-STRUCTURE

In the descriptions of the different types of insect virus diseases we have already learned the general morphology of the viruses-rod-shaped in the nuclear polyhedroses and the granuloses, icosahedral in the cytoplasmic polyhedroses and the non-inclusion diseases. It may be of interest, however, to give here a short account of the double-shadowing technique in electron microscopy whereby it is possible to demonstrate unequivocably the icosahedral, or 20-sided, shape of a virus particle. The experiments in question were carried out on the particles of TIV, which is large and very uniform measuring about 130 mμ in diameter. This virus shows very clearly its non-circular contour and retains, even after drying out of water, its 5- or 6-sided outline (Fig. A2–3). In order to prove that the TIV particle is actually an icosahedron, the double-shadowing was carried out as follows. A model of an icosahedron was made and shadowed by two light sources separated 60° in azimuth and oriented so that an apex of the hexagonal contour points directly to each light source. This throws two shadows, one is 4-sided and pointed and the other is 5-sided with a blunt end. A virus particle was then frozen-dried and shadowed in the same way, resulting in a pointed and a blunt-ended shadow identical with the shadows thrown by the model icosahedron. This indicates with fair certainty that the TIV particle is an icosahedron (Williams and Smith, 1958).

By means of the negative staining technique with phosphotungstic acid (PTA) it is now possible to gain some knowledge of the ultrastructure of viruses. Three types of insect-virus particle have been studied by this technique by Smith and Hills (1962); these are from a nuclear polyhedrosis, a granulosis, and the TIV. There appears to be a difference in the fine structure of the rods from the nuclear polyhedroses and the granuloses, respectively. In the breakdown of the virus rods from the nuclear polyhedroses the first stage in the liberation of the contents of the intimate membrane is the peeling off of the outer capsule. The cap-sules break in the centre and fold back-ward, thus forming two spheres still joined in the middle. These finally break apart and are thought to be the same as Bergold's spherical subunits which he said were discharged from the intimate membrane (Bergold, 1958). The intimate membrane is then exposed; it measures about 20 Å in thickness, and has a slightly different structure at either end. At very high magnification the contents of the intimate membrane give the appearance of a wide-spaced helix; these contents are discharged from either end of the intimate membrane and appear to uncoil as they flow out. This helix is considered to be in part nucleic acid (DNA) and differs markedly from Bergold's subunits.

The morphological detail of the virus rod extracted from the granulosis disease differs in a slight respect from the foregoing. The intimate membrane shows a close-packed helical structure, but whether this is formed by the membrane and its contents is not yet clear. It has not, however, been possible to resolve this helix on empty intimate membranes. Although the actual assembly of the parts forming a new rod has not yet been observed, the presence in both types of virus of a helical structure similar to that observed in the rod of TMV strongly suggests a similar method of assembly. Krieg (1961) has also made a study on the electron microscope of the virus rods from nuclear polyhedroses and considers that they show a helical structure. Based on his former observations of a central hole in the subunits he has proposed a model for the rod-shaped viruses of insects similar to that made by Franklin and Klug (1956) for TMV.

A2–7. METHODS OF SPREAD

In the nuclear and cytoplasmic polyhedroses and in the granuloses there are two main methods of spread of the causal viruses, i.e., by means of the intracellular inclusions and by transovarian spread.

There is no doubt that both types of polyhedra and the "capsules" or granules are ideal media for the dissemination of the virus. These inclusions are extremely stable and are easily carried around by wind or rain; moreover, the polyhedra retain the virus in a viable state for periods of several years. It is doubtful, however, if the "capsules" of the granuloses remain infective for long periods; at Cambridge the "capsules" of the granulosis of *Pieris brassicae* seemed to lose much of their infectivity if stored over winter in the refrigerator.

Ingestion of the polyhedra, or "capsules," by the larva seems essential for infection; mere contact of diseased and healthy larvae is not enough. The intracellular inclusions are spread around by wind and rain, and there may be additional dissemination through the agency of birds and parasitic insects.

The second natural means of spread, by hereditary transmission, is very important, and there is much evidence of its existence. The extreme frequency of latent virus infection is itself conclusive enough. So far most of the evidence concerning transovarial spread is restricted to the polyhedroses and granuloses; instances of the hereditary transmission of the non-inclusion viruses do not seem to have been recorded. There are many well-documented cases of transovarial dissemination, which was first suggested as occurring in the silkworm *Bombyx mori* by Conte (1907) and by Bolle (1908). Larvae of *Telea polyphemus* Cram. have been observed to die of a nuclear polyhedrosis within 48 hours of emergence from the egg (Smith and Wyckoff, 1951). Sometimes the larvae of a certain species may fail to emerge from the egg and subsequent examination reveals the presence of large numbers of polyhedra (Rivers, personal communication). The following is also relevant: during an experiment in Cambridge on the use of a nuclear polyhedrosis to control the larvae of the sawfly *Neodiprion sertifer* (Geoffroy) on pine trees, the virus was introduced into an area where it had not previously existed. At the end of the season some female sawflies were collected and brought back to the laboratory where they were allowed to oviposit under virus-free conditions. A high proportion of the larvae resulting from these eggs died of a nuclear polyhedrosis.

There is much other evidence of a similar nature, and it is now an established fact that transovarial transmission of the inclusion-body viruses does take place. In this connection it is interesting, and perhaps significant, to find a similar transovarial dissemination of certain plant viruses which are known to multiply in their leafhopper vectors.

As already mentioned there does not seem much knowledge about the hereditary transmission of the non-inclusion viruses but the following may be relevant. From a number of larvae of *Pieris brassicae* inoculated with TIV one imago emerged; this butterfly appeared normal but was somewhat undersized. On examination of various parts of this insect by ultrathin sections, a number of particles of TIV were found in the head lying behind the eyes (Fig. A2–4). It is not known whether this insect would have proved fertile or whether the virus would have been transmitted through the egg.

So far as artificial methods of infection are concerned, feeding larvae with contaminated food material is generally sufficient for the inclusion-body diseases. With the non-inclusion viruses, however, the most successful method is injection. The preparation of suitable needles for this purpose has been described by Maramorosch (1951) and by Martignoni (1955). Very good results, however, in the case of larger insects can be achieved by the use of the finest steel hypodermic needles, about 0.01 or 0.02 ml, being injected at a time. So far as the use of TIV is concerned, purity of the virus and absence of contaminating micro-organisms are important; the death rate from extraneous bacterial infection can be greatly reduced by the addition to the inoculum of 200 I.U. of penicillin and 200 I.U. of streptomycin per millilitre, respectively.

A2–8. LATENT VIRUS INFECTIONS

Latency of virus infection is a commonplace phenomenon in all types of organism from bacteria to man, and it is especially common in plants and insects. Anyone who has tried to breed insects, particularly Lepidoptera, through several generations will be aware of this.

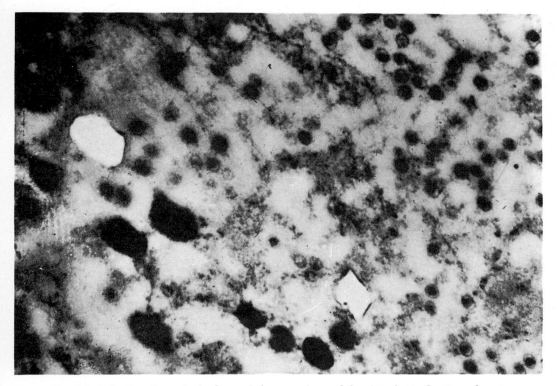

Fig. A2–4. Section through the base of the eye of an adult white butterfly *Pieris brassicae* infected with the *Tipula* iridescent virus; note the virus particles, the large particles are pigment spots. Magnification × 60,000.

It is not known for certain in what form or state the virus remains latent, whether in a pro-virus or fully formed condition. In the case of the inclusion-body diseases the virus is probably not occluded; those adult insects of the Lepidoptera in which polyhedra have been observed are usually in poor condition and seem unlikely to lay fertile eggs.

Latent virus infections can be stimulated into virulence by a number of factors, called "stressors" by Steinhaus (1958). These factors can be grouped under various headings such as temperature and humidity, overcrowding, unsuitable food, and feeding with certain chemicals. The writer has found that inoculation with a foreign virus may stimulate a latent virus infection; inoculation of a caterpillar with a foreign nuclear polyhedrosis does sometimes induce a cytoplasmic polyhedrosis. For example, an inoculation of this type into the larvae of

the winter moth *Operophtera brumata* Linn. and the larvae of *Bupalus piniarius* Linn. induced in each case the development of a cytoplasmic polyhedrosis (Smith and Rivers, 1956). Krieg (1957) states that the application of cytoplasmic polyhedra from *Dasychira pudibunda* Linn. (Lepidoptera) apparently stimulated into virulence a nuclear polyhedrosis in *Neodiprion sertifer* (Geoffroy), the European sawfly (Hymenoptera).

Two recent examples of the stimulation into virulence of a latent virus infection may be given here. In April, 1963, the writer obtained from a dealer in Houston, Texas, a dozen 3d instar larvae of the moth *Automeris io*. In Pittsburgh, however, the particular food plant on which the larvae had been feeding was not available and hawthorn was substituted. The larvae did not take kindly to this change of food and developed slowly. Out of the 12 larvae re-

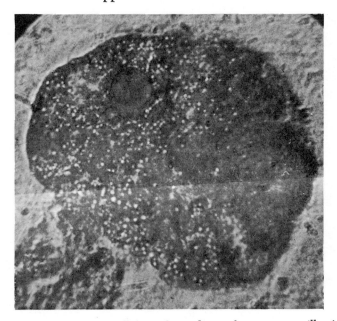

Fig. A2–5. Photomicrograph of a cell from the mid-gut of a tent caterpillar infected with a cytoplasmic polyhedrosis; note the intact nucleus and the polyhedra, which are unusually small, scattered throughout the cell cytoplasm. Magnification × 1500.

ceived only 1 survived to adult stage, the other 11 larvae all died of a cytoplasmic polyhedrosis (Figs. A2–1, A2–2).

In May, 1963, a colony of the common tent caterpillar was collected in the vicinity of Pittsburgh and colonized in the laboratory on a different food plant from that on which they were found and kept under rather confined conditions. Of more than 100 larvae only 6 reached the pupal stage, and of these only 3 adults emerged; all the others died of a cytoplasmic polyhedrosis (Fig. A2–5).

A2–9. TRANSMISSION BETWEEN DIFFERENT SPECIES AND ORDERS

For a number of years the opinion was strongly held by one or two insect virologists that these viruses are species-specific and cannot be cross-transmitted. In view, however, of the large body of evidence to the contrary this view is no longer tenable. A few instances of successful cross-transmission will suffice for the nuclear polyhedroses: Smith (1953) and Smith and Xeros (1952, 1953a,b) reported a number of cross-infection and back-infection tests with about 30 species of insects and obtained a number of positive results. Aizawa (1952) found the nuclear polyhedrosis virus of *Bombyx mori* to be transmissible to *Samia ricini* and back again to *B. mori*. Gershenson carried out successful cross-inoculation tests with 60 species of lepidopterous insects and 6 nuclear-polyhedrosis viruses. He based his conclusions on the assumption that the shape and average size of the polyhedra formed in an insect are characteristic of the virus inoculated. In other words, the virus determines the morphology of the polyhedra and not the host cell (Gershenson, 1955a,b, 1957). It must not be thought, however, that all viruses of nuclear polyhedroses are transmissible to any insect; at present it seems that certain insect species are resistant to infection with certain viruses of the nuclear polyhedrosis type from other insect species.

The viruses of the cytoplasmic polyhedroses seem to have an even wider host-range than those of the nuclear type. Here, however, the situation is slightly more uncertain because of the close similarity between many of the cytoplasmic polyhedrosis viruses, and the possibility of confusing cross-infection with a stimulated latent infection. One recent experiment may be quoted here. A number of larvae, about 50, of *Pieris rapae* were fed on June 25, 1963, with the cytoplasmic polyhedra previously mentioned as having developed in the larvae of *Automeris io*. On July 4 some of the larvae ceased feeding and showed a characteristic yellow tinge quite distinct from the normal green colour. Examination of these larvae showed the gut to be full of cytoplasmic polyhedra. Four days later 33 larvae had died of a cytoplasmic polyhedrosis. Of the 50 control larvae kept under similar conditions 2 died of a cytoplasmic polyhedrosis.

The situation in this experiment is similar to that in a previous experiment (Smith, 1963b) carried out with a number of lepidopterous larvae. In this case also a few control larvae died of a cytoplasmic polyhedrosis, but the number, again, was only a fraction of the deaths among larvae which had actually been inoculated. The fact that in all these experiments a few control larvae died of a cytoplasmic polyhedrosis indicates that the virus may be latent in many of the larvae. If, as seems probable, however, many of the cytoplasmic polyhedrosis viruses are closely similar, if not identical, then it is fair to assume that the 33 larvae in the experiment described above died of a genuine cross-transmission, and the death of a few of the control larvae with a similar disease does not affect the issue. The dividing line between stimulation of a latent cytoplasmic polyhedrosis and genuine infection with a foreign virus becomes indistinct, since the polyhedra from *Automeris io*, from the disease induced by inoculation of *P. rapae* with polyhedra from *A. io*, and from the spontaneous disease in *P. rapae*, are all apparently identical with a characteristic hexagonal outline. It is clear, however, that more work is needed on these cross-transmission experiments with the cytoplasmic polyhedrosis viruses before a definite answer can be given.

So far as cross-transmission with the granulosis viruses is concerned, Huger (1963) considers that there exists a remarkably high degree of host specificity. However, experiments in Cambridge (Smith and Rivers, 1956) showed that a granulosis virus was apparently inter-transmissible between three species of *Pieris—P. brassicae*, *P. rapae*, and *P. napi*. Here, again, the possibility of latent infections must be considered.

All the above experiments refer only to cross-infectivity among species; the first apparently successful transmission of polyhedrosis viruses between different orders seems to have been made by Sidor (1960) and Smith *et al.* (1959b). Carnivorous larvae *Chrysopa perla* Linn. and *Hemerobius stigma* Steven (Neuroptera) when fed upon pieces of larvae of *Porthetria dispar* Linn., which had died of a nuclear polyhedrosis, themselves died of a polyhedrosis. Some recent experiments on the same larvae, but using a cytoplasmic polyhedrosis virus for inoculum, seem to indicate that this type of virus is also transmissible to another insect order (Smith, 1963a).

Undoubtedly the most unequivocable evidence of cross-transmission to different orders and species is given by experiments with TIV. By the use of this virus all the anomalies consequent upon latent infection are avoided. The characteristic shape of the virus particle, the enormous quantities of virus produced, and, above all, the unmistakable iridescence of the infected insect all serve as markers and make identification certain.

Experiment has shown that TIV is inter-transmissible between various species of Diptera, Lepidoptera, and Coleoptera (Smith *et al.*, 1961).

A2–10. VIRUSES MULTIPLYING IN PLANTS AND INSECTS

How far are we justified in drawing a definite line between plant viruses, insect viruses, and viruses of the higher animals? It is true that plant viruses, at least all those so far purified, contain only RNA; but then RNA viruses occur in both insects and the higher animals.

Some of the small viruses affecting plants and animals are morphologically similar; for example, the protein coat (capsomeres) of the potato yellow dwarf virus has processes similar in appearance to those found in the myxoviruses (Black and Markham, unpublished). Furthermore, a leafhopper-transmitted plant virus which multiplies in its insect vector, the wound-tumor virus, shows a similarity in the number of its capsomeres to the group of animal viruses known as reoviruses. Moreover, a recent publication (Streissle and Maramorosch, 1963) suggests a serological relationship between the wound-tumor virus and one of the reoviruses in which the two viruses share a common antigen capable of fixing complement.

Several plant viruses which have leaf-hopper vectors are known to multiply in their insect vectors (Maramorosch, 1963). Indeed, the virus of rice dwarf shows a close resemblance to TIV in some morphological characters, having electron-dense central areas surrounded by less dense regions and an outer membrane. The tendency of the rice virus to orientate into microcrystals enables it to be identified and located within the tissues of infected leafhoppers (Fukushi et al., 1962).

Herold et al. (1960) have studied another leafhopper-transmitted virus affecting corn (maize). By examining sections of leaves in the electron microscope, they have observed rod-shaped virus particles in the cytoplasm around the nucleus. These particles are very regular in size and shape and have a highly differentiated structure with two limiting membranes and a dense, rod-shaped core in the center. The particles have dimensions of 242 mμ in length and 48 mμ in diameter, and they are considered to be very similar in appearance to the rod-shaped viruses of the nuclear polyhedroses of insects.

If it could be shown that insect vectors are themselves diseased or adversely affected by the plant viruses they transmit, then the boundary line between the plant and insect viruses becomes indistinct and doubtful. There is some evidence of this; vectors of peach yellow leaf-roll virus, a strain of Western X-disease, were found to live only half as long as virus-free individuals of the same species, Callodonus montanus (Jensen, 1959). The possibility that the shortened life was due to a toxic substance acquired from the virus-infected plants is largely discounted by the fact that, of the insects feeding on virus-diseased plants, only the active transmitters had the shortened life; non-transmitting individuals lived for the normal period.

Littau and Maramorosch (1956, 1960) describe cytological changes which occur in aster leafhoppers carrying the virus of aster yellows. It has been established that these changes occur in the nuclei of fatbody cells of male leafhoppers 18 to 28 days after acquiring the virus by feeding or injection. In viruliferous insects the nuclei tended to be stellate rather than rounded, and the cytoplasm was reticulate instead of homogeneous with man vacuoles.

There seems to be no valid reason for labelling a virus, which multiplies in both plants and insects, either a "plant" or an "insect" virus. It is merely one which is capable of attacking both types of organisms.

A glance at the wide array of different hosts which are parasitized by some viruses shows their extremely catholic tastes. There is the pig-earthworm-lungworm cycle of the swine influenza virus, poliovirus apparently multiplying in a budgerigar, the chicken sarcoma virus which produces tumors in Primates (Munroe and Windle, 1963), and the TIV which can multiply in practically any type of tissue in insects of different orders.

In view of this versatility it does not seem such an exceptional occurrence for a virus to multiply in both plants and insects. In the future it is highly probable that the artificial barriers of "plant" and "insect" viruses will be further broken down. When a stable system of virus classification is finally achieved we may find that an entirely different conception of virus relationships will be necessary.

* * *

This paper is publication Number 96 of the Department of Biophysics, University of Pittsburgh. Work was supported by U.S. Public Health Service Grant No. GM 10403.

Acknowledgments. The electron micrographs in Figs. A2–1 and A2–2 were made by Zagorka M. Trontl, in Fig. A2–3 by Ramsey Frist, and in Fig. A2–4 by the Virus Research Unit, Cambridge. Dr. Irwin Bendet took the photograph for Fig. A2–5.

A2–11. LITERATURE CITED

Aizawa, K. (1952). J. Sericult. Sci. Japan **21,** 170.

Bergold, G. H. (1947). Z. Naturforsch. **2b,** 122.

Bergold, G. H. (1948). Z. Naturforsch. **3b,** 338.

Bergold, G. H. (1958). In Handbuch der Virusforschung, 60. Springer, Vienna.

Bergold, G. H. (1963). In Insect Pathology: an Advanced Treatise. **1,** 413. Academic Press, N.Y.

Bergold, G. H., and Pister, L. (1948). Z. Naturforsch. **3b,** 406.

Bergold, G. H., and Wellington, E. F. (1954). J. Bacteriol. **67,** 210.

Bird, F. T. (1958). Can. J. Microbiol. **4,** 267.

Bird, F. T. (1959). J. Insect Pathol. **1,** 406.

Bolle, J. (1908). Z. Landwirtsch. Versuchsw. Deut-Oesterr. **11,** 279.

Boudreaux, H. B. (1959). J. Insect Pathol. **1,** 270.

Burnside, C. E. (1945). Am. Bee J. **85,** 354.

Conte, A. (1907). Compt. Rend. 36 Session Assoc. Franc. Avance. Sci. 662.

Franklin, R. E., and Klug, A. (1956). Biochim. et Biophys. Acta **19,** 403.

Fukushi, T., Shikata, E., and Kumura, I. (1962). Virology **18,** 192.

Gershenson, S. (1955a). Mikrobiologia **24,** 90.

Gershenson, S. (1955b). Doklady Akad. Nauk. S. S. S. R. **104,** 925.

Gershenson, S. (1957). Doklady Acad. Nauk. S. S. S. R. **113,** 1161.

Grace, T. D. C. (1958). Science **128,** 249.

Gratia, A., Brachet, J., and Jeener, R. (1945). Bull. Acad. Roy. Med. Belg. **10,** 72.

Herold, F., Bergold, G. H., and Weibel, J. (1960). Virology **12,** 335.

Hills, G. J., and Smith, K. M. (1959). J. Insect Pathol. **1,** 121.

Huger, A. (1961). J. Insect Pathol. **3,** 338.

Huger, A. (1963). In Insect Pathology: An Advanced Treatise. **1,** 531. Academic Press, New York.

Ishimori, J. (1934). Compt. Rend. Soc. Biol. **116,** 1169.

Jensen, D. D. (1959). Virology **8,** 164.

Komärek, J., and Breindle, V. (1924). Z. Angew. Entomol. **10,** 99.

Krieg, A. (1957). Arch. ges. Virusf. **7,** 212.

Krieg, A. (1961). Z. Naturforsch. **16b,** 115.

Krieg, A., and Huger, A. (1960). J. Insect Pathol. **2,** 274.

Littau, V. C., and Maramorosch, K. (1956). Virology **2,** 128.

Littau, V. C., and Maramorosch, K. (1960). Virology **10,** 483.

Lotmar, R. (1941). Mitt. Schweitz. Entomol. Ges. **18,** 372.

Maramorosch, Karl (1951). Nature **167,** 734.

Maramorosch, Karl (1963). Ann. Rev. Entomol. **8,** 369.

Martignoni, M. E. (1955). Science **122,** 764.

Munroe, J. S., and Windle, W. F. (1963). Science **140,** 1415.

Paillot, A. (1926). Compt. Rend. Acad. Sci. **182,** 180.

Paillot, A. (1934). Compt. Rend. Acad. Sci. **198,** 204.

Paillot, A. (1941). Ann. Epiphyt. **7,** 99.

Paillot, A., and Gratia, A. (1939). Arch. Ges. Virusforsch. **1,** 120.

Sidor, D. (1960). Virology **10,** 551.

Smith, J. D., and Wyatt, G. R. (1951). Biochem. J. **49,** 144.

Smith, K. M. (1953). Sci. Progress **163,** 411.

Smith, K. M. (1963a). Viruses, Nucleic Acids and Cancer. Univ. of Texas, Houston.

Smith, K. M. (1963b). In Insect Pathology: An Advanced Treatise. **1,** 457. Academic Press.

Smith, K. M., and Cressman, A. W. (1962). J. Insect Pathol. **4,** 229.

Smith, K. M., and Hills, G. J. (1962). Fifth Internat. Congr. Electr. Microscopy, Vol. 1, Academic Press, N.Y.

Smith, K. M., and Rivers, C. F. (1956). Parasitology **46,** 235.

Smith, K. M., and Wyckoff, R. W. G. (1950). Nature **166,** 861.

Smith, K. M., and Wyckoff, R. W. G. (1951). Research **4,** 148.

Smith, K. M., and Xeros, N. (1952). Nature **170,** 492.

Smith, K. M., Wyckoff, R. W. G., and Xeros, N. (1953). Parasitology **42,** 287.

Smith, K. M., and Xeros, N. (1953a). Parasitology **43,** 178.

Smith, K. M., and Xeros, N. (1953b). Sympos. Interactions Viruses and Cells. Rome 1953, 81.

Smith, K. M., Hills, G. J., Munger, F., and Gilmore, J. E. (1959a). Nature **184,** 70.

Smith, K. M., Hills, G. J., and Rivers, C. F. (1959b). J. Insect Pathol. **1,** 431.

Smith, K. M., Hills, G. J., and Rivers, C. F. (1961). Virology **13,** 233.

Steinhaus, E. A. (1947). Science **106,** 323.

Steinhaus, E. A. (1951). Hilgardia **20,** 629.

Steinhaus, E. A. (1958). Proc. Intern. Congr. Entomol., Montreal, 1956 **4,** 725.

Steinhaus, E. A. (1959). J. Insect Pathol. 1, 435.

Steinhaus, E. A., and Thompson, C. G. (1949). Science 110, 276.

Streissle, G., and Maramorosch, K. (1963). Science 140, 996.

Surany, P. (1960). S. Pacific Comm. Tech. Paper No. 128, 62.

Thomas, R. S. (1961). Virology 14, 240.

Wasser, H. B. (1952). J. Bacteriol. 64, 787.

Wellington, E. F. (1951). Biochim. et Biophys. Acta 7, 238.

Wellington, E. F. (1954). Biochem. J. 57, 334.

White, G. F. (1917). U.S. Dept. Agr. Bull. 431.

Williams, R. C., and Smith, K. M. (1957). Nature 179, 119.

Williams, R. C., and Smith, K. M. (1958). Biochim. et Biophys. Acta 28, 464.

Wyatt, G. R. (1952a). J. Gen. Physiol. 36, 201.

Wyatt, G. R. (1952b). Exptl. Cell Research, Suppl. 2. 201.

Xeros, N. (1962). Biochim. et Biophys. Acta 55, 176.

Yamazaki, H. (1960). Shinano Mainichi Newspaper. 1 p.

Yamazaki, H., Sakai, E., Shimodaira, M., and Yamada, T. (1960). Bull. Nagano Ken. Sericult. Expt. Sta. 61.

ROBERT A. MANAKER

An introduction to the tumor viruses

A3–1. INTRODUCTION

THE FIRST observations of induction of neoplasia in animals treated with cell-free material extracted from diseased tissue were made on chickens more than 50 years ago. The flurry of activity which followed these observations was confined to a few laboratories, and during succeeding years this subsided into a relatively slow-paced experimental effort. Little more than a decade ago, the demonstration of virus-induced mouse leukemia, coupled with advances in tissue culture techniques, ushered in a flood of new developments in tumor virus research. An adequate account of the contributions of the individuals who participated in building the foundation for the present advances is not possible in this presentation. The purpose of this review is to present a general introduction to present-day tumor virus research.

A tumor, or neoplasm, is an abnormal mass of new tissue which persists and grows independently of its surrounding structures and which has no physiologic function (Herbut, 1959). A neoplasm may be benign, showing no tendency to spread, or metastasize. Such a tumor may undergo transformation to malignancy (Foulds, 1961). The malignant tumor, or cancer, possesses the ability to infiltrate and destroy adjoining normal tissue. It may also metastasize by way of the blood and lymph vessels to other parts of the body where new proliferative foci of neoplastic cells are established. The effect of viruses on cells of an infected host range from outright destruction through a graded series of proliferative reactions from simple hyperplasia to autonomous neoplasia. Some virus-induced animal tumors may become malignant and metastasize as do cancers in man. The transformation by virus of normal cells to neoplastic cells is well established. The extent to which viruses are directly implicated in the progression of initially relatively benign lesions to malignant cancers is one of the most challenging problems in cancer research today.

A3–2. THE AVIAN-TUMOR VIRUSES

A. FOWL LEUCOSIS

The avian-tumor group of viruses is associated with tumor induction in tissues of mesenchymal origin. Its members are closely related and have the distinction of being the first viruses with oncogenic potential to be recognized. Leukemia, one of the diseases of chickens now known to be caused by virus, was formerly thought to be a bacterial disease. Moore (1897) reported that he had isolated *Bacterium sanguinarium* from the blood of leukemic fowls and he regarded this organism as the etiological agent of the disease. Butterfield

(1905) indicated that Moore had observed a leukocytosis associated with the bacillary infection and not true leukemia. A description of leukemia in chickens was given by Warthin (1907), who concluded that both aleukemic and leukemic forms of lymphyocytoma were frequent in fowls, analogous in all respects to the similar conditions existing in man. The two conditions appeared to be different stages of the same process. He felt that the nature of these conditions would lead to their interpretation as malignant neoplasms, and that the problem of leukemia was identical with malignant neoplasms in general. All of his attempts to discover an etiological agent in avian leukemia failed, and his plans for transplantation miscarried.

The first successful transplantation of chicken leukemia was reported by Ellermann and Bang (1908). The neoplastic cells were carried through three successive transplant generations by intravenous inoculation into healthy birds of emulsions of bone marrow, spleen, and liver of leukemic donors. The results indicated that the leukemic and aleukemic blood pictures were indicative of the same disease. The word *leukemia* had been proposed by Virchow to delineate a series of diseases recognizable by the characteristic blood changes. Since it was obvious to Ellermann and Bang that the "leukemia" property is only a symptom, the term *leukosis* was suggested to include both the leukemic and the aleukemic forms.

Ellermann and Bang performed two filtration experiments with supernatant fluids from centrifuged extracts of an emulsion of the organs of a leukemic chicken. In the first experiment, the supernatant was filtered through 2 layers of filter paper. Of course, the filtrate could not be considered cell-free. One of 3 chickens inoculated with this filtrate developed leukemia. In a second experiment, the supernatant was filtered through an infusorial earth candle. Two of 5 chickens that were inoculated with the clear filtrate came down with typical leukemia. In a succeeding report (Ellermann and Bang, 1909) these investigators indicated that transplantation of leukemic cells to healthy fowls was successful in about 40% of their trials. Leukemia-induc-

ing activity was also found in cell-free preparations made from all affected organs: bone marrow, liver, spleen, and blood. Such preparations were quite labile, for infectivity was lost after a few days. Regressions were observed in some chickens in which leukemia had been induced. Guinea hens, pigeons, turkeys, and rabbits were resistant to infection. Ellermann and Bang considered avian leukemia to be an infectious disease.

On the heels of the successes with avian leukemia came an attempt to transmit human leukemia to two monkeys (Hirschfeld and Jacoby, 1909). Hirschfeld and Jacoby indicated that a better choice for their effort might have been anthropoid apes, but these were unavailable. Their experimental cynomolgus monkeys died before sufficient time for successful transmission had elapsed. An attempt was also made to pass human leukemias to chickens, apparently without success. Their transmission experiments with a spontaneous leukemia of fowl failed (Hirschfeld and Jacoby, 1910). A leukemic chicken was therefore obtained from Ellermann, and although successful transplants were made with neoplastic tissue from this bird, success was not obtained with Berkefeld filtrates.

The contributions of Ellermann and Bang were not accepted without contest. The leukemia induced in healthy chickens with materials harvested from healthy donors was considered by some to be no more than a leukocytosis (Burckhardt, 1912; Schridde, 1909). Hirschfeld and Jacoby (1912) as well as Ellermann (1914) replied with data supporting their contentions, and shortly thereafter Schmeisser (1915) confirmed the transmission by organic emulsions of avian leukemia in a stock of fowls unrelated to those of previous investigators, who had used successfully only Ellermann's stock.

Subsequent investigations demonstrated that avian leukosis, also designated the "avian leukosis complex" (Jungherr *et al.,* 1941), is a group of diseases with particular pathological characteristics. The most commonly occurring of the specific diseases, visceral lymphomatosis or "big liver disease," is characterized by infiltration of primitive lymphoid cells into the liver and other viscera of the chicken. Other specific diseases are neurolymphomatosis and ocular lymphomatosis, characterized by infiltration of lymphoid cells into the nerve trunks and into the iris of the eye, respectively. Another disease that may occur in combination with any of these forms of lymphomatosis is osteopetrosis, which involves the periosteum and enodosteum and results in an overgrowth of bone. The specific disease conditions described may occur separately or in combination with each other (Burmester, 1952). Abnormal circulating cellular elements are rarely seen in lymphomatosis. In the leukemias, on the other hand, primitive myeloid cells reach the peripheral circulation in myeloblastosis (Furth, 1931a) and primitive red cells in erythroblastosis (Furth, 1931b).

The virus associated with myeloblastosis has a diameter ranging from 80 to 120 mμ. It may reach levels as high as 2×10^{12} particles per ml of plasma in some infected birds, which represents about 1.5 mg of hydrated virus per ml (Beard, 1957a). Line 15 white Leghorns bred for susceptibility to lymphomatosis are also of relatively low resistance to the leukemia viruses. However, there is extremely broad variation in individual susceptibility. In these birds the ID_{50} or median effective dose of myeloblastosis virus is about 26×10^6 particles, and 145×10^9 particles are required for 95% positive infections. Three-day-old chicks are the most susceptible to myeloblastosis virus; older birds become more resistant with age. Primitive cells appear in the circulating blood as early as 9 days post-inoculation, and the average time to death with leukemia is 17 days post-inoculation. The myeloblastosis virus is distinguished from the erythroblastosis and the lymphomatosis viruses by its adenosine triphosphatase activity.

The erythroblastosis virus has a diameter of roughly 100 mμ and is present in plasma in lesser amounts than is myeloblastosis virus. Levels up to 10^{10} particles per ml of plasma have been observed. This virus also is more virulent than myeloblastosis virus, since 2 to 3 logs less virus is required to induce disease at a given incidence level. Older birds appear more susceptible than

young chickens, and the average time to death with large doses is only 9 days post-infection.

The plasma content of lymphomatosis virus is variable. In one plasma 10^{11} particles per ml were observed, but, in most, no significantly identifiable particles could be detected. Birds infected with lymphomatosis virus have a relatively long survival time, about 100 days; younger birds appear more susceptible (Beard, 1957a).

Of the infectious neoplasms of chickens, visceral lymphomatosis is the only one that is highly contagious. Infected chickens need not develop lymphomatosis, but a high percentage of such carrier birds shed virus in their saliva, eggs, and feces. Thus such birds not only contaminate their environment and water supply, but can pass virus to their progeny through the egg. Dams with circulating antibody do passively convey a certain measure of protection to their progeny. Naturally infected chicks pass virus to their uninfected fellows in the incubator and brooder (Burmester, 1957).

In the course of his studies with the RPL 12 strain of lymphomatosis virus, Burmester and his co-workers observed 4 neoplastic conditions in infected fowls. When high doses of the virus were given to young chicks, erythroblastosis was induced within about 4 months. In older birds, or with smaller doses of virus in young birds, visceral lymphomatosis developed 4 months or more post-infection. Both diseases are highly malignant. The other 2 conditions observed were osteopetrosis and hemangiomatosis, a benign tumor of the blood vessels. Other strains of lymphomatosis virus gathered from various sources also were found to cause erythroblastosis under appropriate host or dosage conditions. Fibrosarcomas and myxosarcomas developed in some of the test chickens, but the incidence of myelocytomas, neurolymphomatosis, ocular lymphomatosis, and granuloblastosis was low (Gross *et al.*, 1959; Burmester *et al.*, 1959, 1960).

B. Avian Sarcoma Viruses

Two years after Ellermann and Bang published their first results with avian leukosis, Rous (1910) reported the successful propagation of an avian sarcoma through 4 serial transplant generations, and the following year (Rous, 1911) described tumor induction in healthy birds by cell-free extracts of this tumor. In Japan, Fujinami and Inamoto (1911) reported similar success with another agent. Rous could not transmit the sarcoma to pigeons, ducks, rats, mice, guinea pigs, or rabbits. Young chickens were particularly susceptible. Early transmission was successful only to birds closely related to the chicken in which the tumor arose, but with passage the sarcoma gained the power to grow in chickens of other breeds. A few regressions were noted in healthy fowl, which then proved to be resistant to reinoculation. Metastases were found to take place by way of the blood, usually to the lungs, although tumor nodules were found less frequently in other organs, notably the heart and spleen.

Further experiments with the Rous sarcoma showed dried or glycerinated tissue as well as tumor filtrates to be active in tumor induction. The tumor could be transplanted into the embryonated chicken egg provided it was in contact with mesodermal tissues. Here it grew without the cellular reaction noted as a sign of resistance in the adult. It also grew in the membranes of pigeon or duck embryos (Murphy and Rous, 1912). When cultured *in vitro,* tumor fragments grew almost explosively for a short time with much acid production, but usually failed to grow when reimplanted into fresh medium (Rous, 1913). Variations in structure and behavior of the tumor carried by transplantation in chickens were noted (Rous and Murphy, 1913), and fatal hemorrhages often arose from its substance. In some rapidly-growing tumors, the cells tended to be spherical rather than of spindle-celled form. Giant cells containing from 1 to 40 nuclei were sometimes seen. Some of them exhibited nuclear budding. They were entirely different from the foreign body type of giant cell and lay scattered among the neoplastic spindle cells from which they developed.

Rous and his co-workers obtained from a poultry supply house other transplantable tumors, some of which were filterable. Two tumors differed from chicken tumor No. 1.

One, tumor No. 7, produced cartilage and bone; the other, tumor No. 18, produced a sarcoma with an intracanalicular pattern of blood sinuses (Tytler, 1913; Rous and Lange, 1913). Each of the tumor-inducing agents contained in filtrates of the three tumors gave rise only to growths of the precise kind from which it had been derived (Rous and Murphy, 1914a). At the time this appeared to imply the existence of a myriad of filterable agents, each associated with a particular neoplasm. However, recent findings indicate that this is not true; different neoplasms may be induced by one virus.

Years later in England, Begg (1927, 1929) isolated filterable agents from a fibrosarcoma and an endothelioma (Mill Hill No. 1 and Mill Hill No. 2) of the fowl. Carr and Campbell (1958) investigated spontaneous mucoid chicken tumors similar in morphology to that of Rous chicken tumor No. 1 from which they isolated three tumor-inducing viruses. One, P.R.C. III, is serologically related to, but not identical with, the agent of chicken tumor I, now generally referred to as Rous sarcoma virus (RSV). The other agents, P.R.C. II and P.R.C. IV, are unrelated either to III and Rous virus or to each other. It is evident that different viruses may be associated with avian sarcomata of similar morphology.

Rous felt that the tumor-inducing agent in his chicken tumor I extracts was a filter-passing organism. Others considered the tumors to be induced by an inanimate substance secreted by tumor cells which was capable of causing the malignant transformation of healthy cells. To test the later hypothesis, Murphy and Landsteiner painted the skin of chickens with tar to engender a sarcoma by nonviral means. Two such tumors were obtained. If such a growth contained a filterable agent capable of transmitting the tumor, this would favor the concept of an inanimate principle responsible for neoplasms. The attempts to transmit one of these tumors, No. 9, by filtrates and desiccates were unsuccessful, even after 3 years in transplant passage (Murphy and Landsteiner, 1925; Strum and Murphy, 1928). After tar sarcoma No. 10 had been in transplant passage for about 10 years, Claude demonstrated the presence of a tumor-inducing agent in extracts that had gone undetected because inhibitors masked its activity (Claude, 1937). When the agent was separated from the original filtrate by centrifugation and resuspended in Tyrode's solution, the suspensions were oncogenic in chickens. If some of the supernatant fluid containing the inhibitor were mixed with such active sedimented virus, the mixture produced no tumors. The agent may have been picked up as a passenger during the long period that the tumor was passaged in chickens or it may have been activated by the original tar treatment. Since the agent could be separated from inhibitor by physical means, it had undergone no modification, or at least the reaction between agent and inhibitor was easily reversible.

Inhibitors for the Rous agent were also detected in Rous tumor filtrates (Sittenfield et al., 1931). Sittenfield and co-workers found the inhibitory activity to be confined to the globulin fraction precipitated with ammonium sulfate. Low inhibitory activity was also detected in normal chicken sera. These investigators felt that under these conditions, metastasis probably depends upon migration of live cells, because the agent is probably neutralized by protective substances in the plasma. Murphy and Strum (1932a,b) detected an inhibiting factor in extracts of dried Rous tumor that could be removed by adsorption onto aluminum hydroxide at pH 7.2. It could be released in effective quantities from this combination by basic sodium phosphate solution at pH 9.0. The inhibitor was destroyed when heated over 65°C.

Early in his work with chicken tumor No. 1, Rous recognized that chickens in which an early tumor had regressed were resistant to the tumor-inducing virus as well as to implants of tumor cells (Rous and Murphy, 1914b). Rous et al. (1919) were unsuccessful in attempts to produce an antiserum in rabbits active against the tumor agent, but specific activity against it was demonstrated in immune serum from geese. Gye and Purdy (1931) produced effective antisera in the duck and the goat. Evidence of immunological relationships between the agent of Mill Hill No. 1 fibrosarcoma and the agents of Mill Hill No. 2 endothelioma as well as the Rous No. 1 sarcoma were noted by Andrewes (1931). He found the interpretation of his results to be difficult due to variations both in potency of tumor filtrates and in responses of different birds. A good source of neutralizing antiserum to the Rous No. 1 agent is a chicken which has recovered from induced Rous tumors. Carr (1944) found high serum titers against Rous agent in such birds tested 1–2 years after tumor regression.

Initially, the agent of Rous tumor No. 1 had been considered to be quite specific for the chicken. Duran-Reynals (1942), however, working with the agent some 30 years after its initial isolation, found that 20% of a group of ducklings developed lesions when they had been inoculated intravenously with large doses of sarcoma extract within 24 hours post-hatching. There was detectable hourly increase of resistance to infection. Early lesions that developed in the ducklings within 30 days were sarcomas much like the original Rous tumor. Extracts of these tumors were ineffective in ducks but reproduced the usual disease in chicks and chickens. Late growths that were found in ducks killed several months after injection consisted of 3 sarcomas and a lymphoblastoma in various locations. Extracts of these sarcomas were not effective in chickens, but induced a generalized disease in ducks, one feature of which was the induction of periosteal sarcomas with little or no formation of new bone. In his experiments, Duran-Reynals obtained 6 strains of duck tumor. When he inoculated young chicks with virus from 2 of the duck tumors he again observed early and late disease. The early disease consisted of sarcomas and other tumors like those seen in the duck disease. These tumors could be transmitted by cells through only a few generations of chicks while similar injection into ducks reproduced the original disease of that host. Late lesions that arose in chicks several months after inoculation consisted of leukoses and osteopetrosis. These conditions could not be propagated indefinitely in succeeding generations of chicks. Young turkeys and guinea fowls as well as a few adult pheasants were also susceptible to infection with the agent of chicken tumor No. 1. Differences in the tumors induced in these hosts in comparison with tumors usually produced in the chicken were noted, and evidence of virus variation after passage in these hosts was observed when virus from them was used to induce tumors in chickens (Duran-Reynals, 1943). The pigeon had previously shown resistance to infection with the chicken-grown virus. However, cells from some duck tumors grew to form tumors in adult pigeons (Duran-Reynals, 1947) and a duck tumor filtrate was effective in about 50% of the pigeons inoculated (Borges and Duran-Reynals, 1952). The virus appeared to be "masked" in the pigeon tumors because extracts were not effective when injected into other pigeons, chicks, or ducklings. However, the presence of virus in the tumors could be demonstrated by transplantation of the pigeon tumors into chicks or ducklings. Extracts of the resulting tumor growths showed virus activity. One may conclude that the agent of chicken tumor No. 1 had increased in virulence and decreased in specificity over the years, and was now capable of inducing tumors in a variety of avian hosts. Not only did tumors induced in other hosts differ from those usually arising in the chicken, but variations in virus behavior in chickens were observed after its passage through the alien hosts. Moreover, it is clear that multiplication of virus might vary among species, for the virus was not easily demonstrated in the extracts prepared from pigeons despite the fact that tumors were induced.

Nonneoplastic hemorrhagic lesions were observed in chicken embryos which were inoculated either intravenously or intracoelomically with the agent of Rous tumor No. 1. Only 2 of 64 embryos that developed hemorrhagic lesions also developed tumors. The hemorrhagic lesions could be induced in other embryos by means of extracts, but in chicks and pullets such extracts induced tumors of the usual type (Milford and Duran-Reynals, 1943). Typical hemorrhagic disease and hepatic lesions were observed during serial intracerebral passage of Rous

virus in chicks by Groupé et al. (1957b). Further study showed that both hemorrhagic disease and hepatic lesions resulted from inoculation of a high dose of virus, irrespective of the origin of the virus. Carr (1962) did not believe that the hemorrhagic lesions observed in infected birds were due to necrotizing action of virus on normal or rapidly proliferating capillary endothelium. Nests of lymphoid or myeloid cells are always present in the normal fowl, which lacks a lymphatic system. The hemorrhagic disease was found to be invariably associated with an area of lymphoid or myeloid cells. These areas are probably concerned with extramedullary hematopoeisis, and Carr hypothesized that sudden stimulation of multiplication of the cells which may then be suddenly shed into the blood stream could weaken the single layer of endothelium which usually separates them from the blood. An inflow of blood would result, which is not usual in normal hematopoeisis.

The long-term propagation in vitro of Rous tumor No. 1 without the addition of normal tissue from time to time, has never been achieved. Carrel could maintain cultures of normal chicken embryo fibroblasts in plasma clots for 75–80 days. He observed that explants of the chicken sarcoma frequently died after a few days (Carrel, 1912). The plasma liquified and the tissue degenerated. One small fragment was kept viable for 46 days, after which the growth became small and death occurred without any apparent cause. In his later work with the Rous sarcoma, Carrel (1924, 1925) became convinced that monocytes grown in vitro and infected with the tumor agent secreted the agent, assumed the appearance of fibroblasts, and died prematurely. Carrel was of the opinion that the monocyte, not the fibroblast, was the malignant cell. He noted that Rous virus kept its full activity in the fluid of leucocyte cultures over a period of 13 days. The virus promptly disappeared from the fluid of his fibroblast cultures, but was present for several weeks in the cells themselves. The fibroblasts used for these experiments had been under cultivation for about 13 years (Carrel, 1926). Ludford (1937), among others, disagreed with Carrel. He found it possible to infect fibroblasts in culture with both the Fujinami and the Rous viruses, but not the cells in cultures of buffy coat. An extensive study by Sanford et al. (1952) established that the chicken fibroblast and not the monocyte is the tissue cell susceptible to Rous virus. A detailed description of the morphology of the sarcoma cells in vitro was given by Doljanski and Tenenbaum (1942) and Tenenbaum and Doljanski (1943). Lo et al. (1955) reported that degenerative changes occurred in cultures 1–2 weeks after normal adult chicken fibroblasts had been infected with virus. Manaker and Groupé (1956) developed a method which yielded discrete foci of altered cells in virus-infected monolayer cultures of normal chicken embryo fibroblasts.

The lack of reliable quantitative techniques and of stable and highly virulent virus preparations were major obstacles to investigations with the Rous virus until relatively recent years. Keogh (1938) showed that virus dilutions would induce discrete lesions on the ectodermal layer of the chorioallantoic membrane of the chicken embryo. Not all eggs responded, but when lesions arose, they could be correlated with the dose of virus inoculated. Improvements in method were made by a number of investigators (Rubin, 1955; Groupé et al., 1957a). Prince (1958a) presented evidence that different chicken strains vary widely both in the proportion of embryos that show membrane reactions to Rous virus, and in the uniformity of response of those embryos that do react. In one highly susceptible line, pock counts were found to be normally distributed and linearly related to dose. The resistance of the embryos to infection was demonstrated to be a genetic trait, not related to the distribution of neutralizing substances in maternal sera, yolks, or chorioallantoic membranes (Prince, 1958b). The number of hemorrhagic lesions in chicken embryos has also been demonstrated to be a suitable criterion for quantitation of Rous virus (Lo and Bang, 1955; Borsos and Bang, 1957).

Virus assays may be carried out in posthatched chickens either on the basis of tumor induction or on the basis of death of

host. Carr and Harris (1951) determined the highest dilution of virus which would produce a tumor in young chicks. This yielded an estimate of the "minimal infectious dose" for a given virus preparation. Bryan et al. (1954), plagued by the variation in titer of thawed specimens of a given virus pool, discovered that citrate buffers stabilized the Rous agent. Aliquots of a virus preparation frozen in the citrate diluent yielded reproducible titers when thawed and assayed. Bryan (1955, 1956) reviewed the problems related to virus assay and presented typical data and principles of their analysis for response in chickens inoculated with Rous virus in one subcutaneous site. Taking advantage of the fact that the chicken tumor agent propagates in the brain tissue of newly hatched chicks and results in death, Groupé et al. (1956) developed methods of bioassay based on time to death following intracerebral inoculation. The reciprocal of time-to-death was found to be linearly related to the logarithm of the dose of Rous virus injected. This criterion is not as sensitive as tumor formation in detecting very small amounts of virus, but quantitative assays of relative potency based on time-to-death following intracerebral inoculation were as efficient as those based on the tumor response.

A rough correlation was found between the number of virus particles seen by electron microscopy in thin sections of tumors induced with high and low doses of Rous virus and the potency of extracts of the tumors (Haguenau et al., 1958). They counted more virus in tumors initiated with high doses of virus than in those induced with low doses. Parallel assays showed those extracts obtained from the high-dose tumors to be more potent tumor inducers than similar preparations from the low-dose material. The results indicated that the particles observed either represent, or are quantitatively related to, the agent responsible for the induction of the Rous chicken sarcoma. The particles seen were ovoid and possessed outer and inner membranes surrounding a dense central core averaging 350 Å in diameter. The total diameter of the particles averaged 750 Å.

The technique described by Manaker

and Groupé (1956) for demonstration of focal transformation of cells by Rous virus on chicken embryo cell monolayers was expanded by Temin and Rubin (1958), who introduced an agar overlay to retard secondary infection. When diluted virus was used to infect cultures the counts of foci of transformed cells were correlated with the dose of virus over a range of 2–3 log dilutions. The chick fibroblast altered by Rous virus was transformed into a morphologically new and stable cell type with the same chromosome complement as ordinary chicken embryo cells. If cells of chicken embryo cultures are infected with high concentrations of virus and then transferred to normal cultures, one would expect most of the cells to show evidence of transformation. However, only 10% of the cells produced typical foci. With a cloned cell population, once again 90% of the cells were resistant. Temin and Rubin concluded that the physiological state of the cell determined its susceptibility to infection. Subsequent investigation (Rubin, 1960a) showed that these results were inaccurate. It was found that cells plated for focus formation within a few hours after infection have a low probability for initiating a focus. If the interval between infection and plating is lengthened to 1 or more days, there is a greater chance that the infected cells will either produce virus during a critical period after plating or will multiply to produce daughter cells with a characteristic morphology.

Fetal calf serum was found to contain nondialyzable, heat-labile substances active in focus suppression (Rubin, 1960b). Ordinary calf serum present in more than 10% concentration was also inhibitory. Suppression of morphological transformation was not accompanied by a decrease in the number of infected cells nor by a change in the rate of virus production. Prince (1962) noted that the presence of tryptose phosphate broth markedly favored the production of morphological transformation.

The morphology of the transformed cell is determined by both the virus and the cell. Temin (1960) found the same virus line produced different effects on different kinds of fibroblasts. He also succeeded in isolating 2 strains of virus from the standard virus material obtained from Bryan. One virus line produced spindle-celled foci on cloned fibroblasts and was termed "morph[f]." A second line, termed "morph[r]," produced round-celled foci on similar cultures of fibroblasts. Ectodermal cells in cultures of chicken iris epithelium also produced spindle-form cells growing into areas between epithelial islands when infected with virus "morph[f]" or round-celled foci when infected with the "morph[r]" line (Ephrussi and Temin, 1960). The type change induced is thus a genetic character of the virus line. A cell releasing virus of 1 line could be superinfected with virus of the other line. The virus released by superinfected cells can be of the original type only, of the superinfecting types only, or of both the original and the superinfecting types. Ten generations after superinfection, single cells could continue to release 2 types of virus. In cells which release both types of virus, the virus that controls cell morphology can be either the original or the superinfecting line (Temin, 1961).

Febvre et al. (1963) reported a cytolytic effect when chicken embryo cells infected with their strain of Rous virus were incubated at 40°C. Foci of classical cell transformation were obtained when similarly infected cultures were incubated at 37°C. The "plaques" produced at elevated temperature varied as a function of the relative concentration of the virus, indicating that this property could be utilized for titration.

The kinetics of the growth of Rous virus were studied in the chorioallantoic membrane by Harris (1954) and by Prince (1958c) and in the chick brain by Groupé and Rauscher (1957). Virus disappears at a rapid rate following inoculation in each of these systems. Multiplication is detected in the chorioallantoic membrane in 15–16 hours, provided the infecting dose is large. The period of latency is extended when smaller doses are given. In chick brain, logarithmic increase is detected by the 4th-day post-infection, and maximum titers are achieved in moribund birds at about 10 days. In experiments made by Vigier and Goldé (1959), cultures of chicken embryo cells were exposed to Rous virus for 45 minutes. Only a small fraction of virus was adsorbed, and only a small fraction of the cells became virus producers. With a small inoculum, an eclipse phase of 2 days was observed. Plating showed that only 1–10% of the cells produced an infective center. On subculture, both the virus titer of culture fluids and the number of infective centers increased and eventually most cells appeared to produce virus. About 10–30 pock-forming units (p.f.u.) were produced per cell per day. Virus appeared to be released from cells as soon as it formed. A similar kinetic study made by Temin and Rubin (1959) yielded an eclipse phase of only 12 hours. A final rate of release of 1 focus-forming unit (FFU) per cell per 5–10 hours was reached about 40 hours post-infection. Low temperatures of incubation inhibit virus production. Rabin et al. (1963) tried, unsuccessfully, to obtain virus-free tumors by this means.

Fluorescein-labeled anti-Rous sarcoma virus serums applied to frozen sections of tumor or to Rous virus foci in vitro showed intracytoplasmic virus-specific antigen (Noyes, 1960) as well as an occasional intranuclear fluorescent body (Malmgren et al., 1960; Mellors, 1960). The technique was applied by Vogt and Rubin (1961) to study the localization of viral antigen during successive stages of infection. When a large infecting dose of virus was used, specific viral antigen was detected in 2 days along the borders of occasional cells. The technique was not as sensitive as the infectivity tests of Temin and Rubin (1959), which showed new viral antigen in 12 hours in such cultures. Three days after infection, virus was located extracellularly at the cell membrane as well as in the cytoplasm. With the morphological transformation of the infected cell, the antigen detached itself from the cell wall, and some remained in a matrix-like substance around the cell. Many of the cells also began to synthesize large amounts of intracytoplasmic viral antigen. Greater sensitivity was attained when living cultured cells were treated with fluorescent antibody because antigen associated with the cell membrane could be visualized without the nonspecific background fluorescence of the cytoplasm. This allowed reliable detection of viral antigen at 24 hours after infection (Vogt and Rubin, 1962).

Haguenau and Beard (1962) have reviewed the biology and ultrastructure of the Rous virus-infected cell. The virus has never been found inside the ground cytoplasm; it is usually localized at the surface of the cell. Clusters of small (44 mμ) particles have been found in the ground cytoplasm of 13% of cells of Rous tumors and also in infected cultures. They are not found in other tumors, but their relation to Rous virus has not definitely been established. "Gray bodies" similar to those seen in tissue cultured myeloid cells infected with avian myeloblastosis virus have also been observed in the cytoplasm of Rous virus infected cells cultured in vitro. The phenomenon of the nuclear fluorescent bodies is too rare to be detected in ultrathin sections. Heine et al. (1962) described Rous virus release from the cell by budding. This is the first observation on the mode of elaboration of this virus to be made.

The problem of Rous virus purification was reviewed by Bryan and Moloney (1957). Difficulty centered about small yields of labile virus in admixture with large amounts of cellular constituents. By selective serial passage in chickens, Bryan (1959) increased the titer of his partially purified standard virus preparations thirty-fold. The application of new purification techniques permits further advances in the chemical and physical characterization of the agent. Bather (1957) with partially purified preparations of Rous virus found the purine-bound sugar in lipid-free nucleic acid extracts to be ribose; no deoxyribose was detected. Crawford purified the agent in rubidium chloride density gradients. These preparations contained particles with densities from 1.16 to 1.19. He could find no evidence that his stock consisted of several strains of virus, each with a different genetically-controlled density. The heterogeneity in density was thought to be due to variation in the lipid composition of the outer membrane of the virus particle (Crawford, 1960). Electron microscopic examination showed there were 750 physical particles per infectious unit for tissue culture fluid and 1200 for purified virus preparations, indicating some inactivation in the rubidium chloride density-gradient medium. Particles contained an average of 9.5×10^6 molecular weight units of RNA (Crawford and Crawford, 1961).

In the course of a study on the chemical changes occurring in cultured Rous virus-infected chicken embryo fibroblasts, Goldé (1962) noted that infected cells 2 days after infection grew more slowly than noninfected cells. It appeared that infected as well as noninfected cells exhibited contact inhibition. The quantity of DNA in infected cells remained the same as that in uninfected cultures throughout her experiment. RNA, acid-soluble nucleotides, and protein increased in infected cells in comparison with control cells after the 2d to the 4th day post-infection. 5-fluorodeoxyuridine (FUDR), an inhibitor of thymidylate and, therefore, of DNA synthesis did not interfere with the transformation of chicken embryo cells by Rous virus, nor with the growth of the virus. This is to be expected since this is an RNA virus (Rich *et al.*, 1962). Rous virus production was inhibited by actinomycin D at a concentration of 1.0 μg per ml of medium. This concentration also inhibited RNA synthesis in both normal and infected cells (Bather, 1963). Like other RNA viruses, the Rous virus requires that RNA synthetic pathways remain unaffected.

In the course of his studies on the quantitative aspects of Rous virus infection in chickens, Bryan (1955) found that the yield of virus from tumors induced by strong doses of the agent approached a maximal concentration; but at lower initiating dose levels, the amount of virus extracted from induced tumors was highly correlated with dose. Little or no virus could be recovered from some tumors induced by virus inoculums containing 1 ED_{50} (50% effective dose) or less. Calnan *et al.* (1957) attempted to develop a virus-free Rous tumor by selective transplant passage of slowly-growing tumors of a "low-dose" tumor line but were unsuccessful. The tumor cell has never been dissociated from the virus, and we may conclude that its presence is probably mandatory for maintenance of the transformed cell. The infection of new cells by virus released from infected cells is involved in the progressive development of the Rous tumor. The virus, not tumor cells, has been shown to provoke so-called "metastases" in the lungs of birds infected when high doses of virus were injected (Munroe and Southam, 1961). Rous in his early work showed that true metastasis does occur. Morgan and Andrese (1962) infected chicken embryo fibroblasts with Rous virus *in vitro* and implanted them into susceptible chicks of the opposite sex. The implants developed into tumors. Around the periphery of each were cells with the sex chromatin pattern of the host bird, but the bulk of the tumor was clearly of donor cell origin. This result shows the cells infected *in vitro* to have been transformed into neoplastic entities, and also indicates transformation of the host's cells by virus released by the implanted cells. The same type of an experiment was performed by Pontén (1962b) to ascertain whether the Rous virus-induced tumor was transplantable. By means of the sex chromatin marker he determined that although the growth of implanted tumor resembled transplantation, actually the dominating process was the transformation of the cells of the host by virus. When graded amounts of Rous cells were inoculated, doses larger than 4×10^5 cells were required to obtain detectable metaphases derived from the implanted cells. In a second transplant generation, less than 0.5% of the metaphases were of the same sex as the original Rous cells. The same findings were made by Baluda (1962) in chickens inoculated with neoplastic cells induced by the BAI strain A myeloblastosis virus. Adult chickens resistant to the virus were resistant to the cells, even when their own cells were converted *in vitro* and reimplanted into the donor. On the other hand, Pontén (1962a) could transplant the RPL 12 virus-associated chicken lymphomas in homologous hosts. The infiltration of organs that occurred in advanced cases was due to the transplanted cells, and 100% takes were obtained with 4,900 cells, the lowest amount Pontén tested.

Prince (1959) could detect no virus in 10–20% of the tumors arising in chicks inoculated with less than the 50% dilution end point (ED_{50}). Thus the observations of Bryan et al. (1955) were confirmed. Cultures of tissue from these tumors were resistant to challenge infection with Rous virus. Serial transplantation of noninfective tumors in chickens resulted in the return of virus-containing tumors, although in 2 instances this required 4 transplant generations. Some birds with multiple tumors initiated with less than one ED_{50} of virus carried both noninfective and virus-producing tumors. Prince considered these observations suggestive of a form of cell-virus integration in which infectious virus is only rarely produced.

In the turkey, tumors produced with as much as 10^5 ED_{50} of Rous virus have been found to be noninfective. Rauscher and Groupé (1960) determined that this was due to the presence of specific humoral antibody. Other factors were also involved because some low-dose tumors were noninfective even though the serums of their hosts had no virus-neutralizing activity. Even though trypsinized and washed, cells from birds with high levels of circulating antibody contained little or no detectable virus (Bergs and Groupé, 1962a). However, exposure of tumor cells to antibody for several months in vitro did not free them of virus. Cells of low-dose turkey tumors are resistant to superinfection, but Bergs and Groupé (1962b) could overcome this by repeated challenges with Rous virus. If noninfective tumors from turkeys with high levels of circulating antiviral antibody were transplanted into random-bred turkeys, tumor growth did not occur. This suggests that those tumors that are produced in random birds by cell implantation are actually virus-induced. Rubin (1962a), on the basis of his experiments, concluded that noninfective tumors are all the result of an immunological reaction by the host. The reaction is thought to be mediated by immunologically competent lymphocytes and not by circulating antibody. The lymphocytes attack the sarcoma cell, not the virus. This results in suppression of virus synthesis rather than simply neutralization of virus after its release.

Chicken embryo fibroblasts may be carried through several subcultures to provide cells for Rous virus assay. Some cultures propagated in this fashion become resistant to infection with Rous virus and show a reduced count of foci. Rubin (1961) found this due to interference by a virus of the avian leukosis group. Prior infection of a cell by this "resistance-inducing factor" (RIF) reduces the probability for a successful infection with RSV by a factor of 40 or greater. Interferon does not appear to be implicated. The resistance may be induced with any of the viruses of the avian leukosis complex, and Rubin et al. (1961) found lymphomatosis virus to be serologically indistinguishable from RIF. He also developed an assay procedure for lymphomatosis virus based on its interference with Rous virus. The new technique permitted him to readily confirm previous work done by Burmester and his associates using the more difficult and time consuming bioassay procedure involving intact chickens as test units. Rubin found that congenitally transmitted virus multiplies through embryonic and post-embryonic life in the chicken. The chickens are specifically tolerant to the virus, produce no neutralizing antibody, and have free virus in the blood. They can transmit lymphomatosis virus by contact to uninfected chicks. Tolerant infection can be induced by deliberate infection of the embryo. Uninfected chicks exposed to virus by contact develop transient viremia and almost invariably produce antibody (Rubin, 1962a).

A second virus, which was designated Rous-associated virus (RAV) (Rubin and Vogt, 1962), was isolated from the Bryan high-titer strain of Rous virus (Bryan, 1959). The agent does not induce cytological alterations in cultured cells, but it can be detected because it interferes with infection and focus formation by Rous virus. In stocks of Bryan's Rous virus strain, the titer of RAV is about 4 times higher than that of Rous virus. RAV also induces resistance to Rous virus in cultures much more rapidly than the naturally-occurring RIF. Accurate titers of RAV may be attained. RAV produces no tumor at the site of inoculation in chickens, but it produces erythroblastosis following intravenous inoculation of embryos. This agent is more closely related immunologically to Rous virus than to RIF.

Prince (1960) observed that under certain conditions Rous virus infected cultures of chick fibroblasts exhibited low virus-to-cell ratios. Analysis of clones of cells from such cultures showed that the majority did not produce virus spontaneously, except for very small amounts in some cases. The noninfective clones were resistant to challenge with Rous virus, although, under certain conditions, suboptimal response was noted. About 80% of the noninfective clones followed without challenge did produce small amounts of virus at some time, but this could have been due to contamination of the clones by non-clone-forming, virus-yielding cells. Prince interpreted these observations as suggestive of a virus-cell union comparable to that existing in lysogenicity. Temin (1962) also obtained non-virus-producing clones when he plated infected chick cells on monolayers of mouse cells. In time, some such clones spontaneously produced virus. The non-virus-producing clones could be induced to produce virus by superinfecting with Rous virus, or by avian erythroblastosis or myeloblastosis viruses. Agents such as ultraviolet- or X-irradiation, amethopterin, and mitomycin that induce lysogenic bacteria to release phage did not induce the noninfective clones to release Rous virus. When cells from such noninfective clones were injected into newly-hatched chicks, 25 out of 65 so inoculated developed fibrosarcomas of which 4 did not contain appreciable virus. Similar nonviral tumors developed when noninfective clones were placed on the chorioallantoic membranes of the 10-day-old chick embryo. Temin observed that the production of virus is apparently unnecessary for carcinogenesis.

Hanafusa et al. (1963) interpreted the noninfective clones of cells transformed by Rous virus to be an indication that the agent is a defective virus. In an attempt to free Rous virus of RAV, they isolated foci of transformed cells from monolayers of chick fibroblasts previously infected with high dilutions of their stock virus pool. The transformed cells could be serially trans-ferred onto uninfected chicken embryo cells and most such clones yielded no detectable virus. Rous virus was released when any of several avian tumor viruses or RAV was added. Whenever spontaneous release of Rous virus was observed, RAV was also produced, indicating contamination by that agent. Apparently Rous virus has the ability to transform the chicken fibroblast, but requires a helper virus to permit production of mature virus.

It is interesting to note that the strain of Rous virus carried by Harris in England showed no cross neutralization with the Bryan strain of virus carried in this country (Simons and Dougherty, 1961). Both strains have been through innumerable passages in fowl, and one may but speculate concerning the reason for the lack of serological relationship. The original virus may have been replaced by a tumor-producing contaminant, since such viruses are encountered in chickens from time to time. If Rubin's hypothesis of Rous virus deficiency is correct, the role of the helper viruses in stimulating antigenic change cannot be discounted. Finally, antigenic change is not unknown in viruses, in influenza virus for example, and the Rous virus may spontaneously undergo such change with time. In any event, the Rous virus found its way into other European laboratories, and here strains of the agent have been found to induce tumors in mammals. Zilber (1961) recently reviewed the work in this area. Inoculation of Rous tumor cells into rat embryos or newborn rats resulted in subsequent development of cysts filled with serous transudate which became hemorrhagic. Later, sarcomas appeared in some rats. This was designated the "hemorrhagic disease" of rats. The infection of newborn rabbits resulted in the development of benign multiple fibrous nodules, which when treated with X- or ultraviolet-radiation, sometimes released virus. Serums of infected rats did not contain virus specific antibody, but antiserum was sometimes obtained from affected rabbits. Individual strains of Rous virus differed in their capacity to cause cysts or sarcomas in rats and rabbits. Virus from Carr, Engelbreth-Holm, and Djadkova were compared; Carr's was most active and

Djadkova's was least active (Kryukova, 1961). Karyological studies on a rat sarcoma, 1 of 3 which arose in rats inoculated after birth with Rous sarcoma cells, showed it to be rat tissue. This neoplasm, tumor XC, produced tumors in chicks inoculated with 5×10^7 living tumor cells. Cells frozen and thawed 3 times in doses of 5×10^4 to 5×10^7 as well as extracellular material were ineffective. The chicken tumors that arose following implantation of XC tumor cells contained filterable, tumor-producing virus in relatively high titer which was neutralized by antiserum against Rous virus (Landa et al., 1962; Svoboda, 1962). Although these results suggest release of infective virus by XC tumor cells, tests in chicks failed to show release of Rous virus into the growth medium in cultures of the XC tumor (Simkovic et al., 1962).

Recently, Munroe and Windle (1963) reported that a strain of chicken sarcoma obtained from L. A. Zilber of the Gamaleya Institute in Moscow induced fibrosarcomas in newborn monkeys, *Macaca mulatta*. The tumors that arose at the site at which chicken sarcoma cell suspensions were inoculated were shown by chromosome studies to be composed of cells of the monkey host. The presence of virus in the tumors was demonstrated by inoculation of tumor tissue into the wing web of chickens.

Ahlström and Jonsson (1962a) transplanted subcutaneously the Mill Hill strain of Rous sarcoma into newborn rats and mice. All tumors rapidly regressed after 5–10 days of growth and disappeared. No hemorrhages or subcutaneous cysts were noted. Cortisone was without influence. The discrepancy with other observations in the literature was ascribed to differences in the Rous virus used by different investigators. When Ahlström and Jonsson repeated their experiments with Rous sarcoma obtained from Dr. H. Schmidt-Ruppin of Frankfurt-on-Main-Hoechst, 70% of the rats inoculated when newborn developed after 1 month progressively growing sarcomas at the subcutaneous site of injection (Ahlström and Jonsson, 1962b). Schmidt-Ruppin had received the sarcoma from Prof. Charles Oberling, Paris, and transmitted it in chickens by conventional methods. Cysts filled with bloody serous fluid arose in 30% of the animals in the inguinal, axillary, or cervical areas and sometimes in the retroperitoneal tissue or in the pelvis. The sarcomas were spindle-celled. They metastasized to the retroperitoneal and mediastinal lymph nodes in the lungs and pleural cavities. Some sarcomas developed from cyst walls. Sarcomas developed in rats inoculated at 3 weeks of age, but cysts appeared only after neonatal inoculation. Presumably, cell-free material from chicken sarcomas obtained by centrifugal clarification of tumor homogenate also induced sarcomas in the rat. The rat tumor could be serially transplanted in rats, but cell-free material did not transmit the tumor to other rats. If tumors were transferred to chickens, a Rous sarcoma developed in 4–6 weeks at the site of injection. Sarcomas were also produced in hamsters and guinea pigs (Ahlström et al., 1962; Ahlström and Forsby, 1962). Fibrosarcoma-like tumors developed about 3 weeks after newborn rabbits were inoculated, but soon spontaneously regressed. Some of the rabbits developed cysts in lymph nodes. The Mill Hill and the Schmidt-Ruppin strains of virus evoked foci of usual appearance in cultures of chicken embryo fibroblasts. After 2 weeks giant cells were noted in the foci produced by the latter strain. The Mill Hill strain never produced changes in mammalian cells whereas the Schmidt-Ruppin strain induced foci of granulated cells after about 9 days in cultures of rat, guinea pig, and mouse cells. No changes were produced in rabbit or human fibroblasts (Bergman and Jonsson, 1962).

A3–3. THE MURINE GROUP OF TUMOR VIRUSES

A. Introduction

The murine group of tumor viruses includes agents associated with mammary tumors in mice, polyoma in mice and hamsters, and leukemia of the mouse and rat. Both the leukemia agents and the mammary tumor agent presumably are RNA viruses, which are released at the cell membrane by a budding process and do not appear to involve the cell nucleus. The polyoma virus, a DNA agent which induces multiple tumors in mice, rats, and hamsters, develops within the nucleus. Because this virus is stable, relatively easily quantitated, and transforms cells *in vitro*, it has been the focus of a voluminous literature. More difficulties are associated with the mammary tumor and leukemia agents because an adequate quantitative assay system is not available, and host factors are involved in the expression of their oncogenic potential.

B. The Mouse Mammary Tumor Agent

A brief summary of early work with the mammary tumors of mice and a detailed discussion of their morphology was presented by Dunn (1959). Because he understood the importance of the achievement in relation to cancer biology, C. O. Jensen was credited by Dunn with having performed the first serial transplantation of a mammary tumor in the mouse in 1903. Morau had previously reported a transplantation in 1894, but he thought he was transplanting an infectious agent. Since that time the study of this neoplasm, recognized as a malignant cancer, has contributed to our knowledge of tumor histogenesis and has permitted correlation of histologic structure with biologic behavior. Inbred strains of mice were developed which had a high incidence of mammary cancer. Among these are the C3H strain, which exhibits more than 90% mammary tumors in both virgin and breeding females, and the A strain, which has an incidence below 5% in virgin females. Strains such as CBA, C57 Black, and BALB/c have a low incidence of spontaneous mammary tumors. Hereditary factors and endocrinological factors were known to be important in mammary cancer. The existence of a third extra-chromosomal factor associated with development of this tumor was reported by the Staff of the Jackson Memorial Laboratory at Bar Harbor, Maine (1933). This extra-chromosomal influence in mice was made evident by the fact that a high incidence of mammary tumors developed in the progeny of a high-tumor strain female mated to a low-tumor strain male whereas the progeny resulting from the reciprocal cross had a low-tumor incidence. The transmission of the extra-chromosomal factor through the milk of a high-cancer strain mother was established by Bittner (1936). The factor was also transmitted by inoculation of low-tumor strain mice with mammary, or spleen tissue, from females of high-tumor line (Bittner, 1939) or whole blood from high-tumor line males and females (Woolley *et al.*, 1941). The blood may thus be a vehicle for dispersal of the tumor factor throughout the organs of the body. A high-tumor line of mice could be converted to a low-tumor line by foster-nursing progeny. In such a low-tumor strain A mouse colony, evidence of the tumor factor appeared in the 8th generation in animals that had received no inoculations, but must have been infected in some fashion. Bittner (1941) felt the most consistent explanation for these observations is that the active milk influence is a virus or virus-like agent.

Mice may be infected with the mammary tumor agent (MTA) at any time of life. Although they may not develop mammary cancer, they transmit the agent to their nursing progeny (Bittner, 1943). The MTA is not strain specific; it can be passaged through different strains of mice (Dmochowski, 1944). However, various strains of mice exhibit different degrees of susceptibility, and the inheritance of susceptibility is more important than the milk agent in development of tumors in mice (Warner *et al.*, 1945). Older mice that have fully developed mammary glands have been shown to develop tumors following inoculation with dried tumor tissue, but the quantity of the inoculum required to induce the same tumor incidence is greater than it is in younger mice (Dmochowski, 1945a). Breast tumor tissue from different strains of mice carrying the agent shows differences in tumor-inducing potential, suggesting either the attainment of higher virus titers or the production of more potent virus in mice of some strains than in others (Dmochowski, 1945b).

The MTA can survive in mouse milk for 2 weeks at 8°C, but it is inactivated if heated at 61°–66°C for 30 min (Andervont and Bryan, 1944). It retains its activity in tumor extracts at pH 5.5–10.2, but is not active at pH 4.5. It survives lyophilization and treatment with petroleum ether or acetone (Barnum *et al.*, 1944). The active factor can be sedimented from mouse milk by high-speed centrifugation (Visscher *et al.*, 1942; Bryan *et al.*, 1942).

Virus-like particles were detected by electron microscopic examination of milk or of cultured tumor cells obtained from high-tumor line mice (Graff *et al.*, 1949; Porter and Thompson, 1948). The size of the particles in milk ranged from 50 to 150 mμ with most 80–110 mμ in diameter. Fractions containing these particles were shown to produce the characteristic disease in low-tumor strain C57BL mice. Passey *et al.* (1950) treated extracts from dried cancerous and normal tissues of different strains of high-tumor line mice with petroleum ether after which aqueous extracts were prepared. The extracts were then treated with trypsin, filtered, and examined with the electron microscope. Particles predominantly 15–35 mμ in diameter were observed. Similar, trypsin-treated extracts were tested in mice and found to induce mammary tumors. Such particulate matter or tumor-inducing activity was not present in material prepared in the same fashion from tissues of low-cancer strain mice. With the advent of thin-sectioning techniques, the mammary tumors from mice carrying MTA were found to have 2 types of particle. The first, measuring about 65–75 mμ in diameter, was found within the cell most frequently in the Golgi zone. It consisted of a dense shell with an homogeneous, electron-lucent interior. It is termed the A-particle. A predominantly extra-cellular particle, the B-particle consisting of a thin-walled sac about 105 mμ in diameter with an inner dense nucleoid 20 to 35 mμ in size, eccentrically placed, appeared to be produced by budding from the cell's surface (Bernhard, 1958, 1960). The particles described by Passey *et al.* (1950) may have been the nucleoids.

In the DBA strain of mouse at the Jackson Laboratory, Bar Harbor, mammary tumors arose in about 50 per cent of virgin females. Woolley *et al.* (1939) ovariectom-ized newborn animals of this strain with the expectation of drastic reduction in tumor incidence. Unexpectedly, more than 25% of these animals developed mammary tumors at an average age of 522 days. Removal of the ovaries in some manner allowed nodular hyperplasia of the adrenal cortex; the prolonged action of the latter stimulated the uterus in the older animals, thereby stimulating or replacing ovarian activity. When ovariectomized, the high-tumor C3H strain also showed stimulated uterus, vagina, and mammary glands, and the adrenals exhibited extensive nodular hyperplastic areas. All these organs remained essentially unstimulated in the low-tumor C57BL strain (Woolley *et al.*, 1940). Bittner (1957) has reviewed further studies which developed from these observations. Cross matings between A strain mice with a low incidence of tumors in virgins with C3H strain mice, which have a high incidence of tumors in virgins, yielded progeny with high incidence in virgins. There was no evidence of hormonal stimulation of secondary sex organs in ovariectomized A strain mice and only minor adrenal changes. On the other hand, a correlation existed between postcastrational adrenal hyperplasia and the high incidence in virgin C3H and in the hybrid (C3H $\times$ A)F1 females. Bittner called the chromosomal hormonal mechanism responsible for the induction of mammary cancer in virgins the "inherited hormonal influence." Further crosses between different strains disclosed that the I stock of mice, which does not develop spontaneous mammary cancer, possessed the tumor-inducing hormonal pattern. Crossing with the A strain yields a high-tumor incidence among virgins of the F1 generation. On the other hand, the hormonal pattern transmitted by agent-susceptible CE strain mice produces postcastrational adrenal carcinoma but no high incidence of mammary cancer in (A $\times$ CE)F1 virgin females, indicating lack of the inherited hormonal influence in CE mice. If CE strain females possessing the mammary tumor virus were mated with the I stock mouse which possessed the tumor-inducing hereditary hormonal pattern, over 90% of progeny virgin females developed mammary cancer. Although females of the NH strain of mouse develop adrenal carcinomas, crosses with the A strain of mouse so inhibited or delayed the development of cancer in breeding females of the F1 generation that many died without cancer. Thus there is another hormonal pattern which either inhibits the development of mammary cancer or delays its appearance in both virgin and breeding mice.

Precancerous lesions in mammary glands have been described in mice with and without the MTA (Dunn, 1959). The most important of these consists of a localized area of acinar or alveolar proliferation known as a "hyperplastic nodule." The observations of Mühlbock et al. (1952) on the DBA and foster-nursed DBAb mouse line show that the frequency of nodules and mammary carcinomas which occur spontaneously in old mice is markedly increased in the presence of the MTA. Remains of a nodule are frequently found at the periphery of carcinomas and early carcinomas are found in sections of nodules. Nodules sometimes regress, but differ from normal mammary tissue by remaining unaltered when remaining mammary tissue undergoes involution. They may thus persist for a long time. Of a certain number of nodules, the same percentage becomes carcinomatous in DBA mice whether they be virgins, breeders, "force-breeders," agent-free animals, or agent-bearing animals. Mühlbock and his associates considered both the MTA and breeding to act merely by increasing the number of hyperplastic nodules and thus the incidence of cancer. The agent was thought not to directly influence the progression of adenomatous hyperplasia in a nodule to carcinoma. The MTA thus is regarded by some investigators as an accelerator of developments in the mammary gland which eventually would also take place in the absence of the agent.

The precancerous nature of the hyperplastic nodules was clearly demonstrated by De Ome et al. (1959). They transplanted nodules and normal mammary glands into C3H mouse mammary fat pads previously freed of mammary gland tissue. Under these conditions, mammary tumors developed more frequently from the transplanted nodules than from the similarly transplanted normal glands. Both the pituitary and ovary are necessary for maintenance and growth of the normal lobule transplants, but only the pituitary is required for maintenance and growth of hyperplastic nodules, showing their tendency towards unregulated activity. No tumors develop in transplanted nodules unless the pituitary and either the ovaries or the adrenals are present. De Ome and co-workers found that estradiol-17B, plus somatotropin and either progesterone or deoxycorticosterone are hormone combinations capable of inducing normal alveolar development and nodule formation in situ. Growth and neoplastic development of the transplanted nodules in hypophysectomized-ovariectomized C3H mice was also noted with these combinations of hormones as well as with deoxycorticosterone acetate plus either somatotropin or mammotropin. It appears that the same hormones required for the development of normal lobules and of hyperplastic alveolar nodules are also involved in mammary tumorigenesis (Nandi et al., 1960).

Further experiments were made with mice of different strains. Estrogen, progesterone, and mammotropin were shown to promote lobuloalveolar development while mammotropin plus cortisol induced lactogenesis in all strains of mice tested. Mammary tumor agent-susceptible strains which have a high-tumor incidence in both virgin and parous females responded to combinations in which somatotropin replaced mammotropin. Strains which have a low-tumor incidence in virgin females responded to mammotropin but not to somatotropin. In virgin females, little, if any, mammotropin is secreted; therefore, somatotropin is probably the most important pituitary hormone involved in tumorigenesis in such mice. This suggests that Bittner's "inherited hormonal influence" involves the sensitivity of the mammary gland to somatotropin. In parous females, the pituitary factor active in tumorigenesis may be mammotropin or a combination of this hormone with somatotropin (Nandi and Bern, 1960). An extension of these studies to hypophysectomized-ovariectomized-adrenalectomized youthful

C3H females demonstrated the need for both deoxycorticosterone and corticosterone in conjunction with somatotropin for tumorigenesis in virgin mice. Estradiol enhanced the tumorigenic action of the adrenal corticoids plus somatotropin (Nandi and Bern, 1961). The 2 adrenal corticoids with either somatotropin or mammotropin maintained hyperplastic nodules in all strains of mice even though the hormone requirements for nodule formation differed in the different strains (Nandi, 1961). Attention is being directed to the possible utilization of hyperplastic nodule formation as a rapid means of detecting the virus by inoculating susceptible BALB/c strain mice with the MTA and treating the animals with hormones (Nandi, 1963).

Fairly extensive studies *in vitro* have been made on the mouse mammary carcinoma. Porter and Thompson (1948) observed particulate bodies in their cultures of epithelial cells derived from tumors of a mouse strain carrying the MTA. Pikovski (1953) exposed chicken heart tissue to ground mammary tumor, implanted these tissues in plasma clot, and tested for virus activity at each of 10 subcultures over 156 days. The tumor incidence was higher in mice inoculated with extracts of cultures of the 10th passage than those infected with extracts of the first passage, suggesting not only survival but replication of the agent in the heterologous cells. Despite the promise of these observations, the mammary tumor virus has proven to be most difficult to propagate *in vitro*. Lasfargues *et al.* (1957, 1958) propagated the virus in organ cultures as evidenced by tumorigenic activity of culture material in test mice. The virus particles were not seen in infected cultures on electron microscopic examination, but were detected in the tumors induced in the test animals. Continuous roller tube cultures of pure adult mammary epithelium failed to support the milk agent for a prolonged period. Elias (1958) could maintain normal inactive explants, prelactating lobules and hyperplastic nodules in medium 199 if supplemented with mammotropin, cortisol, and insulin. Secretory activity and distention of both alveoli and terminal ducts were noted. A study to determine whether the MTA persists in long-term cultures of mammary carcinomas propagated as monolayers was initiated by Sanford *et al.* (1961). In cells from some tumors, the agent disappeared; in other cultures, the agent could be demonstrated after 6 months to more than a year of rapid cell proliferation *in vitro*. Lasfargues and Feldman (1963) demonstrated that the release of B particles by strain RIII mouse mammary gland cultures could be induced by appropriate hormonal stimulation. Maximum emission of B particles by explants of glands obtained during early pregnancy was obtained in 199 medium supplemented with estradiol, progesterone, mammotropin, and insulin. Glands explanted during lactation required a hormone supplement of cortisone, mammotropin, and insulin to obtain release of B particles. In each instance the formation of B particles by the cultured epithelium corresponds to a phase of high protein synthesis: lobuloalveolar differentiation of the gland in the first instance and production of milk proteins in the second. This suggests that the production of B particles is closely controlled by the physiologic state of the cell; the role of the hormones is only necessary to establish such a physiological state.

The establishment of the morphological identity of the mammary tumor agent is not yet conclusive. Electron microscopic studies have revealed characteristic virus-like particles in mammary tumors or hyperplastic nodules of supposedly agent-free mice (Dmochowski and Grey, 1957; Pitelka *et al.*, 1960). De Ome (1958) sees no reason to doubt the existence of a virus-like entity actively influencing the development of mammary cancer. However, since the virus-like particles revealed by the electron microscope are associated with preneoplastic mammary hyperplasia in both MTA-infected and MTA-free C3H mice, the biologically active MTA does not seem to be related to the particles, and their role in mouse mammary tumorigenesis remains unknown. Feldman (1963) comments that if neither A nor B particle is related to the MTA, the agent must be "too dispersed to be located with the electron microscope, too small to be resolved by the electron microscope, or not preserved by conventional fixation and embedding techniques." On the basis of data gathered by experiments with strain RIII mouse milk using filtration, free diffusion, irradiation, centrifugation, electrophoretic fractionation, and dialysis, Moore (1962) and Moore et al. (1962) concluded that under certain conditions the milk of agent-bearing mice can contain a complex of tumor-inducing and tumor-inhibiting particles. Hypothetically, the large 100 mμ B particle consists of a sac containing an infective nucleoid about 35 mμ in diameter. Irradiation sufficient to inactivate particles 100 mμ in diameter did not destroy infectivity of the MTA suggesting that the sac is not involved in infection. Free diffusion experiments yielded 3 fractions, one containing the infectious large particles, another containing small 20 mμ to 50 mμ particles which was also infective, and the last consisting of 60 mμ particles which inhibited the activity of the small infectious entity. The small infective particle may be the naked viral nucleoid. The nature of the 60 mμ inhibitor is unknown. Another smaller inhibitor which passes the 2.5 mμ pores of dialysis tubing was demonstrated in the dialysate of skim milk containing MTA. This inhibitor acted on the agent contained in samples of fresh milk. The role of the inhibitors in mammary tumorigenesis in mice is unknown.

The mouse does not develop humoral antibodies to the MTA. Neutralizing antisera have been prepared in the rat and rabbit following a series of injections of tumor tissue centrifugates (Green et al., 1946). Antisera against normal mouse tissue are ineffective. Rabbit antisera to the agent precipitate the agent and also fix complement with the agent (Heidelberger et al., 1952a,b). Normal rabbit serum has an inhibitory effect on the tumor cells, but normal guinea pig or normal chicken sera do not (Imagawa et al., 1954). Antigenic differences have been noted between samples of MTA obtained from different sources. The antigenic properties of the agent in a transplanted tumor may be altered with continued passage of the tumor in agent-free animals (Bittner and Imagawa, 1955). Blair (1963) described experiments showing that an antigenic similarity exists between C3H mammary tissue extracts containing active mammary tumor virus and extract of genetically similar tissues from supposedly agent-free mice containing abundant virus-like particles but without oncogenic activity. The reason for this is unknown. The MTA and the particle from the agent-free mouse lines may be identical, or they may be different but share common antigens. This would suggest either that the biologically active MTA has not been revealed by the electron microscope, or that there are 2 viruses, only 1 of which is oncogenic. There is also a possibility that inactivity of the particles in the low-tumor line may be the result of an inhibitor introduced by the foster parent (Moore et al., 1959a).

At this time, then, there is no agreement among investigators on either the morphology of the entity designated as the "mammary tumor agent" or the manner in which it induces mammary carcinoma. The problem of mammary carcinogenesis in mice includes a complexity of physiological reactions involving the entire animal. Hopefully, the attention presently being directed to mouse mammary cancer will lead to clarification in some of the problem areas in the near future.

C. Murine Leukemia Viruses

Murine leukemia, like mammary carcinoma, has been under study for many years. Lines of inbred mice with high, as well as low, incidence of spontaneous leukemia have been developed. Leukemia is a neoplastic disease of the reticular tissue, that is, of the lymphatic and hemopoietic tissue of the body. Dunn (1954) classified reticular neoplasms by the cell of origin: "stem-cell," lymphocyte, granulocyte; reticulum cell, plasma cell, and mast cell. Of these the most commonly observed are the lymphocytic neoplasms. In certain low-leukemic strains of mice, ionizing radiation, carcinogenic hydrocarbons, estrogens, and viruses have increased leukemia incidence. Genetic factors appear to govern susceptibility to leukemia. In most strains of mice, the thymus is the site of development of lymphocytic leukemia, and thymectomy inhibits leukemogenesis. Implantation of thymus gland in a subcutaneous site in thymectomized mice restores susceptibility to leukemia development. A detailed review of the factors which play a role in leukemogenesis in the mouse was given by Miller (1961) and more recently a review of the viral leukemias in mice was published by Sinkovics (1962).

D. THE GROSS VIRUS

The value of the newborn mouse for leukemia research was demonstrated by Gross (1950). C3H and C57BL mice, inbred strains which have a low incidence of spontaneous leukemia, showed a high incidence of lymphatic leukemia if they had received inoculations shortly after birth of leukemic cells from strain AK mice. The AK strain normally shows a high incidence of leukemia in later life. Extracts of organs of leukemic AK mice also were leukemogenic in the low-leukemia mouse strains, provided injection into the mice was made within 12 hours of their birth. Gross (1951a) concluded that AK mouse leukemia was caused by an agent transmitted from one generation to another, as in chicken lymphomatosis. "Vertical" transmission of virus was evident in one experiment in which 13 out of 27 untreated offspring of infected C3H parents developed leukemia at 14–20 months of age (Gross, 1951b). The milk removed from stomachs of suckling AK strain mice was ineffective in newborn C3H mice, and foster nursing on AK mothers failed to transmit the disease. On the other hand, extracts from ovaries and testes of young, normal AK mice were leukemogenic in test mice. This suggested that the agent is carried in testes and ovaries of healthy AK mice (Gross, 1953a). In further experiments, Gross found that within 8–9 months a high incidence of leukemia developed in the offspring of an infected C3H female, but not in the offspring of an infected male and noninfected female. In the susceptible C57 Brown/cd strain, such transmission of leukemia to offspring was not observed (Gross, 1961a). Litters of C3H mice born to infected parents were exchanged with those born at about the same time to uninfected

parents. Eighty % of the mice born to normal parents but foster-nursed by virus-inoculated females developed early leukemia while only 15% of the mice born to infected mothers and foster-nursed by normal females developed leukemia at a later age. The nursing females had overt leukemia part of the time they were nursing. Whether healthy, virus-carrying females would similarly transmit virus remained undetermined. Under the experimental conditions, foster-nursing did not prevent the development of leukemia (Gross, 1962).

The infectivity of the AK agent is destroyed by ether *in vitro* (Gross, 1956). The virus is inactivated at $50°–55°C$ within 30 min, but it can be stored at $0°C$ for 48 hr or at $−70°C$ for several months without loss of activity. It has been preserved for up to 15 months by lyophilization and by suspension in 50% glycerol, but with decrease in activity. The leukemogenic activity of extracts is not removed by passage through 340 or 200 mμ gradocol membranes (Gross, 1957a).

A more potent strain of the AK leukemia virus was obtained by selective serial passage through mice (Gross, 1957b), a technique developed by Bryan and Moloney (1957) and Bryan (1959) to increase potency of Rous sarcoma virus extracts. With this "Passage A" strain of the AK virus, leukemia developed in C3H mice that were as old as 14 days when inoculated (Gross, 1958). The "Passage A" virus was also effective in the rat. In this animal, localized thymic lymphosarcomas or generalized lymphatic leukemia was observed. Some rats developed stem-cell leukemia (Gross, 1961b).

Thymectomy suppressed development of lymphatic leukemia. Mice that were inoculated with virus after thymectomy did not develop leukemia during 15 months of observation. Mice infected with virus shortly after birth and thymectomized a few weeks later did not develop leukemia until about 9 months of age, whereas unthymectomized controls died with leukemia within about $3\frac{1}{2}$ months. Most of the leukemias were of the lymphocytic type, but an appreciable number of myelogenous leukemias were induced as well (Gross, 1960). Some less frequently observed forms of leukemia such as chloroleukemia and occasionally monocytic leukemia or erythroblastic leukemia also occur in infected, thymectomized C3H mice. A high incidence of myelogenous leukemia develops in unthymectomized strain BALB/c mice following neonatal inoculation of the agent (Gross, 1963). Thus, with laboratory passage, the virus has enlarged its host range to include different strains of mice and a different species, the rat. The disease produced is still predominantly lymphocytic leukemia, but other forms of leukemia have been recognized in certain hosts under particular conditions.

E. The Graffi Virus

In 1954, Graffi and his associates described the cell-free transmission of myeloid mouse leukemia which is manifested frequently as chloroleukemia, that is, granulocytic leukemia with a characteristic green discoloration of lymph nodes, a condition rare in their stock mice. Extensive studies performed with this agent are summarized by Graffi (1957, 1958, 1959) and by Sinkovics (1962). The agent is carried by a number of transplantable mouse tumors from which it can be extracted. About 50–80% of suckling mice infected with cell-free filtrates of the tumor extracts eventually develop myeloid or chloroleukemia at an average age of 4–11 months, depending on the potency of the extract. If mice were splenectomized at birth, either before or several days after injection of leukemogenic filtrates, the development of leukemia was strongly inhibited (Fey and Graffi, 1958). Splenectomy had no effect if done 1–2 months after injection. Previous cytological investigations had indicated that the initial attack of the virus is on the myeloid cells of the bone marrow. Neoplastic cells from the marrow infiltrated into the liver, thymus gland, lymph nodes, and spleen and multiplied in these organs (Graffi, 1957). The virus produced disease in the rat, inducing generalized lymphoid or myeloid leukemia, thymic lymphosarcoma, or reticulum cell sarcoma in about 10% of the rats. When mice were injected with extracts of leukemic rat organs, reticulum cell and lymphatic

leukemia as well as myeloid leukemia were induced by the same filtrate (Fey et al., 1959). In general, cell transplantability of the mouse myeloid leukemias was poor. During cell-free passages, the myeloid leukemia may be converted to a lymphoid type (Bielka et al., 1955). Whole body X-irradiation or carcinogenic hydrocarbons enhanced the leukemic response (Graffi, 1957).

The agent is inactivated by heating at 65°C for 30 min. Activity is reduced by storage in 50% glycerol for one month, but low temperatures (−20°C) are tolerated for some weeks. The virus is stable in the pH range 4.5–9.5. It is inactivated by ether, desoxycholate, concentrated trypsin for long periods, sodium nitrite, and formalin (Graffi, 1958).

The virus is not antigenic in mice; no definite immunization was attained with formalized preparations. Antiserum prepared in the rabbit and incubated with extracts containing the virus reduced but did not eliminate leukemogenic activity (Graffi, 1957). No prophylactic nor therapeutic effect was obtained with the rabbit antiserum in mice (Graffi, 1958).

Virus particles in lymph nodes examined in thin section under the electron microscope were almost exclusively extracellular, although a few cells had intracytoplasmic particles. The particles were round, ranged from 60 to 150 mμ in diameter, and, on the basis of their fine structure, exhibited 4 different forms: simple vesicular particles; a somewhat larger vesicular form with a peripherally-located nucleoid; elements with a fairly large internal nucleoid and outer membrane; and, finally, complex structures comprised of many particles enclosed in a common envelope (Graffi et al., 1960).

RNA and DNA were prepared from leukemogenic extracts of the Graffi virus. The DNA preparations were not leukemogenic, but 11 out of 107 mice that were inoculated with the RNA material developed leukemia. Control animals that received such RNA preparations previously treated with ribonuclease did not develop leukemia. The infectivity of the original extracts was unaffected by this enzyme. Spontaneous leukemia occurred in only 1 of 383 of the stock animals used for the test (Bielka and Graffi, 1959). The results suggest that infective ribonucleic acid was active in the preparations.

F. The Friend Virus

A disease with the character of a leukemia which could be induced in adult Swiss mice within a few weeks following injection of cell-free material was described by Friend (1957). The original observations were made on Swiss mice. Hepatosplenomegaly developed 14 months after the mice had been inoculated with a filtered supernatant from high-speed centrifugation of an extract of Ehrlich mouse ascites tumor. The agent was maintained by serial passage of cell suspensions as well as by cell-free preparations. Splenomegaly may develop in Swiss mice as early as 2 weeks post-infection. The disease is characterized by an invasion of the spleen, liver, bone marrow, kidney, and lung with immature mononuclear cells. These cells appear in the peripheral blood where they may be seen in various stages of mitosis. Terminally the affected animal is anemic, with elevated white cell count and greatly enlarged liver and spleen. The mean value of the logarithm of the spleen weight of mice infected with the Friend virus at some arbitrary time post-infection was found to be a function of the dose of virus inoculated (Rowe and Brodsky, 1959). Estimates of virus potency may be made 2 weeks post-inoculation on the basis of the spleen-weight response to a single dilution of virus. Metcalf et al. (1959) considered the disease produced by the Friend virus to be a virus-conditioned neoplasm characterized by neoplastic proliferation of reticulum cells, and associated with a nonneoplastic erythroblastosis and lymphocytosis. Friend (1957) found that adult DBA/2 and Swiss mice were susceptible to induction of the disease; PRI, C3H, A, C57BL/6, and (C58 × BALB/c)F1 strain mice were resistant. Solid tumors were established from cell grafts of spleen and of liver in DBA/2 mice. After 21 serial transplant generations, the tumors contained appreciable amounts of virus (Friend and Haddad, 1960).

The Friend virus passes gradocol membranes of 220 mµ pore size. It may be lyophilized, stored frozen at −70°C, or subjected to 50,000 r X-irradiation in the spleen without inactivation. Destruction of infectivity occurs on exposure to ether, to a 1 : 200 dilution of formalin, or to heat at 56°C for 30 min (Friend, 1957). Formalin-treated virus has been employed as a vaccine to immunize mice. Eighty % of the vaccinated mice were immune to challenge with active virus. Their sera also specifically neutralized the virus in vitro. Antiserum prepared in rabbits also specifically neutralized virus, but was ineffective in trials of passive immunization of mice (Friend, 1959).

In contrast to Friend's report of anemia in mice infected with her virus (Friend, 1957), Mirand and Grace (1961) noted progressive increase in hematocrit throughout the course of the disease in HA/ICR Swiss mice. There was also early appearance of a marked selective increase in Fe^{59} uptake by the spleen. Splenectomy in these animals eliminated the characteristic leucocytosis and the peripheral erythroblastosis and erythrocytosis. Thus no rise in hematocrit occurred in the splenectomized mouse. Leucocytosis appeared again after gross hepatomegaly. Although the hemopoietic syndrome was modified by splenectomy, the virus-induced reticulum cell disease appeared eventually (Mirand et al., 1961). These results suggest a splenic origin of the increased erythroid and myeloid elements.

Mirand and Grace (1962b) found that the Friend virus induces lymphatic leukemia following its inoculation into newborn Sprague-Dawley CD rats, with an incidence of 60% and an average time to death of 130 days. When adult HA/ICR Swiss mice were inoculated with leukemic rat spleen filtrate, they developed typical Friend disease, but some showed, in addition, hematologic and histologic evidence suggesting myeloid leukemia. The leukemia could be transmitted serially in suckling rats.

In HA/ICR mice, infected mothers transmit the Friend virus disease to about 7% of their offspring (Mirand and Grace, 1962a). The observed average time to death was 212 days for these naturally-infected mice in comparison with 55 days for adults inoculated with virus. No increase in erythropoiesis was noted; instead an anemia developed similar to that first reported by Friend (1957). When passage of filtered splenic extracts from this group of animals was made in mice, the usual reticulum cell disease was observed in 90% of the inoculated newborn and young adult mice. However, there was only a progressive anemia instead of the increased erythropoietic activity associated with infection by the original virus pool. This may be most reasonably explained by considering the transmission of the Friend virus from mother to progeny as having selected a mutant of the virus incapable of stimulating erythropoietic response or as having selected one virus from an original pool containing more than one agent.

Chromosome analyses were made on neoplastic cells from mouse leukemias induced by Friend's virus (Wakonig-Vaartaja, 1961). Two cases were predominantly diploid and one aneuploid, with an easily distinguishable minute chromosome. Aneuploidy apparently is not the primary cause of neoplasia in this disease. However, the nucleus may be involved in virus replication. Immunofluorescent techniques applied in a study of infected cells showed virus antigen appears first in the nucleus and then in the cytoplasm as with the myxoviruses (Friend and Rapp, 1962).

G. The Moloney Virus

Moloney (1959) reported his initial observations on a leukemogenic virus isolated from the transplantable tumor, Sarcoma 37. This anaplastic sarcoma has been maintained in transplant animal passage since 1906. In subsequent reports Moloney (1960a,b) described the disease induced in mice as generalized lymphocytic leukemia. Mice of all ages were highly susceptible, but a consistently high incidence, essentially 100%, was obtained in animals that received as newborns inoculations of the agent. Various strains of mice as well as rats and even hamsters were susceptible. The generalized disease resulted regardless of the route of inoculation, i.e., whether subcutaneous, oral, intraperitoneal, intracerebral, or intravenous. The disease produced was characterized by great enlargement of the thymus gland, lymph nodes, spleen, and liver. The white blood count usually exceeded 30,000 per mm³. The neoplastic cells were found to be freely transplantable in the strain of origin.

The pathogenesis of the virus-induced disease in BALB/c mice was studied by Dunn et al. (1961). Mice 6 weeks of age were infected with a relatively low dose of virus to insure gradual development of leukemia. No changes were noted in infected mice until 8 weeks had elapsed. At that time many megakaryocytes containing granulocytes were observed in the bone marrow. Subsequently, there was a gradual increase in splenic hyperplasia. However, with one exception, it was in the thymus that leukemia was first recognized. Differences in growth, spread, and organ involvement were noted among transplants of a series of the virus-induced neoplasms.

Congenital transmission of Moloney's virus was demonstrated in 2 low-leukemic lines, and one high-leukemic line of C3H mice (Law and Moloney, 1961). Strain RFM mothers apparently do not transmit the agent. There was no evidence that parenterally-infected males transmit virus to their progeny. The mother's milk appeared to be an effective route of transfer. Infected mothers transmitted virus whether or not they eventually became leukemic. A high-leukemic line was established with infected mothers. This could be converted into a low-leukemic line simply by foster-nursing. Reciprocal foster-nursing experiments revealed that transmission of virus can occur from a C3H mother to her offspring during the prenatal period. Foster-nursing combined with thymectomy through successive generations of high-leukemic AKR strain mice does not influence the frequency of, or the mean age to death from the lymphatic leukemia which develops spontaneously in this strain. It is thus considered that transmission of leukemic potentialities not only in the AKR strain but also in other high-leukemic strains such as C58, F, and C3H/Fg is of the chromosomal type (Law, 1962). The mechanism whereby virus is transmitted in these mouse strains is unknown.

H. THE SCHOOLMAN-SCHWARTZ AGENT

Schoolman *et al.* (1957) described a spontaneous lymphoblastoma that arose in a Swiss mouse caged with AKR males. The neoplasm was successfully transplanted in DBA and Swiss mice. Cell-free filtrates of brains of these animals were leukemogenic in Swiss and DBA mice. Evidence of neoplasia occurred as early as 8–10 days post-inoculation. A massive, diffuse intra-abdominal lymphosarcoma developed, and kidneys and genital organs were frequently invaded. An associated ascites was apparent in 10–25% of the animals. Cell-free filtrates of the abdominal tumor were ineffective in test mice. This disease was designated the "L_1" type of leukemia. Another lymphocytic neoplasm, the "L_2" type of leukemia, was observed in low incidence in the mouse stock used. The latter disease differed from the "L_1" type in that it occurred as a generalized form of leukemia much later in the life of the animals (Mitra and Schwartz, 1961). Other laboratories failed to maintain the Schoolman-Schwartz abdominal lymphosarcoma (Sinkovics, 1962).

I. THE RAUSCHER VIRUS

Rauscher (1962) isolated a virus from BALB/c mice which induces a dual type of disease in high incidence in different strains of mice. As early as 7 days post-infection, a rapid proliferation of immature erythrocytes occurs accompanied by splenic enlargement. Spleens are palpable within 10–15 days and continue to enlarge, sometimes to the point of rupture. Death usually occurs within about a month post-inoculation. In mice that survive, the development of lymphatic leukemia is detected 30–45 days post-inoculation. Virus can be extracted from leukemic tissues or from plasma 16 days after inoculation. Titers of 10^7 ID50 have been attained. Rats as well as mice are susceptible to the virus.

The virus is quite stable to storage at 4°C, and can be lyophilized without loss of activity. Slight reduction of activity follows exposure to a 1 : 250 dilution of formalin, but a more marked reduction of activity is noted after overnight exposure to 10% ether at 4°C. Electron microscopic examination of thin sections of mouse plasma pellets disclosed virus-like particles measuring 100 mμ in diameter. The virus can be neutralized by preparations of homologous rabbit antiserum but not by antisera to the Friend virus or to the Moloney virus.

J. THE C-60 VIRUS

A virus, designated C-60, was isolated from tissue cultures of the Schoolman-Schwartz Swiss mouse leukemia (Dalton *et al.*, 1961; Manaker, 1963). The neoplasm had been carried through numerous transplant passages in mice before the isolation was made. Cell-free extracts of spleen and lymph nodes of leukemic mice carrying this virus induced lymphatic leukemia in essentially 100% of Swiss and BALB/c mice inoculated at birth. Death occurred at an average age of about 3 months. This virus was effective in other strains of mice and in the rat. The agent probably represents that indigenous in the Swiss stock mice used by Mitra and Schwartz and designated by them the "L_2" leukemia (Mitra and Schwartz, 1961). The disease induced by the C-60 virus does not have the short period of latency nor the diffuse mesenteric involvement characteristic of the Schoolman-Schwartz "L_1" type of leukemia.

K. OTHER LEUKEMOGENIC AGENTS

Other leukemogenic agents include the Breyere-Moloney isolate (Moloney, 1962), which was recovered from a methylcholanthrene-induced plasma cell tumor of a C3H mouse. This agent induces generalized lymphocytic leukemia in C3H and BALB/c mice. Tennant (1962) isolated a leukemogenic virus from primary and transplanted C58 leukemia extracts. Reticulum cell sarcomas have been regularly induced by virus which Stansly *et al.* (1961) isolated from Ehrlich ascites tumor cells. Viruses associated with reticular disease similar to that induced by Friend's virus were characterized by Bather (1961) and Pope (1962). Pope (1961) also described a chronic disease produced by a virus isolated from a wild mouse. Infected mice have a normal blood picture, moderate splenomegaly, and medullary hyperplasia in lymph nodes. Mirand and Grace (1962c), in the course of their experiments with Friend virus, obtained an agent which induces gross splenic enlargement within 10 days and causes death in 90% of infected animals within 30 days. No thymic changes were noted. The disease has certain characteristics of a myelogenous leukemia. It is not clear whether the agent is a mutant of the Friend virus or an entirely different agent. Lieberman and Kaplan (1959) reported a radiation-induced lymphoid tumor in C57BL/Ka mice that yielded a filterable, leukemogenic agent which is now carried in their laboratory.

L. LEUKEMOGENIC AGENTS IN TISSUE CULTURE

Attempts to propagate the different leukemogenic agents *in vitro* have met with varied degrees of success. Moore and Friend (1958) initially were successful in demonstrating persistence of the Friend virus only in cultures of spleen prepared from leukemic mice. A subsequent report (Moore, 1963) indicates that mouse embryo cultures exposed to leukemic cells regularly released small amounts of virus for almost 2 years. There was no cytopathogenic effect. There was no evidence that the leukemic cells continued to grow in the mouse embryo cultures. On the other hand, mouse embryo cells exposed to leukemic filtrates and subsequently carried through 30 weekly passages by transfer of cells and supernatant fluids did carry virus, but the virus was released only erratically and unpredictably.

Manaker *et al.* (1960) showed that cultures of normal mouse spleen could be infected *in vitro* with cell-free preparations of Moloney's virus. Such infected cultures continued to release virus during 3 months of observation. Serial *in vitro* passage of virus through fresh spleen cultures derived from normal mice was possible provided sufficient time had elapsed to achieve adequate levels of virus in the cultures. An interval of 2 weeks between passages sufficed for the experiments described. There was no evidence of a cytopathic effect nor of neoplastic transformation within the cul-

tures. In other experiments, cultures derived from the spleen of normal BALB/c mice and propagated *in vitro* for 14 months were successfully infected with filtered virus previously passed *in vitro*. These cultures continue to release virus after more than 3 years of observation. Attempts to carry Rauscher's virus in mouse bone marrow cultures gave only limited success. Virus was released over a 6-week period, but infectivity of culture fluids was poor (Manaker, unpublished). Propagation of the Moloney virus *in vitro* was confirmed by Ginsberg and Sachs (1961).

Graffi's myeloid leukemia virus was not successfully propagated on roller tube cultures of mouse fibroblasts, brain, bone marrow, spleen, or whole embryo. Maitland-type cultures with mouse tissues were also inadequate. The nutrient fluids from leukemic lymph node cultures produced about 17% leukemia in test mice. Interestingly the virus was carried through 11 passages on the chorioallantois of the embryonated chicken egg and retained its leukemogenic potential (Graffi, 1959).

Also, Gross *et al.* (1961) successfully maintained the AK-derived "Passage A" virus strain in whole C3H/Bi mouse embryo cultures, but the virus did not reproduce in similar Swiss mouse cultures. The first successful isolation of virus directly from animals with spontaneous leukemia using tissue culture was made by Lemonde and Clode (1962). These investigators filtered and concentrated extracts of organs of AK mice with the spontaneous disease. The concentrates were used to infect spleen cultures from normal C3Hf mice. Tests in mice showed leukemogenic activity in supernatant tissue culture fluids.

M. LEUKEMIA VIRUS MORPHOLOGY

In the murine leukemias, the characteristic particles observed by electron microscopy (Dalton *et al.*, 1961) regularly occur in the intercellular spaces of the lymph nodes, thymus, and spleen. The best source of particles is the megakaryocyte; in these cells the particles collect in the system of intercommunicating channels in the cytoplasm. Particles are also contained within vacuoles in circulating platelets. Free virus may be sedimented from blood plasma.

In mice infected with the Moloney agent, small groups of particles, apparently immature, may exhibit electron-lucent nucleoids. The diameter of the nucleoid averages 60 mμ while the outer diameter of the whole particle varies considerably about a mean value of 100 mμ. The periphery of the electron-lucent nucleoid reacts strongly with lead salts, giving the image a ring-form in profile. The outer membrane is circular or ovoid and smoothly regular in form. A second membrane is located between the inner nucleoid and the outer membrane, and demarcates an area 85 mμ in diameter. The majority of extracellular particles, considered mature particles, have an electron-dense centrally-located nucleoid about 65 mμ in average diameter, an intermediate membrane, and a wrinkled or distorted outer membrane about 100 mμ in diameter. This is the type C particle of Bernhard (1958). In thin sections of cells from leukemic mice infected with the Moloney virus cylindrical particles as well as smaller type A particles are occasionally observed. Such A-type particles also have been reported to occur in mice infected with Graffi virus. The particles in the leukemia induced by the C-60 virus resemble those of the Moloney agent. They are type C particles, average 100 mμ in over-all diameter, have a smaller 74 mμ average diameter for the intermediate membrane, and average 58 mμ in diameter for the central nucleoid.

In mice afflicted with the disease induced by the Friend and the Gross viruses, the mature particles are smaller, averaging about 90 mμ in over-all diameter, while immature particles are 100 mμ in diameter. The electron-lucent nucleoid in the particles observed in mice infected with the Gross virus averages 58 mμ and the electron-dense nucleoid 57 mμ in diameter. The intermediate membrane averages 81 mμ, the same size as that of the Moloney agent. Particles in the Friend virus-induced leukemia have immature and mature nucleoids about 54 mμ in diameter, the smallest in the group of murine leukogenic agents. The diameter of the intermediate membrane is about 80 mμ. The fine structure of all the particles viewed in animals that had developed leukemia after inoculation of cell-free extracts of the different agents was similar. The consistent presence of the C-type particle in these animals is considered significant even though a positive correlation between number of particles and potency of extract has not been demonstrated (Dalton *et al.*, 1961).

The application of the negative-staining technique in electron microscopy using phosphotungstic acid to visualize particles in purified preparations of virus from mice with Moloney leukemia showed mature particles with characteristic hexagonal heads and well-formed tails. The diameter of the heads varied between 100 and 150 mμ and tails were about 250 mμ in length (Dalton *et al.*, 1962). Similar studies on material obtained from mice infected with the Rauscher agent showed 80 per cent of the particles to be tailed. The heads were predominantly hexagonal in shape and averaged 120 mμ in diameter; the tails varied in length up to 500 mμ (Zeigel and Rauscher, 1963).

N. Polyoma Virus Tumors in Mice

In the course of their independent studies with the AK mouse leukemia, both Gross (1953b) and Stewart (1953) had observed the development of neck tumors and subcutaneous sarcomas in some mice inoculated as newborns with extracts prepared from organs of leukemic mice. Stewart recognized the origin of the neck tumors to be in the parotid gland. Among 84 mice that Gross had inoculated with freshly filtered material, 9 died from leukemia and 15 others developed bilateral epitheliomas possibly arising from the salivary glands. Sections of these tumors were examined by Richter and by Furth. The former believed the tumor cells to be epithelial, arising from myoepithelial cells of salivary glands although no fibrils were seen. The latter identified them as tumors of the parotid gland. Furth indicated that the agent might also cause cancer in the mammary gland, and recommended further that the neck tumors be called "salivary gland tumor" (Gross, 1953b). Gross found that the leukemia agent could be sedimented by high-speed centrifugation, leaving the salivary gland tumor agent in the supernatant. The leukemic agent was also much more heat labile, and could be removed from a mixture of the agents by heating at 63° or 64°C. Fine filters would also retain the leukemia agent, and ether treatment would inactivate it. The salivary gland tumor agent was stable to such treatment (Gross, 1953b).

During her attempts to demonstrate the cell-free transmission of AK mouse leukemia to the C3H/He line of mice, Stewart (1953) observed the occurrence of parotid gland tumors 8–10 months post-inoculation. In similar experiments with leukemic extracts, Stewart (1955a,b) observed in inoculated mice pleomorphic tumors of the salivary glands, renal sarcomas, mammary adenocarcinomas, epithelial thymomas, and adrenal medullary tumors. Extracts of parotid tumors inoculated into newborn mice did not produce neoplasms, but when minced tissue from the same tumors was added to tissue cultures of monkey kidney or chicken embryo, the supernatant fluids induced multiple types of tumor in mice which had been inoculated when newborn (Stewart et al., 1957). Cultures of mouse embryo in horse serum medium eventually proved best for virus production. The name "polyoma" was proposed for the virus because it produced a large variety of tumors (Stewart and Eddy, 1958).

A polyoma virus-infected mouse has been observed to carry as many as 8 primary tumors of different types and as many as 26 different neoplasms have been recognized among infected mice. The mouse tumors develop within 2–12 months post-inoculation. The hamster appears more susceptible, for tumors arise as early as 2 weeks after infection. However, the neoplasms induced in hamsters are chiefly sarcomas and angiomas involving many organs. When multiple tumors appear, each appears to be a primary tumor and not the result of metastasis. In the rat, sarcomas and angiomas are induced by the polyoma agent, while in the rabbit only benign, subcutaneous, mesenchymal nodules have been observed. The latter regress in a few months. Neoplasms considered to be undifferentiated sarcomas

are also induced in guinea pigs that received polyoma virus when newborn, or virus plus adjuvant as adults. The tumors arise at the site of injection and, in some guinea pigs also in the liver, lung, spleen, adrenal, and kidney (Eddy et al., 1960).

The polyoma virus is highly antigenic. Antibodies are produced in mice, hamsters, and rabbits following infection (Stewart and Eddy, 1958). Hemagglutination at refrigerator temperature occurs with guinea pig, hamster, and human O red blood cells. The virus elutes from the erythrocytes at 37°C. Pretreatment of erythrocytes with receptor-destroying enzyme prevents hemagglutination. Hemagglutination-inhibiting antibodies are present in sera that inhibit tumor induction (Eddy et al., 1958b). Specific cytopathogenic changes are produced by the virus in mouse embryo tissue cultures (Eddy et al., 1958a). Plaque production by the virus on mouse cell monolayers can be used for quantitative estimation of active virus (Dulbecco and Freeman, 1959; Sachs and Winocour, 1959).

The polyoma virus is found in the nucleus of infected cells. Its nucleic acid is of the DNA type and has been found to be infectious (Di Mayorca et al., 1959). The virus particle has been classed as "type D" by Bernhard (1960). It has cubic symmetry, 42 capsomeres, and is naked (Lwoff et al., 1962). On the basis of these characteristics it falls into the "papova" virus group. Other members of the group include human wart virus, rabbit papilloma virus, and simian virus 40 designated by Melnick (1962) as "papova" viruses. Dourmashkin (1962) has reviewed the observations made on the particles observed in animals and cultures infected with polyoma agents. Besides the type D particle with diameters ranging from 28 to 45 mμ in thin sections, other morphological entities have been observed. These include 50 mμ particles, long filaments, and 100 mμ type C particles. The type D particles, considered to represent the polyoma virus, consist almost completely of electron-dense material. They may have a very thin, closely applied, external membrane. When closely packed, their shape may be polygonal. Hollow forms are also seen. The 50 mμ particles have been found only in the cytoplasm of mouse embryo cell cultures and in mesenchymal cells of infected newborn hamsters. They possess a core 40 mμ in diameter identical to the type D particle. Filaments have a diameter of 30–40 mμ and lengths up to more than 1 micron. Their surface subunits resemble those of the D particles. They are found in the nuclei and sometimes the cytoplasm of cells in infected mouse embryo cultures and in kidney cells of infected suckling hamsters. The 100 mμ type C particles are found in some cell cultures and in salivary gland tumors of some strains of mice infected with polyoma virus. They probably represent a viral contaminant.

The polyoma virus is remarkably stable and can be stored for long periods at 4°C as well as at lower temperatures. Complete inactivation is not obtained on exposure to temperatures as high as 70°C for 30 min. Ether does not affect infectivity, and the virus can be concentrated by precipitation in cold alcohol. It survives lyophilization and storage. Virus contained in hamster tumor tissue stored in 33% glycerol for over 2 months was not affected. Formalin has been successfully used to inactivate virus for vaccine production (Eddy, 1960).

Crawford (1962) studied the adsorption of polyoma virus hemagglutinin to cells in suspension and to cell debris. In such systems an equilibrium exists between free and adsorbed hemagglutinin which depends upon the dilution of the suspension, the temperature, and the pH. Plaque assay of a large dilution of a suspension would show most virus to be free, regardless of whether it had been initially free or not. Maximum hemagglutinin adsorption occurs at refrigerator temperatures. Receptor-destroying enzyme will release adsorbed virus, even at acid pH of 6.8. At this pH, without RDE, 80 per cent of the virus hemagglutinin remains adsorbed. At alkaline pH values of 7.5–8.5 adsorbed hemagglutinin is released. Thus treatment of cells and cell debris with RDE or alkaline buffer would greatly increase the efficiency of virus recovery.

O'Connor et al. (1963) studied the relationship of polyoma virus hemagglutinin to infectivity, using a large-plaque forming strain of virus. During electrophoresis in starch-agar gel at pH 8.6, hemagglutinating and infective biological activity migrated as a single sharp zone. When synthetic macromolecular polyglucose was used as a medium for gradient centrifugation, hemagglutinin was confined to a discrete band of buoyant density 1.17. However, only 5% of the infectivity was associated with this band; the remainder occurred at other densities. It appears that hemagglutinin dissociates from the infective particles in a polyglucose medium.

Density-gradient centrifugation of polyoma virus in cesium chloride solutions separated 2 types of particles (Crawford et al., 1962; Winocour, 1963). Electron microscopic examination of 1 band with buoyant density 1.297 disclosed empty particles. These had hemagglutinating activity but lacked infectivity. The U.V. absorption spectrum was typically protein-like. A second band with buoyant density 1.339 displayed both infective and hemagglutinating potential. Particles in this band appeared "full" in the electron microscope and showed a U.V. absorption spectrum typical of a nucleoprotein. The amount of DNA in "full" particles was estimated as 13.4 per cent.

The subviral infective agent (SIA) obtained by phenol extraction of polyoma virus-infected mouse embryo cultures or infective DNA from purified polyoma virus preparations was investigated by Weil (1961, 1962, 1963). The SIA is sensitive to DNAse, but not to RNAse or to chymotrypsin. Its buoyant density is 1.709 in cesium chloride whereas that of intact virus is 1.34. When the SIA is suspended in saline and heated at 100°C, it is denatured. If heated SIA is cooled rapidly, the denatured state is preserved. In this state it shows increased infectivity for mouse embryo cells, but it is rapidly inactivated by 1.8% formalin. Untreated SIA is relatively resistant to such inactivation. Heat-denatured SIA shows an unusual tendency to renature; more than one-half spontaneously renatured during centrifugation in a cesium chloride gradient. The tendency of the polyoma SIA to renature after heat denaturation is not understood.

When polyoma virus is injected into mice or hamsters of any age, the virus multiplies. Tumors eventually arise if the animals are infected as newborns; tumors do not usually develop following inoculation of adults. The virus is present in the saliva and urine of infected mice and thus contaminates bedding and drinking water (Rowe et al., 1958). In contrast, infected hamsters do not shed virus (Roizman and Roane, 1960). Antibody-positive female mice passively confer protection on their progeny. Transfer of immunity occurs apparently through the placenta during the prenatal period as well as through the mother's milk after parturition (Law et al., 1962). The virus, therefore, is widespread in mice, but neoplasms are not induced as a result of infection under natural conditions.

The reason tumors do not develop in an infected adult mouse is ascribed to immunological rejection of the developing tumor cells. Habel (1961) demonstrated the failure of transplanted polyoma tumor cells to grow in virus-immune mice. Similar results were described independently by Sjögren et al. (1961). The number of cells implanted into the virus-immune hosts is important for the demonstration of tumor rejection. Too large an inoculum will overcome the host reaction and permit tumor outgrowth. The phenomenon appears to be due to a new cellular antigen, which persists even in virus-induced tumor cells that no longer contain demonstrable virus. The newborn mouse becomes tolerant to the new antigen and, therefore, tumors eventually develop. Immunologically competent adult mice react to the neoplastic cells; these are rejected as they appear, and tumors never develop (Sjögren, 1961; Habel, 1962). Sachs (1962) found rejection of transplanted cells of Moloney virus-induced leukemia in mice previously inoculated with the homologous virus.

Some polyoma virus-induced mouse tumors carried by cell transplantation continue to release virus regularly; others appear to be virus free. Even growth in tissue culture does not elicit virus production by cells from the virus-free tumors. Similar observations were made with hamster tumor cells (Habel and Silverberg, 1960). In mouse embryo tissue cultures, the polyoma agent may destroy a large fraction of the cells, but those that remain grow out and repopulate the culture. Of the new population of cells some undergo neoplastic transformation. These are detected by the morphological characteristics of clones obtained by plating suspensions of the infected cells. A virus carrier state may exist in infected mouse cell cultures, and continuous release of virus occurs (Dulbecco and Vogt, 1960). However, not all cells in carrier cultures release virus, and clones of transformed cells apparently virus-free may be obtained, which retain their neoplastic character.

In hamster embryo cultures the virus does not produce cytolytic changes, although virus may be released. The agent transforms a small fraction of the cells (Stoker and MacPherson, 1961; Sachs and Medina, 1961; Stoker, 1962). Virus antigen cannot be detected in clones of transformed cells. An "early" state of transformation and progressive changes to neoplastic "late" transformed cells is discussed by Vogt and Dulbecco (1962a). The conditions affecting transformation were studied by Stoker and his co-workers in an established polyoma virus-susceptible line of hamster cells (Stoker and Abel, 1962). The relationship of the virus to transformed cells which no longer show evidence of its presence has attracted much attention. The experiments of Vogt and Dulbecco (1962b) were planned to determine whether virus was actually present but in forms such as: transforming but noncytocidal virus; incomplete virus detectable by fluorescent antibody or serum-blocking power; infectious nucleic acid; or provirus susceptible to inducing conditions that have been found to be effective in lysogenic bacteria. No evidence was obtained to suggest that virus was present in any of these forms in the affected cells. It was concluded that either virus is present in the transformed cells in a highly integrated state, or the cells do not contain the viral genome.

Variants of polyoma virus have been detected in the course of its propagation in vitro. Hare and Morgan (1963), carrying virus isolate SE-210 on L-cells, encountered a variant that not only had a new antigenic determinant but also was unable to produce hemagglutinin in P388D$_1$ cells or in mouse embryo cells as did the original isolate. In addition, a reduced oncogenic capacity for newborn hamsters was manifested. Two plaque variants of polyoma virus, both similar antigenically, were isolated on mouse embryo monolayers by Gotlieb-Stematsky and Leventon (1960). One of them produced small plaques and the other produced large plaques. The small plaque variant was markedly cytopathogenic for mouse cells, but had low hemagglutinating and oncogenic capacity. The large plaque-former was less cytopathogenic, but had good hemagglutinating and tumor-inducing ability. Rabson and Law (1963) could reduce the oncogenic potency of polyoma virus in mice by propagating it in P388D$_1$ cells cultured in a 20% autoclaved nonfat milk medium. This "M" virus produced plaques on mouse embryo monolayers, most of which were of the small variety, but 0–10% large plaques were observed. Passage of "M" virus through P338 cells in 40% human serum medium converted it to highly oncogenic "S" virus, which produced 28–50% large plaques in admixture with small plaques. The relationship of plaque size to oncogenicity was not determined, but the experiments of Gotlieb-Stematsky and Leventon suggest that these results are due to the relative amounts of each variant present in the inoculum. It is interesting to note that Medina and Sachs (1961) found the most cytolytic activity and the earliest cell transformation *in vitro* to be induced at 37°C by their small plaque variant Sp$_2$ in comparison with the activities of large plaque variants IL 11 and BP5. Higher virus yields were obtained with SP$_2$ because cultures infected with this variant had a greater fraction of virus-producing cells than did cultures infected with the large plaque variants. The SP$_2$ variant was not only more actively cytolytic, but gave a greater percentage of transformed cells (0.8–2.0%) than did BP5 (0.1–0.4%). Thus the virus strain as well as the cultural conditions and the cell-virus ratio influences the degree of polyoma virus-induced cell transformation (Medina and Sachs, 1963).

A3–4. OTHER VIRUSES THAT INDUCE TUMORS IN RODENTS

A. Simian Virus 40

The fact that many viruses have been isolated from monkey kidneys suggested to Eddy and her co-workers that this tissue might provide a tumor-inducing agent. Fluids from monkey kidney cultures were inoculated into newborn hamsters, and eventually undifferentiated sarcomas arose at the site of inoculation (Eddy et al., 1961). The virus responsible for the oncogenic response was identified as the vacuolating virus, SV 40, which Sweet and Hilleman previously had isolated from tissue cultures of monkey kidney cells (Sweet and Hilleman, 1960; Eddy et al., 1962; Girardi et al., 1962). Eddy et al. (1962) successfully reisolated the virus from 2 tumor-bearing hamsters that had been inoculated as newborns. The animals were 203 and 304 days old, respectively, when sacrificed for the virus isolation studies. Besides subcutaneous tumors at the site of injection, occasional tumors were observed in the lungs or kidneys. Intracerebral inoculation of newborn hamsters with large amounts of virus resulted in the formation of ependymomas (Gerber and Kirschstein, 1962). Surprisingly, subcutaneous inoculation of newborn mastomys (*Rattus natalensis*) with SV 40 induced brain tumors with the histopathologic characteristics of papillary ependymomas. Thus the oncogenic activity of this simian virus is not limited to the hamster (Rabson et al., 1962a).

Virus could not be demonstrated in extracts of the hamster ependymomas, but when intact tumor cells were seeded on monolayer cultures of African green monkey cells, the indicator cells for SV 40 cytopathic activity, Gerber and Kirschstein (1962) found that a small fraction of the hamster cells appeared to release trace amounts of virus. No free virus could be detected in tumor cell culture fluids nor in lysates of tumor cells, even after 14 months of cultivation, when these materials were inoculated onto rabbit kidney or monkey kidney cells. However, when 20,000 intact tumor cells were inoculated onto green monkey kidney cultures or onto rabbit kidney cultures, a yield of 10^5 infectious units of virus was detected within 10 days in the former cultures and 10^2 infectious units of virus in the latter. Since rabbit kidney cells fail to absorb intact particles of SV 40, the results suggest that a viral precursor may have been transferred and that viral nucleic acid may have persisted in some of the cells (Gerber, 1963).

Sabin and Koch (1963) noted intermittent release of virus by occasional SV 40-induced hamster tumors carried in serial transplant passage in adult hamsters. No inhibitors or antibodies against SV 40 were involved. *In vitro* cultures of these tumors also did nòt release virus continuously, but in an intermittent fashion. There was no production of infectious virus when large amounts of SV 40 were added to the cultures. Tumors could be produced by transplantation of an average of 2 cells into adult hamsters. Nine of 12 such tumors yielded minute amounts of virus. This is considered to indicate that most, if not all, of the tumor cells carried the SV 40 viral genome in a noninfectious state. Apparently maturation to infectious virus is a rare event in an occasional cell.

SV 40 grows without producing a cytopathic effect in rhesus or cynomolgus kidney cell cultures, but in cultured kidney cells of the green monkey, *Cercopithecus aethiops* (Sweet and Hilleman, 1960), it grows and causes marked cytoplasmic vacuolation within 4–7 days. Rabson and Kirschstein (1962) cultured explants of newborn hamster kidney infected with SV 40. Cell suspensions of the cultures implanted into newborn hamsters produced tumors within 17 days that on histological examination were found to be predominantly undifferentiated carcinomas. However areas of adenocarcinoma, sarcoma, and, in one animal, well-differentiated epidermoid carcinoma were also present. The virus was recovered from infected cultures and from 1 of 2 hamster tumors tested. When primary hamster kidney cell monolayers were infected with SV 40 and held for long-term observation, Black and Rowe (1963) noted nonspecific early cellular degeneration. Regrowth was observed during the second

month of culture, permitting cell passage to be made on the 71st day. SV 40 was continuously demonstrable in the cultures, which consisted of abnormal fibroblasts, areas of epithelial cells, and some polynucleated cells. A decrease in contact inhibition and an increase in acid production as well as in ease of passage were also noted. The cells grew as local tumors within 3–4 weeks after they were implanted subcutaneously in 1-month-old hamsters. The tumors contained fibroblastic and epithelial cells, forms both of which showed heteroploidy with hyperidiploid chromosome counts. Similar transformation of hamster renal cells in tissue culture was observed by Shein et al. (1963). Virus could not be detected in subcultures of the transformed cells. The types of transformed cells observed were similar to those reported by Black and Rowe, namely epithelial, syncytial, and fibroblastoid forms.

The past presence of SV 40 virus in poliomyelitis virus vaccines (Sweet and Hilleman, 1960), although now corrected, is still cause for concern. The virus apparently is capable of infecting man by the respiratory route. Although measures may be taken to cope with the problem of contamination by this agent, the fact that the chance availability of a suitable indicator host system demonstrated the presence of an otherwise nondetectable agent in rhesus monkey kidney cultures raises the question of other as yet undetected viruses in biological reagents. Multiplication of SV 40 was demonstrated in cultures of human kidney, intestine, brain, skin, muscle, lung, liver, heart, adrenal, spleen, and testis (Shein and Enders, 1962). No cytopathic effect was noted during the first passage in these cultures, but subsequent passage in human kidney cells was accompanied by the occurrence in nuclei of vacuoles or eosinophilic inclusions and an increase in cell proliferation and necrosis. Explants of human thyroid (Rabson et al., 1962b) infected with the virus continued to release the agent in quantity over 4 months' observation. Intranuclear virus was noted in about 5% of the cells both by electron microscopy and by fluorescent antibody techniques. Attempts to achieve tumor growth from transplants of SV 40-infected human thyroid in hamsters and in green monkey brain were not successful. Pontén *et al.* (1963) observed alteration of some human skin cells or stable diploid fibroblasts in cultures infected with SV 40, but sustained progressive growth of the transformed cells in mice and rats or in cancer patients could not be demonstrated. Implantation of converted cells into 2 of the original tissue donors gave rise to small nodules which eventually regressed. Immunological mechanisms appeared to be involved in the rejection.

The simian vacuolating virus is included in the "papova" group of viruses (Melnick, 1962). It is without effect in newborn mice or in embryonated eggs. The virus withstands heating at 56°C for 1 hour, is stable to diethyl ether treatment, may be stored at −20°C or −70°C, but loses infectivity on exposure to 1 : 4000 formalin at 37°C. A hemagglutinin has not been demonstrated (Sweet and Hilleman, 1960). A subviral infectious unit sensitive to DNAse but not to RNAse was prepared by Gerber (1962), using cold phenol extraction. Mayor *et al.* (1963) found that the diameter of the whole virus particle averages 45 mμ. The particle has a buoyant density of 1.30 and a molecular weight of 4.4×10^7. Nine % of it is double-stranded DNA, which corresponds to a minimum molecular weight of 4×10^6 avograms of DNA per virus particle. The capsid has 42 protein capsomeres arranged in the icosohedral (5 : 3 : 2) pattern, and calculations show that it is composed of 240 "chemical" subunits, each with an approximate molecular weight of 167,000.

B. ADENOVIRUS

The tumor-inducing potentiality of human adenovirus type 12 was discovered by Trentin *et al.* (1962). Intrapulmonary injection of this agent into newborn hamsters resulted in the appearance of tumors in the thorax and in some cases in the liver. The tumors apparently were the result of specific adenovirus type 12 activity, and not to chance contamination with polyoma virus or SV 40. The susceptibility of hamsters was highest at birth and decreased rapidly with age (Yabe *et al.*, 1962). In animals of a given age, the tumor incidence was directly proportional to virus dose. Animals as old as 3 weeks did not develop tumors following injection of virus.

Huebner *et al.* (1962) screened the 28 human prototypes of human adenoviruses for tumor-inducing ability. They confirmed Trentin's observations and observed similar tumor-inducing activity with the type 18 virus. Three hamsters of 80 inoculated with simian adenoviruses M1-M4 developed tumors. Tumors arose at the site of inoculation when virus was given intrathoracically, intraperitoneally, subcutaneously, or intracerebrally. In the latter instance they apparently arose from the meninges. Interestingly, these 2 adenoviruses are the only nonhemagglutinating members of the group. Infective virus has not been reisolated from tumors induced by them despite the fact that the titer of complement-fixing antibody in the tumor-bearing host reaches a peak at the time tumor appears. This suggests that replication of viral components occurs within the tumor cells. The infection may be abortive, resulting in reproduction of incomplete virus which is still capable of stimulating antibody formation. Huebner *et al.* (1962) emphasized the importance of serological surveys of cancer patients to ascertain the relative prevalence and titers of antibodies against these agents. Data of this type would provide the information necessary to assess the role of these agents in human neoplastic disease.

A3–5. RABBIT TUMOR VIRUSES

A. SHOPE RABBIT PAPILLOMA VIRUS

Many wild cottontail rabbits in the midwestern states develop papillomas on the skin of the neck, shoulders, and abdomen. Their transmission by filtrates to both wild and domestic rabbits was accomplished by Shope (1933). Small, benign papillomas, which sometimes are found in mouths of domestic rabbits, are induced by another virus (Parsons and Kidd, 1936); these tumors do not develop spontaneously in wild cottontails. Humans, horses, cattle, and dogs all develop papillomas or wartlike lesions transmissible by cell-free extracts. Gross (1961c) summarized the information on each of these conditions. At present the

Shope papilloma has been the most extensively studied.

Nothing definite is known of the natural mode of transmission of the agent in wild rabbits, but biting insects such as ticks are suspect because the disease has been passaged by such vectors under laboratory conditions (Dalmat, 1958). The cells of the traumatized germinal layer of the skin must be infected to insure transmission; no tumors develop if virus is introduced by any route not contacting injured susceptible skin cells (Rous and Beard, 1934). The virus is exclusively dermotropic, epithelium from skin follicles and glands and mucosal epithelium being entirely refractory. There is some indication that hormonal factors may affect susceptibility of the animal, for it has been observed that hypophysectomized rabbits exhibit some resistance to development of lesions following inoculation with the Shope virus (Lacassagne and Nyka, 1936).

When domestic rabbits (Rous and Beard, 1935a,b) or wild rabbits (Syverton and Berry, 1935) have borne the virus-induced papillomas for several months, carcinomas may develop through transition of the benign lesions. Syverton (1952) kept rabbits for an extended period to learn the natural papilloma-to-carcinoma sequence. Twenty-five % of wild cottontails and 75% of domestic rabbits with papillomas which were held for longer than 6 months developed cancers. The specific role of the virus in the formation of carcinomas is unknown.

Infectious papilloma virus may be extracted from the warts of cottontail rabbits in large quantities. The virus is not detectable in the rapidly multiplying germinal cells, although they are obviously infected. Virus is located in intact nuclei of differentiating cells in the horny upper layers of the wart (Moore et al., 1959b; Stone et al., 1959; Noyes and Mellors, 1957; Noyes, 1959). The papillomas induced in domestic rabbits yield extracts with apparently little or no tumor-inducing potency. By means of fluorescent antibody studies (Mellors, 1960) relatively few antigen-containing foci are demonstrable in the domestic rabbit papillomas in comparison with the numbers seen in lesions of wild rabbits. A higher humoral antibody titer is also detectable in wild rabbits from which much virus is recovered (Kidd, 1938 a,b) than in domestic rabbits. Although the tumors of the domestic rabbit usually appear to contain no infectious virus, antibodies specific for the Shope virus arise in hosts in which these tumors are induced or transplanted. Thus, Syverton (1952) observed that if cottontail papilloma virus were not available as a reagent to establish immunologic evidence for the presence of virus, the induced growth in the domestic rabbit would inevitably fall into the category of a nonviral mammalian tumor, even though its viral etiology might be suspect.

Although the malignant carcinomas associated with old papillomas grow with difficulty in other domestic rabbits, one such growth, the VX2 carcinoma, was successfully maintained in transplant whole-cell passage. The rabbit hosts which carried the neoplasm for at least the first 5 years developed antibodies against the papilloma virus. When tests were again made several years later, antibody was no longer detected (Kidd, 1942; Smith et al., 1947). Whether this loss of specific antigenicity is due to loss of the agent or to change in its antigenic structure is unknown. In other carcinomas derived from papilloma-bearing rabbits, virus antigen could be demonstrated by the evocation of immune responses in wild rabbits (Kidd, 1950). The VX7 carcinoma which was started in transplant passage by Rous many years ago continued to induce specific antibody against the Shope papilloma viral antigen through its 47th passage. Fluorescent antibody techniques showed viral antigen to be localized in the nuclei of the VX7 carcinoma cells (Mellors, 1960).

The apparent absence of infective virus from papillomas of their malignant derivatives which retained immunizing capacity suggested that virus was present in "masked form." Beard (1957b) considered that the low sensitivity of the test-host to papilloma induction by virus provided the basis for the assumption of a noninfective or masked form of the virus. Indeed, when the skin was treated with turpentine and acetone or with methylcholanthrene to induce hyperplasia, it was much more susceptible to infection. Protection of the inoculated skin area with paraffined gauze increased the sensitivity of response (Friedewald, 1942, 1944; Friedewald and Kidd, 1944; Friedewald and Rous, 1944). This permitted detection of virus in tumors in which it would previously have been considered to be masked.

During the first 6 months post-infection, 25–35% of the animals naturally reject their tumors. The regression rate may be increased to between 50 and 90% by inoculating the rabbits with vaccine made of fresh homologous tumor cells (Evans *et al.*, 1962a). The natural regression of papillomas may, therefore, be a consequence of a specific immunological reaction against the tumor cells. Specific antiviral immunity has no influence on tumor regression. Inoculation of rabbits with the tumor cell vaccine also reduced the successful transplantation of the VX7 carcinoma from 100 to 50% (Evans *et al.*, 1962b). Kreider (1963) sought to determine whether the papilloma regression mechanism was directed specifically against papilloma cells by attempting to demonstrate anamnestic response in animals in which papillomas had regressed upon secondary exposure to autologous papilloma tissue. Chips of skin, washed free of antiviral antibody, were infected in organ cultures. They were then autografted to uninoculated, to virus-immune, and to papilloma-bearing rabbits. Papillomas developed in all of the explants. If similar grafts were made to animals whose papillomas had previously regressed, tumors either did not develop or soon regressed. On the other hand, washed skin from regressor animals treated with virus became papillomatous when transplanted to the cheek pouch of cortisonized hamsters. These results suggest that specific immunity directed against papilloma cells develops in regressor animals. To Syverton *et al.* (1950), it seemed that regression resulted from failure of the germinal layers to multiply. Since regression may occur in all tumors in a given animal at the same time, Evans *et al.* (1962a) consider it most plausible that a systemic, specifically immune process is operative. Whether the process is humoral or cell-associated and whether the antigen is "viral" or "cellular" remains to be established.

A tumor-producing factor sensitive to DNAse, unaffected by antisera against Shope papilloma virus, was extracted from cottontail papilloma tissue (Ito, 1960; Ito and Evans, 1961). Tumor-producing DNA extracts were also obtained from domestic rabbit tumors and purified virus. Carcinomas also eventually arose at sites of papillomas induced by the DNA extracts. DNA extracts from some primary carcinomas evoked papillomas in test animals. Successful induction of papillomas with 3.6% incidence was accomplished with DNA extracted from the transplanted VX7 carcinoma. Thus functioning viral nucleic acid may exist in these cells (Ito, 1963). Hodes *et al.* (1963) confirmed Ito's work but failed to demonstrate infective DNA in extracts prepared from the VX2 or VX7 carcinomas.

The Shope papilloma virus is a member of the "papova" group of DNA viruses. It resists temperatures of 65°C for 30 min. The particles observed in thin sections in the electron microscope are 26–29 mμ in diameter, with a densely-staining, thick threadlike or granular material comprising most of the demonstrable substance of the particle (Haguenau *et al.*, 1960). Numerous electron-lucent "ghost" forms are also evident in these preparations. Four bands have been obtained on centrifugation in cesium chloride density gradients (Breedis *et al.*, 1962). The heaviest particles, with density 1.34, contained the highest proportion of DNA and probably represent the complete virus. Intermediate layers of densities 1.33 and 1.32 had less DNA, and the top layer of density 1.29 had little or none. The lightest particles seemed to be loose aggregates of capsomeres, many of which disintegrated into free capsomeres on the electron microscope grid. Their structure was suggestive of hollow cylinders or cups.

B. The Rabbit Fibroma Virus

Shope observed small, egg-shaped, subcutaneous nodules on the legs of a wild rabbit killed near Princeton, N.J., in 1931. He (Shope, 1932a) described the tumors as resembling spindle-celled sarcomas but atypical in that lymphocytic infiltration was apparent at their bases, and the overlying epidermis extended down in bulbous masses into the substance of the tumor. The tumors could be transplanted in domestic rabbits and sometimes persisted for 10–15 days, but usually regression began in 2–3 days. In a wild rabbit, a tumor induced by tumor cell suspension persisted for 77 days. The fibroma virus may be transmitted by filtrates, but is not contagious. Mosquitoes and fleas can transmit the virus to normal rabbits (Kilham and Woke, 1953). Fibromas, similarly transmissible by filtrates, have been observed in grey squirrels (Kilham et al., 1953) and deer (Shope, 1955).

The rabbit fibroma virus is immunologically related to the squirrel fibroma virus and to rabbit myxoma (Shope, 1932b). The myxoma virus induces a contagious, rapidly fatal disease of domestic rabbits. Myxomatosis was first reported by Sanarelli (1898). It is characterized by firm, gelatinous nodular tumors around the nose, ears, mouth, and genitalia of the affected rabbit. Cells in the nodules undergo dissolution and vesicles appear in the epidermis. If the animal lives long enough, crusts capping the nodules replace the vesicles (Rivers, 1930). The myxoma virus does not produce disease in the cottontail, but inoculated rabbits become resistant to fibroma infection. However, their sera show only doubtful neutralization of myxoma or fibroma virus. Serum from domestic rabbits which had recovered from infection with fibroma virus did not neutralize myxoma virus, but serum from one domestic rabbit that survived myxoma infection neutralized both myxoma and fibroma virus (Shope, 1932b).

Berry and Dedrick (1936) showed that viable fibroma virus could reactivate heated myxoma virus. When viable fibroma virus was mixed with heat-inactivated myxoma virus and inoculated into domestic rabbits, fatal myxomatosis developed in some of the recipients. Kilham (1957, 1958) reproduced the reactivation phenomenon in tissue cultures of rabbit kidney or testis by inoculating them with heat-inactivated myxoma virus and either rabbit or squirrel fibroma virus. The reactivation phenomenon is not limited to these viruses, but is general among the pox group of viruses (Hanafusa et al., 1959; Fenner et al., 1959).

Fibroma virus inoculation into newborn rabbits gives rise to a generalized disease with widespread tumors and results in death of the animals when larger doses are given (Duran-Reynals, 1940). A similar pattern of disease can be produced in adult rabbits by treating them with massive doses of cortisone (Harel and Constantin, 1954) or total body irradiation (Clemmesen, 1938). Whereas a small tumor arises and soon regresses in normal adult rabbits inoculated by the subcutaneous route, enormous sarcoma-like tumors are induced by similar inoculation of a rabbit previously given one injection of tar intramuscularly or subcutaneously (Ahlström and Andrewes, 1938).

Fibroma virus is a member of the pox group of DNA viruses. The agent develops in a matrix or "viroplasm" in the cytoplasm of the infected cells. The matrix has the form of an inclusion body under the light microscope. The morphology of the virus particle resembles that of vaccinia virus when dried and shadowed with chromium. Bernhard et al. (1954), working with thin sections, have reported the diameter of the particles to be between 220 and 240 mμ. The particles have a well-defined limiting membrane. In some instances an eccentrically-placed dense nucleoid, 60–70 mμ in diameter, is found close to the membrane. Febvre (1962) described the appearance of the particles in the electron microscope and reviewed the literature on this virus.

The fibroma virus does not produce discrete lesions on the chorioallantoic membrane of the embryonated hen's egg, nor does it agglutinate red cells. The adult rabbit has been used as a test animal to assay pools of virus, but Febvre (1962) indicates that the newborn rabbit is a more sensitive indicator host. Febvre has also used with success a sensitive line of rabbit testis cells for in vitro assays. Verna and Eylar (1962) described a plaque assay for the virus on rabbit cell cultures. They observed a linear relationship between the virus concentration and the plaque count. The composition of the nutritional medium was found to influence the number of plaques obtained.

A3–6. YABA VIRUS

Another pox virus, which produces subcutaneous nodules in rhesus monkeys, was observed at the West African Institute for Medical Research at Yaba, near Lagos. The disease can be serially transmitted by subcutaneous or intradermal inoculation. The nodules which arise regress in a month or more. Filtrates passed through a 650 mμ gradocol membrane are active. Cytoplasmic inclusions and elementary bodies are observed in nodules and in infected cells in rhesus monkey kidney cultures. The nodules contain many large polyhedral cells with densely-staining, Feulgen-positive material in paranuclear masses or as fine granules (Andrewes *et al.*, 1959). The virus is ineffective in newborn or adult rodents or in embryonated eggs (Feltz, 1951). Immunity follows regression in the monkeys *Macaca mulatta* and *Macaca irus*.

Niven *et al.* (1961) considered the pleomorphic polygonal cells in the nodules induced by the agent to be most likely derived from fibrocytes. Light and electron microscopic examinations of the affected cells showed developmental stages resembling those of the pox viruses. Unlike vaccinia virus the agent appeared to be specific for the monkey, and also differed from the former in the lesions produced and its tissue cell specificity. In limited cross-immunity tests, no relationship to vaccinia was evident. Although lesions developed in monkey kidney cell cultures, the virus was not maintained therein for more than 3 passages. Sproul *et al.* (1963) noted innumerable growths in the skeletal muscle, subcutaneous tissues, and internal organs of monkeys given intravenous injection of the agent. They consider the disease to be a disorder of histiocytic derivation.

A3–7. PLANT TUMOR VIRUSES

A. THE WOUND-TUMOR VIRUS

Black (1945) described woody tumors on the roots of plants susceptible to the virus *Aureogenus magnivena*. Forty-three species of plants in 20 families were found to be susceptible, and perhaps many susceptible species remained undiscovered. In most species, veins of leaves are irregularly enlarged, and enations or vein tumors form on the under side of leaves. Tumors are also produced on crowns of some hosts and on the petioles of others. The stems of *Melilotus alba* as well as the roots become afflicted. The names "wound-tumor disease" and "wound-tumor virus" were suggested for the disease and the virus, respectively, because evidence indicated wounds were involved in the origin of at least some of the tumors. The high frequency of root tumors was ascribed to the wounds made by lateral roots as they break through the endodermis, cortex, and epidermis from their origin as meristems in the pericycle. Wounds made with pins on stems of infected plants usually gave rise to one or more stem tumors, indicating the systemic nature of the infection (Black, 1946).

Valleau (1947) reported a systemic disease of tobacco which seemed to resemble Black's wound-tumor disease. The disease was given the name "clubroot" because it resembled clubroot of cabbage. Affected tobacco plants develop short upper leaves, but the lower leaves are normal giving the plant a pyramidal shape. Growth is stunted. On young roots, tumors develop where rootlets originate, while old roots increase in size until the whole root becomes an irregular mass of tumor tissue. The symptoms of the diseases produced in Turkish tobacco by wound-tumor virus and by the clubroot virus are quite similar, though not identical, suggesting that the viruses may be related to each other. However, some indication of a lack of relationship between the 2 viruses has been obtained by Selsky (1961), using serological methods.

The wound-tumor virus (WTV) is transmitted by the leafhoppers *Agalliopis novella*, *Agallia constricta*, and *Agallia quadripunctata* (Maramorosch *et al.*, 1949). The insects become infected if they feed on diseased plants for 2 weeks or more. The virus is transmitted to other plants on which the insects feed. Such transmission cannot be attained in plants by mechanical means, but in the leafhoppers the virus may be established by intra-abdominal injection of extracts from either infected insects or plants. The incubation period of the virus in the insect is about 2 weeks at temperatures of 25°–30°C (Maramorosch, 1950). At lower temperatures the incubation period is extended and transmission is poor. At 37°C there is no transmission of WTV. At a given temperature, the incubation period in the plant appears to be related to that in the insect. Once infected, the insect carries virus until it dies. About 1.8% of the progeny of infected females of *Agalliopis novella* also carried the WTV (Black, 1953), apparently transmitted through the egg.

The WTV belongs to the RNA group of viruses. It has been estimated to have an over-all diameter of about 60 mμ, 92 subunits in the capsid, and a core of 35 mμ (Bils and Hall, 1962). The agent survives drying and storage at 0°C. In crude extracts, infectivity is not lost after 10 min at 50°C, but no activity remains after similar incubation at 60°C. The agent is inactivated within an hour at pH below 4 or above 9 (Brakke *et al.*, 1953).

Purified WTV was used to prepare antiserum in the rabbit (Black, 1954). Virus from either plant or insect sources yielded common antigenic reactions. A small second antigen was associated with the virus in infected hosts and is perhaps the same entity as a small antigen that is observed when purified virus breaks down in suspensions. Precipitation, complement-fixation, and specific neutralization were demonstrated with the antiserum. By precipitin ring tests, soluble antigen (WTSA) was detected in most insects of the species *A. constricta* infected with massive doses of WTV (Whitcomb and Black, 1961). Insects negative for WTSA failed to transmit virus to plants, but some positive for WTSA also failed to transmit the agent. Fluorescein-conjugated antibody applied to infected sweet clover plant sections showed WTV antigen to be concentrated in the pseudophloem issue of root and stem tumors and in a few thick-walled cells in the xylem region; specific staining was not observed in other tissues (Nagaraj and Black, 1961). The morphological similarity of WTV to the reoviruses led Streissle and Ma-

ramorosch (1963) to test for serological relationships between these agents by complement-fixation. The results showed serological cross reactivity indicating the presence of a common complement-fixing antigen between these animal viruses and WTV.

A3–8. OTHER TUMOR VIRUSES

Tumor-inducing agents have been associated with the induction of mast cell sarcoma in dogs (Lombard and Moloney, 1959) and melanotic tumors in *Drosophila melanogaster* (Friedman *et al.*, 1957; Burton *et al.*, 1957), and they may be related to some tumors of fish (Nigrelli, 1952; Wessing and von Bargen, 1959). Lucké (1934) detected interesting tumors in the kidneys of leopard frogs in Vermont. A virus extracted from such tumors induced similar neoplasms in other leopard frogs (Duryee, 1956). The early tumors do not tend to metastasize, but as they grow to large size, infiltrating and destroying kidney tissue, metastatic tumor is carried to other organs, notably the lungs and liver. Prominent acidophilic inclusions are present in some of the tumor cells. A higher tumor incidence is promoted by high environmental temperatures and advanced age (Rafferty, 1962).

A3–9. VIRUSES ASSOCIATED WITH HUMAN LEUKEMIA

With the successful demonstration of the cell-free transmission of the murine leukemia a renewed effort is under way to determine the role of viral agents in the human disease. At this time no virus has been proven to be related to human leukemia. Bergol'ts and Shershul'skaia (1958) propagated a "human leukemic factor" in embryonated eggs which was detected in the allantoic fluid with the aid of anaphylactic reaction with desensitization. Bergol'ts (1958a) observed increased incidences of leukemia in low-leukemia strains of mice (C57, C3Ha and noninbred strains) which had received inoculations of Seitz-filtered extracts of tissues from leukemic humans.

The animals had been given a series of cortisone injections, beginning 1 month post-inoculation. Mice which had been inoculated with extracts of brain showed an incidence of leukemia as high as 25% with an average period of latency of 3.7 months. Eleven % reacted similarly to leukemic blood. Control animals which had received "normal" brain filtrate had an incidence of 3.4%. The leukemia factor from human leukemics was serially propagated on the chorioallantoic membrane of chicken embryos for over 3 months. The allantoic fluids with added cortisone were used for passage and for inoculation of mice. Leukemoid reactions were noted in many animals, and true leukemias were observed in 15–20% as compared with 2.7% leukemia in controls (Bergol'ts, 1958b).

Schwartz *et al.* (1956) also demonstrated leukemogenic activity in extracts of human leukemic brain by mouse inoculation. They used young adults of the high-leukemia strain AKR mice. These animals were shown not to develop spontaneous leukemia under 22 weeks of age, while all those inoculated with brain extracts died with leukemia within a few weeks post-injection. The active factor could be passaged blindly through Swiss mice and still showed high-leukemogenic activity in the AKR mouse test system (Schwartz *et al.,* 1958).

De Long (1960) used filtrates of human leukemic tissues and De Carvalho *et al.* (1960) used RNA preparations from similar sources to inoculate mice. An increased incidence of mouse leukemia was observed in each instance. Such leukemic responses have not been limited to mice, for Ageenko (1962) found human leukemic tissue extracts to have leukemogenic activity in rats.

Tissue culture techniques have been employed for some years in the search for virus in human reticular neoplasms. Despite the wealth of interesting observations suggestive of viral activity, no agent specifically related to the human diseases has been established in the laboratory. Bostick (1952) has summarized early work with Hodgkin's disease. Tissue cultures of diseased tissue showed various abnormalities of behavior which were no more than suggestive of virus activity. Multinucleated giant cells were prominent and cytoplasmic inclusions and phagocytic activity were prevalent, but all this is seen in most cultures of other lymphomas and in some normal cultures, although not to the degree observed with the Hodgkin's tissue (Bostick, 1952). De Carvalho (1959) inoculated preparations from human leukemic tissues into human amnion cultures. Culture fluids as well as the RNA preparations were tumorigenic in mice (De Carvalho *et al.,* 1960). Sykes *et al.* (1962) recorded the presence of cytoplasmic inclusions and alterations in the perinuclear zone of cultured cells from 50% of cases of leukemia and Hodgkin's disease. These changes were not seen in cultures of nonleukemic lymph nodes. The changes could not be serially transmitted in freshly isolated or stable lines of human cells. The actual presence of a virus in these preparations remains to be demonstrated. Since tumor cells may carry viruses unrelated to the neoplastic condition, no special significance can be attributed to the presence of virus in leukemic nodes without direct proof of an association of the agent with the disease condition.

A3–10. LITERATURE CITED

Ageenko, A. I. (1962). Acta Unio Intern. Contra Cancrum 18, 140.

Ahlström, C. G., and Andrewes, C. H. (1938). J. Pathol. Bacteriol. 47, 65.

Ahlström, C. G., and Forsby, N. (1962). J. Exptl. Med. 115, 839.

Ahlström, C. G., and Jonsson, N. (1962a). Acta Pathol. Microbiol. Scand. 54, 136.

Ahlström, C. G., and Jonsson, N. (1962b). Acta Pathol. Microbiol. Scand. 54, 145.

Ahlström, C. G., Jonsson, N., and Forsby, N. (1962). Acta Pathol. Microbiol. Scand. Suppl. 154, 127.

Andervont, H. B., and Bryan, W. R. (1944). J. Nat. Cancer Inst. 5, 143.

Andrewes, C. H. (1931). J. Pathol. Bacteriol. 34, 91.

Andrewes, C. H., Allison, A. C., Armstrong, J. A., Bearcroft G., Niven, J. S. F., and Periera, H. G. (1959). Acta Unio Intern. Contra Cancrum 15, 760.

Baluda, M. A. (1962). Cold Spring Harbor Symp. Quant. Biol. 27, 415.

Barnum, C. P., Ball, Z. B., Bittner, J. J., and Visscher, M. B. (1944). Science 100, 575.

Bather, R. (1957). Brit. J. Cancer 11, 611.

Bather, R. (1961). Brit. J. Cancer 15, 114.

Bather, R. (1963). Proc. Amer. Assoc. Cancer Res. 4, 4.

Beard, J. W. (1957a). Ann. N. Y. Acad. Sci. 68, 473.

Beard, J. W. (1957b). D. L. Walker, R. P. Hanson and A. S. Evans (eds.), Symposium on Latency and Masking in Viral and Rickettsial Infections. 20. Burgess Publ. Co., Minneapolis.

Begg, A. M. (1927). Lancet 212, 912.

Begg, A. M. (1929). Brit. J. Exptl. Pathol. 10, 322.

Bergman, S., and Jonsson, N. (1962). Acta Pathol. Microbiol. Scand. Suppl. 154, 130.

Bergol'ts, V. M. (1958a). Bull. Exptl. Biol. Med. (U.S.S.R.) (English Transl.) 45, 731.

Bergol'ts, V. M. (1958b). Bull. Exptl. Biol. Med. (U.S.S.R.) (English Transl.) 47, 849.

Bergol'ts, V. M., and Shershul'skaia, L. V. (1958). Bull. Exptl. Biol. Med. (U.S.S.R.) (English Transl.) 5, 604.

Bergs, V. V., and Groupé, V. (1962a). J. Nat. Cancer Inst. 29, 723.

Bergs, V. V., and Groupé, V. (1962b). J. Nat. Cancer Inst. 29, 739.

Bernhard, W. (1958). Cancer Res. 18, 491.

Bernhard, W. (1960). Cancer Res. 20, 712.

Bernhard, W., Bauer, A., Harel, J., and Oberling, C. (1954). Bull. Cancer 61, 423.

Berry, G. P., and Dedrick, H. M. (1936). J. Bacteriol. 31, 50.

Bielka, H., and Graffi, A. (1959). Acta Biol. Med. Ger. 3, 515.

Bielka, H., Fey, F., and Graffi, A. (1955). Naturwissenschaften 42, 563.

Bils, R. F., and Hall, C. E. (1962). Virology 17, 123.

Bittner, J. J. (1936). Science 84, 162.

Bittner, J. J. (1939). Public Health Rep. (U.S.) 54, 1827.

Bittner, J. J. (1941). Cancer Res. 1, 113.

Bittner, J. J. (1943). Cancer Res. 3, 441.

Bittner, J J. (1957). Proc. II Internat. Symposium on Mammary Cancer. Univ. Perugia. P. 491.

Bittner, J. J., and Imagawa, D. T. (1955). Cancer Res. 15, 464.

Black, L. M. (1945). Am. J. Botany 23, 408.

Black, L. M. (1946). Nature 158, 56.

Black, L. M. (1953). Phytopathology 43, 9.

Black, L. M. (1954). Phytopathology 44, 482.

Black, P. H., and Rowe, W. P. (1963). Virology 19, 107.

Blair, P. B. (1963). Cancer Res. 23, 381.

Borges, P. F., and Duran-Reynals, F. (1952). Cancer Res. 12, 55.

Borsos, T., and Bang, F. B. (1957). Virology 4, 385.

Bostick, W. L. (1952). Ann. N. Y. Acad. Sci. 54, 1162.

Bostick, W. L., Smith, M. E., and Siegel, B. V. (1958). Federation Proc. 17, 430.

Brakke, M. K., Maramorosch, K., and Black, L. M. (1953). Phytopathology 43, 387.

Breedis, C., Berwick, L., and Anderson, T. F. (1962). Virology 17, 84.

Bryan, W. R. (1955). J. Nat. Cancer Inst. 16, 287.

Bryan, W. R. (1956). J. Nat. Cancer Inst. 16, 843.

Bryan, W. R. (1959). Acta Unio Intern. Contra Cancrum 15, 764.

Bryan, W. R., and Moloney, J. B. (1957). Ann. N. Y. Acad. Sci. 68, 441.

Bryan, W. R., Calnan, D., and Moloney, J. B. (1955). J. Nat. Cancer Inst. 16, 317.

Bryan, W. R., Moloney, J. B., and Calnan, D. (1954). J. Nat. Cancer Inst. 15, 315.

Bryan, W. R., Kahler, H., Shimkin, M. B., and Andervont, H. B. (1942). J. Nat. Cancer Inst. 2, 451.

Burckhardt, J. L. (1912). Z. Immunitaetsforsch. 14, 544.

Burmester, B. R. (1952). Ann. N. Y. Acad. Sci. 54, 992.

Burmester, B. R. (1957). Ann. N. Y. Acad. Sci. 68, 487.

Burmester, B. R., Fontes, A. K., and Walter, W. G. (1960). J. Nat. Cancer Inst. 24, 1423.

Burmester, B. R., Gross, M. A., Walter, W. G., and Fontes, A. K. (1959). J. Nat. Cancer Inst. 22, 103.

Burton, L., Friedman, F., and Mitchell, H. K. (1957). Ann. N. Y. Acad. Sci. 68, 356.

Butterfield, E. E. (1905). Folia Haematol. **2**, 649.

Calnan, D., Kvedar, J. P., and Bryan, W. R. (1957). J. Nat. Cancer Inst. **19**, 941.

Carr, J. G. (1944). Brit. J. Exptl. Pathol. **24**, 138.

Carr, J. G. (1962). Brit. J. Cancer **16**, 626.

Carr, J. G., and Campbell, J. G. (1958). Brit. J. Cancer **12**, 631.

Carr, J. G., and Harris, R. J. C. (1951). Brit. J. Cancer **5**, 83.

Carrel, A. (1912). J. Exptl. Med. **15**, 516.

Carrel, A. (1924). Compt. Rend. Soc. Biol. **91**, 1069.

Carrel, A. (1925). J. Am. Med. Assoc. **84**, 151.

Carrel, A. (1926). J. Exptl. Med. **43**, 647.

Claude, A. (1937). Science **85**, 294.

Clemmesen, J. (1938). Acta Pathol. Microbiol. Scand. **38**, 47.

Crawford, L. V. (1960). Virology **12**, 143.

Crawford, L. V. (1962). Virology **18**, 177.

Crawford, L. V., and Crawford, E. M. (1961). Virology **13**, 227.

Crawford, L. V., Crawford, E. M., and Watson, D. H. (1962). Virology **18**, 170.

Dalmat, H. T. (1958). J. Exptl. Med. **108**, 9.

Dalton, A. J., Haguenau, F., and Moloney, J. B. (1962). J. Nat. Cancer Inst. **29**, 1177.

Dalton, A. J., Law, L. W., Moloney, J. B., and Manaker, R. A. (1961). J. Nat. Cancer Inst. **27**, 747.

De Carvalho, S. (1959). Proc. 3rd Canad. Cancer Conf. R. W. Begg. 329. Academic Press, New York.

De Carvalho, S., Rand, H. T., and Meyer, D. P. (1960). J. Lab. Clin. Med. **55**, 706.

De Long, R. (1960). J. Lab. Clin. Med. **56**, 891.

De Ome, K. B. (1958). Federation Proc. **21**, 15.

De Ome, K. B., Faulkin, L. J., Jr., Bern, H. A., and Blair, P. B. (1959). Cancer Res. **19**, 515.

Di Mayorca, G. A., Eddy, B. E., Stewart, S. E., Hunter, W. S., Friend, C., and Bendich, A. (1959). Proc. Nat. Acad. Sci. U.S. **45**, 1805.

Dmochowski, L. (1944). Brit. J. Exptl. Pathol. **25**, 138.

Dmochowski, L. (1945a). Brit. J. Exptl. Pathol. **26**, 192.

Dmochowski, L. (1945b). Brit. J. Exptl. Pathol. **26**, 267.

Dmochowski, L., and Grey, C. E. (1957). Ann. N. Y. Acad. Sci. **68**, 559.

Doljanski, L., and Tenenbaum, E. (1942). Cancer Res. **2**, 776.

Dourmashkin, R. R. (1962). A. J. Dalton and F. Haguenau (eds.), Tumors Induced by Viruses: Ultrastructural Studies. 151. Academic Press, New York.

Dulbecco, R., and Freeman, G. (1959). Virology **8**, 396.

Dulbecco, R., and Vogt, M. (1960). Proc. Nat. Acad. Sci. U.S. **46**, 1617.

Dunn, T. B. (1954). J. Nat. Cancer Inst. **14**, 1281.

Dunn, T. B. (1959). F. Homburger (ed.), The Physiopathology of Cancer. 2d ed. 38. Hoeber-Harper, New York.

Dunn, T. B., Moloney, J. B., Green, A. W., and Arnold, B. (1961). J. Nat. Cancer Inst. **26**, 189.

Duran-Reynals, F. (1940). Yale J. Biol. Med. **13**, 99.

Duran-Reynals, F. (1942). Cancer Res. **2**, 343.

Duran-Reynals, F. (1943). Cancer Res. **3**, 569.

Duran-Reynals, F. (1947). Cancer Res. **7**, 103.

Duryee, W. R. (1956). J. Franklin Inst. **261**, 377.

Eddy, B. E. (1960). Adv. Virus Res. **7**, 91.

Eddy, B. E., Stewart, S. E., and Berkeley, W. (1958a). Proc. Soc. Exptl. Biol. Med. **98**, 848.

Eddy, B. E., Borman, G. S., Berkeley, W. H, and Young, R. D. (1961). Proc. Soc. Exptl. Biol. Med. **107**, 191.

Eddy, B. E., Borman, G. S., Grubbs, G. E., and Young, R. D. (1962). Virology **17**, 65.

Eddy, B. E., Borman, G. S., Kirschstein, R. L., and Touchette, R. H. (1960). J. Infect. Diseases **107**, 361.

Eddy, B. E., Rowe, W. P., Hartley, J. W., Stewart, S. E., and Huebner, R. J. (1958b). Virology **6**, 290.

Elias, J. (1958). Presented at 9th Ann. Meeting Tissue Culture Assoc. Philadelphia, Pa. Apr. 9-10.

Ellermann, V. (1914). Z. Klin. Med. **79**, 43.

Ellermann, V., and Bang, O. (1908). Centr. f. Bacteriol. Parasitenk. Ite Abt. Orig. **46**, 595.

Ellermann, V., and Bang, O. (1909). Z. Hyg. Infektionskrankh. **63**, 231.

Ephrussi, B., and Temin, H. M. (1960). Virology **11**, 547.

Evans, C. A., Weiser, R. S., and Ito, Y. (1962a). Cold Spring Harbor Symp. Quant. Biol. **27**, 453.

Evans, C. A., Gorman, L. R., Ito, Y., and Weiser, R. S. (1962b). J. Nat. Cancer Inst. **29**, 277.

Evans, C. A., Gorman, L. R., Ito, Y., and Weiser, R. S. (1962c). J. Nat. Cancer Inst. **29**, 287.

Febvre, H. (1962). A. J. Dalton and F. Haguenau (eds.), Tumors Induced by Viruses: Ultrastructural Studies. 79. Academic Press, New York.

Febvre, H., Rothschild, L., and Arnoult. J. (1963). Compt. Rend. Acad. Sci. (Paris) **256**, 534.

Feldman, D. G. (1963). J. Nat. Cancer Inst. **30**, 477.

Feltz, E. T. (1951). Proc. Am. Assoc. Cancer Res. **3**, 224.

Fenner, F., Holmes, I. H., Joklik, W. K., and Woodroofe, G. M. (1959). Nature **183**, 1340.

Fey, F., and Graffi, A. (1958). Naturwissenschaften **45**, 471.

Fey, F., Gimmy, J., and Graffi, A. (1959). Acta Biol. Med. Ger. **3**, 598.

Foulds, L. (1961). Acta Unio Intern. Contra Cancrum **17**, 148.

Friedewald, W. F. (1942). J. Exptl. Med. **75**, 197.

Friedewald, W. F. (1944). J. Exptl. Med. **80**, 65.

Friedewald, W. F., and Kidd, J. G. (1944). J. Exptl. Med. **79**, 591.

Friedewald, W. F., and Rous, P. (1944). J. Exptl. Med. **80**, 101.

Friedman, F., Burton, L., and Mitchell, H. K. (1957). Ann. N. Y. Acad. Sci. **68**, 349.

Appendix 3—R. A. Manaker

Friend, C. (1957). J. Exptl. Med. **105**, 307.

Friend, C. (1959). J. Exptl. Med. **109**, 217.

Friend, C., and Haddad, J. R. (1960). J. Nat. Cancer Inst. **25**, 1279.

Friend, C., and Rapp, F. (1962). Federation Proc. **21**, 454.

Fujinami, A., and Inamoto, K. (1911). Gann **5**, 13. Cited by: Foulds, L. (1934). Imperial Cancer Research Fund. 11th Sci. Rept. Inv. Taylor and Francis. London.

Furth, J. (1931a). J. Exptl. Med. **53**, 243.

Furth, J. (1931b). Arch. Pathol. **12**, 1.

Gerber, P. (1962). Virology **16**, 96.

Gerber, P. (1963). Science **140**, 889.

Gerber, P., and Kirschstein, R. L. (1962). Virology **18**, 582.

Ginsberg, H. and Sachs, L. (1961). Virology **13**, 380.

Girardi, A. J., Sweet, B. H., Slotnick, V. B., and Hilleman, M. R. (1962). Proc. Soc. Exptl. Biol. Med. **109**, 649.

Goldé, A. (1962). Virology **16**, 9.

Gotlieb-Stematsky, T., and Leventon, S. (1960). Brit. J. Exptl. Pathol. **41**, 507.

Graff, S., Moore, D. H., Stanley, W. M., Randall, H. T., and Haagensen, C. D. (1949). Cancer **2**, 755.

Graffi, A. (1957). Ann. N. Y. Acad. Sci. **68**, 540.

Graffi, A. (1958). Z. Ges. Inn. Med. Ihre Grenzgebiete **13**, 961.

Graffi, A. (1959). Acta Unio Intern. Contra Cancrum **15**, 737.

Graffi, A., Heine, U., Helmcke, J. G., Bierwolf, D., and Randt, A. (1960). Klin. Wochschr. **38**, 254.

Green, R. G., Moosey, M. M., and Bittner, J. J. (1946). Proc. Soc. Exptl. Biol. Med. **61**, 115.

Gross, L. (1950). Cancer **3**, 1073.

Gross, L. (1951a). Proc. Soc. Exptl. Biol. Med. **76**, 27.

Gross, L. (1951b). Proc. Soc. Exptl. Biol. Med. **78**, 342.

Gross, L. (1953a). Acta Haematol. **10**, 18.

Gross, L. (1953b). Proc. Soc. Exptl. Biol. Med. **83**, 414.

Gross, L. (1956). Acta Haematol. **15**, 273.

Gross, L. (1957a). Ann. N. Y. Acad. Sci. **68**, 501.

Gross, L. (1957b). Proc. Soc. Exptl. Biol. Med. **94**, 767.

Gross, L. (1958). Proc. Soc. Exptl. Biol. Med. **97**, 300.

Gross, L. (1960). Proc. Soc. Exptl. Biol. Med. **103**, 509.

Gross, L. (1961a). Proc. Soc. Exptl. Biol. Med. **107**, 90.

Gross, L. (1961b). Proc. Soc. Exptl. Biol. Med. **106**, 890.

Gross, L. (1961c). Oncogenic Virus. 17. Pergamon Press, New York.

Gross, L. (1962). Proc. Soc. Exptl. Biol. Med. **109**, 830.

Gross, L. (1963). Acta Haematol. **29**, 1.

Gross, L., Dreyfuss, Y., and Moore, L. A. (1961). Proc. Am. Assoc. Cancer Res. **3**, 231.

Gross, M. A., Burmester, B. R., and Walter, W. G. (1959). J. Nat. Cancer Inst. **22**, 83.

Groupé, V., and Rauscher, F. J. (1957). J. Nat. Cancer Inst. **18**, 507.

Groupé, V., Dunkel, V. C., and Manaker, R. A. (1957a). J. Bacteriol. **74**, 409.

Groupé, V., Rauscher, F. J., and Bryan, W. R. (1957b). J. Nat. Cancer Inst. **19**, 37.

Groupé, V., Rauscher, F. J., Levine, A. S., and Bryan, W. R. (1956). J. Nat. Cancer Inst. **16**, 865.

Gye, W. E., and Purdy, W. G. (1931). J. Pathol. Bacteriol. **34**, 116.

Habel, K. (1961). Proc. Soc. Exptl. Biol. Med. **106**, 722.

Habel, K. (1962). Cold Spring Harbor Symp. Quant. Biol. **27**, 433.

Habel, K., and Silverberg, R. J. (1960). Virology **12**, 463.

Haguenau, F., and Beard, J. W. (1962). A. J. Dalton and F. Haguenau (eds.), Tumors Induced by Viruses: Ultrastructural Studies. 1. Academic Press, New York.

Haguenau, F., Dalton, A. J., and Moloney, J. B. (1958). J. Nat. Cancer Inst. **20**, 633.

Haguenau, F., Bonar, R. A., Beard, D., and Beard, J. W. (1960). J. Nat. Cancer Inst. **24**, 873.

Hanafusa, T., Hanafusa, H., and Kamahora, J. (1959). Biken's J. **2**, 85.

Hanafusa, H., Hanafusa, T., and Rubin, H. (1963). Proc. Nat. Acad. Sci. U.S. **49**, 572.

Hare, J. D., and Morgan, H. R. (1963). Virology **19**, 105.

Harel, J., and Constantın, T. (1954). Bull. Cancer **41**, 482.

Harris, R. J. C. (1954). Brit. J. Cancer **8**, 731.

Heidelberger, M., Graff, S., and Haagensen, C. D. (1952a). J. Exptl. Med. **95**, 333.

Heidelberger, M., Leon, M. A., Graff, S., and Haagensen, C. D. (1952b). J. Mt. Sinai Hosp. **19**, 210.

Heine, U., De Thé, G., Ishiguro, H., and Beard, J. W. (1962). J. Nat. Cancer Inst. **29**, 211.

Herbut, P. A. (1959). Pathology. 249. Lea and Febiger, Philadelphia.

Hirschfeld, H., and Jacoby, M. (1909). Berlin. Klin. Wochschr. **46**, 159.

Hirschfeld, H., and Jacoby, M. (1910). Z. Klin. Med. **69**, 107.

Hirschfeld, H., and Jacoby, M. (1912). Z. Klin, Med. **75**, 501.

Hodes, M. E., Palmer, C. G., Beaty, L. E., Sivenson, M. K., and Hubbard, J. D. (1963). J. Nat. Cancer Inst. **30**, 1.

Huebner, R. J., Rowe, W. P., and Lane, W. R. (1962). Proc. Nat. Acad. Sci. U.S. **48**, 2051.

Imagawa, D. T., Syverton, J. T., and Bittner, J. J. (1954). Cancer Res. **14**, 1.

Ito, Y. (1960). Virology **12**, 596.

Ito, Y. (1963). Proc. Am. Assoc. Cancer Res. **4**, 31.

Ito, Y., and Evans, C. A. (1961). J. Exptl. Med. **114**, 485.

Jungherr, E., Doyle, L. P. and Johnson, E. P. (1941). Am. J. Vet. Res. **2**, 116.

Keogh, E. V. (1938). Brit. J. Exptl. Pathol. 19, 1.

Kidd, J. G. (1938a). J. Exptl. Med. 68, 703.

Kidd, J. G. (1938b). J. Exptl. Med. 68, 737.

Kidd, J. G. (1942). J. Exptl. Med. 75, 7.

Kidd, J. G. (1950). Symposia Sec. Microbiol., N. Y. Acad. Med. 161. Columbia Univ. Press, New York.

Kilham, L. (1957). Proc. Soc. Exptl. Biol. Med. 95, 59.

Kilham, L. (1958). J. Nat. Cancer Inst. 20, 729.

Kilham, L., and Woke, P. (1953). Proc. Soc. Exptl. Biol. Med. 83, 296.

Kilham, L., Herman, C. M., and Fisher, E. R. (1953). Proc. Soc. Exptl. Biol. Med. 82, 298.

Kreider, J. W. (1963). Proc. Am. Assoc. Cancer Res. 4, 35.

Kryukova, I. N. (1961). Probl. Virol. (U.S.S.R.) (English Transl.) 6, 340.

Lacassagne, A., and Nyka, W. (1936). Compt. Rend. Soc. Biol. 121, 822.

Landa, Z., Svoboda, J., and Jirasek, J. (1962). Folia Biol. (Prague) 8, 12.

Lasfargues, E. Y., and Feldman, D. G. (1963). Cancer Res. 23, 191.

Lasfargues, E. Y., Moore, D. H., and Murray, M. R. (1958). Proc. Am. Assoc. Cancer Res. 2, 318.

Lasfargues, E. Y., Murray, M. R., and Moore, D. H. (1957). Proc. II Intern. Symp. Mammary Cancer. Univ. Perugia 719.

Law, L. W. (1962). Proc. Soc. Exptl. Biol. Med. 111, 615.

Law, L. W., and Moloney, J. B. (1961). Proc. Soc. Exptl. Biol. Med. 108, 715.

Law, L., Rowe, W. P., Hartley, J. W., and Dawe, C. J. (1962). J. Nat. Cancer Inst. 28, 629.

Lemonde, P., and Clode, M. (1962). Nature 193, 1191.

Lieberman, M., and Kaplan, H. S. (1959). Science 130, 387.

Lo, H. Y., and Bang, F. B. (1955). Bull. Johns Hopkins Hosp. 97, 238.

Lo, H. Y., Gey, G. O., and Chapras, P. (1955). Bull. Johns Hopkins Hosp. 97, 248.

Lombard, L. S., and Moloney, J. B. (1959) Federation Proc. 18, 490.

Lucké, B. (1934). Am. J. Cancer 20, 352.

Ludford, R. J. (1937). Am. J. Cancer 31, 414.

Lwoff, A., Horne, R., and Tournier, P. (1962). Cold Spring Harbor Symp. Quant. Biol. 27, 51.

Malmgren, R. A., Fink, M. A., and Mills, W. (1960). J. Nat. Cancer Inst. 24, 995.

Manaker, R. A. (1963). Med. et Hyg. 21, 295.

Manaker, R. A., and Groupé V. (1956). Virology 2, 839.

Manaker, R. A., Strother, P. C., Miller, A. A., and Piczak, C. V. (1960). J. Nat. Cancer Inst. 25, 1411.

Maramorosch, K. (1950). Phytopathology 40, 1071.

Maramorosch, K., Brakke, M. K., and Black, L. M. (1949). Science 110, 162.

Mayor, H. D., Jamison, R. M., and Jordan, L. E. (1963). Virology 19, 359.

Medina, D., and Sachs, L. (1961). Brit. J. Cancer 15, 885.

Medina, D., and Sachs, L. (1963). Virology 19, 127.

Mellors, R. C. (1960). Cancer Res. 20, 744.

Melnick, J. L. (1962). Science 135, 1128.

Metcalf, D., Furth, J., and Buffett, R. F. (1959). Cancer Res. 19, 52.

Milford, J. J., and Duran-Reynals, F. (1943). Cancer Res. 3, 578.

Miller, J. A. F. P. (1961). Adv. Cancer Res. 6, 291.

Mirand, E. A., and Grace, J. T., Jr. (1961). Virology 14, 145.

Mirand, E. A., and Grace, J. T., Jr. (1962a). Virology 16, 344.

Mirand, E. A., and Grace, J. T., Jr. (1962b). Virology 17, 364.

Mirand, E. A., and Grace, J. T., Jr. (1962c). Proc. Am. Assoc. Cancer Res. 3, 345.

Mirand, E. A., Hoffman, J. G., Grace, J. T., Jr., and Trudel, P. J. (1961). Proc. Soc. Exptl. Biol. Med. 107, 824.

Mitra, S., and Schwartz, S. C. (1961). Acta Haematol. 26, 360.

Moloney, J. B. (1959). Proc. Am. Assoc. Cancer Res. 3, 44.

Moloney, J. B. (1960a). J. Nat. Cancer Inst. 24, 933.

Moloney, J. B. (1960b). Nat. Cancer Inst. Monograph 4, 7.

Moloney, J. B. (1962). Federation Proc. 21, 19.

Moore, A. E. (1963). J. Nat. Cancer Inst. 30, 885.

Moore, A. E., and Friend, C. (1958). Proc. Am. Assoc. Cancer Res. 2, 328.

Moore, D. H. (1962). A. J. Dalton and F. Haguanau (eds.), Tumors Induced by Viruses; Ultrastructural Studies. 113. Academic Press, New York.

Moore, D. H., Pollard, E. C., and Haagensen, C. D. (1962). Federation Proc. 21, 942.

Moore, D. H., Stone, R. S., Shope, R. E., and Gerber, D. (1959b). Proc. Soc. Exptl. Biol. Med. 101, 575.

Moore, D. H., Lasfargues, E. Y., Murray, M. R., Haagensen, C. D., and Pollard, E. C. (1959a). J. Biophys. Biochem. Cytol. 5, 85.

Moore, V. A. (1897). Twelfth and Thirteenth Annual Reports, U.S. Bureau of Animal Industry. 185.

Morgan, H. R., and Andrese, A. P. (1962). J. Exptl. Med. 116, 329.

Mühlbock, O., Tongbergen, W. van E., and Rijssel, T. G. (1952). J. Nat. Cancer Inst. 13, 505.

Munroe, J. S., and Southam, C. M. (1961). J. Nat. Cancer Inst. 26, 775.

Munroe, J. S., and Windle, W. F. (1963). Science 140, 1415.

Murphy, J. B., and Landsteiner, K. (1925). J. Exptl. Med. 41, 807.

Murphy, J. B., and Rous, P. (1912). J. Exptl. Med. 15, 119.

Murphy, J. B., and Strum, E. (1932a). J. Exptl. Med. 56, 107.

Murphy, J. B., and Strum, E. (1932b). J. Exptl. Med. **56**, 705.

Nagaraj, A. N., and Black, L. M. (1961). Virology **15**, 289.

Nandi, S. (1961). J. Nat. Cancer Inst. **27**, 187.

Nandi, S. (1963). Proc. Am. Assoc. Cancer Res. **4**, 47.

Nandi, S., and Bern, H. A. (1960). J. Nat. Cancer Inst. **24**, 907.

Nandi, S., and Bern, H. A. (1961). J. Nat. Cancer Inst. **27**, 173.

Nandi, S., Bern, H. A., and De Ome K. B. (1960). J. Nat. Cancer Inst. **24**, 883.

Nigrelli, R. F. (1952). Ann. N. Y. Acad. Sci. **54**, 1076.

Niven, J. S. F., Armstrong, J. A., Andrewes, C. H., Periera, H. G., and Valentine, R. C. (1961). J. Pathol. Bacteriol. **81**, 1.

Noyes, W. F. (1959). J. Exptl. Med. **109**, 423.

Noyes, W. F. (1960). Virology **12**, 488.

Noyes, W. F., and Mellors, R. C. (1957). J. Exptl. Med. **106**, 555.

O'Connor, T. E., Oroszlan, S. I., and Mora, P. T. (1963). Proc. Am. Assoc. Cancer Res. **4**, 49.

Parsons, R. J., and Kidd, J. G. (1936). Proc. Soc. Exptl. Biol. Med. **35**, 441.

Passey, R. D., Dmochowski, L., Reed, R., and Astbury, W. T. (1950). Biochim. Biophys. Acta **4**, 391.

Pikovski, M. (1953). J. Nat. Cancer Inst. **13**, 1275.

Pitelka, D. R., De Ome, K. B., and Bern, H. A. (1960). J. Nat. Cancer Inst. **25**, 753.

Pontén, J. (1962a). J. Nat. Cancer Inst. **29**, 1013.

Pontén, J. (1962b). J. Nat. Cancer Inst. **29**, 1147.

Pontén, J., Ravdin, R. A., and Koprowski, H. (1963). Proc. Am. Assoc. Cancer Res. **4**, 53.

Pope, J. H. (1961). Australian J. Exptl. Biol. Med. Sci. **39**, 521.

Pope, J. H. (1962). Australian J. Expt. Biol. Med. Sci. **40**, 263.

Porter, K. R., and Thompson, H. P. (1948). J. Exptl. Med. **88**, 15.

Prince, A. M. (1958a). J. Nat. Cancer Inst. **20**, 147.

Prince, A. M. (1958b). J. Nat. Cancer Inst. **20**, 843.

Prince, A. M. (1958c). Virology **5**, 435.

Prince, A. M. (1959). J. Nat. Cancer Inst. **23**, 1361.

Prince, A. M. (1960). Virology **11**, 400.

Prince, A. M. (1962). Virology **18**, 524.

Rabin, H., Heyen, C. F. A., Foard, M., and Bang, F. (1963). J. Nat. Cancer Inst. **30**, 467.

Rabson, A. B., and Kirschstein, R. L. (1962). Proc. Soc. Exptl. Biol. Med. **111**, 323.

Rabson, A. S., and Law, L. W. (1963). J. Nat. Cancer Inst. **30**, 367.

Rabson, A. S., Malmgren, R. A., O'Connor, G. T., and Kirschstein, R. L. (1962b). J. Nat. Cancer Inst. **29**, 1123.

Rabson, A. S., O'Connor, G. T., Kirschstein, R. L. and Branigan, W. J. (1962a). J. Nat. Cancer Inst. **29**, 765.

Rafferty, K. A., Jr. (1962). J. Nat. Cancer Inst. **29**, 253.

Rauscher, F. J. (1962). J. Nat. Cancer Inst. **29**, 515.

Rauscher, F. J., and Groupé, V. (1960). J. Nat. Cancer Inst. **25**, 141.

Rich, M., Perez, A. G., and Eidinoff, M. L. (1962). Virology **16**, 98.

Rivers, T. M. (1930). J. Exptl. Med. **51**, 965.

Roizman, B. and Roane, P. R., Jr. (1960). Nature **188**, 1134.

Rous, P. (1910). J. Exptl. Med. **12**, 696.

Rous, P. (1911). J. Exptl. Med. **13**, 397.

Rous, P. (1913). J. Exptl. Med. **18**, 183.

Rous, P., and Beard, J. W. (1934). J. Exptl. Med. **60**, 701.

Rous, P., and Beard, J. W. (1935a). Proc. Soc. Exptl. Biol. Med. **32**, 578.

Rous, P, and Beard, J. W. (1935b). J. Exptl. Med. **62**, 523.

Rous, P., and Lange, Linda B. (1913). J. Exptl. Med. **18**, 651.

Rous, P., and Murphy, J. B. (1913). J. Exptl. Med. **17**, 219.

Rous, P., and Murphy, J. B. (1914a). J. Exptl. Med. **19**, 52.

Rous, P., and Murphy, J. B. (1914b). J. Exptl. Med. **20**, 419.

Rous, P., Robertson, O. H., and Oliver, J. (1919). J. Exptl. Med. **29**, 305.

Rowe, W. P., and Brodsky, I. (1959). J. Nat. Cancer Inst. **23**, 1239.

Rowe, W. P., Hartley, J. W., Brodsky, I., Huebner, R. J., and Law, L. W. (1958). Nature **182**, 1617.

Rubin H. (1955). Virology **1**, 445.

Rubin, H. (1960a). Virology **10**, 29.

Rubin, H. (1960b). Virology **12**, 14.

Rubin, H. (1961). Virology **13**, 200.

Rubin, H. (1962a). Cold Spring Harbor Sym. Quant. Biol. **27**, 441.

Rubin, H. (1962b). Nature **195**, 342.

Rubin, H., and Vogt, P. K. (1962). Virology **17**, 184.

Rubin, H., Cornelius, A., and Fanshier, L. (1961). Proc. Nat. Acad. Sci. U.S. **47**, 1058.

Sabin, A. B., and Koch, M. A. (1963). Proc. Nat. Acad. Sci. U.S. **49**, 304.

Sachs, L. (1962). J. Nat. Cancer Inst. **29**, 759.

Sachs, L., and Medina, D. (1961). Nature **189**, 457.

Sachs, L., and Winocour, E. (1959). Virology **8**, 397.

Sanarelli, G. (1898). Centr. Bakt. Abt. **23**, 865.

Sanford, K. K., Andervont, H. B., Hobbs, G. L., and Earle, W. R. (1961). J. Nat. Cancer Inst. **26**, 1185.

Sanford, K. K., Likely, G. D., Bryan, W. R., and Earle, W. R. (1952). J. Nat. Cancer Inst. **12**, 1317.

Schmeisser, H. C. (1915). J. Exptl. Med. **22**, 820.

Schoolman, H. M., Spurrier, W., Schwartz, S. O., and Szanto, P. B. (1957). Blood **12**, 694.

Schridde. (1909). Deut. Med. Wochschr. **35**, 280.

Schwartz, S. O., Schoolman, H. M., and Szanto, P. B. (1956). Cancer Res. **16**, 559.

Schwartz, S. O., Schoolman, H. M., Spurrier, W., and Yates, L. (1958). Proc. Soc. Exptl. Biol. Med. **97**, 397.

Selsky, M. I. (1961). Phytopathology **51**, 581.

Shein, H. M., and Enders, J. F. (1962). Proc. Soc. Exptl. Biol. Med. **109**, 495.

Shein, H. M., Enders, J. F., Levinthal, J. D., and Burket, A. E. (1963). Proc. Nat. Acad. Sci. U.S. **49**, 28.

Shope, R. E. (1932a). J. Exptl. Med. **56**, 793.

Shope, R. E. (1932b). J. Exptl. Med. **56**, 803.

Shope, R. E. (1933). J. Exptl. Med. **58**, 607.

Shope, R. E. (1955). Proc. Soc. Exptl. Biol. Med. **88**, 533.

Simkovic, D., Valentova, N., and Thurzo, V. (1962). Folia Biol. (Prague) **8**, 221.

Simons, P. J., and Dougherty, R. M. (1961). Virology **15**, 200.

Sinkovics, J. G. (1962). Ann. Rev. Microbiol. **16**, 75.

Sittenfield, M. J., Johnson, B. A., and Jobling, J. W. (1931). Proc. Soc. Exptl. Biol. Med. **28**, 517.

Sjögren, H. O. (1961). Virology **15**, 214.

Sjögren, H. O., Hellström, I., and Klein, G. (1961). Cancer Res. **21**, 329.

Smith, W. E., Kidd, J. G., and Rous, P. (1947). Fourth Intern. Cancer Res. Congr. 84. St. Louis.

Sproul, E. E., Metzgar, R. S., and Grace, J. T., Jr. (1963). Cancer Res. **23**, 671.

Staff, Jackson Memorial Laboratory (1933). Science **78**, 465.

Stansly, P. G., Ramsey, D. S., and Soule, H. D. (1961). Cancer Res. **3**, 270.

Stewart, S. E. (1953). Anat. Record **117**, 532.

Stewart, S. E. (1955a). J. Nat. Cancer Inst. **15**, 1391.

Stewart, S. E. (1955b). J. Nat. Cancer Inst. **16**, 41.

Stewart, S. E., and Eddy, B. E. (1958). Proc. VIIth Intern. Congr. Hematol. 596. Intern. Soc. Hematol. II Pensiero Scientifico, Roma.

Stewart, S. E., Eddy, B. E., Gochenour, A. M., Borgese, N. G., and Grubbs, G. E. (1957). Virology **3**, 380.

Stoker, M. (1962). Virology **18**, 649.

Stoker, M., and Abel, P. (1962). Cold Spring Harbor Symp. Quant. Biol. **27**, 375.

Stoker, M., and MacPherson, I. (1961). Virology **14**, 359.

Stone, R. S., Shope, R. E., and Moore, D. H. (1959). J. Exptl. Med. **110**, 543.

Streissle, G., and Maramorosch, K. (1963). Science **140**, 996.

Strum, E., and Murphy, J. B. (1928). J. Exptl. Med. **47**, 493.

Svoboda, J. (1962). Folia Biol. (Prague) **8**, 215.

Sweet, B. H., and Hilleman, M. R. (1960). Proc. Soc. Exptl. Biol. Med. **105**, 420.

Sykes, J. A., Dmochowski, L., Schullenberger, C. C., and Howe, C. D. (1962). Cancer Res. **22**, 21.

Syverton, J. T. (1952). Ann. N. Y. Acad. Sci. **54**, 1126.

Syverton, J. T., and Berry, G. P. (1935). Proc. Soc. Exptl. Biol. Med. **33**, 399.

Syverton, J. T., Dascomb, H. E., Koomen, J., Jr., Wells, E. B., and Berry, G. P. (1950). Cancer Res. **10**, 379.

Temin, H. M. (1960). Virology **10**, 182.

Temin, H. M. (1961). Virology **13**, 158.

Temin, H. M. (1962). Cold Spring Harbor Symp. Quant. Biol. **27**, 407.

Temin, H. M., and Rubin, H. (1958). Virology **6**, 669.

Temin, H. M., and Rubin, H. (1959). Virology **8**, 209.

Tenenbaum, E., and Doljanski, L. (1943). Cancer Res. **3**, 585.

Tennant, J. R. (1962). J. Nat. Cancer Inst. **28**, 1291.

Trentin, J. J., Yabe, Y., and Taylor, G. (1962). Proc. Am. Assoc. Cancer Res. **3**, 369.

Tytler, W. H. (1913). J. Exptl. Med. **17**, 466.

Valleau, W. D. (1947) Phytopathology **37**, 580.

Verna, J. E., and Eylar, O. R. (1962). Virology **18**, 266.

Vigier, P., and Goldé, A. (1959). Virology **8**, 60.

Visscher, M. B., Green, R. G., and Bittner, J. J. (1942). Proc. Soc. Exptl. Biol. Med. **49**, 94.

Vogt, M., and Dulbecco, R. (1962a). Cold Spring Harbor Symp. Quant. Biol. **27**, 367.

Vogt, M., and Dulbecco, R. (1962b). Virology **16**, 41.

Vogt, P. K., and Rubin, H. (1961). Virology **13**, 528.

Vogt, P. K., and Rubin, H. (1962). Cold Spring Harbor Symp. Quant. Biol. **27**, 395.

Wakonig-Vaartaja, R. (1961). Brit. J. Cancer **15**, 120.

Warner, S. G., Reinhard, M. C., and Goltz, H. L. (1945). Cancer Res. **5**, 584.

Warthin, A. S. (1907). J. Infect. Diseases **4**, 369.

Weil, R. (1961). Virology **14**, 46.

Weil, R. (1962). Cold Spring Harbor Symp. Quant. Biol. **27**, 83.

Weil, R. (1963). Proc. Nat. Acad. Sci. U. S. **49**, 480.

Wessing, A., and von Bargen, G. (1959). Arch. Ges. Virusforsch. **9**, 521.

Whitcomb, R. F., and Black, L. M. (1961). Virology **15**, 136.

Winocour, E. (1963). Virology **19**, 158.

Woolley, G., Fekete, E., and Little, C. C. (1939). Proc. Nat. Acad. Sci. U. S. **25**, 277.

Woolley, G., Fekete, E., and Little, C. C. (1940). Proc. Soc. Exptl. Biol. Med. **45**, 796.

Woolley, G., Law, L. W., and Little, C. C. (1941). Cancer Res. **1**, 955.

Yabe, Y., Trentin, J. J., and Taylor, G. (1962). Proc. Soc. Exptl. Biol. Med. **111**, 343.

Zeigel, R. F., and Rauscher, F. J. (1963). J. Nat. Cancer Inst. **30**, 207.

Zilber, L. A. (1961). J. Nat. Cancer Inst. **26**, 1295.

501

Bibliographical Index

Bibliographical Index

Bibliographical Index

Bibliographical Index

Subject Index

Subject Index

518

Subject Index

Hyadaphis xylostei, 332
Hyalestes obsoletus, 185
Hybridization, 99–100
Hydrangea macrophylla, 353
Hymenoptera, 445, 451
Hyoscyamus mosaic, 20

Icosahedral particle design, 285–89
Identification of plant virus, 69, 101–2
Illumination effect, 51–52, 59
Immunity, 18, 69, 103–10, 357–59
Immunization techniques, 236–41
  blood-sample acquisition, 239–40
  combination of injection routes, 238–39
  intramuscular injection, 238
  intravenous injection, 237
  subcutaneous injection, 239
Immunoelectrophoresis, 247
Immunology, 235–36
Impurity detection, 231–33
Inactivators, 338–39
Inarching, 40
Inazuma dorsalis, 181, 188, 189
Inclusion bodies, 76
Incubation period, 177
Infection with mild virus strains, 339, 349
Infection with plant viruses, 374–81
Infectious canine hepatitis, 416
Infectious chlorosis, 3, 17, 178
Infectiousness, correlation with characteristic virus particle, 429
Infectiousness, the destruction of, 430
Infectious nucleic acid, 292
Infectious variegation virus, 110
Infectivity, 194
Influenza virus, 412, 416
Infrared spectrophotometry, 318
Inhibitors, 54–57, 78, 111, 166, 167, 172, 207, 338–39
Initial-buffer determination, 212
Inoculation, 4, 39, 40, 47–59, 70, 71, 72, 74, 75, 78, 81, 90, 149, 151, 170–90, 200–203, 208–9
  by aphids, 170–73
  by leaf rubbing, 40
Inoculum, sources of, 53, 54, 58, 59
Insecticides, 335, 336–37, 348, 349–51
Insects, as vectors, 3, 75, 107–8, 197–98, 331, 334, 453–54. See also under individual insects
Interference, 4, 103–4, 108, 110–14
Internal browning disease, 31
Internal cork disease, 35
Ionic-strength changes, 220
Ipomoea setosa, 150
Iris mosaic, 36

Irradiation, 159–60, 161, 167, 168, 169, 170
Isoelectric points, 101
Isoelectric precipitation, 220–21, 230
Isolation of virus 343–45, 447–48

Japanese aster yellows virus, 183
Japanese beetles, 26
Japanese wheat mosaic, 120
Jasminum, white, 1
Jasminum, yellow-striped, 1
Jassid, 334
Jessamine (Jasminum) mottle, 1
Juice extraction, 212–13

Kaolin, 50
Katahdin, 358
Kenaf, 153
Koksaghyz yellows, 28, 183
Kringerigheid, 122

Labial tapping, 157
Lactuca, 125, 135
  sativa, 62
Lambert mottle of sweet cherry, 29, 30, 35
Laothoe populi, 443
Latent-mosaic of potato virus, 7
Latent virus infections, 450–51
Leaf abnormalities, 19–27
Leaf curl, 358
Leaf curl disease of tobacco, 179
Leafhopper, 3–4, 5, 17, 18, 40, 41, 42, 43, 72, 81, 83, 175, 176, 177, 180–82, 183, 184, 188, 189, 190, 197, 238, 244, 248, 331, 333, 342, 343, 346, 350, 352, 376, 454, 491
Leaf mottle, 352
Leaf-pucker disease of apple, 30
Leaf rolling mosaic, 369
Leaf roll virus, 24, 34, 36, 40, 331, 333, 334, 335, 340, 341, 345, 348, 352, 355, 356
Legumes, 74, 89
Legume viruses, 89, 250
Leguminosae, 46, 59, 323
Lepidoptera, 445, 446, 450–51, 453
Lesions, primary, 18
Lettuce, 12, 13, 27, 44, 45, 120, 125, 133, 134, 135, 136, 330, 331, 333, 334, 341, 342, 343, 345, 346, 348, 350, 353
Lettuce big vein virus, 12, 60, 61, 118, 120, 124–25, 132, 133–34, 135, 136, 137, 138, 141
Lettuce calico, 121
Lettuce mosaic virus, 12, 25, 27, 28, 44, 45, 62, 155, 173, 330, 334, 336, 341, 343, 354
Lettuce ringspot form, 120, 121, 128, 132
Lettuce yellow mosaic, 20
Lettuce yellows virus, 350
Leukemia, 457–93
Leukemogenic agents in tissue culture, 480
Light, 206–7

Lilac witches' broom, 60, 61
Lily, 341
Lily mosaic, 102
Lily rosette, 25
Lily yellows flat disease, 24, 38
Lima bean mosaic virus, 44, 102
Lime, 20, 23
Line pattern virus, 353
Little cherry disease, 29, 31
Little leaf disease, 32
Little peach disease, 14, 24, 29, 31, 102, 110
Local-lesion assay of plant virus, 94, 194–96, 198–209
  dilution curve, 198–200
  influential factors, 205–9
    inoculation methods, 208–9
    inoculum inhibitors, 207
    light, 206–7
    temperature, 207
    test plant, 205–6
  relative infectivity, 200–5
    accuracy of local-lesion method, 203–5
    inoculation schemes, 200–203
    test plants, 203
      local-lesion hosts, 203, 211
      starch-iodine lesions, 203
Locusts, 445
Loganberry dwarf disease, 24, 31, 32
Longevity in vitro, 77, 80
Longidorus, 127, 128, 129, 131, 137
  attenuatus, 128, 132
  elongatus, 126, 128, 131, 132, 137, 139, 140, 141
  macrosoma, 128
Lucerne, 123
Lucerne mosaic, 332
Lupin mosaic virus, 163
Lupines, 12
Lupinus luteus, 62
Lycopersicon esculentum, 51, 63, 74, 318

Macrosiphum euphorbiae, 156
  solanifolii, 335
Macrosteles, 185
  divisus, 5
  fascifrons, 180, 183, 184, 185, 346, 350
  laevis, 183
Mahaleb rootstock, 33
Maize, 29, 127, 141, 142, 189, 342, 349, 454
Maize leaf fleck, 21
Maize rough dwarf virus, 349
Maize streak virus, 21, 24, 345
Maize stripe, 21
Maize virus, 50
Mangold, 70, 344
Manila hemp plant, 14
Marble disease of cardamon, 22
Mauche, 122
Mealybug, 179, 331, 333, 355, 357
Measles virus, 416
Mechanical inoculation, 57–59, 71

519

Subject Index

Subject Index

Subject Index

Tomato spotted wilt virus, 21, 30, 31, 34, 47, 50, 56, 60, 61, 81, 99, 100, 102, 178, 179, 330, 332, 346
Tomato stolbur, 60, 61
T phages, 410–11
Transmission of virus, 2, 69, 71, 89
  between different species and orders, 452–53
  in series, 70
  See also Vectors
Transovarial-passage technique, 181
Treehoppers, 177–78
"Tree-top" disease, 440
Trefoil, 342
Trichodorus, 127, 128, 129, 131, 132, 140
  christiei, 127, 128, 129, 139
  pachydermus, 128, 131
  primitivus, 128
  teres, 128, 139
  viruliferus, 128
Trifolium incarnatum, 50
Tristeza disease, 14, 19, 23, 26, 28, 34, 100, 331, 334, 339, 353
Triticum aestivum, 62
Tropaeolum majus, 56
Tube precipitin test, 242
Tulare apple mosaic virus, 60, 61, 244, 247
Tulip, 124, 141, 338
Tulip breaking virus, 1, 39, 337
Tulip color-adding disease, 27
Tulip mosaic, 1, 27, 102
Turnip, 11, 140, 164
Turnip crinkle virus, 242, 294, 412, 413
Turnip mosaic virus, 11, 25, 113, 150, 152, 160, 166, 171, 242
Turnip yellow mosaic virus, 10, 20, 86, 88, 216, 242, 243–44, 264–65, 285, 293, 294, 296, 299, 303, 318, 325, 380, 386, 412, 413–14, 415, 416, 417
Tumor, defined, 457
  viruses, 457–93
Two-phase systems, 224, 230

Ulmus americana, 62
Ultracentrifugation, 195, 224, 230, 232, 431
Ultrafiltration, 228–29, 430–31
Ultrastructure of arthropod viruses, 449
Ultraviolet absorption spectra, 195
Ultraviolet radiation experiments, 378
Uptake, 149–51, 155–64, 170, 171

Vaccinia virus, 416
Valleau's yellow ringspot virus, 106
Varicella virus, 416
Vectors, 3, 5, 12, 17, 72, 81, 83, 89, 100, 101, 118, 126, 127, 128, 129, 137, 138, 148–91

Vectors—*Continued*
  aerial, 119
  control of, 342–51
  identification of, 91
  as virus separators, 71
Vector-virus relationship, 178, 72, 81, 89, 128, 175–91
Vein-banding mosaic virus, 20, 332, 352
Vein chlorosis virus, 352, 353
Vein mottle, 352
Velocity constants, 79
Veronica persica, 135
Vicia faba, 20, 25, 34, 62, 74
Vigna sesquipedalis, 62
  sinensis, 62, 74
Vinca flowers, 27, 28
Vinca yellows, 60
Vine mosaic, 21, 23
Viral diseases in the arthropods, 439–54
Viral diseases in plants, abnormalities as symptoms, 19–38
  of buds, 34–35
    in dormancy, 35
    in structure, 35
    in viability, 35
  of flowers, 27–29
    in blossom timing, 28–29
    in color, 27–28
    in egg viability, 28
    in number, 28
    in persistence, 29
    in pollen, 28
    in position, 28
    in shape, 28
    in size, 28
  of foliage, 19–27
  of fruit, 29–32
    in color, 30
    in death, 31–32
    in flavor, 31
    in habit, 30
    in maturation, 31
    in number, 29
    in persistence, 31
    in seed, 31
    in shape, 29–30
    in size, 29
    in texture, 30–31
    in yield, 31
  of leaf, 19–27
    in color, 19–22
      line patterns, 21–22
      mottling, 20
      over-all color, 19–20
      ring patterns, 21
      spotting patterns, 21
      vein patterns, 20
    in cytology, 25
    in death, 26–27
    in histology, 25
    in luster, 24
    in miscellaneous physiological processes, 25–26
    in number, 22
    in position, 24–25
    in shape, 22–24
    in size, 24
    in texture, 24

Viral diseases in plants—*Continued*
  of plant as a whole, 36–38
    in chemical composition, 37
    in growth habit, 37–38
    in growth rate, 37
    in histology, 37
    in latex flow, 37
    in length of life, 36–37
    in size, 37
    in transpiration, 37
    in turgidity, 36
    in yield, 36
  of root, 35–36
    in chemical composition, 35
    in color, 35
    in death, 36
    in number, 35
    in shape, 35
    in size, 35
    in texture, 5
  of stem, 32–34
    in bark, 33
    in chemical constitution, 34
    in color, 33
    in death, 34
    in growth habit, 32
    in gum production, 34
    in histology, 33
    in internode length, 32
    in number, 32
    in physiology, 34
    in rigidity, 33
    in shape, 32–33
  assay method, 194–98
    biological, 197–98
      transmission by dodder, 197
      transmission by grafts, 197
      transmission by insects, 197–98
      transmission by mechanical inoculation, 198
    chemical, 196
    physical, 195–96
      dilution end-point of stream double refraction, 195–96
      dry-weight determination, 195
      optical density and ultraviolet-absorption spectra, 195
      particle count method, 195
    serological, 196–97
  beneficial effect of, 189–90
  control of, 330–59
  genetic variability, 381–84
  hybridization, 99–100
  identification of, 68–91
    choice of criteria, 68, 88–89
    descriptions, 89–90
    determination of number of viruses in disease, 70–71
    determination of virus presence, 69–70
    general approach, 71–72
    names, 89–90
    routine diagnoses, 90–91

Subject Index